INTRODUCTION TO GEOPHYSICAL PROSPECTING

INTRODUCTION TO GEOPHYSICAL PROSPECTING

FOURTH EDITION

Milton B. Dobrin
Late Professor of Geology
University of Houston

Carl H. Savit
Adjunct Professor of Geology and Geophysics
Rice University
Western Geophysical Company (retired)
Houston
Assisted by Heloise Bloxsom Lynn with
additional chapters by Norman Neidell,
Yoram Shoham, and Ozdogan Yilmaz

McGRAW-HILL BOOK COMPANY

New York   St. Louis   San Francisco   Auckland   Bogotá
Caracas   Colorado Springs   Hamburg   Lisbon   London   Madrid   Mexico   Milan   Montreal   New Delhi
Oklahoma City   Panama   Paris   San Juan   São Paulo   Singapore   Sydney   Tokyo   Toronto

This book was set in Times Roman by Better Graphics, Inc.
The editors were John Zumerchik and Steven Tenney;
the production supervisor was Salvador Gonzales.
The drawings were done by J & R Art Services, Inc.
The cover was designed by Joseph Gillians.
R. R. Donnelley & Sons Company was printer and binder.

INTRODUCTION TO GEOPHYSICAL PROSPECTING

1 2 3 4 5 6 7 8 9 0 DOCDOC 8 9 3 2 1 0 9 8

ISBN 0-07-017196-3

Library of Congress Cataloging-in-Publication Data

Dobrin, Milton B. (Milton Burnett)
  Introduction to geophysical prospecting.

   Bibliography: p.
   Includes index.
   1. Prospecting—Geophysical methods.   I. Savit,
Carl H.   II. Title.
TN269.D6   1988   622'.15   88-566
ISBN 0-07-017196-3

ABOUT
THE AUTHOR

Carl H. Savit is a consulting geophysicist. After 38 years of service with Western Geophysical Company, he retired as Senior Vice President, in which position he had been responsible for the technical activities of the organization. In 1970–71 he took a leave of absence to serve on the White House staff as Assistant for Earth, Sea, and Air Sciences to the President's Science Advisor. Among offices he has held are Editor of *Geophysics,* President of the Society of Exploration Geophysicists, and Chairman of the NRC-NAS Committee on Seismology. He has been and continues to be a member of many governmental and organizational advisory boards, panels, and visiting committees. He is an honorary member of SEG, a fellow of the GSA, and a member of other professional societies, as well as holding California licenses in both geology and geophysics. He holds more than 41 U.S. patents and has written numerous papers and articles in his field.

CONTENTS

PREFACE TO THE FOURTH EDITION

In characterizing the state of exploration geophysics today, I am prompted to refer to the first sentences of the prefaces of the second and third editions of this text. The lead sentence to the second edition reads "In the eight years since the first edition of *Introduction to Geophysical Prospecting* was published, there have been more extensive technical advances in the field of geophysical exploration than in any similar period since the earliest years of the art." The third edition reads "Revolutionary changes since 1960 in all aspects of geophysical technology have necessitated a much more thorough revision of this text than is usually required between successive editions of a book."

At the risk of being repetitious, I would begin *this* preface with the observation that the pace of technological advance in geophysical prospecting, like that in most other technical disciplines is, if anything, accelerating. Even in so short a time as in the four years that this edition has been in preparation, whole sections have had to be revised, added, or omitted to keep pace with progress in technology.

In exploration geophysics, progress has been made along a broad and diversified front. More data are gathered in the field. For example, within the last 60 years, the number of bits of information gathered in a seismic survey per mile of line surveyed has increased more than 10,000-fold. A further 10-fold increase is in the offing. Additionally, more types of data are being acquired. An example is gradient information in potential fields or shear-wave information in seismic prospecting.

Because the power of computers (internal memory size multiplied by computation rate) has for 30 years or more been increasing 10-fold about every 2¾ years, computers have almost kept abreast of geophysical data flow, but, more importantly, greater precision is being achieved in the results of exploration and new geologic parameters are being extracted from computer processing of the acquired data.

In the early years of exploration geophysics, progress was most rapid in instrumentation, so that now most measurements of physical properties or fields can be made and recorded as precisely and frequently as the inherent uncertainty of the quantities measured will permit. In recent years and for some time in the future, rapid progress has been and will be made in field techniques and in the analysis and interpretation of data.

The present edition of this text is thus necessarily a "freeze frame" of exploration geophysics as it was when those of us who contributed to the final result wrote. Nevertheless, the fundamental physical and geological principles embodied in the discussions and derivations of the text will probably remain valid for a considerable time.

While the essence of *Introduction to Exploration Geophysics* is and will remain the work of the late Dr. Milton Dobrin, in the task of preparing this edition I have had invaluable assistance from Dr. Heloise Bloxsom Lynn, without whose manifold talents and broad knowledge I would have found it impossible to complete the work. Special gratitude is expressed to three distinguished geophysicists who wrote either new or largely new chapters in keeping with their special expertise. Dr. Norman Neidell wrote Chapter 9 on interpretation techniques, Dr. Ozdogan Yilmaz wrote the totally new Chapter 10 on three-dimensional seismic surveying, and Dr. Yoram Shoham completely rewrote Chapter 18, with special emphasis on the magnetotelluric method which has come into prominence since the third edition.

Because Dr. Lynn and I have specialized in seismic exploration, we have depended on experts in other fields to bring up to date the chapters on nonseismic methods. For undertaking those endeavors I express my sincere appreciation to Dr. Richard J. Blakely, Mr. Gerald Connard, Mr. Eduard deRidder, Dr. Robert A. Fowler, Dr. Richard O. Hansen, Dr. Alan T. Herring, Dr. Robert Jachens, Dr. Patrick Taylor, and Dr. Robert Simpson, Jr.

I am particularly appreciative of the efforts of Barbara Anki, CPS, for her patience in typing the entire text, correcting my errors and omissions, and making what must have seemed like an interminable number of revisions and corrections. Finally, I express my deepest gratitude to my wife Sandra for her patient acceptance of my late hours and constant preoccupation with the work and for proofreading every word of what she must have felt to be an interminable text.

While Dr. Dobrin and all the people I have acknowledged have contributed to a greater or lesser extent to the work, I take full responsibility for the final text in that the ultimate decisions on what was or was not included and in what manner the material is presented was mine.

Carl H. Savit

PREFACE TO THE THIRD EDITION

Revolutionary changes since 1960 in all aspects of geophysical technology have necessitated a much more thorough revision of this text than is usually required between successive editions of a book. The present edition is different in so many ways from the previous one that it can almost be looked upon as a new book rather than as a revision.

Three chapters (on acquisition of seismic data at sea, seismic data enhancement in digital processing centers, and direct detection of hydrocarbons using seismic data) are entirely new. The need for such chapters reflects the great advances made during the past decade or so in digital recording and processing of seismic data as well as in techniques for seismic prospecting in offshore areas.

The development during the 1960s of a new generation of high-speed digital computers has had an enormous impact on all phases of applied geophysics—from the acquisition of data in the field to its ultimate interpretation. The computer has not only made it possible to obtain better-quality seismic data but also to derive from them new kinds of geological information that until recently were not considered obtainable by geophysics at all. To give such developments proper coverage has required the introduction of material on many aspects of geophysics that were not even in existence when the second edition of this book was published in 1960.

A significant innovation in the present edition is the use of elementary calculus in presenting the basic principles of the various geophysical methods. In earlier editions the calculus was not employed because of concern that many geologists using the book might not have studied this subject. Now nearly all geological curricula leading to a bachelor's degree in geology require at least a year of calculus, and the restriction against its use observed in previous editions no longer appears necessary. It is unlikely that those readers who are not familiar with calculus will encounter any real difficulty if they skip over the equations which use it, assume them to be correct, and determine their significance from pertinent discussions in the text.

Applied geophysics has become so specialized in recent decades that few readers are likely to be equally interested in all its phases. Even in elementary courses in the subject, the emphasis on different topics will vary with the background and interests of the instructor. Among those working in the field of exploration some will be primarily concerned with techniques used in oil exploration and others with those most widely applied in the search for metallic minerals. Those involved with geophysics in either the oil or mining industry will probably have different areas of concentration, e.g., field operations, instruments, data processing, or geological interpretation. It is hoped that the needs of all such users will be met in this book.

To meet the needs of instructors offering a one-semester course in applied geophysics who would like to use this time for more intensive study of specific aspects of the subject rather than for broad coverage of the entire book, the individual chapters have been designed to be self-contained so far as that is possible.

The present edition, like previous editions, was written with the needs of geologists in mind and I have emphasized the geological applications of geophysics. It is not possible for the geologist to use geophysical tools most effectively unless he has a thorough understanding of the physical principles behind the various methods, particularly those involved in the recording of field data and its processing. Geological considerations should guide all aspects of geophysical prospecting from choice of field recording parameters and processing programs to final mapping of results in geological terms.

The book is also intended for students of geophysics who want a broad view of all phases of geophysics, particularly those outside their own areas of specialization. It is hoped that the book will be helpful to professional geophysicists who would like to review basic principles and at the same time keep up to date on new developments. Continuing education courses in geophysics have been well attended in recent years, indicating a widespread need for such updating.

It is hoped that this book will serve a broader purpose than the mere presentation of technical information. Geophysical prospecting is a field of activity that is of particular current importance because of its bearing on the maintenance of the world's industrial economy as well as living standards in many parts of the world. Both of these are highly dependent on the continued extraction of needed energy and mineral resources from the earth. As the challenge of finding such resources has grown, there has been an increasing need for dedicated individuals of exceptional ability to choose applied geophysics as a career. It would be most gratifying if this book could lead students with the necessary qualifications to consider careers in a field that can offer the dual satisfaction of helping meet society's material needs as well as of meeting the challenge, more and more exacting as time goes on, of unravelling the fragmentary clues left by nature to the location of the treasures still hidden in the earth.

Many people have helped me with this edition in numerous ways during the time when I was writing it. I should like to acknowledge such assistance from Terry Spencer, of Texas A and M University; Carl Savit, of Western Geophysical Co.; Harry Mayne, of Petty-Ray Geophysical; Leroy Brow, of Exxon, Inc.; Robert E. Sheriff, of Seiscom-Delta, Inc.; Harold Mooney, of the University of Minnesota; and Fred Hilterman, of the University of Houston; all of them have given me valuable information or material.

Several geophysicists have reviewed portions of the manuscript relating to their areas of specialization and have given me the benefit of their comments. Among these are Mr. Savit, Mr. Mayne, and Dr. Sheriff as well as Thomas R. LaFehr of Edcon, Inc., and Ralph C. Holmer and George V. Keller of Colorado School of Mines. Ralph B. Ross, a consultant and John C. Hollister, retired chairman of the Geophysics Department of Colorado School of Mines, have read the entire manuscript. All of these reviewers have made many valuable suggestions for improving the book and their assistance is deeply appreciated.

I am particularly indebted to Bernard F. Bash and John Hough, students at the University of Houston, for invaluable help in assembling the material for the book and to Mrs. Doris Segelhorst for her patient typing of what must have appeared to be an endless number of drafts of the text.

Milton B. Dobrin

INTRODUCTION TO GEOPHYSICAL PROSPECTING

CHAPTER 1

THE PLACE OF GEOPHYSICS IN OIL AND MINERAL EXPLORATION

The extraction at a continually increasing rate of fossil fuels and useful minerals from the earth has raised the specter of impending shortages that could threaten the economy and way of life of the civilized world. Events of the middle 1970s have demonstrated how well founded this concern can be. The amounts of oil, gas, and metallic minerals that actually exist in the earth, both known and undiscovered, are of course limited, but the immediate problem as established reserves become scarce is to find new supplies in the earth that will replace those which have been consumed. The exploration for energy supplies and mineral resources has become increasingly difficult as the "easy" sources are discovered and exploited.

To meet the challenge, earth scientists have developed more and more sophisticated techniques of exploration. Until well into the twentieth century the search for oil and solid minerals was confined to deposits directly observable on the surface in the form of seeps and outcrops or other exposures. When all accumulations in an area that could be discovered by such simple means had been found, it was necessary to deduce the presence of buried deposits indirectly by downward projection of geological information observable on the surface. As this approach reached the point of diminishing returns, new methods of studying the subsurface were needed. They did not require any geological observations, but they did involve physical measurements at the earth's surface that would give information on the structure or composition of concealed rocks that might be useful for locating desired deposits.

1-1 GEOPHYSICS AND GEOLOGY

We designate the study of the earth using physical measurements at or above the surface as *geophysics*. While it is not always easy to establish a meaningful border line between geology and geophysics, the difference lies primarily in the type of data with which one begins. Geology involves the study of the earth by direct observations on rocks, either from surface exposure or boreholes, and the deduction of its structure, composition, or history by analysis of such observations. Geophysics, on the other hand, involves the study of those parts of the earth hidden from direct view by measuring their physical properties with appropriate instruments, usually on or above the surface. It also includes interpretation of the measurements to obtain useful information on the structure and composition of the concealed zones. The distinction between the two branches of earth science is not clear-cut. Well logs, for example, are widely used in geological studies, even though they present the results of purely instrumental observations. The term *borehole geophysics* is often used to designate such measurements.

In a broader sense, geophysics provides the tools for studying the structure and composition of the earth's interior. Virtually all of what we know about the earth below the limited depths to which boreholes or mine shafts have penetrated has come from geophysical observations. The existence and properties of the earth's crust, mantle, and core have been determined by observations upon seismic waves from earthquakes, as well as by measurements of the earth's gravitation, magnetic, and thermal properties. The tools and techniques developed for such studies have been used in exploration for hydrocarbons and minerals. At the same time, geophysical methods devised for prospecting applications have been put to use in more academic research on the nature of the earth's interior. While this book will emphasize the economic applications of geophysics, it should be stressed that the areas of "pure" and "applied" geophysics have so much interdependence that the separation is artificial at best.

1-2   THE TECHNOLOGICAL CHALLENGE OF GEOPHYSICS

Geophysical exploration is a relatively new area of technology. Ferrous minerals were sought with magnetic compasses as early as the 1600s, but only during the past century have special instruments been put to use in mining exploration. Geophysical prospecting for oil and gas is in its sixties, the first oil discovery attributable to geophysics having been made in 1924. Throughout its history, the tools and techniques of exploration geophysics have been continually improved, both in performance and economy. This progress has been in response to an unrelenting pressure to develop new capabilities after existing ones have become inadequate to find enough new deposits. Except in areas newly opened to exploration, most geophysical surveys are undertaken where previous ones have failed because the instruments, field techniques, or interpretational methods were not good enough. In other words, those accumulations which are capable of being located with existing technology are the only ones that will be discovered at a given time. Those remaining will not be found until the technology improves sufficiently to bring them to light.

Thus the exploration geophysicist finds himself in the same situation as a man on an accelerating treadmill who must run faster and faster just to stay where he is. This problem is also faced by others involved in the exploration process, such as geologists and drilling engineers.

The technological improvements in geophysical exploration have been of several types. In some cases, new techniques have been developed to solve problems associated with the environment where exploration is to be carried out. In offshore areas, or in deserts, Arctic tundra, or lava-covered terrain, special logistics are needed. Moreover, unique types of "noise" in such areas often cause interference with desired geophysical information, and special techniques must be developed to suppress such interference. The introduction of analog computer technology in the 1950s and digital computers in the 1960s brought about new capabilities in the recording and processing of all kinds of geophysical data, making it possible to extract useful information otherwise concealed by undesired noise.

The technological revolution following World War II brought about many scientific developments which have contributed greatly to the effectiveness of geophysical exploration. Electronic computers, microminiature electronics, information-processing techniques, and navigation satellites, to cite some examples of pertinent space-age developments, have all been put to extensive use by geophysicists searching for oil and other natural resources.

1-3   REVIEW OF GEOPHYSICAL PROSPECTING METHODS

The geophysical techniques most widely employed for exploration work are the seismic, gravity, magnetic, electrical, and electromagnetic methods. Less common methods involve the measurement of radioactivity and temperature at or near the earth's surface and in the air.

Some of these methods are used almost entirely in the search for oil and gas. Others are used primarily in exploring for solid minerals. Most of them may be employed for either objective. Seismic, magnetic, and gravity prospecting are the chief tools for hydrocarbon exploration; seismic and electrical methods are the two chief tools used for mineral exploration. In the U.S.S.R., in former French territories, and, more recently, in parts of the United States, electromagnetic methods have been applied routinely to the search for oil. Magnetic and electromagnetic methods are employed for both types of prospecting.

Seismic Reflection Method   With this method—by far the most widely used geophysical technique—the structure of subsurface formations is mapped by measuring the times required for a seismic wave (or pulse), generated in the earth by a near-surface explosion, mechanical impact, or vibration, to return to the surface after reflection from interfaces between formations having different physical properties. The reflections are recorded by detecting instruments responsive to ground motion. They are laid along the ground at distances from the point of generation, which are generally small compared with the depth of the reflector. Variations in the reflection times from place to place on the surface usually indicate structural features in the strata below. Depths to reflecting interfaces can be estimated from the recorded times and velocity information that can be obtained either from the reflected signals themselves or from surveys in wells. Reflections from depths of 30,000 ft or more can normally be observed by combining the reflections from the repeated source applications, so in most areas geologic structure can be determined throughout the sedimentary section.

In recent years, reflection data have also been used for identifying lithology, generally from velocity and attenuation characteristics of the transmitted and reflected seismic waves, and for detecting hydrocarbons, primarily gas, directly on the basis of reflection amplitudes and other seismic indicators.

The reflection method comes closer than any other prospecting technique to providing a structural picture of the subsurface comparable to what could be obtained from a great number of boreholes in close proximity. Modern reflection record sections are similar in appearance to geologic cross sections, and geologists must sometimes be cautioned not to use them as such without taking into consideration some potential hazards that might lead to erroneous interpretation, even with good-quality reflection data. Under ideal conditions, structural relief can be determined with a precision of about $\frac{1}{2}$ percent of depth below the surface.

This method makes it possible to produce structural maps of any geologic horizons that yield reflections, but the horizons themselves usually cannot be identified without independent geological information such as might be obtained from wells. Reflection data can be used to determine the average velocities of seismic waves between the surface and the reflector. More important from a geological viewpoint, the velocities of seismic waves through depth intervals of a few percent of depth from the surface can now be obtained and often provide a good indication of lithology. The usefulness of such information depends on the layering as well as on the problem at hand.

With reflection methods, one can locate and map such features as anticlines, faults, salt domes, and reefs. Many of these are associated with the accumulation of oil and gas. Major convergences caused by depositional thinning can be detected from reflection sections. The resolution of the method is now approaching a fineness adequate for finding stratigraphic traps such as pinchouts or facies changes. However, successful exploration for stratigraphic oil accumulations by reflection techniques requires skillful coordination of geological and seismic information.

While current technological improvements have made it possible to obtain usable reflection data in many areas where reflections were formerly too poor to map, there are still places where reflection does not yield reliable information even though highly sophisticated data acquisition and processing techniques are used. In such intractable areas, other geophysical and geological methods must be employed.

Seismic Refraction Method In refraction surveying, the detecting instruments record seismic signals at a distance from the shot point that is large compared with the depth of the horizon to be mapped. The seismic waves must thus travel large horizontal distances through the earth, and the times required for the travel at various source-receiver distances give information on the velocities and depths of the subsurface formations along which they propagate. Although the refraction method does not give as much information or as precise and unambiguous a structural picture as reflection, it provides data on the velocity of the refracting beds. The method made it possible to cover a given area more quickly and economically than with the reflection method, though with a significant loss of detail and accuracy.

Refraction is particularly suitable where the structure of a high-speed surface, such as the basement or the top of a limestone layer, is the target of geological interest. If the problem is to determine the depth and shape of a sedimentary basin by mapping the basement surface, and if the sedimentary rocks have a consistently lower seismic velocity than do the basement formations, refraction was in the past an effective and economical approach for achieving this objective. Airborne magnetics and, to some extent, gravity have replaced seismic refraction for such purposes. Because velocities in salt and evaporites are often greater than in surrounding formations, refraction has been useful in mapping diapiric features such as salt domes. Under favorable circumstances, this technique has been used to detect and determine the throw of faults in high-speed formations, such as dense limestone and basement materials.

Despite its advantages, refraction is now rarely employed in oil exploration because of the larger-scale field operations required. Also, the reflection method has developed to the point that it can now yield nearly all of the information that refraction shooting could produce as well as relatively unambiguous and precise structural information unavailable from refracted waves.

Gravity Method   In gravity prospecting, one measures minute variations in the pull of gravity from rocks within the first few miles of the earth's surface. Different types of rocks have different densities, and the denser rocks have the greater gravitational attraction. If the higher-density formations are arched upward in a structural high, such as an anticline, the earth's gravitational field will be greater over the axis of the structure than along its flanks. A salt dome, on the other hand, which is generally less dense than the rocks into which it is intruded, can be detected from the low value of gravity recorded above it compared with that measured on either side. Anomalies in gravity that are sought in oil exploration may represent only one-millionth or even one-ten-millionth of the earth's total field. For this reason, gravity instruments are designed to measure variations in the force of gravity from one place to another rather than the absolute force itself. Modern gravimeters are so sensitive that they can detect variations in gravity to within less than one-hundred-millionth of the earth's total field.

The gravity method is useful wherever the formations of interest have densities that are appreciably different from those of surrounding formations. It is an effective means of mapping sedimentary basins where the basement rocks have a consistently higher density than the sediments. It is also suitable for locating and mapping salt bodies because of the generally low density of salt compared with that of surrounding formations. Occasionally it can be used for groundwater studies and for direct detection of heavy minerals such as chromites. Recently, extremely sensitive gravimeters have been used to detect underground tunnels and the locations of burial chambers in pyramids.

Data from gravity surveys are more subject to ambiguity in interpretation than with seismic surveys, because any gravity field can be accounted for equally well by widely different mass distributions. Additional geophysical or geological information over a gravity anomaly will reduce the ambiguity and increase the usefulness of the gravity data.

Gravity measurements are routinely made in conjunction with marine seismic work and are used as a minor supplement. Gravity surveys, unaccompanied by other methods, are no longer employed in oil and gas exploration except on rare occasions.

Magnetic Method   Magnetic prospecting maps variations in the magnetic field of the earth that are attributable to changes of structure, magnetic susceptibility, or remanence in certain near-surface rocks. Sedimentary rocks generally have a very small susceptibility compared with igneous or metamorphic rocks, which tend to have a much higher magnetite content, and most magnetic surveys are designed to map structure on or inside the basement or to detect magnetic minerals directly. The magnetic method was initially used for petroleum exploration in areas where the structure in oil-bearing sedimentary layers appeared to be controlled by topographic features, such as ridges or faults, on the basement surface.

Since the development of aeromagnetic methods, most magnetic surveys undertaken for oil exploration are carried out to ascertain the thickness of the sedimentary section in areas where such information is not otherwise available (usually frontier areas). Interpretation of such data is complicated by the fact that intrabasement susceptibility changes usually have a much more significant effect on the observed magnetic field than does structural relief on the basement surface itself.

In mining exploration, magnetic methods are employed for direct location of ores containing magnetic minerals such as magnetite. Intrusive bodies such as dikes can often be distinguished on the basis of magnetic observations alone.

Interpretation of magnetic data is subject to the same uncertainty as is found in gravity work, because of the lack of uniqueness inherent in all potential methods. Here again, the more geological information is available, the less the uncertainty in the final interpretation.

Electrical Methods   Electrical prospecting uses a large variety of techniques, each based on some different electrical property or characteristic of materials in the earth. The resistivity method is designed to yield information on formations or bodies having anomalous electric conductivity. The induced-polarization method, employed in the exploration for disseminated ore bodies such as sulfides, will give diagnostic readings where ionic exchanges take place on the surfaces of metallic grains. Such effects cause perturbations in the falloff of voltage across the ore mass when current passed through the mass from surface electrodes is suddenly cut off. The resistivity method has been used for a long time to map boundaries between layers having different conductivities. It is employed in engineering geophysics to map bedrock and in groundwater studies to determine salinity and the depth to the water table. Most recently it has been applied in the search for geothermal power because subterranean steam affects the resistivity of formations in a way that can often be diagnostic.

Telluric current and magnetotelluric methods use natural earth currents (the latter involving natural alternating magnetic fields as well), and anomalies are sought in the passage of such currents through earth materials. In this respect, these methods are different from resistivity and induced polarization, which require artificial introduction of electricity into the earth. Magnetotelluric methods have been found to be the only effective method of oil and gas exploration in areas where seismic work is not practicable, particularly where multiple sheets of volcanic rocks overlie the sedimentary section.

The self-potential method is used to detect the presence of certain minerals and metallic bodies that react with electrolytes in the earth in such a way as to generate electrochemical potentials. A sulfide body oxidized to a greater extent on its top than along its bottom will give rise to such potentials, which are detectable with electrodes at the surface.

Electromagnetic methods detect anomalies in the inductive properties of the earth's subsurface rocks. An alternating voltage is introduced into the earth by induction from transmitting coils either on the surface or in the air, and the amplitude and phase shift of the induced potential generated in the subsurface are measured by detecting coils and recorded. Ore of base metals can often be detected by this technique.

The resistivity and magnetotelluric methods are used extensively in the U.S.S.R. for mapping sedimentary basins at the early stages of exploration for petroleum in new areas. Other electrical methods, such as the telluric, have been employed by French geophysicists in Europe and Africa. Elsewhere in the world, electrical techniques have been employed for engineering purposes and in the search for solid minerals, water supplies, and geothermal energy.

Radioactive Methods   Radioactive prospecting for minerals containing uranium has involved the use of geophysical tools (geiger counters and scintillation counters) and must therefore be looked upon as a geophysical method. Much of the surface exploration for uranium is carried out by amateurs equipped with detecting instruments. Industrial prospecting involves radioactive logging of exploratory drill holes and airborne surveys with scintillation counters. Earlier editions of this book contained chapters on exploration for radioactive minerals, but the subject will not be covered in this edition because more coverage is needed for the state of the art in the more widely used areas of geophysics.

Well Logging   Well logging involves probing the earth with instruments that give continuous readings recorded at the surface as the instruments are pulled up through the borehole. Among rock properties currently being logged with such instruments are electrical resistivity, self-potential, gamma-ray generation (both natural and in response to neutron bombardment), density, magnetic susceptibility, and acoustic velocity.

Although well logging is one of the most widely used of all geophysical techniques, it would require a book as long as this even to introduce this subject properly. For this reason, well logging will not be covered here except for special applications such as velocity or density measurement. The reader interested in logging is directed to other publications devoted specifically to the subject.

1-4   GEOPHYSICS IN OIL EXPLORATION

Geophysics and Our Future Oil Supply

During the latter part of 1973, the matter of maintaining needed supplies of petroleum products became one of the most critical issues faced by most Western countries since World War II. As long ago as 1956, Hubbert predicted that the United States would reach its peak petroleum production in 1969 or 1970, and that from then on new reserves would not keep pace with increased consumption. His prediction for the United States was reaffirmed[1] in 1969, and statistics now available indicate that his projections were correct. Since 1973, the dependence of the United States upon imported oil has increased, but it was not until the embargos of 1973 that limitations on the availability of oil were really felt, not only in the United States but in most other countries as well. The impact of the sudden shortage upon the economy and way of life in affected countries illustrates the value of effective oil exploration in maintaining the equilibrium of our industrialized economy.

Hubbert[1] also predicted that peak production for the world as a whole would be reached between 1990 and 2000, the former year applying if the most pessimistic published estimates were used. Figure 1-1 shows these projections.

Hubbert's analysis proves that any oil surplus or ''glut'' that we may experience is bound to be a temporary phenomenon. Our continued use of this resource must inexorably reduce the world's supply, so eventually the price of oil (and gas) will have to increase to the point that alternative sources become economic.

The hydrocarbons now being extracted from petroleum to meet the demand for energy need not come from conventional sources, because they can, in principle at least, be extracted from tar sands or oil shales or be synthesized from coal. But the technological, economic, and environmental problems of changing over to such alternative sources are so formidable that we shall be almost entirely dependent on oil and gas in their present form for many years. Even when the capacity for large-scale conversion of other fossil fuels is achieved, there will be demand for all the conventional petroleum that can be produced as long as the costs of exploration and production do not become so great that other sources can be exploited more cheaply.

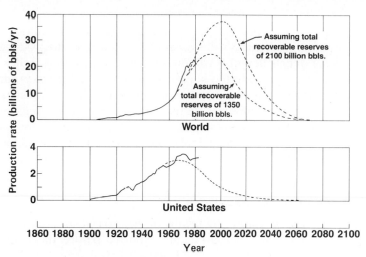

FIGURE 1-1   Crude oil production for the United States and world since 1900 and projected into the 21st century. (*From Hubbert*[1] *and API.*)

Present geophysical exploration techniques are limited in their usefulness in many long-known petroliferous areas. To find substantial new oil and gas reserves requires further technological development of geophysical methods or new frontiers to explore. Many undiscovered deposits are located under water or in environments, e.g., desert or tundra, where conventional geological exploration is not very promising. Other undiscovered deposits are entrapped in such a way that existing geophysical techniques are incapable of finding them, and the only effective means of discovery is costly wildcat drilling. Many such oil deposits have never been discovered because geophysical methods that will locate them have not yet been developed. The limitation also applies to some oil located in stratigraphic (as opposed to structural) traps, although the appearance since 1970 of techniques for direct detection of gas by seismic reflection is changing the prospects. Other potential improvements are discussed by Dobrin.[2]

In consideration of these facts, the conclusion seems reasonable that no technical factor may be as important in governing the future supply of conventional oil as the development of improvements in geophysical techniques. Two areas for potential advances are particularly significant: (1) the attainment of capability for mapping productive structures in places where no usable data can be obtained by existing methods and (2) the further development and use of effective geophysical techniques for locating oil in stratigraphic traps.

Of the many important technical advances in geophysics since its introduction as a tool for oil exploration in the early 1920s, none has been responsible for any really significant increase in discovery rates. As pointed out by Lyons,[3] the ratio of discoveries in exploration wells located by geophysics remained constant through the 1950s at about one in six. Improvements in technology had thus done no more than keep pace with the increasing difficulty of finding oil as the easier-to-locate deposits were found. The inexorable decline of supply and continuing demand will sooner or later combine to produce increases in the real price of petroleum. It will then pay to look for the smaller or more inaccessible deposits that were too hard to find and too costly to produce. In any case, the inevitable future shortages of petroleum make it especially important that geophysical techniques be brought to the greatest degree of effectiveness that natural limitations allow. The incredible pace of technological development in geophysics and related fields since 1960 appears to be, if anything, accelerating and gives assurance of many more years of oil and gas discoveries.

Historical Development of Petroleum Geophysics

The earliest efforts to locate oil-bearing structures by geophysical tools involved gravity measurements. Shortly before the beginning of the present century, Baron Roland von Eötvös, of Hungary, completed development of the torsion balance that bears his name. This was a field device for measuring the distortions in the earth's gravitational field that would result from buried bodies, such as salt domes, that have anomalous densities. In 1915 and 1916 the torsion balance was employed to detail the structure of what was then a one-well oil field at Egbell, now in Czechoslovakia. According to Eckhardt,[4] this survey was highly successful. In 1917, Schweidar detailed a known salt dome at Hanigsen in Germany with a torsion balance, and the predicted structure was confirmed by subsequent drilling. Early in 1922, according to DeGolyer,[5] Shell surveyed the Horgada field in Egypt with this type of instrument, and later that year the Spindletop field in Texas was traversed by a torsion balance, yielding a striking anomaly over the known salt structure.

Early Gulf Coast Surveys   In 1922 the torsion balance was used for the first time to explore for oil over areas where the structure was completely unknown. This was in the Gulf Coast of the United States, where the association of oil with salt domes had been well established, making the torsion balance particularly suitable as an exploration tool. Immediately afterwards, the instrument was introduced in Mexico.

At about the same time, seismic refraction equipment, very crude by modern standards, was brought from Germany to look for salt domes in the Gulf Coast.*

In 1919, Ludger Mintrop had applied for a German patent on locating and measuring depths to subsurface features by refraction profiling. The earliest work, in 1923, was in Mexico, but later in the year a refraction (fan-shooting) survey was undertaken along the Mexia fault zone in the Texas Gulf Coast.

Both the torsion-balance and refraction campaigns were successful in locat-

---

* Most of the material presented here on the early history of seismic prospecting is from Weatherby.[6]

ing salt domes as early as 1924. The gravity surveys led to the discovery of the productive Nash domes, and the seismic shooting was responsible for finding the Orchard dome, both in Texas. These successes led to more widespread application of the two techniques, and by 1929 virtually all the piercement-type domes in the Gulf Coast had been discovered.

Refraction in Iran   Meanwhile, in 1928, the seismic refraction method was introduced into the Middle East by the D'Arcy Exploration Company (which subsequently became British Petroleum). This technique turned out to be highly effective for finding the large oil-bearing limestone structures in Iran and was used successfully there for two decades.

Early Reflection Work   The earliest experiments with the seismic reflection method were carried out by J. C. Karcher from 1919 to 1921. To demonstrate the potential of the method for oil exploration, he mapped a shallow reflecting bed in central Oklahoma early in 1921. On the fiftieth anniversary of this event, in April 1971, a monument (Fig. 1-2) was dedicated at the site where these tests had been conducted. Karcher was present at the ceremonies. Two of the first reflection records he shot there, as well as his interpretation of them, are shown in Fig. 1-3.

It was not until 1927, however, that the reflection method was put to work for routine exploration. In that year, the Geophysical Research Corporation used the technique to discover the Maud Field in Oklahoma. By the early 1930s, reflection became the most widely used of all geophysical techniques, a status it has maintained ever since.

Gravity after the Torsion Balance   The torsion balance was slow and cumbersome to operate, and more fieldworthy instruments were developed for measuring gravity by the early 1930s. A simple pendulum system was introduced by Gulf Research & Development Company in 1932, and it was used in the field until about 1935. In 1935, the first gravimeter (an instrument giving direct readings of gravity differences) was put to use in commercial prospecting, and in a short time gravimeters virtually displaced all other gravity-measuring tools in oil exploration work. Light-weight gravity meters appearing in the late 1940s increased the speed and economy of land surveys. Bottom meters were introduced for water work before World War II, and shipborne meters were in use by the early 1960s.

Early Seismic Work in Water-Covered Areas   Ever since the later 1920s, when seismic surveys were conducted from houseboats and barges in the bays and bayous of the Gulf Coast, geophysics has been used to explore for oil in water-covered areas. After the end of World War II, seismic surveys were being undertaken in the open ocean, both off the Gulf Coast and off California. In the early 1950s, marine surveys had been carried out in the Gulf of Mexico, on the California shelf, in the Persian Gulf, and in Lake Maracaibo, Venezuela.

FIGURE 1-2 Monument unveiled in 1971 at Belle Isle (Oklahoma City), Okla., to commemorate 50th anniversary of first reflection shooting by J. C. Karcher. (*SEG*)

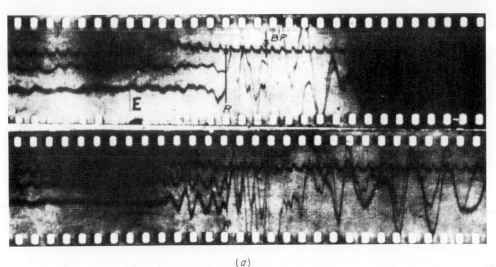

(a)

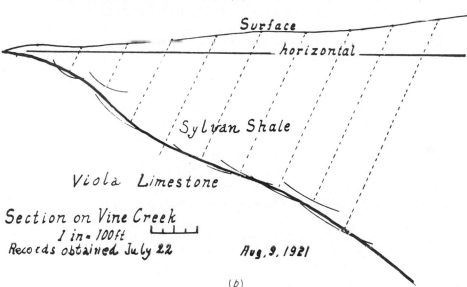

(b)

FIGURE 1-3 (a) Two of the earliest reflection records ever shot. Recorded by J. C. Karcher and colleagues at Belle Isle, Okla., in 1921. (b) Karcher's interpretation of his earliest reflection line, Belle Isle, Okla., 1921.

But it was not until the middle 1960s that marine exploration was extended to include almost all the shelf areas of the world, with widespread use of gravity, magnetic, and seismic instruments.

Advances after World War II Since the end of World War II, continual progress has been made by oil companies, geophysical companies, and equipment manufacturers in developing new and improved geophysical tools. Most of the advancements in the seismic reflection method were initiated with the primary objective of eliminating noise that interferes with reflections. A number of innovations were introduced to achieve greater safety, economy, or flexibility in field operations. Most of the new energy sources that have appeared since the 1950s are in this category.

Presentation of tape-recorded data on time-corrected record sections became common practice during the later 1950s. In 1963, digital recording equipment was first employed on a widespread basis, and digital computers were programmed to process the data thus acquired. The recording and processing techniques have been greatly improved over the years, full advantage being taken of the increased storage capacity and speed of the computers as well as other advances made by communications engineers and applied mathematicians in signal-processing technology.

Other developments related to field operations have increased the economy and effectiveness of the seismic reflection method. Mechanical impactors, such as land air guns, and vibrators operating on the surface have displaced explosives in shot holes as sources of seismic energy in about one-half of land exploration. For some years, the Thumper (trademark, Petty-Ray Geophysical Inc.) and the Dinoseis (trademark, ARCO), impulsive sources that produce signals similar to those of explosives, were used, but have now virtually disappeared from the scene. About half of present-day land reflection work is done with the vibroseis source, which generates a continuous wave of slowly varying frequency. Data from this source require special processing procedures before they can be used. Another highly significant development was common-depth-point recording, in which signals from different shot-point–receiver pairs are time-corrected and composited for reduction of noise. This technique was invented by Harry Mayne of Petty Geophysical Engineering Company in the early 1950s,* but it did not come into widespread use until about a decade later, when processing technology had been developed that made it economically feasible.

The universal use of common-depth-point techniques in offshore seismic work led to the development of ship-towed streamer cables more than 2 mi long, with large numbers of pressure phones per channel. Such cables record reflections with less interference from noise than was usually possible with earlier types. The most striking innovation in marine geophysics, however, has been the replacement of explosives by special energy sources, such as the nearly ubiquitous air guns, and the lesser used water guns, sparkers, and propane-oxygen exploders.

Gravity and magnetic instruments have also been adapted for work at sea. Shipborne gravity meters that give a continuous record of gravity variations from a moving ship make such surveys more economical than those made with

---

* A technique for determining velocities by use of a similar approach in the field was introduced in the early 1930s by Cecil H. Green.

water-bottom meters of the type previously employed in offshore gravity work. Such shipborne meters are on gyroscopically stabilized platforms which compensate for accelerations resulting from ship motion. Proton and optical-pumping magnetometers are often used for obtaining magnetic data on marine surveys undertaken primarily for seismic recording.

Direct Detection of Hydrocarbons (Bright Spots)

One of the most significant developments in the entire history of exploration geophysics is the capability demonstrated in 1960 (Savit[7]) and put into use in the early 1970s for direct detection of gaseous hydrocarbons, usually in water-covered areas, by proper processing of seismic reflection data. Until this capability was established, it was generally taken for granted that geophysics could locate structures and, in some cases, stratigraphic features favorable for oil and gas accumulation but could not locate the hydrocarbons themselves. Its development can thus be looked upon as a revolutionary breakthrough in geophysical prospecting.

The detection technique is based on the principle that there is a *greater* contrast in velocities at an interface when one formation is charged with gas than when the same formation is saturated with oil or water. Gas-saturated sands have a lower velocity than adjacent water- or oil-saturated sands; the greater velocity contrasts across surfaces bounding the gas zones above or below give reflections of higher amplitude than those observed from the same interface on either side of the gas zones. Miller[8] in 1948 was the first to document his calculations of this phenomenon. Processing techniques that allow true relative amplitudes to be observed on seismic record sections make it possible to observe the high reflection amplitudes directly on the sections in the form of *bright spots* (see Chap. 9).

Although there have been numerous verifications by drilling of gas accumulations predicted by bright spots, many predictions have not been borne out because certain shale masses and small, noncommercial gas accumulations at anomalously high pressure also yield bright spots. The bright-spot technique has, however, developed into a technique for quantitative study of reflection amplitudes. Those amplitudes have been translated into quantities closely related to the velocity of sound in the reflecting layers. Velocity data in turn make possible much finer discrimination between potentially productive zones and false alarms.

Statistics on Oil-Exploration Activity

Since 1933 the Society of Exploration Geophysicists (SEG) has published statistics on the level of geophysical activity expressed in terms of crew-months. Curves based on the statistics thus presented show how greatly such activity fluctuates because of economic and political factors.

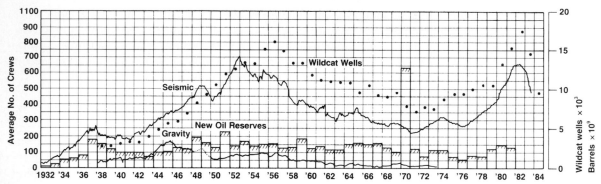

FIGURE 1-4 Statistics on crew activity and gravity prospecting in the United States along with number of wild-cat wells drilled and new reserves discovered, 1933–1984. (*Data from SEG activity reports and American Petroleum Institute.*)

Figure 1-4 illustrates the variation of seismic exploration activity in the United States since 1933 and that of gravity exploration activity since 1938 (expressed by the number of crews operating) along with corresponding statistics on exploratory drilling and on new oil discovered in the United States. It is evident that the level of seismic activity in the United States has peaked twice, once in 1952 and once in the early 1980s, both times followed by precipitous declines. Gravity activity has decreased significantly since 1945. The count of crew-months does not, however, tell the entire story. Marine activity off the coasts of the United States has shown a long-term increase, but it is not evident from statistics based on number of crews alone that a marine seismic crew can cover 20 times as many miles of line per day as a typical land crew. Furthermore, today's marine crew using modern cables, sources, and navigation techniques can cover three or four times as much ground in its 24-hour day than could comparable but daylight-bound crews only 20 years ago. Moreover, a modern land crew using common-depth-point shooting techniques and digital recording accounts for a vastly greater expenditure and volume of subsequent data-processing activity than a typical crew doing land work required as recently as the early 1960s. Therefore, the seismic activity peak in the early 1980s represents substantially more miles and crew effort than does the peak in 1952.

The plots of oil discovery and drilling activity when properly smoothed show correlation with geophysical activity if the time lags between exploration work and consequent drilling (sometimes as great as 6 years) are taken into account. The anomalously high level of new reserves indicated for 1970 reflects the discovery of the Prudhoe Bay field in Alaska, the reserves estimates for which became official in that year.

It should be emphasized that the growth in worldwide geophysical activity since the early 1950s has compensated to a large extent for the decline in United States domestic work. During this period, geophysical surveys have been carried out at an increasing rate in almost every part of the world where

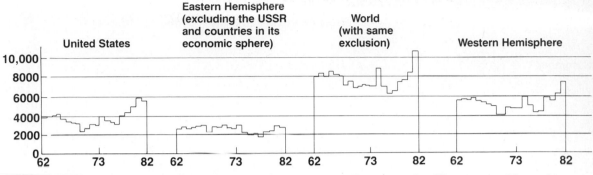

FIGURE 1-5 Distribution of geophysical activity in crew-months per year for different parts of the world, 1962–1982. (*Data from SEG activity reports.*)

there are known petroleum prospects (see Fig. 1-5). Nowhere has the increase been as pronounced as in offshore areas (see Fig. 1-6), although it is difficult to demonstrate this because published statistics on marine activity in various parts of the world were not reliable before 1967.

Of great significance to the industry and profession of exploration geophysics is the recent application of seismic reflection technology to the development and production of oil and gas fields after their discovery. By surveying parallel seismic lines as close together as one or a few hundred feet, scientists can obtain enough data to account for three-dimensional propagation effects and to map a volume of the subsurface quite accurately. Interpreted by means of interactive computer graphics, the results guide the placement and drilling of

FIGURE 1-6 Worldwide seismic marine activity since 1944. (*Data from C. H. Johnson and D. M. Blue, Offshore Technology Conf., proc., 1969 and SEG activity reports.*)

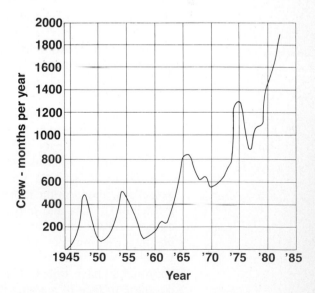

development wells in the newly discovered field and the sequence and progress of secondary and tertiary recovery activities in the mature field.

Summary

Geophysics has occupied a most important place in the exploration for oil and gas since its introduction in the early 1920s, but its effectiveness is nevertheless limited. Although it is now possible to directly detect some hydrocarbon deposits by seismic reflection methods, many operators have not developed the confidence and the skills to abandon their primary reliance on structural information. However, purely structural choices of well locations are fraught with perils. If there are no source beds, or if rocks needed as reservoirs do not have the necessary porosity or permeability, structures that look highly favorable from a geometrical standpoint will inevitably be dry. The record of geophysics in locating stratigraphically trapped oil has been quite poor, although the newer techniques are beginning to improve its performance (Savit and Wu[9]). The likelihood that the record of success can be generally applied to stratigraphic accumulations depends on the geological characteristics of the trap itself and on the amount of geological information available. Reefs, usually classified as stratigraphic features, that may serve as hydrocarbon traps can often be found by seismic reflection as easily as most structural traps. Pinchouts can usually be located, but operators remain reluctant to drill them because they must rely on velocity data to select the pinched-out bed or beds into which to drill. The place of seismic prospecting in locating stratigraphic oil has been discussed by Lyons and Dobrin.[10] The book in which this article appears contains numerous case histories illustrating all degrees of success with geophysics, the extent depending on the geologic nature of the accumulation. More recent case histories based on velocity techniques have only begun to appear as this was being written.

The only real limitations in finding structural traps with the seismograph have been inadequate resolution and interference by noise. Dramatic advances in seismic recording and data processing over the past two decades have brought about great improvements in the capability of the seismic method for overcoming both limitations. Many structures with potential for oil accumulation can be located now that would not have been discoverable a few years ago. Further improvements should lend still greater effectiveness to finding and verifying stratigraphic as well as structural traps favorable for oil accumulation.

As more oil is found, and as the amount of oil remaining to be discovered decreases, exploration targets are becoming deeper and the search extends farther out to sea and into deeper water. Moreover, the exploration effort is being extended more and more into remote areas and into those with more hostile environments and more difficult logistics. It also moves into areas where new techniques show their ability to obtain useful data after earlier approaches have failed. This is the challenge that geophysics faces and will continue to face in meeting the world's needs for energy from hydrocarbons.

1-5   THE USE OF GEOPHYSICS IN MINING EXPLORATION

Geophysics and the World Supply of Minerals

Just as our society is critically dependent on petroleum products for its energy requirements, it is equally dependent on mineral supplies for maintenance of the industrial economy that is the basis of our modern civilization. The rate at which such mineral supplies are being extracted to meet the increasing demands of an ever-expanding economy has created great concern among economic geologists lest we run out of critically important minerals sooner than is generally realized. In 1968 Charles F. Park, Jr.,[11] said, "whereas in the past many minerals were at times in troublesome surplus, it now appears that the world is about to enter a period when shortages of several minerals may well develop in the next decade." His statement is even more applicable now.

Although supplies of most common metals are not now in jeopardy, the world's annual consumption of them is enormous. Furthermore many critical metals are found in only one or a few areas that are remote or felt to be politically unstable or subject to hostile control. The combination of economic and political factors is perceived to require a high level of exploration activity to maintain adequate supplies. To the extent that geophysics can help in the discovery of such reserves, its place should become increasingly important as mineral shortages become more imminent.

Excellent surveys of geophysical techniques in mining can be found in Parasnis[12] and in Ref. 13. Geophysical methods have been most successful in locating two types of ores: (1) sulfides, both massive and disseminated, and (2) iron ores. Other minerals such as chromites and gold have been discovered by geophysical surveys but not nearly with the same degree of success.

The principal metals found in massive sulfide ore bodies are copper, nickel, lead, and zinc. The most common minerals in which they are found are chalcopyrite, pyrrhotite, galena, and sphalerite. Most such ore bodies are characterized by high conductivity, high density, and often, because of the frequent occurrence of magnetite as "guest" mineral, high magnetic susceptibility. The electromagnetic, resistivity, and induced-polarization techniques appear best for detecting conductivity anomalies associated with such bodies. Gravity measurements are desirable for observing density anomalies where they are significant, and magnetometer surveys for measuring any diagnostic magnetic anomalies.

Disseminated sulfide ores are favorable sources of porphyry copper and molybdenum. Among the minerals appearing most frequently in this form are chalcopyrite, chalcocite, bornite, molybdenite, and pyrite. The most effective geophysical tool for finding ores of this type is the induced-polarization technique.

Iron ores of greatest economic interest contain magnetite and hematite. Magnetite has the highest magnetic susceptibility of all minerals, and magnetic techniques are most suitable in the search for iron in this form. Hematite is not particularly magnetic, but it is often related genetically or stratigraphically to lithologic units which do contain magnetic minerals, so the magnetometer may be suitable in exploring for it as well as for magnetite. Since the density of magnetite and hematite is often greater than that of the host rocks containing these minerals, gravity surveys may be useful in the search for both kinds of ores.

Recent discoveries of massive deposits of polymetallic sulfide ores at vents in the ocean bottom give hope that it will be many centuries before the world experiences a real shortage of nonferrous metals. The true significance of these deposits must await development of mining and transport techniques. Exploring for these deposits is, however, well within the capabilities of present-day geophysical technology.

History of Mining Geophysics

Geophysical tools were applied to mineral exploration almost three centuries before geophysics was used in the search for oil. The magnetic compass was employed in prospecting for iron ores as early as 1640, but it was not until about 100 years ago that a special type of instrument, the Swedish mining compass, was developed for such investigations. Its magnetic needle was so suspended that it could be rotated about both horizontal and vertical axes. American versions of this compass were used to explore for iron ore in New Jersey and Michigan during the last decades of the nineteenth century.

One of the earliest pioneers of exploration geophysics was Robert Fox, who in 1815 discovered that certain minerals exhibit spontaneous polarization. He proposed measurement of this effect as a means of prospecting for such ores. It was not until almost a century later, however, that a commercial discovery was made by this technique. In 1913, Conrad Schlumberger used it to locate a sulfide deposit at Bor. About the same time, he developed practical field techniques for resistivity and equipotential-line prospecting, techniques which were based on experiments carried out by Osborn and others before the turn of the century in the Great Lakes mining area.

From 1915 to 1920, dip needles of various types were introduced for magnetic-mineral prospecting. The Schmidt magnetometer, still in occasional use, appeared about this time. Airborne magnetometers (based on the flux-gate principle) under development for exploration were used for submarine detection during World War II and applied to prospecting shortly after the war. Nuclear magnetometers, both for ground and airborne surveys, appeared around 1955, and the even more precise optical-pumping-type (cesium- and rubidium-vapor) magnetometers were introduced into exploration work around 1961. The airborne magnetic gradiometer came into use in the middle 1960s. All these magnetic instruments have been employed both in mining and petroleum exploration.

During the 1920s, improved techniques were developed for resistivity prospecting involving multiple-electrode configurations. Electromagnetic methods were introduced by Hans Lundberg in the middle 1920s, and they were adapted for airborne surveys about 1947.

Before World War II, the theoretical basis for mining exploration was quite limited, and interpretation was often only qualitative. Since the war, there have been significant advances in the theory behind the interpretation methods used in mining geophysics, particularly with the magnetic and electromagnetic techniques.

A number of geophysical methods for mining exploration have come into widespread use since World War II. In 1948, the induced-polarization, or overvoltage, method was introduced commercially in the search for sulfide ores. Magnetotelluric methods, including audio magnetotellurics, were also introduced after the war.

Statistics on Activity in Mining Geophysics   Mining geophysics appeared to enter a period of intensive growth from 1963 to 1968 (see Fig. 1-7). From the standpoint of dollar volume, worldwide geophysical activity in mining exploration increased by a factor of more than 3 from 1961 to 1968. This is a much greater rise than can be accounted for by inflation alone. By the late 1970s, expenditures for mining geophysics were up by another 50 percent. Since 1968, ground-method expenditures have fluctuated, but in real terms they have declined. Airborne-method expenditures from 1968 to the late 1970s have doubled. This doubling represents a fairly constant level of activity when corrected for the worldwide inflation during that interval. The statistics on expenditures separated into ground methods, airborne methods, and research, are presented in Fig. 1-7. On the same plot is shown the total number of person-

FIGURE 1-7   Worldwide activity in mining geophysics, separated by types of methods. All curves for expenditures are cumulative with respect to those below them. (*Data from SEG activity reports.*)

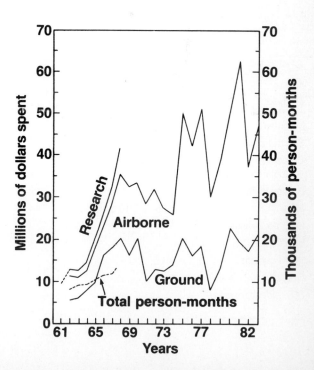

TABLE 1-1   PERCENTAGE OF MINING GEOPHYSICS EXPENDITURE BY METHOD: GROUND METHODS

Method	1974	1975	1976	1977	1978	1979	1980	1981	1982
Magnetic	9.3	7.6	6.8	8.9	1.6	4.2	2.5	4.1	4.7
Resistivity	9.8	8.2	4.85	40.8	14.0	10.7	4.2	2.1	0.8
Induced polarization	18.35	14.9	18.05	11.8	9.7	14.4	13.05	15.6	5.3
Earth currents	1.5					0.15			
Self-potential	0.8				0.1		0.55	0.5	0.15
Electromagnetic	4.2	5.1	4.5	7.3	4.5	6.45	6.1	14.8	11.05
Gravity	6.9	9.9	9.05	10.3	9.0	4.2	10.7	6.1	6.5
Seismic	22.01	31.6	33.1	10.5	45.6	44.8	55.0	48.8	44.5
Radioactivity	12.4	4.9	8.75	2.3	1.5	1.4	0.9	1.15	2.7
Drill-hole logging	0.1								
Electrical	0.1								
Gravity/magnetic	2.4	10.8	5.8						
Magnetotelluric		0.5		0.1	3.1	3.2		0.8	5.4
Combined magnetic/ electromagnetic	7.6	2.8	7.4	5.5	9.9	6.4	3.7	2.7	6.6
Neutron activation	0.6	0.5		1.2					
VLF	0.5	0.9	1.3	0.5	0.1	0.3	0.7	1.4	1.0
Other	3.2	2.3	0.4	0.8	0.9	3.8	2.6	1.8	1.3
	100.0	100.0	100.0	100.0	100.0	100.0	100.0	100.0	100.0

TABLE 1-2   PERCENTAGE OF MINING GEOPHYSICS EXPENDITURE BY METHOD: AIRBORNE METHODS

Method	1974	1975	1976	1977	1978	1979	1980	1981	1982
Magnetic	60.9	66.8	45.8	47.6	51.7	33.0	27.0	40.45	42.2
Electromagnetic	0.5	0.3	0.3	0.45	0.7	0.9	3.65	8.2	
Combined magnetic/ electromagnetic	15.15	9.6	5.4	7.5	9.9	19.9	7.45	18.8	29.0
Radioactivity	8.6	12.6	31.2	29.5	31.5	6.25	17.0	13.15	7.5
Input	14.75	10.5	15.7	14.95	6.0	33.2	41.9	11.3	17.9
Remote sensing		0.1	0.4						
VLF		0.1	1.2			0.65		1.0	0.1
Earth current	0.1							0.1	3.3
Gravity						2.2			
R.S. sidescan radar					0.2	3.9	3.0	7.0	
	100.0	100.0	100.0	100.0	100.0	100.0	100.0	100.0	100.0

months applied to the search for minerals from 1962 to 1968. Its growth was much less (about 50 percent) than that of the expenditures during this period, indicating that the cost of equipment per geophysical employee more than doubled between 1962 and 1968.

Mining exploration involves a greater number of geophysical techniques than does petroleum prospecting, and prior to 1978 there is a more even distribution of activity among the methods. Tables 1-1 and 1-2 show the relative expenditure for the different ground and airborne geophysical methods used in mining over the period 1961 to 1982. Induced-polarization activity increased during the years from 1961 to 1969, then decreased from 1974 to 1982, while seismic activity increased. After 1978, 45 percent or more of the ground-method expenditures were for seismic methods.

1-6 UNIT ABBREVIATIONS USED IN THIS BOOK

With the exception of gals (not abbreviated) and milligals (abbreviated mgal), abbreviations for units follow the style of the Système International (SI), now being adopted in most fields. In this system, units named after people are given abbreviations that start with a capital letter, e.g., volt (V), joule (J), bel (B), and oersted (Oe). The name hertz (Hz) replaces cycles per second. Note that the capitalization applies only to the abbreviation for the unit; when it is spelled out, it is lowercase, as before. Units not named after people are given lowercase abbreviations, e.g., second (s), meter (m), and hour (h). To show multiples and submultiples of units, prefixes corresponding to certain powers of 10 are attached to the unit abbreviation (see Table 1-3). Many of these combinations, e.g., kg (kilogram), mm (millimeter), and kΩ (kilohm), are probably familiar to most readers.

In some contexts, we have departed from SI units and abbreviations when citing references or when common practice in the field is to use other systems.

TABLE 1-3   SI PREFIXES FOR POWERS OF 10*

			Example	
Multiple	**SI prefix**	**Abbreviation**	**Unit**	**Abbreviation**
10^6	mega	M	megahertz	MHz
10^3	kilo	k	kilocalorie	kcal
10^{-1}	deci	d	decibel	dB
10^{-2}	centi	c	centimeter	cm
10^{-3}	milli	m	millisecond	ms
10^{-6}	micro	μ	microsecond	μs
10^{-9}	nano	n	nanosecond	ns

* Abbreviations for powers of 10 not used in this text are omitted.

REFERENCES

1 Hubbert, M. King: "Resources and Man," National Academy of Sciences and the National Research Council, Freeman, San Francisco, 1969.

2 Dobrin, Milton B.: Geophysics and Our Future Oil Supply, in *Proc. Southwest Leg. Found., Explor. Econ. Pet. Ind.*, vol. 8, Matthew Bender, 1970.

3 Lyons, Paul L.: Economics of Geophysics in Oil Exploration, *Geophysics*, vol. 27, pp. 121–127, 1962.

4 Eckhardt, E. A.: A Brief History of the Gravity Method of Prospecting for Oil, *Geophysics*, vol. 5, pp. 231–242, 1940.

5 DeGolyer, E.: Notes on the Early History of Applied Geophysics in the Petroleum Industry, pp. 245–254, in "Early Geophysical Papers," Society of Exploration Geophysicists, Tulsa, Okla., 1947.

6 Weatherby, B. B.: The History and Development of Seismic Prospecting, *Geophysics*, vol. 5, pp. 215–230, 1940.

7 Savit, C .H.: Preliminary Report: A Stratigraphic Seismogram, *Geophysics*, vol. 25, pp. 312–321, 1960; Use Seismic Data to Find Stratigraphic Traps, *Oil and Gas J.*, April 11, 1960.

8 Miller, J. W.: The Possible Relation of Reflection Seismic Record Amplitudes to the Presence of Oil and Gas in a Simple Structure, MS Thesis, The Rice Institute (now Rice University), May 1948.

9 Savit, C. H., and Changsheng Wu: Geophysical Characterization of Lithology— Application to Subtle Traps, pp. 11–30, in *Am. Assoc. Petrol. Geol. Mem. 32*, 1982.

10 Lyons, Paul L., and M. B. Dobrin: Seismic Exploration for Stratigraphic Traps, pp. 225–243, in "Stratigraphic Oil and Gas Fields," *Am. Assoc. Petrol. Geol. Mem. 16* and *Soc. Explor. Geophys. Spec. Pub. 10*, 1972.

11 Park, Charles F., Jr.: "Affluence in Jeopardy," Freeman Cooper, San Francisco, 1968.

12 Parasnis, D.: "Mining Geophysics," Elsevier, New York, 1966.

13 Society of Exploration Geophysicists: "Mining Geophysics," vol. 1, Tulsa, Okla., 1966.

CHAPTER 2

HOW SEISMIC WAVES PROPAGATE

The seismic wave is the basic measuring rod used in seismic prospecting. If we are to understand how it works and evaluate the information we get from it in geological terms, we must be familiar with the basic physical principles governing its propagation characteristics. These include its generation, transmission, absorption, and attenuation in earth materials and its reflection, refraction, and diffraction characteristics at discontinuities. Seismic waves are generally referred to as elastic waves because they cause a nonpermanent deformation of the material in which they propagate like that in an elastic band when it is stretched. The deformation consists of alternating compressions and dilatations as the particles in the material move closer together and farther apart in response to forces associated with the traveling waves.

Many decades before the advent of seismic prospecting, the characteristics of elastic waves traveling in the earth were studied by seismologists concerned with signals from earthquakes. While the scale, both with respect to the wavelengths and distances involved, is much larger for natural earthquake waves than for those generated in seismic prospecting, both types of wave propagation are described by the same physical laws.

In introducing the basic concepts of elastic-wave propagation in the earth, we shall emphasize the physical and geological significance of the concepts rather than their formal mathematical expression.

2-1 ELASTIC CHARACTERISTICS OF SOLIDS

Stress and Strain Seismic waves propagate in solids as patterns of particle deformation traveling through the materials with velocities that depend upon

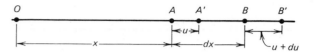

FIGURE 2-1   Quantities used in deriving expression for linear strain.

their elastic properties and densities. To show the nature of this dependence, we shall describe these deformations in terms of the forces which cause them and define the useful concepts of stress and strain. The relation between them for a particular material enables us to describe the elastic properties of the material as well as the characteristics, such as velocity, of waves propagating therein.

Dilatational Strain   Let us consider the changes in position of two points A and B inside a solid after a linear deformation (in this case tensional) (Fig. 2-1). A and B are a distance dx apart. A dilatational motion has shifted A to A' and B to B', the former having moved a distance u and the latter a distance $u + du$. Defining the *strain* as ratio of the change in separation to the original separation, we express the component of ϵ_x in the x direction as

$$\epsilon_x = \frac{u + du - u}{dx} = \frac{\partial u†}{\partial x} \tag{2-1}$$

Taking dv as the differential elongation in the y direction and dw as that in the z direction, we similarly define

$$\epsilon_y = \frac{\partial v}{\partial y} \quad \text{and} \quad \epsilon_z = \frac{\partial w}{\partial z}$$

The strains observed when seismic waves pass through a material are much too small to be seen by the eye, falling in the neighborhood of 10^{-6} for most linear deformation.

Shear Strain   If a cubic block is cemented to an immovable surface along its bottom face, as shown in Fig. 2-2a, and a horizontal traction is exerted along the upper face, the initially vertical faces perpendicular to the paper will be inclined after distortion, the surface initially vertical now making an angle α with its original direction. For a more general analysis, we should relinquish the constraint we have introduced along one face and leave the block free to rotate under shear as well as to deform elastically. This is because shearing deformation actually involves a combination of lengthening along one diagonal, shortening along another, motion along the diagonal, and rotation of the diagonal. Figure 2-2b shows the geometry. The angle (very much exaggerated in the

---

† The strain must be expressed as the partial derivative $\partial u / \partial x$ rather than as the total derivative du/dx because we must assume that y and z do not vary when x varies.

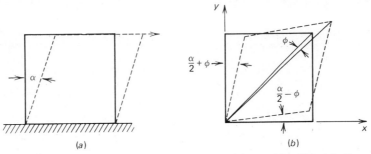

FIGURE 2-2   Two definitions of shear strain for cubical block: (*a*) one side of block in firm contact with rigid surface; (*b*) block fixed at one point and free to rotate as well as to deform under shear.

diagram) between the deformed surface originally lying in the *yz* plane and the reference plane (*yz* coordinate plane), which is $\alpha/2 + \phi$, where ϕ is the angle of rotation of the diagonal, is small enough to be approximated by its tangent, which is the rate of increase of deformation in the *x* direction with increasing *y*, or $\partial u/\partial y$. Similarly, $\alpha/2 - \phi$ can be approximated by $\partial v/\partial x$. We then solve for α, the shear strain, and ϕ, the rotation as follows:

$$\frac{\alpha}{2} + \phi = \frac{\partial u}{\partial y} \tag{2-2}$$

$$\frac{\alpha}{2} - \phi = \frac{\partial v}{\partial x} \tag{2-3}$$

$$\alpha = \frac{\partial u}{\partial y} + \frac{\partial v}{\partial x} \tag{2-4}$$

$$\phi = \frac{1}{2}\left(\frac{\partial u}{\partial y} - \frac{\partial v}{\partial x}\right) \tag{2-5}$$

Dilatation   When a three-dimensional body deforms in the same sense (either by extension or contraction) along all three coordinate axes, there will be an expansion of volume in the case of tensile deformation or a contraction of volume in the case of compressive deformation. The ratio of the change in volume to the volume before deformation is called *cubical dilatation*.

Assume a rectangular element *dx dy dz* before strain. When there is strain, the respective sides become $dx\,(1 + \epsilon_x)$, $dy\,(1 + \epsilon_y)$, and $dz\,(1 + \epsilon_z)$ and the resulting volume, as indicated in Fig. 2-3, is

$$dx\,dy\,dz\,(1 + \epsilon_x)(1 + \epsilon_y)(1 + \epsilon_z)$$
$$= dx\,dy\,dz\,[1 + (\epsilon_x + \epsilon_y + \epsilon_z) + (\epsilon_x\epsilon_y + \epsilon_x\epsilon_z + \epsilon_y\epsilon_z) + \epsilon_x\epsilon_y\epsilon_z] \tag{2-6}$$

The third and fourth terms on the right side are of second and third order, respectively, compared with the first term and may be neglected. Then the cubical dilation θ becomes, by definition,

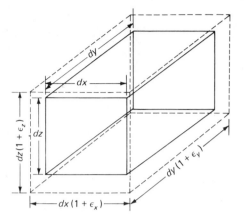

FIGURE 2-3   Expansion of rectangular parallelepiped under cubical dilatation.

$$\theta = \frac{dx\ dy\ dx\ (1\ +\ \epsilon_x\ +\ \epsilon_y\ +\ \epsilon_z)\ -\ dx\ dy\ dz}{dx\ dy\ dz} = \epsilon_x\ +\ \epsilon_y\ +\ \epsilon_z \quad (2\text{-}7)$$

Definition of Stress   Let us consider a small plane area ΔA on the surface of an irregular solid as shown in Fig. 2-4. Such an area could be taken in its interior as well. Assume that an element of force ΔF is exerted uniformly over the area in a direction to make an angle ψ with the normal to the plane surface. This force can be resolved into components $\Delta \bar{F}_N$ normal to the plane and $\Delta \bar{F}_T$ tangential to the plane in the directions indicated in the figure. The *stress S*, which is a vector since it has both magnitude and direction, is defined as the ratio of the force $\Delta \bar{F}$ to the area ΔA. As the area becomes infinitesimally small, S is expressible as the derivative

$$S = \frac{d\bar{F}}{dA} \quad (2\text{-}8)$$

FIGURE 2-4   Resolution of force acting on a small area of a solid into its normal and tangential components.

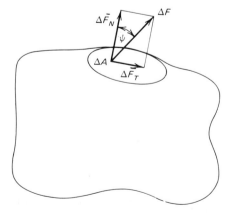

The limiting ratio of the normal component of force F_N to the area is defined as the *dilatational stress* dF_N/dA and the ratio involving the tangential component as the *shear stress* dF_T/dA.

To express stress in a more general way, we shall set up an *xyz* coordinate system and designate the orientation of the surface element upon which the force is exerted by the direction of its normal (Fig. 2-5). Let us consider a rectangular area with boundaries *dy* and *dz* with a normal in the *x* direction. A stress making an arbitrary angle ϕ with the normal would have one component X_x of dilatational stress and two components Y_x and Z_x of sheer stress. In this notation, the capital letter represents the direction of the force component, and the subscript indicates the direction of the *normal* to the area on which it is acting. If we draw two other rectangles representing elementary areas in the *xy* and *xz* planes and then resolve the corresponding stress elements with respect to them, we have a total of nine stress components, X_x, Y_y, and Z_z being dilatational stresses and the other six (such as X_y, Z_x, etc.) being shear stresses. As stresses in pairs, such as X_y and Y_x, are equal to each other, the actual number of independent stress components is six rather than nine.

Relations between Strain and Stress   When an "ideal" elastic solid is subjected to linear deformation in a single direction, the specification of the material as elastic implies a direct proportionality between the compressional or dilatational stress and the linear strain of the form

$$X_x = E\frac{\partial u}{\partial x} \tag{2-9}$$

where E, the proportionality constant, is *Young's modulus*. For most materials, E is the order of a megabar (10^{12} dyn/cm^2).

FIGURE 2-5   Resolution of stress acting on an element of area in the *yz* plane into one dilatational component (X_x) and two shear components (Y_x and Z_x).

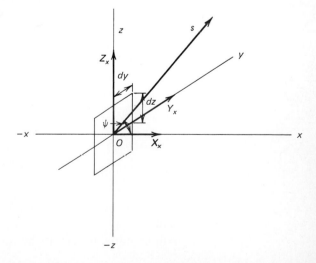

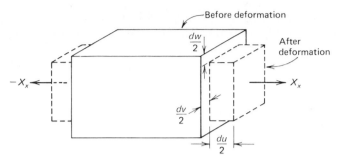

FIGURE 2-6   Deformation of rectangular parallelepiped by dilatational stress acting in one direction.

For a three-dimensional body, the relation between stress and strain is somewhat more complex. A tensional stress X_x will cause an elongation du in the x direction, as shown in Fig. 2-6, but at the same time there will be contractions in the y and z directions of dv and dw, respectively. It is evident that dv and dw will be less than du, both being related to du by the same proportionality constant σ, which is *Poisson's ratio*.

The relationship can be expressed by the equations

$$E\frac{\partial u}{\partial x} = X_x \qquad E\frac{\partial v}{\partial y} = -\sigma X_x \qquad E\frac{\partial w}{\partial z} = -\sigma X_x \qquad (2\text{-}10)$$

the minus signs representing contractions, so that σ can be expressed as $-\partial v/\partial u$ and $-\partial w/\partial u$.

If there is no volume change when a unidirectional stress is applied, σ becomes 0.5, the maximum value it can have. For highly consolidated, un-weathered rocks such as fine-grained limestones or deeply buried crystallines, σ ranges from 0.2 to 0.3, while for most nonindurated clastic sedimentary rocks it ranges from 0.05 to 0.02, depending on porosity and weathering.

Let us consider the case where tensile (or compressive) stresses act along all three principal axes, which may be designated X_x, Y_y, and Z_z. Each strain component can be written in terms of these stress components as

$$E\frac{\partial u}{\partial x} = X_x - \sigma Y_y - \sigma Z_z$$

$$E\frac{\partial v}{\partial y} = -\sigma X_x + Y_y - \sigma Z_z \qquad (2\text{-}11)$$

$$E\frac{\partial w}{\partial z} = -\sigma X_x - \sigma Y_y + Z_z$$

If the stress results from an excess hydrostatic pressure ΔP above the ambient pressure, all three of the stress components will be the same and each will be equal to ΔP. If the three equations of (2-11) are added, we have

$$E\left(\frac{\partial u}{\partial x} + \frac{\partial v}{\partial y} + \frac{\partial w}{\partial z}\right) = (1 - 2\sigma)(X_x + Y_y + Z_z)$$

$$= (1 - 2\sigma)3\Delta P \qquad (2\text{-}12)$$

or
$$E\theta = (1 - 2\sigma)(3\Delta P)$$

where
$$\theta = \frac{\Delta V}{V} \qquad (2\text{-}13)$$

Now define $(\Delta V/V)/\Delta P = \theta/\Delta P$ as the *compressibility* β of the material and $1/\beta = k$, the *bulk modulus*; then

$$k = \frac{\Delta P}{\theta} = \frac{E}{3(1 - 2\sigma)} \qquad (2\text{-}14)$$

This formula relates the constant for cubical dilatation resulting from pressure to the constants relating linear strain and linear stress.

The relationship between shear stress and shear strain is quite simple. For the small deformations involved in seismic-wave propagation, shear stress is proportional to shear strain, the proportionality constant being μ, as in the relation

$$X_y = Y_x = \mu\alpha = \mu\left(\frac{\partial u}{\partial y} + \frac{\partial v}{\partial x}\right) \qquad (2\text{-}15)$$

μ is called the *rigidity modulus*. For most rock materials it ranges from 0.1 to 0.7 Mbar.

The rigidity modulus can be expressed in terms of Young's modulus and Poisson's ratio as

$$\mu = \frac{E}{2(1 + \sigma)} \qquad (2\text{-}16)$$

A derivation of this relationship can be found in Dix[1] (pp. 300–303). Equations (2-14) and (2-16) illustrate the interrelation between the four basic elastic constants E, σ, k, and μ.

By algebraic manipulation of Eq. (2-11), the nine components of stress defined in the previous section can be linearly related to corresponding strain components. Dix[1] (pp. 303–305) shows that a dilatational stress like X_x can be expressed in the form

$$X_x = 2\mu\frac{\partial u}{\partial x} + \lambda\left(\frac{\partial u}{\partial x} + \frac{\partial v}{\partial y} + \frac{\partial w}{\partial z}\right) \qquad (2\text{-}17)$$

where λ, one of Lamé's coefficients, is related to Young's modulus E and Poisson's ratio σ as follows:

$$\lambda = \frac{E\sigma}{(1 + \sigma)(1 - 2\sigma)}$$

Generalizing from Eqs. (2-15) and (2-17), we can write

$$X_x = 2\mu\frac{\partial u}{\partial x} + \lambda\theta \qquad X_y = Y_x = \mu\left(\frac{\partial u}{\partial y} + \frac{\partial v}{\partial x}\right)$$

$$Y_y = 2\mu\frac{\partial v}{\partial y} + \lambda\theta \qquad Z_x = X_z = \mu\left(\frac{\partial w}{\partial x} + \frac{\partial u}{\partial z}\right) \qquad (2\text{-}18)$$

$$Z_z = 2\mu\frac{\partial w}{\partial z} + \lambda\theta \qquad Y_z = Z_y = \mu\left(\frac{\partial v}{\partial z} + \frac{\partial w}{\partial y}\right)$$

These are *Hooke's relations* for all stress components in terms of strains. They apply to "ideal" elastic solids (homogeneous and continuous) for deformations which are small enough to fall within the range of linearity implied by the equations.

2-2 PROPAGATION CHARACTERISTICS OF COMPRESSIONAL AND SHEAR WAVES

We shall next show how the propagation characteristics of seismic waves, particularly their velocities,* depend on the elastic constants defined in the previous section. To do this, we must show how one obtains the classical wave equation from Hooke's relations.

The general form of the wave equation, which is most applicable to the propagation of seismic waves through the earth, assumes deformation in three directions, each component of stress being associated with strain in more than one direction, as indicated in Eqs. (2-17) and (2-18).

The logic by which the more general equation is derived can be demonstrated very simply when applied to the case where the stress and strain are both confined to a single direction. This is what occurs when a thin rod is subjected to elastic deformation along its axis, as illustrated in Fig. 2-7. This rod, of area dA, has a Young's modulus E and density ρ. An element of the rod having a length of dx will be moved from the position bounded by the full lines to the position bounded by the dashed lines when subjected to an elastic stress

---

* The term *velocity* is, strictly speaking, a vector expressing both the magnitude, referred to as *speed*, and the direction of motion. In this book, velocity will be considered to be synonymous with speed.

FIGURE 2-7   Elastic deformation in element of thin rod caused by longitudinal stress wave along axis.

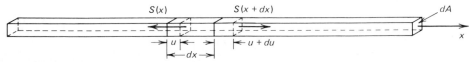

$S(x)$ in the axial direction x. The force on any surface is the stress times the area. The net force on such an element will be the difference between the forces $S(x)\,dA$ and $S(x + dx)\,dA$, where $S(x + dx)$ is the stress at the position $x + dx$. This net elastic force will equal the mass $\rho\,dx\,dA$ (density multiplied by volume) of the element times the acceleration d^2u/dt^2 of a particle having the instantaneous deformation u. This relation is expressed in the form

$$[S(x + dx) - S(x)]\,dA = \rho\frac{d^2u}{dt^2}dx\,dA \tag{2-19}$$

Now $S(x + dx) - S(x) = (dS/dx)\,dx$, and from Eq. (2-9), $S = E\,du/dx$ (the partial derivative not being needed because the deformation is only in the x direction). Differentiating the term for S, we get

$$E\frac{d^2u}{dx^2}dx\,dA = \rho\frac{d^2u}{dt^2}dx\,dA \tag{2-20}$$

and we can write the equation of motion

$$\frac{d^2u}{dx^2} = \frac{\rho}{E}\frac{d^2u}{dt^2} \tag{2-21}$$

This is the form of the classical one-dimensional wave equation

$$\frac{d^2q}{dx^2} = \frac{1}{V^2}\frac{d^2q}{dt^2} \tag{2-22}$$

where V is the velocity of propagation. A convenient solution is

$$q = A\sin k(Vt - x) \tag{2-23}$$

and this can be verified by differentiation. In the case of the elastic wave in a rod, comparison of Eqs. (2-21) and (2-22) shows that

$$V = \sqrt{\frac{E}{\rho}} \tag{2-24}$$

so that velocity of this wave depends only on the elastic modulus and the density.

The three-dimensional wave equation, which can be derived in a similar way, is essentially analogous. For compressional deformation it is

$$\frac{\partial^2\theta}{\partial x^2} + \frac{\partial^2\theta}{\partial y^2} + \frac{\partial^2\theta}{\partial z^2} = \frac{\rho}{\lambda + 2\mu}\frac{\partial^2\theta}{\partial t^2} \tag{2-25}$$

where θ is the cubical dilatation. For shear deformation, it is

$$\frac{\partial^2 \alpha}{\partial x^2} + \frac{\partial^2 \alpha}{\partial y^2} + \frac{\partial^2 \alpha}{\partial z^2} = \frac{\rho}{\mu} \frac{\partial^2 \alpha}{\partial t^2} \tag{2-26}$$

where α is the shear strain.

By comparing Eq. (2-22) with Eqs. (2-25) and (2-26), it is easy to show that the velocity V_P for compressional waves is

$$V_P = \sqrt{\frac{\lambda + 2\mu}{\rho}} \tag{2-27}$$

and the velocity V_s for shear waves is

$$V_s = \sqrt{\frac{\mu}{\rho}} \tag{2-28}$$

The solution to the wave equation can be expressed as a displacement (or pressure) that maintains its form as distance x and time t change as long as x and t are so related that $Vt - x$ is constant. This is another way of saying that the wave propagates at a velocity equal to x/t. Such a solution has the general form $f(Vt - x)$. The significance of this function is illustrated in Fig. 2-8.

A more complete and realistic form of the wave function, which holds for a pulse of any shape, is the Fourier series, which can be expressed as

$$f(Vt - x) = \sum_{n=1}^{n=\infty} [A_n \cos nk_1(VT - x) + B_n \sin nk_1(Vt - x)] \tag{2-29}$$

where A_n and B_n are the Fourier coefficients for the nth harmonic term and k_1 is 2π divided by λ, the fundamental wavelength (normally the length of the initial pulse). The n's are successive integers (1, 2, 3, . . .). Another form of Eq. (2-29) is

FIGURE 2-8   Movement along x axis of pulse having a waveform $y = f(x)$ and velocity v during time interval t_1.

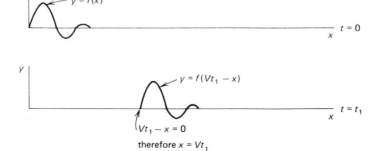

$$f(Vt - x) = \sum_{n=1}^{n=\infty} \left[A_n \cos 2\pi n\left(\frac{t}{T_1} - \frac{x}{\lambda_1}\right) + B_n \sin 2\pi n\left(\frac{t}{T_1} - \frac{x}{\lambda_1}\right) \right] \qquad (2\text{-}30)$$

where T_1 is the fundamental period. $T_1 = 1/f_1$ with f_1, the fundamental frequency, being equal to V/λ_1. This means that a seismic pulse can be looked upon as the summation of an infinite number of sine and cosine waves, each having a frequency that is an integral multiple of the fundamental frequency. The amplitudes of the frequency components can be determined by the conventional techniques of Fourier analysis if the initial waveform is known.

2-3 TYPES OF SEISMIC WAVES

In the previous section, we summarized the relationship between the velocities of propagation for compressional and shear waves, generally referred to as *body waves,* and the elastic constants of the solid material in which they travel. In this section, we shall endeavor to describe the characteristics of such waves in a way that is easier to visualize. We shall also consider the two types of surface waves, Rayleigh waves and Love waves, most widely observed in seismic prospecting and earthquake seismology.

Compressional Waves The particle motion associated with compressional waves consists of alternating condensations and rarefactions during which adjacent particles of the solid are closer together and farther apart during successive half cycles. The motion of the particles is always in the direction of wave propagation. It has been demonstrated by Dix[2] that a pressure pulse traveling as an expanding sphere through an elastic medium must have an oscillatory character and that the pulse passing any point involves at the very least an initial compression of the particles followed by a rarefaction and then a second compression before quiescence is restored. This is illustrated in Fig. 2-9.

FIGURE 2-9   Particle separations during passage of compressional pulse.

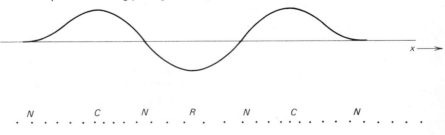

C   at maximum compression
N   normal
R   at maximum rarefaction

If a pressure is suddenly applied, as by an impact, at a point inside a homogeneous elastic medium of infinite size, the region of compression will move outward from the disturbance as an expanding spherical shell, the increase of radius having the compressional wave velocity V_P as designated in Eq. (2-27). Behind this, we observe another expanding shell representing maximum rarefaction and later, at an approximately equal distance, the second compressional pulse as shown in Fig. 2-10.

The relation between compressional velocity V_P and the elastic constants λ, μ, and ρ is given in Eq. (2-27). This velocity can be expressed in terms of other constants also, as indicated by the relations

$$V_P = \sqrt{\frac{k + \frac{4}{3}\mu}{\rho}} = \sqrt{\frac{E}{\rho}\left(1 + \frac{2\sigma^2}{1 - \sigma - 2\sigma^2}\right)}$$

$$= \sqrt{\frac{E}{\rho}\frac{1 - \sigma}{(1 - 2\sigma)(1 + \sigma)}} \tag{2-31}$$

These expressions were derived by applying Eqs. (2-14) and (2-16) to Eq. (2-27). More than 95 percent of exploration seismology is concerned with compressional waves.

Shear Waves   When shear deformation propagates in an elastic solid, the motion of individual particles is always perpendicular to the direction of wave propagation. The velocity V_S of such waves was shown in Eq. (2-28) to be $\sqrt{\mu/\rho}$. An alternative expression is

$$V_S = \sqrt{\frac{E}{\rho}\frac{1}{2(1 + \sigma)}} \tag{2-32}$$

FIGURE 2-10   Spherical spreading of compressional pulse in plane through source at center of expanding spheres. Particle separations indicated by density of dots.

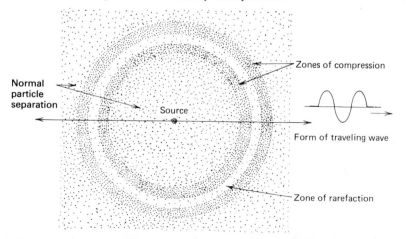

Comparing Eqs. (2-31) and (2-32), we see that the ratio of compressional to shear velocity is

$$\frac{V_P}{V_S} = \sqrt{\frac{k}{\mu} + \frac{4}{3}} = \sqrt{\frac{1 - \sigma}{\frac{1}{2} - \sigma}}$$

Either expression tells us that the compressional speed will always be greater than the shear speed in a given medium. Both radicals must be greater than 1: the first because k and μ are always positive, the second because σ cannot be greater than $\frac{1}{2}$ in an ideal solid. If, during the passage of a shear wave, the particles all move in parallel lines, the wave is said to be *polarized* in the direction of the lines. A horizontally traveling shear wave so polarized that the particle motion is all vertical is designated as an *SV wave*; when its motion is all in the horizontal plane, it is called an *SH wave*. For most consolidated rock materials V_P/V_S is between 1.5 and 2.0. As shear deformation cannot be sustained in a liquid, shear waves will not propagate in liquid materials at all. The outer portion of the earth's core is assumed to be liquid (even though its density is approximately that of lead) because it does not transmit shear waves from earthquakes.

Figure 2-11 shows the nature of the particle motion in an oscillatory shear pulse passing through an elastic medium. Note that the actual movement in the material is perpendicular to the direction of wave propagation.

Rayleigh Waves   Rayleigh waves travel only along the free surface of a solid material (Fig. 2-12a). The particle motion, always in a vertical plane, is elliptical and retrograde with respect to the direction of propagation. The amplitude of the motion decreases exponentially with depth below the surface. The speed of Rayleigh waves is slower than for any body waves, being about nine-tenths that of shear waves in the same medium. The mathematical relationships are derived by Richter.[3]

When a low-speed surface layer overlies a much thicker material in which the speed of elastic waves is higher, the Rayleigh-wave velocity varies with frequency. For wavelengths very short compared with the layer thickness, the speed is about nine-tenths of the shear velocity in the material comprising the surface layer. The properties of this layer govern the speed since such short waves will not penetrate the underlying material.

FIGURE 2-11   Particle deformation along line of wave travel during passage of shear pulse through solid material.

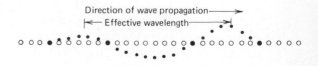

Direction of wave propagation⟶
⟵ Effective wavelength ⟶

○ Normal position of particle

● Position during passage of shear pulse

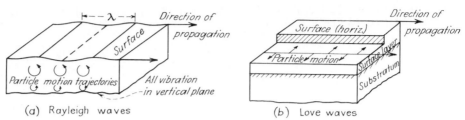

FIGURE 2-12 Characteristics of (a) Raleigh waves and (b) Love waves in traveling along surface of solid.

For very long wavelengths, the speed is nine-tenths the shear velocity in the substratum material since the effect of the surface layer is negligible when most of the wave travels in the zone below it. For intermediate wavelengths, the velocity falls between these extremes. This variation of velocity with frequency or wavelength is known as *dispersion*. A dispersive wave, in which different wavelengths travel with different speeds, will appear as a train of events in which successive cycles have increasing or decreasing periods. When a low-speed surface layer is thin compared with wavelength, the longer wavelengths will have higher velocities as they penetrate farther into high-speed material. The periods will then decrease from the beginning of the train to the end. Some examples of such dispersion are illustrated in Dobrin.[4] By analysis of the dispersion of Rayleigh waves on earthquake records, seismologists have been able to derive a great deal of useful information on the layering in the earth's crust and upper mantle.

Rayleigh waves are believed to be the principal component of *ground roll*, the common designation for low-velocity, low-frequency surface waves which often obscure reflections on seismic records obtained in oil exploration. They seem to be particularly troublesome in the Gulf Coast of the United States.

Love Waves Love waves are surface waves which are observed only when there is a low-speed layer overlying a higher-speed substratum. The wave motion is horizontal and transverse (Fig. 2-12b). The British mathematician A. E. H. Love demonstrated that these waves propagate by multiple reflection between the top and bottom surface of the low-speed layer.

All Love waves are dispersive, the velocity increasing with wavelength. The Love-wave speed is equal to that of shear waves in the upper layer for very short wavelengths and to the speed of shear waves in the lower medium for very long wavelengths. Because their particle motion is always horizontal, Love waves are seldom recorded in the course of seismic prospecting operations for which the detectors respond to vertical ground motion only. They are used extensively, however, in earthquake seismology to study the earth's near-surface layering. For a more advanced discussion of surface waves the reader is referred to Grant and West[5] (pp. 95–107).

2-4 ATTENUATION, REFLECTION, REFRACTION, AND DIFFRACTION OF ELASTIC WAVES

Falloff of Energy with Distance   The energy of a wave in a given medium is proportional to the square of its amplitude (which may be expressed in terms either of pressure or displacement). As a spherical wave spreads out from its source, the energy must be distributed over the area of the sphere, which increases as the square of the sphere's radius. Thus the energy per unit area varies inversely as the square of the distance from the source; the amplitude, which is proportional to the square root of the energy per unit area, should be inversely proportional to the distance the wave has traveled. In addition to the loss of amplitude due to spreading out of the wave, there is also a certain loss from absorption, due to frictional dissipation of the elastic energy into heat. The loss from this source is exponential with distance and will be considered in more detail later in this chapter.

Combining both mechanisms of attenuation, we note that for a homogeneous material

$$I = I_0 \frac{r_0}{r} e^{-\alpha(r - r_0)} \tag{2-33}$$

where I = amplitude at distance r from source
I_0 = amplitude at distance r_0 from source
α = absorption coefficient

The value of the absorption coefficient depends on the material.

Huygens' Principle   Waves in a homogeneous medium, as previously pointed out, spread out from a point source as expanding spheres. *Huygens' principle* states that every point on a wavefront is the source of a new wave that also travels out from it in spherical shells. If the spherical waves have a large enough radius, they can be treated as planes. Lines perpendicular to the wavefronts, called *wave paths* or *rays*, can often be used to describe the wave propagation more conveniently than can wavefronts.

Reflection   Let us apply Huygens' principle to a plane longitudinal wave impinging obliquely upon an interface between two elastic media having respective compressional velocities of V_{P1} and V_{P2}, shear velocities of V_{S1} and V_{S2}, and densities of ρ_1 and ρ_2 (Fig. 2-13). Consider the incident wavefront AB. The point A will become the center of a new disturbance, from which both longitudinal and transverse waves spread out hemispherically into each medium. Considering only the waves that return into the upper medium, we see that by the time the ray that passed through B reaches the interface at C, a distance x from B, the spherical compressional wave from A will also have

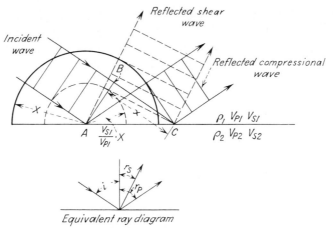

FIGURE 2-13   Reflection of plane compressional wave at interface.

traveled a distance x and the spherical shear wave a distance $(V_{S1}/V_{P1})x$. Drawing a tangent from C to the first sphere, we get the wavefront of the reflected compressional wave, which has an angle of reflection r_P (with the perpendicular to the interface) equal to the angle of incidence i. This is so because the incident and reflected compressional waves travel at the same speed. A tangent to the smaller circle represents the reflected wavefront for the shear wave, which will make an angle r_S with the interface, determined by the relation

$$\sin r_S = \frac{V_{S1}}{V_{P1}} \sin i \tag{2-34}$$

In the case of normal incidence ($i = 0$), the ratio of reflected *energy* in the compressional wave E_r to the incident energy E_i is

$$\left.\frac{E_r}{E_i}\right|_{i=0} = \frac{(\rho_2 V_{P2} - \rho_1 V_{P1})^2}{(\rho_2 V_{P2} + \rho_1 V_{P1})^2} \tag{2-35}$$

The square root of this ratio, known as the *reflection coefficient R*, gives the relative *amplitudes* of the reflected and incident waves. This can be expressed in the form

$$R = \frac{A_r}{A_i} = \frac{\rho_2 V_{P2} - \rho_1 V_{P1}}{\rho_2 V_{P2} + \rho_1 V_{P1}} \tag{2-36}$$

The amount of energy reflected in this case is thus seen to depend on the contrast in the product of density by velocity (acoustic impedance) on opposite sides of the interface and is independent of the side from which the incident wave approaches. When the medium in which the incident wave travels has a smaller acoustic impedance than the medium across the interface from it, there is no phase change on reflection. When the incident wave is from the side of the interface having the higher acoustic impedance, the reflected wave shows a phase shift of 180°, as follows from the fact that the numerator of Eq. (2-35) becomes negative. Thus, a compression becomes a rarefaction upon reflection from a medium having a lower product of seismic velocity and density.

From a practical standpoint, the reflection coefficient depends mainly on the velocity contrast on opposite sides of the interface, since the variation in density among different kinds of rocks is usually small. It is theoretically possible for the velocity to increase and the density to decrease across an interface in such proportions that there will not be any contrast in acoustic impedance. Under such conditions, no reflection would be expected.

Refraction; Snell's Law   When an incident wave strikes an interface, each point along the interface (according to Huygens' principle) becomes the center of a new hemispherical elastic wave that travels into the second medium with a speed of V_{P2} for compressional-wave propagation and with a speed of V_{S2} for the shear wave. From Fig. 2-14, one sees that the compressional wavefront in the lower medium travels a distance AD while the wavefront in the upper medium travels the distance x from C to B. The resulting refracted wave makes an angle R_P with the interface. From the diagram it is evident that

FIGURE 2-14   Refraction of plane compressional wave across interface.

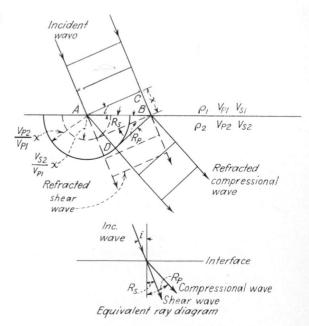

$$\sin i = \frac{BC}{AB} \quad \text{and} \quad \sin R_P = \frac{AD}{AB} = \frac{V_{P2}BC}{V_{P1}AB}$$

so that
$$\frac{\sin i}{\sin R_P} = \frac{V_{P1}}{V_{P2}} \tag{2-37}$$

This is *Snell's law*.

For the shear wave, the angle of refraction R_S is expressed by the relation

$$\frac{\sin i}{\sin R_S} = \frac{V_{P1}}{V_{S2}} \tag{2-38}$$

When $\sin i = V_{P1}/V_{P2}$, $\sin R_P$ becomes unity and R_P becomes 90°. This means that the refracted wave does not penetrate the medium but travels along the interface betwen the two materials. The angle $i_c = \sin^{-1}(V_{P1}/V_{P2})$ is known as the *critical angle* for refraction of the compressional wave. For any value of i greater than this critical value, there is no refraction into the second medium and the wave is *totally reflected*. This concept of the critical angle is most important in seismic refraction work, since the ray used in refraction surveying (the *head wave*) is the one which impinges on the top surface of a high-speed bed at the critical angle, travels horizontally along this surface, and is refracted back to the earth's surface at the same angle.

Reflections and Refractions at Oblique Incidence   According to Eq. (2-35), the ratio of incident energy normal to the interface that is reflected upward is dependent only on the relation between the acoustic impedances on opposite sides of the interface. When the ray path makes any other angle than 90° with the interface, the reflected energy depends on the angle; also any compressional wave obliquely incident on the interface will be transformed into the four kinds of waves illustrated in Fig. 2-15: reflected compressional, reflected shear, refracted compressional, and refracted shear.

The partitioning of energy among the four types of waves depends on the angle of incidence and on the velocities (shear and compressional) and densities on each side of the interface. The relationships are expressed by Knott's or Zoeppritz's equations, which are rather involved and will not be presented here. Interested readers are referred to Richter[3] for their derivation. At vertical incidence, no shear waves are generated at the interface. When the angle exceeds the critical angle, perceptible amounts of shear energy are reflected upward and also refracted into the medium below. Compressional reflections maintain an almost constant energy at small angles, but as the critical angle is approached, the percentage of compressional energy that is reflected increases sharply.

The change in the reflected energy with increasing angle of incidence, i.e., increasing source-receiver separation, is a recent topic of investigation and of

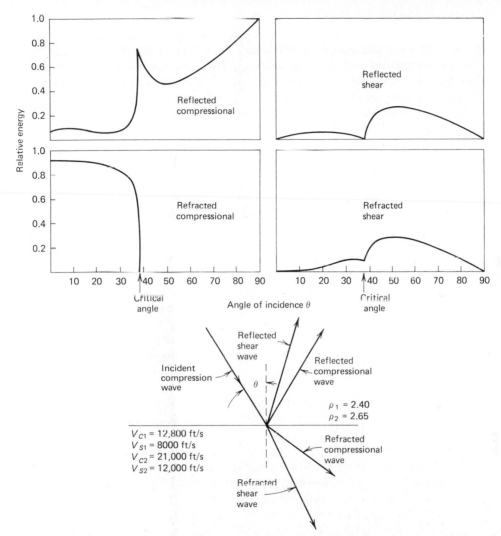

FIGURE 2-15   Partition of energy of incident compressional wave at boundary between materials having specified velocities and densities. Where the incident ray is not perpendicular to the boundary, four kinds of waves are generated and the energy in each type depends on the angle of incidence θ, as shown in the plots. (*After Richards.*[6])

interest to explorationists. The goal is to achieve a better understanding and measurement of the velocity-density contrasts that produce the reflection. The payoff is, of course, locating porosity or hydrocarbons through determination of lateral changes in velocity-density contrasts.

Energy of the refracted compressional wave remains almost constant with increasing angle of incidence until the critical angle is reached, at which point it is, of course, cut off. There is an increase in the conversion to shear energy, both reflected and refracted, as the critical angle is approached, the maximum shear amplitude being observed at an angle somewhat beyond. The curves of Fig. 2-15 were computed by Richards[6] for a typical interface between deep elastic formations and dense limestones. They are based on Knott's equation for partition of energy at an elastic interface. McCamy et al.[7] have published a more complete set of curves for the distribution of the energy among the four phases as a function of the angle of incidence and the velocities and densities on each side of the interface.

Diffraction   When seismic waves strike any irregularity along a surface such as a corner or a point where there is a sudden change of curvature, the irregular feature acts as a point source for radiating waves in all directions in accordance with Huygens' principle. Such radiation is known as *diffraction*. Figure 2-16 illustrates a buried corner at *A*, from which waves, excited by radiation downward from a source at the surface, spread out in all directions along paths which are rectilinear as long as the velocity is constant. Those waves shown in the drawing are returning to the surface along the indicated paths. A diffracted wave will reach the surface first at a point directly above the edge, because the path is shortest to this point. The event will be observed at successively later times as one moves along the surface away from the point. The amplitude of a diffracted wave falls off rapidly with distance from the nearest point to the source. Diffracted events are frequently recorded on seismic data, but they are not always recognized as such.

Limits of Applicability of Elastic Theory in Earth Materials   Up to this point, we have been studying the laws of elastic-wave propagation in ideal materials having properties not often found in the earth. In such materials, there is microscopic and macroscopic homogeneity; stress and strain have a linear relationship; there is no volume change in shear deformation; and no energy is lost due to friction resulting from the wave motion. Yet any theoretical treatment that endeavors to take into account the deviations of the properties of earth materials from those of ideal solids can rapidly become too complex to handle, so that elastic theory (with all its inadequacies) provides the best groundwork for studying seismic properties of earth materials.

FIGURE 2-16   Diffraction from an edge. The source *A* of diffracted radiation has been set into oscillation by waves generated on surface. Radial lines with arrows are ray paths; circular arcs are wavefronts.

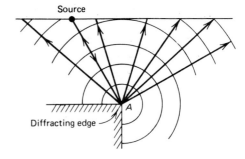

2-5 GENERATION OF SEISMIC WAVES FOR PROSPECTING APPLICATIONS

Until now our discussion of basic principles has been equally applicable to earthquake seismology and seismic prospecting. The two kinds of seismic waves are generated by processes that are quite different. Originally, explosive sources such as dynamite were detonated in boreholes for virtually all seismic prospecting operations. Since the middle 1960s, however, impactive and vibratory mechanical sources of energy, which operate on the earth's surface, have also been employed; moreover, a large variety of nondynamite energy sources have virtually replaced dynamite and other explosives for generation of seismic waves in marine exploration.

The physical theory behind the generation of seismic energy has not been worked out as satisfactorily as that for other aspects of the seismic exploration process (such as attenuation, reflection, and refraction) because materials in the immediate vicinity of most energy sources are subjected to nonlinear deformation and the physics of such deformation is much more complex than it is for elastic-wave propagation.

The mechanics of generating traveling waves by underwater explosions was investigated quite thoroughly during World War II, and we know more about the physical processes involved in shooting underwater than those that occur when a shot is fired in a borehole. The behavior of underwater energy sources in generating seismic waves will be covered briefly in Chap. 5, while vibratory or impactive surface sources used on land will be discussed in Chap. 4. In this section, we shall consider the mechanics of generating seismic waves only with explosives in boreholes. While such holes are generally drilled below the weathered layer, the material is for the most part only semiconsolidated, and when explosives are detonated at the bottom of the hole, a more or less spherical or cylindrical cavity is formed in the rock surrounding the explosion, as shown schematically in Fig. 2-17. Inside the wall of the cavity is a shell of

FIGURE 2-17 Deformation of earth when explosive is detonated underground: (a) locations of zones representing different types of deformation around cavity left by shot; (b) stress-strain relation in zone A; (c) stress-strain in zone B. (After Dix.[1])

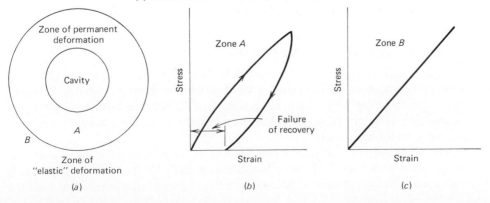

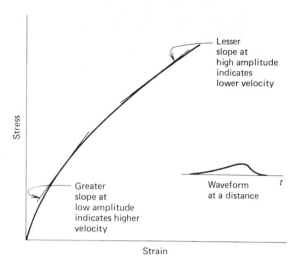

FIGURE 2-18   Spreading of pulse in soft material with nonlinear stress-strain curve. (*After Dix.*[1])

rock material which has been compacted beyond the limit of elastic recovery. This is indicated on the stress-strain diagram for silty clay under very high stress. The curve shows a high degree of hysteresis (permanent displacement after removal of stress).

Dix[1] has used the form of the stress-strain curve in relatively unconsolidated materials (as in zone *A* of Fig. 2-17*a*) to explain the characteristics of the wave recorded from an explosion which takes place in such materials. The steeper the slope of the curve the greater the effective Young's modulus and (because of the relation between this constant and the velocity, at least over the linear parts of the curve) the higher the velocity of propagation of the seismic pulse. In Fig. 2-18, the slope is highest where the stress is least, and the smaller amplitudes thus travel at the higher speeds. As the energy of the explosion builds up, the slope decreases, so that the higher-amplitude part of the impact will generate waves with progressively lower velocities as the pressure continues to build up. This effect results in the spreading out of the wave and yields a waveform which shows a relatively slow buildup of energy with time rather than the near-vertical rise that one associates with shock waves.

2-6   ABSORPTION OF SEISMIC WAVES IN EARTH MATERIALS

The absorption of elastic waves in rocks has been the subject of extensive theoretical and experimental study. Attenuation constants have been measured for a variety of earth materials (as in sec. 8 of Clark[8]), but the mechanism for attenuation in many types of rocks, particularly softer sedimentary rocks, is not very well understood.

The amplitude of a seismic wave falls off with distance *r* from the source in accordance with Eq. (2-33), which contains a term $1/r$ for spherical spreading and an exponential term $e^{-\alpha r}$ for absorption. The symbol α is referred to as the *absorption coefficient.* Experiments by Born[9] with samples of shale, sandstone, limestone, and cap rock indicated that α is proportional to the first power of frequency for the types of rocks which transmit seismic waves in the portion of the geologic section where oil is generally sought. This kind of dependence would suggest that the mechanism of absorption is solid friction associated with the particle motion in the wave.

The coefficient α can be easily related to δ, the logarithmic decrement (the logarithm of the ratio of amplitude of any cycle to that of the following one in a train of damped waves) and Q, which is π/δ. α can be expressed in terms of δ as $\delta f/v$ or in terms of Q as $\pi f/Qv$, where f is frequency and v is propagation velocity. Both δ and Q are frequently used in the literature to designate attenuation characteristics of materials.

In 1940, Ricker[10] published the first of a series of papers on the form of seismic pulses as governed by the absorption characteristics of the earth materials through which they propagate. He derived equations for the waveform that would be observed after an impulsive signal has traveled through absorbing material in terms of first-power, second-power, and fourth-power dependence of the absorption coefficient on frequency. The shape of the wave he computed for second-power dependence seemed to resemble observed waveforms rather closely. Such a dependence would indicate a viscoelastic frictional loss of the type usually associated with highly viscous liquids. Assuming this attenuation law, he developed equations predicting waveforms for both ground displacement and ground-motion velocity; computed waveshapes for the two at a number of distances from the source are shown in Fig. 2-19. The symmetrical wave representing the velocity at very large distances is referred to as a *Ricker wavelet.*

Waveforms having this appearance and some of the characteristics predicted for it by Ricker's theory have been observed in the Pierre shale of Colorado,[11] but subsequent experiments in the same formation reported by McDonal et al.,[12] which involved Fourier analysis of observed waveforms, indicated an

FIGURE 2-19 Change in waveforms of displacement and particle velocity at increasing distances from explosion in shothole. (*After Ricker.*[11])

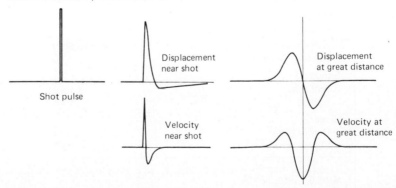

absorption proportional to the *first power* of the frequency, implying solid friction of the type indicated in Born's laboratory experiments. The preponderance of evidence now appears to support the solid-friction hypothesis, and this is accepted by most geophysicists.

The Ricker wavelet has frequently been employed as a convenient representation of the basic seismic pulse in attenuating material. The equation for it is a useful mathematical expression for a seismic signal in the design of recording instruments as well as of programs for data processing.

Table 2-1 shows attenuation characteristics as observed in the laboratory or field for rock samples representing most major rock types of interest to exploration geophysicists. The values of the attenuation coefficient α have been computed for a frequency of 50 Hz from measurements tabulated in the literature of Q at various frequencies using the relation $\alpha = \pi f / Q v$, where f is frequency and v velocity. There is an appreciable overlap in the attenuation values, but it is evident that sedimentary rocks are generally more absorptive than igneous rocks. Actually, there is a large range of variation among different samples for the same type of rock, as is indicated in the tables in sec. 8 of Clark.[8] The great number of papers that have appeared in the literature on attenuation of seismic waves in rocks indicates the importance of this question to geophysicists.

But regardless of the physical mechanism within the rock fabric or the precise law of attenuation, the absorption of higher-frequency energy at a greater rate than lower-frequency energy is well established. This property of

TABLE 2-1 ATTENUATION COEFFICIENTS FOR 50-Hz SEISMIC WAVES

Material and source of sample	Velocity, km/s (ft/s)	Attenuation α, km^{-1}
Granite:		
Quincy, Mass.	5.0 (16,400)	0.21–0.32
Rockport, Maine	5.1 (16,700)	0.237
Westerly, R.I.	5.0 (16,400)	0.384
Basalt:		
Painesdale, Mich.	5.5 (18,000)	0.414
Diorite	5.78 (19,000)	0.21
Limestone:		
Solenhofen, Bavaria	5.97 (19,600)	0.04
Hunton, Okla.	6.0 (19,700)	0.366
Sandstone:		
Amherst	4.3 (14,100)	0.71
Navajo	4.0 (13,100)	1.77
Shale:		
Pierre, Colo.	2.15 (7,100)	2.32
Sylvan, Okla.	3.3 (10,800)	0.68

SOURCE: Data from Sydney P. Clark, Jr. (ed.), "Handbook of Physical Constants," rev. ed., *Geol. Soc. Am. Mem.* 97, 1966, Table 8-1.

rocks causes a progressive lowering of apparent frequency of seismic events with increasing distance of travel through the earth.

2-7 VELOCITIES OF SEISMIC WAVES IN ROCKS

Most igneous and metamorphic rocks have little or no porosity, and the velocities of seismic waves depend mainly on the elastic properties of the minerals making up the rock material itself. This is also the case with massive limestones, dolomites, and evaporites. Sandstones, shales, and certain kinds of soft limestones, on the other hand, have more complex microstructures with pore spaces between grains which may contain fluids or softer types of solid material such as clay. For such rocks, velocity is very much dependent on the porosity and on the material filling the pores. Table 2-2 gives compressional and shear velocities for rocks of different types based mainly on laboratory measurements upon representative samples.

TABLE 2-2   COMPRESSIONAL AND SHEAR VELOCITIES IN ROCKS

Material and source	Compressional velocity		Shear velocity	
	m/s	ft/s	m/s	ft/s
Granite:				
Barriefield, Ontario	5640	18,600	2870	9470
Quincy, Mass.	5880	19,400	2940	9700
Bear Mt., Tex.	5520	17,200	3040	10,000
Granodiorite, Weston, Mass.	4780	15,800	3100	10,200
Diorite, Salem, Mass.	5780	19,100	3060	10,100
Gabbro, Duluth, Minn.	6450	21,300	3420	11,200
Basalt, Germany	6400	21,100	3200	10,500
Dunite:				
Jackson City, N.C.	7400	24,400	3790	12,500
Twin Sisters, Wash.	8600	28,400	4370	14,400
Sandstone	1400–4300	4620–14,200		
Sandstone conglomerate, Australia	2400	7920		
Limestone:				
Soft	1700–4200	5610–13,900		
Solenhofen, Bavaria	5970	19,700	2880	9500
Argillaceous, Tex.	6030	19,900	3030	10,000
Rundle, Alberta	6060	20,000		
Anhydrite, U.S. Midcontinent, Gulf Coast	4100	13,530		
Clay	1100–2500	3630–8250		
Loose sand	1800	5940	500	1650

SOURCE: Sydney P. Clark, Jr. (ed.), "Handbook of Physical Constants," rev. ed., *Geol Soc. Am. Mem.* 97, 1966.

Igneous and Metamorphic Rocks In general, igneous rocks have seismic velocities which show a narrower range of variation than sedimentary or metamorphic rocks. The average velocity for igneous rocks is higher than that for other types. The range for 15 samples of granite taken from the earth's surface, which are listed in Clark[8], is from 16,500 to 20,000 ft/s. For basalts from four locations, the range is from 17,800 to 21,000 ft/s. The fastest rock is dunite, an ultrabasic rock that some believe may be an important constituent of the earth's mantle, for which the speeds measured for five samples range from 22,400 to 28,500 ft/s. Most types of metamorphic rocks show an even wider range of variation in velocities. Gneiss, for example, has speeds ranging from 11,600 to 24,800 ft/s, and marble velocities are listed from 12,400 to 23,000 ft/s.

Variation of velocity with depth, usually simulated in the laboratory by putting samples under high pressures, is rather small for most igneous rocks. As the pressure was raised from 10 bars (only slightly more than atmospheric) to 10,000 bars (corresponding to a 115,000-ft depth of burial) the compressional velocity of three granite specimens increased less than 15 percent. Sedimentary rocks generally exhibit a much greater percentage increase in velocity with overburden pressure for reasons which will be considered in the following paragraphs. Figure 2-20 shows the effect of depth of burial upon velocity for one sample of igneous rock (granite) and one sample of sedimentary rock (sandstone) as determined by laboratory measurements.

Sedimentary Rocks The velocity characteristics of sedimentary rocks are quite different for different types. Most evaporites such as rock salt and

FIGURE 2-20   Increase of compressional velocity with depth for a typical granite and a typical sandstone. Leveling off of increase in velocity at shallow depths probably caused by closing of cracks in granite and maximum reduction of pore space in sandstone.

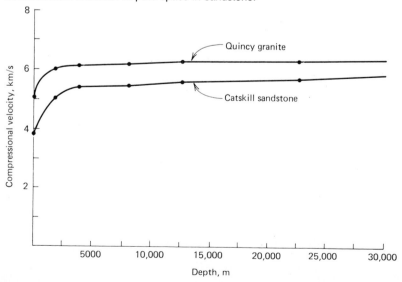

anhydrite have velocities which lie in the same range as igneous rocks. Rocks of this kind show little variation in speed even for different depths of burial. Dolomites exhibit a limited range of variation, and this is quite close to that for many types of evaporitic rocks. The highest reported velocity in sedimentary rock is about 25,000 ft/s in a dolomitic limestone encountered in many wells in the Alberta basin of Canada. Velocities of limestones, sandstones, and shales vary over a much wider range. The key to the variation appears to be the density and (a closely related quantity) porosity. Figure 2-21 shows how all sedimentary rocks except anhydrites exhibit a 0.25 power relationship between velocity and bulk density.

Such a correspondence between density and velocity is not confined to sedimentary rocks. Nafe and Drake[14] have plotted seismic velocity versus bulk density for a wide variety of materials ranging from muds at the bottom of the sea to ultrabasic igneous rocks. Figure 2-22 illustrates their results. The best line through the points, which has surprisingly little scatter about it, indicates

FIGURE 2-21   Velocity-versus-density relationships for different types of rocks. (*Gardner, Gardner, and Gregory.*[13])

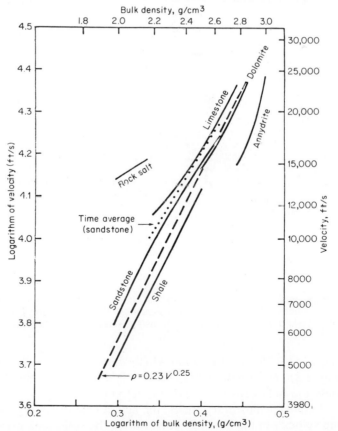

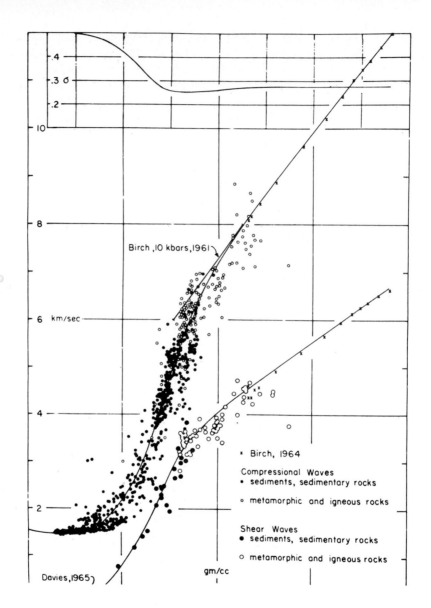

FIGURE 2-22 Velocity versus density for compressional and shear waves in all types of rocks. Poisson's ratio versus density at top of figure. (*Data assembled by John E. Nafe, Lamont-Doherty Observatory. From Ludwig et al., "The Sea," vol. 4, part 1, Wiley-Interscience, New York, 1970.*)

the same 0.25 power relation which shows up clearly in the logarithmic plot of Fig. 2-21. This relation makes it possible to estimate the velocity of rocks when only the bulk density is known, and vice versa.

In most sedimentary rocks, the actual velocity is dependent upon the intrinsic velocity in the minerals constituting the solid rock matrix, the porosity, the pressure, and the velocity in the fluid filling the pore spaces. It also depends on the composition of any solid cementing material between the grains of the primary rock constituents.

At shallow depths of burial, the velocity of most sedimentary rocks increases rapidly with increasing pressure. For rocks consisting of grains that are approximately spherical, a theoretical relationship developed by Gassmann predicts that the velocity should be proportional to the pressure raised to the one-sixth power, the constant of proportionality being expressed in terms of the elastic constants and density of the rock material itself. For rocks such as quartzites that have almost no porosity, very small cracks are often present near the surface which tend to close under the weight of the overburden at depth, the result being a rapid increase in velocity in the first few thousand feet and a leveling off at greater depths.

Beyond the depth where such consolidation is reached, the influence of variation in pressure on velocity becomes small, and then porosity and mineral composition of the grains become dominant in governing velocity. A very simple linear relationship between the reciprocal of the velocity and porosity has been found by Wyllie et al [15] to be valid for water-saturated sandstones at depths greater than a few thousand feet:

$$\frac{1}{V} = \frac{\phi}{V_F} + \frac{1 - \phi}{V_M} \tag{2-39}$$

where V = velocity in saturated rock
   ϕ = fractional porosity
   V_F = velocity of fluid in pore space
   V_M = velocity of solid material making up rock matrix

Equation (2-39) is referred to as the *time-average relationship*. Where it holds, the velocity V would be equal to V_M at zero porosity and V_F at 100 percent porosity, its reciprocal $1/V$ being linearly related to ϕ for values in between. Figure 2-23 is a plot of V versus ϕ for several types of sedimentary rocks. The observed velocities for sandstone show a close adherence to the time-average relationship over the porosity range between zero and 30 percent. The other rocks represented, exhibiting higher porosities, have a different matrix velocity, but there is too small a porosity range to test the validity of the time-average law for these materials.

A similar equation developed from theoretical considerations by Pickett [16] is

$$\frac{1}{V} = A + B\phi \tag{2-40}$$

where A and B depend on lithologic parameters and depth of burial. The equation appears to be valid for a wider range of sedimentary rocks.

A large-scale statistical study of sedimentary-rock velocities has been made

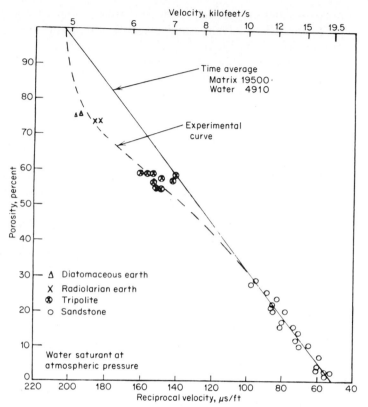

FIGURE 2-23 Velocity versus porosity for various silicic rocks. Straight line represents predicted time-average relationship. (*After Wyllie, et al., Geophysics, 1958.*)

by Faust,[17] who showed that for sandstones and shales the velocity V (in feet per second) can be expressed empirically as

$$V = KZ^{1/6}T^{1/6} \qquad (2-41)$$

where $K = 125.3$ when Z is in feet, T in years, and V in feet per second
      $Z =$ depth of burial
      $T =$ age of formation

Although this relation is purely empirical, being based on conventional well-velocity surveys made before the days of velocity logs (so that velocities of sections hundreds of feet thick had to be used in compiling the averages), the correspondence between Faust's one-sixth power dependence on depth and Gassmann's theoretically determined one-sixth power relation with pressure is quite interesting even though it may be coincidental. The geologic age relationship cannot be so easily related to the physical mechanisms governing

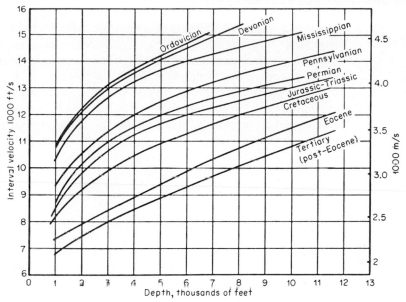

FIGURE 2-24   Compressional velocities as determined from borehole surveys in sandstone and shale. (*After Faust.*[17])

velocity, but increasing induration and grain cementation with time might be expected to lead to an increase in seismic velocity.

Figure 2-24 shows some curves based on Faust's law indicating velocities of sands and shales as a function of depth for rocks of different ages.

2-8 PRINCIPLES INVOLVED IN MEASURING SEISMIC-WAVE CHARACTERISTICS

The immediate objective of all seismic field measurements is to obtain a record in the most useful form possible of the ground motion resulting from the arrival at the surface of seismic waves reflected or refracted from subsurface formations. The record made in the field, whether on paper or on magnetic tape, will not be an exact representation of the actual ground motion because the characteristics of the measuring system introduce distortions that change the waveforms, often appreciably. These distortions are inevitable, but they can often be effectively removed in the processing stages by means of filters.

An important concept in the interpretation of records showing ground motion is filtering, which is the process of changing the waveform of a signal. In Chap. 3, we shall consider electronic filters used in recording. In Chap. 6, we shall study the principle of filtering as carried out in processing data with electronic computers. Still another type of filtering occurs in the earth itself, and it is appropriate for us to consider it in connection with our investigations of the propagation characteristics of earth materials.

We have seen how earth material changes the shape of the pressure impulse from an explosion, an impulse which initially has the form of a spike with a negligible time duration, into an oscillatory pulse having a breadth which increases with distance of travel. This is one sense in which the earth acts as a filter, changing the form of the input much more drastically than most electronic filters are capable of doing. When the filtering action of the recording system is separated from that of the earth, the seismic record becomes an expression of the earth's filtering behavior. Such filtering action depends on the earth's structure and lithology. In Chap. 8, which is on reflection interpretation, we shall apply filter theory to deduce the layering characteristics of reflecting formations from the waveforms of the signals which they return to the surface.

REFERENCES

1 Dix, C. H.: "Seismic Prospecting for Oil," Harper, New York, 1952.

2 Dix, C. H.: On the Minimum Oscillatory Character of Seismic Pulses, *Geophysics,* vol. 14, pp. 17–20, 1949.

3 Richter, C. F.: "Elementary Seismology," Freeman, San Francisco, 1941.

4 Dobrin, Milton B.: Dispersion in Seismic Surface Waves, *Geophysics,* vol. 16, pp. 63–80, 1957.

5 Grant F. S., and G. F. West: "Interpretation Theory in Applied Geophysics," McGraw-Hill, New York, 1965.

6 Richards, T. C.: Motion of the Ground on Arrival of Reflected Longitudinal and Transverse Waves at Wide-Angle Reflection Distances, *Geophysics,* vol. 26, pp. 277–297, 1961.

7 McCamy, Keith, R. P. Mayer, and Thomas J. Smith: Generally Applicable Solutions of Zoeppritz Amplitude Equations, *Bull. Seismol. Soc. Am.,* vol. 52, pp. 923–955, 1962.

8 Clark, Sydney P., Jr. (ed.): "Handbook of Physical Constants," rev. ed., *Geol. Soc. Am. Mem.* 97, New York, 1966.

9 Born, W. T.: The Attenuation Constant of Earth Materials, *Geophysics,* vol. 6, pp. 132–148, 1941.

10 Ricker, Norman: The Form and Nature of Seismic Wavelets and the Structure of Seismograms, *Geophysics,* vol. 5, pp. 348–366, 1940.

11 Ricker, Norman: The Form and Laws of Propagation of Seismic Wavelets, *Geophysics,* vol. 18, pp. 10–40, 1953.

12 McDonal, F. J., F. A. Angona, R. L. Mills, R. L. Sengbush, R. G. Van Nostrand, and J. E. White: Attenuation of Shear and Compressional Waves in Pierre Shale, *Geophysics,* vol. 23, pp. 421–439, 1958.

13 Gardner, G. H. F., L. W. Gardner, and A. R. Gregory: Formation Velocity and Density: The Diagnostic Basis for Stratigraphic Traps, *Geophysics,* vol. 39, pp. 770–780, 1974.

14 Nafe, John E., and Charles L. Drake: Variation with Depth in Shallow and Deep Water Marine Sediments of Porosity, Density and the Velocities of Compressional and Shear Waves, *Geophysics,* vol. 22, pp. 523–552, 1957.

15 Wyllie, M. R., A. R. Gregory, and G. H. F. Gardner: An Experimental Investigation of Factors Affecting Elastic Wave Velocities in Porous Media, *Geophysics,* vol. 23, pp. 459–493, 1958.

16 Pickett, George R.: Principles for Application of Borehole Measurements in Petroleum Engineering, *Log Anal.,* May–June 1969, pp. 22–33.

17 Faust, L. Y.: Seismic Velocity as a Function of Depth and Geologic Time, *Geophysics,* vol. 16, pp. 192–206, 1951.

CHAPTER 3

SEISMIC RECORDING INSTRUMENTS

Seismic records obtained in prospecting show the motion of the earth's surface, as generated by explosives or other energy sources, at different, usually closely spaced, observing positions. On land, the motion is actually indicated in terms of particle velocity versus time rather than of particle displacement versus time. In marine operations, the observed quantity is the pressure variation in the water resulting from the passing seismic waves. The proper translation of the signals thus obtained into geological information requires us to know as much as possible about the behavior of seismic waves as they propagate through earth materials, but we must also understand the characteristics and performance of the instruments that record the waves when they return to the surface. The properties of the seismic waves in the earth were taken up in Chap. 2; the operation of the recording instruments is considered in this chapter.

It is important for the geologist to realize how the instruments with which reflection records are obtained can affect the interpretation of the data on the records. Unrecognized, instrumentally generated distortions of the signals on seismic records could result in spurious geological conclusions.

The primary elements of modern instrumental systems used to record seismic ground motion are geophones on land or hydrophones at sea, amplifiers, digital recorders (with associated hardware), and units such as galvanometric or electrostatic cameras for monitoring. In recent years, special-purpose digital computers have been put into the recording trucks and seismic ships to control the entire recording process in the field. They are generally used both for regulating and monitoring the field operations and for preliminary processing of the data more or less concurrently with the shooting.

3-1 GEOPHONES

The *geophone*, sometimes referred to as the detector or the seismometer, is the unit in direct contact with the earth that converts the motion of the earth resulting from the shot into electric signals. These signals constitute the input into an instrumental system, the end product of which is the presentation of subsurface geological information in some visible form, usually as a record section, which, except for distortions of scale, is comparable to a geologic cross section.

Electromagnetic Geophones   Nearly all geophones currently used for seismic recording on land are of the electromagnetic type. This kind of detector consists of a coil of wire and a magnet, one of the two elements being fixed as rigidly as possible to the earth's surface so that it will move along with the earth in response to seismic disturbances. The other element is inertial and is suspended by a spring from a support attached to the portion that moves with the earth. Relative motion between the two produces an electromotive force between the coil and magnet, the voltage being proportional to the velocity of the motion.

Figure 3-1 shows the principle of operation for a unit in which the magnet is inertial and the coil moves with the earth. In most geophones designed for exploration work, however, the coil is incorporated in the inertial element and the magnet is attached to the case, which moves when the earth on which it is planted moves. When the coil is the inertial element, it is ordinarily attached to a mass suspended by a spring. For the geophone in Fig. 3-2, the coil is wound about a bobbin, and the combination of the two acts as the inertial mass.

The sensitivity of an electromagnetic geophone depends on the strength of the magnet, the number of turns of wire in the coil, and the geometry governing the interaction of the magnetic flux lines and the coil. Geophones have become steadily smaller as new magnetic materials of greater strength have become available. Some geophone elements used regularly in field operations are not much bigger than golf balls (Fig. 3-3).

Every seismic detector, whether designed to record natural earthquakes or the sound waves generated in seismic prospecting, has a natural period which depends on the mass and the restoring force of the spring suspension. In an electromagnetic geophone, the natural period T depends on the mass m of the

FIGURE 3-1   Schematic diagram of electromagnetic geophone. The magnet is the inertial element, and the case moves with the earth.

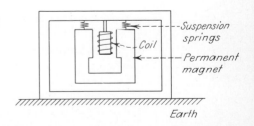

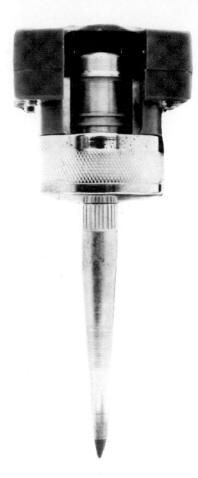

FIGURE 3-2 Cutaway of electromagnetic geophone with spike for good coupling to soft earth. Other bases are used on hard ground, in snow, etc. The main assembly of the geophone is 1 in by 1.3 in. Spike is $3\frac{1}{2}$ in long. (*Litton Resources Systems.*)

suspended inertial member (whether it is the magnet or the coil) and the stiffness coefficient k of the spring. The latter quantity is the proportionality constant between the force on the spring and the elongation attributable to the force. The period T is dependent on m and k as follows:

$$T = 2\pi\sqrt{\frac{m}{k}} \qquad (3\text{-}1)$$

For frequency, which is the reciprocal of the period, the relation is

$$f = \frac{1}{2\pi}\sqrt{\frac{k}{m}} \qquad (3\text{-}2)$$

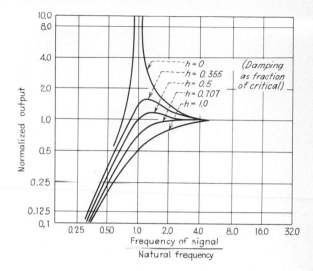

FIGURE 3-3 Normalized frequency-response curves for electromagnetic geophone with various values of damping (h is fraction of critical damping).

If the damping in the geophone system is small, any seismic impulse setting the spring suspension into motion will generate an oscillatory or "ringy" output signal with a frequency that is the reciprocal of the natural period. This type of oscillation is generally undesirable in seismic recording. For one thing, the response to any component of the input signal that occurs at the natural period would be greatly accentuated compared with all other components.

By introducing proper damping, it is possible to make the geophone response approximately equal at all frequencies above the resonant frequency. When this is the case, the geophone output gives a high-fidelity representation of the ground motion. Originally geophone damping was effected by filling the case with oil to produce viscous mechanical damping. Modern geophones use electrical damping to suppress mechanical oscillation by means of the eddy-current effect. The degree of damping is controlled by a resistor connected across the terminals and the effect of a conductive bobbin, which acts as a shorted turn.

While most geophones used in exploration are designed to have a relatively flat response, there are special circumstances where it is desirable for the response curve to be peaked at a predetermined frequency. If detection of a signal (such as the first break in refraction recording) is more important than precise registration of its waveform, and if the signal is immersed in a high level of background noise, sharp tuning of the detector to the dominant frequency of the expected signal may be the only way to observe it at all.

The three variable parameters in a geophone system are thus the mass m of the suspended element, the stiffness coefficient k, and the damping, which is linearly dependent (the proportionality constant being R) upon the velocity of the moving element. The differential equation for the displacement from equilibrium u of a system where there is an external force F_0 (the ground motion) oscillating at frequency f is

$$m\frac{d^2u}{dt^2} + R\frac{du}{dt} + ku = F_0 \sin 2\pi f_0 t \qquad (3\text{-}3)$$

This equation for forced, damped oscillatory motion is a classic one in mathematical physics. The solution (see p. 28 of Morse[1]) approaches the steady-state value

$$u = \frac{F_0}{2\pi f \sqrt{R^2 + (2\pi fm - k/2\pi f)^2}} \sin(2\pi ft - \phi) \qquad (3\text{-}4)$$

$$\text{where } \phi = \tan^{-1}\frac{2\pi fm - k/2\pi f}{R}$$

is the phase angle between input and output for frequency f.

The output of an electromagnetic geophone will be proportional to the velocity of the coil, which is the first derivative of Eq. (3-4). This is

$$v = \frac{du}{dt} = \frac{F_0}{\sqrt{R^2 + (2\pi fm - k/2\pi f)^2}} \cos(2\pi ft - \phi) \qquad (3\text{-}5)$$

Figure 3-3, based on Eq. (3-5), shows a set of characteristic curves for geophone response as a function of the frequency of earth motion and of damping. Such curves can be obtained experimentally by putting the geophone on a shaking table that is set into oscillation at various frequencies.

Each curve of Fig. 3-3 corresponds to a different amount of damping. The ordinate is the voltage output divided by the output which would be obtained with an excitation having the same velocity amplitude and a frequency much higher than the natural frequency. The uppermost curve is for an updamped system.

Theoretically, the absence of damping results in an infinite response at resonance. As damping is introduced in increasing amounts, the amplitude and sharpness of the peak at the resonance frequency diminish. The maximum amount of damping that will just eliminate the oscillatory character of the response is referred to as critical damping, which is reached when $R = 2\sqrt{km}$. If the damping is half its critical value ($h = 0.5$), a maximum will still be observed but it will be a somewhat higher frequency than the natural one. This is considered by many to be the most acceptable degree of damping for reflection recording.

At a damping 0.707 times the critical value, the peak disappears and the output increases smoothly with increasing frequency, approaching its maximum value asymptotically. The curve for critical damping ($h = 1.0$) follows a similar pattern. If there is any substantial component of earth motion in the neighborhood of the detector's natural frequency, it is desirable to flatten this portion of the response curve by introducing enough damping resistance to remove the peak. Otherwise the effect of that component will be exaggerated in the output. If, for example, a geophone of natural frequency 6 Hz were used for reflection work in an area where the dominant frequencies to be recorded are in the neighborhood of 30 Hz, the damping would not have to be adjusted so carefully as in refraction work, where frequencies as low as 5 Hz are encountered.

The choice of natural frequency, which can be set by use of a spring with the proper k value, should be governed by the minimum frequency of the signal to be recorded. At one time, it was considered desirable to restrict reflection frequencies to the higher portion of the range passed by the earth and to suppress lower frequencies (which might be associated with ground roll) by using the geophone itself as a high-pass filter. It was common then for natural frequencies of geophones to be set at 30 Hz or higher. Now that ground roll can be suppressed in the field by shot and geophone patterns and there is greater interest in reflection signals from deep formations that may have useful components far below 20 Hz, there has been a trend toward geophones with lower natural frequencies (6 Hz, 8 Hz). It is simplest, as can be seen from Fig. 3-3, to set the natural frequency of the geophones at the lower limit of the range of frequencies it is desired to record. Refraction geophones, for example, should always have a natural period well below 10 Hz (actually below 5 Hz for exceptionally long shot-detector distances). Commercial geophones with natural frequencies ranging from 4.5 to 100 Hz are now available for reflection work. Variable shunts can be inserted to provide any desired degree of damping.

Geophones are rarely used singly. Normally several (as many as 20 or more) are electrically connected to each other in a group in such a way that the outputs of the individual phones are effectively summed. The information from each group must be transmitted via cables to the recording truck. In modern land recording with 48, 96, or more group recordings, the cables are long and heavy and often add noise to the recording, especially in the presence of powerlines or water.

Pressure Phones (Hydrophones) While electromagnetic geophones with moving coils are the standard detecting units for work on land, pressure geophones are more commonly used for receiving seismic signals in appreciable depths of water. Special waterproof cases have been designed (Fig. 3-4) to permit planting of moving-coil phones in marshy ground. Pressure-sensitive phones, often referred to as hydrophones, use piezoelectric crystals or comparable ceramic elements as pressure sensors. They generate a voltage proportional to the instantaneous water pressure associated with the seismic signal. It can be shown that this pressure is proportional to the velocity of the water particles set into motion by the signal.

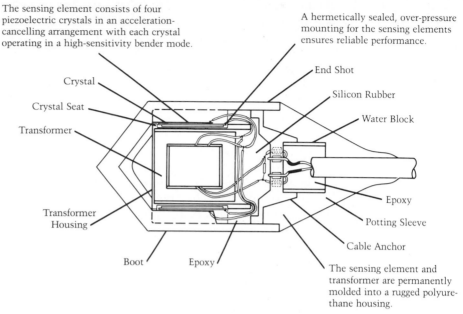

The sensing element consists of four piezoelectric crystals in an acceleration-cancelling arrangement with each crystal operating in a high-sensitivity bender mode.

A hermetically sealed, over-pressure mounting for the sensing elements ensures reliable performance.

Crystal

Crystal Seat

Transformer

End Shot

Silicon Rubber

Water Block

Transformer Housing

Epoxy

Potting Sleeve

Cable Anchor

Boot   Epoxy

The sensing element and transformer are permanently molded into a rugged polyurethane housing.

FIGURE 3-4   Pressure phone (hydrophone) schematic. (*Litton Resources Systems.*)

One type of pressure phone is ordinarily placed inside a plastic hose filled with oil that transmits the pressure variations in the water to the sensitive element in the detecting unit. This type of cable is generally referred to as a streamer. Pressure phones of the type used in marine cables will be discussed further in Chap. 5.

3-2 ANALOG RECORDING

For the first 30-odd years of seismic reflection recording, all registration of signals from geophones or hydrophones was in continuous form, as was the case with the "wiggly lines" observed on paper oscillograms, or (since the early 1950s) with magnetic tape having a magnetization continuously varying along the tape. This type of storage, called analog recording, is to be contrasted with digital recording, which has been employed to an increasing extent since the early 1960s and is now found on nearly all seismic equipment. In digital registration, signal amplitudes are recorded at discrete sampling intervals in a form that encodes a number for each sample, with no recording of the signal at times between the sampling instants. Figure 3-5 illustrates the basic differences between the two types of recording.

Although almost all seismic recording for oil exploration is now digital, we should review the techniques of analog recording for a number of reasons. Even on digital crews, the amplifiers into which the geophone signals are

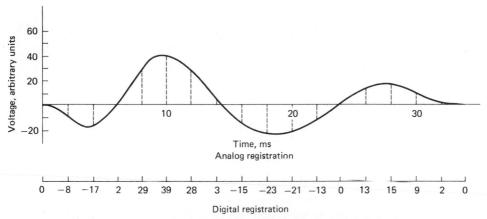

FIGURE 3-5   Analog and digital registration of the same signal. Sampling interval for the digital data is 2 ms.

passed before being digitized are analog. Moreover, in some parts of the world analog equipment is still being used, the signals being digitized for processing subsequent to recording. Also, a large amount of seismic data still in the active files of oil companies has been recorded by analog techniques. Geologists and geophysicists involved in the processing or the interpretation of such data should understand how the original recording was carried out.

Analog Amplifiers   The primary problems encountered in designing amplifiers for seismic reflection work result from the exceptionally wide range of ground-motion amplitudes that the geophone picks up over the few seconds after the shot is fired. The ground motion in the vicinity of a shot point may have a million or more times the amplitude immediately after the explosion that it has at the end of the record, when the energy that is recorded has traveled many tens of thousands of feet to a deep reflector and back. The dynamic range of analog magnetic tape is between 40 and 45 dB (corresponding to an amplitude factor of 100 to 200), so that the range of 1 million in the signal amplitudes must be somehow compressed in the amplifier if it is to be stored properly on analog tape. For direct registration on paper records of the type used for the first 25 years or so of seismic recording, only about 20 dB of dynamic range is available, making the requirements for signal compression even more stringent.

To compress the signal so that it can be recorded by media having such limitations, analog amplifiers have special circuitry for expanding or suppressing the gain level during recording in the form of automatic gain control (AGC). The characteristic curve of Fig. 3-6 shows how a 10^6:1 range of input voltages is reduced to a range of approximately 2:1 at the output of one type of analog system.

Early AGC systems operated with diode bridge circuits, which required balancing in the field to maintain stability. Such balancing is no longer neces-

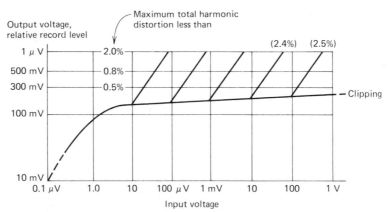

FIGURE 3-6   Characteristic curve for automatic gain control illustrating relative constancy of output for 10^6:1 range of input voltages. Diagonal lines represent response to and distortion from simulated noise burstouts with a 35-Hz input signal. (*SIE, Inc.*)

sary. The rate at which the AGC action is applied and relaxed after the signal has passed can be varied on some amplifiers. Special gain controls are used to regulate the amplitude levels at the beginning and end of the record.

Analog Filters for Recording and Playback   Filtering of seismic signals from geophones is often necessary before they can be recorded in a really useful form. Such filtering is done both in field recording and in subsequent processing of the recorded data. In the days before reproducible recording, filters in the field truck were used to remove undesired noise from seismic data before registration on the paper records used for the ultimate interpretation. Even after magnetic tape was introduced, it was sometimes desirable to remove higher-amplitude spurious signals, such as low-frequency surface waves, by prefiltering before registration on the tape so as to avoid saturation effects. Analog filtering is still carried out in conjunction with digital recording to avoid spurious signals on records.

Analog filters of the type that were used in the field trucks before the advent of digital systems had a choice of high- and low-cut frequency limits to be selected with knobs on the amplifier panel. The same types of filters were used for playing back tapes in the field to monitor the recorded data and for data processing in analog playback centers. Slopes of the analog filter curves, ranging from 18 to 36 dB/octave, are generally much gentler than those obtained with digital processing filters.

In digital recording, analog filters must be employed in the field to prevent aliasing, a spurious effect associated with the sampling process, which will be discussed in Chap. 6. The typical performance of filters available with field amplifiers is illustrated by the curves of Fig. 3-7.

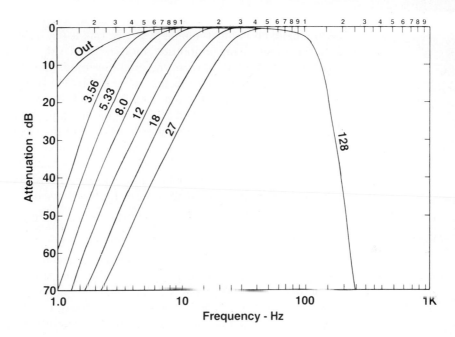

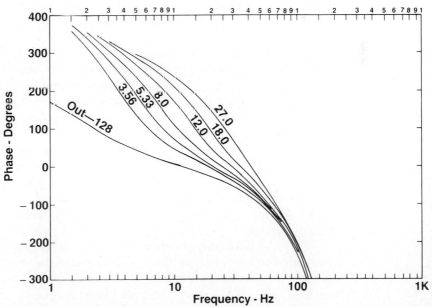

FIGURE 3-7   Frequency attenuation and phase response diagrams of the DFS V recording system (2-ms sample rate, 128-Hz high-cut). (*Texas Instruments.*)

Magnetic Analog Recorders   Two basic types of tape-recording units have been employed in most analog systems, one using frequency modulation (FM) and the other using amplitude modulation (AM). In the former type, the amplitude of the output from the amplifier modulates the frequency of a 3000-Hz carrier signal over the seismic range (10 to 300 Hz). The signal representing geophone motion is extracted upon playback by demodulation. In the other type, the signal is impressed directly upon the tape, as in sound recording, the magnetization of the tape being proportional to the strength of the signal up to the limit of the tape's dynamic range (usually about 45 dB). In either type of recording the tape is stretched around a drum which revolves, during the time the recording is going on, past a bank of heads. There is one head for each trace plus one for timing and several more for auxiliary data channels.

3-3   DIGITAL RECORDING EQUIPMENT

One of the most significant developments in seismic technology has been the introduction of digital recording in the field. The first use of digital equipment for actual exploration work was in 1963. The advantages of digital recording over analog recording had long been recognized, but it was not until computer technology reached the stage where speed and storage capacity were adequate for handling multichannel seismic signals in real time that the approach became feasible for seismic operations. There are a number of elementary explanations of seismic recording by digital means in the literature. An early paper on the subject was by Dobrin and Ward.[2] The reader is also referred to Silverman,[3] Evenden and Stone,[4] and Dohr[5] for further information.

Principles   The analog signals constituting the amplified outputs of the geophone groups on the ground are digitized by analog-to-digital converters, the digital output being recorded on magnetic tape. In playback, the data on the tapes are introduced into digital computers, which, through filtering, time shifting, compositing, and other operations, put them into the form desired for presentation after digital-to-analog conversion. The description of the digitizing process that follows does not refer to any existing systems of digital recording; their operation is too complicated for presentation at an elementary level. What we shall consider is a schematic system chosen for pedagogic simplicity rather than for close correspondence to current practice.

All seismic signals that are recorded digitally are registered in the form of binary numbers.

Figure 3-8 is a highly simplified demonstration of how seismic signals can be presented on tape in digital form. The output of the seismic amplifier, shown at the left, is sampled at uniform intervals, in this case 2 ms, and the amplitudes at each sampling position are converted into binary form as shown in the middle part of the figure.

The sample having an amplitude of 28, for example, is written in seven-digit binary form as 0011100, the zero at the beginning being the coefficient of 2^6, the second of 2^5, and the two zeros at the end being the multipliers of 2^1 and 2^0,

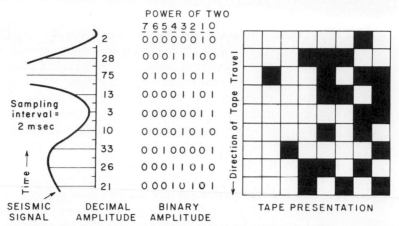

POWER OF TWO
7 6 5 4 3 2 1 0

SEISMIC SIGNAL	DECIMAL AMPLITUDE	BINARY AMPLITUDE	TAPE PRESENTATION
	2	0 0 0 0 0 0 1 0	
	28	0 0 0 1 1 1 0 0	
	75	0 1 0 0 1 0 1 1	
	13	0 0 0 0 1 1 0 1	
Sampling interval = 2 m sec	3	0 0 0 0 0 0 1 1	
	10	0 0 0 0 1 0 1 0	
	33	0 0 1 0 0 0 0 1	
	26	0 0 0 1 1 0 1 0	
	21	0 0 0 1 0 1 0 1	

FIGURE 3-8   Representation of a seismic signal sampled at 2-ms intervals on digital magnetic tape. Black squares indicate binary digit 1, and white squares binary digit 0. This format is schematic and is not used in practice. (*Dobrin and Ward.*[2])

respectively. For tape recording of digital information, the binary system has the great advantage that any number can be represented on tape by a series of blocks, each of which when magnetized corresponds to the digit 1 or when not magnetized corresponds to the digit 0. This "yes" or "no" combination is all that is needed to represent any number on magnetic tape, regardless of its magnitude, if enough elements, or bits, are available. The crossword puzzle pattern on the right represents a strip of tape on which the binary numbers shown to the left of it are encoded. This arrangement would be used for a tape system having eight recording heads, each corresponding to a different binary digit. Actually, no systems with as few as 8 bits are used in modern seismic recording.

For virtually every type of recording it has been demonstrated that far fewer bits are required than are used in practice. The incremental cost and complexity of additional bits up to at least 16 in modern instruments is, however, negligible with the result that 16-bit systems are common and 22-bit systems have been introduced.

Figure 3-9 shows a block diagram of a system for converting analog signals

FIGURE 3-9   Schematic diagram illustrating operation of an analog-to-digital converter. (*Dobrin and Ward.*[2])

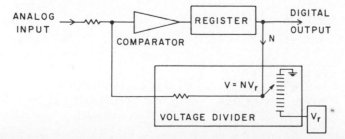

into digital form. It is called an *analog-to-digital converter*. The input at the upper left could be the voltage output of a seismic amplifier in the field. V_r, at the lower right, is a constant reference voltage which is fed into a voltage divider where a variable fraction N of it is picked off for balance against the input voltage. By successive approximations the digitally controlled comparator locates at each instant the value of N that will null the voltage in the loop containing it and the voltage divider. This value is stored digitally in the register, and when the nulling voltage is found, a command is given for the contents of the register to spill out the digits for N in proper sequence, thus producing the output signal in digital form.

In Fig. 3-10, we see how the signals on 24 information channels corresponding to a conventional multitrace seismic system can be transferred to a single channel for storage and processing. For seismic frequencies, a sampling of the signal at short intervals such as 2 ms preserves all significant information. During this interval, an electronic switch, called a multiplexer, sweeps each of the 24 input channels sequentially. The output, still an analog-type signal, consists of a series of chopped-up fragments corresponding to the respective samples, each continuous portion having a duration of 83 μs (2 ms divided by 24). This signal, shown below the multiplexer block, is next passed into the sample-and-hold unit. In it each 83-μs continuous signal is sampled, and the value thus obtained is fed into a capacitor, which holds it in storage before digitization. The output of the sample-and-hold system now goes into an analog-to-digital converter, which operates as depicted in Fig. 3-9. The emerging signal is now in the form of discrete pulses or pips having uniform height. Each 83-μs interval includes one binary number consisting of eight digits which are either 1 or 0. Bits represented by pulses correspond to the binary digit 1; those without a pulse correspond to 0.

FIGURE 3-10 Digital recording of 24 seismic channels using multiplexer, analog-to-digital converter, and other elements. (*Dobrin and Ward.*[2])

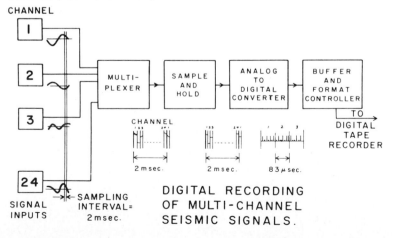

The final element through which the signals pass before being recorded on digital tape is the buffer and format controller. This holds them in storage until they go into the tape recorder, and it also programs the sequence of the digits so that the samples from the different channels can be kept in order for redistribution upon playback. The tape recorder has a separate head for each bit. In most recording systems, each sample is represented by two or more 8-bit "bytes" in sequence on the tape. The seismic signals are recorded on the tape in real time, i.e., the time that was actually required to register them initially. Later processing of the tape in a digital computer can be either in real time or at a faster or slower rate.

Dynamic Range in Digital Recording   A conspicuous advantage of digital recording is its dynamic range, which is the ratio of the maximum amplitude to the minimum amplitude that can be meaningfully stored. Being limited only by the number of bits in the recording system, the system can be designed to have a dynamic range that is as great as necessary to recover the entire signal with fidelity. It is true that the dynamic range of the analog elements, such as geophones and amplifiers, that precede the digitizing stage sets a limit to the performance of the entire recording unit.

When digital systems were first introduced, they were designed to record "words" (amplitude values of 13 bits plus 1 for sign), each corresponding to a dynamic range of almost 78 dB. This should be compared with the 45-dB maximum range available in analog recording systems. Binary-gain-ranging amplifiers, which automatically shift the gain by steps corresponding to a factor of 2, increase the effective dynamic range by another 78 dB. With such a capacity, it is possible to record the entire seismic signal on digital tape with preservation of true relative amplitudes over the entire length of the record. Moreover, the capability of recovering a weak reflection signal in the presence of a very strong noise is enhanced by the higher dynamic range of digital systems. A reflection signal, superimposed on a stronger noise amplitude that might be irretrievably lost in an analog tape recording can still be recoverable in undistorted form with the dynamic ranges that are obtainable on digital recordings. The doubling of dynamic range made possible by binary-gain equipment is particularly valuable in recording true amplitudes for obtaining a characterization of lithology, porosity, and fluid content.

When binary-gain amplifiers were first introduced in the summer of 1966, electronic switching circuitry could operate only with limited speed. As a consequence, separate gain-changing circuits were used for each channel and the changes were made in response only to changes in the peak values of signal amplitude. The result was a limitation of effective dynamic range when the signals underwent rapid, large changes in amplitude. Shortly afterwards, high-speed switching circuits became available, and a single gain-switching unit and analog-to-digital converter could service 12 or 24 multiplexed channels at each sample interval.

Modern recording systems are accordingly described as *instantaneous float-*

ing-point (IFP) in that they effectively record floating-point numbers ("scientific notation").

Typical floating-point values calculated by contemporary instruments consist of one sign bit, a 2-bit exponent base 16 or a 4-bit exponent base 2, and a fractional part of 11 to 16 bits. The instruments internally convert these calculated values and record them on tape in a standardized form conventionally accepted by commercial digital computers.

All commercial IFP recording systems today are capable of recording the entire dynamic range of seismic reflection signals.

Field Recording Systems The complexity of recording seismic signals digitally in the field might lead one to expect digital field systems to be very large and bulky, requiring a greater truck capacity than was needed in analog recording. Yet thanks to miniaturization of electronic components, digital systems are exceptionally compact. Figure 3-11 shows a typical 96-channel recording system. The tape transport and various control units are shown in the pictures. The approximate dimensions of the hardware in Fig. 3-11 are $3\frac{1}{2}$ ft wide, $3\frac{1}{2}$ ft high, and 2 ft deep.

Figure 3-12 is a simplified block diagram illustrating the basic elements of a

FIGURE 3-11 A 96-channel digital recording system. (*Sercel.*)

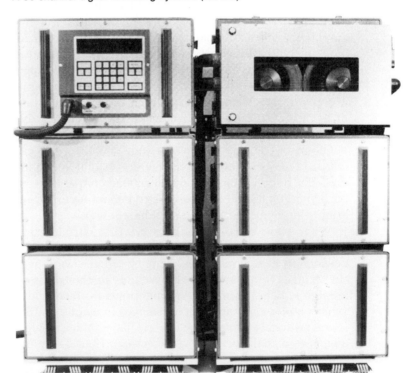

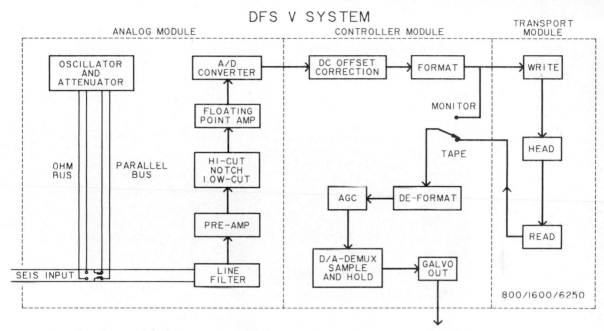

FIGURE 3-12 Simplified block diagram of DFS V field recording system. (*Texas Instruments.*[6])

DFS V (DFS five) field system, from geophone input to tape transport, that is designed expressly for digital recording. The signal passes through a line filter, then a preamplifier and various other filters (high-cut, notch, and low-cut) before going into the IFP amplifier. The antialiasing filter must be set to provide a high cut no higher than half the sampling frequency, this value being referred to as the *Nyquist frequency*, considered in more detail in Chap. 6.

The floating-point amplifier measures the input signal and sets its own gain to the power of 2 that will bring the amplified signal to a preselected range within which the A/D converter operates. After amplification, the signal is converted from analog to digital format. The gain value for each sampling instant (normally at 1- or 2-ms intervals) is computed and stored for permanent recording if absolute amplitude reconstruction should be desired at some later time. Then the DC (zero frequency) and low-frequency components are removed. The numbers are then formatted into an order specified by industry standards.

The system is designed to sense the signals stored on the digital tape after the recording by a read-after-write element, which is used as a monitor. This sensing is done by special reading heads, the outputs of which are converted into a format suitable for AGC and convenient digital-to-analog conversion. The analog output of this converter unit passes into the demultiplexer, which unscrambles the multiplexed signal into the separate channels originally recorded. The outputs go through filters and amplifiers with AGCs to keep the signals within a practical amplitude range for recording on paper and to make them intelligible to the operator. A galvanometer camera is used to print the signal on photographic paper. In some units, electrostatic printers are used to make dry copy for immediate use.

Figure 3-13 shows a typical nine-track recording transport unit employing $\frac{1}{2}$-in tape. A common tape format for such a tape recording is illustrated in Fig.

FIGURE 3-13   DFS V 120-channel recording system with tape transport unit. (*Texas Instruments.*)

3-14. The portion shown is for a typical scan of data over four of the channels being multiplexed at a particular sampling instant. The column at the right-hand side of each row is reserved for parity bits, which are used to detect certain classes of recording errors in the corresponding row. The two gain-code rows at the top of the figure define the respective gains (in 4 bits for each) corresponding to the first set of four seismic data words. Each word follows in subsequent pairs of rows. It consists of a sign bit, 14 bits expressing magnitude, and a blank bit (designated by 0). The gain code for channels 5 to 8 follows the information channels that are shown.

Before the gain and magnitude information for a scan as shown in the figure are recorded, some preliminary data (not indicated in the illustration) are registered. The start of the scan is signified by four rows of 0s in all bit positions except one (position 7, which contains 1s). There are then coded time identifications for the scan, the uphole time, and the time break. The eight rows following the portion of the format shown present the same kind of signal amplitude information for channels 5 to 8 as is indicated for channels 1 to 4. The sequence of gain and amplitude data is repeated until all the channels are covered, whereupon the starting code (all 0s but one) is repeated before starting the next scan.

Needless to say, the programming or software necessary to route such a complex array of information properly into the recording heads represents a remarkable engineering accomplishment. Equal competence in computer technology is required to extract the information from the tape with playback heads and put it into ultimately usable form. Fortunately, geophysicists do not have to devise this software, but they must still work closely with the computer manufacturers and programmers to ensure that it will meet their needs efficiently.

Recent additions to the selection of recording instruments are various types of seismic group recorders and telemetered recording systems. Seismic group recorders are small boxes (approximately 13 in $\times$ 12 in $\times$ 7 in) that record the output of one or two groups on tape cassettes, thus replacing the conventional

FIGURE 3-14 Format (SEG B) for beginning information channels of a seismic record as registered on nine-track digital tape. (*Geo Space Corp.*)

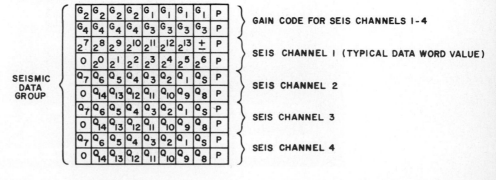

cables and doghouse (recording truck). The group recorder contains the amplifiers, filters, A/D (analog-to-digital) converter, and recording system which preserves the day's shooting. Usually, each night the cassette's information is transcribed to conventional field tape in the field processing center. The telemetered recording systems relay each group's recording through the air to the recording truck, thus obviating the use of cables. A cable-free recording system enables seismic crews to record across, or through, rivers, marshes, hilly terrain, and other inhospitable terrains where cables cannot be laid, or, if laid, are damaged (cows, rats, water, etc.). There is also greater flexibility in deployment since the stations are no longer physically connected.

3-4 OTHER FIELD INSTRUMENTATION

Monitoring Cameras In digital recording, as in analog recording, it is desirable to obtain a visible record in the field of what has gone on the tape. Such a monitor record tells the observer whether all the traces were recording and gives some idea whether source conditions (charge size and depth, for example) were appropriate or whether they should be changed,

For this purpose, a galvanometer and camera are used to register the read-after-write signal taken from the digital tape immediately after recording. There is usually one channel of the galvanometer for each geophone signal recorded

FIGURE 3-15 Visual display, computer terminal, monitoring status of field operation. Groups on lines 21 through 116 are "alive," i.e., recording for the present shot. (*Western Geophysical Company.*)

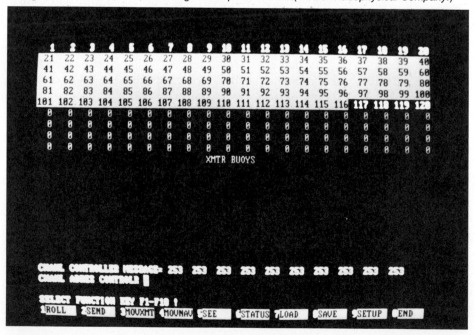

by the digital system. Cameras in the field use a "dry-write" process, and neither a dark room nor a developing tank is needed to bring out the signal traces on the recording paper.

Computers for Control of Recording In recent years, it has become increasingly common to have special-purpose computers in the recording truck to handle many functions in the data acquisition that were previously carried out by the field observer. Tests of such items as continuity of the connections to each geophone group on the ground can be performed automatically by the computer, which can also guide the operator through the various steps in the initial field setup. At the same time, it can establish a sequence of operations which is followed automatically until changed by the observer. Operational parameters are monitored with the aid of a visual display unit (Fig. 3-15), which presents questions and indicates acceptance or rejection of the answers, depending on whether they fall within predetermined limits of tolerance.

REFERENCES

1 Morse, P. M.: "Vibration and Sound," 2d ed., McGraw-Hill, New York, 1948.
2 Dobrin, Milton B., and Stanley H. Ward: Tools for Tomorrow's Geophysics, *Geophys. Prospec.*, vol. 10, pp. 433–452, 1962.
3 Silverman, Daniel: The Digital Processing of Seismic Data, *Geophysics*, vol. 32, pp. 988–1002, 1967.
4 Evenden, B. S., and D. R. Stone: "Seismic Prospecting Instruments," vol. 2, "Instrument Performance and Testing," Borntraeger, Berlin, 1971.
5 Dohr, Gerhard: "Applied Geophysics," Enke, Stuttgart, Germany, 1974.
6 Texas Instruments, DFS V Performance Manual No. 966180-9701, Rev. D, revised April 8, 1980.

CHAPTER 4

ACQUIRING SEISMIC REFLECTION DATA ON LAND

In this chapter, we shall review the field procedures used in seismic reflection prospecting on land. This is a phase of the art which one might expect to change less than those involving the development of recording instrumentation and the processing and ultimate presentation of data. Yet advances in operational techniques, particularly since the middle 1950s, have brought about spectacular improvement in data quality as well as in operating efficiency. Many of the most fruitful innovations in field methods have been made possible because of recording instruments or processing capabilities that have been introduced in recent decades.

Since 1955, several new energy sources have come into use as alternatives to dynamite, and new arrangements of source and receiving elements have been introduced to improve data quality by minimizing noise. The new sources have many advantages in areas where older shooting methods were unproductive or uneconomical. More channels for recording have become widely available. The overall improvement in data quality and depth of penetration has been phenomenal.

4-1 SINGLE-FOLD FIELD PROCEDURES

We shall first consider the basic field techniques that had been used for reflection recording in the first three decades of the art. In areas where only shallow information is needed and data quality is good, these techniques might still yield adequate geological information, although they are seldom employed.

Need for Multiple-Channel Recording of Reflection Signals In recording ground motion from reflected seismic waves it is customary to receive the signals with a large number of geophones (actually geophone groups) spread out along a line extending from the shot point for a distance of thousands of feet. Each group transmits its data to the recording instruments on one information channel. With such an arrangement, each shot yields information on the structure of a subsurface interface at a large number of reflecting points distributed along the line. An important reason for multiple-channel recording is the need to identify the reflections as such and separate them from ground motion due to other sources. Much of the undesired ground motion, which we refer to in this context as *noise*, is associated with the shot and might result from waves that have traveled along the earth's surface or that have been scattered or diffracted by surface or subsurface irregularities. A large portion of such spurious ground disturbance can be removed by proper recording and data-processing procedures, many of which will be discussed later in this chapter and in subsequent chapters, but it is not likely that all undesired events can be eliminated.

There is generally no way of distinguishing the reflections from the noise on a single trace displaying the ground disturbance recorded by a detector group. But when several closely spaced groups are laid out along a line with the shot, the time (or phase) relations between corresponding events (such as peaks or troughs) in the signals on the respective traces from contiguous geophone channels make it possible to identify the reflectors on the basis of the patterns they show in their correlation from trace to trace.

Simple Geophone Spread Arrangements Figure 4-1 illustrates the ray-path geometry for a spread of 13 geophone groups* distributed equally between two adjacent shot points *A* and *B*. We refer to geophone groups rather than geophones because the individual phones are almost invariably planted in electrically connected patterns for cancellation of noise. Each group might consist of as few as three or as many as several hundred phones connected in series or in parallel. The output, which goes into a single amplifier channel, represents the average ground motion over the group and is attributed to the center of the group. The design of such geophone patterns will be considered later in this chapter. In practice, the group at the source location is usually disconnected, so that in the simplified example of Fig. 4-1 only 12 groups record at any time.

In planning the layout of shots and geophones along a reflection profile, one must remember that the subsurface depth point computed from a reflection recorded by a particular geophone group can be assumed to apply (for gentle dips) at a point midway between the shot and the phone. Since continuous depth control is desired along a profile, the detector groups are uniformly

---

* This small a number of groups is almost never used in current practice and is introduced here only for simplicity of description. In most present-day operations, 96 or more groups are laid out at a time, the positioning of the shot points being more complex than the figure suggests.

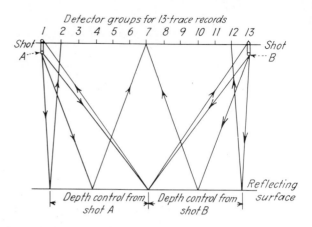

FIGURE 4-1
Obtaining continuous depth control (single fold) along profile by recording shots from opposite directions with same geophone spread. This arrangement of shots and receivers yields one trace (one fold) for each reflecting point in the subsurface.

spaced between adjacent shot points and each group will record reflections from successive shots on opposite sides of the spread. Each shot gives depths beneath the half of the spread nearest it, as shown in Fig. 4-1. The term ''100 percent'' or ''single-fold'' coverage refers to the one channel per reflecting point in the subsurface. Later in the chapter, multifold (CDP) coverage will be discussed, wherein there are recorded many traces per reflecting point (Fig. 4-20). When the bed is inclined, the depth point will of course be displaced updip from its position midway between shot and receiver; methods for correcting the error that is introduced by plotting the trace at the midpoint will be

FIGURE 4-2
Split-spread arrangement for single-fold shooting. Shot point at B.

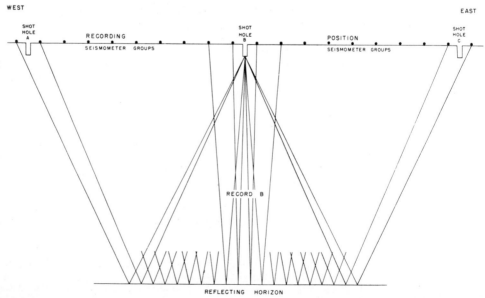

discussed in a later chapter. Because of this displacement of reflecting points, the term CMP (common midpoint) is often preferred over CDP (common depth point).

With the *split spread* (Fig. 4-2), by far the most common arrangement for conventional coverage, an equal number of geophone groups is laid out* on each side of the shot hole. All 20 groups between shot hole *A* and shot hole *C* record the shot from *B* simultaneously.

Sample Monitor Record for Split Spread   Figure 4-3 illustrates a 36-channel oscillographic (wiggly-line) record made from a split spread. This is the kind of record on which all interpretation was carried out for the first quarter century of reflection prospecting. Wiggly-line records like this have been superseded by variable-area (Fig. 4-5) and combined-mode record sections corrected for variations in reflection time not related to the structure of the reflecting surfaces. Yet the greater detail that can generally be brought out on conventional oscillographic traces and the opportunity such a presentation affords the interpreter to examine raw, uncorrected data could give old-fashioned records of this type certain advantages over more modern modes of presentation.

Each trace of the record represents the ground motion of a single group of geophones. The centers of adjacent groups are spaced 200 ft apart. All phones in each group are connected in series, and the resultant signal is transmitted by one pair of a multiconductor cable to an amplifier in the recording truck. The output of the amplifier is registered on magnetic tape, either analog or digital. Total distance from the shot (which is located between the phone groups corresponding to channels 18 and 19) to the farthest detector groups (corresponding to channels 1 and 36) is 3500 ft in each direction from the shot.

Times from the shot moment (labeled "time break") can be read by use of the vertical lines. The light lines are at 0.010-s intervals, the lines of intermediate weight at 0.050-s intervals, and the heavy lines at 0.100-s intervals. The interval of time represented by the portion of the record shown is about 2.5 s.

After the time break, we see that the two center traces stay quiescent until a time of about 0.025 s when "down kicks" are registered. The farthest traces are quiet for more than 0.4 s before motion of the ground is observed. For the traces between, the times at which the first movement is observed appear to increase more or less linearly with distance from the shot to the geophone group for each trace. This lineup of first-break times results from the near-horizontal paths followed by the rays responsible for these events on the record. The waves travel along the base of a thin, low-velocity surface layer and reach the detectors before any other events.

At about 0.8 s, the first well-defined reflections are recognizable by the way corresponding peaks or troughs on successive traces tend to fit into each other

---

* Here again the number of receiving groups does not correspond to what is now used in practice. In present-day split-spread shooting, usually 48 or more groups are laid out on each side of the source.

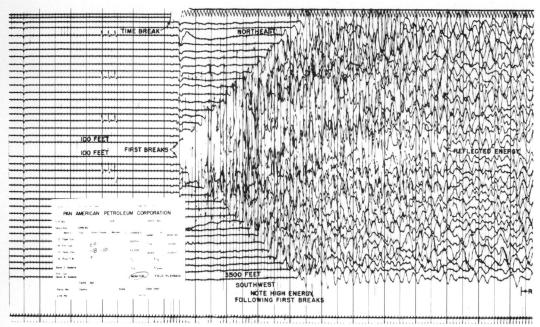

FIGURE 4-3 Typical oscillographic reflection record, consisting of 36 channels, as made in the field recording truck to monitor the digital data. (*Amoco Production Co.*)

even though there are generally systematic (if usually small) shifts in time between one trace and the next. The troughs for some of these reflection events are marked. The pattern of each reflection across the record is rather like an umbrella having a horizontal shaft located between the center traces. Note that the curvature decreases progressively with increasing time on the record. The time delay that produces the curvature is usually termed "*normal moveout*" or, sometimes, "angularity." The increase in time with distance from the shot results from the fact that the length of the travel path of the reflected waves becomes greater at larger offset distances.

Progression of Split Spreads for Single-Fold Shooting For the first three decades of reflection prospecting, split spreads were used to obtain continuous reflection-point coverage (single-fold) without the duplication that is characteristic of modern shooting. It is instructive to begin our discussion of recording maneuvers in seismic operations by describing split-spread, single-fold shooting. Later in the chapter, we shall cover the more complicated operational logistics involved in today's CDP procedures.

With single-coverage shooting, only half the split detector spread is shifted between shots at successive shot holes. For example, after the shot has been fired in *B* (Fig. 4-2), the detector groups between *B* and *C* are left for recording the shot from *C* while the groups from *A* to *B* are moved to cover the interval

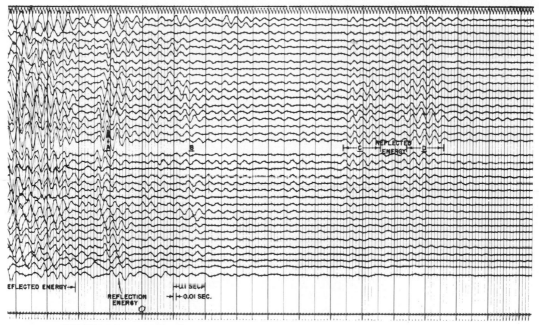

FIGURE 4-3   continued

from C to a new shot point D, located the same distance to the right of C that B lies to the left. Figure 4-4 shows a sample set of records made from spreads of this type before CDP shooting came into universal use. Correlations of the reflections between adjacent end traces for continuous records are clearly defined.

Trends in Multiplicity of Recording Channels   The number of channels used in seismic recording has continually increased since the earliest days of reflection prospecting. Originally, seismic records contained as few as two traces. By 1936, the standard number was 6; by the early 1940s it was 12. From the end of World War II until the beginning of the 1970s, 24-channel recording was standard. Now 96- or 120-channel systems are the most common, but more channels, up to 1024, are sometimes used and there is every reason to expect that the number will become even greater as time goes on.

4-2   CHARACTERISTICS OF SEISMIC NOISE TO BE SUPPRESSED IN FIELD RECORDING

A major impetus for the development of new energy sources and new field techniques in reflection recording has been the necessity for eliminating or suppressing spurious seismic signals from ground motion not associated with reflections. Such signals are generally referred to as *noise*.

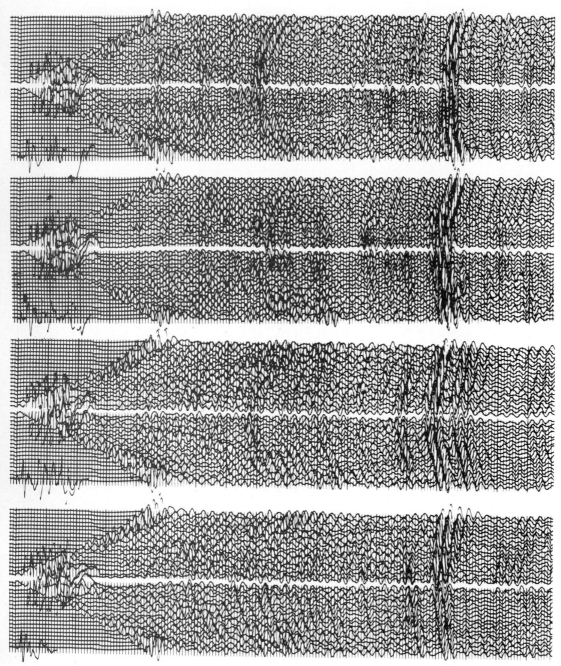

FIGURE 4-4 Oscillographic records from four adjacent shot points set up for 100 percent coverage. Note the correlations of reflection events between records. (*Amoco Production Co.*)

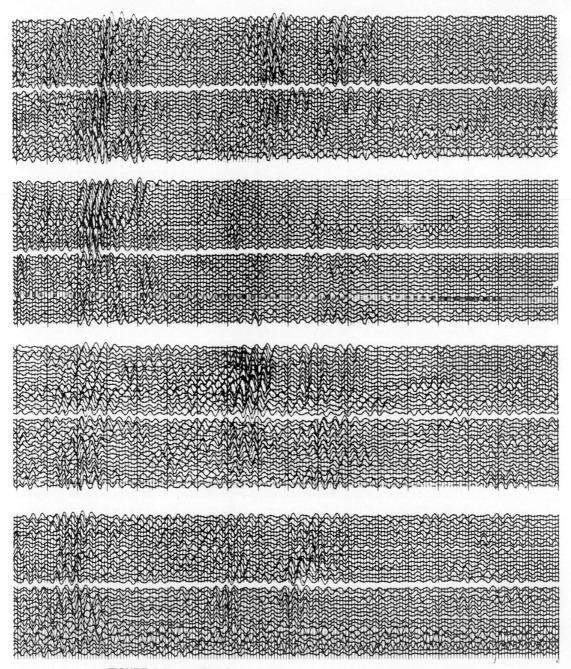

FIGURE 4-4 continued

Noise has always been the most troublesome problem in seismic prospecting. In some areas, it still poses more of a challenge than can be met by the present state of the art. Until the late 1950s, noise-suppression techniques consisted primarily of filtering, to suppress selectively those frequencies in which noise predominated over signal, and judiciously arranged groups of phones and sources to average out unwanted energy components. Unfortunately, noise and signal frequencies, directions of arrival, and other relevant factors varied from place to place, requiring constant expert tuning and adjustment of noise-suppression techniques.

In the six decades of seismic acquisition, the signal-to-noise ratio appears to have increased about 50 dB. In comparing the average number of bits of information gathered per mile then and now, we see an increase of about 10,000:1 based on the number of phones per group, number of groups per shot, number of shots per mile, and fold. From information theory, the improvement obtained by averaging redundant information is about equal to the square root of the number of values averaged. Since the square root of 10,000 is 100, averaging alone has produced about 40 dB of the improvement. It follows that most of the staggering improvement in seismic data quality can be traced to the increase in sheer quantity of data gathered. Averaging more information has allowed better estimates of the signal that was concealed beneath the noise. Extensive research and development was nevertheless needed to generate the complex processing techniques for properly aligning the data to be composited or averaged. Sophisticated filtering techniques, such as deconvolution and *f-k* filtering (see Chap. 6) have contributed the rest of the improvement.

The principal types of noise associated with land shooting are surface and near-surface waves, scattered or incoherent noise, and multiple reflections.

Surface and Near-Surface Waves   In the early days of reflection shooting in the Gulf Coast area, low-velocity, low-frequency surface waves with an amplitude level that is high compared to reflections would often override useful reflection information. These events were referred to as ground roll. Because the frequencies of the waves were usually much lower than those for reflections, low-cut filters were introduced into the amplifier circuits to eliminate interference from this source. Somewhat later, groups of series-connected geophones were laid out over distances corresponding to one or more wavelengths of the ground roll. Such an arrangement would result in suppression of the horizontally traveling ground roll and enhancement of vertically traveling reflections.

In the early days of seismic prospecting, it was assumed that ground roll consisted primarily of Rayleigh waves (see page 37). Subsequent research, however, has shown that Rayleigh waves account for only a part of such interference. In some areas, e.g., one in east Texas studied by Dobrin, Simon, and Lawrence,[1] dispersive Rayleigh waves are readily recognizable. In other areas, e.g., one in west Texas described by Dobrin, Lawrence, and Sengbush,[2] more complex physical mechanisms may be responsible for much of the interference. Among these mechanisms are refracted waves multiply reflected in a surface layer, shear refractions, and guided waves trapped in a near-surface layer with a lower speed than that in the material above and below.

A typical reflection record on which ground roll causes perceptible interference with reflections is illustrated in Fig. 4-5. Along with it is another record showing how the ground roll can be removed by low-cut filtering alone, leaving the reflection in a more easily interpretable form. Where frequency filters alone do not yield such good discrimination, multiple geophones or multiple shots must be used, with the number of units and spacings selected to give optimum cancellation of the wavelengths observable in the ground roll. The procedures involved in determining the geophone and/or shot patterns that will be most effective in removing such interference from surface waves will be considered later in this chapter.

Scattered and Other Incoherent Energy   The surface and near-surface waves discussed in the previous paragraphs are coherent, traveling events which can be followed for substantial distances along the receiving profile. Cancellation of certain noise wavelengths can be accomplished by applying principles of directivity similar to those used in designing antennas for receiving radio waves. A different type of interference which is generally more difficult to cancel comes from *incoherent noise,* sometimes referred to as *random noise*. This is usually associated with scattering from near-surface irregularities.

Incoherent noise is particularly common when the shot point overlies or is close to gravel, boulders, or vuggy limestone, all of which can cause scattering of waves. The strength of such scattered waves is inversely related to the distance of the scatterers from the shot and receivers. Sometimes the scattering occurs where stream banks and other topographic irregularities diffract energy from the shot and return it to the recording line in the form of incoherent noise. Figure 4-6 illustrates a record section on which most of the useful reflections appear to have been obscured by incoherent-noise signals.

Incoherent noise observed at one point on the surface should by its very nature be entirely unrelated to that at another point only a short distance away. This would not be the case with coherent noise, where there would be a predictable relationship between the two signals. Addition of signals containing incoherent noise should result in some cancellation of the noise, and the more signals are added the more complete the cancellation to be expected. The multiplicity factor N is the product of the number of source elements s and the number of receiver units r from which signals are added. The cancellation effect is proportional to the square root of N. To obtain the greatest suppression of incoherent noise, one would therefore use as many shots and as many receivers (geophones per trace) as possible. Yet addition of signals from 100 receiving elements per trace results in only 3 times the noise cancellation that would be obtained if only 10 elements were used per trace. A major advantage of most surface sources such as vibrators lies in the fact that it is a simple

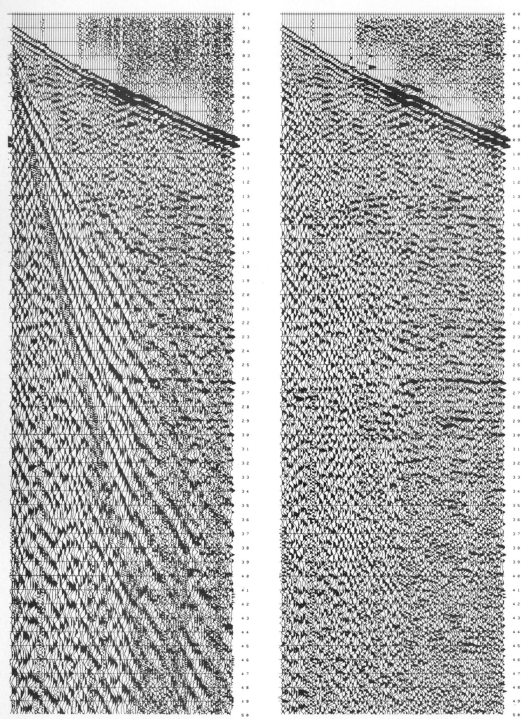

FIGURE 4-5 Field records, 96-channel recording with ground roll from Primacord source: as displayed in variable area (VA) mode (*a*) without filtering and (*b*) with filtering (12–48 Hz bandpass filter). (*Union Oil Company of California.*)

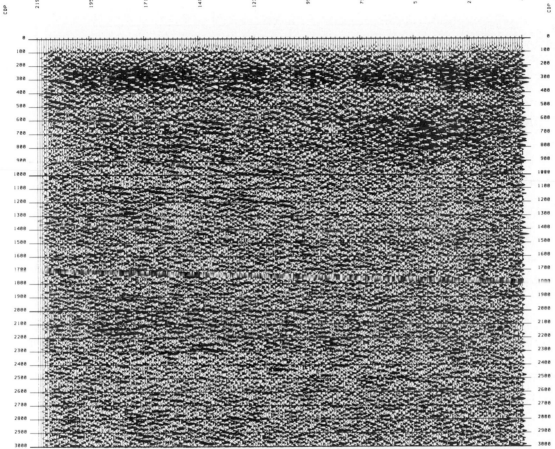

FIGURE 4-6   A poor reflection record section. There are no usable data between CDP 1 and 99. The reflections from CDP 99 to 219 are poor to 1.2 s and are not usable below that time. (*Trinidad and Tobago Oil Co. Ltd.*)

matter to generate a great number of individual signals within a limited area by moving the source a short distance between application points, whereas it would be economically prohibitive to drill an equivalent number of holes for shooting dynamite.

Multiple Reflections   A common and particularly troublesome type of interference is that from multiple reflections, which can look so much like primary reflections that the geophysicist may not always be able to identify the multiples as such. Multiple reflections can be of many kinds, some of which are shown in Fig. 4-7, but the simplest and probably the most common is the surface multiple (Fig. 4-7*b*), which arrives at twice the time of the primary reflection from the same bed. Other types of multiples are the interbed reflection (Fig. 4-7*c*) and the more complex kind in Fig. 4-7*d*. Elimination of the

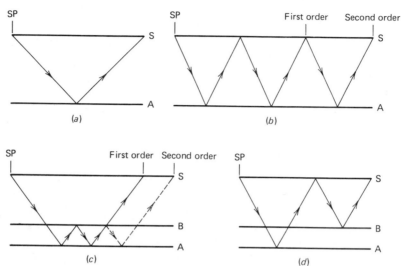

FIGURE 4-7   Several types of multiple reflections: (*a*) primary; (*b*) surface multiple; (*c*) interbed multiple; (*d*) combination multiple. *S* is earth's surface. *A* and *B* are reflecting interfaces. (*Amoco Production Co.*)

surface multiples is best accomplished by proper application of CDP shooting, discussed in detail later in this chapter. Often there is a distinct frequency change between the primary and multiple reflections because of differences in the materials through which the respective waves travel as well as differences in path lengths. In such cases, it may be possible to achieve some discrimination between the two by frequency filtering.

4-3   ENERGY SOURCES FOR REFLECTION SHOOTING ON LAND

Although a number of nonexplosive energy sources have come into use for reflection prospecting since the middle 1950s, the source employed for about 50 percent of all work on land is still dynamite exploded in shot holes. During the first 25 years of reflection activity, this was the only source which provided sufficient energy to yield satisfactory reflection data. The introduction of magnetic-tape recording and compositing systems in the 1950s made it possible to build up usable signals from mechanical impactors and similar low-energy sources by adding properly synchronized returns from a multiplicity of individual impacts. These newer sources offered economic and operational advantages over dynamite in many areas, and the percentage of land crews that use them has risen steadily since their introduction. In 1975, nondynamite sources were used in 56 percent of the land surveying in the United States and 48 percent of all such work outside the U.S.S.R. In 1983, nondynamite sources were used in 60 percent of U.S. land seismic surveying and 54 percent of all such work worldwide outside the U.S.S.R. Such sources are now employed for virtually all seismic work at sea; some of them will be discussed in Chap. 5.

Dynamite*

The mechanism for generation of energy by exploding dynamite in a shot hole was discussed in Chap. 2 (pages 45–46). Because of the impulsive nature of the seismic signal it creates and the convenient storage and mobility it provides for energy that can be converted into ground motion, dynamite should constitute an ideal seismic source from many points of view. There are, however, a number of drawbacks to its use: (1) In seismic operations, the dynamite is planted in sticks or cans in boreholes (usually about 4 in in diameter) that may range from 30 ft to several hundred feet in depth; this requires drilling the holes, which is difficult and expensive in many areas, particularly in hilly terrain into which heavy drilling equipment cannot be easily moved or in desert areas where water is not readily available. (2) Dynamite can be dangerous. Although the safety record of the geophysical industry has been remarkably good, the hazard involved in using dynamite has led to legal restrictions, some reasonable and others perhaps not, upon its transportation, storage, and handling, which often cause considerable inconvenience and expense.

Dynamite ordinarily comes in cylindrical plastic-covered sticks 20 in long with a diameter of about 2 in and a weight of 5 lb. The principal constituent of dynamite, nitroglycerin, is mixed with a sufficient amount of inert material to be stable at ordinary temperatures. Detonation converts the active material into very hot gases whose expansion is responsible for the violent impact against the earth that generates the seismic signal.

The amount of dynamite needed for a reflection shot varies from less than a pound to several hundred pounds, depending on the nature of the material in which the shot is fired, the lithologic characteristics of the geological section below the shot, and the depth of penetration desired.

To maximize the amount of explosive energy transmitted into the earth, it is customary to fill the hole with a heavy drilling mud, which prevents the pressure generated by the explosion from being released too easily into the air. The tamping effect of the mud increases the efficiency of the shooting and improves the signal quality. Sometimes a delayed expulsion of the mud into the air produces a geyser that can be quite spectacular and noisy (Fig. 4-8).

In areas where interference from noise is severe, shots are often fired in linear or areal patterns for noise reduction. The same considerations that govern the geometry of geophone patterns apply in determining the geometry of shot-hole patterns as well. The design of such patterns will be discussed later in this chapter.

Buried Primacord

Noise can be reduced by exploding dynamite in arrays of shot holes, achieving the same directivity effects as those obtained with multiple geophones. The

---

* Although dynamite as invented by Alfred Nobel used nitroglycerin as the active constituent, it is customary to designate other explosives used for seismic-energy generation, such as nitrocarbonitrate as "dynamite" also.

FIGURE 4-8 "Hole blow" created by the explosion of Primacord in trenches. (*Western Geophysical.*)

greatest possible enhancement of downward-traveling energy over horizontally traveling energy can be obtained with a continuous source horizontally elongated. Such downward directivity can be achieved by burying a proper length of Primacord (Trademark of Ensign Bickford Co.), an explosive extruded into a ropelike form, detonating it at one end (or at its center), and letting the explosive disturbance propagate along it at a speed (22,000 ft/s) much greater than the speed of seismic propagation in the near-surface material within which it is buried. (See Fig. 4-8 for example of Primacord trench blow.) The Geoflex (Trademark of Imperial Chemical Industries, Ltd.) source system operates on this principle. It is used in lengths of several hundred feet, being plowed into the ground to a depth of 2 or 3 ft. Burial is necessary to suppress noise and increase the efficiency of energy transfer into the earth. If the velocity of detonation of the cord were infinite, the energy would propagate vertically downward in phase and there would be maximum vertical directivity. Because the velocity is finite, the sharpest and highest-amplitude pulse will be directed forward at an angle whose sine is the velocity in the earth divided by that in the cord. The ray path will generally be at an angle of 20 to 30° with the vertical, as shown in Fig. 4-9. It is evident that the greatest seismic effect is observed in the direction of in-phase wave propagation shown in the figure. The variation with angle in the time duration of the signal gives rise to a filtering effect such that

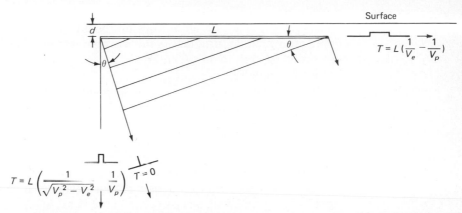

FIGURE 4-9   Use of Primacord planted in plowed trench as seismic source. L = length of Primacord, V_e = velocity of seismic waves in earth, V_p = velocity of detonation in Primacord, θ = direction of maximum amplitude with vertical, T = duration of pulses in different directions.

the highest frequencies are observed at the angle θ and the lowest in the horizontal direction.

Nondynamite Surface Sources

The advantages of distributed generation of energy for attenuating horizontally traveling noise have led to the development of nondynamite sources, which allow an almost unlimited number of effectively identical impulses to introduce energy over any desired distance along the surface without the cost of drilling or plowing and without the hazards involved in using dynamite. These sources involve mechanical impact upon the earth's surface or shaking of the surface with a mechanical vibrator. Multiplicity of the impulses necessary for noise suppression is obtained by a combination of multiple source units and by storage and subsequent compositing of reflected signals sequentially generated at locations close to one another along the surface.

All sources of this type are so disposed in the field that signals received from impacts (or sweeps in the case of vibratory source systems) are applied to the earth over a linear distance comparable to what would be used for a line of shot holes at a shot point or (where necessary and feasible) over an area that would be used for a two-dimensional array of shot holes. The signals so generated are composited to simulate the effect conventionally obtained from a single extended shot point.

Land Air Gun   The land air gun is one of the nondynamite, impact sources presently in use. The source module containing the air gun, water, diaphragm, and pan is lowered to the earth's surface, with most of the vehicle's weight applied downward on the module so that the pan is held firmly against the ground. The air gun is charged to high pressure (about 130 to 140 atmospheres);

a quick-acting valve releases the air into the water surrounding the gun. The energy of the released air is transmitted by the water and expands the diaphragm, which, in turn, drives the pan against the ground (see Fig. 4-10). The upwardly moving main assembly is caught before it can drop to initiate a secondary impulse.

Other impact sources are hydraulic power or diesel detonations to drive a plate or pan that imparts a controlled impact to the earth.

Vibroseis The mechanical impactor systems we have discussed, like dynamite, introduce an impulsive seismic signal into the earth. The wave put into the earth by a vibroseis source is oscillatory rather than impulsive and persists for many seconds, the frequency changing slowly over the duration of the signal. The returned signals recorded in the field cannot be interpreted directly,

FIGURE 4-10 A land air gun. "A shooting cycle begins when the module is lowered to the surface. This action also applies part of the vehicle weight to the cage. This weight on the cage acts through bumpers to pre-load the pan against the ground. The air gun within the water-filled bell is then charged by an air compressor to operating pressure, typically 137 atmospheres."

"When a fire command is received, the air gun is triggered by an electrically-actuated valve. The explosive release of high pressure air into the water abruptly expands the elastomeric diaphragm, which in turn drives the pan downward against the ground."

"The upward reaction of the main assembly (shaded in the drawing) is slowed and gently lowered by the catch cylinders so as to avoid generating secondary impulses. Six seconds is required for the spent air to pass through the separator, and the unit is then ready to deliver another shot." (*Bolt*.[18])

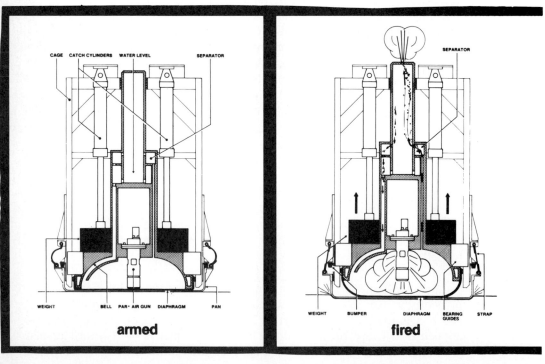

FIGURE 4-11   Four vibroseis trucks operating in line. (*Western Geophysical*.)

as is generally possible with the other sources. The recorded data must be processed by cross-correlation of the signals received by the geophones with the oscillatory source signal itself. The technique involves a comparison of the two signals with progressively increasing delay times. Reflections and other seismic events related to the source signal give a greater degree of correlation with the generated waveform than with random noise.

Operational Procedures   The vibroseis technique was developed during the 1950s by Continental Oil Company after a long period of experimentation. The earliest account of this system is by Crawford et al.[3] A typical source consists of a 3-ton mass with a hydraulic vibrator controlled by a preprogrammed sinusoidal wave signal of continuously varying frequency activated by a starting "beep" sent by the recording truck.

Vibroseis operations, like those with impact sources, involve the use of several trucks, usually four or more simultaneously, as shown in Fig. 4-11. In open fields, the trucks travel along parallel trajectories; when confined to roads, they operate in tandem. In difficult terrain, vibrators are mounted on specialized articulated vehicles similar to those used in construction and logging operations. They stop for vibratory sweeps at intervals determined by the total number of sweeps needed per shot point, all units sweeping simultaneously for times lasting 4 to 30 s. Records are made from the combined outputs of the series-connected geophone groups, and data from all sweep positions within the distance range designated as the shot point are composited into a single channel, usually by a digital summing unit in the field truck.

Like the impact sources, the vibroseis source is employed with 48 or more geophone groups, and sweep patterns may be placed to coincide with every group or every other group, depending on the multiplicity of subsequent CDP compositing (see Sec. 4-5). A common field arrangement for a linear source array is shown in Fig. 4-12.

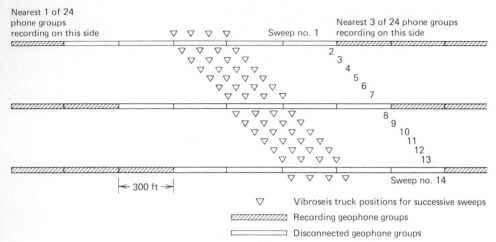

FIGURE 4-12 Progression of vibroseis sweep positions along geophone line in four-truck operation. Note change in recording connections at the final sweep for one field record.

Processing of Vibroseis Data Because the signal put into the ground persists for a long time (generally many seconds), the reflection signals actually recorded in the field are entirely incoherent to the eye and special processing is necessary, as has been pointed out, to convert the data into usable form.

A reflection record obtained from a vibroseis source consists of superimposed signals from each of the reflecting surfaces, as illustrated in Fig. 4-13. Each reflection has approximately the same waveform (but not the same amplitude) as the source signal, but the wave train corresponding to each reflector is delayed by the time required for it to travel from the source to the reflecting interface and back. All the individual reflections (curves 3, 4, 5) are in essence added together, yielding the field record (curve 2). Curve 2 has all the information needed but is uninterpretable without cross-correlation.

Qualitatively, it might be instructive to look on the cross-correlation process as a test of the fit of the source signal (1 in Fig. 4-13) and the recorded signal (2 in Fig. 4-13) which contains the reflections at successive relative displacements of the two signals along the time scale. The initial fit is tried with the beginnings (time zero) of the two signals coincident, and then the fits are determined with the respective zero positions progressively shifted by constant increments, such as 2 ms (i.e., the sampling interval).

The degree of fit is determined at each juxtaposition by multiplication of the two signals over their entire length at closely sampled ordinate positions (time shifts) followed by addition of the products. The greater the sum, the greater will be the cross-correlation coefficient obtained in this way. If the two signals are randomly related, the cross-correlation is zero. The cross-correlation coefficient at each time shift is output to tape and used thereafter as the reflection data value.

At a time shift equivalent to the two-way travel time for a reflection, the returned signal displays a partial coincidence with the source signal (only partial because other reflections and noise will be superimposed). When such a coincidence occurs, the cross-correlation value (degree of fit) will be a maximum. Elsewhere the relation between the two signals is random, and the cross-correlation value is low. If the cross-correlation so determined is plotted against the time shifts, the reflections will show up as high-amplitude events that look like reflections on conventional recordings from impulsive sources, the portions of each trace between being more or less quiescent, depending on the noise level.

If a signal is correlated with itself the result is called an *autocorrelation*. The autocorrelation of a vibroseis sweep is the wavelet equivalent to that of an impulsive source forming the same reflection record.

Advantages of Vibroseis   Energy from a vibroseis unit can be introduced into the earth over the entire range of seismic frequencies, although the efficiency of transmission by the earth varies with the nature of the surface material. The frequency content of a signal from an impulsive source is not subject to control and, in the case of dynamite, is influenced by the material and its moisture content in which the explosion occurs, by the charge size, by the hole depth, and by other factors. In many places, the best signal-to-noise ratio is observed over a limited range of frequencies which can be specifically programmed into the vibroseis source signal. Relatively shallow reflections, for example, would call for a sweep over a range of frequencies at the high end of the usual seismic spectrum (20 to 100 Hz) while deep reflections would call for a sweep at the low end, such as from 8 to 32 Hz.

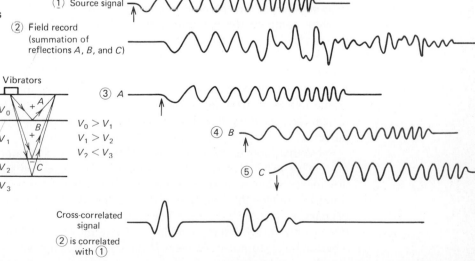

FIGURE 4-13
Recording and analysis of a vibroseis source signal reflected from three interfaces. (*Continental Oil Co.*)

Another advantage of vibroseis lies in the fact that a signal from it, being spread out over many seconds, will have a much lower amplitude level at the source than will an impulse in which all the energy is injected into the earth within a few milliseconds. This feature makes it possible to use vibroseis in populated areas where explosions would not be acceptable. Vibroseis surveys have been carried out near the centers of Chicago and Los Angeles, to cite two examples.

Harmonic Ghosting There is a certain type of noise that can occur in vibroseis data. It is termed "harmonic ghosting" because the vibrator-earth system may introduce a frequency that is twice the fundamental frequency being sent out This distortion appears to be caused by the earth's interaction with the vibrator-mass system. For example, a 36- to 6-Hz sweep may also have a 72- to 12-Hz harmonic. Upon cross-correlation with the sweep, the harmonic yields a visible correlation pulse, termed the harmonic ghost, which may be mistaken for a reflection.

The arrival time of the ghost may be determined by the equation

$$ t = \frac{F_L\, T}{F_0 - F_t} $$

where t = the time difference between the primary (real) event and its closest possible ghost (first harmonic)
F_L = the lowest frequency in the sweep
F_0 = the initial frequency in the sweep
F_t = the terminal frequency of the sweep
T = the time duration of the sweep

This equation is for use with sweeps of more than 1 octave. (An octave is one doubling of frequency, e.g., 8 to 16 Hz.) Today, sweeps are 2 or more octaves long in practice, so the equation is useful for practically all vibroseis data.

Now compare the ghosting effect in an upsweep (e.g., 6 to 36 Hz) and a downsweep (e.g., 36 to 6 Hz). For the illustration, let the time duration of the sweep be 15 s. In the downsweep, the first harmonic ghost arrival time is + 3 s, meaning it arrives 3 s after the primary of which it is the ghost. If the last reflection of interest arrives before 3 s after the first primary, then the ghost would not cause trouble. In the upsweep, the first harmonic ghost arrival time is negative, meaning it will appear before time 0 and so will not affect primary pulses.

Note that there are thus two commonly used ways of handling the ghost. The first is to use an upsweep. An upsweep is easier on the vibrators than a downsweep and so is often preferred. The other way is to use a long sweep time; the longer the sweep, the deeper the ghost is "pushed," relative to its primary reflection. A long sweep provides the additional benefits of more power into the ground per oscillation point and through the correlation process a better signal-to-noise recovery (Laing[4]). If short upsweeps are to be used, the ghosts may nevertheless be suppressed by changing the sweep duration or frequency ranges slightly between successive sweep applications. The ghosts resulting from each such sweep will bear a somewhat different time relationship to the primaries and will be reduced or "averaged out" when the correlated data are summed. This process requires "correlation before stack (sum)," a procedure that has additional noise-cancellation properties and has only been practical since the early 1980s.

4-4   SHOT AND GEOPHONE ARRAYS

In the earliest days of seismic reflection prospecting, it was customary to use a single shot hole and one geophone for each trace. By the later 1930s, groups of geophones spread out over tens to hundreds of feet were connected in series or in series-parallel arrangements, and the combined outputs of the geophones were fed into a single amplifier channel corresponding to the group as a whole. The purpose of the grouping, which at first involved three to six phones, was for cancellation of ground roll and other horizontally traveling noise. In areas such as west Texas, where noise was particularly severe, patterns consisting of 100 or more geophones became common during the late 1940s. At the same time, it became customary to drill shot holes in patterns over areas where it appeared desirable to reinforce the noise attenuation obtainable with the geophone groups alone. In west Texas, Florida, and New Mexico, where usable reflections are hard to get, it had been customary to use patterns involving as many as 36 shot holes per shot point and 96 geophones per trace. Figure 4-14 shows records obtained with shot and geophone patterns typical of those employed in Florida during the early 1950s. It is from a paper by McKay[5] that illustrates the effectiveness of many types of patterns, some of which are exceptionally large.

Nondynamite sources make it possible to achieve the advantages of shooting a large number of distributed shots without the disadvantage of drilling many shot holes. Digital tape-recording techniques make it possible to record individual phones or small groups separately for later combination into groups after making corrections for geometry and terrain variations.

Principles   The theory of noise attenuation by patterns is the same whether applied to the shot or the geophone end of the wave trajectory. The basic idea is to design both groupings so that waves traveling vertically or nearly vertically are reinforced while those traveling horizontally are reduced.

Figure 4-15 shows a four-geophone group which covers a horizontal distance equal to a wavelength of the surface wave to be canceled. With this arrangement, at any given time the horizontal wave will cause upward motion in two detectors of each group and downward motion in the other two. If all four are connected in series, the net signal from this source will be very nearly zero because of cancellation. Reflected waves, on the other hand, are very nearly vertical when they reach the source, and all four detectors of each group will

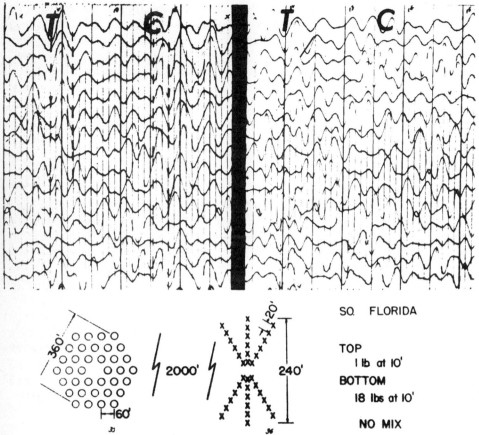

SO. FLORIDA

TOP
I lb at 10'

BOTTOM
18 lbs at 10'

NO MIX

FIGURE 4-14 Comparison of record obtained using single hole, 36 phones per trace, 1 lb at 10 ft (right) with record obtained along same spread with pattern of 36 holes, 36 phones per trace, and 18 lb per hole at 10 ft (left). The respective shot and geophone patterns are shown in the lower part of the figure. (*From McKay.*[5])

FIGURE 4-15 Eliminating effects of ground roll by use of multiple geophones in series.

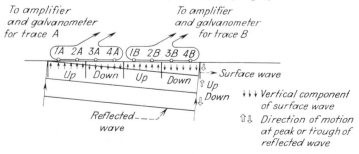

respond to them by moving in the same direction at the same time. The outputs for the reflection signals should therefore be additive. Proper grouping of geophones should thus reinforce reflected events and cancel horizontally traveling noise.

The optimum number of elements in a shot or geophone pattern and the best spacing of the units within the pattern are determined by applying the same principles as those used in designing radio antennas. The theory is reviewed by Lombardi,[6] Parr and Mayne,[7] and Savit et al.,[8] the basic concept being illustrated by Fig. 4-16. Here we have an array of five uniformly spaced geophones, the separation between adjacent phones being D. We can calculate the response of the phones to waves of various wavelengths most expeditiously at the instant a peak of the traveling wave coincides with the center phone of the group. If the wavelength λ equals the spacing D ($\lambda/D = 1$), the signals picked up by the phones are in phase and the output when all phones are connected together is 5 times the peak value for the center phone. If $\lambda/D = 2$, the first, third, and fifth phones record maximum *positive* (upward) motion, while the second and fourth phones record the maximum *negative* (downward) motion. The sum is thus the peak output for a single phone or one-fifth the output for $\lambda = D$.

Similarly, it is evident that both for $\lambda/D = 3$ and $\lambda/D = 4$ the downward motion exceeds the upward motion by one unit. The sign is not of significance in evaluating attenuation characteristics, and we can consider the response for these to be effectively equivalent to that for $\lambda/D = 2$. When $\lambda/D = 5$, the positive and negative contributions are equal and cancel one another, leaving zero response. As the wavelength gets very large compared with D, it ap-

FIGURE 4-16 Cancellation of waves of different wavelengths using five geophones separated by a distance D. Numbers in right-hand column represent relative amplitudes of outputs for the array.

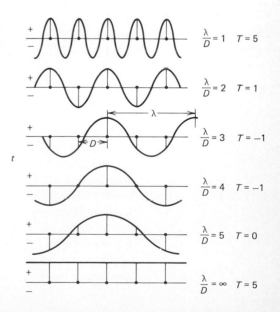

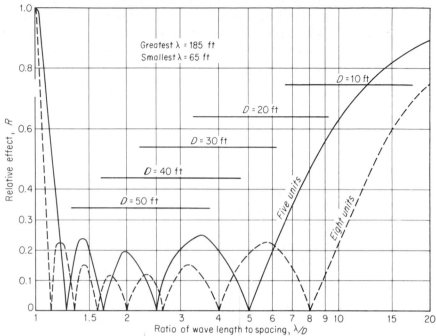

FIGURE 4-17 Noise-cancellation curves for five and eight geophones in groups. Relative response referred to amplitude of a wave recorded from a single geophone. To illustrate use of curve, suppose eight phones of group were spaced 20 ft apart. For wavelength of 100 ft $\lambda/D = 5$; the chart shows that only 20 percent of the original wave amplitude is recorded by the system. The bars illustrate the range of λ/D values from an area where the noise wavelengths lie between 65 and 185 ft. (*Adapted from Parr and Mayne.*[7])

proaches the limit of $\lambda/D = \infty$ at which value the peak output for five units is observed again, just as with $\lambda/D = 1$.

Figure 4-17, based on the model just considered, shows how the respective outputs from groups of five and eight phones vary as λ/D changes. For the five-unit group, one sees that there are four values of λ/D at which there is complete cancellation. There are three λ/D values at which transmission is a maximum. The corresponding attenuation curve for an array with eight units shows seven positions along the λ/D axis at which cancellation is complete and six positions for maximum transmission. From these two examples, we can make several generalizations. The number of zeros (positions where the geophones have no output) on the curve is 1 less than the number of phones, and the number of peaks or lobes between the zeros is 2 less than the number of phones. The greater the number of phones the lower one can draw the envelope (line tangent to the peaks) of the attenuation curve, indicating less transmission of horizontally traveling waves. Also, the greater the number of phones the wider the zone along the λ/D axis within which significant reduction of horizontal noise takes place. This means that the range of noise wavelengths that can be effectively reduced increases with the number of phones per group.

The equation for the fractional transmission T by an array of N geophones a distance D apart for horizontally traveling waves having a wavelength λ is

$$T = \frac{1}{N} \frac{\sin (2\pi N\lambda/D)}{\sin (2\pi\lambda/D)}$$

where T is the ratio of the signal observed with the N phones a distance D apart to that which would be recorded if they were all in a huddle (at zero distance apart).

Determination of Optimum Phone Spacing   To determine the optimum geophone spacing for a given number of phones per trace in an area where the characteristics of the noise are not known, it is advisable to carry out special measurements in the field. These tests are designed to establish the nature of the noise (whether coherent or incoherent) and (for the coherent noise) to determine the range of wavelengths encompassed. A series of records is made with geophones (generally single) spaced 5 to 30 ft apart, the spread being moved (or, alternatively, if the geophone spread is held fixed, the source being moved) so that there is continuous geophone coverage from the shot point itself out to distances as great as several thousand feet. This type of data set is often termed a "wave test" or "noise spread" and is illustrated in Fig. 4-18.

All events on the section having a lineup at a low enough velocity to be associated with horizontally traveling surface and near-surface waves are readily identifiable on such sections, and their velocities are determined simply by dividing the distance between the nearest and farthest phone receiving the event by the differential time required to traverse this distance. The wavelength is the velocity multiplied by the period (time between successive peaks or troughs) of the traveling wave. A range of wavelengths is determined for all noise events of this type, and a spacing is selected that will optimize the noise attenuation.

Above the curves in Fig. 4-19 are drawn a series of bars indicating the range of λ/D values corresponding to noise events from an area where tests of the type described show the noise wavelengths to lie between 65 and 185 ft/cycle. The respective bars correspond to trial values of D ranging from 10 to 50 ft. Taking the envelope of the respective attenuation curves for five and eight units, we see that the 50-ft spacing gives optimum cancellation for the five-phone group, while the 40-ft spacing appears best for the eight-phone group.

Savit et al.[8] have shown that an improvement in the signal-to-noise ratio (S/N) is obtained if the sensitivity of the geophones in the patterns is tapered or weighted in such a way that the greatest response is at the center of the group, with the response of the phones decreasing in both directions as one goes toward the outermost geophones. The taper can be obtained by individual

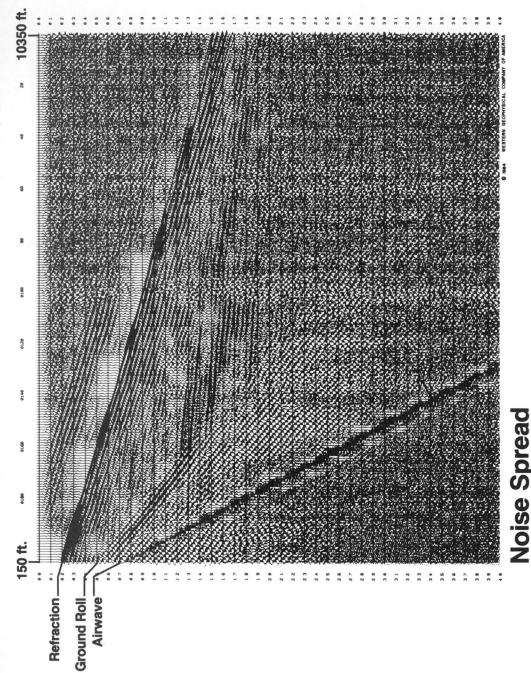

Noise Spread

FIGURE 4-18 Traveling waves recorded over spread 150 ft to 10,350 ft from source. Trace-to-trace separation is 50 ft. The air wave has a velocity of 1100 ft/s. The ground roll (or possibly shear wave) velocity is about 2500 ft/s. Its wavelength is about 125 ft/cycle. The nearly flat events from about $\frac{1}{25}$ s to $\frac{1}{85}$ s are reflection signals. (*Western Geophysical*.)

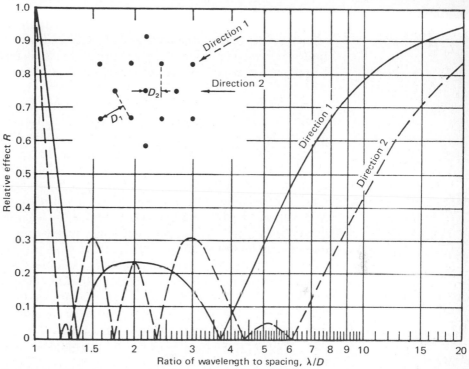

FIGURE 4-19 Cancellation curves for an areal pattern of geophones consisting of 13 units. Note the differences in cancellation for the two directions of approach of the wave to be attenuated. (*Parr and Mayne.*[7])

controls, such as potentiometers, built into the cable at each geophone connection. The desired effect can also be achieved by placing two or more phones side by side or by changing the spacing between adjacent units. For example, a five-unit array with equally spaced phones could yield as much as double the noise cancellation if extra phones were added so that three phones would stand in a huddle at the center position, two phones together at the second and fourth positions, and single phones at the first and last positions. However, experience with tapered geophone arrays and with computer simulations has shown that the substantial increase in S/N predicted by theory usually cannot be obtained, due to the variation in geophone plants (phone-to-earth coupling) and the often radical changes within geophone groups in surface materials.

Either of the above situations destroys the desired uniformity of impedance match between the earth and the recording system. The considerable increase in the number of available channels, however, presents the opportunity to obtain the predicted S/N improvement. The S/N improvement can come from array forming in the computer. The data can be amplitude balanced and appropriately time shifted prior to summation with the proper weighting (array forming). Note that marine data, already acquired with many short groups, in a uniform surface condition (water) provide raw data suitable for optional array forming in the computer and subsequent S/N enhancement.

Areal Arrays   Noise often travels in directions that are not coincident with the direction of the radial line extending outward from the shot. This happens when the noise which initially travels in a direction different from that of the geophone spread is reflected back to the line of phones by some feature such as a vertical escarpment or river bank or even a hidden lateral irregularity below the earth's surface. Where this occurs, it is necessary to have geophones in areal, i.e., two-dimensional, rather than in linear patterns. A properly designed areal pattern should yield adequate attenuation regardless of the direction in which the horizontally propagating noise approaches. A good discussion of coherent and incoherent noise with real data examples is found in Larner et al.[9]

Areal patterns may be rectangular (for example, 24 phones may be in four rows x ft apart with 6 phones in each row spaced y ft apart) or along concentric circles, depending on the nature of the noise and on the space available for the array. In a wooded area, it may not be feasible to bulldoze clearings that would allow circular symmetry of phones around the center position for each group. Yet it might be quite feasible to lay out the phones in an elongated rectangular array.

In determining the attenuation for an areal array, one must specify the direction of the wave travel. The attenuation curves (transmission versus λ/D) for a star pattern consisting of 13 geophones will be different for different directions of propagation, as shown in Fig. 4-19. To use conventional attenuation curves designed for linear arrays with areal patterns, the position of each phone would have to be projected on a line in the direction of wave travel, as shown in the figure.

The detailed procedures followed in designing areal shot and detector patterns will not be discussed here. Reynolds[10] describes a spoke-and-wheel pattern which has worked successfully in many areas. McKay[5] has published a large collection of sample records showing the improvement in reflection quality that is possible with elaborate two-dimensional shooting and receiving patterns.

Where the noise is incoherent and traveling events cannot be followed between geophones only a few feet apart, cancellation techniques of the type described will not be effective. Statistically, incoherent noise can be reduced by a factor proportional to $\sqrt{n}$, where n is the number of detectors in the group irrespective of spacing. Where m shots are used along with the n phones per trace, the improvement in S/N is proportional to $\sqrt{mn}$. This may be a difficult way to obtain the necessary degree of cancellation. Yet in some areas, e.g., the

Sahara desert or in west Texas, where there is a high level of incoherent noise, the only way to obtain usable reflections is with very large shot-hole patterns and an even larger number of phones per trace. Patterns comprising 48 shots and 36 phones in a star configuration for each trace were not unusual in west Texas, and much larger patterns have been used for work in the Sahara Desert (see Pieuchot and Richard[11]).

4-5 COMMON-DEPTH-POINT SHOOTING

Common-depth-point (CDP) shooting is the mode used since the early 1960s, because it offers further cancellation of noise, i.e., multiples and random noise. The use of simple arrays of shots or geophones for canceling noise is practical only where the noise has wavelengths that are not appreciably greater than the lengths of the arrays themselves. Too long an array can severely attenuate reflection signals originating from other than horizontal surfaces directly below the shot point. The effects of arrays of different lengths and configurations on both noise and signal are illustrated in Savit et al.[8] Moreover, the length of most arrays is often limited to a distance that is not substantially greater than the separation between group centers along the spread. Thus, noise with wavelengths of more than a few hundred feet usually cannot be handled satisfactorily by conventional arrays.

Occasionally, high-speed refracted or diffracted events are observed with apparent velocities of 15,000 ft/s or more corresponding to wavelengths as great as 500 to 1000 ft. Such wavelengths will not be adequately canceled by the geophone groups having a much shorter length that are customarily employed in reflection work. A more common, and even more troublesome, type of long-wavelength noise is that associated with multiple reflections. The multiple events ordinarily have a different *moveout* from the primaries arriving at the same time because of the difference in average velocities for the respective paths. (Moveout refers to the trace-to-trace time delay of the reflection on a seismic record. See Fig. 4-4 for an example of this change of arrival time with offset.) Thus, when primary reflections are corrected to have no normal moveout, multiple events at appreciable distances from the shot will appear to make a small angle on the corrected record with the primaries, cutting across them in roughly the same way as very high velocity long-wavelength noise events.

The CDP technique is designed to cancel noise of large apparent wavelength, regardless of its origin. As with cancellation by means of arrays, outputs of phone groups distributed over a distance exceeding a wavelength are summed. The loss of definition which averaging over such an extensive baseline would otherwise cause is averted by a special arrangement of shots and geophones that attempts to combine only those signals reflected from the same region of the subsurface.

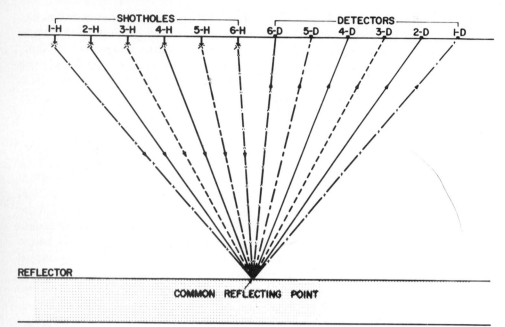

FIGURE 4-20
Ray paths for reflections from a single point in sixfold common-depth-point shooting.

The method for doing this has been described by Mayne,[12] the inventor of the technique. Basically, signals associated with a given reflection point, but recorded at a number of different shot and geophone positions, are composited in a processing center after appropriate time corrections are applied to compensate for the increasing length of ray path as the shot-geophone distances are increased. Figure 4-20 illustrates the recording arrangement when six signals are composited.

In an actual field setup, such CDP shooting (or multifold coverage) involves a greater number of shot points per unit distance along the line than single-fold shooting does. With 24 recording stations, threefold coverage will be obtained if the shots are separated by four geophone-group intervals, fourfold if by three intervals, and sixfold if by two intervals. If the shooting is twelvefold, there is a shot for every geophone group center. Twenty-four-fold shooting on land, which is common, requires 48-channel recording and shooting on every group. Figure 4-21 shows the successive shot positions for a set of single-end shooting spreads giving sixfold multiple coverage. Consider the reflecting point halfway between geophone positions 10 and 11. Reflection takes place at this position when the shot is at shot position 1 and the phone at geophone position 21, also when the shot is at position 2 and the geophone at 17. Such a reflection also occurs with shots and geophones at the four other combinations of positions shown on the left side of the figure.

To composite, or *stack*, the data for this reflecting point, the playback in the 1960s was so programmed that after all signals are corrected for normal moveout, the information on channel 21 of the tape from shot point 1 is added to that from channel 17 of the tape made from shot point 2, with similar contributions from the respective tapes corresponding to the four shot points 3 through 6. Today, the trace manipulation is carried out in the processing-center computer after the proper corrections are made to the data.

At the bottom of the figure, the dots show reflection points which correspond to all recorded wave paths. It is seen that there are six such paths for each subsurface position. Adding the proper signals for coincident subsurface reflection positions ("common depth points") as indicated on the diagram and plotting the output traces thus obtained on a record section is referred to as *stacking*. The bottom half of Fig. 4-21 is an example of a stacking diagram. Stacking diagrams constructed by hand are still useful for analyzing the line layout in old seismic lines of complicated shooting in which there were many groups irregularly not shot or not recorded or in which the spatial relationship of the recording groups to the source location changed often and radically.

"Well-behaved" lines have a systematic progression of field records in which the source is always in a certain position with respect to the recording

FIGURE 4-21
Shot and geophone combinations giving sixfold multiplicity for two subsurface reflecting points. Pattern at bottom shows reflecting points for successive spreads. (*Mayne.*[12])

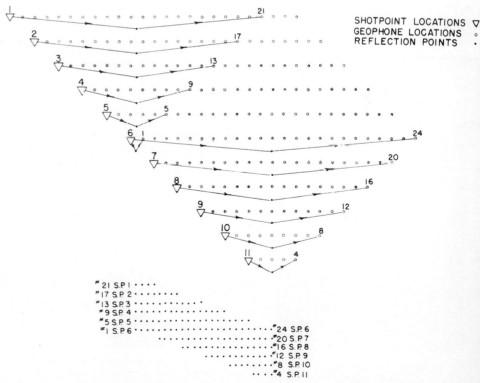

groups, and in which there is a minimum of skipped shooting locations or nonfunctional recording stations. In such lines, it is quite easy to describe the shooting and recording geometry for the whole line so that stacking diagrams would not need to be made by hand.

The shooting of the CDP data is carried out continuously along a line, the phone groups at the rear being picked up four, six, or more at a time and moved to the front of the spread in a kind of leapfrog maneuver as the shooting progresses. This procedure is referred to as *rollalong*.

Figure 4-22 illustrates how multiple reflections are attenuated by CDP stacking. The primary reflection and the multiple shown in the diagram at the upper left arrive at the near-offset geophone group at the same time. The far-offset groups receive the multiple reflection later in time than the primary reflection. This delay is due to the average velocity for the primary being higher than that for the multiple when the velocity increases with depth; thus the multiple travels through formations having an average speed slower than the average along the path taken by the primary. The moveout times for the multiple and primary are plotted against horizontal receiving distance. The multiple shows a greater moveout time (greater curvature) than the primary event. If a moveout correction is made using the velocity for the primary and the traces thus corrected are then added together, all primary reflections should have phase coincidence and the signal after summation should have accentuated ampli-

FIGURE 4-22 Cancellation of multiple reflections by common-depth-point processing for five shot-geophone distances. Difference in arrival times for the multiple at these distances covers a wave period, resulting in cancellation upon addition of the signals. (*Mayne.*[12])

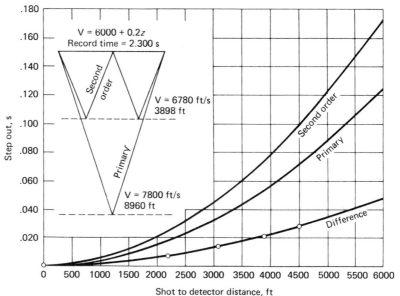

tudes for such events. The multiples, however, will be out of phase, and addition of such signals for equally distributed distances from 0 to 6000 ft will tend to result in cancellation. In this example, the total range of differences in time between the two corrected events over a 6000-ft distance is more than 40 ms, which is greater than the periods of most seismic reflection events.

It is evident from the diagram that the deeper the primary event to be brought out over a multiple that arrives at about the same time, the smaller the moveout differential over a given spread length. Yet the deeper the primary reflection the greater the likelihood that there will be interference from multiples. The only way to increase the time differential from moveout is to lengthen the spread. For this reason, spreads are much longer with CDP shooting than they were with single-fold coverage. Spreads allowing recording 10,000 ft from the shot point are common. Where feasible and practical, spreads are often designed to be about as long as the target formation is deep, within the limits of available field equipment.

Actually, the cancellation of multiples would be more complete if the shot-geophone distances were such as to allow equal time intervals between successive samples along the difference curve. The practical difficulties of laying out spreads in which the distances between phones are nonuniform would make such an arrangement infeasible. The irregularity of time intervals can be minimized, however, if there is an appreciable offset distance between the shot and the nearest phone, as is customary (to reduce surface-wave interference) when nondynamite sources are employed. With the nearest phone at a large offset distance, all the phones lie along the portion of the difference curve that approaches linearity. The nearer the differential time-distance curve is to being linear the more nearly equal the phase differences for successive intervals and the better the cancellation to be expected.

Whether the shooting should be programmed for 24-fold, 48-fold, or 96-fold coverage depends on the quality of the data and the relative amplitudes of the multiple reflections to be canceled. Now that CDP data are used to compute interval as well as average-velocity information, it is usually desirable to shoot with as great a degree of multiplicity as is operationally feasible (24-fold or more) so as to attain the greatest possible precision in the resultant velocity. Current techniques for determining velocities from seismic records shot in CDP configuration will be described in a later chapter.

4-6   SHEAR-WAVE DATA ACQUISITION

Shear-wave reflection work is gaining more interest. This chapter will conclude with the field techniques and equipment used in shear-wave data gathering, and later chapters will discuss why shear-wave reflection data are useful.

As discussed in Chap. 2, shear waves are characterized by polarized particle motion perpendicular to the advancing wavefront. The two polarizations used in reflection shear work are SH, polarization transverse to the seismic line, and

SV, polarization parallel to or in line with the seismic line. Any polarization can be generated and recorded by appropriate orientation of the sources and receivers, but most shear sources have been deliberately designed for efficient SH data acquisition. The newest shear-wave sources have been designed to provide alternative orthogonal polarizations. Upon reflection in an isotropic, homogeneous, flat-layered earth, SH shear waves, unlike SV, will not mode convert some of their energy to P waves. The lack of mode conversion makes SH shear-wave data "simpler" (in theory) to process and interpret, and thus "preferable."

Sources The available shear-wave sources are shear vibrators, inclined impact sources, horizontal hammers, and P-wave sources in special arrays adapted to maximize shear-wave energy generation.

The shear-wave vibrator truck is similar to the P-wave vibrator truck in concept except that the driving oscillation is horizontal and transverse to the forward direction of the truck. The baseplate usually has large inverted pyramidal or conical cleats (6 to 18 in deep, 6 to 18 in wide) on its base. During oscillation, the pad is held in contact with the ground by the cleats and the weight of the vibrator truck. With this baseplate, bulldozers may have to follow the vibrators to backfill the resulting holes. Shear vibrators have demonstrated the acquisition of adequate to good SH data in many different locations (Robertson and Pritchett[13]). As with conventional P-wave vibrator surveys, four to eight or more shear vibrators are used together. For SH reflection work, the required baseplate oscillation is perpendicular to the line direction, and the trucks simply drive straight down the line, stopping at appropriate places to vibrate. Should SV reflection work be desired, the truck must turn sideways at each oscillation in the in-line direction. A shear vibrator truck that allows the baseplate or vibrating mechanism to be rotated and secured for SH or SV work would be more flexible and allow faster and, hence, cheaper SV data acquisition.

The horizontal hammer was used more for engineering geophysics, i.e., a penetration of a few thousand feet or less, but modern versions (MARTHOR™, ARIS™) have generated reflections from about 10,000 ft. In the MARTHOR source, two hammers, located on opposite sides of the cleated baseplate, strike alternately. Subtraction of the records of the two blows allows enhancement of shear reflections, and attenuation of P-wave energy. Good coupling of the baseplate to the ground is essential. The ARIS source uses an inclined weight drop to generate a shear wave. The weight is alternately dropped in opposite directions, left and right for SH waves, forward and back in the line direction for SV. The records for the two opposite directions are subtracted to produce the final product.

The P-wave sources adapted to shear-wave energy generation are a three-trench or three-hole technique, and P-wave vibrators used in the SHOVER™ technique. Three trenches are dug parallel to the line direction. Primacord or other explosives are buried in the trenches; the explosive in the center trench is detonated first to create an air cavity to absorb some of the subsequently generated sideways propagating energy. To gather data, the right trench is fired and the reflections recorded, then the left trench. In processing, the second recording is subtracted from the first, which removes most (in theory, all) of the P-wave energy, and adds in phase the SH polarized energy with first motion to the right of the line. This concept can also be executed by placing dynamite charges in three holes oriented in a manner similar to that of the three-trench method and firing, recording, and subtracting in the same order. An explosive shear source system and a large recording system allow the simultaneous gathering of P-wave data and shear-wave data. One needs the collocated P-wave data to interpret the shear-wave data in terms of the underlying geology.

Another P-wave source system adapted to shear wave generation is the SHOVER technique in which four, six, or more P-wave vibrators are placed in pairs down the line. All the trucks on the right side of the line oscillate 180° out of phase with the trucks on the left side of the line, thus creating a right, left, right, left, etc., oscillation on the earth to simulate sideways (SH) motion. Edelmann[14] published comparisons of SHOVER field data to shear vibrator field data. Shear reflections to 3 s were recorded using both techniques, although the amplitudes and the penetration displayed by the two P-wave vibrator SHOVER experiment were inferior to those of the three-shear vibrator survey. However, Edelmann proposed that by increasing the number of P vibrator couples and by using other measures, the data quality could improve to perhaps rival that of shear vibrator surveys.

Receivers A shear-wave geophone is a low-frequency (4.5, 6, 8 Hz, etc.) phone that has the coil horizontally oriented, so that shear waves polarized parallel to coil direction are detected. Each geophone has an arrow on the lid of the case, indicating coil direction, so that all phones may be oriented properly with respect to the source polarization. Many areas are characterized by azimuthal anisotropy that causes a propagating shear wave to split and rotate into the "natural" coordinate system. Most shear-wave surveys, therefore, use two-component horizontal recording (see Alford,[15] Willis et al.,[16] and Crampin[17]). Modern shear-wave phones are specially constructed to level the coil internally. Manual leveling of geophones not so constructed is time consuming and has a low probability of success.

Once the sources and receivers have been chosen and deployed, conventional cables, recording systems, and CDP shooting methods are used.

REFERENCES

1 Dobrin, M. B., R. F. Simon, and P. L. Lawrence: Rayleigh Waves from Small Explosions, *Trans. Am. Geophys. Union*, vol. 32, pp. 822–832, 1951.
2 Dobrin, M. B., P. L. Lawrence, and Raymond Sengbush: Surface and Near-Surface Waves in the Delaware Basin, *Geophysics*, vol. 19, pp. 695–715, 1954.

3 Crawford, John M., W. E. N. Doty, and M. R. Lee: Continuous Signal Seismograph, *Geophysics*, vol. 25, pp. 95–105, 1960.

4 Laing, W. E.: Some Basics and Applications of the Vibroseis System of Exploration, 1972, *J. Petrol. Tech.*, or *Soc. Petrol. Engineers J.*, from 1972 Reg. Conf. SPE-AIME.

5 McKay, A. E.: Review of Pattern Shooting, *Geophysics*, vol. 19, pp. 420–437, 1954.

6 Lombardi, L. V.: Notes on the Use of Multiple Geophones *Geophysics*, vol. 20, pp. 215–226, 1955.

7 Parr, J. O., Jr., and W. H. Mayne: A New Method of Pattern Shooting, *Geophysics*, vol. 20, pp. 539–565, 1955.

8 Savit, C. H., J. T. Brustad, and J. Sider: The Moveout Filter, *Geophysics*. vol. 23, pp. 1–25, 1958.

9 Larner, K. L., R. Chambers, M. Yang, W. Lynn, and W. Wai: Coherent Noise in Marine Seismic Data, *Geophysics*, vol. 48, pp. 854–886, 1983.

10 Reynolds, F. F.: Design Factors for Multiple Arrays of Geophones and Shot Holes, *Oil Gas J.*, April 19, 1954, pp. 145–146.

11 Pieuchot, M., and H. Richard: Some Technical Aspects of Reflection Seismic Prospecting in the Sahara, *Geophysics*, vol. 23, pp. 557–573, 1958.

12 Mayne, W. Harry: Common Reflection Point Horizontal Data Stacking Techniques, *Geophysics*, vol. 27, pp. 952–965, 1962.

13 Robertson, J. D., and W. C. Pritchett: Bright Spot Validation Using Comparative P-Wave and S-Wave Seismic Sections, *Soc. Expl. Geophys.*, *53rd Int. Meeting Expanded Abstracts*, pp. 355–356, 1983.

14 Edelmann, H. A. K.: SHOVER Shear Wave Generation by Vibrating Orthogonal to the Polarization, *Geophys. Prosp.*, vol. 29, pp. 541–549, 1981.

15 Alford, R. M.: Shear Data in the Presence of Azimuthal Anisotropy: Dilley, Tx., *1986 Int. SEG Convention Expanded Abstracts*, pp. 476–479, 1986.

16 Willis, H. A., G. L. Rethford, and E. Bielanski: Azimuthal Anistropy: Occurrence and Effect on Shear Wave Data Quality, *1986 Int. SEG Convention Expanded Abstracts*, pp. 479–480, 1986.

17 Crampin, S.: Evaluation of Anistropy by Shear-Wave Splitting, *Geophysics*, vol. 50, pp. 142–152, 1985; Evidence for Aligned Cracks in the Earth's Crust, *First Break*, vol. 3, pp. 12–15, 1985.

18 Bolt Associates, Inc. Schematic for LSS-3B Air Gun, (U.S. patent no. 4,108,271, U.S.A., issued Aug. 22, 1978).

CHAPTER 5

ACQUISITION OF SEISMIC DATA IN WATER-COVERED AREAS

In Chap. 4 we considered techniques for seismic recording on land. Some of the topics discussed there, e.g., use of multiple receivers and common-depth-point techniques, are equally applicable to seismic work at sea. Other aspects of seismic data acquisition, however, are uniquely associated with marine applications. For example, the physical processes by which seismic energy is generated in the water are quite different from those involved when the generation is in solid earth materials. Special energy sources can thus be used at sea which are not generally applicable on land. Receiving transducers and cables are designed quite differently, and position location for marine exploration may require methods which have been specifically developed for solving the special problems encountered at sea.

While the seismic method has been used in offshore oil exploration since before World War II, most marine activity was confined to the Gulf and Pacific Coasts of the United States until the early 1960s, when the amount of offshore seismic exploration in other parts of the world began to increase at a rapid rate. Concurrent with this expansion of activity was a rapid development of new and improved equipment and techniques which have led to greatly increased efficiency and economy in marine operations as well as to much better data quality. Today, the 24-h shooting schedule of most marine crews allows a high production rate (typically 750 to 1000 mi/month compared with 50 to 100 mi/month for a land crew). The per-mile cost of marine data acquisition is thus about 10 to 20 percent of that on land.

Because of the vast amount of data recorded each day in a seismic operation at sea, digital recording was put to use for nearly all marine shooting within a few years after its introduction. From the middle 1960s on, virtually all marine reflection work has employed multifold (common-depth-point) coverage. Since late 1967, explosives have only rarely been used as sources of seismic energy except for special detonating systems in which small ($\frac{1}{2}$ lb or less) charges confined in cans or plastic jackets are exploded. Even this limited use of explosives effectively ceased by 1980. Marine acquisition can be 2-D, with seismic lines spaced 1000 ft or more apart, or 3-D, with seismic lines spaced 100 to 500 ft apart. Considerations common to both 2-D and 3-D marine acquisition are presented in this chapter; special concerns of 3-D acquisition are presented in Chap. 10.

5-1 GENERATION OF SEISMIC ENERGY UNDERWATER

The function of any underwater source of seismic energy, whether or not it involves the detonation of dynamite or similar explosives, is to introduce a sudden positive (or sometimes negative) pressure impulse into the water. This impulse involves a compression (or rarefaction) of the water particles, creating a shock wave that spreads out spherically into the water and then into the earth. A delayed effect of the shock wave is an oscillatory flow of water in the area around the explosion, which gives rise to subsequent pressure pulses designated as bubble oscillations. A simple description of these phenomena, published by Kramer et al.,[1] will be summarized here.

Formation and Properties of the Gas Bubble in Water Shooting   The properties of the seismic signals generated by all marine energy sources are strongly dependent upon the bubble oscillation, which in the case of dynamite and certain nonexplosive sources such as air guns is associated with an actual bubble in the water. With other types of sources where little or no bubble exists, periodic pressure pulses are generated which have characteristics similar to those from the bubble oscillations. To understand how these pulses are generated for all types of sources, let us consider what happens to a gas bubble created underwater by an explosion of dynamite.

If we assume a spherical charge of dynamite 1 ft in diameter to be detonated at its center, we shall have a very rapid conversion of the solid material constituting the explosive into high-temperature, high-density gas. That gas in turn causes a detonation of the still undetonated portions of the sphere. The detonation front propagates at a velocity as high as 22,000 ft/s and causes gasification of the solid explosive material with which it makes contact. The pressure in the interior of the solid shell has a peak value of 2 million pounds per square inch. When the outward traveling detonation front reaches the surface of the spherical charge 23 μs after the detonation, the water immediately outside the sphere becomes highly compressed and a strong shock wave is initiated in it. At a time of 30 μs from the detonation, the peak pressure of the shock wave, now traveling in the water, has been reduced to 550,000 lb/in^2. The falloff in pressure on either side of the shock front is sharp, as is demonstrated in Fig. 5-1.

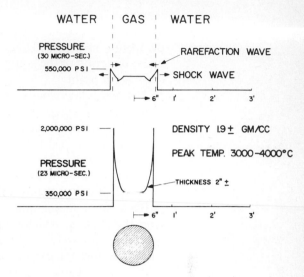

FIGURE 5-1
Pressure fields in vicinity of spherical dynamite charge 23 μs (*below*) and 30 μs (*above*) after detonation at center. (*From Kramer, Peterson, and Walter.*[1])

From this point on, the process of generation is the same whether the source is dynamite, an air gun, an electric sparker creating a steam bubble in the water, or any other system that suddenly injects a bubble of gas into the water. The important consideration from the standpoint of putting seismic energy in the earth is the creation of a shock wave by sudden compression of the water that occupies the space adjacent to the bubble immediately after it is generated.

As the shock front progresses outward, its pressure and particle velocity continue to decrease. Figure 5-2 shows both quantities as functions of distance from the point of detonation at a time of 630 μs. At this time (still less than 1 ms

FIGURE 5-2
Pressure and particle velocity versus distance from source 630 μs after underwater explosion. (*From Kramer, Peterson, and Walter.*[1])

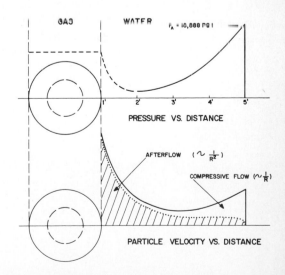

after the explosion) the gas bubble is 2 ft in diameter, and the shock front is a spherical surface having a radius of 6 ft. The water pressure at the outer edge of the front is now 16,000 lb/in². Just inside the shock front the pressure decreases in the direction of the source, reaching a minimum at a distance of 2 ft from the detonation point.

The particle velocity in the water consists of two components: (1) the outward-directed *compressive* flow of water required to fill the rarefaction left behind the shock front which transports water under compression away from the source, and (2) the *afterflow* which supplies water to accommodate the tangential expansion that occurs as the shock front travels. The afterflow represents a production of kinetic energy which is converted into a pressure wave when the outward flow of water is reversed.

Because of momentum, the gas bubble continues to expand until 200 ms after the shot, at which time its radius is about 10 ft. The pressure inside the bubble is now only 2 lb/in², which is 35 lb/in² below the ambient hydrostatic pressure. Here the expansion stops and contraction begins. The rapid shrinking of the bubble causes an increasing inward velocity of the water and a rapidly increasing pressure in the contracting bubble. At 400 ms the bubble has col-lapsed to its smallest diameter and highest pressure, and expansion starts again.

Figure 5-3 demonstrates this cycle of bubble oscillation. The depth of the bubble stays almost constant, while its diameter is large because the resistance of the water above it inhibits upward motion. When the bubble diameter is smallest, the water resistance is the least and the bubble rises at its greatest rate of speed.

This description of bubble behavior is, of course, highly idealized. In the real world, the shape of the bubble is not perfectly spherical because, in the case of explosives, the explosive itself is not spherical and is not detonated from its

FIGURE 5-3
Variation of bubble radius and position in water with time after dynamite explosion. (*From Kramer, Peterson, and Walter.*[1])

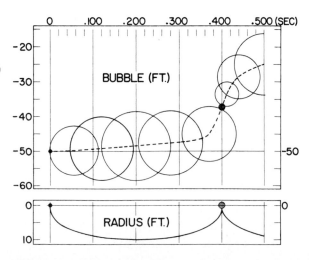

center, while in the case of air guns the air is discharged in preferential directions through ports. Furthermore, the pressure of the water body is less at the upper parts of the bubble than it is at the bottom.

Because of these asymmetries and because the original and subsequent bubbles create considerable energy-dissipating turbulence, the bubble oscillations die out after only a few cycles. Nevertheless the theoretical calculations have been found to be a good first-order approximation to actual bubble behavior encountered with sources in use before about 1985.

Relation between Oscillation Period of Gas Bubble and Energy of Source   The period of the bubble oscillation is of great practical importance because each oscillation generates a new seismic impulse. The seismic signal associated with the initial pressure injection is thus repeated at intervals equivalent to this period. Such multiple repetitions in the down-traveling source signal cause reverberation effects in the reflection signals that often obscure desired information. Fortunately, the magnitude of the bubble oscillation can be minimized by proper design of the source and by the use of appropriate shooting procedures, as discussed later in this section. In some cases the entire bubble train can be used as an effective energy source by recording the original bubble sequence and using an appropriate mathematical filter (of a type to be discussed in Chap. 6) for simplifying the desired reflection signal.

The relation between the bubble-oscillation period T and the potential energy associated with the oscillation was developed by Willis[2] on the basis of an equation previously published by Lord Rayleigh[3] for the dependence of the period of the bubble upon its radius and its ambient hydrostatic pressure. Lord Rayleigh's equation, originally developed to explain the sounds made by steam bubbles in a teakettle, is

$$T = 1.83 A_m \sqrt{\frac{\rho}{P_0}} \tag{5-1}$$

where T = period of bubble oscillation, in seconds
A_m = maximum radius of bubble, in centimeters
ρ = density of the fluid, in grams per cubic centimeter
P_0 = ambient pressure, in dynes per square centimeter

Willis' equation introduced the relation between Q, the potential energy in the bubble, and its pressure and volume:

$$Q = \tfrac{4}{3}\pi A_m{}^3 P_0 \tag{5-2}$$

Eliminating A_m, we obtain the following relationship between T and Q:

$$T = 1.14 \, \rho^{1/2} \, P_0^{-5/6} \, (KQ)^{1/3} \tag{5-3}$$

where K is a constant depending on the units of Q. It is 1.0 if Q is in ergs,

1.00×10^{10} if in kilojoules, 1.36×10^7 if in foot-pounds, and 4.18×10^{10} if in kilocalories. If we assume a density of 1.024 g/cm^3 for seawater and replace P_0 by $d + 33$, where d is the depth in feet of the center of the bubble below the water surface, this equation becomes, for T in seconds,

$$T = \frac{0.000209(KQ)^{1/3}}{(d + 33)^{5/6}} \tag{5-4}$$

If we operate on the assumption that the potential energy of the bubble Q is proportional, for any particular type of source, to the intrinsic energy in the source, we have a means of determining the relative efficiency of different sources and of comparing the effective performance of the sources on the basis of the oscillation period, which is often easily measurable. The Rayleigh-Willis diagram, discussed later in this chapter (see page 130), was used for many years to relate the bubble-oscillation period to the potential energy available for seismic signal generation. It is less used now, because it does not relate to the newer sources without bubbles.

The mechanism for pressure generation by bubble-pulse oscillation is somewhat different for sources which do not create an actual bubble in the water. Several sources have been used in which a detonation of fuel and oxygen takes place inside a device. The detonation causes a part of the device to expand impulsively, producing a shock wave in the water. Other sources create an underwater, water jet which is then abruptly cut off. Inertia of the moving water creates a cavity and an abrupt rarefaction. The mechanism is that of the familiar water hammer in domestic plumbing. Even in these cases, however, there is an oscillation effect caused by the buildup of potential energy in the afterflow, which is generated whenever there is a shock wave. As with explosives, the period of the oscillation depends upon the potential energy associated with the source. For impulsive sources where there is no actual bubble, the signal will still exhibit all the effects of a bubble oscillation because of the afterflow mechanism, which is inextricably associated with the shock wave. Mechanical oscillations or abrupt movements in the internal workings of many sources will themselves produce unwanted sound waves in the water. The amplitude of the pressure signal associated with such oscillations will, in general, be lower than those produced by bubbles of air or gas.

5-2 MARINE ENERGY SOURCES

It is not feasible to describe all the energy sources that have been developed and used for marine seismic work, but the number of basic types now in use is relatively small, and examples of each will be discussed. Previous editions of this and other geophysical textbooks dealt with then-current marine source types.

To illustrate the basic principles involved, and because of their historical importance, we shall begin with explosives. While explosives are now rarely if ever used as marine sources, many existing and important data sets were produced through the use of explosives. In addition, much of present governmental regulation and public perception of marine seismic activity is based on phenomena associated with explosive methods in use prior to about 1967.

Our discussion of present-day marine sources will be confined to air guns and water guns, with a brief listing of other types of sources that are no longer popular but still used to fill special needs, as well as some presently under development.

Dynamite

Referring to dynamite and other high explosives, Kramer et al.[1] wrote in 1968:

> Probably no other type of source provides such a compact package of concentrated energy and no other source provides such a simple means for rapid and almost instantaneous release of energy. However, for various economic, technological, and political reasons, the last few years have seen a rapid increase in the use of alternative types of energy sources, particularly in marine seismic surveying operations.

Dynamite was used as an explosive for early seismic work at sea until the early 1950s, when it was largely replaced by nitrocarbonitrate (NCN). In the middle 1960s the percentage of work making use of NCN decreased almost to zero until specially controlled NCN sources such as Flexotir (trademark of Institut Français du Pétrole) and Maxipulse (trademark of Western Geophysical Co. of America), described later in this chapter, came into extensive use. In 1974, 20 percent of all marine shooting employed small NCN charges. By about 1982 the use of explosives as a marine seismic source had effectively ceased.

In shooting explosives at sea, it had been customary to detonate the charge at such a shallow depth that the bubble would break through the surface of the water and not oscillate. Lay[4] found that the maximum depth d (in feet) at which the bubble will break is related to the charge weight w (in pounds) by the formula

$$d = 3.8w^{1/3} \tag{5-5}$$

Worzel and Ewing[5] reach a similar conclusion in a memoir on shallow-water seismic-wave propagation.

The explosion of NCN at such shallow depths substantially lowers the efficiency of the operation because there is always a pressure node at the free surface of the water at which any excitation should theoretically have no effect. The most efficient input of energy is actually at an antinode, which occurs at depths equal to any odd number of quarter wavelengths. One-quarter of a wavelength for a typical seismic reflection signal in water is 20 to 40 ft.

The bubble-oscillation period in water for an NCN charge of 1 lb detonated at 30 ft is about 120 ms, and for a charge of 50 lb it is about 700 ms. Such long intervals cause repetitions of reflection events on records, which can make proper interpretation very difficult. Thus before the advent of effective digital "debubbling" procedures, large charges always had to be fired at shallow enough depths to destroy the bubble in spite of the loss in efficiency that results when a large part of the energy of the explosion is released into the air.

There are many reasons for the great decrease in the use of explosives for marine seismic work during the later 1960s. Most of them relate directly to the potential hazards, both to life and to property, associated with explosives as conventionally used. For example, it was generally not considered safe to handle explosives after dark for any seismic crew, land or marine. This restriction limited offshore operations to daylight hours and, depending on latitude and time of year, could cut down on productivity by 50 percent or more. Also, the explosive was seldom fired from the ship that contained the recording equipment and towed the receiving cable because any misconception about location of the charge under the water surface could result in the loss of a cable costing more than $100,000 (late 1960s dollars) or even the destruction of the recording ship. The need for two ships in such operations (one for shooting and one for receiving) involved a much greater initial investment and operating expense than did the single ship that could suffice for both purposes if a less hazardous source were used.

Another important reason for abandoning explosives detonated just below the surface was their low efficiency. A large part of the energy of the detonation went into the geyser that each shot created instead of into seismic events. The cost of using many charges having such poor effectiveness became prohibitive with the introduction of common-depth-point shooting.

Also the logistic difficulties and governmental restrictions in shipping, storing, and handling large quantities of explosives, particularly in parts of the world that are far from factories where they are manufactured or in politically sensitive areas, added complications and delays that were not encountered with other energy sources.

Finally, there was the danger of destroying fish by dynamite, a danger which has led to restrictions on seismic activity in many areas where fishing is important. Such restrictions could prohibit such activity altogether at certain times of year. In areas such as the Cook Inlet of Alaska and the Bay of Biscay, the severity of regulations against underwater explosions made it particularly urgent that some seismic-energy source be found which would be acceptable to the agencies charged with protecting the fisheries industry.

Although the devices that have largely replaced conventional high explosives for offshore seismic work are ordinarily referred to as nonexplosive sources, this terminology has euphemistically come to include systems that involve the detonation of NCN charges under such conditions that safety and economy are not compromised.

Sources Using Controlled Charges of Dynamite

Flexotir   In one such system, developed by the Institut Français du Pétrole and designated Flexotir, the source itself is a small pellet of dynamite weighing about 2 ounces embedded in a plastic cartridge. The charge is detonated at the center of a multiply perforated cast-iron spherical shell about 2 ft in diameter which is towed behind the ship at a depth of about 40 ft. There are 130 perforations in the shell, each 2 in across. A flexible hose conveys the charge from the fantail of the ship into the sphere, the driving force being water pumped down the hose under high pressure. The sphere must be replaced after about 2000 explosions.

The mesh made by the perforations in the spherical enclosure has the effect of breaking up the bubble, in accordance with a principle first established by Knudsen,[6] so that oscillation is aborted and the undesired effects of bubble-pulsing on the signal are suppressed. Because the shooting depth is about a quarter wavelength for typical seismic reflection waves, the efficiency of the explosion for generating seismic energy is much greater than for detonation just below the surface and, as Lavergne[7] has shown, the effective seismic signal is as strong as that for a much larger charge fired at conventional depths.

Flexotir systems had their greatest use from the mid-1960s to the early 1970s.

Maxipulse Another source containing dynamite, the Maxipulse, is also designed for detonation under conditions that combine safety, efficiency, and elimination of bubble-pulse effects. The charge, about $\frac{1}{2}$ lb, is packed in a can which is injected into the water at a depth of about 20 to 40 ft by a delivery device trailed from the ship. The detonation takes place about 1 s after the injection, the delay making it possible for the can to explode far enough from the injector to avoid damaging it. The arrangement is illustrated in Fig. 5-4a.

Upon detonation, a bubble is formed, and it expands and collapses with a period of approximately 100 ms. A detecting hydrophone on the injector device picks up the signal generated by the source, including the bubble oscillations (Figs. 5-4b and 5-8c). In the final processing of the data, this signal is compared with the reflection signal, and the bubble oscillations are reduced to negligible proportions by use of a filter program, discussed in Chaps. 6 and 7, that yields an output equivalent to what could have been obtained if the source had generated a single sharp pulse (Fig. 5-4b). Similar reduction of the oscillatory wave train (coda) can be obtained for other types of sources when it is possible to record or otherwise determine the form of the complete source waveform at or near the source.

Nonexplosive Sources

Air Gun The most widely used of all nonexplosive sources is the air gun. As with explosives and some other sources, it was originally employed for academic studies of subbottom geological structure in marine areas. It was also used for research on sound transmission in the ocean.

The PAR (trademark of Bolt Associates) air gun of Bolt Technology, was the first air gun used in commercial operations and dominated that field from the late 1960s until the 1980s. It is manufactured in a number of models with

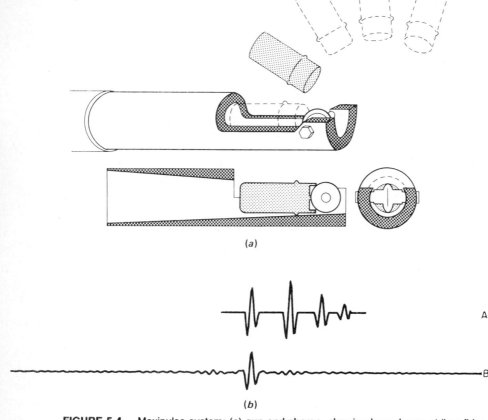

(a)

(b)

FIGURE 5-4 Maxipulse system: (*a*) gun and charge, showing how charge strikes firing wheel and how it is subsequently ejected; (*b*) collapse of bubble pulse by computer processing. Waveform *A* includes bubble pulses as generated. Waveform *B* shows collapsed waveshape after the processing. (*After C. H. Savit, Copyright Offshore Technol. Conf., Houston, 1970, vol. I, p. 604.*)

capacities ranging from 1 to 2000 in^3 or more of air and typically operates at a pressure of about 2000 lb/in^2.

In the mid 1970s a series of 5000-lb/in^2 air guns came into use. These guns were the descendants of air guns that had been used as substitutes for explosives in coal-mining operations in the 1940s and 1950s. Use of the higher pressure allowed the guns to be smaller and easier to handle than those that used the lower pressure. The higher pressure also contributed a somewhat higher frequency range to the seismic signal.

Figure 5-5 shows how the PAR source works. High-pressure air, which passes through a hose from the compressor to the towed submerged unit, enters through the connection at the upper left. It flows into the upper cham-

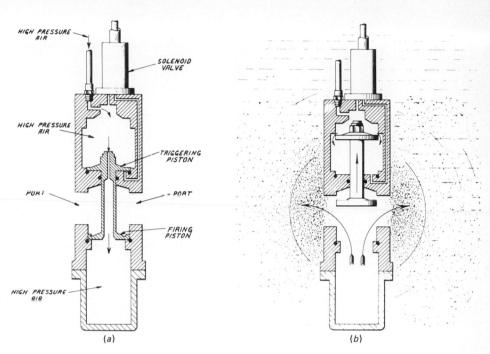

HIGH PRESSURE
AIR

SOLENOID
VALVE

HIGH PRESSURE
AIR

TRIGGERING
PISTON

PORT

- PORT

FIRING
PISTON

HIGH PRESSURE
AIR

(a)

(b)

FIGURE 5-5
Bolt PAR air gun,
showing two stages of
the firing cycle: (a)
armed; (b) fired. (Bolt
Associates, Inc.)

ber, across which is fitted the top piston of a shuttle consisting of a shaft with a triggering piston at the upper end and a firing piston at the lower. There is a hole in the shaft through which the air from the upper chambers enters the lower one.

Although the same pressure is developed in each chamber, the area of the triggering piston above is somewhat greater than that of the firing piston below, and the net downward force on the shuttle causes it to move down until it is stopped by the base of the upper chamber. At the instant the gun is to be fired, a solenoid opens a valve that injects high-pressure air between the triggering piston and the base of the upper chamber through the opening on the right side of this chamber. The sudden introduction of the air through the solenoid-controlled valve upsets the equilibrium of the system, and the shuttle moves upward at a high velocity. As the firing piston passes the four large ports (two of which are shown in Fig. 5-5), most of the high-pressure air from the lower chamber is suddenly spilled out into the water, creating an air bubble quite similar to that from a dynamite explosion and giving rise to repetitive bubble pulses at a rate determined by the oscillation period of the air mass thus generated: the larger the volume of the air, the longer the period. Figure 5-6 shows the waveform obtained from an air gun at different depths. The decrease in oscillation period with depth conforms to the Rayleigh-Willis prediction that the period should fall off as the five-sixth power of source depth. The amplitude of the initial impulse is necessarily greater than that of any produced by

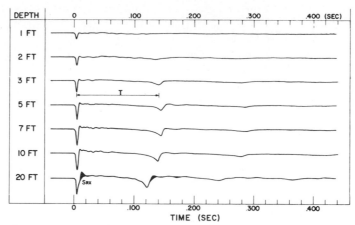

FIGURE 5-6   Air-gun pressure signature at various depths. (*Kramer, Peterson, and Walter.*[1])

subsequent collapses of the bubble because energy is lost each time the bubble expands and collapses. Often, however, the seismic record will show the first bubble pulse to be substantially stronger than the initial impulse. The explanation of this anomaly lies in the frequency content of the initial impulse and of the subsequent bubble pulses. Because the initial impulse is produced by the abrupt mechanical release of compressed air, the acoustic signal has a sharp onset and most of the acoustic energy is contained in the first few milliseconds of the pulse. In other words, the energy of the initial impulse is largely contained in the higher frequencies. The collapsing bubbles, on the other hand, produce signals with a much more gradual onset. The energy of the bubble pulses, therefore, tends to be concentrated in the lower frequencies, well within the seismic band. Since seismic recording instruments are generally set to reject energy outside the restricted band in which deeper seismic reflections are observed, they can reject a substantial part of the energy of the initial impulse and pass all of the bubble energy. This effect is even greater when the initial impulse is produced by an explosive charge.

The effect of the bubble-pulse repetition (see Fig. 5-8*b*) is to give an oscillatory and, hence, unsatisfactory reflection record. Special measures are therefore taken in the shooting and in the processing center to eliminate the bubble oscillations. The most effective way of doing this in the field is to use an array of guns having a variety of air-chamber capacities and all fired in synchronism. The intervals between the initial pulse and the first bubble pulse will be different for each gun having a different air capacity. The pressure signal actually recorded from the array will consist of an impulse representing the sum of the initial pulses from all the guns followed by a train of much weaker bubble pulses spread out over a period of time and partially canceling one another. Provided that the guns could be synchronized to emit their initial pulses nearly simultaneously, and provided that the guns are far enough apart that they do not interact substantially, the initial-pulse sound pressure produced at a great distance below the array is equal to the sum of the sound pressures of the individual guns. If also the sizes of the individual guns are sufficiently varied, the first and subsequent bubble pulses all occur at different times and so their maximum level is no greater than that of the strongest one. Because perfect synchronization is not attainable in practice, the best primary-to-bubble ratio attainable in practice for signals in the seismic reflection band is about 10. Properly processed seismic data show no discernible differences between data taken with arrays yielding primary-to-bubble ratios more than about 3 or 4.

The large guns generate a signal richer in low frequencies than do the small guns whose signals are relatively richer in high frequencies. Through judicious choice of large, medium, and small guns, the geophysicist can achieve an approximately balanced frequency spectrum.

Some operators use "tuned" arrays in which two or more guns are spaced apart at a distance at which the primary pulses interact minimally but sufficiently close together that their air bubbles merge (Fig. 5-7c). The result is a bubble period of a gun having the combined capacity of the individual guns but with a much larger primary pulse than could be obtained from a single gun of equal capacity (see Figs. 5-7 and 5-8b and d).

A different technique for bubble-pulse suppression is to add air to the bubble at the stage when it begins to contract, thus weakening the force of the contraction and hence the pressure in the pulse generated when the bubble reaches minimum diameter. While effective, this method uses much more compressed air than is required for equal results obtained from a properly designed array.

Water Gun   Water guns are often used when sharp, clean, bubble-free impulses are needed and greater source power is not as important. A water gun generally consists of an underwater metal chamber filled with water and a mechanism for rapidly pushing that water out. Upon activation, the water gun accelerates its contained water to a high velocity, producing a jet or current in the surrounding water body. When all of the water has been driven out of the chamber, the jet abruptly terminates. Inertia produces a void behind the moving slug of water. Collapse of the surrounding water into the void produces an implosion which, in turn, generates an acoustic pulse.

In contrast to the compression pulse produced by explosives, air guns, gas guns, and other sources, the water gun produces an initial rarefaction (see Fig. 5-8a). Because the collapse is into a void, there is no gas or air to be compressed. Absence of air in the void allows the resulting impulse to have a shorter onset than is produced by the collapse of an air bubble. Furthermore there is no compressed air to store energy for a subsequent expansion; hence there is no succession of bubble pulses.

As of this writing, no water gun can generate an impulse equal in strength to that of the more powerful air guns. In addition, beginning the acceleration of the water in the gun produces a compressive acoustic impulse in advance of the

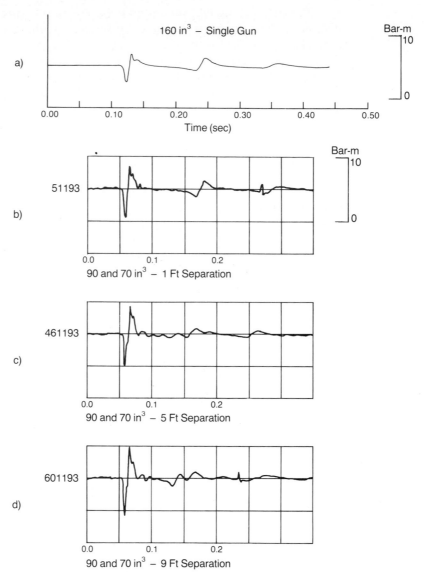

FIGURE 5-7 The comparison of marine source signatures of one large gun (160 in³) with that of a gun array (90 and 70 in³) with different separations of the guns.

(a) 160 in³, single gun. (b) 90- and 70-in³ guns, 1-ft separation. The bubble period is the same as that of the single gun (a), but the amplitude of the primary pulse is twice that of (a). (c) 90- and 70-in³ guns, 5-ft separation. Notice the change in the character and timing of the bubble, and the much larger primary pulse, compared to (a). (d) 90- and 70-in³ guns, 9-ft separation.

The source signatures from the gun array all exhibit larger primary/bubble ratios than that of the single gun. (*Western Geophysical.*)

main, rarefaction impulse (see Fig. 5-8a). In short, elimination of the bubble-train coda of other sources has been purchased at the cost of an undesired precursor.

Other Nonexplosive Sources   The extent to which various marine sources have been put to use has changed with time. Some that were once used quite extensively are no longer used on a large scale, often for operational or economic reasons. For many years the Aquapulse (trademark of Western Geophysical Co.) or sleeve exploder source was second only to the air gun in popularity. This was a source consisting of a cylindrical cage of metal pipes inside a rubber tube. Inside the cage a mixture of propane and oxygen gases was detonated by a spark plug. The resulting detonation caused the rubber tube to expand abruptly in the surrounding water. A vacuum pump on board the ship removed the combustion products after the detonation. The cage of pipes kept the rubber tube from collapsing with the internal gas, and seawater passing through the pipes that formed the cage prevented the rubber from overheating. The source waveform of the Aquapulse sleeve exploder system is shown in Fig. 5-8e. Despite their relative freedom from bubble-pulse effects, sleeve exploders have largely been replaced by the more powerful air guns.

Other sources in the less frequently used or abandoned category are sparkers, boomers, mechanical imploders, steam guns, and marine versions of the

FIGURE 5-8   Comparisons of different marine source waveforms: (a) water gun; (b) single air gun (note high-amplitude bubbles); (c) Maxipulse; (d) array of air guns (bubbles come at different times and most add destructively); (e) Aquapulse. (*Western Geophysical.*)

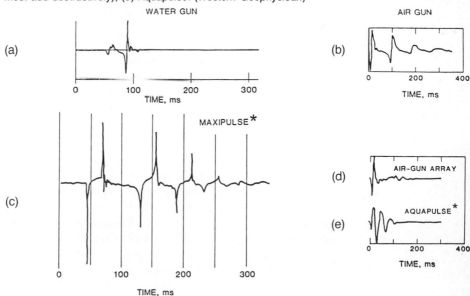

*WESTERN GEOPHYSICAL COMPANY OF AMERICA REGISTERED TRADEMARK

vibroseis and Dinoseis land sources. In nearly all cases these sources have been replaced by the air gun, which generates more acoustic energy at less cost. For shallow penetration (300 m or so), high-resolution (50 to 2000 Hz) reflection work, the sparker-type of electrical discharge source is commonly used.

In some sources the energy is generated along a line rather than at a point. An example is the Aquaseis (trademark of Imperial Chemical Industries), which employs a 100-ft length of towed explosive in ribbon form such as Primacord (trademark of Ensign Bickford Co.). The detonation travels along the cord at a speed of about 20,000 ft/s, the effect of the distributed explosion being to generate a host of small bubbles with minute pressure pulses from each so that oscillation effects are substantially absent. This source represents the ultimate in asymmetry of the bubble.

A comparison of different marine source waveforms is shown in Fig. 5-8.

Evaluation of Marine Sources

For many years attempts have been made to establish test procedures or measurements by which the effectiveness of marine sources can be judged. At first, sources were judged solely on the basis of their power. The Rayleigh-Willis diagram (Kramer, Peterson, and Walter[1]) compared every source to a dynamite standard on the basis of potential energy stored in the bubble. Sources such as imploders, which did not produce a bubble, could not be fitted into this scheme.

After a few years, it became customary to specify the strength of a source on the basis of measurement of the actual pressure excursion produced by the source or source array in the "far field," that is at a substantial distance directly below the source or the center of the array. The distance chosen is such that the receiver is substantially the same distance from every source in the array. The far-field criterion is usually satisfied at a depth 10 to 20 times the maximum dimension of the array. The receivers are positioned below by means of a sonobuoy or by a "deep tow," as will be discussed later in the chapter.

A calibrated receiving system is used to record the pulse train produced by the source. The difference between the maximum and minimum pressures in the initial pulse is expressed in units of bars (1 bar is 1 standard atmosphere at sea level) and divided by the distance between the source, or array center, and the receiver. The resulting quotient is taken to be the strength of the source or array in bar-meters. Inherent in this process is the assumption of spherical spreading of the acoustic wave, whereby the amplitude of the pressure wave decreases as the inverse first power of the radial distance from the source. It is also customary to specify over what frequency band the measurement was made. Typically, measurements are quoted in the "seismic band" of 0 or 3 to 125 Hz. In other words, energy above this band is not considered as contributing to exploration requirements. The strength of sources in common use ranges from about 20 to 100 bar-meters.

A second criterion of quality of marine sources is the primary-to-bubble ratio, which was discussed earlier in this section.

While strength and primary-to-bubble ratio are important in judging marine sources, it has been found that two sources having equivalent values of both can still differ markedly in their ability to produce an optimum seismic reflection section. Such differences are associated with the detailed shape of the acoustic pulse produced by the source. Usually, the shape is specified by the frequency spectrum of the pulse. It is felt that a smooth, broad spectrum is desirable, although a consensus is developing that greater energy at higher frequencies, i.e., a rising characteristic, is desirable to compensate, at least in part, for the greater attenuation of higher frequencies in the earth.

5-3 CABLES USED IN MARINE SHOOTING

In the early years of seismic exploration in water-covered areas, gimbal-mounted geophones were attached to cables designed to keep the phones 6 to 15 ft below the surface. In those days, cables were seldom more than 1000 ft long. Cables in use today are considerably longer, more expensive, and more sophisticated in design.

Multiple-Channel Streamer Cables The streamer cable, originally developed for antisubmarine warfare in World War II, is the most widely used type for modern seismic recording. This cable, a plastic tube $2\frac{1}{2}$ to 3 in in diameter, is nearly neutrally buoyant and filled with oil. In common practice, the cable is maintained at approximately 1 percent positive buoyancy so that the cable will float to the surface if it becomes detached from the towing vessel. If the density of the water changes because of temperature or salinity variations, the overall density of the cable can be changed to maintain desired buoyancy by adding or removing thin lead sheets wrapped around the cable. The hydrophone elements, wires, and transformers are inside the plastic tube, which is acoustically transparent and generally also optically transparent. Also inside the tube are steel cables, the strain members, that provide the mechanical strength to tow the entire length of the cable. The seismic waves pass through both the plastic and the oil to reach the hydrophones without noticeable interference. In general, the cable consists of detachable and interchangeable sections, about $66\frac{2}{3}$ to 100 m in length.

Most marine recording makes use of cables 3000 or more meters long, which contain 96 to 240 recording segments, each feeding a separate channel. Individual "live" segments are 12 to 30 m long, and each may contain 6 to 15 hydrophones. Some cables are designed for only 48 channels, while others have as many as 480.

Until about 1979 all marine cables in regular use were of the analog type. This is, the individual pressure-sensitive hydrophones were connected in groups to wire-pairs that conducted their electrical output directly to the recording vessel, where those signals were converted to digital form for recording on magnetic tape. When the number of separate channels or groups in these cables reached and passed 96, many cables came to be constructed with plugs in the junctions between sections, which enabled the entire cable to be configured with several different arrangements of the hydrophone groups and hence with a selectable number of channels.

When 240-channel cables were being planned, it became apparent that analog cables had reached their limit. The 500 or so individual wires needed to carry the 240 separate electric signals generated by the hydrophones as well as auxiliary and control signals required difficult design compromises. In practice, the wires were made very thin to reduce their weight enough so that the cable would still float.

It was clear that 240 channels was a breakpoint and that a radically new design would be needed to handle the larger number of channels that were sure to come. By 1985 about one-fourth of all marine cables in use were of the "digital" type. In this type of cable the electric hydrophone signals are carried in analog form only as far as a digitizing module built into the cable or into connectors between cable sections.

Highly miniaturized electronic components make it possible to provide 12 to 16 channels of analog-to-digital conversion circuitry, control logic, and telemetry drivers in a cylinder as small as $2\frac{3}{4}$ in in diameter and 12 in long. These cylinders are then made integral with the cable, and all of the data from 500 or more channels can be sent, in multiplexed digital form, down a coaxial cable, an optical fiber, or as few as 12 to 16 electrical line-pairs.

By 1986 it became practical to have separate highly miniaturized analog-to-digital converters inside the cable for each channel and, thus, to eliminate the instrument cylinders.

Figure 5-9 shows the configuration of a 480-channel cable as it is towed in actual use. There is a heavy armored lead-in cable, usually about 200 m long, from the ship to the beginning of the neutrally buoyant streamer cable. The heavy, long, lead-in cable is used to depress the hydrophone cable to its operating depth and to provide some isolation from the pitching and tossing

FIGURE 5-9   Schematic diagram of streamer cable being towed from ship. (*Western Geophysical.*)

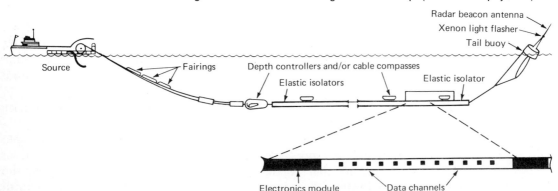

motion of the ship and from the noise of the ship's machinery. Usually rubber strips or sheets, called fairings, are fastened to the forward part of the lead-in to cut down the turbulence that ordinarily follows an object towed transversely through the water. Were it not for such fairings, the lead-in would strum and transmit noise to the towed streamer.

After the lead-in is a section of streamer cable called a "stretch" section. It usually contains no hydrophones, and its stress member or members are made of nylon rope or similar resilient material. Within the stretch section the electric conductors or optical fibers are loosely coiled or bunched so that the entire section can stretch as much as 30 percent without rupturing. Much of the vibration that is not attenuated by the lead-in is presumed to be absorbed by the stretch section. In streamer cables used by naval forces to detect submarines, the stretch section is called a *vibration isolation module* (VIM).

At the after end of the streamer there is usually about 200 m of rope to which a buoy is attached. The buoy serves to mark the end of the cable and is essential to recovery of a severed cable.

At suitable intervals along the cable, 8 or 10 pressure-sensitive depth controllers or "birds" of a type developed by Continental Oil Company keep the cable at the optimum depth. Each unit contains wings that lift or lower the cable, depending on the angle they make with the horizontal. The controller is set for the desired depth, and a pressure gauge actuates the wings when the actual depth of the cable begins to deviate from that for which the setting was made. Some depth controllers can be reset remotely from the towing ship to alter the towing depth of the cable. This feature is especially useful in areas of heavy ship traffic to depress the cable when a large ship threatens to cross and sever it.

Under tow, the streamer does not, in general, form a straight line in the direction of the towing ship's course. Because undersea currents are found in every ocean, the streamer is usually diverted from its desired course. To enable the shape and orientation of the cable to be determined, remote-reading magnetic compasses are attached to the streamer at six or eight positions along its length. Also high-frequency acoustic signal generators are sometimes deployed off each side of the ship's stern and used for sound ranging to the front end of the cable. By combining the compass data with the sound-ranging information, both the shape and position of the cable can be determined relative to the ship. This information is automatically recorded and used in subsequent data processing and in the generation of base maps to show the actual location of the seismic line. (See Chap. 10 for use of such data during 3-D acquisition and processing.)

Streamer cables perform satisfactorily in most areas where marine shooting is carried out, but they are not suitable in shallow water where the depth is not much greater than (or sometimes not as great as) the level corresponding to quarter-wavelength optimum submergence. For shallow-water exploration, bottom-reference cables, for which sensors maintain a constant elevation above the water bottom, or cables which lie on the bottom are frequently used.

Distributed Systems

When the area to be surveyed covers the "transition zone," that is, the area from the shore to deeper water in which marine streamers can be used, or in deeper water where reefs, platforms, or other structures prevent the towing of cables, recourse is had to distributed systems that do not employ cables. In these systems each data channel, corresponding to a single phone or group of phones, is represented by a separate module containing an amplifier and either a cassette tape recorder or, most commonly, a radio transmitter. The electronic module is contained in a buoy which is generally moored in the shallow water and contains batteries, transmitting antenna, and control apparatus.

Earlier systems transmitted the received seismic signals in analog form to a master station, usually aboard a mother ship, where they were digitized and recorded. In the early 1980s systems were introduced in which each module contained digitizing electronics and could transmit the data in digital form to the master station. These systems record one seismic shot in a memory in the module for transmission to the control station upon receipt of a radio command. Some of these systems are designed to transmit data sequentially from the modules, one at a time. With a hundred or more channels the transmission time can be excessive. In at least one system, however, transmission from 120 channels is simultaneous on 120 separate radio frequencies.

Single-Channel Streamers   In shallow reconnaissance exploration as well as in engineering surveys, it is more expedient and more economical to record from a single channel than from a long multichannel spread. On marine reflection surveys carried out for academic rather than exploration studies, single-

FIGURE 5-10   Noise level versus towing speed for streamer cable. (*From M. Schoenberger and J. F. Mifsud, Geophysics, vol. 39, p. 788, 1974.*)

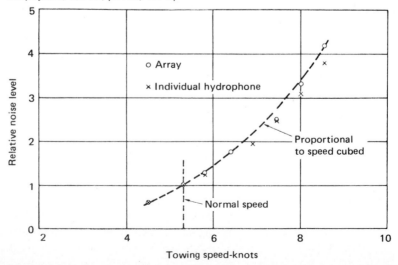

channel recording had been employed for many years. (More recently, multi-channel cables, with 6 to 48 channels have been used for this type of research.) The cable used for single-channel surveys is of the streamer type. Because only one channel is used, it is economically feasible to introduce many more hydrophone elements than would be possible for each element of a multichannel cable. As many as 100 elements may be built into a 300-ft length of cable when it is to be used in this way. This number results in a better response to high frequencies than is usual for 30 elements per channel. Figure 5-10 shows noise as a function of water speed, illustrating how the increase of noise with speed is similar for a single phone or an array.

5-4 REFLECTION PROCEDURES AT SEA

Most marine reflection surveys today are carried out as single-ship operations. With explosives in conventional form no longer being used, the same ship tows both the energy source and the recording cable. Such an arrangement has obvious economic advantages over any requiring two ships for recording one line of profile.

With the advent of 3-D shooting (see Chap. 10) and with the recent trend to conduct reflection surveys during the course of field development, it has become the practice in such situations to use two ships simultaneously. Each ship is equipped with both a source array and a recording cable. The two ships travel abreast a few hundred feet apart. Typically the two ships alternate firing their source arrays. In the simplest configuration for such two-ship operations, three subsurface profiles are recorded during the traverse of a line. Subsurface coverage thus produced by each ship would be one and one-half times as much as that obtained by the one ship acting alone. Of course, because only alternate shots from each ship can be used, the ships must be slowed down somewhat. Nevertheless a saving in cost could still be realized because turns and trips to and from the prospect can be traversed at full speed and because such ancillary services as onshore navigation installations can be shared.

As illustrated in Fig. 5-11, however, a judicious deployment of source arrays and streamer cables can make it possible to run four simultaneous profiles from two ships. A substantial saving in cost can thus be realized. In any event, the two-ship survey configuration permits the surveying of lines directly beneath drilling rigs, reefs, or other impediments to a ship's passage.

In the early 1980s experimental work was begun on the use of marine sources similar to the land vibroseis in principle. With such sources it would be possible to conduct two-ship operations with both ships activating their sources simultaneously as long as the two sweeps they generate are orthogonal (Goupillaud[8]). Orthogonal sweeps are sweeps whose cross-correlation is zero or very small. A simple example of a pair of orthogonal sweeps is an upsweep and a downsweep of the same duration and frequency range.

Nearly all energy sources in common use are towed at a distance far enough from the stern of the ship to avoid the possibility of damage to the ship's hull. As noted in our discussion of marine cables, there is generally a distance of

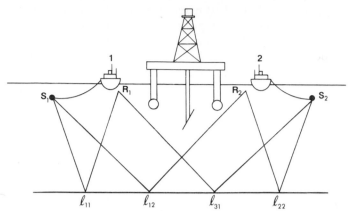

FIGURE 5-11   Two-ship shooting. This schematic drawing in a vertical plane perpendicular to the lines of survey and through a drilling platform illustrates the methods of shooting four survey lines from two ships and "undershooting" the drilling platform. The source arrays are offset from the ship's course by means of paravanes adapted from devices originally designed for naval mine-sweeping operations. Receiver arrays are towed behind the ship, sometimes offset from the ship's center line by a small distance.

Ships 1 and 2 are shown towing sources S_1 and S_2 and receiver arrays R_1 and R_2. The four subsurface lines of coverage correspond to the four possible combinations of source and receiver. To obtain uniformly spaced subsurface lines the distance between the two receiver arrays must be twice the distance between source and receiver for each boat individually.

about 30 m between the source and the center of the nearest receiver group on the cable. With the recording portion of the cable generally 3200 m in length, the total distance from the ship to the end of the cable can thus be 2 mi or more. It is important to know the actual position of the cable as it is towed through the water. When, because of cross currents, the cable drifts away from the line of motion of the ship and the positions of the geophones are different from those assumed in making time corrections for common-depth-point stacking, appreciable deterioration of the processed data could result. With a neutrally buoyant streamer cable, visual or radar contact can only be made with the tail buoy, which is hard to see. The buoy is therefore designed to be observable on the radar screen and it generally contains a light for visibility at night so that its position will always be known.

The adverse effects of excessive *feathering*, as this type of deviation is called, upon data quality depend to a large extent on the dip and structural relief of the reflecting formations. The greater the relief the less such deviation can be tolerated. Many oil companies require that operations be shut down when the current across the shooting line becomes strong enough for the deviation of the cable due to feathering to go beyond specified limits.

In 3-D operations feathering is accepted and the positions of sources and individual cable sections are recorded for each shot. The ship is usually steered in accordance with a computer program and display that keeps track of the feathering to achieve a preplanned pattern of reflection points over the survey area. (See Chap. 10.)

Virtually all marine reflection work is carried out with common-depth-point shooting. The time interval between the shots depends on the degree of multiplicity. In sixfold coverage, for example, the shot is fired every two geophone intervals, which is about 200 m (or once a minute at 6 knots). Twelvefold shooting would involve shots every 100 m (about once every 30 s with a 6-knot speed). Now that more rapid repetition rates are feasible with most sources, the practice is to use 24- or 48-fold coverage (as frequently as one shot every 25 m or 10 s at 6 knots). Ninety-six-fold coverage is not unknown. The timing may be determined from the ship's position either automatically or as indicated on a screen associated with the electronic navigation (discussed later in this chapter), or the shots may be fired at constant intervals of time determined from the ship's speed.

With sources such as air-gun arrays allowing fast repetition of energy impulses, several shots can be fired at uniform intervals between the predetermined common-depth-point shooting positions. Where this is done, the signals from all shots nearest to each position (between one midpoint and the next) are composited, the sum constituting the input for that position. The compositing may either be done on the ship, using a special summing system, or during subsequent playback. This procedure, designated as *vertical stacking*, increases multiplicity and should therefore reduce noise. To reduce the amount of subsequent computation, it had been common to composit two to four shots for each input, thereby reducing the volume of resulting data by a factor of 2 or 4. The vastly increased speed and power of computers available after about 1980 have made this practice unnecessary.

5-5 MARINE REFRACTION

Until the later 1960s, all refraction work at sea was carried out with dynamite as the energy source, making use of separate ships for sending and receiving. Such work involved considerably greater expense than reflection because of the cost of the explosives as well as the cost of operating two ships instead of one. These costs tended to price refraction shooting out of the market, in spite of some possible advantages it has demonstrated over reflection for reconnaissance in previously unexplored offshore areas. Since 1968, a sonobuoy receiver, based on one developed by the U.S. Navy for submarine detection from aircraft, has been used for refraction exploration with nondynamite energy sources. This development, which allows single-ship refraction operations, made marine refraction economical, and the volume of activity of this type had a brief resurgence in exploration work.

Sonobuoy Refraction System   Sonobuoys are self-contained systems for receiving sound waves in the water and transmitting them to a distant receiving point by radio. A hydrophone or array of hydrophones is suspended from the buoy, which contains sonic amplifiers and a radio transmitter with an antenna projecting upward from the floating buoy. Figure 5-12 illustrates a sonobuoy refraction recording operation. If a sonobuoy is not used, two ships are usually employed.

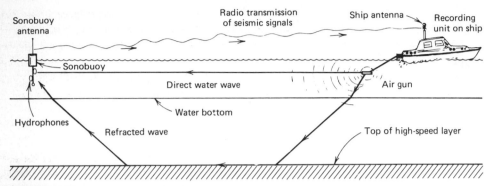

FIGURE 5-12
Sonobuoy refraction
recording operation.

Sonobuoys have been employed for several decades in academically oriented marine refraction surveys, using dynamite as a source. One such survey was carried out in the English Channel to determine the subbottom geology there (Giles[9]). It was only in the late 1960s that refraction techniques involving sonobuoy receivers became practical for petroleum exploration. These techniques involve the use of air gun or other nonexplosive sources and expendable sonobuoy receivers.

FIGURE 5-13   Refraction sonobuoy disassembled. (*Select International, Inc.*)

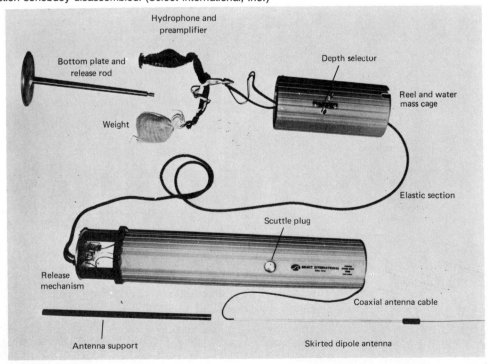

When the buoy is thrown into the water from a ship, the hydrophones drop from the bottom of the floating buoy to a depth of about 60 ft, and a 3-ft antenna for transmission of the hydrophone signals by radio springs into the air from its top.

Figure 5-13 shows a disassembled sonobuoy of this type. Originally four hydrophone elements were suspended 18 in apart along a cable. More recently, a single phone has been used along with a preamplifier. The main amplifier and the circuitry for the radio transmitter are on cards inside the buoy. Power is from a battery activated by seawater.

Sonobuoys are today rarely used for refraction surveys but are still frequently used to measure the signature of sources or source arrays. In such use, the hydrophone is lowered to a depth of hundreds to a thousand feet or more beneath the buoy. Naturally, the location is chosen so that the water depth is substantially greater than the depth of the phone. The ship fires its source or source array repeatedly as it travels past the buoy. Recordings at one or more depths are compared for the different shots. Those recordings, from a given depth, corresponding to the minimum travel time from source to hydrophone are presumed to represent the far-field array signature. Selecting the minimum-time recording is necessary, since it is not generally possible to assume that the phone or phones are vertically beneath the buoy.

An alternative means of detecting the signal at depths of several hundred feet is to tow a short hydrophone streamer cable by means of deep-tow vehicles developed for oceanographic studies and for military purposes.

5-6   NOISE PROBLEMS IN MARINE SEISMIC WORK

In the previous chapter we considered the various types of noise encountered in reflection work on land. We pointed out that most of the major improvements that have been made in seismic recording and data-processing techniques have been devised with the objective of eliminating noise and enhancing the quality of desired reflections. Some types of noise which are recorded on land are also observed on marine records. One type of noise, rarely encountered in land work, is predominantly associated with marine shooting. This is *surface-layer reverberation*, also referred to as *ringing* or *singing*. It is caused by multiple reflection of waves, both at the source and receiving ends of the reflection path, that bounce back and forth between the top and bottom of the water layer.

Figure 5-14 shows the frequency spectrum computed by Backus[10] for reverberation in a water layer 100 ft deep with a "hard" bottom, i.e., a bottom having a sound speed much higher than that of the water. In this case, the fundamental frequency is one-fourth of the reciprocal of the one-way time through the water layer, and frequencies for higher harmonics are odd multiples of this frequency, as expressed by

$$f_n = \frac{(2n - 1)V_w}{4d_w}$$

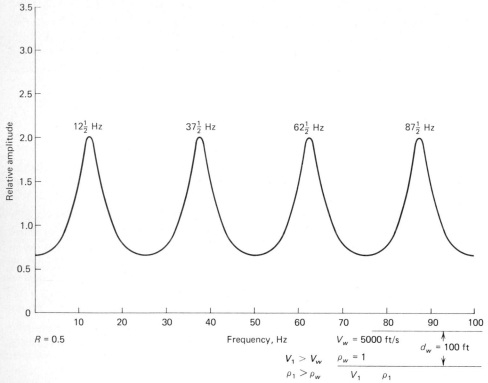

R = 0.5

Frequency, Hz

V_w = 5000 ft/s

d_w = 100 ft

$V_1 > V_w$ $\rho_w = 1$

$\rho_1 > \rho_w$ V_1 ρ_1

FIGURE 5-14
Frequency spectrum
for reverberation of
pressure pulse in water
layer 100 ft deep.
(*After Backus.*[10])

where f_n = frequency of nth harmonic (n = any integer)
  V_w = velocity of sound in water = 5000 ft/s
  d_w = water depth

For the example given, the fundamental frequency would be $12\frac{1}{2}$ Hz with harmonics at $37\frac{1}{2}$, $62\frac{1}{2}$, $87\frac{1}{2}$, . . . Hz.

The net effect of multiple reflection in the water is to give all reflections the same frequency characteristics as those of the water reverberation itself. Each peak in the spectrum [corresponding to the various harmonics of Eq. (5-5)] can be related to repetitive events in the reverberating signal, but as the individual trains are superimposed, it is not generally possible to resolve them on the recorded signal. On a variable-area record section these events will often have the appearance of uniformly spaced stripes which entirely obscure the desired reflections from subbottom interfaces. Figure 6-22 illustrates such a ringing record.

Reverberation effects can be effectively reduced or eliminated by proper processing of the records, making use of digital filter programs that effectively cancel the undesired filtering effect of the water layer. This process, known as *inverse filtering* or *deconvolution*, will be discussed in Chaps. 6 and 7.

Once the reverberation has been properly attenuated through deconvolution, correctly acquired marine data are generally better than land data. The relatively uniform water environment surrounding the receivers and the sources, and the absence of the highly irregular and absorptive weathering layer (on land), are the two significant causes of the better data quality.

5-7 POSITION LOCATION FOR MARINE SURVEYS

The precise determination of position coordinates is an important aspect of all geophysical surveys, whether on land or in marine areas. In most land work, long-established surveying procedures have generally been adequate, providing all the precision needed to meet geophysical requirements. For marine operations, however, no position-location techniques usable over areas out of sight of land were in existence until World War II. To meet wartime and other requirements for guidance of ships and aircraft, a number of radio navigation systems were developed in the 1940s. Among these were reflection radar, Loran, Shoran and continuous-wave, phase-comparison methods such as Decca and Raydist.

The earliest techniques to be employed in radio-position location were reflection radar and Shoran. The continuous-wave methods were first applied in petroleum exploration during the later 1940s, and for two decades they were used more extensively than any other positioning systems in offshore geophysical surveys, mainly because of their great range and high accuracy. In 1968, the Transit satellite system, initially developed by the U.S. Navy and operated by it since 1964, was first put to use in geophysical exploration work, and it is being employed in almost all seismic surveying.

Line-of-Sight Methods

Radar reflection and Shoran both involve the direct propagation of pulsed microwaves along a line-of-sight path. For this reason, they are applicable only at relatively short distances from shore. The range limitation may not be too restrictive in areas where transmitters can be located on high mountains close to the coastline. The range of such methods has been constantly increased through various electronic techniques which will not be described here.

Radar can be used in two ways: (1) A transmitter on board the ship can send out radar waves that are returned by reflection from passive targets at known locations near shore or from buoys at predetermined positions in the water. Measurement of the times required for waves to make the round trip from the same source to a number of targets make it possible to determine the ship's location quite precisely, as the velocity of the radar waves, like that of all electromagnetic radiation (3×10^{10} cm/s), is well known. (2) The other approach is to set up two radar transmitters at known positions on shore and to time the reflections from the ship, feeding the times by radio into a shipborne plotter, which produces a continuous track of the ship's position.

Shoran makes use of two transmitting stations on land, but there is a third station located on the ship. Pulses sent out from the ship's unit are received by the land stations. After a brief but precisely known delay, a transmitter at the land station broadcasts the signal back to the ship. The time required for each round trip minus the delay determines the distance from the ship or plane to the corresponding fixed point on land. The intersection on a chart of the radii representing ranges from the two stations on a chart gives the location of the ship.

Each pulse is transmitted at a frequency between 210 and 320 MHz and has a duration of less than 1 μs. With such high frequencies, an accuracy of ±25 ft is possible under favorable conditions. For a transmitter 1000 ft above sea level (as on a mountain near shore), the range is about 40 mi.

More recent versions of such "range-range" systems have increased their effective range and some (e.g., Syledis) can accommodate more than one user at a time by use of coded transmissions and time-division multiplexing of signals.

Continuous-Wave Systems

Continuous-wave systems give results almost as accurate as those of Shoran, but they are usable over much greater distances from shore. The first continuous-wave systems were Decca, Raydist, and Lorac, all of which are quite similar in design and performance. More recent systems such as Syledis, Argo, and Omega operate on basically similar principles but with higher accuracies or greater ranges. Because the systems involve the use of continuous waves, it is not possible to measure absolute distances, only differences in distance between one position and another. These differences are determined by counting the number of wave cycles, or "lanes," in the standing-wave pattern surrounding each shore station that are crossed as the ship moves from one position to another.

Hyperbolic Systems The hyperbolic technique involves the use of three shore stations. *Differences* (usually expressed as integers) in lane count between two adjacent pairs of stations are plotted on a map as a family of hyperbolas for each pair. The differences as measured for the respective pairs are located on the map. The actual position is plotted at the intersection point of the respective hyperbolas.

Figure 5-15 shows a family of curves (the heavy lines) representing such locations one lane apart. Each of these lines is a hyperbola, the locus of a point whose distances to two other fixed points, called foci, differ by a constant. In this case the foci are the two transmitter locations A and B. If the output of a receiver tuned to the frequency of the two transmitters is fed to a phasemeter, the reading will be zero along any of the hyperbolas, but elsewhere it should have some value between 0 and 360°. The phase angle will be proportional to the distance of the point from the nearest line of zero phase difference. If the

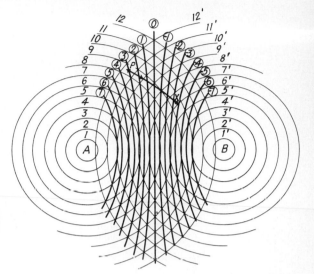

FIGURE 5-15
Contour map showing lines of zero phase difference in vicinity of two sources (*A* and *B*) of synchronized radio waves of same frequency. Light lines are successive waves spreading out from source at any time. Heavy lines are hyperbolas representing path-length differences of integral wavelengths as labeled. Ship moving from *P* to *X* must cross six such hyperbolas.

phase can be read to the nearest degree, the position can be established to $\frac{1}{360}$ times the distance between adjacent hyperbolas in the vicinity of the point. At 1000 kHz, a wavelength corresponds to about 1000 ft, and the distance between adjacent hyperbolas, which is a half wavelength, will be about 500 ft. In this case the interpolation could be made with a theoretical accuracy of the order of 1 ft. Because the propagation paths of the radio signals are not actually straight lines, and because the propagation velocity of radio waves is affected by air temperature and humidity, accuracies are generally of the order of 300 to 500 ft, but a given position will be found to have the same hyperbolic coordinates within about 100 ft on repeated readings on different days.

Lane Identification Although a phasemeter will enable one to interpolate precisely between adjacent lines of zero phase difference, it cannot distinguish among the lines themselves and thus cannot locate positions absolutely. With continuous waves generated at the source, a phasemeter cannot identify individual waves. If, however, the receiver is at a known location at one point along one of the hyperbolas, it is possible to count cycles as the shipboard receiver moves away from the known position.

Suppose the receiving ship starts at point *P* (Fig. 5-15), known to be on hyperbola 3 (which represents a difference of three cycles between the wave from *B* and that from *A*), and moves eastward as shown. Before reaching point *X* it crosses six lanes, which means that the phasemeter would make six revolutions (up to hyperbola −3) and then a fractional part of a revolution equal to the distance from line −3 to point *X* divided by the distance between lines −3 and −4. If the phasemeter were linked to a counter, such as an odometer (the mileage indicator on a speedometer), which is set at 3 when the

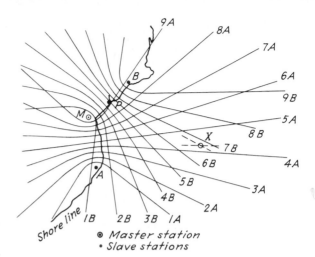

FIGURE 5-16
Use of three transmitting stations
(one master, two slaves) in continuous-wave position location.

receiver is at position P, it will shift six counts in the negative direction and
read -3 at the end of the run. The fractional distance between -3 and -4 can
be read directly from the phasemeter dial.

This does not give the position in itself but only one locus (or "line of
position," LOP). Another pair of transmitters (one of which is usually common
to both pairs) will give the position on a second hyperbola in the same way. The
two hyperbolas can intersect in two points, but one of these points is usually so
located that it can be readily ruled out, leaving the position specified uniquely
within the limits of accuracy discussed. Figure 5-16 illustrates how three
transmitters give two sets of hyperbolas from which actual positions are located on a specially designed chart. The common transmitting station M is
called the *master*, and the other two, A and B, are called *slaves*.

Assume that the ship containing the receivers starts from a dock at point P,
located at the intersection of lane 9 for station pair MB, the respective meter
dials being initially set at these values. At position X on the map the B counter
will read 6 and the B phasemeter 300°, while the A counter will read 5 and the A
phasemeter 270°.

With the early hyperbolic systems, it quite frequently occurred that either
transmission or reception could be interrupted for a few minutes or more and
there would be no way to determine in which lane the ship was located. In the
U.S. Gulf Coast, and elsewhere, a service grew up to meet this problem. The
ship, having lost count of lanes since leaving port, would radio to shore and an
airplane equipped with a compatible positioning system, would fly out to the
ship to deliver a "lane count." With the passage of time some systems were
provided with two distinct frequencies and could thus produce lanes of different width. Reconciliation of the two resulting phase measurements reduced the
ambiguity enough so that, for all practical purposes, the ship knew its location
to the maximum resolution of the system. Most recently, satellite fixes and

TABLE 5-1 CURRENT POSITIONING SYSTEMS

System	Operational range (km)	Accuracy (m)	Limitations
Omega	Worldwide	3000–1500	Limited accuracy
Loran-C	300–1500	500–50	General navigation
NNSS (Transit)	Worldwide	300–30	Long interval between updates
Pulse 8	300–1500	500–50	
Decca-Seafix/Mainchain	300–600	500–30	
Toran	100–400	250–30	Limited accuracy
Lorac	100–400	250–30	Good for large area
Raydist-N/RAC	100–400	250–20	Recon surveys
Decca hi-fix 6	100–300	50–20	
Raydist-DRS	100–300	50–20	
Argo	100–300	25–10	Signal degradation
Maxiran	60–200	30–10	Sky-wave interference/limited range
Syledis	60–150	20–5	Limited operational range
Artemis	30	25–2	
Motorola mini-ranger	20–50	12–4	Line-of-sight operations
Trisponder	20–40	12–4	

integrated navigation systems (described later in this chapter) have made it unnecessary to fly lane counts.

A sampling of the various electronic positioning systems available in many parts of the world is contained in Table 5-1.

Satellite Navigation

The U.S. Navy Navigation Satellite System makes use of a number of navigation (or Transit) satellites operating in polar orbit. Tracking stations and monitoring or injection stations check and maintain the accuracy of the system by frequent correction of the information each satellite transmits. The nominal number of operationally effective transit satellites in orbit is five, but that number has on occasion fallen to as low as three. The configuration of a typical orbit is shown in Fig. 5-17. The satellites are in trajectories that are measured from the tracking stations whenever the satellite comes within range. The tracking information is transmitted to a computing center, where the information is used for calculating orbit constants. Updated as frequently as twice a day, the constants are injected into the satellite by radio. The satellite continuously retransmits this orbital information on two carrier frequencies, 400 and 150 MHz. A short book by Stansell[11] presents an elementary discussion of the theory and operation of the transit satellite navigation system.

Principles of Position Location from Satellite Data The receiver on board the ship, which is completely passive, picks up the signals from the satellite that

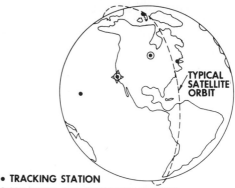

FIGURE 5-17
Navigation satellite monitoring and
update stations.

• TRACKING STATION
⊙ TRACKING AND INJECTION STATION
◈ TRACKING, INJECTION AND COMPUTATION STATION

provide the information necessary to determine the height, latitude, and longitude of the satellite at any time of day. Once the position of the satellite is
established as a function of time, it is only necessary to determine the distance
or range of the satellite at the instant of closest approach to determine the
ship's position. This is found by observing the doppler shift in the frequency of
the radio signals broadcast from the satellite. The actual shift varies with time
as shown in Fig. 5-18. The instant at which the doppler shift changes sign from
positive to negative gives the time of the satellite's closest approach to the ship.
The sharpness of the slope of this curve is a function of the *distance of closest
approach*, so that the distance can be computed from the variation of the
doppler shift with time. The trajectory constants contained in the beamed
signal are stored in a small shipboard computer. The computer is used to
calculate the distance of the satellite at its closest approach by use of the
measured frequency-time relationships, which are also stored. The position
coordinates of the ship are then determined by applying the updated satellite
trajectory constants. Uncertainties concerning the pressure and moisture content of the atmosphere and the height and intensity profile of the ionosphere are
translated into unknown variations in the velocity of the radio signals from the
satellites and hence in range determinations. Much of this uncertainty is resolved by comparing the signals received at the two broadcast frequencies. The
technique is described by Stansell.[11] The latitude and longitude of the ship are
fed electronically to all of the equipment on the ship that requires location
information. It is also displayed on a CRT (cathode ray tube, computer screen)
both in the instrument room and on the bridge. It may also be printed out on the
computer printer.

Frequency and Precision of Fixes   For accurate position data, information
should be used only from satellite passes in which the elevation of the satellite
at closest approach is within the range from about 20 to 70° above the horizon.
If two or more satellites are above the horizon at the same time, their signals
usually interfere and no useful information can be obtained. If six satellites are

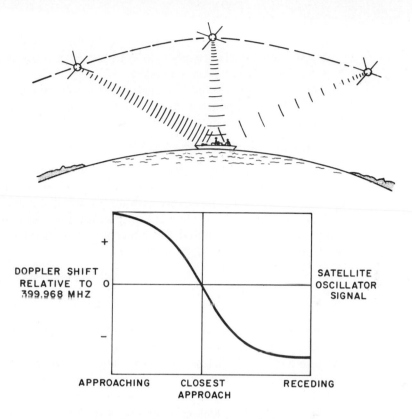

SATELLITE TRAVEL RELATIVE
TO NAVIGATOR POSITION

FIGURE 5-18   Use of doppler-shift characteristics to determine range of satellite at closest approach. Frequency shift is plotted versus time.

in orbits, there should be about 24 passes per day falling within the acceptable range at middle latitudes. This means that there should be an average of one recording every hour. The intervals between usable passes will vary, depending on the relation, which tends to be random, of the trajectories for the different satellites that are in orbit at the same time. Particularly at lower latitudes and when there are few satellites in favorable orbits, intervals can range up to 16 h or more. An accuracy of readings within about 300 ft can generally be obtained provided the north-south component of the ship's velocity is accurately known. This is usually measured in shallow water (less than 1000 ft) by doppler Sonar or by recourse to available electronic systems or by both.

Advantages and Disadvantages of Transit Satellite Positioning   There are a number of advantages of satellite navigation over other positioning techniques such as those making use of continuous waves:

1 There is no limitation in the applicability of the system because of distance from shore.

2 Atmospheric disturbances do not restrict operations to daylight hours.

3 No shore installation is needed.

4 Because only a satellite receiver and small computer are required by the user, the overall expense is less than for other positioning systems employed in operations far from shore.

The principal disadvantages of satellite navigation are:

1 Within 50 to 100 mi from the coast the uncertainty in positioning is usually greater with satellite navigation than with range-measurement techniques. The difference decreases, however, with increasing distance from shore.

2 As readings can be obtained only at intervals of minutes to hours, additional hardware is required for interpolating positions between readings to track the ship's course continuously.

Methods used for such interpolation will be discussed in the following paragraphs.

Interpolation between Satellite Fixes   Interpolation between satellite positions was initially carried out by dead-reckoning procedures. Starting at a satellite fix, the navigator plotted the ship's position on the map from the best velocity and heading information he could get. When the next satellite fix was plotted, there would generally be a discrepancy between the position of the fix on the map and the position along the trajectory plot for the time the fix was made. On the basis of such differences a least-squares iterative adjustment was made in the trajectory plot that would correct the velocities to those giving the best agreement at all fix positions.

In some geophysical surveys on which satellites were used for position location, velocities were determined by devices that measure the ship's speed with respect to the water. When there are water currents, the velocities thus measured will deviate from the actual ship speed by the amount of the current. Among the current meters used for measuring water speed were the pit log (incorporating a pitot tube), the spinner log, and the Electrolog (trademark of Chesapeake Instrument Company), which injects electric current into the water between electrodes trailed from the ship and then measures the ship's speed through the water by determining the rate at which the magnetic field generated by the current is cut by a detecting coil trailed along with the electrode assembly.

More accurate position information can be obtained between fixes if velocities can be measured with respect to the bottom itself. If such an arrangement is used, water currents do not affect the measurement. The only system which measures absolute speed referred to the bottom is doppler Sonar, which beams very-high-frequency (150- to 300-kHz) continuous-wave sound signals to the bottom at an angle with the vertical and measures the doppler shift in frequency (due to the ship's motion) in the waves scattered back to the ship.

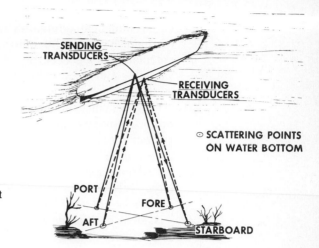

FIGURE 5-19
Use of doppler Sonar to determine velocity of ship with respect to bottom. View from below hull of ship. (*The Marquardt Company.*)

Four beams are sent to the bottom, as illustrated in Fig. 5-19. The fore and aft shifts are averaged to determine the component of velocity along the ship's axis, and the port and starboard shifts are averaged to obtain the athwartships component of velocity.

Because of attenuation of the high-frequency sound waves, the doppler Sonar system will not operate reliably in water deeper than about 1200 ft.

Scattering layers in the water resulting from a high density of marine life, such as plankton, sometimes limit the depth range even further. The accuracy of distance measurement is often rated as 0.2 percent. This means that in water less than 1000 ft deep, a ship moving at 6 knots should not go more than about 100 ft off the course plotted from the output of a doppler Sonar system during a typical 90-min interval between satellite fixes. In water between 600 and 1000 ft deep, the error may be somewhat greater than it is at depths less than 600 ft. A system employing the satellite receiver and ocean-bottom doppler Sonar in relatively shallow waters (100 ft) has an accuracy of 200 to 500 ft and is considered at least comparable to the best radio-positioning systems that can be used beyond line-of-sight ranges.

Integrated Positioning Systems

Because no one positioning system is universally applicable or, for that matter, available, in all marine areas, most geophysical vessels now carry computer-based, integrated positioning systems. A typical such system includes inputs for receivers of several types of electronic positioning signals, a Transit satellite receiver, and an ocean-bottom doppler Sonar. Often the system can also receive and process signals from cable compasses and cable trilateration subsystems.

A powerful computer in the system produces a "best estimate" of ship and cable position at frequent intervals (usually substantially less than 1 s) by judging the relative reliability of the different information it receives. Sophisticated statistical estimation techniques such as Kalman filtering are used to distinguish random fluctuations from solid information. Positions are generally calculated on a geocentric, global, polar-coordinate system used by the Transit satellites and then transformed to the coordinate systems (and geoid) of the locally furnished maps and charts.

The system also furnishes firing signals to the seismic sources so as to obtain uniform coverage. If, for some reason, the sources are independently fired, the system records the actual firing locations for all shots. All raw positioning information is also recorded for recomputing after the survey is completed. Recomputation generally results in more accurate results because positions can effectively be interpolated rather than merely extrapolated.

Global Positioning System (GPS, NAVSTAR)   In the early 1980s the U.S. Department of Defense began experimental deployment of a totally new satellite navigation system intended ultimately to replace all other navigation and positioning systems. When the system becomes operational in the 1988–1990 time frame, there will be a "constellation" of at least 18 satellites whose high orbits are so designed that at least four satellites are visible at any time from any place on earth. Each satellite is separately tracked from government base stations so that the orbit of each is precisely known to within a few feet. Each satellite is provided with a precise clock whose accuracy is also tracked by the base stations.

As with the transit satellites, the base stations repeatedly inject updated orbit parameters into the satellites. In operation each satellite broadcasts its orbital position and time constantly over two widely separated frequencies. The two frequencies are used to correct for variations in the velocity of radio waves from satellites to receivers.

GPS receivers are equipped with powerful, special-purpose computers. When a position determination is required, the receiver tunes in to all satellites in view. While all the satellites broadcast on the same two frequencies, their signals are modulated with unique codes so that their messages can be sorted out by the receiver-computer. Each message gives the geocentric position of the satellite and the time. With four such messages there is enough information to solve for four variables: the geocentric latitude, longitude, and elevation of the receiver, and the time of reception. Reception time is not one of the desired quantities but is needed in the computation to derive the intermediate quantities of range to each of the satellites.

At the time of this writing the Department of Defense plans to broadcast two different codes from the satellites. One code is to be reserved for the military and can be used to determine positions with an accuracy of a few tens of feet. Civilian users are restricted to a code that yields a position uncertainty 10 times as great, an accuracy calculated to be insufficient to improve the guidance of hostile ballistic missiles.

For geophysical use, however, a family of techniques has been devised to obtain an accuracy equivalent to that of the military without, at the same time, providing guidance to missiles. All of these techniques depend on the installation of an auxiliary receiving station at a fixed location within a thousand miles or so of the planned ship positions. Comparison of signals received at the ship and the fixed location enables the ship position to be calculated accurately.

REFERENCES

1 Kramer, F. S., R. A. Peterson, and W. C. Walter: "Seismic Energy Sources, 1968 Handbook," Bendix United Geophysical Corporation, Pasadena, Calif., 1968.

2 Willis, H. F.: Underwater Explosions: Time Interval between Successive Explosions, *Br. Admir. Rep.* WA-47-21, 1941.

3 Rayleigh, Lord: On the Pressure Developed in a Liquid during the Collapse of a Spherical Cavity, *Phil. Mag.*, vol. 34, pp. 94–98, 1917.

4 Lay, Roy L.: Repeated P-Waves in Seismic Exploration of Water Covered Areas, *Geophysics,* vol. 10, pp. 467–471, 1945.

5 Worzel, J. L., and Maurice Ewing: Explosion Sounds in Shallow Water, in "Propagation of Sound in the Ocean," *Geol. Soc. Am. Mem.* 27, 1948.

6 Knudsen, W. C.: Elimination of Secondary Pressure Pulses in Offshore Exploration, *Geophysics,* vol. 26, pp. 425–436, 1961.

7 Lavergne, M.: Emission by Underwater Explosions, *Geophysics,* vol. 35, pp. 419–435, 1970.

8 Goupillaud, Pierre L.: Signal Design in the Vibroseis Technique, *Geophysics,* vol. 41, pp. 1291–1304, 1976.

9 Giles, Ben I.: Pneumatic Acoustic Energy Source, *Geophys. Prospec.,* vol. 16, pp. 21–53, 1968.

10 Backus, M. M.: Water Reverberations: Their Nature and Elimination, *Geophysics,* vol. 24, pp. 233–261, 1959.

11 Stansell, T. A.: "The Transit Navigation Satellite System," Magnavox Government and Industrial Electronics Company, Torrance, Calif., 1978, reprinted 1983.

CHAPTER 6

COMPUTER SYSTEMS AND DIGITAL FILTERING CONCEPTS IN SEISMIC-DATA PROCESSING

The greatest impact of the digital computer upon seismic prospecting has been in the processing of seismic data. Such processing had its beginnings when field systems were introduced in the early 1950s for reproducible recording on analog magnetic tape, but it was not until modern high-speed digital computers became available that the full potential of processing techniques could begin to be realized for improving the quality and usefulness of seismic field data.

The basic objective of all seismic processing is to convert the information recorded in the field into a form that can be used for geological interpretation. The data initially recorded on magnetic tape (digital or analog) are transformed in the processing center into a record section comparable in some ways to a geological structure section. One object of the processing is to eliminate or at least suppress all noise (defined here as signals not associated with primary reflections, particularly those which might obscure or be confused with such reflections). Actually we are not particulary interested in reducing the absolute level of noise but in increasing the ratio of signal level to noise level, the signal-to-noise ratio. Another is to present the reflections on the record sections with the greatest possible resolution and clarity and in the proper geometrical relationship to each other.

Reproducibly recorded data and playback facilities have made it economically feasible to implement new field recording systems designed to facilitate the suppression of noise relative to reflection signals. Many of these systems require processing of the data as an integral part of the data acquisition. Among these are common-depth-point recording and vibroseis, as well as many marine systems, all described in the preceding two chapters. Most nondynamite sources require summing of signals, which can be carried out either on special digital compositing units in the field or, at a later stage, in a playback center.

Data processing is a lengthy affair, comprising five major types of corrections or adjustments: time, amplitude, frequency-phase content, data compression, and data repositioning. Our primary concern in this chapter is with the computer system components that accomplish these processes and with the principles of digital filtering. Digital filtering makes up a large part of all data processing. The principle of data compression, or stacking, was introduced in Chap. 4 in connection with common-depth-point recording.

Seismic-data processing will be considered in Chap. 7. Chapter 8, which presents the interpretation methods, also discusses how processing affects interpretation. The importance of processing to preserve relative reflection-amplitude relations is discussed in Chap. 9, which is devoted to direct hydrocarbon detection and seismic stratigraphy.

6-1 DATA PROCESSING WITH ANALOG SYSTEMS

Some of the processing operations now carried out on digital computers were done, if only on an experimental basis, with analog systems before suitable digital approaches became available. Even now, however, analog filters are widely used in field recording systems prior to digitization. The phase shifts those filters introduce should be removed in later processing, when stratigraphic information is sought to be derived from the seismic data.

In analog processing systems, shifting of times and compositing of signals, particularly for common-depth-point stacking, were routinely accomplished by mechanical, electrical, and optical means long before digital systems were available for such operations. Earlier editions of this book discussed the mechanics of the analog computers that performed analog data processing.

Analog Filtering   During the period between the introduction of reproducible seismic recording on analog magnetic tape and the advent of digital techniques, it was customary to play the recorded data back through analog filters both in the field and in playback centers. Most analog equipment used for such filtering consisted of conventional electrical elements for high-pass or low-pass frequency cutoffs. Filters of this type are discussed in Chap. 3 (pages 66 to 67).

A filter can be specified either in the frequency domain by its pass-reject zones, or in the time domain. The principles involved in analog filtering in the time domain are similar to those of time-domain digital processing. Since use of the time domain in analog filtering is probably easier to visualize than in digitial processing, it is worthwhile to introduce the concepts involved.

To express the action of a filter in the time domain, we must transform its frequency- and phase-response curves into the correlative function of time called its *impulse response*. This is the output signal from the filter in response to the input of a spike of unit amplitude having a time duration too short to observe on conventional recording modes. The output signal on the right side

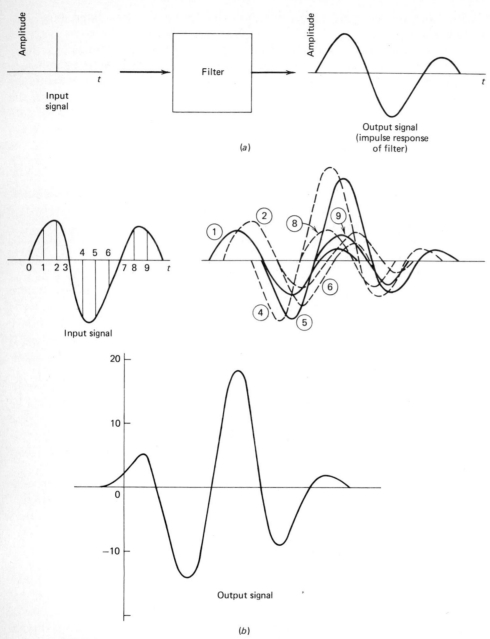

FIGURE 6-1 (a) The impulse response of a filter as the output signal when the input is a spike. (b) Use of impulse-response characteristic for filtering input signal of finite duration. Numbers on curves in diagram with superimposed signals represent sequence of corresponding spikes on left.

of Fig. 6-1*a* is the impulse response for the filter shown at the center. It is evident that the filter has the effect of spreading out the spike and converting it into an oscillating pulse of finite duration.

Even if the input signal is extended in time, we can still use the impulse response of the filter to predict the output. To do this, as shown in Fig. 6-1*b,* we sample the input to form a series of uniformly spaced spikes, each having a height corresponding to the signal amplitude at the instant that the spike occurs. Every spike can be looked upon as independent of all the others so that the output it generates is simply the impulse-response curve with an amplitude proportional to the height of the spike and a time for its beginning, equivalent to the time when that spike occurs on the signal. The amplitude of the input thus acts as a weighting factor to be applied to the impulse-response function. If the spike is negative (pointing downward), the output signal corresponding to it will be negative also. The actual output is closely approximated by the sum of the outputs corresponding to the individual spikes. As the interval between the spike samples gets smaller, the sum of the weighted impulse responses approaches the true output more and more closely until in the limit they coincide.

It is easy to demonstrate that the same output signal would be obtained if the impulse-response function were the input signal and the original input signal were the impulse response. In other words, filtering is a commutative process.

6-2 DIGITAL COMPUTER SYSTEMS USED FOR SEISMIC-DATA PROCESSING

Analog systems for seismic-data recording and processing had reached an advanced stage of development by the mid-1960s to the extent that they could perform such operations as applying static and dynamic corrections, muting, stacking, applying time-variant amplitude control, and some rudimentary deconvolution and deghosting in addition to conventional filtering. Patents granted by the U.S. government document the progression of analog processing capabilities.[1-5] The processes listed above will be described later in this chapter, as they are now carried out by digital methods. Nevertheless all such analog systems suffered from limited dynamic range; limited accuracy and precision; and difficult, mechanical, and highly restrictive programming processes. Much of the power of digital processing over analog stems from the ease, versatility, and scope of stored programs available in modern digital equipment.

Only data in digital form can be processed with digital computers. If the initial recording is digital, the signals on the tape are demultiplexed (which will be discussed in Chap. 7) and fed into computer storage directly. If the initial recording is on analog tape, the analog signals are digitized before being put into the computer. Once the data are introduced into the computer, the processing programs operate on the data in the same way, regardless of whether the data were originally recorded analog or digital.

Computer System Elements

A computer system designed for seismic-data processing consists of input and output ports, the central processing unit (CPU), various data storage areas, various peripheral devices that perform specialized (dedicated) computations exceedingly fast, and hard-copy devices (plotters). The input and output ports for data are tape drives or disks or some combination of them. Human input (commands) and system responses are traded at terminals, usually equipped with cathode-ray tubes (CRTs). The numerical calculations are either performed in the CPU or allocated to a special peripheral device (e.g., an array processor). At the time of this writing, a new generation of computers, called *vector computers*, were being used in the computer centers of a few major oil companies and contractors. Because these computers have their vector capabilities within the CPU and also incorporate especially large internal memories, they outperform the older machines with peripheral array processors by a factor of 10 or more. The effect upon the geophysicist, as bigger and faster computers become available, is that more sophisticated algorithms and techniques move from the "too expensive to use" category to the "available" category.

After a process or step has been completed, the output may be saved on disk or tape. Line printers output the typewritten records of the job, which include the processing history, the processing parameters, and other information. At the end of a long job consisting of many processes, the data output is usually written to tape, since tape is more practical and cheaper than disk as a long-term storage device.

To obtain plots, one usually reformats the data by a plot program, since most standard plotters can handle only a small subset of the full range of numbers used by the computer system. Color plots are the only type of plot capable of displaying the range of values present in the original data. Plotting of seismic data is also discussed in Sec. 7-9 and Chap. 9. The importance of plots (hard copy) cannot be overemphasized, because all of the millions of dollars spent on acquisition, processing, and processing systems must be recouped through the geophysicist's interpretation of the data as presented on paper or on a CRT.

Digital computing systems work with stored data and have available the entire time history of events. A given input sample can be operated upon while accessing all past and future time samples. Some of the power in digital processing over analog comes from this extended operating base. The further advantages of digital systems over analog are speed and, above all, flexibility to modify parameters and even processes on the basis of observed data values.

The plotting of processed data on record sections can be done either with analog or digital equipment. The most widely used analog system for presentation of digitally processed data, the Geo Space plotter, operates by photography of the seismic signals displayed on a cathode-ray screen. Photographic paper or film is fastened to a rotating drum. This device can be used for registering data from analog tape or from multiplexed digital tape. The motion of the spot on the scope is controlled by the stored digital seismic signal and produces a plot along a horizontal line perpendicular to the time axis. Motion along that axis is provided by the rotation of the drum, which moves the film or paper wrapped around it in the vertical direction. A digital-to-analog converter is provided to drive the spot in response to the digitally stored signals.

This system provides all the usual modes of presentation, i.e., wiggle trace, variable area, and variable density (see Figs. 8-1, 4-5), the selection depending on control of the beam on the scope. For a wiggly-line trace, the beam is focused on the scope face at a point. For variable-area registration, the length of an elongated line on the scope is modulated by the signal amplitude, and for variable density the intensity of the beam is modulated and the light is focused on the screen as a line. The electronic optics of the scope can be readily adjusted for a combined-mode, e.g., the commonly used wiggly-line plus variable-area, presentation.

The plotting may be carried out with 6, 12, 18, or 24 channels at a time, depending on the number of multiplexed signals that can be accommodated on the oscilloscope screen. A precision mechanism advances the recording drum along its axis as the plotting proceeds.

Two kinds of plotters in current use register digital signals directly without prior conversion to analog form. One type is electrostatic, as exemplified by the Gould and Varian plotters. The other transforms the digital signal into a dot matrix on a CRT, which is photographed in the same way as with the Geo Space analog plotter. The Petty-Ray Photo-dot system is of this type.

Electrostatic plotters are generally used for processing in the field with minicomputers, such as the PreSeis, Phoenix, or ComMand systems, or for plotting of intermediate results or quality control displays in a processing center. The definition is not generally sharp enough for final, permanent presentation of the data, and other types of plotters, such as the Geo Space or Photo-dot, are generally employed for this purpose. Permanent storage of plotted seismic data can be accomplished by plotting the seismic section on heavy film for storage, or by photographing the final sections at a reduced scale (often 1 in/s) and storing the negatives. Permanent storage of the final processed data can be accomplished by archiving the tape in a reliable tape library system.

In the early 1970s a variety of data presentation modes were introduced which required the use of color. The techniques of color photography and of several color-proofing systems prevalent in the printing industry were tried but were found to be time-consuming and costly. After a few years the first of the digitally controlled, fully automatic color, hard-copy devices became available. The Applicon plotter operated by means of three ink jets that squirted the three primary colors against a sheet of paper or plastic wrapped around a rotating drum. A microprocessor-controlled magnetic field diverted the ink flow into a drain when the particular primary color was not to be applied to the part of the paper directly in front of the jet. This apparatus required a considerable amount of maintenance to keep the inks flowing at their design rates, but the results were of good quality and could be obtained on almost any kind of paper and on many plastics.

By the early 1980s a growing demand for color displays prompted the introduction of a full-color electrostatic printer by Versatec. This device is capable of printing on continuous rolls of paper and obtains its color capabilities by running the paper several times through the printing mechanism to print a different primary color or black on each pass. The process is completely automatic, and the equipment requires relatively little maintenance.

Interactive Work Stations   The "real-time" manipulation of seismic data to optimize the processing parameters or the interpretation in an iterative fashion is accomplished at an interactive work station. The geophysicist can test different interpretive hypotheses or processing attempts and view the result immediately. A work station will usually equip the geophysicist with an input CRT terminal to communicate with the operating system, a CRT (equipped with a pointing or selecting device) capable of displaying seismic data, another CRT to display calculated data value fields, a digitizing table, and a hard-copy device. The software should allow the geophysicist to obtain hard copy from any of the display CRTs. Supporting the work station is a minicomputer (often dedicated to the work station) or a shared, large computer, a computer operator/technician, several tape drives, several disks, and preferably an array processor or two.

Demands of Seismic-Data Processing on a Computer System

In seismic-data processing, heavy demands are placed upon the computer with respect to speed of operation and storage capacity. A seismic line can typically be 20 mi long. A shot-point spacing of 330 ft will yield 320 shot points (320 field records). With 96-channel recording, a 2-ms sample rate, 6-s recording, there will be 9.2×10^7 (about 100 million) samples per line. The processing from start to finish can take from 1 to 2 h (or more) of CPU time on a computer in which a multiply/add step takes 1 ns. Large processing centers can have many hundreds of lines in active processing.

Filtering

As digital filtering generally requires the use of filter operators that are actually impulse-response functions for the desired filters expressed as time series, it is necessary to put each filter function into storage (along with instructions as to how the function is to change with record time in the case of time-varying filters) so that it can be called from memory during subsequent filtering of the seismic signals. The position in storage of each term in the filter operator must be indexed for instantaneous access during the operation. The filtering itself, which generally involves the convolution of the input signal with the filter operator, breaks down into a programmed succession of multiplications, additions, and time shifts.

Filter operators used in seismic processing vary greatly in length, but a typical one can be 200 ms long. With 2-ms sampling, such an operator consists of 101 points. The necessary conversions between the time domain and the frequency domain in digital filtering require the calculation of Fourier transforms. A technique introduced about 1965 by Cooley and Tukey,[6] called the *fast Fourier transform*, has greatly reduced the time necessary for carrying out this process.

When digital processing of seismic data began to be done on a large scale in the mid-1960s, processing time and, hence, cost was dominated by the need to do several filtering steps and, hence, by the speed at which the multiply/add operation could be performed. A rapid succession of special hardware improvements and additions were implemented by the computer manufacturers, culminating in the introduction of array (transform) processors, also known as ATPs. ATP and vector processors (e.g., the Cray computer) have speeded the multiply/add operation by three orders of magnitude. Furthermore, modern array processors and vector processors have built-in instructions to perform the fast Fourier transform as well as dozens of other specialized algorithms.

The conceptual basis for digital filtering of seismic data was brought to its present state of usefulness during and after World War II by mathematicians and electrical engineers who, as Silverman[7] has pointed out, were faced with the problem of improving the signal-to-noise ratio for radar, radio, and telephone systems. In all these applications, a signal of known form is introduced into the system at the input end and must be extracted from noise at the output end. In seismic prospecting, the problem is more complex. The input signal, a nominal spike at the shot end of the seismic-wave path, is so changed by the earth materials through which it travels that one can seldom, if ever, identify the input signal in the waveform of the output. Actually, the changes in the signal resulting from the earth's own transmission and reflection characteristics (both associated with the geology of the subsurface) are what we are trying to observe. The earth thus acts as a filter, and we can look upon a seismic trace as the output of this earth filter, the input being the signal (a simple pulse except in the case of vibroseis) that is introduced by the energy source. In addition to filtering, computers carry out many other operations in seismic-data processing, among them velocity and relative-amplitude determination, frequency analysis, and migration (presentation of the reflections in their true positions on the seismic section). All these applications will be discussed in subsequent chapters.

6-3 PRINCIPLES OF DIGITAL FILTERING

The main objective of filtering in seismic reflection work is to remove undesired signals (collectively referred to as noise) from the record, leaving, ideally, only primary reflections having geological meaning. Two properties of the noise can be used as a basis for separating it from the signal. One is frequency; the other is apparent velocity. Frequency filtering is a single-channel operation. Apparent-velocity filtering is a multichannel operation.

Frequency filtering can be carried out in conjunction with field recording to remove low-frequency ground roll (surface waves) from the records so that reflections, generally of higher frequency, would not be obscured. Because such filtering in the field is essentially irreversible, there is danger that useful information may be forever lost. Accordingly, wherever possible, all filtering steps should be done in the playback center subsequent to recording. Only if the recording system does not have the dynamic range to record the signal in the presence of the expected noise is it preferable to filter before recording. Of course the antialiasing filters required in digital recording must precede the analog-to-digital conversion step in field recording. (See Chap. 3.) Other types of noise can also be rejected by frequency discrimination, but because overlap is common between the frequency ranges covered by the noise and the reflection signals, the process often requires intricate control of the discrimination characteristics. Only digital filtering gives the flexibility necessary for optimizing filter performance in such cases. The need for sharp discrimination can be demonstrated where there is a large amount of scattered, incoherent noise mixed with a reflection signal, as illustrated in Fig. 6-2. Analog filters generally have such gentle slopes that it would be difficult to extract the reflection from the noise by frequency filtering, but the nearly vertical slope that can be obtained from a properly programmed digital filter does allow such discrimination.

The techniques of manipulating the waveforms of seismic signals by digital computers to maximize the desired information and minimize noise were developed from information theory, a relatively new and mathematically sophisticated branch of electrical engineering. To appreciate how digital filters work, one need not be familiar with all aspects of this theory; yet one must understand its basic concepts. Most of them can be explained intuitively without the use of advanced mathematics. Several elementary discussions of digital filtering principles are available which cover the subject in more detail than is possible here. Treatments by Silverman,[7] Sheriff and Geldart,[8] Robinson and Treitel,[9] Peterson and Dobrin,[10] Anstey,[11] and Yilmaz[12] are particularly recommended for those who wish to explore digital processing further.

Earlier in this chapter, when discussing time-domain filtering by analog methods, we showed how the action of a filter can be described by its impulse response as well as by its frequency-response curve. The impulse response is in the time domain, as is the input signal itself. The frequency-phase-response curves conventionally used by engineers are in the frequency domain. Each mode of expression is a function of the other; i.e., if one is known, the other can be derived from it.

In digital filtering, either domain can be employed, but both the seismic signal and the characteristics of the filter must generally be converted into the same form. If the operation is to be in the time domain and only the frequency characteristic of the filter is specified, the frequency curve must be expressed as an impulse response (in the time domain) before the operation can be carried out. Fourier transformation provides the physical basis for such conversions from one domain to the other.

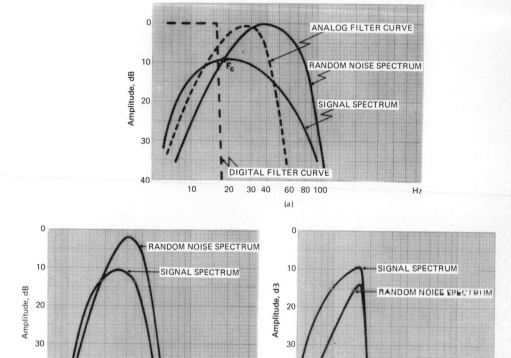

FIGURE 6-2   Comparison of performance of digital and electric analog filters designed for extracting reflections from high-frequency scattered noise: (*a*) before filtering, (*b*) after optimum analog filtering, and (*c*) after optimum digital filtering.

The Fourier Transform

The concept of Fourier transformation is based on the Fourier series, which expresses any function, such as a time signal of limited length, as a summation of an infinitely long series of sine waves and cosine waves (see Sec. 2-2, page 34).

A typical seismic trace is 6 s long. (Although reflections arriving later than 6 s are usually beyond drilling depths, there are cases in which one needs to record greater than 6 s—for example, in areas in which the steeply dipping edges of salt domes or steeply dipping beds are the imaging targets.) The fundamental frequency f_0 is $\frac{1}{6}$ Hz, and by adding up a series of sinusoids having frequencies $f_0, 2f_0, 3f_0, \ldots, kf_0$, and a constant, the Fourier series is formed. A harmonic is a simple multiple of the fundamental frequency: the more harmonics included, the better the representation of the time series. The Fourier series is expressed in terms of the amplitude coefficients and phase values for each of the harmonic terms. The phase values specify the displacement, in fractions of a cycle, of the starting point (zero crossing) for each sine (or cosine) wave in the series. The amplitude coefficients and phase shifts for each term are determined by Fourier analysis, the theory of which is covered in most textbooks on engineering mathematics.

The *Fourier transform* is an integral expression for a Fourier series applied to an infinitely long signal. As the signal becomes infinitely long, the fundamental frequency approaches zero. All harmonics of this fundamental are separated by infinitesimal increments, and the Fourier series, consisting of amplitudes and phases for the successive harmonics, becomes a continuous function. Fourier-transform techniques are used to express a time function as a continuous function of frequency and also to synthesize a function expressed in terms of amplitude versus frequency (a frequency spectrum) into the function of time to which it corresponds. Of course, in seismic-data processing, the signals we analyze are finite in length and discrete (digitized), not continuous. Nevertheless, for ease in manipulating the mathematics, nearly all proofs and derivations are done with continuous functions.

Transformation of Frequency Spectrum to Time Signal   Let us now consider how a continuous frequency spectrum can be transformed into a time signal by Fourier methods. Figure 6-3a illustrates an amplitude and phase spectrum, the frequency coverage being limited to a rather narrow range. The individual sinusoidal waves shown in Fig. 6-3b have different frequencies, increments between the successive frequencies being small. Amplitudes for each frequency are least at the top and bottom of the frequency range and greatest in the middle, as would be expected from the spectrum of Fig. 6-3a. At the same time the positions of the peaks for each frequency, when measured with respect to the reference marks indicating a constant time, shift systematically in accordance with the phase spectrum.

The sum of all the sinusoidal waves gives the time signal shown at the bottom of Fig. 6-3b. The process constitutes a Fourier transformation from the frequency function (amplitude and phase) to the corresponding time function.

It is often convenient to express Fourier transforms or series in terms of separate sine and cosine transforms or series rather than as one or the other with phase terms. The alternative formulations are mathematically equivalent.

Transformation of a Time Signal into Frequency Spectra   Let us now apply the principle of Fourier transformation to determine the frequency spectrum of a seismic signal. In the limit we want a continuous spectrum, but we shall start by obtaining components of it at discrete frequencies 2 Hz apart. The input seismic signal is shown in Fig. 6-4a. Figure 6-4b displays one frequency, 22 Hz, of the many frequencies for which the analysis is carried out. Figure 6-4c to f shows the amplitudes of all the discrete cosine and sine terms calculated over the range of frequencies generally used in seismic reflection work, as well as

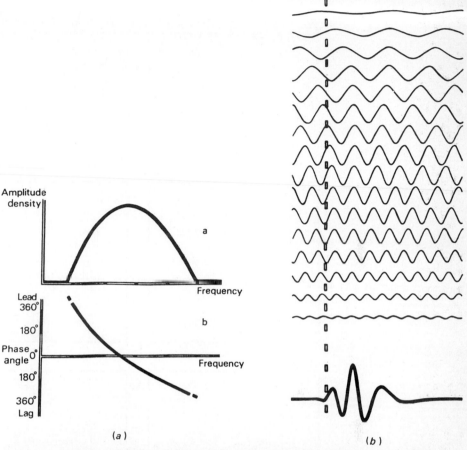

FIGURE 6-3   Fourier representation of seismic waveform: (a) amplitude and phase spectra; (b) synthesis of the waveform (at bottom) by summation of sinusoidal waves having amplitudes and time shifts corresponding to these spectra. (*From Anstey.*[11])

the resultant amplitude and phase spectra determined from the sine and cosine coefficients plotted in Fig. 6-4c and d.

To determine the cosine transform of the seismic signal at our 22-Hz frequency, we align it with a 22-Hz cosine wave and determine the degree of fit between the two curves. A window 500 ms long is used, and the origin is taken at the center. The cosine wave should be symmetrically placed with respect to the origin. Corresponding amplitude samples of the signal and the cosine wave are taken every 2 ms and multiplied at each instant of sampling. The sum of these products is plotted in normalized form, each at a sampling point such as P, where the spike observed on the cosine plot gives a measure of the amplitude component at this frequency.

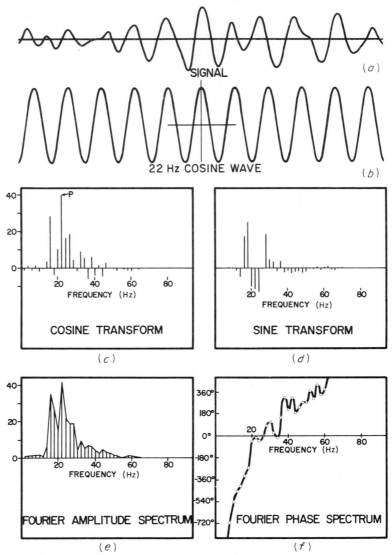

FIGURE 6-4 Fourier analysis of seismic signal by use of cosine and sine waves of different frequencies to derive cosine and sine portions of Fourier spectra: (a) signal, (b) 22-Hz cosine wave, (c) cosine transform, (d) sine transform, (e) Fourier amplitude spectrum, (f) Fourier phase spectrum.

If the seismic signal is itself a pure 22-Hz cosine wave, all products will be positive and the summation will yield a maximum value at this frequency. If the signal has no component of frequency at 22 Hz, there will be a random relation between it and the 22-Hz wave, so that there will be as many negative products (plus times minus or minus times plus) as positive ones (plus times plus or minus times minus). The net contribution to the spectrum will then be zero. In between, the relative contribution at each frequency is indicated by the net positive or negative value after the summation.

The process shown for the 22-Hz reference signal is repeated with cosine signals having all other frequencies between 2 and 100 Hz and then with sine signals over the same range of frequencies. Each sine wave is different from the cosine curve having the same frequency only because its origin comes at zero amplitude (midway between a trough and a peak) instead of at its peak value. The cosine and sine components of the spectrum are plotted as a series of discrete spikes. Conventional cosine and sine transforms can be obtained if the tops of the spikes are connected to produce smooth curves.

The spectrum is represented by two functions, in Fig. 6-4*e* and *f*. One is expressed as amplitude versus frequency, and the other as phase versus frequency. The amplitude term for each frequency is the square root of the sum of the squares of the sine and cosine terms for that frequency, and the phase term is the angle whose tangent is the sine term divided by the cosine term.

Mathematical Expression of Fourier Transforms   The integral expression for a Fourier transform is in two parts, one for the frequency spectrum $F(n)$ in terms of the time function $f(t)$, and the other for the time function in terms of the frequency spectrum. The frequency function $F(n)$ can be obtained from the time function $f(t)$ by the integral

$$F(n) = \int_{-\infty}^{\infty} f(t) \cos 2\pi nt \, dt - i \int_{-\infty}^{\infty} f(t) \sin 2\pi nt \, dt \qquad (6\text{-}1)$$

Time here is designated by t and frequency by n.

Similarly, the transform $f(t)$ of the frequency function $F(n)$ can be expressed by the integral

$$f(t) = \int_{-\infty}^{\infty} F(n) \cos 2\pi nt \, dn + i \int_{-\infty}^{\infty} F(n) \sin 2\pi nt \, dn \qquad (6\text{-}2)$$

The integral containing the cosine term is designated as real, while that containing the sine term is designated as imaginary; hence the use of the coefficient i. This complex representation is a mathematical convenience, as the two terms cannot be added directly but must be added vectorially; the sum has a magnitude and phase angle (proportional time delay) for each frequency which can be determined by following the rules for addition of complex quantities.

Designating the cosine integral in Eq. (6-1) as $C(n)$ and the sine integral as $S(n)$, we can show that the amplitude $A(n)$ of the spectrum at frequency n is

$$A(n) = \sqrt{C(n)^2 + S(n)^2} \qquad (6\text{-}3)$$

and the phase angle, also a function of frequency, is

$$\phi(n) = \tan^{-1}\frac{S(n)}{C(n)} \qquad (6\text{-}4)$$

The computation of Fourier transforms is simplified for functions that are symmetrical about the respective axes for which time or frequency are zero. With such functions, termed "even functions," the imaginary sine term of the transform disappears, because in the integration between $-\infty$ and ∞ each positive product on the right side of the axis is canceled by an equal negative product the same distance on the left side. The sine wave, being an odd function, conforms to the relation

$$f(t) \sin 2\pi n t = -f(t) \sin 2\pi n(-t) \qquad (6\text{-}5)$$

An important property of transforms is their complementary nature, which can be expressed as follows:

1 If $F(n)$ is the Fourier transform of $f(t)$, then $f(t)$ is the Fourier transform of $F(n)$.

2 If $f(t)$ is the Fourier transform of $F(n)$, then $F(n)$ is the Fourier transform of $f(t)$.

This reciprocal relationship has widespread application in seismic filtering.

Equation (6-1) may also be written

$$F(n) = \int_{-\infty}^{\infty} f(t)e^{-i2\pi n t} \, dt \qquad (6\text{-}6)$$

and Eq. (6-2) may be written

$$f(t) = \int_{-\infty}^{\infty} F(n)e^{i2\pi n t} \, dn \qquad (6\text{-}7)$$

Square Wave   To illustrate how a transform is determined for a simple function of time, we shall demonstrate the derivation of the frequency spectrum of a square wave of amplitude A and breadth T which is symmetrical about the zero time axis. Its waveform is expressed by the relations

$$f(t) = \begin{cases} A & \text{when } t \geq -\dfrac{T}{2} \leq \dfrac{T}{2} \\[4mm] 0 & \text{when } t \leq -\dfrac{T}{2} \geq \dfrac{T}{2} \end{cases} \qquad (6\text{-}8)$$

as illustrated in Fig. 6-5.

Symmetry in time indicates a zero-phase function, and the phase component of the Fourier transform is given by the sine term. Thus, in the Fourier transform of this boxcar time function, the sine term is zero. The cosine integral is zero for times outside the range $-T/2$ to $T/2$ bounded by the sides of the square wave, so we will use only the cosine term in our integration and change the effective limits in Eq. (6-1) to encompass this range alone, obtaining the frequency spectrum

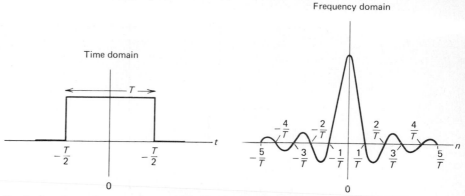

FIGURE 6-5   Fourier transform of a square wave of width T in the time domain.

$$F(n) = \int_{-T/2}^{T/2} A \cos 2\pi n t \, dt = \left[\frac{A}{2\pi n} \sin 2\pi n t \right]_{-T/2}^{T/2} \tag{6-9}$$

$$= \frac{A}{2\pi n} 2 \sin \frac{2\pi n T}{2} = \frac{A}{\pi n} \sin \pi n T \tag{6-10}$$

$$= AT \frac{\sin \pi n T}{\pi n T} = AT \frac{\sin u}{u} = AT \operatorname{sinc} u \tag{6-11}$$

where $u = \pi n T$ and sinc x is a shorthand notation for $(\sin x)/x$.

Plotting the spectrum $F(n)$ versus n, as we do on the right side of Fig. 6-5, we see that the function becomes zero at values of frequency equal to $1/T$, $2/T$, $3/T$, etc., with the maximum amplitude at zero frequency. The frequency at which the first zero crossing occurs and the frequency intervals between successive crossings are inversely proportional to the breadth of the square wave. The width of the central peak is twice as great as the width of the lobes alongside it (generally referred to as *side bands*), and both widths are inversely propor tional to the width of the square wave constituting the original time signal. Thus the longer the duration of the square wave, the narrower are the lobes and the greater is the concentration of the energy of the wave at low frequencies. Because the frequency is in the denominator of the expression, the peak amplitude for each half cycle of the sinc function decreases with increasing frequency, approaching zero as a limit.

The appearance in a spectrum of amplitude values at negative frequencies equivalent to the amplitudes observed at the corresponding positive values of the frequency may be somewhat confusing to the reader who is accustomed to thinking of frequencies from a practical engineering standpoint. The signifi- cance of a negative frequency can best be visualized by considering a wheel which can rotate in either direction, the rates of clockwise rotation representing positive frequencies and those of counterclockwise rotation, negative frequen- cies. Mathematically it can be shown that the spectra are valid for both positive

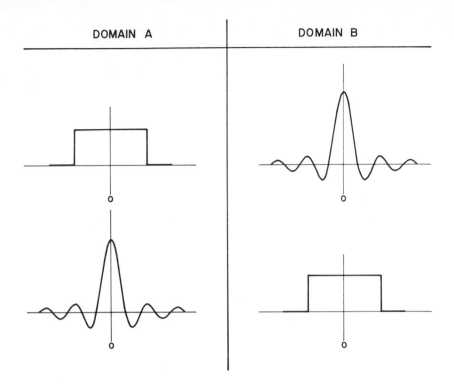

IF DOMAIN A IS TIME, DOMAIN B IS FREQUENCY
IF DOMAIN A IS FREQUENCY, DOMAIN B IS TIME

FIGURE 6-6   Reciprocity of Fourier-transform pairs. The transformation is the same regardless of the domain of the signal to be transformed. (*From Peterson and Dobrin.*[10])

and negative values. It is therefore necessary to plot both, in symmetrical patterns, for proper representation.

The reciprocal relation between the transforms is illustrated for this case in Fig. 6-6, which demonstrates that a time function in the form of a square wave will have a frequency spectrum which is a sinc function, while a time signal in the form of a sinc function has a frequency spectrum which is a square wave. As the sinc function theoretically extends from minus infinity to plus infinity, it is necessary for practical reasons to cut it off at predetermined positive and negative values, whether it represents a time signal or a frequency spectrum. Such cutoff should be at distances from the origin where the amplitude of the function is negligibly small. Later we shall see how the truncation of the sinc function affects the performance of a filter with a frequency characteristic that can be represented by a square wave.

Spike Impulse   The Fourier transform of a sharp impulsive signal that has the appearance of a spike on a seismic recording is exceedingly simple. On a

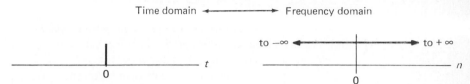

FIGURE 6-7   Fourier transform of a spike or delta function at zero time.

plot of amplitude versus frequency, it is a horizontal line raised a constant distance above the frequency axis, indicating a uniform amplitude level for all frequencies (Fig. 6-7). To obtain this transform mathematically is rather difficult. Yet it is intuitively evident that a spike represents a square wave with a width of zero, so that the breadth of the central peak (the distance between the zero crossings nearest the central axis) on the corresponding transform becomes infinite, approaching a horizontal line. If, on the other hand, the square wave has infinite breadth, the sinc function contracts to a spike representing zero frequency.

When the spike is at zero on the frequency axis, it represents the dc (or 0-Hz) component in the time domain. The dc component in time is a bias or horizontal line raised a constant distance above the time axis.

Cosine Wave   When the signal is a wave having the form $A \cos (2\pi t/T)$ (amplitude A, period T), as shown in Fig. 6-8, the transform, or frequency spectrum, is particularly evident. It consists of two spikes symmetrically placed around the zero-frequency axis, one at frequency n equal to $1/T$ and the other at frequency n equal to $-1/T$. As the function is symmetrical about zero time, the phase term in the transform is zero, and this is another "zero-phase" function.

Although the derivation of this transform is somewhat complicated, it is easy to see intuitively that the frequency spectrum of an infinitely long cosine wave having a period of T would have to be confined to the frequencies $n = 1/T$ and $n = -1/T$ (the negative term being required because the cosine wave could be generated by either clockwise or counterclockwise rotation). There is obviously no component of the signal at any other frequency.

FIGURE 6-8   Fourier transform of an infinitely long cosine wave.

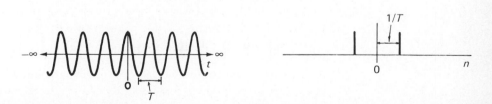

Infinite Series of Equally Spaced Spikes   Let us now consider a time signal consisting of an infinitely long succession of spikes separated by equal time intervals having a value of T. This function is known as the *sampling* or *replicating* function. The transform of this array (as shown in Fig. 6-9) is also a series of spikes separated by a uniform frequency interval which is equal to the reciprocal of the time interval between the spikes in the time function. For symmetrical arrays of spikes that include a spike at zero time, there is no phase term in the transform. The mathematical derivation of this transform is beyond the scope of this chapter.

Let us investigate the physical significance of the frequency function for this case. The spike at zero frequency represents the dc component of the signal, which exists because all spikes have positive amplitudes, so that the net flow of the current for a spike representing an electric voltage would be unidirectional and uniform. The two spikes nearest to, and on opposite sides of, the one at zero frequency correspond to cosine waves at the fundamental frequency n_1, which is the reciprocal of the repetition period of the time signal (n_1 being equal to $1/T$). The pair of spikes at frequency n_2, which is twice the frequency of n_1, represents cosine waves having the second harmonic frequency ($n_2 = 2/T$). By the same token, the frequency n_3, which is $3/T$, is the third harmonic of n_1, and so on, there being an infinite number of harmonic-frequency components, all having the same amplitude. We shall consider later what happens when the pulses that are periodically repeated consist not of spikes but of square waves having a finite width. We shall also take up the case of a finite number of uniformly spaced pulses, which has more practical significance than an infinite number.

Phase as a Function of Frequency   Whenever there are both sine and cosine terms in the transform, as is the case for time functions that are not either symmetrical or antisymmetrical about zero time, it follows from Eq. (6-4) that phase as well as amplitude will have to be taken into account in specifying the frequency spectrum. Physically, we may picture the phase as the time (expressed as a fraction of the wave period multiplied by 360° or 2π rad) that a sinusoidal Fourier component of the signal must be shifted to bring its zero crossing to zero on the time axis. This shift in time will be different for different

FIGURE 6-9   Fourier transform of a uniformly spaced series of spike signals extending to infinity in both directions.

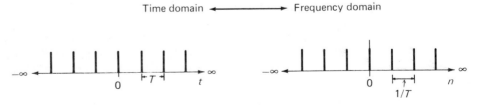

Time domain ⟷ Frequency domain

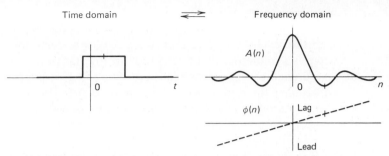

FIGURE 6-10   Phase shift introduced when square wave is displaced from its symmetrical position. (*From Peterson and Dobrin.*[10])

frequencies. For most signals of the type encountered in seismic work, a plot of phase angle versus frequency turns out to be a smooth, continuous curve.

To illustrate the nature of the phase-frequency relationship, let us consider a square wave that is shifted in time away from a position of symmetry about the $t = 0$ axis, as in Fig. 6-10. This shift of the square-wave function in the frequency domain represents a bandpass filter that is commonly used in processing. The amplitude term of the transform is unchanged, but the phase curve shows that the phase angle (the tangent of which is the sine transform divided by the cosine transform) passes through the origin and increases linearly with increasing frequency. A linear phase curve of this kind means that all frequency components of the signal are shifted by an equal amount of time, as would be necessary if the signal itself were shifted with no change in waveform.

The need for considering phase as well as amplitude is seen in Fig. 6-11. It shows two signals, each made up by adding two infinitely long sinusoidal waves of equal amplitude. One of the two waves has a frequency double that of the other. The only difference between (*a*) and (*b*) is in the phase of the higher-

FIGURE 6-11   Effect of phase relation upon signal obtained by summation of two sinusoidal waves: (a) addition of two cosine waves with one having double the frequency of the other; (b) addition of the same waves after 90° phase shift of the higher-frequency event. Note the difference in the synthesized waveforms. (*From Anstey.*[11])

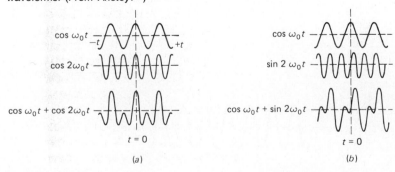

frequency component. The higher-frequency wave is symmetric about zero time in Fig. 6-11a (cos $2\omega_0 t$), but is phase shifted 90° in Fig. 6-11b (sin $2\omega_0 t$), with the result that its zero crossing is now at zero time. The lower-frequency wave is symmetric about zero time in Fig. 6-11a and b. The difference in the appearance of the waves made up by adding respective Fourier components which have the same amplitudes and frequencies but different phase relations is quite striking. In case (a), since both components are zero phase (time symmetric), the sum is zero phase.

Sine Wave   Let us now consider the transform of an antisymmetrical time signal, one having the form $A \sin (2\pi t/T)$. It differs in phase from that of the cosine wave previously discussed because the sine wave, as can be seen in Fig. 6-12, is not symmetrical about $t = 0$. It is evident that the phase of the sine wave is shifted 90° with respect to the cosine wave. For a sine wave the spike in the transform at frequency $n = -1/T$ has a sign opposite to that of the spike in the transform at $n = 1/T$. The times at $\pm 1/T$ are dashed because they represent imaginary numbers. A real and odd (antisymmetic) function in time has a Fourier transform which is imaginary and odd.

Hilbert Transforms   A seismic-data trace as recorded in the field is a time series which is real (no imaginary components in time) and causal (no arrivals before time zero, the time of source initiation). These two properties cause the Fourier transforms of seismic-trace data to have special properties. Let

$$f(t) = \text{real, causal time series}$$
$$f(t) \leftrightarrow F(n), \text{ the frequency-domain equivalent}$$

As in Eq. (6-1), the Fourier transform, $F(n)$, of the time series consists of real and imaginary parts.

$$F(n) = G(n) + iB(n)$$

$B(n)$ is the Hilbert transform of $G(n)$.

FIGURE 6-12
Fourier transform (amplitude and phase) of infinitely long sine wave.

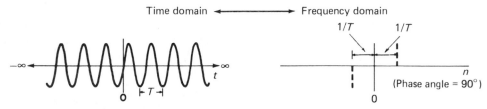

Time domain ⟷ Frequency domain

(Phase angle = 90°)

The Hilbert transform of a function $f(x)$ is defined as a convolution (see next page)

$$F_{\text{Hi}}(x) = \left(\frac{-1}{\pi x}\right) * f(x)$$

or   (6-12)

$$F_{\text{Hi}}(x) = \frac{1}{\pi} \int_{-\infty}^{\infty} \frac{f(x') \, dx'}{x' - x}$$

At $x' = x$, the Cauchy principal value of the integral is taken. The Hilbert transformation is a type of filtering that passes the amplitudes of the spectral components unchanged, but alters the phases of the spectral components by $\pi/2$ (90°). For more information, see Bracewell.[13]

Hilbert transforms are also used in complex trace and attribute analysis (Taner and Sheriff,[14] Taner et al.[15]). The analytic signal $A(t)$ is the associated complex function computed from a real function, e.g., seismic trace, $f(t)$:

$$A(t) = f(t) - iF_{\text{Hi}}(t)$$

The Hilbert transform which computes the imaginary part of the analytic signal is also referred to as the quadrature function of $f(t)$. As Fig. 6-13 shows, the real part of the analytic signal, $f(t)$, is the projection of the analytic signal onto the plane defined by the time axis and the axis of reals; the quadrature function $F_{\text{Hi}}(t)$ is the projection onto the plane defined by the time axis and the imaginary axis.

FIGURE 6-13
The analytic signal, its real projection, and its imaginary projection (the quadrature function). The Hilbert transform is used to calculate the quadrature function from (real) seismic data. (*From Bracewell.*[13])

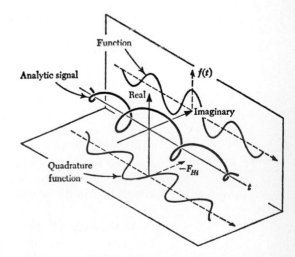

Complex trace and attribute analysis are used in stratigraphic interpretation and in structural mapping of low-amplitude events, as will be discussed in Chaps. 8 and 9.

Significance of Fourier Transforms To those whose primary concern with Fourier transforms is in their application to seismic-data processing, the physical significance of the concepts involved is likely to be of more interest than is their mathematical expression. From the standpoint of geophysical applications, the following aspects of Fourier transforms are most important:

1 The Fourier transform of a time function, such as a seismic signal, is the frequency and phase spectra of the signal.

2 The Fourier transform of a frequency function, such as a filter-response curve, is a time function. An example of such a time function is the impulse response of a filter, as shown in Fig. 6-1. It is sometimes more efficient to perform digital filtering in the time domain than in the frequency domain. A Fourier transformation makes the necessary conversion to the time domain where the filter characteristics are initially specified in terms of frequency.

3 It follows from items 1 and 2 that any function of time can be expressed as a corresponding function of frequency, and vice versa.

4 Reciprocity exists between the appearance of a function and its transform regardless of whether the initial function is in the time or frequency domain.

Convolution

"*Convolution*" as used in exploration geophysics is the change in waveshape as a result of passing through a linear filter (Sheriff[16]). Earlier in this chapter we introduced the concept of convolution by defining the impulse response to be the output of a filter when the input is a spike of unit amplitude. We then showed how the impulse response is used to form the output of this filter for any input wave. The output was formed by replacing each element of the input function with an output function scaled according to the magnitude of the input elements and then superimposing the results. This "replacement" method is one time-domain method to perform convolution. Another time-domain method to perform it is by "folding," where the impulse response of the filter is reversed in time and slid past the input, the output for each position being the sum of the products of inputs and impulse responses for corresponding points. Still another way to perform convolution is by multiplying the z transforms of the two functions (which shall be discussed later). Convolution in the time domain may also be accomplished by multiplication in the frequency domain, which is also discussed later.

Mathematical Expression of Convolution Consider two functions of time $f(t)$ and $g(t)$. The first might be a seismic signal. The second might be the impulse response of a filter through which the signal is passed. The output of the filter, which we call the convolution product of the two functions $f(t)$ and $g(t)$, can be expressed in the form

$$h(t) = \int_{-\infty}^{\infty} f(\tau)g(t - \tau) \, d\tau$$

or   (6-13)

$$h(t) = f(t) * g(t)$$

the symbol $*$ meaning "convolved with."

The physical significance of this mathematical operation is illustrated by Fig. 6-14. The input signal $f(t)$ is plotted in Fig. 6-14a, and the impulse response of the filter $g(t)$ in Fig. 6-14b. Convolution is commutative, so $f(t) * g(t) = g(t) * f(t)$. To demonstrate the folding technique of convolving $f(t)$ with $g(t)$, we will time reverse $g(t)$ and multiply the reversed function by the unreversed function ordinate by ordinate, sum these products as the value of the convolu-

FIGURE 6-14   Convolution of two functions $f(t)$ and $g(t)$ to obtain convolution product $h(t)$. If $f(t)$ is an input signal and $g(t)$ the impulse response of a filter, $h(t)$ is the output signal. (a) Plot of $f(t)$ versus t; (b) plot of $g(t)$ versus t; (c) multiplication of $f(\tau)$ and $g(t-\tau)$ versus τ, products shown by dashes; (d) plot of $h(t)$ versus t.

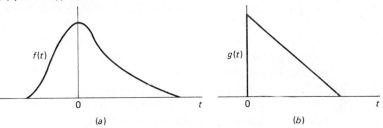

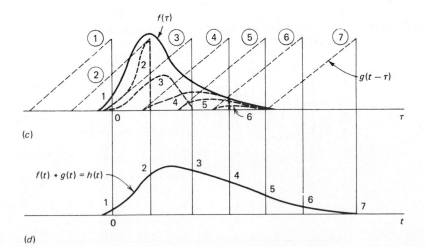

tion at that time shift, t, and perform this operation for all time shifts. In doing this we change the designation of the time variable t to τ, so that $f(t)$ becomes $f(\tau)$ and $g(t)$, because of its reversal, becomes $g(t - \tau)$. The argument of g indicates that its original zero-time value has been shifted an amount τ.

When the two functions are lined up so that their respective zero-time positions coincide along the time axis, τ is zero, as shown for position 2 in Fig. 6-14c. The separation τ of the two zero positions can be either positive or negative. For position 1 for $g(t)$ in Fig. 6-14c, τ is negative; for positions 3 to 7 it is positive. For each of the six time shifts (including zero), the product $f(\tau)$ and $g(t - \tau)$ is plotted versus τ using the heavy dashed lines in Fig. 6-14c. The areas under these lines, which correspond to the integral in Eq. (6-13), are plotted versus t after changing the time variable back to t as shown in Fig. 6-14d. The value of the integral is the convolution product $h(t)$, which is the output signal.

Convolution of Sampled Data The folding approach applied to continuous data in Fig. 6-14 can be used to convolve sampled data. Figure 6-15 illustrates how a signal represented by six samples equally spaced in time (1, 1, 1, 2, 2, 2) is convolved with the impulse response of a filter which consists of three samples (4, 2, 1). The series representing the impulse response is time reversed and swept across the input signal in the steps shown.

The need to reverse the impulse response with respect to the input can be visualized more easily if it is remembered that both functions are conventionally plotted with time increasing from left to right. The output signal has its beginning when the earliest part of the input (the left end) interacts with the beginning (also the left end) of the impulse-response function. The termination of the output signal is associated with the interaction of the latest part (right end) of the input signal with the corresponding end of the impulse response. This interaction can be visualized most readily if one of the functions is reversed so that the contacts representing successive increments of time in the

FIGURE 6-15 Convolution of two sampled signals (1, 1, 1, 2, 2, 2) and (4, 2, 1). The first time series represents the input signal, the second the impulse response, and the eight-term series shown as a diagonal, the output. Note reversal of second term. (*From Peterson and Dobrin.*[10])

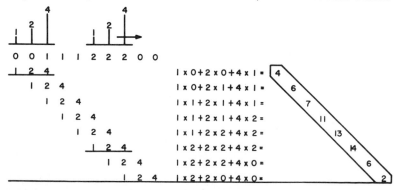

outputs can be looked upon as the sweeping (from left to right) of the reversed and unreversed signals, as shown in Figs. 6-14 and 6-15.

At each position of the sweep, the products obtained by multiplying each input sample by the appropriate weighting function associated with the impulse response are added to give the output at the instant corresponding to that position. The successive shift, multiply, and add operations provide the basic sequence of steps involved in filtering by convolution, the type most widely used in digital processing of seismic signals.

Applications   It is easy to understand from the foregoing discussion that the product of convolution, the output signal, will have a length that is one sample less than the sum of the lengths of the input and the impulse response. The effect of filtering is to lengthen the input signal by a time equal to the duration of the filter operator with which the input is convolved. (In practice, however, the number of samples per trace is fixed, and the excess samples after convolution are dropped.) The effect of the filtering is to remove the undesirable frequency components, thus enhancing the desired signal frequencies. If the signal is convolved with a spike, it follows from Fig. 6-14 that the signal is shifted without change of waveform by the amount that the spike is displaced from the zero-time reference of the filter operator.

Relation between Fourier Transformation and Convolution (the Convolution Theorem)

One of the most important and most useful relationships in data processing is expressed by the *convolution theorem*. This states that the Fourier transform of the convolution of two functions is equal to the product of the transforms of the individual functions. Convolution in one domain is thus equivalent to multiplication in the other domain. Interchangeability of the two filtering approaches is extensively used in programming digital computers for filtering seismic data.

If $F(n)$ is the Fourier transform of the function $f(t)$, $G(n)$ the Fourier transform of $g(t)$, and $H(n)$ the Fourier transform of $h(t)$, the convolution product of $f(t)$ and $g(t)$, we can write

$$h(t) = f(t) * g(t)$$
$$H(n) = F(n)G(n)$$

(6-14)

This means that the function obtained by the convolution of any two functions can also be obtained by taking the Fourier transform of each function, multiplying the transforms, and then taking the transform of the product. Since the amplitude spectrum is the magnitude of the complex transform and the phase spectrum, its angle, we can obtain the amplitude spectrum of $H(n)$ by multiplying the amplitude spectra of $F(n)$ and $G(n)$. The phase spectrum of $H(n)$ is obtained by adding the phase spectra of $F(n)$ and $G(n)$.

If, instead of time functions, we want to convolve the two frequency functions $F(n)$ and $G(n)$, the reciprocal relation holds. Defining

$$Q(n) = F(n) * G(n)$$

gives $$q(t) = f(t)g(t)$$

where $q(t)$ is the Fourier transform of $Q(n)$.

The convolution theorem is often applied to compute Fourier transforms of functions for which the determination by integration would involve much more labor. The calculation, for example, of the transform for an infinitely long, equally spaced series of square waves (shown in Fig. 6-16) would be very tedious by direct calculation. But if we were to build up the series of square waves by convolving an infinite succession of equally spaced spikes with a single square wave of the desired width, we could obtain the transform simply by multiplying the transform for the spikes by that for the square wave (the sinc function shown as a dashed line), the results being indicated by the suite of vertical lines on the right side. The effect of going from the spikes to the square waves is to reduce the amplitudes of the higher-harmonic terms for the spikes (see page 170) in such a way that those beyond a certain order become negligibly small.

Suppose, as another example, that we replace the infinite series of square waves with a finite succession of such events. How is the Fourier transform affected? We can find out, as shown in Fig. 6-17, by multiplying the original infinitely long train of pulses by a square wave with a breadth equal to the length desired for the finite series of square waves. To get the transform of this product, we simply convolve the respective transforms of the two time functions that were multiplied. In the resulting transform obtained by this convolution, the spikes for the infinite succession of square pulses have been spread out into a series of sinc functions having distances between zero crossings that are inversely proportional to the number of pulses contained in the truncated series.

FIGURE 6-16   Fourier transform of an infinite series of square waves of width T with centers separated by interval t_1. Convolution theorem used to obtain frequency function. Dashed line shows how heights of spikes were derived.

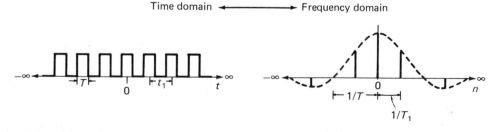

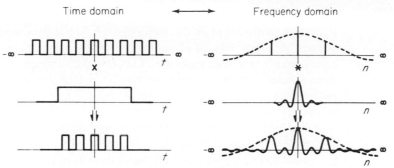

FIGURE 6-17   Development using convolution theorem of Fourier transform of truncated series of uniformly spaced square waves. (*From Peterson and Dobrin.*[10])

By the same procedure, we can show how the truncation of an infinitely long cosine function will broaden the simple two-spike spectrum shown for this type of signal in Fig. 6-8. When this infinitely long function is multiplied by a square wave of appropriate length, as in Fig. 6-18, the transform of the truncated train of cosine waves now consists of two sinc functions instead of two spikes, as each spike has been convolved with a sinc function corresponding to the transform of the square wave. The width of each sinc function decreases as the number of cosine cycles increases. This is because the breadth of the square wave used in the multiplication is proportional to the number of cycles involved.

Other applications of the convolution theorem will be considered when we take up the design of filter operators for digital processing of seismic signals.

FIGURE 6-18
Development using convolution theorem of Fourier transform of truncated cosine wave. (*From Peterson and Dobrin.*[10])

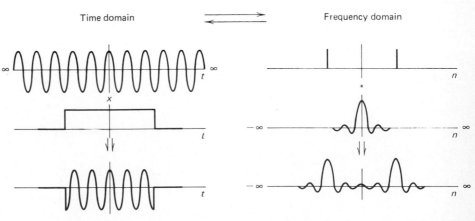

Autocorrelation

Fourier transforms provide one approach to the frequency analysis of seismic signals. Another way of obtaining the frequency spectrum that is used extensively involves autocorrelation. This requires a series of mathematical operations similar to those in convolution except that the two functions operating on each other are the same and one of them is not reversed with respect to the other.

Initially the two identical functions are aligned with each other as shown in Fig. 6-19. The ordinates of the respective curves are picked off at equal time intervals. The samples are multiplied at each of the ordinate positions, and the products are added to give what is defined as the *autocorrelation function* at zero time lag. The function has its highest value at this lag because all coincident ordinate values are equal. Sample by sample, the function is shifted relative to itself, the amount of shift being the lag, and the sum of the products being the output for that lag value. Now consider the case of a half-cycle shift, *A*, between the identical functions. Because of the shift, the products of the ordinate values are mostly negative, so that the sum shows a peak negative value when plotted against the time lag, designated here as *A*. Shifting the lower curve still farther to *B*, we obtain a positive autocorrelation value.

FIGURE 6-19
Determination of autocorrelation function illustrated by matching curve with itself at zero time lag and three other values of lag. (*From Peterson and Dobrin.*[10])

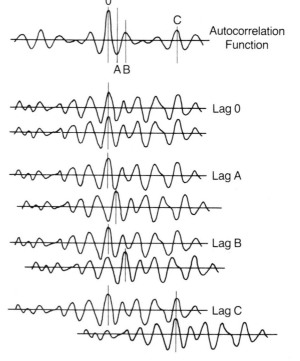

Another peak is shown when the lower curve lags by an amount C, which apparently represents another periodicity in the original function.

The equation for the autocorrelation function of $F(t)$ is

$$\theta_{11}(t) = \int_{-\infty}^{\infty} f(\tau)f(\tau - t) \, d\tau \tag{6-15}$$

where τ is the time shift between the two identical functions. Note its resemblance to the expression for convolution [Eq. (6-13)], except that there is no time reversal.

The autocorrelation function will have its largest value at zero lag time. It will have large positive values at time shifts corresponding to periodicities or repetition times in the signal that is correlated with itself. The reciprocals of such times will represent dominant frequencies. Note that the autocorrelation function is symmetric about zero lag time because a time shift to the right of τ units yields the same sum of products as a time shift of τ units to the left. Autocorrelation functions are zero-phase functions.

If we take the Fourier transform of the autocorrelation function, we get the square of the frequency spectrum of the signal. A spectrum obtained in this way contains amplitude information but none of the phases of the various frequency components. A spectrum giving the square of the amplitude as a function of frequency but containing no phase information is referred to as a *power spectrum*.

Cross-Correlation

The same mathematical or graphical procedure that is used in autocorrelation is known as *cross-correlation* when it is applied to analyze the relationship between two different functions. Cross-correlation measures the similarity as a function of lag or time shift between two functions. The process involved was shown in Fig. 4-15 along with our discussion of vibroseis recording. The equation for the cross-correlation of the time function $f(t)$ and $g(t)$ is

$$\theta_{12}(t) = \int_{-\infty}^{\infty} f(\tau)g(\tau - t) \, d\tau \tag{6-16}$$

At a lag τ of zero, the two functions are juxtaposed so that their individual zero time axes are coincident. They are then progressively moved apart, and at each value of time lag τ ordinate values sampled at closely spaced intervals are multiplied and the individual products added. For any values of the lag τ at which the functions tend to have the same shape and thus seem to fit into each other or correlate, the cross-correlation function will have a local maximum.

Notice the similarity between the cross-correlation equation (6-16) and the convolution equation (6-13). Using Sheriff and Geldart's[8] mathematical developments, we express cross-correlation as

$$\theta_{xy}(\tau) = \sum_k X_k Y_{k+\tau}$$

Convolution is

$$X(t) * Y(t) = \sum_k X_k Y_{\tau-k}$$

Figure 6-20 illustrates the cross-correlation of $x(t)$, $(1, \frac{3}{4}, \frac{1}{2})$, and $y(t)$, $(1, \frac{1}{2}, -1)$. As in Fig. 6-20b, positive lag in $y(t)$ (one Δt shift to the left) yields the same sum of the products (cross-correlation value) as a negative lag in $x(t)$ (one Δt shift to the right), which can be written

FIGURE 6-20 The cross correlation of two functions, $x(t)$, $(1, \frac{3}{4}, \frac{1}{2})$, and $y(t)$, $(1, \frac{1}{2}, -1)$. The maximum value of the cross-correlation function is at a shift of -1, indicating the lag that best time-aligns the two functions. (*Modified from Sheriff and Geldart.*[8])

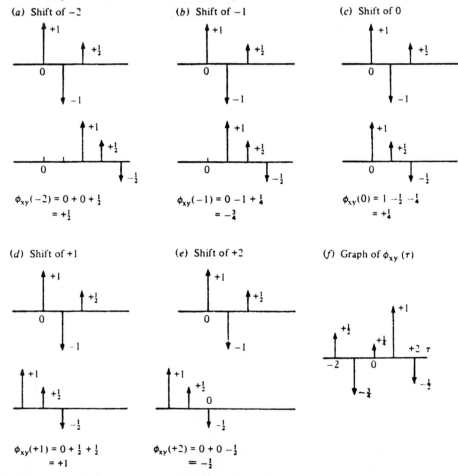

(a) Shift of -2

$\phi_{xy}(-2) = 0 + 0 + \frac{1}{2}$
$\qquad = +\frac{1}{2}$

(b) Shift of -1

$\phi_{xy}(-1) = 0 - 1 + \frac{1}{4}$
$\qquad = -\frac{3}{4}$

(c) Shift of 0

$\phi_{xy}(0) = 1 - \frac{1}{2} - \frac{1}{4}$
$\qquad = +\frac{1}{4}$

(d) Shift of $+1$

$\phi_{xy}(+1) = 0 + \frac{1}{2} + \frac{1}{2}$
$\qquad = +1$

(e) Shift of $+2$

$\phi_{xy}(+2) = 0 + 0 - \frac{1}{2}$
$\qquad = -\frac{1}{2}$

(f) Graph of $\phi_{xy}(\tau)$

$$\theta_{xy}(\tau) = \theta_{yx}(-\tau) = \sum_k Y_k X_{k-\tau} = \sum_k Y_k X_{-(\tau-k)}$$
$$= y(t) * x(-t) = x(-t) = x(-t) * y(t) \qquad (6\text{-}17)$$

Equation (6-17) shows that cross-correlation can be performed by time reversing the first data set and convolving. We have already stated that convolution
requires a time reversal and that it is commutative. Thus, the effective two time
reversals of the same function implied in Eq. (6-17) "cancel" each other,
leaving correlation being the simple sum of products of two functions.

Cross-correlation in the time domain corresponds to the frequency-domain
operation of multiplying the amplitude spectra and subtracting the phase spectra. The phase spectra are subtracted in cross-correlation, instead of the addition performed in convolution, because reversing the trace in time (before the
convolution) changes the sign of the phase spectrum.

A widely used application of cross-correlation in seismic exploration is the
reduction of vibroseis data, discussed in Chap. 4. To recapitulate, a varying-
frequency signal of many seconds' duration emitted from the source reflects
from a bed at a depth corresponding to a two-way travel time of t. It is
superimposed on reflection signals of similar duration from other beds, so that
it will probably not be identifiable on the record made in the field. If, however,
the ground motion as actually recorded is cross-correlated with the signal as
initially generated, a high value of the cross-correlation coefficient at a lag of
time t indicates the presence of a reflection at that time. When the shift is of this
amount, the source signal and the portion of the recorded signal made up of
reflected energy from the bed in question will coincide, resulting in a maximum
cross-correlation value for this time lag. Each reflection event will show a
cross-correlation maximum at a time shift equivalent to its two-way reflection
time, so that the cross-correlation of a vibroseis recording with the input signal
should be equivalent in appearance to a reflection record generated by a band-
limited impulse source. A second important use of cross-correlation is in the
determination of static values (see Sec. 7-4).

A vibroseis record after cross-correlation with the pilot (the swept wave
train) is the earth's reflectivity (with noise) convolved with the autocorrelation
wavelet of the sweep. Autocorrelation functions are zero phase (symmetric
about time zero). Since vibroseis data contain the zero-phase autocorrelation
wavelet as its basic wavelet, some vibroseis data have been found to be more
nearly zero phase than minimum phase. If a data set is truly more zero phase
than minimum phase, care must be exercised in the use of some of the later
processing steps, especially in common deconvolution processes, which assume the data to be minimum phase.

Bandpass Filtering

A relatively simple type of frequency filtering is bandpass filtering. All signals
above one specified frequency are passed, or all frequencies below another

specified frequency are passed, or both occur. Such filters are generally designated as high-pass, low-pass, or bandpass. In designing digital filters that operate in the time domain, we express the desired filter characteristic as a function of frequency and then compute the Fourier transform of this function so as to set up a filter operator as a function of time.

Suppose we want to design a low-pass filter in the time domain that transmits all frequencies from 0 to 40 Hz without attenuation but allows no frequencies above 40 Hz to pass. Remembering that frequency-characteristic curves must be symmetrical about zero, as they apply equally to positive and negative

FIGURE 6-21 Design of low-pass filter operator based on convolution theorem. Desired cutoff at 40 Hz cannot be achieved exactly because the operator must be of finite length and the frequency function in the form of the square wave shown at the upper right would require an infinitely long filter function. (*From Peterson and Dobrin.*[10])

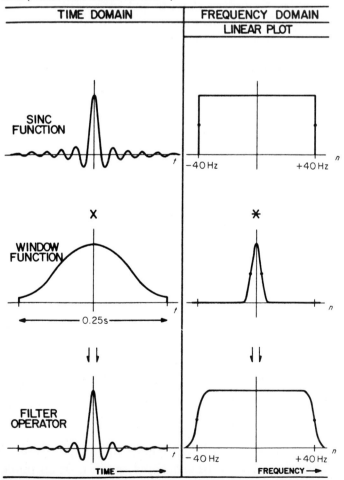

frequencies, we can draw the characteristic curve for the desired filter in the form of the square wave shown at the upper right of Fig. 6-21. This has uniform transmission between frequencies of -40 and 40 Hz and zero transmission outside this range. The time representation of this rectangular frequency function, which is its Fourier transform, is a sinc function having zero crossings at ± 0.0125, ± 0.025, ± 0.0375, . . . s.

The times of these crossings are, as we saw on page 167, equal respectively to 1, 2, 3, . . . divided by the width, 80 Hz, of the square wave as measured on the frequency scale. Even though the amplitudes of the lobes thus obtained attenuate rapidly as time increases in the positive and negative directions, the sinc function must be infinitely long to represent an accurate transform of the square wave. An infinitely long filter operator is, of course, not physically realizable, and we must consider what effect truncation of such an operator will have on its filter characteristics. One way of truncating the time operator is to multiply it by a rectangular (square-wave) function having a time duration of proper length, but the sharp corner at the cutoff point would leave undesired side-band effects. A common solution of this problem is to truncate the operator more gradually by multiplying it by a *window function* of the type shown at the left center of Fig. 6-21. This function consists of one cycle of a cosine wave with its trough raised slightly above zero; it is called a *Hamming window*.

The frequency transform of the window is shown at the right of the function itself. It consists of a peak at zero with a fairly sharp drop on either side. The purpose of the window function is to reduce the side bands to the point where they have no perceptible effect on the output.

When the infinitely long sinc function is multiplied by this window function, we get a time operator having a length of 0.250 s. What effect does the truncation have on the frequency characteristic of the filter? We can find out by convolving the original square filter curve with the transform of the window in accordance with the convolution theorem. Instead of a vertical cutoff, we have an inclined cutoff curve centered at 40 Hz, the slope depending on the width of the truncation window: the broader the window, the steeper the slope; thus the longer the filter operator, the sharper the cutoff at the desired frequency.

The convolution of what is effectively a single-peak spectrum for the window function with the desired square-wave frequency function yields a filter with a frequency characteristic that has sloping rather than vertical sides. Even so, the slope is almost always steeper than can be obtained with the sharpest analog filters ordinarily used.

Deconvolution

We have shown that the output, $h(t)$, of a filter, $e(t)$, with a known input signal, $f(t)$, can be computed by convolving the input with the impulse response of the filter; i.e.,

$$h(t) = f(t) * e(t)$$

Suppose, however, that the output $h(t)$ is known and we would like to recover the form of the signal, $f(t)$, as it was before it was modified by the filter. To do this, we need to find another filter with a response $k(t)$ through which $h(t)$ might be passed to recover $f(t)$; $k(t)$ would then be an inverse filter with respect to $e(t)$. The process of canceling the effect of a filter with a second filter designed to be its inverse is called *deconvolution* or *inverse filtering*.

The equation for the deconvolution operation is

$$f(t) \;=\; h(t) * \frac{1}{e(t)} \;=\; h(t) * k(t) \tag{6-18}$$

or, in the frequency domain,

$$F(n) \;=\; \frac{H(n)}{E(n)} \;=\; H(n)\,K(n) \tag{6-19}$$

where $F(n)$, $H(n)$, $E(n)$, and $K(n)$ are the frequency spectra or Fourier transforms of the respective time functions $f(t)$, $h(t)$, $e(t)$, and $k(t)$.

In practice, we deconvolve seismic signals to convert the waveform of a reflection complicated by the filtering that takes place in the earth (such as by

FIGURE 6-22
Marine record section: (a) before deconvolution; (b) after deconvolution. (*Prakla-Seismos.*)

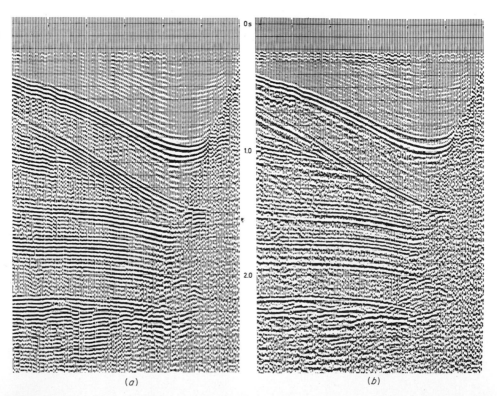

(a)   (b)

reverberation within a water layer or near-surface layers on land) into a simple pulse representing the reflection waveform before the filtering took place. (See Fig. 6-22.) Also, the long initial waveform of a marine source can be transformed into a short wavelet. A long source waveform hinders the interpretation of seismic data and can cause erroneous interpretations, as shown in Fig. 6-23.

Land data have an initial shot waveform consisting of a short pulse which is broadened by the filtering action of the earth with a consequent decrease in resolution. Any reverberations of the pulse in shallow layers alter the waveform still more, interfering further with the desired definition of reflection events. Processes that remove such distortions of the initial pulse improve

FIGURE 6-23   An interpretation problem caused by a long source waveform, as illustrated on model data. A pinchout might be interpreted on the upper panel in the circled area, but it is only an artifact, caused by the long source waveform. (*From Neidell.*[25])

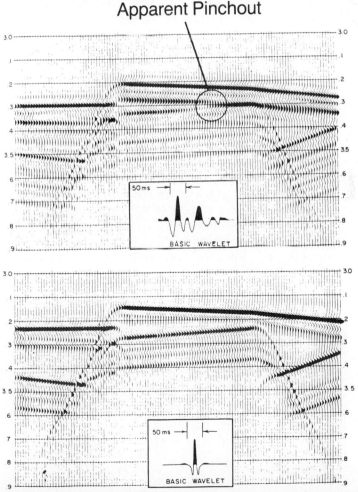

reflection quality. The compression of the basic seismic wavelet increases the *temporal* resolution. It also improves the results of subsequent data analysis techniques (e.g., velocity analysis and automatic static routines). In deconvolution we endeavor to compensate for the undesired filter characteristics of the earth itself or a long source waveform by creating a new filter that is the inverse of the unwanted filter.

The first step is to measure the spectrum of the signal and to manipulate this spectrum in a way that makes it approach the uniform character of the transform associated with a single spike. Computer programs determine the spectrum (often by autocorrelation), design the inverse filter according to specified criteria supplied by the geophysicist, and apply the designed filter to input data. Practical aspects of this process will be discussed in the next chapter.

Wiener Filtering

Wiener filtering is a method widely used in deconvolution and in filtering. Since there are many different applications of Wiener filtering, it is an important concept to understand. During World War II, Norbert Wiener of M.I.T., one of the foremost mathematicians of this century, was asked to develop a technique for extracting radar signals from noise. The method of filtering he worked out turned out to have many other applications to information processing, including enhancement of seismic reflection data.

In formulating his filtering technique, Wiener assumed that an information trace, e.g., in a seismogram, consists of a desired signal immersed in noise. Criteria were developed for deriving a filter operator that when convolved with the recorded trace would yield an output as close as possible to the desired signal. Starting with the observed trace, one would only need to specify the desired signal in order to determine this operator.

The mathematical theory of Wiener filtering is too advanced for presentation here in more than rudimentary form. Its application to seismic processing is well explained by Robinson and Treitel[17] and Foster et al.[18] The earliest work on adapting Wiener's pioneering studies to seismic data was reported by

FIGURE 6-24
Principle of Wiener filtering. Desired output signal provides basis for designing filter. (*From Robinson and Treitel.*[17])

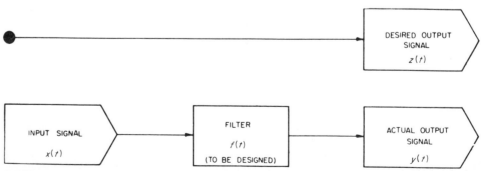

DESIRED OUTPUT SIGNAL
$z(t)$

INPUT SIGNAL
$x(t)$

FILTER
$f(t)$
(TO BE DESIGNED)

ACTUAL OUTPUT SIGNAL
$y(t)$

Wadsworth et al.,[19] who were associated with the geophysical analysis group at M.I.T.

Figure 6-24 illustrates the principle of a simple Wiener filter. Three signals are shown: the input $x(t)$, the desired output $z(t)$, and the actual output $y(t)$. The problem is to determine the filter operator $f(t)$ that brings $y(t)$ as close as possible to $z(t)$ by minimizing the differences (on a least-squares basis) between $y(t)$ and $z(t)$. The agreement shown between the actual output and the desired output in Fig. 6-25 is remarkably good, considering the very small number of terms used in the time series for the filter.

An approach like this is not generally employed in processing operations. An equation developed by Wiener and Hopf, however, provides a convenient basis for determining the filter operators. This equation makes it possible to determine the filter coefficients from the autocorrelation function of the input signal and the cross-correlation function between the desired output and the input signal. The two correlation operations can usually be performed by standard subroutines. As with the least-squares approach to filtering previously considered, simultaneous equations (called the "normal equations") are set up which are solved by the computer to obtain the respective coefficients of the desired filter operators. The derivation and application of the Wiener-Hopf equation to seismic filtering are presented by Robinson and Treitel.[17]

The output function obtained by convolving the input with the optimum filter operator will not coincide exactly with the desired output, but the differences can be minimized in a least-squares sense. Lines and Treitel[20] have

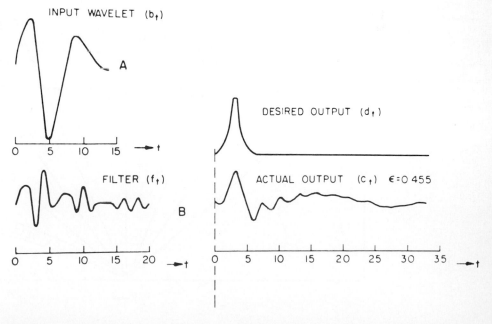

FIGURE 6-25
Comparison of desired output and actual output from Weiner filter. (From Robinson and Treitel.[17])

written a tutorial on least-squares inversion, with an example of its use in Wiener filtering.

Wiener filters can be used either in single-channel or multichannel processing. The most widespread and well-known use of Wiener filtering is in predictive deconvolution. (See Sec. 7-2.)

Velocity (or Multichannel) Filtering

Velocity filtering is one of the processing steps that attenuate coherent noise. Coherent noise on reflection records, first discussed in Chap. 4, has a different moveout or apparent velocity than have the desired reflection events. The time differential for a particular event between adjacent traces is the criterion on which the filtering operation is based. The filtering may be accomplished in the time domain or in the frequency–wave-number domain. We will examine first the frequency-domain operation, and then turn to the time-domain operation. Section 7-2 also discusses *f-k* filtering, and shows some field data examples.

The seismic data, either before stack in the shot-record form, or after stack, is 2-D Fourier transformed. Figure 6-26 shows the range of moveouts for reflections and low-velocity coherent noise on a plot of wave number (reciprocal of wavelength) versus frequency, which is effectively a conventional

FIGURE 6-26
Ranges of noise events in frequency–wave-number (*f-k*) representation. (*Embree et al.*[21])

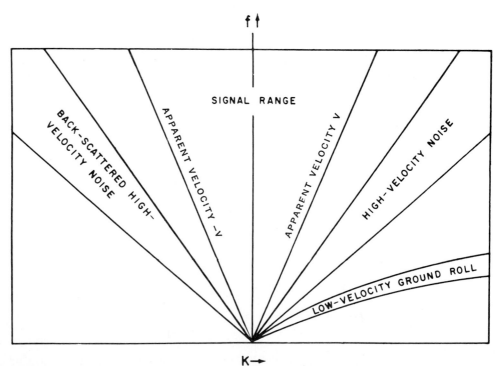

time-distance plot rotated by 90°. This is referred to as an *f-k* plot (frequency *f* versus wave number *k*), and the slopes on it are proportional to the apparent velocities of the events on the record rather than to the reciprocals of the apparent velocities, as on a time-distance plot. A reflection will normally have a small moveout across the record, and even when there is steep dip, the moveout will often be relatively small compared with most traveling noise, such as surface waves, which usually have low velocities. Reflections will fall within a narrow wedge that is centered on the frequency axis. Low-velocity noise, such as ground roll, falls within wedges closest to the *k* (wave number) axis; high-velocity noise falls within wedges of intermediate slope. Transformation of the data into the frequency–wave-number domain has thus effected a separation of noise and signal.

Ground roll is conventionally suppressed by a combination of low-cut frequency filtering and wave-number filtering, the latter being equivalent to the discrimination accomplished by using multiple shots and/or geophone arrays. High-velocity noise, on the other hand, cannot be rejected in this way without risking deterioration of the reflections, particularly those associated with steeply dipping beds. The object of velocity filtering is to suppress high-velocity noise without detriment to the reflection quality.

Referring again to Fig. 6-25, we set up a condition that all signals be passed without modification in the range of apparent velocities from V to $-V$. The filter response is specified not as a function of frequency alone but as a two-dimensional function of frequency and wave number that can be represented on an *f-k* plot of the type shown in this figure. A transmission of unity (no filtering effect) is desired in the range where k has values between $-|f|/|V|$ and $|f|/|V|$ (the vertical bars represent absolute values irrespective of the sign of f). For all k values outside this range, the transmission is specified to be zero. The transition between pass and reject zones needs to be smooth and appropriately set in order to minimize a "ringing" effect upon the output data. Thus, velocity filtering can be accomplished in the frequency domain.

The calculation of the time-domain velocity filter operator is discussed by Embree et al.[21] These filters generally tend to introduce a certain amount of spatial smearing, termed *mixing*, which is an artificial increase in the horizontal coherence. Cassano and Rocca[22] presented a technique to determine the coefficients of the time-domain operators by solving a matrix equation in the frequency domain. This approach is fast and results in minimum mixing effects.

Figure 6-27 shows the form the time-domain filter operator takes for six pairs of traces, each member of the respective pairs, such as 6, 7; 5, 8; etc., representing the same distance x_m from the source. Input signals corresponding to increasing distances from the output position at the center are fed into low-pass filters with progressively lower cutoff frequencies. Looking at the filtering action in a qualitative way, we might say that the highest-frequency components of the desired signal are passed only by the two channels nearest the center of the array, but the relative contribution of these components to the output signal is raised to its proper level by the high amplitude of the weighting

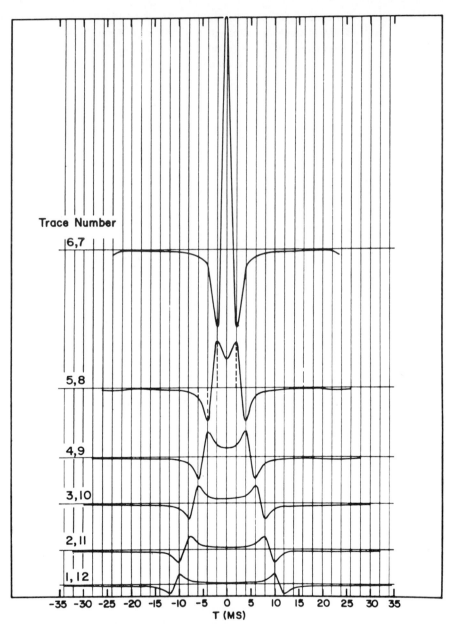

FIGURE 6-27 Filter operators used with pairs of traces at progressively greater distances from shot point in velocity filtering by the pie-slice process. (*Embree et al.*[21])

function. Successively lower frequencies can be composited over a successively greater number of traces without attenuation. A further discussion and examples of the use of velocity filtering is found in Sec. 7-2.

Principles of Sampling in Seismic Processing

Although the theory of sampling enters into analog time-domain filtering, as pointed out by Swartz and Sokoloff[23] in an important paper published some years before the digital revolution, some aspects of it are unique to digital technology. The basic difference between digital and analog methods, as pointed out in Chap. 3, is that the analog data represent a continuous flow of (usually varying) voltage, whereas digitally recorded data represent a discontinuous series of voltage values, expressed as numbers sampled at discrete time intervals, such as every 2 or 4 ms. Between sampling instants there is no registration of the voltage.

The parameters associated with digitizing of seismic data that are of greatest concern in processing are the sampling interval and the number of bits (or binary digits) for each sample. The former quantity governs the frequency range over which the processing system gives usable results, while the latter governs the dynamic range, resolution, and precision of the processed information.

Effect of Number of Bits   As pointed out in Chap. 3 (page 68), seismic signals are stored digitally in binary code. The number of bits available for encoding the analog voltages at the sampling points sets a limit on the precision with which the data can be registered. Suppose that a peak voltage of 123.53 mV is to be encoded on analog tape with only 7 bits available. We could express 123 mV by the digits 1111011 and 124 mV by the digits 1111100, but there would be no way of designating any values in between. With 7 bits our final result can be read only to the nearest millivolt, and this does not appear to be precise enough for most seismic registration. A real digital recording system is usually felt to require at least 14 bits for encoding the input voltage with the degree of precision inherent in seismic data. Fourteen bits allow resolution to the order of microvolts.

The real limitation on the number of bits required for any digital recording system is derived from the expected minimum level of the irreducible background noise that the system is expected to encounter. Experimentally that level can be determined by taking a seismic record under the quietest conditions with no shot being fired. If the rms (root-mean-square) level of the minimal noise can be expressed as the least significant binary digit, there is no need for more digits of lesser significance. This conclusion is reached by the following reasoning. It is obvious that digitization by itself produces an error equal to at most one-half the value of the least significant bit (provided that the digitized value is a rounded off expression of the precise value). That error can be considered to be an additional, additive noise and is uniformly distributed between zero and half the least significant bit. The mean-squared value of noise uniformly distributed between 0 and $\frac{1}{2}$ is $\int_0^{1/2} x^2 \, dx = \frac{1}{24} = 0.04$. If the rms value of the minimum noise is unity, the mean-squared value is also unity and the rms value of the sum of the minimum noise and the digitizing noise is $\sqrt{1.04} = 1.02$. In other words, digitization by rounding off to where the rms value of the minimum noise is 1 bit increased the noise level by only 2 percent, an absolutely negligible quantity. An additional bit would reduce this increase to 0.25 percent.

As a practical matter, experiments have shown that for seismic field work a digitization consisting of a sign, a 4-bit exponent to the base 2, and 8 bits of fractional value (mantissa) is more than adequate. For vibroseis work the fractional part need only be 1 bit rounded, or 2 bits truncated. Because there is little or no extra cost entailed in recording and processing much longer digital words, these minimal word lengths are not used in practice.

Sign-Bit Recording

In the late 1970s, Geophysical Systems Corporation introduced a field recording system that was able to record up to about 1000 channels with the digitization consisting of using only the sign of the received signal. In other words, the digitization consisted of 1 bit; a 1 represented a received signal of one polarity, and a 0 a signal of the opposite polarity.

Since this sign-bit recording system was meant to be used in vibroseis operations, it was provided with a correlator that consisted of an AND gate, an adder, and a shifter. Since the emitted sweep signal was also digitized to 1 bit, correlation was accomplished by the AND gate, which would send a 1 to the adder if a sample of the received signal were of the same sign as the corresponding sample of the sweep, and a -1 if they were different.

For a 16-s sweep sampled every 2 ms, the maximum sum in the adder could be 8000 and the minimum nonzero sum would be 1, producing a dynamic range of 8000 or 78 dB, equivalent to a 13-bit word.

It can be shown that provided the received signal-to-noise ratio is sufficiently low, the correlogram resulting from single-bit recording is as accurate as that which would be obtained by means of a recording system with an unlimited number of bits (Ref. 24). In practice, however, there are situations which the sign-bit system cannot handle adequately, such as the combination of a strong reflector closely followed by a weak reflector. The sign-bit system is nevertheless advantageous when many channels are needed or when the multiplicity available from the many channels can overcome the disadvantages of the less precise recording. Since the sign-bit system was introduced, the number of "full-precision" channels practicably available in the field has been increasing to the point that full-precision, 1000-channel systems can now displace the less precise, sign-bit system.

Amplitude Relations   The lower the sampling rate is (the smaller the number of samples per second), the lower the cost of digital recording and processing is. What factors govern the lowest sampling rate that will yield acceptable data quality? The answer to this question depends on the upper limit of seismic frequencies that are of interest.

Let us consider first the effect of sampling rate on the amplitude measurement. The reconstruction in analog form of a digitized signal is accomplished by a digital-to-analog converter that passes the voltage corresponding to each sampling instant into a storage element. This value is held in storage until the next sampling instant, at which point the voltage in the hold element is switched abruptly to its next sampled value. The result is the staircase pattern shown in Fig. 6-28. The original signal, indicated by a dashed line, is a 62.5-Hz sine wave with an amplitude of 100 units, and the sampling is every 2 ms. The staircase signal can be transformed by filtering to a sinusoidal wave having a frequency of 62.5 Hz which has an amplitude of 97 units plus a series of higher-order harmonics which are superimposed on the 62.5-Hz signal as a ripple. The ripple components are removed by a proper high-cut filter, but the reconstructed signal has now been reduced 3 percent in amplitude.

If the sampling positions are shifted somewhat to fall at points along the sine wave different from those shown in Fig. 6-28, the distortion in amplitude will probably have a different value; it will depend on the amplitude of ripple components which are observed with the new distribution of sampling points.

Frequency Relations   Sampling has no adverse effect on the fidelity with which desired frequency components can be reproduced so long as the sam-

FIGURE 6-28
Reconstruction of a sampled signal in digital-to-analog conversion. Ripple removed by filtering. (*From Peterson and Dobrin.*[10])

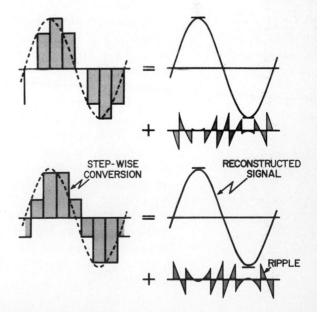

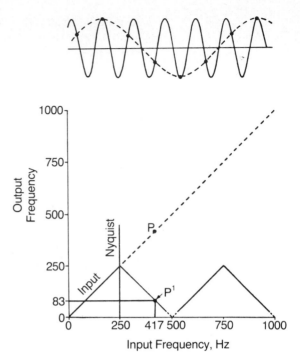

FIGURE 6-29
Frequency folding, or aliasing, in case where sampling frequency is greater than half-signal frequency. As input frequency increases beyond half of the sampling frequency (Nyquist value), output no longer follows input. The dashed output signal at 83 Hz is spurious. (*From Peterson and Dobrin.*[10])

pling frequency is more than twice the highest-frequency component of interest in the signal. If the sampling frequency is less than this, we can expect a serious distortion of output frequency, which is generally referred to as *aliasing*.

Figure 6-29 illustrates the principle involved. The sine wave at the top has a frequency of 417 Hz and is sampled at a frequency of 500 Hz. The sampling frequency is thus considerably less than twice the signal frequency. The output frequency is obtained by drawing the best smooth curve through the sampling points; this turns out to be 83 Hz.

The lower part of the figure illustrates the relation between input and output frequencies as the input frequency increases. Here the sampling frequency is 500 Hz (2-ms sample rate). For inputs up to 250 Hz, the output has the same frequency as the input. This limit of half the sampling frequency is referred to as the Nyquist frequency.[26,27] Inspection of Fig. 6-29 shows why the Nyquist frequency has been termed *the folding frequency*. Frequencies higher than the Nyquist are "folded" back spuriously onto lower-frequency components.

Above 250 Hz, the output frequency decreases linearly with increasing input frequency until at 500 Hz the output frequency is zero. As the frequency increases beyond 500 Hz, the output repeats the pattern that began at zero frequency, reaching a peak of 250 Hz at 750-Hz input and reaching zero again at 1000 Hz.

As discussed in Chap. 3, antialiasing filters are used in the field prior to digitization to remove the frequencies which would be aliased. The antialias filter chosen obviously depends upon the sample rate in effect during digitization. A 2-ms sample rate (500 samples/s) has a Nyquist frequency of 250 Hz. A commonly used antialias filter begins to attenuate frequencies above 125 Hz, and above 250 Hz the reject level is at least 65 dB down (see Fig. 3-8).

z **Transforms**   The *z* transform provides a mathematically convenient means for carrying out convolution and deconvolution of sampled signals with a computer. Using it, one expresses the amplitudes of successive samples taken at uniform intervals as a polynomial in *z*.

The exponent of the variable *z* indicates the time of the sample for which the amplitude constitutes the coefficient. Specifically, the power of *z* is the ordinal number of the sample, and the coefficient for each term is the value of the sample. For example, suppose the seismic signal of Fig. 6-30 is sampled so that at zero time the first amplitude is 1, and successive samples, uniformly spaced, are 4, 3, and 2; then we could express the entire sampled signal in the form

$$F(z) = 1 + 4z + 3z^2 + 2z^3$$

If the signal is convolved with a filter having a response characteristic that can be represented by samples with a corresponding time series, 2, 4, 3, the filter operator can be expressed in the form $g(z) = 2 + 4z + 3z^2$ and we can obtain the output $h(z)$ of the filter by multiplying the polynomials as follows:

$$h(z) = (1 + 4z + 3z^2 + 2z^3)(2 + 4z + 3z^2)$$
$$= 2 + 12z + 25z^2 + 28z^3 + 17z^4 + 6z^5 \qquad (6\text{-}20)$$

The time series for the output is obtained by listing the successive coefficients corresponding to the increasing powers of *z* as follows:

$$2, 12, 25, 28, 17, 6$$

This representation follows from the fact that each exponent of *z* designates the time at which the sample with the amplitude equivalent to its coefficient occurs in the output signal.

Multiplication of the terms corresponding to $f(z)$ with those corresponding to $g(z)$ makes use of the same shift-and-add operations that are carried out in conventional convolution processes.

The *z* transform provides a handy mathematical approach to deconvolution also. If the output signal is to be a spike at time zero, its time-series representation 1, 0, 0, 0, 0, . . . becomes 1 in *z*-transform notation. If the input signal is 1, 0.5 (in *z*-transform notation, $1 + 0.5z$), we can determine the inverse filter function $f(z)$ which when operating on the input will yield a spike as its output.

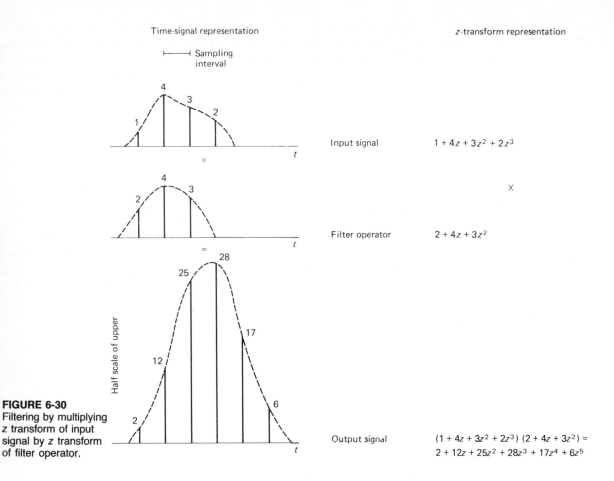

Time-signal representation

z-transform representation

Sampling interval

Input signal $1 + 4z + 3z^2 + 2z^3$

Filter operator $2 + 4z + 3z^2$

Half scale of upper

FIGURE 6-30
Filtering by multiplying
z transform of input
signal by z transform
of filter operator.

Output signal $(1 + 4z + 3z^2 + 2z^3)(2 + 4z + 3z^2) =$
$2 + 12z + 25z^2 + 28z^3 + 17z^4 + 6z^5$

This is a deconvolution operation which can be carried out by simple poly-nomial division as follows. Starting with

$$(1 + 0.5z)f(z) = 1$$

$$f(z) = \frac{1}{1 + 0.5z} \tag{6-21}$$

the function can be approximated by binomial expansion as the polynomial

$$f(z) = 1 - 0.5z + (0.5)^2 z^2 - (0.5)^3 z^3 + (0.5)^4 z^4 + \cdots \tag{6-22}$$

so that the desired inverse filter operator can be specified by the converging time series

$$1, -0.5, 0.25, -0.125, 0.0625, \ldots$$

The convergence indicates that only a limited number of terms is needed to construct a usable filter operator, as later terms in the infinite series become too small to be significant.

z can be set equal to $e^{-i\omega t}$, where $\omega = 2\pi f$, which allows one to relate z transforms to Fourier transforms. z transforms are also useful for determining if a given waveform is minimum phase or not. For further discussion of z transforms see Sheriff,[8,16] Bracewell,[13] and Claerbout.[28]

Recursive Filtering and z Transforms z transforms are used to describe a ghost on seismic data. Once the ghost is so defined, its inverse can be calculated and applied to the data. Recursive filtering uses previously derived values to determine the current output value.

Following Sheriff and Geldart's[8] development, we will start with the time series, $f(t)$, of the down-going source wave train, containing a ghost n time samples after the source; $(1, 0, 0, \ldots, -R, 0, 0, \ldots)$, R being the reflection coefficient at the base of the weathering. The z transform of $f(t)$ is $F(z)$, which equals $(1 - Rz^n)$. The inverse to $F(z)$ is written

$$F^{-1}(z) = \frac{1}{1 - Rz^n} = 1 + Rz^n + (Rz^n)^2 + (Rz^n)^3 + (Rz^n)^4 + \cdots \quad (6\text{-}23)$$

Since R is less than 1, the series converges. A seismic trace containing ghost effects is $g(t)$, with z transform $G(z)$. The convolution of $g(t)$ with the inverse of the ghost filter, $f^{-1}(t)$, can be expressed with z transforms and the convolution theorem as

$$G(z)F^{-1}(z) = H(z) \quad (6\text{-}24)$$

$H(z)$ is the deghosted output. Manipulating the terms, we can rewrite $H(z)$ as

$$H(z) = \frac{G(z)}{1 - Rz^n}$$
$$H(z)(1 - Rz^n) = G(z)$$
$$H(z) - H(z)Rz^n = G(z)$$
$$H(z) - G(z) = H(z)Rz^n \quad (6\text{-}25)$$

In time notation the last equation is written

$$h_t = g_t + Rh_{t-n}$$

A previous output value, h_{t-n}, is scaled, then added to the current value to obtain the output value. This technique of recursive filtering is practical in that not many terms are needed to achieve complete deghosting. z-transform analysis is a powerful processing tool in this and other data-processing tasks.

REFERENCES

1 Salvatori, H., M. J.Wells, and H. Glenn: U.S. Patent No. 3,044,041, July 10, 1962.

2 Savit, C. H., and M. J. Wells: U.S. Patent No. 3,144,651, Aug. 11, 1964.

3 Strange, B. B., and M. J. Wells: Re. 26,574, April 29, 1969.

4 Savit, C. H., T. L. Slaven, and M. J. Wells: U.S. Patent No. 3,289,153, Nov. 29, 1966.

5 Wells, M. J., T. L. Slaven, and C. H. Savit: U.S. Patent No. 3,402,387, Sept. 17, 1968.

6 Cooley, J. W., and J. W. Tukey: An Algorithm for the Machine Calculation of Complex Fourier Series, *Math. Comput.,* vol. 19, pp. 297–301, 1965.

7 Silverman, Daniel: The Digital Processing of Seismic Data, *Geophysics,* vol. 32, pp. 988–1002, 1967.

8 Sheriff, R. E., and L. P. Geldart: "Exploration Seismology," vol. 2, "Data Processing and Interpretation," Cambridge Univ. Press, New York, 1983.

9 Robinson, E. A., and S. Treitel: Principles of Digital Filtering, *Geophysics,* vol. 29, pp. 395–404, 1964.

10 Peterson, Raymond A., and Milton B. Dobrin: "A Pictorial Digital Atlas," United Geophysical Corp., Pasadena, Calif., 1966.

11 Anstey, N. A.: "Signal Characteristics and Instrument Specifications," vol. 1 of "Seismic Prospecting Instruments," Borntraeger, Berlin, 1970.

12 Yilmaz, Ozdogan: "Seismic Data Processing," Society of Exploration Geophysicists, Tulsa, Okla., 1987.

13 Bracewell, R.: "The Fourier Transform and Its Applications," McGraw-Hill, New York, 1965.

14 Taner, M. T., and R. E. Sheriff: Application of Amplitude Frequency and Other Attributes to Stratigraphic and Hydrocarbon Determination, pp. 301–328, in "Seismic Stratigraphy—Applications to Hydrocarbon Exploration," (ed., C. E. Payton), AAPG Memoir 26, Tulsa, Okla., 1977.

15 Taner, M. T., F. Koehler, and R. E. Sheriff: Complex Seismic Trace Analysis, *Geophysics,* vol. 44, pp. 1041–1063, 1979.

16 Sheriff, R. E. (compiler): "Encyclopedic Dictionary of Exploration Geophysics," 2d ed., Society of Exploration Geophysicists, Tulsa, Okla., 1984.

17 Robinson, Enders A., and Sven Treitel: Principles of Digital Wiener Filtering, *Geophys. Prospec.,* vol. 15, pp. 311–333, 1967.

18 Foster, M. R., R. L. Sengbush, and R. J. Watson: Design of Sub-Optimum Filter Systems for Multi-Trace Seismic Data Processing, *Geophys. Prospec.,* vol. 12, pp. 173–191, 1964.

19 Wadsworth, G. P., E. A. Robinson, J. G. Bryan, and P. N. Hurley: Detection of Reflections on Seismic Records by Linear Operators, *Geophysics,* vol. 18, pp. 539–586, 1953.

20 Lines, L. R., and S. Treitel: Tutorial: A Review of Least-Squares Inversion and Its Application to Geophysical Problems, *Geophys. Prospec.,* vol. 32, pp. 159–186, 1984.

21 Embree, Peter, John P. Burg, and Milo M. Backus: Wide-Band Velocity Filtering: The Pie-Slice Process, *Geophysics,* vol. 28, pp. 948–974, 1963.

22 Cassano, E., and F. Rocca: After-Stack Multichannel Filters without Mixing Effects, *Geophy. Prospec.,* vol. 22, pp. 330–344, 1974.

23 Swartz, C. A., and V. M. Sokoloff: Filtering Associated with Selective Sampling of Geophysical Data, *Geophysics,* vol. 19, pp. 402–419, 1954.

24 Gimlin, D. R., and J. W. Smith: A Comparison of Seismic Trace Summing Techniques, *Geophysics,* vol. 45, pp. 1017–1041, 1980.

25 Neidell, N. S.: Stratigraphic Modeling and Interpretation: Geophysical Principles and Techniques, *Am. Assoc. Petrol. Geol. Education Course Note Series #13,* Tulsa, Okla., 1984.

26 Nyquist, H.: Certain Topics in Telegraph Transmission Theory, *Trans. A.I.E.E.,* vol. 47, pp. 617–644, 1928.

27 Whittaker, E. T.: On the Functions Which Are Represented by Expansion of Interpolation Theory, *Proc. Roy. Soc. Edinburgh,* vol. 35, 1915.

28 Claerbout, Jon F.: "Imaging the Earth's Interior," Blackwell Scientific, Palo Alto, Calif., 1984.

CHAPTER 7

SEISMIC-DATA PROCESSING

This chapter will present the components of seismic-data processing. No actual computer programs will be developed. Our object is to explain the digital processing tools used in seismic-data processing and the geophysical problems that can be solved with typically available hardware and software. Hardware and software are, however, continually being updated. The latest developments in seismic-data processing (and all aspects of geophysical exploration) are presented at the annual convention of the Society of Exploration Geophysicists, to which we refer those interested. The Expanded Abstracts from the national SEG conventions are the record of the technical presentations and are thus a valuable source for state-of-the-art techniques and information.

Seismic-data processing is composed of basically five types of corrections and adjustments: time, amplitude, frequency-phase content, data compressing (stacking), and data positioning (migration). These adjustments increase the signal-to-noise ratio, correct the data for various physical processes that obscure the desired (geologic) information of the seismic data, and reduce the volume of data that the geophysicist must analyze.

The geologic information desired from seismic data is the shape and relative position of the geologic formations of interest. In areas of good data quality it is possible to produce estimates of the lithology based upon velocity information. From the amplitudes of reflections, it is even possible to make estimates of the pore constituents, since gas accumulations often generate amplitude anomalies. Knowing the shape of the structures at depth allows oil company explorationists to assign probabilities of finding commercially exploitable hydrocarbons in the area surveyed. The velocities of seismic waves in the earth can be derived from seismic data or measured in wells, and they are used to convert the known reflection times into estimated reflector depth. We shall present a brief overview of the five types of corrections, followed by the expanded discussion.

Time adjustments fall into two categories: static and dynamic. Static time corrections shift a whole trace. The correction is constant over time. Dynamic time corrections (normal moveout) are a function of both time and offset and convert the times of the reflections into coincidence with those that would have been recorded at zero offset, that is, to what would have been recorded if source and receiver were located at the same point.

Amplitude adjustments correct the amplitude decay with time due to spherical divergence and energy dissipation in the earth. There are two broad types of amplitude gain programs: structural amplitude gaining or automatic gain control (AGC), and relative true amplitude gain correction. The first scales amplitudes to be nearly alike and is generally chosen for structural mapping purposes. The second attempts to keep the relative amplitude information so that the amplitude anomalies associated with facies changes, porosity variations, and gaseous hydrocarbons are preserved.

The frequency-phase content of the data is manipulated to enhance signal and attenuate noise. Appropriate bandpass filters (one-channel filtering) can be selected by reference to frequency scans of the data which aid in determining the frequency content of the signals. Deconvolution is the inverse filtering technique used to compress an oscillatory (long) source waveform, often seen on marine data, into as near a spike (unit-impulse function) as possible. Ghosts, seafloor multiples, and near-surface reverberations can often be attenuated through deconvolution approaches. Many deconvolution techniques use the autocorrelation of the trace to design an inverse operator that removes undesirable, predictable energy.

The data-compression technique generally used is the common midpoint (CMP) stack. It sums all offsets of a CMP gather into one trace. Forty-eight- to 96-fold stacks are common. Conventional 2-D seismic data initially exist in a 3-D space: the three axes are time, offset, and a coordinate x along the line of survey. Three-dimensional data consist initially of a 4-D data set; the coordinates being time, offset, and two horizontal spatial coordinates, x and y. Stacking compresses the offset axis onto the zero offset, which lies on the midpoint axis.

The data-positioning adjustment is migration. Migration moves energy from its CMP position to its proper spatial location. In the presence of dip, the CMP location is not the true subsurface location of the reflection (Fig. 10-10). Migration collapses diffractions to foci, increases the visual spatial resolution, and corrects amplitudes for geometric focusing effects and spatial smearing. Migration techniques have been developed for application pre-stack, post-stack, or a combination of both.

An overview chart of seismic-data processing is given in Fig. 7-1.

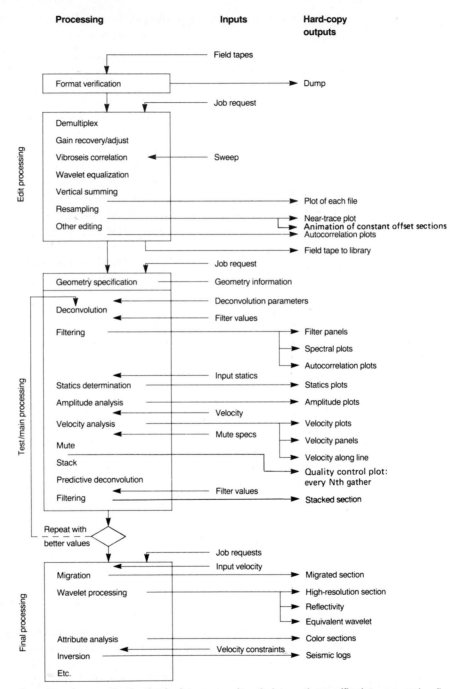

FIGURE 7-1 Overview of generalized seismic-data processing. A data set's specific data-processing flow will be tailored to handle the requirements and problems of the individual data set. (*Modified from Sheriff and Geldart[2]*).

7-1 DEMULTIPLEX, GEOMETRY SPECIFICATION, AND OTHER FRONT-END PROCESSING

Field tapes customarily arrive at the processing center written in multiplexed format because that is the way the sampling is usually done in the field— successive samples on the tape represent the succession of channels at the same instant in time. Multiplexed data thus use time, not channel, as the primary index. In general, the early stages of processing (geometry description, statics, etc.) require channel-ordered, or trace-ordered, data. Demultiplex is thus the first step in processing. The data samples for shot 1, group 1 are assembled in the order of increasing time and output first, then the corresponding samples for shot 1, group 2, and so forth, to create the output demultiplexed data set. Samples corresponding to times beyond a preselected maximum (typically 6 s) are not included. This output organization of data is a *common-shot gather* or a *field record* because the source location is common to the first N channels of data. Later processing steps will rearrange the data for efficient processing to "common-receiver" ordered data or "common-midpoint" ordered data, in which receiver location or source-receiver midpoint is the major sort index.

The layout of receivers for each shot record, the location of all shots along the line, and all such field information must be described in detail to the computer for the geometry-specification step. Most geometry programs can access the digitized base-map file. Computer access is particularly necessary for processing crooked lines in which sources and receivers are not uniformly distributed along a straight traverse. The geometry program must calculate a source-receiver midpoint based on the two ground locations, not by selecting the arithmetic mean of the source-receiver indices. All relevant geometric information is retained in the trace headers on the tape so that each trace is uniquely and accurately located. Later programs will time shift or filter as a function of ground location, offset, and/or other spatial coordinate(s) and time.

Noisy traces are zeroed, and various quality checks are made on the data. If vibroseis data were cross-correlated with the pilot recorded on each record, the autocorrelations of each pilot used across the line are checked for consistency. A near-trace plot yields single-fold coverage across the line for a first look at the data, the geologic structures present, and noisy areas. If resampling (usually to a coarser time rate) is desired, it can be done now. Seismic signals are generally sampled at either 1-, 2-, or 4-ms intervals, 2 ms being most common with marine data. During processing a seismic sample is usually expressed in a floating-point, 32-bit word, 24 bits for the mantissa, 8 bits for exponent and sign. In Sec. 7-8, a data-reduction step usually performed at the start of data processing is presented: array forming and beam steering.

7-2 DECONVOLUTION AND FILTERING

As previously pointed out in Chaps. 5 and 6, the purpose of deconvolution is to remove undesirable filtering effects introduced in the process of acquisition and in passage through the earth. By passing through the earth and the instruments, the (desired) simple reflection pulses from subsurface interfaces change, becoming more complicated and broadened. It is desired that the end product of deconvolution be reflection signals that are simple wavelets with the shortest duration allowed by the earth's absorption characteristics. Mathematically, the ideal reflection signal is an impulse (spike) of finite energy and minimal time duration. Figure 6-23 illustrated the undesirable effects of a long or complicated source waveform.

Deterministic Inverse Filtering

In certain cases, the distorting filter is known fairly explicitly, and its inverse can be calculated directly. Most deconvolution of marine data falls in this category and is carried out for two purposes: (1) to compress a long source waveform, and (2) to cancel irregularities superimposed on the spectrum of the reflected signal by reverberation in the water layer. These two purposes can be accomplished by convolving the recorded data with a filter operator that is the inverse of the undesired filter. Another known distorting filter is that of the recording system. The distortions we wish to remove are usually the phase-shifting effects of the system, which is why applying its inverse is often called *dephasing* the data.

For marine data, an attempt is often made to record the source waveform. Usually, however, the source waveform must be synthesized from a selection of observed parameters and some geometric assumptions (see Dragoset[1]). Convolution of each shot record with the inverse of its source waveform compresses long source waveforms and can correct for shot-to-shot variations (gun misfires, etc.). If the seafloor is reasonably deep and its reflection is a simple one, a procedure is available to determine the source waveform from that reflection. Figure 6-22 shows the effect of a typcial deconvolution on a section in which the reflection information is seriously obscured by marine reverberations.

Reverberation in near-surface layers and ghosting (see Sec. 6-3) modify the waveforms of down-traveling and emerging seismic impulses and, as such, are filtering mechanisms within the earth. In the case of a reflection pulse returning from the subsurface, the spectrum of the wave reaching the layer from below is multiplied by the spectrum associated with the reverberation system. Figure 7-2 shows how a wavelet spectrum would be changed by multiple reverberations within a water layer overlying a hard bottom. For $T = 40$ ms, the reverberatory marine system has its frequency characteristic illustrated in Fig. 5-14. Section 5-6 discussed the calculation of the frequency spectrum of a reverberatory system for a given water depth.

Predictive Deconvolution

Predictive deconvolution uses the autocorrelation of a trace to ascertain the periodicities within the data. The geophysicist determines from the autocor-

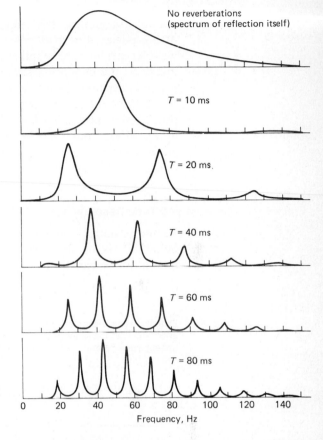

No reverberations
(spectrum of reflection itself)

$T = 10$ ms

$T = 20$ ms

$T = 40$ ms

$T = 60$ ms

$T = 80$ ms

Frequency, Hz

FIGURE 7-2 Spectra of reverberating pulses in water layer. T is two-way "thickness" (in time) of layer. (*From F. J. McDonal and R. L. Sengbush, Proc. 7th World Petrol. Congr. Mexico, vol. 2, p. 591, 1967.*)

relation(s) the necessary operator length, usually a few hundred milliseconds, that will span the significant reverberation-caused energy on the autocorrelation, and a gap, or delay time after the zero lag value. The autocorrelation values after the gap for the length of the operator constitute the timing information of the reverberations that will be predicted (see Fig. 6-19). The filter designed from the autocorrelation, when convolved with the data trace, predicts reverberations and multiples. The predicted trace is subtracted from the observed trace to give the prediction error, which should be the trace with the predicted reverberations and multiples removed. Primaries are considered unpredictable, so they remain, while the (predictable) reverberations and multiples are removed. The prediction-error trace is output as the result of the process. Use of the earlier part of a seismic trace to predict and ultimately deconvolve the latter part of the trace gave rise to the name of the process. For a mathematical development of predictive deconvolution, see Sheriff and Geldart.[2]

Spiking Deconvolution   Spiking deconvolution is a type of predictive deconvolution in which the operator is to predict (and thus remove) energy starting within a sample or two, or at the first zero crossing, after the zero lag value of the autocorrelation. The effect of this type of filter is to concentrate the energy of the pulse as near as possible to the front of the wavelet, i.e., to turn the wavelet into as near a spike as possible. As with all predictive deconvolution methods, the data are assumed to be minimum phase. The earth's reflectivity series is assumed to be random (i.e., knowledge of the amplitude and time of the shallow reflections does not help in predicting those values for the deeper reflections) and the earth's impulse response to be minimum phase. Data from an explosive source are thought to be approximately minimum phase, while correlated data from a vibroseis source are supposed to be more nearly zero phase.

Frequency Spectrum and Time Resolution

As the frequency content of reflections with which we work is seldom much below 10 Hz or above 90 Hz, the frequency spectrum representing the best resolution we can normally expect consists of a pair of rectangles lying between

FIGURE 7-3 Determination using convolution theorem of waveform corresponding to a symmetrical frequency spectrum with flat response from 10 to 90 Hz and sharp cutoffs at both limits. Narrowness of resultant pulse (upper right) should result in good resolution.

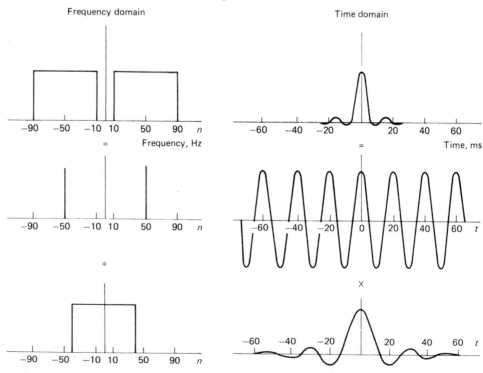

these limits on the positive and negative sides of the frequency axis, as shown in Fig. 7-3. This spectrum can be obtained by convolving the transform of an infinitely long cosine wave having a frequency of 50 Hz with a rectangular frequency function 80 Hz in breadth. The time signal corresponding to the rectangular frequency function is a sinc function with a central peak 0.025 s wide having side bands 0.0125 s in breadth. Multiplying this by a cosine wave with a period of 0.020 s (the reciprocal of 50 Hz) results in a pulse 0.010 s wide at its first zero crossings. This waveform represents the best resolution that can be expected from a reflection signal traveling in a medium that passes frequencies from 10 to 90 Hz.

To illustrate how the principle operates in an actual case, let us consider the spectrum observed from shallow-water shooting shown in Fig. 7-4 (along with the waveform on which it is based). The sharp peak at about 38 Hz is about

FIGURE 7-4   Waveforms and spectra of reflection signal from North Sea before (input) and after deconvolution (output). (*Spectra from D. W. Rockwell, Geophysics, vol. 32, p. 262, 1967. Waveforms computed from spectra assuming minimum phase.*)

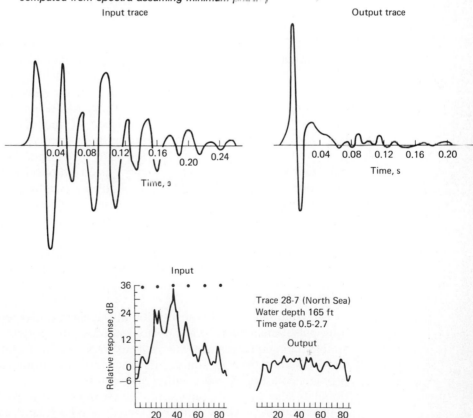

25 Hz broad at its base. This peak frequency corresponds to an oscillation period of 0.026 s, which is in the neighborhood of what is observed on the record. After deconvolution, the peak is removed, and an essentially flat (white) spectrum is observed from 15 to 80 Hz. Assuming vertical cutoffs at these frequencies, we would expect that seismic pulses would have a breadth approximately equal to the zero-to-zero width of the central peak of the sinc function corresponding to a rectangular frequency curve 65 cycles wide. The expected breadth, which is twice the reciprocal of this value, is about 0.030 s. The portion of the seismic record obtained after deconvolution shows discrete pulses about as wide as predicted.

Peaking in the frequency spectrum due to repetition of signals by multiple reflection is most prevalent in but not confined to water layers. Any other layering with strong reflection coefficients at both top and bottom can give rise to pronounced reverberation effects. Permafrost, which generally is characterized by a seismic velocity much higher than that of the underlying unfrozen rock material, is responsible for strong ringing effects observed on reflection records shot on the North Slope of Alaska. The physical mechanism is quite similar to that for water-layer reverberation in the case of a soft bottom.

Spectral Whitening and Temporal Resolution

The optimum ''wavelet'' on band-limited seismic data is a spike of small duration. A spike of infinitesimal duration has a frequency spectrum that is ''white''; i.e., components at all frequencies from plus to minus infinity have equal amplitudes. The earth's reflectivity series (response) is often viewed as random, thus implying a spectrum in which all frequencies are equally probable. Consequently, a spike of small duration convolved with the earth's (random) reflectivity series will have a white (flat) spectrum over the seismic bandwidth. When the actual frequency spectrum of the data can be converted to ''whiteness'' by introduction of a suitable inverse filter, and provided that all reflections are minimum phase, the principle of Fourier transformation tells us that all reflection events will more nearly approach spikes and the greatest conceivable resolution in reflection character will be achieved. This step, often termed *time-variant, spectral whitening*, can significantly improve both the signal-to-noise ratio (S/N) and the temporal resolution of the data. There are many different ways to perform this task, each organization having its own proprietary method.

Attenuation caused by absorption in the earth of the less-than-millisecond-long pulse emanating from the shot broadens the pulse to the point where a simple reflection signal will have a measurable width after it has traveled only a short distance from its source. Its frequency spectrum, no longer white, approximates a square wave with a high cutoff at a frequency inversely proportional to the width of the pulse, which might be looked upon as a crude approximation to a sinc function. Once the high frequencies (in the kilohertz range) are removed (i.e., reduced to a level below that of ambient noise) by absorption, they cannot, of course, be restored by any kind of inverse filtering. It is possible, however, to obtain a spectrum by inverse filtering that is approximately white over the seismic bandwidth (approximately 10 to 90 Hz), a bandwidth that can normally be transmitted through substantial thickness of sedimentary rocks: the wider the zone of flatness in the spectrum, the narrower the corresponding wave pulse and the better the overall resolution.

Not only is the high end of the frequency spectrum not recorded, but also the lowest frequencies (0 to 4 or 8 Hz) are not recorded or are greatly attenuated. Geophones do not record energy from 0 to about 4 or 5 Hz with fidelity. Also, vibrators cannot mechanically input frequencies less than about 4 to 6 Hz. It would, however, be desirable to retain the low end of the spectrum in seismic data so that inversion techniques (which convert seismic traces into pseudosonic logs) could replicate the "blocky" appearance of sonic logs. (See Chap. 9 for further discussion of inversion.)

Adaptive Deconvolution and Other Time-Variant Deconvolution Techniques

The deconvolution techniques discussed above assume a time-invariant wavelet, i.e., that the statistics of the waveshape do not change with time (stationarity). There are, however, various physical processes that do lengthen or change the wavelet with time, such as the attenuation of higher frequencies with time, and the addition of "peg-leg" multiples. It is possible continuously to update the statistics upon which the prediction filter is based, and thus to change the prediction filter to allow for a time-variant wavelet. Burg[3] has developed an adaptive deconvolution program effective on seismic data. A data set with predictable primary reflections, for example, cyclically bedded suites, would not be handled properly by an adaptive deconvolution program—the program will remove all predictable energy. Also, adaptive deconvolution can be expensive in computer time.

A simpler time-variant deconvolution approach is to determine an operator based on an early portion of the data and another based on the later portion of data, with each portion being 1 s or longer to allow valid estimates of the periodicities present. The early operator is applied from time zero to the center (or end) of its design window; there is a merge zone between the two design windows in which the weight of an operator is a ramp function of its distance from its design window; and the later operator is applied in the lower portion of the data. Care should be exercised to center a design window around the target zone and not put the target zone(s) within merge zones. If a deconvolution operator does a good job in its design window as well as away from its design window, time-variant deconvolution would not appear to be necessary. If a deconvolution operator does a poor job away from its design window, a time-variant approach could be considered. If a deconvolution operator performs poorly throughout the entire trace (which is often its design window), the geophysicist might suspect that changing periodicities and/or a changing wavelet presented (unsurmounted) difficulties in building the prediction filter.

Wavelet Processing or Wavelet Shaping

Wavelet processing is "a variety of different processes which involve determining, assuming, or operating on the effective wavelet shape . . . to: 1. attempt to make the wavelet shape everywhere the same; 2. change the effective wavelet shape to some 'more desirable' shape, or; 3. endeavor to separate the earth's reflectivity from wavelet shape effects" (p. 44 in Sheriff and Geldart[2]). Some types of wavelet shaping, for example, deconvolution to compress a long marine source waveform, are done early in the flow, other types are done later (Fig. 7-1). A phase-shifting filter which removes the phase shifts induced by the recording instruments, geophones, and/or cable, is a type of wavelet-shaping process. In the last stage of processing, one widespread wavelet-processing technique is to zero-phase the data so that the basic wavelet approximates a symmetric wavelet with the energy concentrated in the center lobe. An example of some stacked data before and after wavelet processing is given in Fig. 7-5, from Wood.[4] Here, a deterministic approach was used, one in which well logs from the well close to the line were needed in order to determine the reflectivity series. "The reflectivity series was correlated with the field data traces nearest the well to extract the wavelet. Once the wavelet was estimated, an inverse filter can be designed and applied to the field data to convert the wavelet's phase to zero" (p. 77 in Wood[4]). A statistical approach to wavelet processing would not require the use of well data, but would generally make some assumption concerning the phase of the data (e.g., minimum phase, etc.). A further discussion of wavelet processing is in Chap. 9.

Bandpass Filtering

Bandpass filtering is designed to pass signal and reject noise. Filter scans are generated from the data, in which many different narrow, bandpass filters are applied and the results plotted (see Fig. 7-6). The geophysicist designs the final filter to pass the frequencies containing coherent energy (reflections) and to reject those frequencies containing mostly noise and no apparent reflections.

Time-variant filters are often applied to the data in order to pass higher frequencies shallow in the section and lower frequencies at greater depths.

Velocity Filtering

Coherent noise was discussed in Chap. 4, since it is a chief reason for the use of source and receiver arrays. It was mentioned that processing techniques are also used to attenuate coherent noise. Velocity filtering (also termed pie-slice or *f-k* filtering, see Sec. 6-3) discriminates either against or for such linear

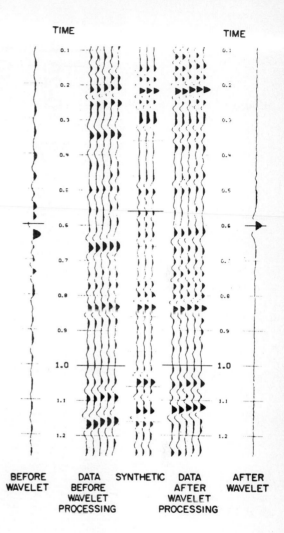

FIGURE 7-5 Illustration of wavelet processing. The well logs near this location were used to calculate the reflectivity series of the earth. The wavelet present on the field data was determined (shown on the left), its inverse estimated and applied to the field data, with the result shown on the right. Note the significant improvement in the match of the synthetic (in which a zero-phase wavelet was used) to the wavelet processed field data. (*From Wood*.)[4]

arrivals on reflection data. (Beam steering, or array forming, is another processing technique to attenuate coherent noise; it is discussed in Sec. 7-8.) Linear arrivals have either "positive" or "negative" dip; program documentation specifies how to determine the sign of the dip. A velocity filter can pass or reject dips of either or both signs. Most of the time, the linear events are rejected because they are ground roll (or other coherent noise). In certain circumstances, such as refraction statics, discussed later, the refracted waves, linear arrivals, are the signals sought, so velocity filtering can be used to enhance such signals by attenuating all other energy.

Velocity filtering can be done in either the time domain or the frequency domain. The derivation of the time-domain operator can be accomplished by solving a set of equations in $f\text{-}k$ space, as demonstrated by Cassano and Rocca.[5]

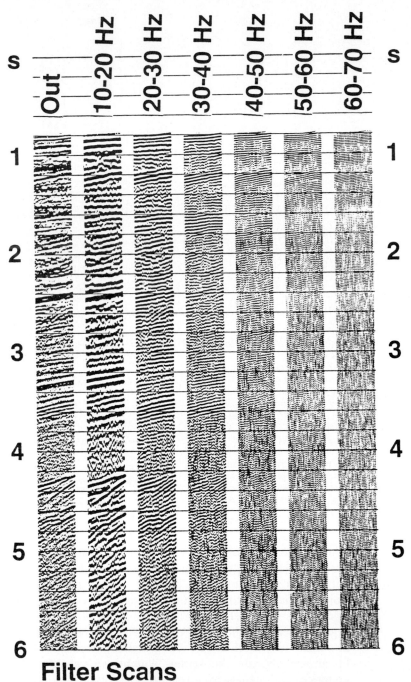

Filter Scans

FIGURE 7-6   Example of filter scans (right) on raw field data (left). The bandpass of the filter used for each panel is annotated at the head of each panel. The low-frequency signals are at least 10 Hz (and probably lower). The high-cut of the filter should be time-variant here: higher than 60–70 Hz could be cut after 1.5 s; higher than 50–60 Hz could be cut after 1.5 s; higher than 50–60 Hz could be cut after 2.4 s; higher than 40–50 Hz could be cut after 4 s. (*Western Geophysical*.)

An example of a time-domain operator is found in Fig. 6-27. Figure 7-7 provides a field data example of velocity filtering in the frequency domain. The marine field record (Fig. 7-7a) and its f-k transform (Fig. 7-7c) contain strong coherent noise. f-k filtering will reject a pie-slice-shaped region near or around the wave-number axis and pass pie-slice-shaped regions centered on the frequency axis. The fan boundary is shown by the radiating lines (Fig. 7-7d). Care is taken to make the fan widths not too narrow and to have a gentle transition (taper) from reject zone to pass zone. The field data result is Fig. 7-7b.

Velocity filtering is also used in multiple suppression, as will be discussed in Sec. 7-6, where velocities and normal moveout are presented.

Velocity filtering works on events sufficiently sampled in space. Occasionally, coherent noise is spatially aliased. Spatial aliasing is undersampling in space, that is, sampling less than two samples per spatial wavelength. Certain trace-interpolation schemes, not using Fourier-transform techniques, can generate enough traces between the input traces so as to create sufficiently sampled data. The interpolated data set can then be velocity filtered.

7-3   GEOMETRY OF REFLECTION PATHS

Geometrical versus Physical Optics in Seismic Analysis

In Chap. 2 we considered the physical processes involved in the reflection of seismic waves at an interface between rocks having different elastic constants and presumbly different lithologies. The percentage of the seismic energy reflected at such an interface was shown to depend on the acoustic impedances (products of velocity and density) of the materials on respective sides of the interface and the angle of incidence of the down-going wave. At normal incidence, the amplitude of the reflection is simply proportional to the difference between these acoustic impedances divided by their sum, the relation becoming more complex at oblique angles of incidence, as shown in Fig. 2-15.

When there is a series of interfaces separating individual formations having different velocities and the distances between the interfaces are large compared with the seismic wavelengths employed, a separate reflection should theoretically be observed from each interface, although this does not always occur for a number of reasons to be discussed later.

The times required for the waves to travel from a near-surface source to the reflectors and back to receivers on the surface are used, along with all available information on seismic velocities, to determine the structure of the reflecting surface. This process forms the geometrical basis for the reductions used with the reflection method.

Actually, the separations of individual reflecting interfaces in the earth are often much smaller than a seismic wavelength, so that resolution of reflections from every lithological boundary in the geologic section would require the input of additional geologic information (see Sec. 9-2; and Gelfand and Larner[6]). In considering the ray-path geometry of seismic reflections, we shall initially work with models of discrete interfaces that are separated from adjacent boundaries

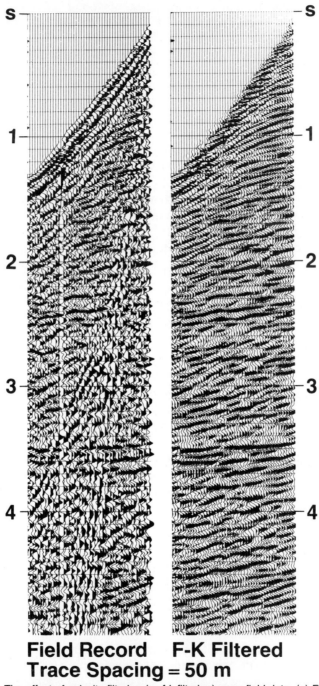

Field Record   F-K Filtered
Trace Spacing = 50 m

FIGURE 7-7   The effect of velocity-filtering (or *f-k* filtering) upon field data. (a) Field record, unfiltered. (b) *f-k* filtered field record. (c) Frequency-domain representation of field data before filtering, and (d) after filtering. The portions of *fk* space below the line, containing noise were reduced or zeroed [see (d)], so that, upon 2-D Fourier transformation back into *tx* space, only reflected signals remained (b). (*Western Geophysical.*)

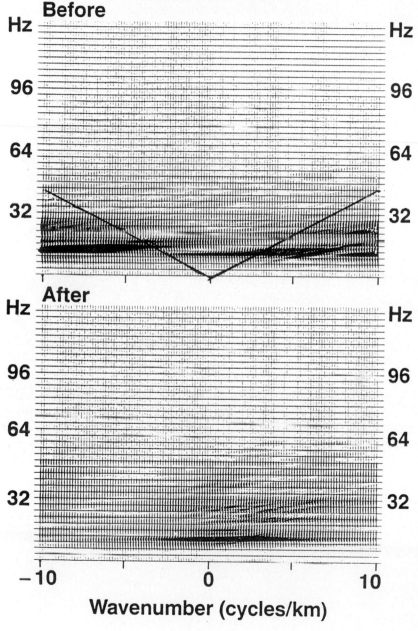

**F-K Dip Filtering
2D Amplitude Spectra**

by distances large compared with seismic wavelengths. In the next chapter we shall consider the more usual case of boundaries that are closer together than a wavelength. Both physical optics and geometrical optics must be taken into account in the interpretation of seismic reflections from this more complex kind of layering.

Reflection from Horizontal Surfaces   Let us assume a horizontal reflecting interface, as shown in Fig. 7-8, at a depth z below the earth's surface. The seismic velocity above the interface is V_0, and that below is V_1. The path of a reflected wave generated at the shot point and received by a detector at a distance, x, consists, as indicated in the diagram, of two rectilinear segments that have traveled from the surface to the reflecting interface and back to the surface. The total path length L is related to x and z by the formula

$$L = 2\sqrt{z^2 + \left(\frac{x}{2}\right)^2} = V_0 T \qquad (7\text{-}1)$$

where T is the total travel time. For a horizontal reflector (z = constant) it is evident that the relation of T to x is hyperbolic. Solving for T, we have

$$T = \frac{2}{V_0}\sqrt{z^2 + \left(\frac{x}{2}\right)^2} \qquad (7\text{-}2)$$

Similarly,

$$z = \tfrac{1}{2}\sqrt{(V_0 T)^2 - x^2} \qquad (7\text{-}3)$$

Figure 7-9 shows the relation between travel time and horizontal distance for this reflected ray. The curve is a symmetrical one in this case of a flat interface, as it holds for negative as well as positive values of x, the portion corresponding to the negative values not being shown. The axis of symmetry of the hyperbola

FIGURE 7-8   Wave reflected from single interface. Speed constant at V_0 between source and reflecting surface.

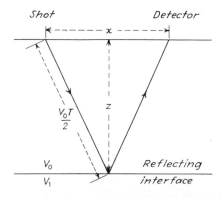

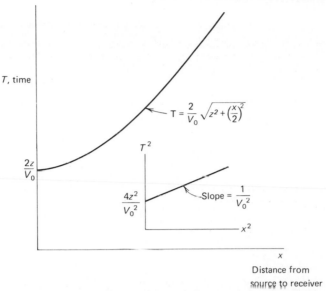

T, time

$$T = \frac{2}{V_0}\sqrt{z^2 + \left(\frac{x}{2}\right)^2}$$

T^2

$\frac{2z}{V_0}$

$\frac{4z^2}{V_0^2}$

Slope $= \dfrac{1}{V_0^2}$

x^2

x

Distance from
source to receiver

FIGURE 7-9   Time-distance relation for a wave reflected from a horizontal surface at depth z in a medium of constant velocity V_0. Inset shows linear relation between square of time and square of distance.

representing the relationship is the line $x = 0$. The inset shows the linearity between T^2 and x^2 that results from squaring Eq. (7-1). The velocity V_0 can readily be determined from the slope of the line thus obtained.

As the inclination of the down-going ray decreases (the angle with the vertical increases), the down-traveling ray eventually approaches the boundary at the critical angle, $\sin^{-1}(V_0/V_1)$. At angles smaller than critical, a large proportion of the energy in the wave is transmitted (refracted) downward into the layer below the interface, as shown in Fig. 2-14. At critical-angle incidence, the refracted wave travels horizontally along the boundary at the speed of the underlying medium. At any greater angle of incidence, there is total reflection, and the wave does not penetrate into the lower material at all. Reflection continues to take place at angles greater than the critical angle, but it is evident from Fig. 7-10 that the ray refracted horizontally along the interface that is returned to the surface at the critical angle will reach a distant point on the surface before the reflected wave reaches the same point. Up to the distance x_{cross} which is shown on the diagram, the direct waves that have taken a horizontal path along the earth's surface will be the first events to arrive.

The depth z can be determined from the time-distance relation for the waves returned to the surface after refraction along the interface. This is the basis of the seismic refraction method, which will be discussed later in this chapter in connection with refraction statics. Refraction statics, or "first break statics," uses refraction theory and the first arrivals to determine the nature of the low-speed weathered zone just below the earth's surface.

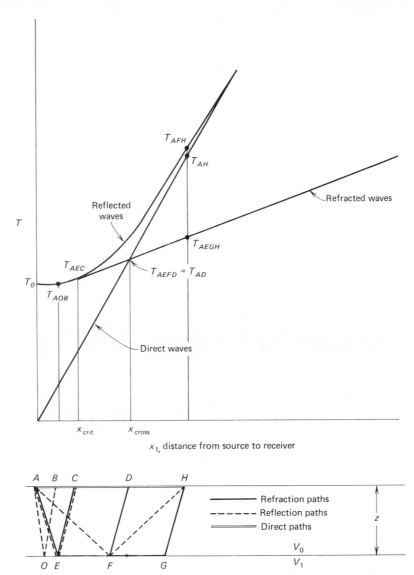

FIGURE 7-10 Relation between times for waves reflected and refracted from a horizontal interface. Times for direct wave also shown.

The above discussions of propagating seismic waves use ray theory, not wave theory. Ray theory follows the methodology of geometric optics and is dependent on the assumption that waves propagating in a medium have wavelengths that are small compared to the distances and dimensions involved in the problem. Reflecting surfaces are assumed to be specular, that is, mirrorlike or perfectly smooth. Ray theory adequately calculates travel times for propagating waves, but not amplitudes or phases. Wave theory handles all three quan-

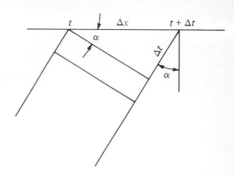

FIGURE 7-11   Determination of emergence angle α.

tities. Modeling (the forward problem), migration (one type of the inverse problem), and other inverse programs can be based either on ray theory or wave theory. Wave-theoretical calculations cost substantially more than do ray-theoretical ones. Ray-theoretical programs are used if only the time of the wave is needed; wave-theoretical are used if the time and amplitude and phase of the wave are needed. The complete theory for the wave-theoretical inverse problem has not yet been worked out. (The "inverse problem" is defined in Sec. 9-2.)

Angle of Emergence   The angle at which a seismic wave returned by reflection or refraction reaches the earth's surface, generally referred to as the *angle of emergence* α, can be determined from the difference Δt between the arrival times at two nearby receivers a distance Δx apart along the surface (Fig. 7-11):

$$\sin \alpha = \frac{V \Delta t}{\Delta x} = V \frac{dt}{dx} \quad \text{as } \Delta x \to 0 \tag{7-4}$$

where V is the velocity at the surface. A knowledge of this angle makes it possible to trace the ray toward its source, allowing calculation of the dip of the reflecting or refracting boundary from which it comes to the surface. The value of dt/dx can be determined by taking the slope of the time-distance curve at the receiving point.

Reflections from Dipping Beds

Let us consider the case of a reflecting surface, as shown in Fig. 7-12, dipping at an angle ϕ and underlying a homogeneous medium having a velocity V_0. The source is at O, and receivers are located on both sides of it as shown. The shot and geophones are laid out in a split-spread arrangement, as described in Chap. 4.

Above the cross section showing the wave paths is a plot of reflection times as a function of distance along the line. The path lengths for the reflection are

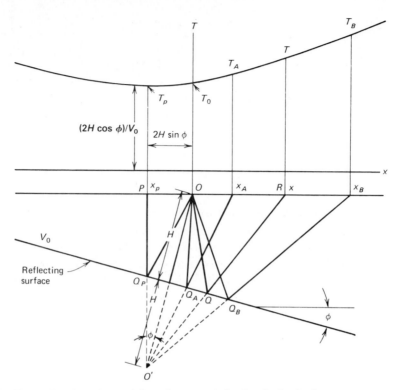

FIGURE 7-12 Ray-path trajectories and time-distance relation for dipping bed.

best determined by locating the mirror-image point O' along the perpendicular to the reflecting surface a distance below the surface equal to the distance H.

Consider the path OQR, which is equal to $O'QR$, where R is a distance x from the source O, the origin of our coordinate system. From the law of cosines we can write

$$
\begin{aligned}
(V_0 T)^2 &= (2H)^2 + x^2 - 2(2H)x \cos(90° + \phi) \\
&= 4H^2 + x^2 + 4Hx \sin \phi
\end{aligned}
\tag{7-5}
$$

This can be shown to be the equation of a hyperbola whose vertical axis of symmetry passes through the point P (shown on the upper part of Fig. 7-12) having the coordinates

$$
x_p = -2H \sin \phi \quad \text{and} \quad T_p = \frac{2H \cos \phi}{V_0}
\tag{7-6}
$$

This displacement in the updip direction of the minimum-time position on the x scale as well as the minimum-time values can be used to determine the dip angle ϕ. Dividing the first part of Eq. (7-6) by the second, we get

$$\tan \phi = - V_0 \frac{x_p}{T_p} \qquad (7\text{-}7)$$

The tangent is negative only because of the sign convention chosen. If the dip were in the opposite direction, it would be positive.

Another way of measuring dip from these data is to observe the reflection times T_A and T_B at distances x_A and x_B, respectively, as shown in Fig. 7-12. Substituting these times in Eq. (7-5), we get

$$\begin{aligned} (V_0 T_A)^2 &= (2H)^2 + x_A^2 + 4Hx_A \sin \phi \\ (V_0 T_B)^2 &= (2H)^2 + x_B^2 + 4Hx_B \sin \phi \end{aligned} \qquad (7\text{-}8)$$

We then subtract the first of these equations from the second, getting

$$V_0^2(T_B^2 - T_A^2) = (x_B^2 - x_A^2) + 4H(x_B - x_A) \sin \phi \qquad (7\text{-}9)$$

so that

$$\begin{aligned} \sin \phi &= V_0^2 \frac{(T_B^2 - T_A^2)}{4H(x_B - x_A)} - \frac{x_B^2 - x_A^2}{4H(x_B - x_A)} \\ &= \frac{V_0^2(T_B^2 - T_A^2)}{4H(x_B - x_A)} - \frac{x_B + x_A}{4H} \end{aligned} \qquad (7\text{-}10)$$

If $(T_A + T_B)/2$, the average of T_A and T_B, is designated as T_{av}, the time difference $T_B - T_A$ as ΔT, and $2H$ as $V_0 T_0$, where T_0 is the time of a reflection received at the shot point ($x = 0$), we can write Eq. (7-10) in the form

$$\sin \phi = \frac{V_0 T_{av} \Delta T}{T_0 (x_B - x_A)} - \frac{x_B + x_A}{2V_0 T_0} \qquad (7\text{-}11)$$

If receiver A is located at the shot point ($x_A = 0$),

$$\sin \phi = \frac{V_0 T_{av} \Delta T}{x_B T_0} - \frac{x_B}{2V_0 T_0} \qquad (7\text{-}12)$$

If the reflecting bed is flat ($\phi = 0$), $\sin \phi = 0$ and the time differential at x_B with respect to a vertical reflection from the same interface will be

$$\Delta T = \frac{x_B^2}{V_0^2(T_0 + T_B)} \qquad (7\text{-}13)$$

For a split spread with $x_A = -x_B$ we have

$$\sin \phi = \frac{V_0^2(T_B^2 - T_A^2)}{8Hx_B} = \frac{2V_0^2(T_{av})\Delta T}{4V_0 T_0 x_B} = \frac{V_0 T_{av}}{2T_0} \frac{\Delta T}{x_B} \qquad (7\text{-}14)$$

These relations hold only for the plane of the wave paths. If the shooting line is not in the direction of dip, the angle ϕ is the *apparent dip*, which is related to the angle of true dip, by the equation

$$\sin \phi = \cos \psi \sin \delta \tag{7-15}$$

where ψ is the angle between the shooting line and the direction in which the reflecting surface actually dips and δ is the true dip.

True dip can be obtained by determining the angle (in degrees) of apparent dip in two different directions, not necessarily perpendicular to each other. A simple geometrical construction can then be used for obtaining the magnitude and direction of the true dip of the reflecting interface from the apparent dips in the two respective directions. Figure 7-13 illustrates the chart designed for solving this problem. The mathematical justification for this construction can be found in Slotnick[7] (p. 164). The tangents of the two apparent dip angles are

FIGURE 7-13
Use of chart to determine true dip from two dip components making an arbitrary angle with each other. (*Geophysical Service, Inc.*)

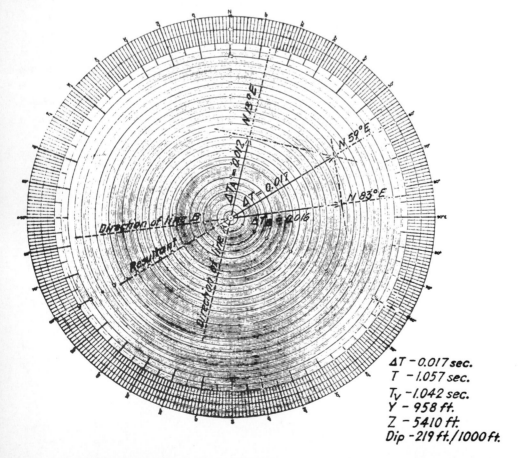

$\Delta T - 0.017\,sec.$
$T\ -1.057\,sec.$
$T_V - 1.042\,sec.$
$Y - 958\,ft.$
$Z - 5410\,ft.$
$Dip - 219\,ft./1000\,ft.$

plotted from the center of the chart in the directions of the respective shooting lines. Perpendiculars are drawn from the end of each line. The direction of true dip is obtained by drawing a line from the center to the point of intersection of these perpendiculars. The length of the line is the tangent of the true dip angle. For angles small enough (less than 10°) that the ratio of the angles can be considered equal to the ratio of the tangent of the angles, the chart may be used with the angles themselves.

The dip angle in degrees is often troublesome to measure directly. A better quantity is the tangent of the dip angle: It is used geologically to express the dip as change in elevation (e.g., in feet) per unit lateral distance (100 ft, 1000 ft, etc.), since the change in elevation is often more accurately measured in the field than the dip angle. In many similar circumstances, such as with stacked seismic sections, it is likewise easier to express dip as change in milliseconds per unit lateral distance (km, 1000 ft, 10 shot points, etc.), and have velocity act as a scale factor, held constant for simplicity's sake. Thus the tangent of the dip angle can be expressed in milliseconds per unit lateral distance, and its value can be determined graphically as illustrated in Fig. 7-13. An alternative analytic expression will be derived below for determining dip with a computer program.

In Fig. 7-14 we assume true dip is expressed by a vector D whose magnitude is the tangent of the dip angle (or proportional to the tangent if expressed in milliseconds per unit distance) and whose azimuth is θ. The components of dip along two survey lines are expressed as vectors A and B whose magnitudes are the respective dip components expressed in the same units used in D and whose directions are the azimuths θ_a and θ_b of the respective survey lines. Then

$$A = |D| \cos(\theta - \theta_a)$$
$$B = |D| \cos(\theta_b - \theta) \tag{7-16}$$

$$\frac{A}{B} = \frac{\cos(\theta - \theta_a)}{\cos(\theta_b - \theta)} = \frac{\cos\theta \cos\theta_a + \sin\theta \sin\theta_a}{\cos\theta \cos\theta_b + \sin\theta \sin\theta_b}$$

$$= \frac{\cos\theta_a + \tan\theta \sin\theta_a}{\cos\theta_b + \tan\theta \sin\theta_b}$$

FIGURE 7-14   Geometrical determination of true dip, D, from two seismic measurements of apparent dip (A, B). The length of each vector is the component of dip in the direction of that vector. Vector direction is given as azimuth measured from north.

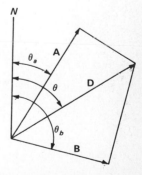

Solving, we obtain

$$\tan \theta = \frac{A \cos \theta_b - B \cos \theta_a}{B \sin \theta_a - A \sin \theta_b}$$

and

$$\theta = \tan^{-1} \frac{A \cos \theta_b - B \cos \theta_a}{B \sin \theta_a - A \sin \theta_b} \tag{7-17}$$

The magnitude of true dip may be obtained by substituting this value of θ into either equation of (7-16).

If, as is frequently the case, the lines of survey are perpendicular to each other—i.e., $\theta_b = \theta_a + \pi/2$, Eqs. (7-16) and (7-17) simplify to

$$\theta = \theta_a + \tan^{-1} \frac{B}{A}$$
$$D = \sqrt{A^2 + B^2} \tag{7-18}$$

True Dip Calculations from Field Records

In the years before programmable normal moveout correction and common-depth-point (CDP) stack, true dip calculations were made from field records (from which normal moveout had been removed) from crossing lines (p. 154 in Slotnick[7]). For dip angles less than 10°, in which the tangent of the angle is approximately equal to the sine of the angle, Slotnick has shown that the (pre-stack, pre-normal moveout removal) time differential of two in-line receivers an equal distance on either side of the source location is proportional to the tangent of the apparent dip angle as measured from the field record. In these circumstances, this time differential of the two receivers, offset from the source a distance p, is plotted for each seismic line as shown in Fig. 7-13. The true dip direction is derived as above, and the Δt derived as above is used in the following equation to calculate the true dip angle, d:

$$\frac{\Delta t}{2p} = \frac{2h(\sin d)}{v^2 t_0} \tag{7-19}$$

where p = source-receiver offset
h = perpendicular depth to reflector under the source
d = true dip angle of the reflector
v = velocity to the reflector
t_0 = the zero-offset dipping-reflector travel time

7-4 STATIC TIME CORRECTIONS

To obtain the greatest amount of information possible from seismic data, it is necessary to correct reflection times for predictable irregularities not associated with structure at the depths of interest. One obvious source of such irregularity is surface elevation. If reflection waves from a flat subsurface interface were received by geophones spread over a hill, valley, or other topographic feature, the reflection times would indicate a structure that could be associated with the elevations at the earth's surface rather than with those of the subsurface formations being mapped. From a knowledge of the elevations and near-surface velocities, one can compute the variations in reflection time at points along the surface that are attributable to such topographic irregularities. Observed reflection times can be corrected for the effects of these irregularities by proper subtraction or addition of the time increments thus determined. Many interpreters compare a surface topographic map to their final structure map: If a direct or inverse correlation is found between the two, the velocity used to correct to a reference surface, the datum, may have been too slow or too fast, respectively.

The weathered layer just below the earth's surface is a source of irregularity concerning which we usually have the least amount of information. It generally consists of unconsolidated rock or soil materials, usually above the water table, and varying in thickness from essentially zero to several hundred feet. Its quite low seismic velocity, often between 750 and 3000 ft/s, causes a disproportionately great and variable time delay in the arrival of the desired deeper reflections. The velocity and thickness of this layer can change with the level of the water table; the thickness of the weathered layer can decrease over hilltops and increase in stream valleys, and can change radically over short distances along the line of survey. Lateral changes are particularly troublesome where paleotopographic relief (old stream channels, limestone ledges, etc.) occurs in the subsurface.

The weathering layer is also characterized by significant absorption of the higher frequencies. Scattering caused by short-wavelength waves striking small features results in more seismic noise. Due to the velocity contrast between the weathered layer and the underlying formations, a high reflection coefficient is often encountered which can cause multiple reflections and reverberations. The travel paths through the weathering layer tend to be nearly vertical due to Snell's law, regardless of their direction of travel below the low-velocity layer (LVL).

There are two main types of techniques to determine the thickness and velocity of this layer at each detector station: directly measuring it through shot-hole information and calculating it through refraction static routines. Techniques are also available to determine the required corrections directly from reflection data by reconciling the time shifts needed to align different observations of the same reflections. Such methods are usually applied only to refine the corrections determined by the other two methods. A knowledge of the thickness and velocity of the LVL increases the accuracy and the validity of the static time shifts applied. The compensation for the LVL is one of the most difficult to do correctly and one of the most important. When done incorrectly, through insufficient information or other causes, oil or gas fields are missed and false prospects are drilled.

In areas of known static problems, a source of irretrievable error in acquisition is to make the geophone groups too long. Time shifts within the group, termed *intragroup statics*, will degrade the signal and cannot be removed through later processing. Where intragroup statics pose problems, the coherent noise attenuation afforded by long groups can be achieved better through array forming in the computer (see Sec. 7-8) after static corrections.

In the early days of seismic exploration, the elevation and weathering corrections were made after reflection times were read from the records. Now the elevations of source and receiver are stored in the header of each trace, to be used in the automatic calculation and application of elevation corrections.

Elevation Corrections

Since the paths of reflected waves through the LVL are usually close to vertical regardless of offset and angle of propagation below the LVL, the correction for elevation difference can be made simply by subtracting (or adding) the time required for the wave to travel the vertical distance between a reference elevation and that of the earth's surface at the point in question. The reference plane is generally chosen to be below the base of weathering. In a mature hydrocarbon region, where there have been decades of seismic exploration, maps of the customary reference plane and velocity to reference plane are often available. The new seismic data are referenced to the regional standard to allow easy integration of new data with old data. Generally, the elevation correction is done at the same time as the weathering correction; in this discussion the concepts are introduced separately for clarity.

The usual method, illustrated in Fig. 7-15, is to make a correction that puts both the shot and detectors on the chosen datum plane below the depth of shot and, usually, at the base of the weathered zone. Sometimes the datum is chosen to be at ground level. For the situation in Fig. 7-15, the times required for the wave to travel down to the datum plane from the shot and up from the datum

FIGURE 7-15 Elevation corrections by putting shot and geophones on the datum plane, thus effectively removing the effect of the weathered layer.

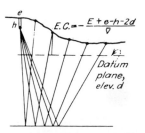

$$E.C. = -\frac{E + e - h - 2d}{\bar{v}}$$

plane to the detector are then removed. The excess times are computed simply by dividing the differences in elevation between shot and datum and also between detector and datum by the near-surface velocity. Surface source data will use either a refraction-type estimation of the near-surface velocity to correct to datum, or the velocity field customary in the area.

Weathering Corrections

The effect of variations in the LVL on the apparent structure of reflectors is illustrated in Fig. 7-16. The velocity in the surface layer is so much lower than the average speed of the material between the base of the layer and the reflecting surface that any change in its thickness or its velocity is observed on the record as a much greater change in the apparent depth of the reflector. The decrease in the weathering thickness of 40 ft gives an anomaly in two-way time of 30 ms, and when this time difference is multiplied by half the 8000 ft/s average velocity to the flat reflecting bed, the reflector has an apparent relief of 120 ft. Unless a correction is made for the change in thickness of the low-speed zone, a spurious pull-up of 120 ft will be indicated on the final map.

Weathering Corrections Using Uphole Information

The most accurate of all weathering correction methods is made from dynamite data in which the source is below the base of weathering. The uphole time, the depth of source, and the ground elevation of the source point are all stored in the trace header to be used later in the calculation and application of datum statics.

In many areas where surface sources are customarily used, information concerning the LVL is acquired by uphole surveys. Uphole times in a deep hole are measured by firing an explosive source at several different depths and recording the arrival times (see Fig. 7-17).

FIGURE 7-16   Spurious structure introduced at depth by failure to take local thinning of weathered zone into account. Note magnification of relief at deep reflection because of increase in velocity.

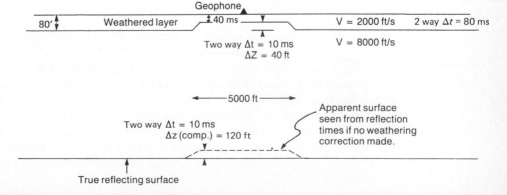

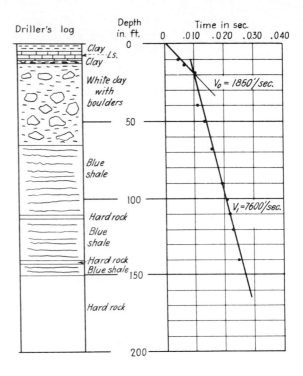

FIGURE 7-17 Vertical velocity distribution near the surface determined by "shooting up the hole." (*Geophysical Service, Inc.*)

Using Waters'[8] (1978) development, we will determine the time components of the static correction for a trace. Let T_r be the uncorrected reflection time for a shot at E_1 received at E_2 (see Fig. 7-18). T_r^c is the corrected time for this trace given with respect to the reference plane, E_s.

$$T_r^c = T_r - \frac{E_1 - d_{s1} - E_s + E_2 - d_{s2} - E_s}{V_0} - t_{uh2} \qquad (7\text{-}20)$$

where d_s is the depth of shot. Some programs using Eq. (7-20) or similar equations allow V_0 to be specified as a function of shot point, i.e., spatial coordinate along the line.

Weathering Corrections Using First Arrivals (Refraction Statics) The first events to arrive at the geophones on a reflection profile have traveled either directly through the weathered layer or by refraction along the top of the high-speed zone just below the weathered layer. Using the time-distance curves of the first arrivals for shots from opposite directions, one can calculate the thickness of the weathered layer by conventional refraction methods, discussed below. There are many algorithms that automatically pick refraction arrivals, fill matrices with the first arrival times, and then invert to get a least-squares best estimate of the vertical time to the refractor associated with each group location.

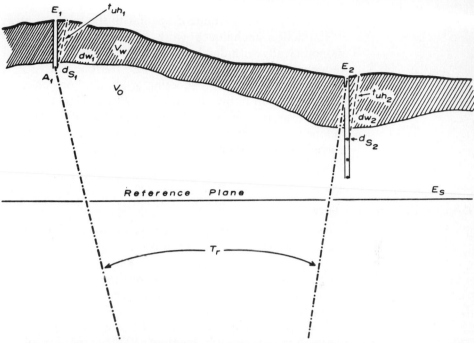

FIGURE 7-18 Definition of terms used to describe the time referencing of a trace to datum. E_1 and E_2 are the ground elevations of the group locations. t_{uh1} and t_{uh2} are the uphole times of the two group locations, dw_1 and dw_2 are the depths of weathering, d_{s1} and d_{s2} are the depths of the shot, V_w is the weathering velocity, and E_s is the datum plane elevation. (*From Waters*[8])

Refraction Statics The principles of refraction calculations are covered in Chap. 10 and in other publications (Refs. 7, 9). For best results, geophone groups should be small in linear or areal extent, because the refracted energy is arriving at an angle and would thus be attenuated by a long group. The greater the offsets and the closer spaced are the groups, the better. Refracted arrivals from a horizontal bed can be plotted upon a *t-x* diagram. The slopes of the lines (Fig. 11-2) yield V_0 and V_1 for flat refractors. With that information and the intercept time (discussed later), one can calculate the depth z to the refracting layer. If the refracting layer is present on the whole line, and preferably in a whole area, the datum plane can be placed at or beneath the refracting boundary.

Determination of the dip of the refracting layer requires a reversed profile, and since split spreads are customarily used in land acquisition, reversed profiles are almost always available. A reversed profile is a profile shot from opposite directions into the same set of receiver positions. If single-end shooting was performed, a split-spread profile can be generated by use of the reciprocity principle. Reciprocity states that a receiver at a first location with a source at a second location will record the same wave field as would be recorded by a receiver at the second with a source at the first. Occasionally in practice, the prerequisites for reciprocity may not be met: for example, the source array may be quite dissimilar to the receiver array.

Refraction techniques work best with subsurface velocities increasing monotonically with depth. If there is a velocity reversal, i.e., if any bed in the sequence has a lower velocity than the one above it, that bed will not be detectable by refraction shooting at all. The presence of such an undetected LVL will result in the computation of erroneous depths to interfaces below it. If the presence of an LVL is suspected, it becomes necessary to obtain independent information on velocity as a function of depth in order to make a correct interpretation. A method of operating with such estimates is given by Savit.[10]

Automated Statics Routines

With multifold CMP data, there is redundant information to estimate static corrections. The static time shifts can generally be assumed to be "surface consistent"; i.e., each group location has its own static value independent of the path by which the energy reaches that group. The need to make the static "correction" is attributed to local variation in the velocity or thickness of the weathering zone or to some other anomalous near-surface condition. Implicit is the assumption that the travel path through the LVL for all offsets is effectively vertical at that group's location. If the condition of surface consistency is removed, the static shifts at each group will be a function of offset. With surface-consistent statics, the source static is normally set equal to the receiver static for each group location. That is, the upgoing travel time through the LVL is taken to be equal to the downgoing travel time. An example of the improvement in data quality that automatic static routines can achieve is shown in Fig. 7-19.

We shall discuss three types of approaches to automatic or residual static corrections, following Waters'[8] development. Residual static corrections are the extra time shifts after elevation corrections have been made. Surface-source data, e.g., vibroseis, are prime candidates for these techniques since they lack direct uphole information on the LVL. Surface-source data have only their first arrivals for determining weathering-type static parameters (refraction statics approach). Unfortunately, vibroseis acquisition often employs long arrays to attenuate the horizontally traveling ground roll that interferes with the reflected arrivals. Refraction arrivals, on the other hand, have a large horizontal component and are thus attenuated by long arrays, thus destroying the information needed to perform refraction statics. Some receiving systems attempt to resolve this dilemma by providing the ability to switch to a single central geophone from each geophone array for separate weathering "shots."

Automatic statics determination using reflection events can best be performed after normal moveout (NMO) corrections, but determining the NMO is significantly affected by unremoved statics. Thus an iterative approach is often employed: the elevation statics are removed, NMO estimated and removed,

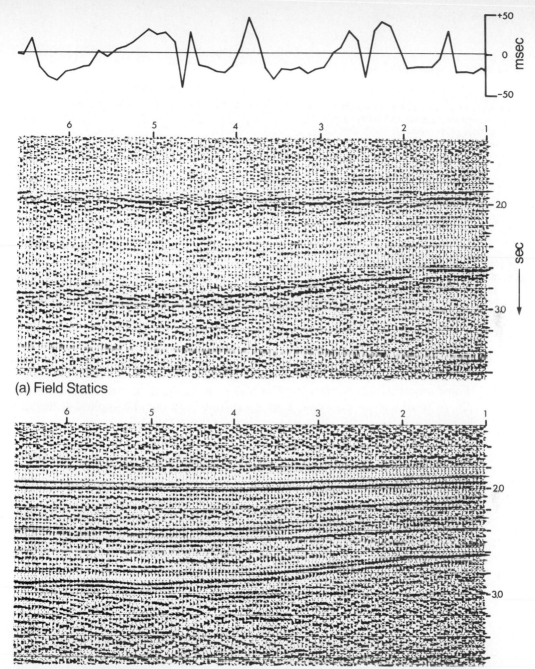

(a) Field Statics

(b) Automatic Statics

FIGURE 7-19 Example of the improvement possible with automatic or residual static corrections. (*a*) Only field statics (reference-to-datum statics) applied. (*b*) Automatic or residual statics applied. The magnitude of the residual (automatic) receiver static applied by the program is shown in the graph on the top of the figure. The automatic statics program also calculated what residual normal-moveout corrections were necessary. Those corrections were also applied. (*Western Geophysical.*)

FIGURE 7-20 Series of cross-correlation functions between a reference trace and the individual traces within the gather. The maximum value of the cross-correlation function, within a prescribed window, is an estimate of the residual static shift needed for that trace. The last cross-correlation shows large correlation values at B and C: these values are probably incorrect estimates of the static. A properly set window of allowable static shifts would exclude C, but B might be chosen by the program, instead of the correct value. In this case, we would rely on the logic of the program to minimize the effect of a poor estimate upon the final determination of the static shift. (*From Waters.*[8])

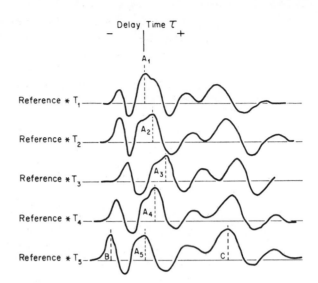

Delay Time τ

and automatic statics estimated. The statics are then applied to the data uncorrected for NMO, followed by a reestimate of NMO and automatic statics. Some automatic statics programs generate an estimate of both the statics and the residual normal moveout. Both corrections can then be applied to the data in one pass. This procedure was applied to the data in Fig. 7-19.

The cross-correlation function is typically used to find the time shift that produces the maximum similarity between two traces. A range of allowed time shifts is chosen, perhaps $+20$ ms to -20 ms, depending upon the area. (Trace-to-trace static shifts larger than 100 ms are not unknown in some areas.) A window of the data is chosen that contains prominent reflections, minimum noise, and good normal moveout correction. The outcomes of the cross-correlations will look similar to Fig. 7-20, in which the time shifts of the various traces may be read from the maximum peaks of the cross-correlations. Due to the redundancy of traces in multifold shooting, each source and receiver group location will have several estimates of the correct static shift. Statistical analysis can then be used to determine the static shift associated with each group location.

The set of equations that relates the static shifts resulting from the cross-correlations to the unknown components of the observed shifts cannot be "solved" in a deterministic way. There are far more equations than there are unknowns, but there are not enough *independent* equations to permit a deterministic solution for any unknown. The usual recourse is to use an iterative method of approximation. Such a method requires the exercise of judgment to stop the iteration sequence at a "best" approximation and before the solutions begin to deteriorate.

The static correction for each trace consists of a shot position component, a receiver position component, and various sources of error (noise, normal moveout, dip, etc.). One problem is to separate change in time due to near-surface irregularities from those caused by structural relief on the reflector.

Common-Midpoint Technique   Hileman et al.[11] published one method for surface-consistent statics estimation. Cross-correlation functions are used to measure the relative time shifts of each trace within a common-depth-point gather.

The time shift, t, calculated by the cross-correlation of two traces may be expressed as

$$t = t_D + t_{WS} + t_{WR} + t_{NMO} + t_n \tag{7-21}$$

where t_D = dip time difference (structural relief of reflector)
t_{WS} = weathering at shot point
t_{WR} = weathering at receiver
t_{NMO} = time difference due to incorrect normal moveout calculation
t_n = noise

The choice of a CMP gather in which to estimate statics should minimize the effect of the dip term. Some programs test for a hyperbolic fit to the event in order to model residual normal moveout (RNMO). Calculating the statics follows the removal of the RNMO.

An arbitrary reference trace is used for correlating the individual signals for which static shifts are desired. The reference trace is usually the near-offset trace in which NMO, and hence NMO error, is least. The reference trace in low S/N data sets is often the average of all the nonshifted traces. The danger of the latter is that the static shifts may be so large that the nonshifted sum does not match any of the individual traces. Many schemes exist for calculating the reference trace. Figure 7-21 shows the computation array that Hileman et al.[11] use for their correction technique. Time shifts obtained by cross-correlation are averaged over the rows to obtain the correction associated with the shot corresponding to each row. The value for the receivers can be obtained by averaging the time shifts in the columns representing particular detecting groups.

"High-frequency" statics (statics within one spread-length) can be estimated well, but "long-period" statics, that is, static shifts between traces that are far apart, are measured poorly. Thus, even though the use of a CMP gather to estimate statics minimizes the effect of dip (structural relief on the reflector), errors made in this static estimation scheme can affect the perceived dip.

Equivalence of Source and Receiver Statics

Automatic static routines can also operate on common-source and common-receiver gathers after moveout and elevation corrections. The source static of Eq. (7-21) will be constant within a common-source record. An estimate of the

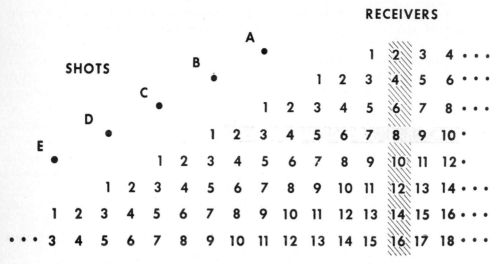

FIGURE 7-21   Array for computing static corrections with sixfold shooting geometry. Time shifts common to the same shots lie along the rows, and time shifts common to the same geophones lie along the columns. (*From Hileman et al.*[11])

dip and NMO components can be made for comparison with the common-receiver-gather calculations. After all the common-source gathers have been analyzed for the component time shifts, the data are reorganized to common-receiver gathers, to estimate t_{WS} and the other time-component shifts. The assumption is then made that t_{WS} at a given location equals t_{WR} at the same location. Statistical methods can then be used to estimate t_{WR} and t_D.

Constant-Offset Static Corrections   In this case, t_{NMO} from Eq. (7-21) drops out as long as the average velocity to the reflection window is constant. Adjacent traces, from adjacent sources, of the same offset, are cross-correlated to determine the time shift.

The time shift so calculated is the sum of a source static, a receiver static, a dip (or structural relief of reflector moveout), and a noise component. The time shift necessary to remove the static shift must not also remove the dip component (a desired geologic signal). Various schemes are employed to estimate and retain the dip component.

Wave Equation Statics and Wave Equation Datuming

In certain marine areas, the water layer (the local LVL) varies substantially in thickness. On land, a thick LVL can change in thickness and laterally in velocity. In both cases, the surface-consistent static concept is inappropriate. A surface-consistent static is offset independent, consisting of the vertical path travel time through the LVL under the group location. The true ray paths through a thick LVL are substantially slant paths for the farther offsets, and the static shift associated with a group location varies with offset (source-receiver separation).

There are several different techniques in use to calculate and apply statics in this situation. The necessary information is the velocity, $V = V(x, z)$, where x and z are the customary variables of midpoint or spatial coordinate and depth, respectively, of the LVL and its configuration (thickness along the line). Marine data presents the simplest situation—the water-bottom reflection is picked and input to define the shape of the water layer. For land data, the information is usually derived from a refraction-type analysis and/or near-trace reflection plot.

One method is to ray-trace the different travel paths through the LVL of the model to calculate the appropriate static shift for each trace, and then apply that static shift. A 300-shot-point line with 96-channel recording will thus require the tracing of 28,800 rays to determine the statics.

A thick LVL of variable thickness or velocity presents other problems in addition to offset variable statics. Velocity anomalies (time push-downs or pull-ups) seriously distort the time image of the subsurface. A pre stack technique developed to treat this problem is called *wave equation datuming*. The less expensive version is done with stacked data (Berryhill[12]). That version does not address the offset-dependent static problem, but only the velocity anomaly problem.

The wave field is downward continued (see Sec. 7-10, Migration) to a reference plane below the base of the LVL using the correct low velocity and correct rock (indurated) velocity. Then the wave field is upward continued to the surface, substituting the rock (indurated) velocity of the second layer for the low-velocity first layer. Thus the distorting lens of low-velocity material has been replaced with a uniform velocity layer, and the time pull-up or push-down that is the velocity anomaly produced by the LVL variation is removed.

The more expensive version is performed pre-stack. When the data are sorted into common-source gathers, the extrapolation of receivers from datum 1 to datum 2 can be accomplished through wave equation operators. As always, the velocity and configuration of the distorting lens (the LVL) must be known and input as the depth-velocity model to the program. The data are reordered to common-receiver gathers, in which reciprocity allows the extrapolation (moving) of sources from datum 1 to datum 2 (Berryhill[13]). The data are then extrapolated from datum 2 or datum 1 using the indurated rock velocity. The power of this approach is to correct pre-stack for the slant ray paths through the LVL *and* for the time pull-ups and push-downs. At the time of this writing, the hardware and software requirements for pre-stack wave equation datuming place this technique beyond the capabilities of most processing centers. The less expensive version performed after stack obviously does not address the problem of offset-dependent statics, but does address, to a considerable extent, the time pull-up and push-down problem.

7-5   AMPLITUDE CORRECTIONS

There are two general types of amplitude compensation: structural (AGC or automatic gain control) and relative, true amplitude gain preservation. The physical causes that necessitate correcting the amplitudes are discussed in Chap. 2 and Sec. 9-4.

AGC

AGC attempts to make amplitudes similar for all offsets, for all times, and for all midpoints. A typical method of calculating the gain to be applied is to calculate the median or average amplitude within sliding windows down the trace, and then to calculate the multipliers needed to equalize the median values in all the windows. The multipliers are normally smoothed over time and then applied. A separate gain function is calculated and applied for each trace. Once AGC is applied, it cannot be removed unless a record is kept of the applied multipliers.

Relative, True Amplitude Gain Preservation

In many circumstances, such "homogenization" of amplitudes removes precisely that standout of high-amplitude events and the relative amplitudes of reflections for which the interpreter is looking. An example of a data set processed with AGC versus the true amplitude gain is in Figs. 9-21 and 9-22. Therefore, other gain schemes exist that attempt to preserve relative true amplitudes. The simplest of relative, true amplitude gain schemes involves either a linear or quadratic increase of gain with time

$$G(t) = kt \qquad \text{or} \qquad G(t) = kt^2$$

where k is an arbitrary constant.

To multiply by time to the first power is to compensate for spherical divergence. The wavefront is expanding in three dimensions at once, resulting in the surface area increasing in proportion to radius squared. The energy of the wavefront is distributed over a surface that is expanding in proportion to time squared. Seismic amplitudes are proportional to the square root of the energy, resulting in a linear function of time. The second power of time can arise from a simple absorption calculation (Claerbout[14]). Both gain functions use a homogeneous, constant-velocity earth model. Since this type of medium does not exist, we must also try to compensate for scattering, instrumental effects, variety in geophone and source coupling, array directivity, superimposed noise (especially ground roll), and the interference effect of different events. Relative, true amplitude gaining will also preserve detrimentally the amplitude standout of noise bursts and strong coherent noise. Muting (zeroing) of high-amplitude noise before relative, true amplitude gain becomes far more important here than in AGC-gained data. Simple gain functions, such as the ones we have discussed, can be removed from the data if the original amplitudes are desired at a later date.

A velocity function for an area can be used so that the spherical divergence correction depends upon distance rather than travel time. Sometimes a data-dependent, smooth, gain curve is applied rather than a t or t^2 gain curve. Such a gain curve is obtained from an amplitude decay analysis over selected records or traces. The high amplitudes contained in noise, such as first breaks, coherent noise waves, or noise bursts, may deleteriously affect the amplitude decay analysis. Care should therefore be exercised in muting and in placing the analysis windows. The gain curve applied to the whole line, based upon the amplitude decay analysis, can be offset dependent or offset independent.

In determining the relative true amplitude gain functions for marine data, one faces fewer complicating factors than for land data. The receivers are uniformly coupled. The source strengths will vary only accidentally (gun malfunctions, etc.). Source-strength equalizations usually involve the use of source-constant multipliers. The time-variant gain scheme can be one described above, or one standard gain function can be used over an entire area.

7-6 DYNAMIC TIME CORRECTIONS—DETERMINATION OF SEISMIC VELOCITIES

The hyperbolic curvature of a reflection event must be transformed to time coincidence with zero offset prior to CMP stack so that all the peaks and troughs will add (stack) in phase. The NMO correction that accomplishes this alignment defines the correct stacking velocity. An incorrect stacking velocity leaves remnant hyperbolic curvature on the event, degrading the stack and hindering interpretation. A second consideration is the extraction of the rms velocity functions from the stacking velocity functions for converting reflection times to depths and for migration purposes. On a dip line, rms velocity is determined by multiplying the stacking velocity by the cosine of the dip of the event.

In Chap. 2 we considered the factors governing seismic velocities in rocks. Our concern here is the measurement of the actual velocities in or near the plane of the seismic profile. These velocities can be measured directly in boreholes, or they can be estimated from the data. The spreads now used in recording by common-depth-point techniques are generally so long (up to 3 mi) that analytical methods are considerably more accurate than they were when the shorter spreads used for single-coverage shooting were common.

In many areas, seismic velocity data can also be used to identify lithology in discrete formations within the geologic section.

Definition of Terms

At this point it is desirable to define the different kinds of velocities that enter into seismic-data reduction and interpretation. The following types are referred to most frequently in the geophysical literature.

Average Velocity   This is simply the depth z of a reflecting surface below a datum divided by the observed one-way reflection time t from the datum to the surface so that

$$V_{av} = \frac{z}{t} \qquad (7\text{-}22)$$

If z represents the sum of the thicknesses of layers z_1, z_2, z_3, . . . , z_n, the *average velocity* is defined as

$$V_{av} = \frac{z_1 + z_2 + z_3 + \cdots + z_n}{t_1 + t_2 + t_3 + \cdots + t_n} = \frac{\sum\limits_{1}^{n} z_k}{\sum\limits_{1}^{n} t_k} \qquad (7\text{-}23)$$

The average velocity is used for time-to-depth conversions and for migration.

Interval Velocity   If two reflectors at depths z_1 and z_2 give reflections having respective one-way times of t_1 and t_2, the *interval velocity* V_{int} between z_1 and z_2 is defined simply as $(z_2 - z_1)/(t_2 - t_1)$.

Instantaneous Velocity   If the velocity varies continuously with depth, its value at a particular depth z is obtained from the formula for interval velocity by contracting the interval $z_2 - z_1$ until it becomes an infinitesimally thin layer having a thickness dz. The interval velocity computed by the formula above becomes the derivative of z with respect to t, and we designate it as the instantaneous velocity V_{inst}, defined as

$$V_{inst} = \frac{dz}{dt} \qquad (7\text{-}24)$$

Root-Mean-Square Velocity   If the section consists of horizontal layers with respective interval velocities of V_1, V_2, V_3, . . . , V_n, and one-way interval travel times t_1, t_2, t_3, . . . , t_n, the root-mean-square (rms) velocity is obtained from the relation

$$V_{rms}^2 = \frac{V_1^2 t_1 + V_2^2 t_2 + V_3^2 t_3 + \cdots + V_n^2 t_n}{t_1 + t_2 + t_3 + \cdots + t_n} = \frac{\sum\limits_{1}^{n} V_k^2 t_k}{\sum\limits_{1}^{n} t_k} \qquad (7\text{-}25)$$

The slope of this line in t^2, x^2 space, using the reflection from a flat bed, is shown in Fig. 7-22. Kleyn[15] offers a further discussion of velocity.

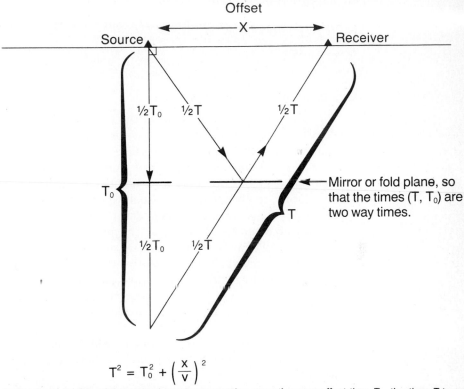

$$T^2 = T_0^2 + \left(\frac{X}{V}\right)^2$$

FIGURE 7-22   A simple derivation of the normal-moveout equation uses the zero offset time T_0, the time T to a given offset x, a fold plane at the time of the reflector, and the Pythagorean theorem. V_{st}, the stacking velocity, is the processing parameter that achieves the best time alignment of a reflection at an offset with the zero-offset reflection time.

Stacking Velocity   Stacking velocity, V_{st}, is based on the relation

$$T^2 = T_0{}^2 + \frac{x^2}{V_{st}{}^2} \qquad (7\text{-}26)$$

where x is the source-receiver offset for a common-midpoint sequence of shots, T is the travel time of the reflection at x, and T_0 is the travel time at the zero offset. The derivation of V_{st} is simple, and uses the Pythagorean theorem as illustrated in Fig. 7-22. The stacking velocity is used to correct the quasi-hyperbolic primary reflection event to time alignment with zero offset. Appropriate values for T_0, x, and T can be read from data plots, preferably CMP gathers, when manual calculation of the stacking-velocity function is necessary.

Stacking velocity is almost always greater than average velocity. The relationship between V_{rms} and V_{st} has been described by many authors, notably Kleyn.[15] V_{rms} is the inverse slope at its origin of an event on a t^2-x^2 plot. V_{st} is the best fit over all offsets of hyperbolic moveouts derived from Eq. (7-26) to the actual reflection events. In general,

$$V_{av} \leq V_{rms} \leq V_{st}$$

Velocity Survey, Check Shot Survey, or Well Shooting

An independent measurement of the earth velocity function is obtained by a velocity survey. (The other names for this experiment are above.) Explosive charges are detonated near the surface, or a vibroseis unit is operated alongside a deep borehole, and the arrival times of waves received by a geophone suspended in the borehole at a number of depths are recorded. In marine operations, an air-gun array is usually employed as a sound source. Figure 7-23 illustrates the setup and shows interval- and average-velocity curves of the type that are obtained from such data. The interval velocity is obtained by taking the distance between successive detector positions in the well and dividing it by the difference in arrival times at the two depths after the arrival times have been corrected for angularity of the wave path. The average velocity is either the actual distance from source to receiver divided by the observed time or the vertical component of distance divided by the appropriately corrected time. Assuming flat layers, one can use either the average velocity or the interval velocity to compute the rms velocity which can be used for the initial NMO correction. The velocities measured in check shot surveys are also useful for migration (Sec. 7-10).

Values from a number of widely separated wells can be averaged to obtain a velocity function which is used as the initial V_{st} over the area between the wells. The seismic reflection data can then be analyzed to refine the estimate of V_{st} and to supply velocity values away from the wells. In many cases, the velocity to one or more horizons is plotted or contoured over the prospect or

FIGURE 7-23   Well-shooting arrangement with typical interval-velocity and average-velocity curves thus obtained.

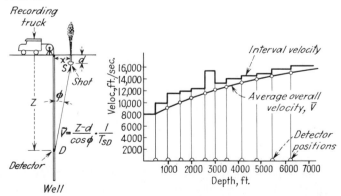

the entire area being mapped. Considerable variation in velocity to a given horizon is sometimes found over relatively short distances. These changes often have geologic significance and could cast light on the geology of the area involved. Changes in velocity are critical in the interpretation of the time map of the horizon; the depth map is the genuine article desired from interpretation, and that is constructed from the time map and the velocity map of the horizon.

Graphical (Manual) Velocity Determination from Reflection Data

Velocities from reflection data have always been determined using the relationship between reflection times and shot-receiver distances. The earliest procedure, proposed by Green,[16] involves plotting the square of the travel time T to and from a reflector at depth z versus the square of the receiving distance x, using the relation

$$T^2 = \frac{4}{V^2} z^2 + \frac{1}{V^2} x^2 \tag{7-27}$$

A plot of this type is shown in Fig. 7-24. In the early days, spreads were short (500 to 1000 ft), so the line fitted to these near offsets represented $1/V_{rms}^2$. If $2z/V$ is designated as T_0, the travel time of a reflection received by a geophone at the shot point ($x = 0$), we can write

$$T^2 = T_0^2 + \frac{x^2}{V^2} \tag{7-28}$$

For a reflection event, T, T_0, and x can be measured from a gather (CMP, common source, or common receiver) and inserted into Eq. (7-28) to determine V, which is V_{st}. If common-source or common-receiver gathers are used, the dip of the reflector will exert a first order effect upon the V_{st} so calculated, which is why V_{st} is usually calculated from CMP gathers.

FIGURE 7-24 Determination of average velocities to three horizons by analysis of reflections on velocity spreads.

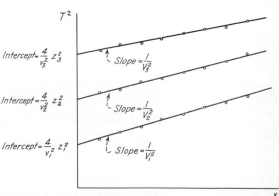

If there are two horizontal reflectors having times of T_1 and T_2 with respective rms velocities V_1 and V_2 (determined as outlined in the last paragraph), Dix[17] showed that the interval velocity V_{i12} between the reflectors can be obtained from the relation

$$V_{i12}^2 = \frac{V_2^2 T_2 - V_1^2 T_1}{T_2 - T_1} \tag{7-29}$$

This formula, known as the *Dix equation*, has been widely used to determine interval velocities between two flat or uniformly dipping reflectors from rms velocities.

Computer-Aided Velocity Determination

With almost universal digitization of reflection data, it is now customary to use computers to determine velocities directly from reflection data. A number of approaches have been programmed for such computations.

Velocity Spectra Common-depth-point (common-midpoint) shooting makes it possible to obtain velocities from reflection times at various receiving distances much more accurately than by the earlier techniques described above. Computers can determine velocities by carrying out calculations based on the time-distance relationship that would be too tedious to perform manually, and programs are available for automatic plotting of the velocity-reflection-time relationships thus obtained.

A commonly used technique for this purpose presents stacking velocity as a function of time in a form called a *velocity spectrum*, the technique having been published by Taner and Koehler.[18] As with all analytical methods for obtaining velocities from actual reflection data, the accuracy and usefulness of the results depend on the quality of the input data.

The time T_x of a reflection event at shot-receiver distance x is related to the time T_0 at the originating point ($x = 0$) by the equation

$$T_x^2 = T_0^2 + \frac{x^2}{V^2} \tag{7-30}$$

Here V^2 is the stacking velocity, more closely related to the rms velocity than to the average velocity. From this equation it is evident that the moveout time, $T_x - T_0$, designated ΔT, can be written

$$\Delta T = \sqrt{T_0^2 + \frac{x^2}{V^2}} - T_0 \tag{7-31}$$

Data arranged in CMP-gather format have a common reflection point in the subsurface only if the reflectors are horizontal. (See Fig. 7-25.) When reflectors

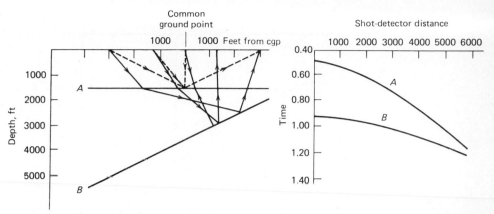

FIGURE 7-25   Schematic time-distance relation for two reflections obtained in common-depth-point shooting arrangement with horizontal and dipping reflectors. *(Modified from Taner and Koehler.[18])*

dip there can be an undesirable "smear" in subsurface coverage. Later in this section, and in Sec. 7-10, Migration, we shall discuss dip moveout, a technique to compensate for this problem. Each reflection, A and B in Fig. 7-25, has a respective moveout, Δt, $T_x - T_0$. The appropriate moveout is a function of offset. When the appropriate value of Δt is subtracted from the time of each reflection, all the reflected events should have their arrivals at the same time. If the traces are added after the appropriate times are subtracted, the sums should be greater than at any other alignment (based on another set of Δt values) of the respective events.

In carrying out this manipulation, different values of V are tested, the computer determining the Δt's corresponding to each V for the respective traces using Eq. (7-31). The Δt's thus obtained are subtracted from the observed reflection times, and the time-shifted signals for all traces are added. The trial value of V which will give the best lineup for each reflection will yield the greatest reflection amplitude after addition (stack). All velocities over the entire range that might be plausible for the area are tried, usually at intervals of 100 ft/s.

Figure 7-26 illustrates the principle of the technique. In the top part, hyperbola 1, shown by a dashed line, corresponds to an assumed velocity slower than the true velocity. When the data are corrected with time shifts based on this velocity and stacked, the sum will be as shown on the plot to the right.

Hyperbola 2 shows Δt versus x for the correct velocity. The sum of the amplitudes over all the traces at the times determined by this curve is greater than that for hyperbola 1. Hyperbola 3, the dotted line, represents a velocity faster than the correct value. The sum of trace amplitudes for times determined from this function also turns out, as was the case with hyperbola 1, to be lower than for hyperbola 2. The velocity for which this sum is maximum can thus be considered as the correct velocity for the time chosen for the calculation.

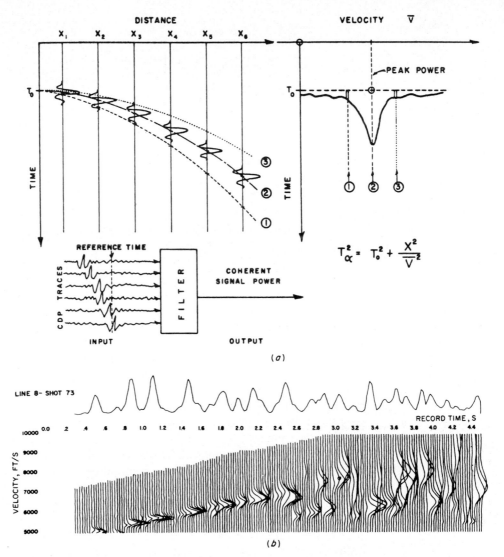

$$T_{\alpha}^2 = T_0^2 + \frac{X^2}{\bar{V}^2}$$

FIGURE 7-26 Velocity spectra: (*a*) alignment of reflections along traces for different shot-receiver distances with shooting configuration for common-depth-point, time-distance relations shown for three assumed velocities; (*b*) typical display of velocity versus time from reflection record. (*From Taner and Koehler.*[18])

An unresolved statics problem in the data will manifest itself as scatter in the lineup of the reflection event. This scatter will lead to a decrease in the amplitude of the correct V_{st} peak power, whereas the amplitudes of erroneous V_{st} peak powers will be affected randomly.

If we choose T_0 values at regular, closely spaced intervals over the length of the record, we can obtain a series of such amplitude-versus-velocity curves, one for each T_0 value, indicating the average velocity as a function of reflection time at the shot point. The lower part of Fig. 7-26 illustrates a spectrum of the type obtained when good reflections occur at frequent intervals on the record. The anomalously low velocities which begin to show up at about 2.6 s probably correspond to multiple reflections, as their values are the same as those for times half as great. In determining a continuous velocity function, it is necessary to interpolate velocity values over portions of the time scale where reflections are not recorded.

Velocity Scans An exceptionally simple method for determining stacking velocity as a function of record time is the velocity scan. An example is shown in Fig. 7-27. A series of trial velocities is assumed with this technique, as with the velocity spectrum, but in a velocity scan the same trial velocity is used for computing moveouts at all times on the record. A separate record is made for each velocity. At times for which the trial velocity is too high, a corrected reflection will show upward convexity like half an umbrella. The event is "undercorrected," because not enough moveout (Δt) has been applied. When the velocity is correct, the reflection will have a horizontal or nearly horizontal lineup. When the velocity is too low, the pattern is like a half-umbrella which points downward. The event is now "overcorrected," for too much moveout has been applied. It is necessary to remember that moveout and velocity have a reciprocal relationship. If the records corrected in this way with continuously increasing velocities are placed side by side, as in Fig. 7-27, the increase of velocity with record time is evident to the eye by the shift downward and to the right of the flat segments corresponding to successively deeper reflections. The time and velocity for each such flat event is plotted to obtain the desired stacking-velocity–time relationship.

In conjunction with these constant-velocity gathers (CVGs), constant-velocity stacks (CVSs) are used. CVSs depict on a suite of stacked traces the effect of increasing velocities. A single trial velocity is used for stacking all events from the beginning to the end of the record, instead of being allowed to vary with time as is conventionally done. Only when the velocity is proper for stacking does a well-defined reflection appear at all. Figure 7-28 illustrates an array of records made for a velocity determination of this type. The correct stacking-velocity function is indicated by the line connecting the points where each reflection seems to show up best. A CVS is normally used along with a CVG taken from one of the common midpoints contained in the CVS panel.

Careful inspection of Fig. 7-28 will also reveal that as the stacking velocities increase, so does the apparent arrival time of an event. An incorrect stacking velocity not only degrades the character of the reflection event but also creates a faulty arrival time, which in turn introduces error onto the time map of the reflector.

Horizon-Event Analysis In complex data areas, horizon-event, velocity analysis can greatly aid in data analysis, interpretation, and modeling. Key

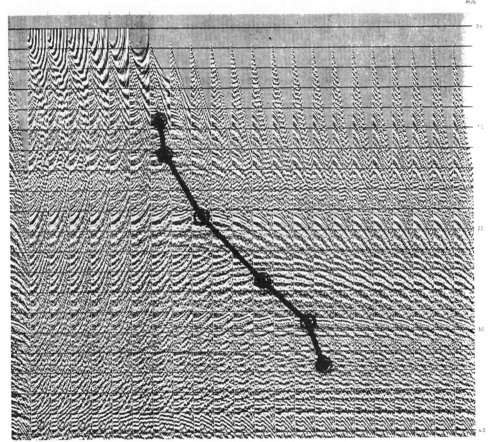

FIGURE 7-27 Velocity scan for typical reflection recording. Each record strip from left to right is corrected for moveout at a successively higher uniform velocity. The stacking velocity-time function obtained by this method is shown below. (*Prakla Seismos.*)

Time, s	0.90	1.25	1.87	2.50	2.90	3.33
Stacking velocity, m/s	1870	2010	2170	2700	3370	3550

horizons, often the mapping horizons, are chosen, and the stacking velocity is estimated in a detailed fashion laterally. The times of the horizons of interest are usually digitized from the best stack available and input to guide the window about the proper T_0. A suite of trial velocities appropriate for the T_0's is analyzed; the outputs are displayed as a function of midpoint location and V_{st}; and the peak power is determined for the given velocity, over the length of the line. A field data example of horizon-event, velocity analysis is in Fig. 7-29*b*. The geophysicist picks the velocity generating the peak power for each

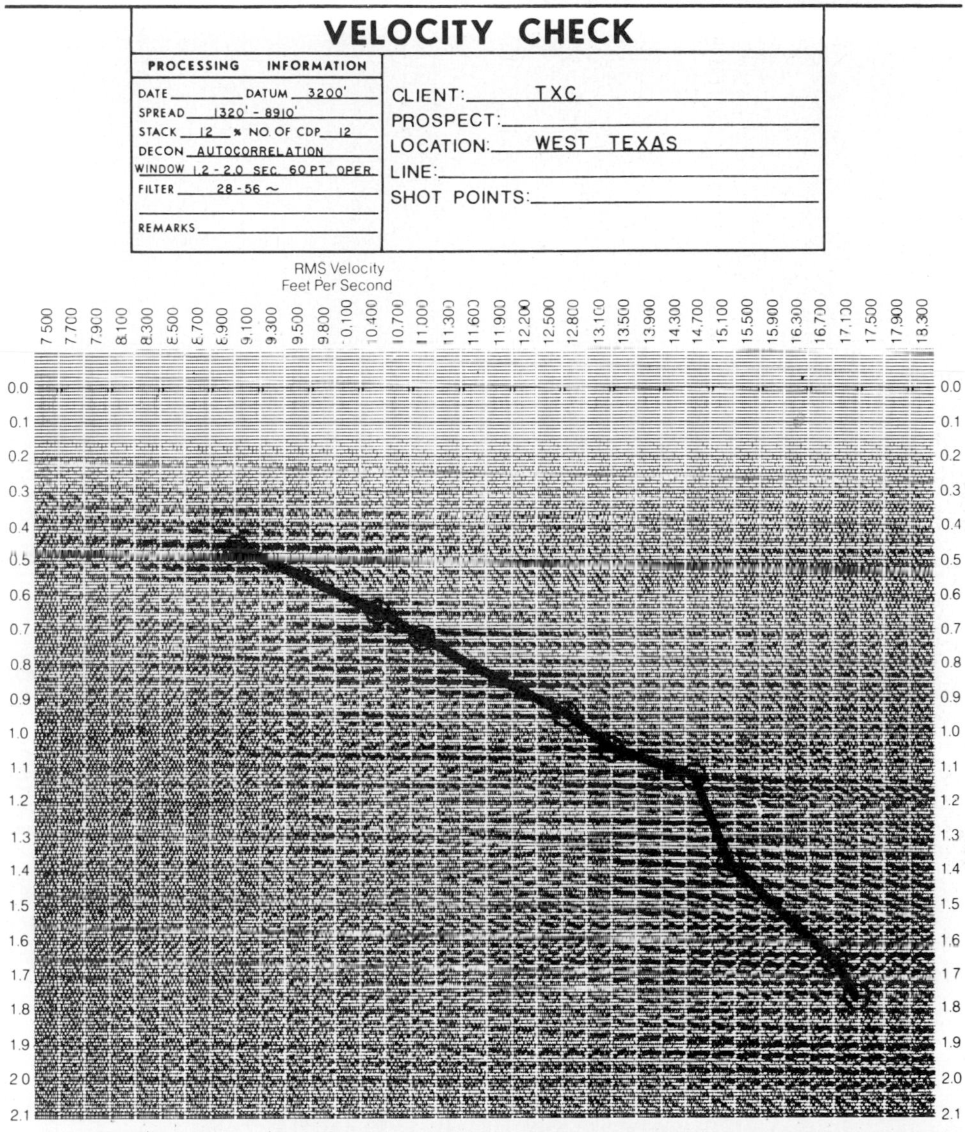

VELOCITY CHECK

PROCESSING   INFORMATION

DATE_____ DATUM __3200'__

SPREAD____1320' - 8910'__

STACK __12__ % NO. OF CDP__12__

DECON __AUTOCORRELATION__

WINDOW 1.2 - 2.0 SEC. 60 PT. OPER.

FILTER _____28 - 56 ~_____

REMARKS_____

CLIENT:_____TXC_____

PROSPECT:_____

LOCATION:____WEST TEXAS_____

LINE:_____

SHOT POINTS:_____

FIGURE 7-28 Determination of stacking velocity by stacking with series of trial velocities from 7500 to 18,300 ft/s. Trial velocity that gives best stack at each time is the correct one for that time. The velocity function shown by the heavy line was obtained by connecting positions where stack is optimum. (*Teledyne Exploration Co.*)

CMP, and these velocity picks are applied by the computer. The output shows the V_{st} field as a function of space and time. The V_{st} information can be corrected by the cosine of the dip to calculate the rms velocity field, which may then be input to subsequent migration or modeling programs. Dip increases the stacking velocity:

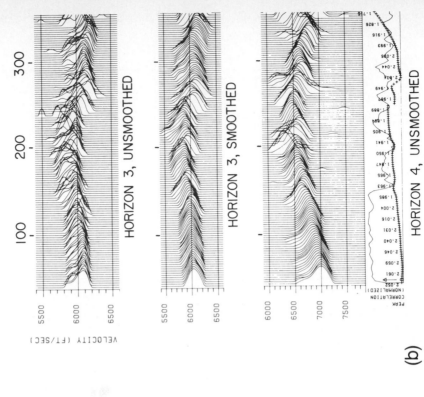

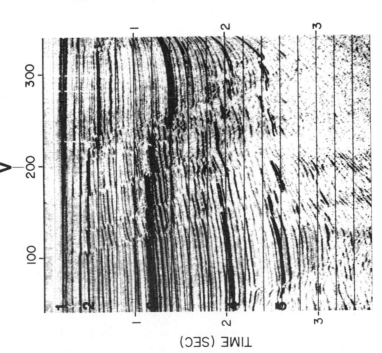

FIGURE 7-29 Example of horizon-event velocity analysis. (a) Stacked data, from which T_0 is chosen for several horizons (1, 2, 3, 4, 5). (b) Display of some of the horizons' velocities, as they vary along the line. (*Western Geophysical.*)

$$V_{st} = \frac{V_{rms}}{\cos \alpha}$$ (7-32)

where α = the dip of the bed in the subsurface. Later in the chapter we will discuss the fairly common problem of having two reflection events of different time dips arrive at the same time on the CDP stack.

Interval velocities for much of a section may be calculated from several horizon-velocity analyses and displayed on a time section as shown in Fig. 7-30.

A depth model, constructed from the time model, can be used for offset modeling in which the stacking velocities can be calculated for comparison with

FIGURE 7-30 Interval velocities, as determined from the rms velocities of horizons 1 through 5. The letter after each interval velocity value indicates the statistical uncertainty of the estimate. (A represents ± 25 ft/s, B ± 50 ft/s, etc.) Underlined values indicate increased uncertainty due to presence of fault(s). Because the illustration is much smaller than the original, most of the values determined by the program could not be reproduced here. (*Western Geophysical*.)

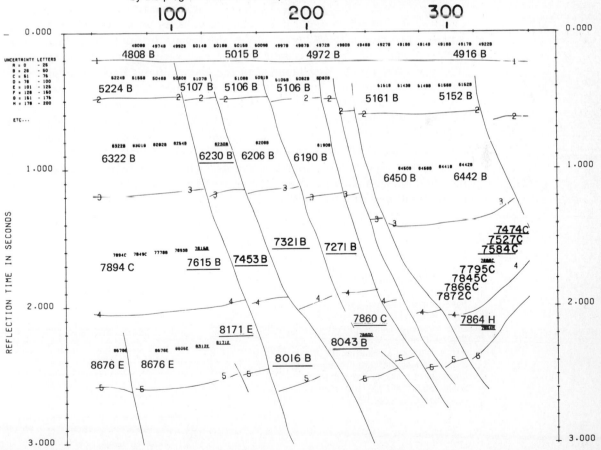

the stacking velocities measured from the data. This method can be a powerful interpretation tool in complex data areas. Once the depth model produces results in acceptable accord with the real data, a depth migration or other expensive imaging technique can be run with confidence.

Other Sources of Velocity Information On CMP stacks, the diffraction hyperbolas yield earth velocities (average velocity) to the diffracting point. Migration can be used as a scanning technique to determine what velocities yield the best (visual) section.

Anomalies in V_{st} Due to Lateral Velocity Variation

In the presence of significant lateral velocity variation, the stacking-velocity field displays a characteristic aberration (see Figs. 7-31 through 7-33 from Lynn and Claerbout [19]). This artifact in the stacking-velocity field can cause problems when the stacking-velocity information is incorporated into the seismic travel inversion (see Sec. 9-4).The aberration is caused by the nonhyperbolic shape of the reflection event due to lateral velocity variation within a spread length. Conventional NMO programs do not regard the nonhyperbolic shape of the event and still try to determine the "best average" hyperbolic match to the nonhyperbolic event. Misalignment of the event follows hyperbolic moveout. Lynn and Claerbout suggested the use of a particular velocity estimation operator, based upon the second lateral derivative of the rms slowness, which decreases the amplitude of the stacking-velocity artifact, and increases the accuracy of the rms velocity estimation. Offset ray tracing using the geophysicist's estimate of the true rms velocity field will calculate the nonhyperbolic trajectories expected for primary events, which will then be used as the moveout function for the data. The result is the alignment of the reflection events that optimizes the quality of the stack.

FIGURE 7-31 Model used for the velocity estimates plotted in Figs. 7-32 and 7-33. The velocities of the layers are given in ft/s. Travel times for the common midpoint gathers were generated by ray tracing at CMP locations 1 through 200. The CMP gathers were 24-fold with a midpoint spacing of 100 ft, a group spacing of 200 ft, and a far offset of 5000 ft. The discontinuity occurs at CMP 100. (*From Lynn and Claerbout.*[19])

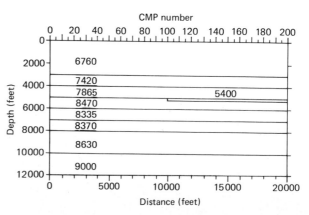

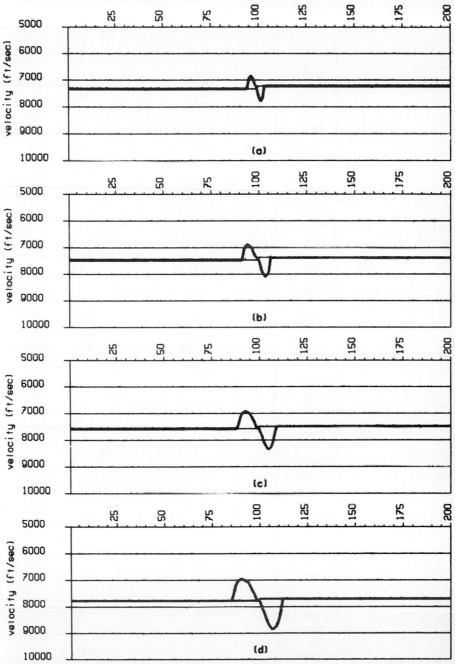

FIGURE 7-32 Stacking (bold lines) and true rms (light lines) velocities to the interfaces at (a) 6000 ft, (b) 7000 ft, (c) 8000 ft, and (d) 10,000 ft. The low velocity zone discontinuity occurs at CMP 100, and its effect is manifested in the large fluctuations in the stacking-velocity estimates. Ideally, the rms velocity should change abruptly at CMP 100, being less for midpoints greater than 100. (*From Lynn and Claerbout.*[19])

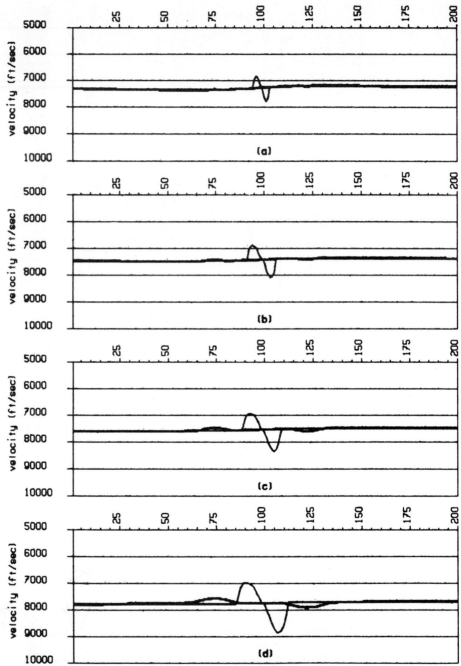

FIGURE 7-33   Estimated rms velocities, using the lateral derivitive operator (bold line), for the model in Fig. 7-31. The light line is the unsmoothed stacking-velocity estimate from Fig. 7-32. (*a*) Estimated velocity to the interfaces at 6000 ft; (*b*) 7000 ft; (*c*) 8000 ft; and (*d*) 10,000 ft. (*From Lynn and Claerbout.*[19])

Multivalued V_{st} Problem

In the presence of dipping events adjacent to, or coincident with, nearly flat events, as illustrated in Fig. 7-34a, the problem arises that two or more V_{st}'s are needed at the same time in order to preserve the several events on the stack. The flat events need a slower velocity, and the dipping events need a faster velocity. It is not possible to apply several NMO functions simultaneously with conventional moveout programs. A process termed pre-stack partial migration (PSPM) or dip moveout (DMO) addresses this problem. Both flat and dipping events need to be stacked in, so that the migration (post-stack) will be able to present all the signals originally in the data set.

The technique converts nonzero offset data to data that are more nearly zero offset. The correction is a 2-D filtering operation performed on each set of common offset data after the NMO correction has been applied and before the data are stacked (Yilmaz and Claerbout;[20] Deregowski and Rocca;[21] Hale[22]). The correction is a wave-theoretical process that converts the NMO-corrected data recorded at any nonzero offset to true nonzero offset. DMO corrections move finite-offset events updip to their true reflection points and thus remove reflection-point smear. The dip dependence of V_{st} is also removed. For these two reasons a better estimate of V_{rms} and a better stack will be obtained when the velocities are reestimated after DMO. The original NMO function is restored to the data after the DMO correction. The velocity analysis will now yield rms velocities, not the usual dip-dependent stacking velocities. The data will be moved out and stacked with the improved velocity functions. Now, all primary events, independent of dip, will be stacked in (see Fig. 7-35). Migration of the DMO stack (Fig. 7-35b) will produce for less total cost a section effectively equivalent to a pre-stack time migration.

NMO and Dip Filtering

As mentioned before, NMO stack is a powerful discriminant for primaries and against multiples. Further multiple suppression can be achieved by use of NMO and velocity filtering. The data are ordered into CMP gathers, and an NMO function is applied that is intermediate between primary and multiple velocities. The result is that the primaries are overcorrected and the multiples are undercorrected. A velocity filter that rejects "positive" dips (curving down with offset) is used on the data, thus removing the "tail" of the multiple. Obviously, since all energy curving down with offset is removed, care must be taken to have all the primaries overcorrected so that they will be preserved.

General Aspects of Velocity Determination by Computer

Interval velocities can be determined by any of these techniques from velocity-time relations and Eq. (7-29) (the Dix formula), but it must be realized that the precision of the interval values thus determined is necessarily less than that of the stacking velocities.

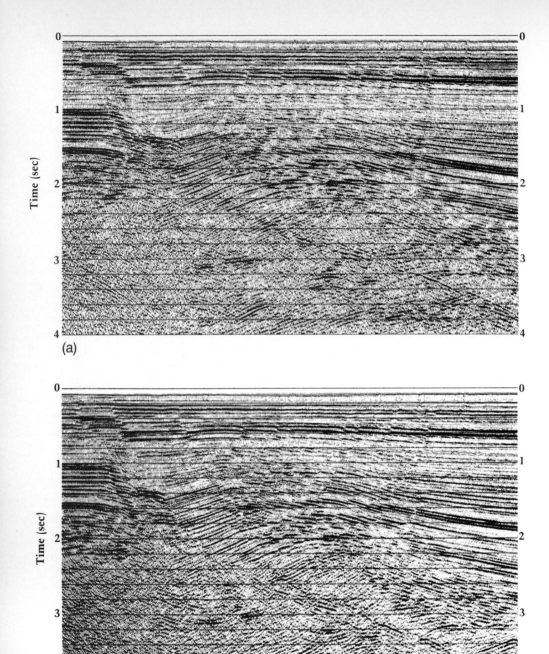

(a)

(b)

FIGURE 7-34 Illustration of the multivalued stacking-velocity problem on conventionally processed data. (*a*) Conventional CMP stack: events with different dips arriving at the same time are not preserved through NMO and stack. For adequate imaging, either DMO (Fig. 7-35) is required, or pre-stack time migration, which is much more expensive and more difficult to do correctly. (*b*) The post-stack time migration of section (*a*). Note the loss of detail in and around the fault-plane reflections on both sections, as compared to Fig. 7-35. (*Western Geophysical*.)

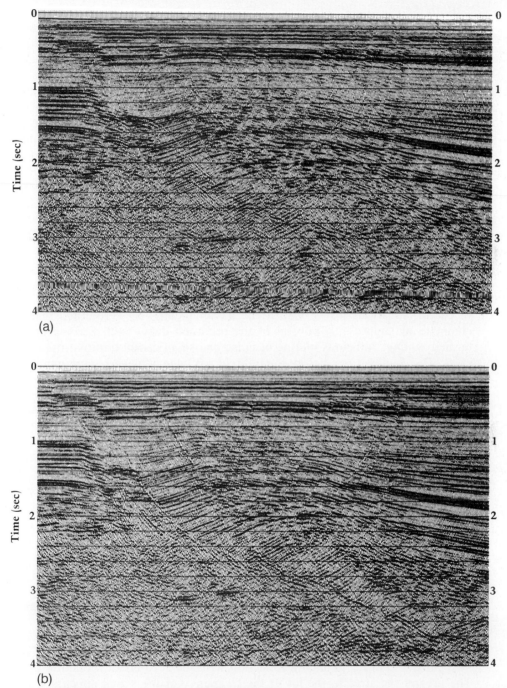

(a)

(b)

FIGURE 7-35   The effect of DMO processing. (a) The same field data as Fig. 7-34a, but with DMO applied pre-stack. (b) The post-stack time migration of section (a). Note the improvement in reflection data quality and the definition of the numerous fault-plane reflections and adjacent sediments, as compared to Fig. 7-34. (*Western Geophysical*.)

Both the velocity-spectrum and velocity-scan methods are programmed for automatic computation from reflection data corrected for statics and adequately gained (usually AGC). The decisions made by the geophysicist are the choice of shot-point positions at which the analyses are to be made, the range and separation of the trial velocities to be used, and, for the velocity spectra, the interval between the times for which successive determinations are made.

Other computer techniques have also been employed for determining velocity. One method involves the assumption of a velocity function based on whatever information is available and the determination of corrected residual moveouts by cross-correlation of all traces with a reference trace obtained by averaging a number of near-offset traces. The residual times provide a time-distance relation from which a more accurate velocity function can be computed. The residual moveout corrections can also be specified manually by the geophysicist for application by the computer. The geophysicist is supposed to be more alert than are automated RNMO programs to the presence of multiples.

7-7 MUTING

In certain situations it has been found advantageous to "zero-out," that is, eliminate or suppress, a portion of the recorded data. Such zeroing out is termed *muting*. Judicious muting of noise can significantly improve the CMP stack. For shallow time, before the full fold has been achieved, good muting is critically important. Noisy traces can either be zeroed or windows within the noisy trace can be zeroed to remove the noise and leave the discernible signal. We will briefly discuss the main types of mutes: first-break muting, NMO-stretch muting, and inner-trace muting.

First-Break Muting

Certain processing flows will require first-break muting. This processing step has been around for a long time—a patent on it was granted to B. B. Strange[23] in the early days of playback capability. Today, first-break muting is required whenever subsequent calculations will be perturbed by the first breaks. For example, if a data-dependent amplitude adjustment program is run early in the flow, the high amplitude of the first breaks can distort the calculation of the early gain factors.

NMO-Stretch Muting

Normal moveout stretches the time axis of the far offsets more than that of the near offsets in order to align a reflection with the zero-offset reflection time. The greater the stretch, the lower the frequency of the signal appears to be. Most NMO programs have an option to mute data stretched more than a certain percentage. The usual limit of acceptability of stretch is around 50 percent. Best results are often achieved by allowing a 2:1 stretch, and then specifying a handpicked mute pattern after viewing the data. The NMO-stretch mute can be integral with the first-break mute and, in effect, defines the maximum extent of the mute beyond the first break themselves.

Inner-Trace Muting

Deep reflections, arriving late in time, have minimal or negligible moveout stretch. These events are usually low frequency and suffer from competition with multiples. An inner-trace mute can help the signal-to-noise ratio here, because the inner traces do not contain the necessary differential stepout of primary and multiple. A straight-line mute is often specified by a mute "velocity," i.e., its inverse slope on the record being muted.

7-8   CMP STACK: MIDPOINT DISPLAY OF DATA SUMMATION

The CMP gather is stacked (summed) after all necessary time, amplitude, and frequency-phase adjustments are made. Stacking is a data compression of one to two orders of magnitude. The signal-to-random-noise ratio is increased through an N-fold stack by $\sqrt{N}$. After stack, the data are displayed at the surface location of the midpoint between source and receiver. When all adjustments to the data have transformed the offset data into time and phase coincidence with the zero-offset trace, a stack trace is used as the approximation to the zero-offset trace. With flat reflectors, the common midpoint (CMP) is the common depth point (CDP). The terms CMP and CDP are both widely used, often interchangeably. With dipping reflectors, however, the CMP after conventional processing is not the CDP. The correct positioning of reflecting points will be discussed in Sec. 7-10, Migration.

Any time-shift errors, or misalignments, remaining in the data will affect the high-frequency components more than the low-frequency components upon stacking. Therefore, unless moveout and statics are done very carefully, CMP stack can act as a high-cut filter. Any processing step that adds or repositions energy can act as a high-cut filter when error is present. The high frequencies are desirable for resolution and for waveshape character. In practice, the high-frequency content of the stack can be compared (visually, by the geophysicist) to that of the near-offset traces in the CMP gather. If the frequency contents of reflected events at comparable times in the two data sets are reasonably similar, one concludes that there were not significant time-shift errors remaining in the data. The frequency content of background noise is not affected by stacking errors.

Array Forming and Beam Steering

Some data summation steps, beam steering and/or array forming, are normally done in the field or in the first stages of data processing. These steps are presented here because knowledge of NMO is required for the following discussion.

The number of channels (traces) recorded per shot is customarily 96, but 120 to 480 channels are not unusual. When as many as 480 or more channels are recorded, particularly in marine operations, data summation steps such as array forming and/or beam steering are often used to reduce the number of traces per record to a more manageable number (such as 96 to 120) and to increase the signal-to-noise ratio (S/N). Array forming is the summation of several traces into one trace. Arrays, however, act as high-cut filters due to intragroup moveout at the farther offsets. This undesirable effect is circumvented by applying dynamic (time-variant), offset-dependent time shifts to the component traces before summing, a process generally called *beam steering* (Ref. 24). Dramatic improvements in high-frequency signal content and in S/N are obtainable. These time shifts, correcting for differential NMO across the array, or intragroup moveout, are distinctly separate from ordinary normal moveout corrections. The exact velocity function in the area does not have to be known in order to perform beam steering. Because it is only necessary to estimate the differential NMO across the traces to be summed (beam steered), only a crude idea of the velocity function is needed to beam steer with an accuracy of better than 1 ms. Even if the velocity used is grossly in error, the beam-steered data will be superior to array-formed data.

7-9 PLOTTING OF SEISMIC DATA

Record sections are conventionally plotted versus time, as shown in Fig. 7-36, but the time axis can be converted to a depth axis through the velocity functions. On a depth section, usually made after a migration, the wavelengths of the plotted seismic events lengthen with increasing depth. Compare Figs. 7-36 and 7-37. This effect is caused in part by the increase of average velocity with depth. Thus, at greater times, equal time intervals correspond to ever greater depth intervals. The earth's natural filtering action, which results in lower-frequency signals being observed from greater depths even on time sections, accentuates the wavelength stretch. The presentation of seismic signals on a depth scale is more helpful after migration, for diffractions are collapsed and crossing-time dips are separated and moved back to a more nearly correct subsurface spatial position, thus simplifying the structural image. A depth section demonstrates, in geologically meaningful terms, the limitation in the resolution of seismic reflection signals as well as the decrease in the resolution attainable as depth increases. The differences in appearance are quite conspicuous, providing evidence of velocity variation within the section.

Types of Plots

The standard black-and-white plots have already been introduced. They present amplitude as a function of time and spatial location. Variable-density plots, in which the positive amplitudes are shaded from gray to black according

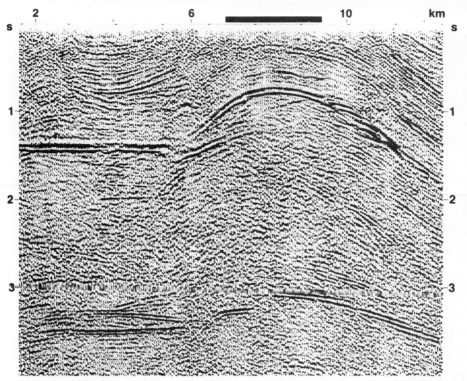

FIGURE 7-36   CDP stack, not migrated, plotted in time. Migrations of this data set are shown in Figs. 7-37 and 7-47. (*Western Geophysical.*)

to amplitude, allow a significantly greater range of amplitudes to be discerned than do variable-area plots.

Variable-area and variable-density plots focus attention primarily on the peaks. A rectified plot (that is, a plot of the absolute values of the trace) allows direct comparison of peaks to troughs. The plot may have both positive and negative values shaded in gray according to amplitude (variable density), or the peaks may be shades of red and the troughs of blue (or any other pair of contrasting colors). A plot in which the peaks are shaded a different color than the troughs, with or without the rectifying of the wiggle trace, is sometimes referred to as a *polarity plot*.

Color Plots   The use of color in the display of seismic data is becoming more important. The color encoding of amplitude onto a wiggle trace (CMP stack) can allow the eye to detect 60 dB or more of amplitude variation, a range far exceeding any black-and-white plot. Substantial increases in the amount of information that can be displayed are possible through the use of color. Actual increases in the dynamic range depend, of course, on the color selection. Grading colors by use of shades of single colors offers the least improvement

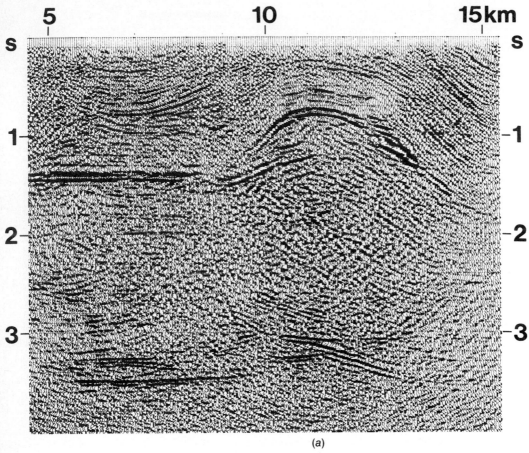

(a)

FIGURE 7-37 (a) Post-stack time migration of Fig. 7-36. Vertical scale is in time. (b) Conventional depth section (after a post-stack time migration). Vertical scale is in depth. The time axis of (a) was converted to depth by use of the appropriate velocity functions. (*Western Geophysical.*)

while sharply contrasting color steps can offer improvements as great as 15-fold. Different color schemes are designed for detecting small amplitude variations over a certain amplitude range or for studying amplitude variation over a broad range of values.

Color amplitude plots have the capability to depict a wide range of amplitudes faithfully and with great consistency. Variable-density plots, which are the black-and-white plots capable of conveying the greatest amount of information can vary greatly in quality from day to day and from plotter to plotter due to plotter drift, chemical strength of the developing fluid, and human factors.

The simplest of all conventional plots is a black wiggle-trace plot displaying amplitude as a function of time and space. Color-encoded information displayed on top of a wiggle trace may come from the trace itself (single-channel measurements) or from adjacent channels (multichannel measurements). Taner

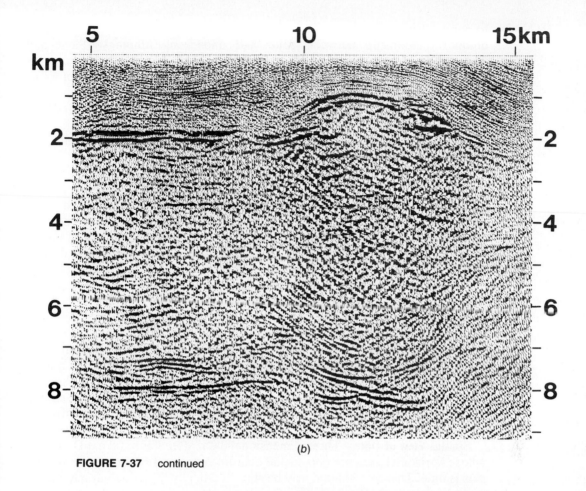

(b)

FIGURE 7-37   continued

and Sheriff[25] and Taner et al.[26] have introduced a number of single-channel measurements, called *seismic attributes*, which are color plotted and displayed upon the wiggle trace. These quantities include instantaneous phase, instantaneous frequency, and envelope amplitude. Multichannel measurements can look at any quantity over the dimensions of space, time, and/or offset. Stacking velocity, amplitude change with offset, and cross-dip (component of dip perpendicular to the plane of section) in swath shooting or 3-D data are a few of these quantities.

Two, three, or four independent attributes or derived quantities from the seismic data can simultaneously be displayed in color by the expedient of having the magnitude of each of the attributes control the intensity of one of the three primary colors and the gray scale. Every combination of the primary colors and the gray scale will produce a unique result. It is expected that when methods are devised to derive not only *P*-wave velocity but such quantities as attenuation, shear-wave velocity, or Poisson's ratio, and two or more are used to control primary components of color, the result will be a unique (or near-unique) relationship between color and underlying lithology (Savit and Mateker[27]).

Color plotting of stacking velocity presents important information in a format easily used by the geophysicist. Lateral changes of stacking velocity or rms velocity can reveal velocity anomalies (push-downs or pull-ups) and indicate potential lithologic changes. The interval velocity determined by using Dix's equation [Eq. (7-29)] can also be color plotted. See Sec. 9-4 for examples and discussion of the interpretation of such plots.

Another example, in which information from one of the compressed axes is "preserved," is the change of amplitude with offset, which can be color plotted upon the conventional CMP wiggle-trace plot. The change of amplitude with offset must be quantified in some consistent manner in order to encode the information. The type of gain applied prior to measuring the change of amplitude with offset is critical and under debate. Comparison of real seismic data so plotted with color plots generated by sophisticated modeling packages allows the testing of hypotheses for the presence of gas or porosity, or any geologic circumstance that can affect the reflection coefficient.

Three-dimensional data or "swath shooting," in which three to seven lines are shot in a band a few hundred feet apart, allow the estimation of cross-dip components (component of dip perpendicular to the plane of section). This information can be color plotted on the CMP stack. Shades of red and orange could, for example, indicate amount of dip to the right; shades of blue and green, amount of dip to the left. A more expensive algorithm would present the dip information as a function of azimuth by the use of a rainbow spectrum.

Spatial View of Data   Three-dimensional data, after stack, fill a 3-D "cube" whose horizontal axes are two spatial coordinates, x and y, and whose vertical axis is time. This data volume may be sliced vertically at any azimuth to yield a "conventional" (2-D) seismic line. The data volume can also be sliced horizontally to view all x and y for a given time. Time-slice plots have been used for structural mapping purposes (see Figs. 10-36 through 10-38) and to show paleostream meanders (Ref. 28). A time-slice plot has a counterpart in 2-D seismic data. Conventional (2-D) seismic data fills a 3-D cube (offset and midpoint being the two horizontal axes and time being the vertical axis), so a horizontal slice through this cube will yield the amplitude for all offsets at all midpoints at a given time (personal communication, Hayward).

Note that a vertical slice from a properly migrated 3-D data volume may not duplicate a corresponding 2-D migrated profile (see Sec. 7-10 and Chap. 10). Data from out of the plane of the section may well appear on a conventional 2-D migrated survey line. In a 3-D migrated volume those data will have been properly placed in space and so will not appear on the slice (see Sec. 10-1 for data examples). Conversely, a reflection that can be seen only on another 2-D migrated line may appear on the 3-D migrated slice.

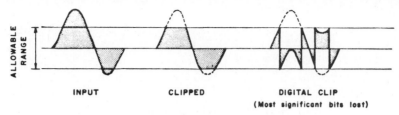

FIGURE 7-38   The two types of clipping: analog and digital. (*From Sheriff*.[29])

The dB Scale

Plots often have to be regenerated due to overscaling or underscaling by a constant in the zone of interest. Plot programs achieve an overall balanced plot, but the geophysicist is usually more interested in some parts of the plot than others. To regenerate the plot, the geophysicist often uses the dB scale to state the gain correction. The dB scale is also widely used in general comparisons of amplitudes. The ratio of two quantities is expressed in dB:

$$\text{Ratio in dB} = 20 \log \left(\frac{A_2}{A_1}\right) \tag{7-33}$$

where A_1 and A_2 are different amplitudes. Thus, 6 dB is a multiplier of 2; dB's add, and multipliers multiply. For example, if A_2 is 4 times greater than A_1, A_2 is 12 dB above A_1. If the amplitude ratio is greater than 1, the dB value is positive; if the ratio is less than 1, the dB value is negative.

To obtain a visible increase in the amount of wiggle-trace deflection, a gain increase of 6 dB is normally used. If a record section comes back with barely visible deflections on the wiggle traces, i.e., the gain is seriously too low, an 18-dB gain should solve the problem. Standard wiggle-trace plots have a "usable" range of approximately 30 dB: a 30-dB gain will take a record section of one or two barely visible deflections to a "clipped" record section. A clipped trace is a display in which amplitudes in excess of a certain amount are not shown. There are two types of clipping, digital and analog, which are illustrated in Fig. 7-38 (from Sheriff[29]).

7-10 MIGRATION

Migration is the process that repositions reflected energy from its common-midpoint position to its true subsurface location (for 2-D data in a 2-D world). Dipping reflectors on a CMP stack are plotted downdip from and with less dip than their true position, as shown in Fig. 10-10. Structures in the earth (e.g., anticlines, synclines, etc.) often have curvatures exceeding that of the seismic wavefront. In such cases, these structures look diffuse or complicated on time stacks (Fig. 8-8*b*). In tight synclines, reflections originate nearly simul-

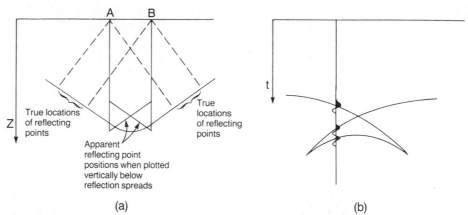

(a)   (b)

FIGURE 7-39 (a) Tight syncline showing the true and apparent spatial locations of the reflected dipping energy. (b) The "bow-tie effect" that is the time response over the syncline. A further discussion of this effect is found in Secs. 8-3 and 8-5.

taneously from several points on the curved surface (Fig. 7-39*a*) leading to the triple arrivals (termed "bow-tie effects") illustrated in Figs. 7-39*b* and 8-19. Figure 8-18 shows on field data the complicated appearance of a tight syncline before migration. Migration moves the reflected energy in these situations to the correct spatial location and thus clarifies the structural features. Diffractions, important indicators of discontinuities, are collapsed or focused back to the "discontinuity point."

The need for migration has been recognized since the first reflection surveys [Jakosky[30] (pp. 670–696)]. Figure 7-40 traces the development of migration techniques.

FIGURE 7-40 Development of migration techniques. (*From Johnson and French.*[32])

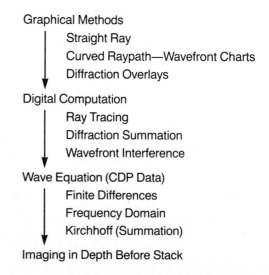

Graphical Methods
    Straight Ray
    Curved Raypath—Wavefront Charts
    Diffraction Overlays

Digital Computation
    Ray Tracing
    Diffraction Summation
    Wavefront Interference

Wave Equation (CDP Data)
    Finite Differences
    Frequency Domain
    Kirchhoff (Summation)

Imaging in Depth Before Stack

When discussing migration topics, certain variables have widespread pre-assigned meanings:

z = depth
t = one-way time
ω = frequency
x = spatial location (the midpoint axis)
y = the second spatial coordinate, orthogonal to x, used in 3-D situations
v = velocity

Manual and Graphical Methods

Straight-Ray (Constant-Velocity) Manual Method   Manual approximate migration can be performed by use of the correct average velocity overlying the dipping event, on the assumption of stratified media. Using Claerbout's[14] formulation, we can associate an apparent location (t_0, x_0) and an apparent time dip, $\theta_a = dt/dx$, with each reflection on the CDP stack. We wish to find its migrated position (t_m, x_{mo}) and dip, θ_m. From Fig. 7-41 we see that

$$\sin \theta_m = v \frac{dt}{dx} \tag{7-34}$$

where v is the overlying velocity. The basic geometric equation linking the unmigrated and the migrated dips is

$$\sin \theta_m = \tan \theta_a \tag{7-35}$$

which can be observed from triangles OX_1D' and OX_1D.

FIGURE 7-41   Diagram of terms used in development of hand-migration equations. θ_m = migrated dip, θ_a = apparent dip. The basic geometric equation linking the unmigrated and migrated dips is $\sin \theta_m = \tan \theta_a$.

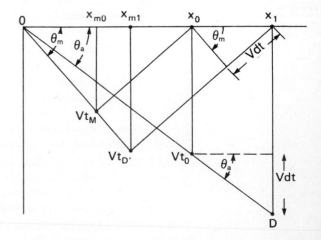

$$\tan \theta_a = v \frac{dt}{dx} \tag{7-36}$$

The migrated time is

$$t_m = t_0 \cos \theta_a = t_0 \sqrt{1 - \left(\frac{dt}{dx}\right)^2 v^2} \tag{7-37}$$

The lateral location after migration is

$$x_{mo} = x_0 - t_0 v \sin \theta_a = x_0 - t_0 \left(\frac{dt}{dx}\right) v^2 \tag{7-38}$$

where $v \sin \theta_a$ is a horizontal component of velocity. The migrated dip of the reflection segment, p_m, is given by

$$p_m = \frac{\tan \theta_a}{v} = \frac{\theta_a}{1 - \theta_a^2 v^2} \tag{7-39}$$

Migration by Means of Graphs and Charts   Hand-drafted sections with migration by means of precomputed graphs and tables that gave depth, displacement, and dip values based on "standard" velocity functions was an almost universal norm in areas of significant dip until the advent of record sections in the mid-1950s. Drafted time sections were used almost exclusively in areas of little dip. Migration by use of diffraction overlays and wavefront charts for use with record sections was introduced by Hagedoorn[31] in 1954. In the late 1960s Hagedoorn's concepts became the basis for most pre-wave equation digital migration code.

Figure 7-42a illustrates a diffraction overlay, also termed a surface of maximum convexity. It is determined from the average velocity field of the data for a 2-D stratified earth. Each curved line represents the time along a slant path that would be required for a reflection or diffraction curve. Charts of maximum convexity are made by combining individual curves of maximum convexity for successively deeper times. When a diffraction is overlaid by the appropriate curve, keeping time zero of the chart on time zero of the data, the location of the diffracting point on the time section is given by the apex of the diffraction curve. It is assumed that velocities are horizontally stratified [$v = v(z)$, not $v = v(x, z)$].

In manual migration using Hagedoorn's technique, one needs two charts, a wavefront chart (chart of equal reflection times as shown in Fig. 7-42b) and a maximum convexity chart for closely spaced vertical reflection times. Wavefront charts show the successive positions of a wave emanating from a point source at uniform time intervals after source initiation. The velocity field appropriate to the data is used to generate the wavefront chart. The two curves are placed in juxtaposition over the data with zero time and central positions

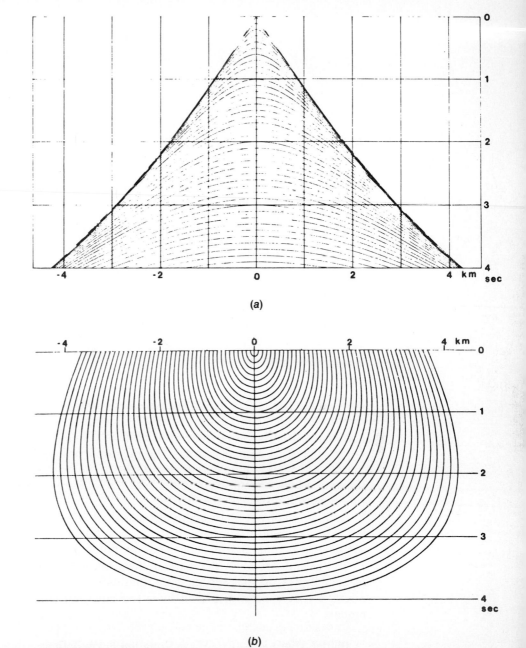

(a)

(b)

FIGURE 7-42   (a) Diffraction overlay, also known as a surface of maximum convexity. (b) Wavefront chart, showing the positions of seismic wavefront at 100-ms increments of time, for a given velocity function. (*From Kleyn.*[15])

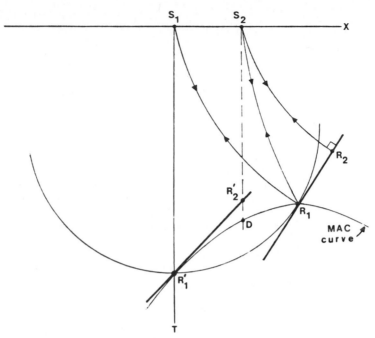

FIGURE 7-43   The use of the maximum convexity curve and a wavefront curve to migrate a dipping event, R_1, to its correct location, R_2, and determine its true dip. (From Kleyn.[15])

coincident. The reflecting-dip segment to be migrated is located along a curve on the wavefront chart at the central (vertical) axis of the chart. The maximum convexity chart is slid laterally until a lineup is found tangent to the diffraction curve (Fig. 7-43 from Kleyn[15]). The migrated position of the point is at the vertex of this diffraction curve, and the dip of the migrated segment is found by drawing a line tangent to the wavefront circle corresponding to the reflection time where it intersects this vertex.

Both a wavefront chart and a diffraction overlay are constructed based on the best estimate of earth velocities $v = v(z)$ in the vicinity of the dipping segment to be migrated. Geophysical textbooks issued from 1940 through the 1970s deal extensively with the use of these and other charts and analog devices to accomplish manual seismic-data migration. These older methods of hand migration have been displaced by wave equation computer migration techniques.

Digital Migration—Pre–Wave Equation Formulations   Before the advent of explicitly wave-equation-based migration code (Claerbout and Johnson[33]), digital migrations of data were based on ray-theory concepts. These programs did not correctly maintain the amplitude and phase relationships of the input data, and they introduced considerable noise. Since all digital migration schemes currently in use are approximations or explicit formulations of the acoustic wave equation, the need to discuss these older techniques has vanished. Seismic reflection textbooks issued in the 1970s deal adequately with this topic.

Wave Equation Migration

There are many good overviews of wave equation migration techniques: Johnson and French,[32] Sheriff and Geldart,[2] Kleyn,[15] and Waters.[8] Claerbout[14] extensively discusses the physics, mathematics, and coding of wave-equation-based computer techniques that image the earth's interior, with emphasis on finite-difference techniques.

Wave equation migration may be accomplished in the time domain, in the frequency domain, or in combinations thereof. The different formulations involve different assumptions and different approximations: which migration algorithm will best migrate the data is a function of the complexity of the geologic problem presented by the data. The types of migrations currently performed are time migration, depth migration, event migration, 3-D migration, and time migration before stack. Migration normally connotes a post-stack process, unless explicitly described as pre-stack. Time migration is the cheapest and practically as widespread as deconvolution. Impressive S/N improvements are achieved through time migration and the cost is minimal compared to the benefit received. Time migration before stack is quite expensive and done only if subtle features must be imaged. Migration before stack usually yields only an incremental improvement over post-stack migration, and yet the cost is many times greater. Particularly expensive migration techniques include reverse-time migration (no approximations to the acoustic wave equation), and depth migration before stack.

Time migration is a particular type of image reconstruction that works well for data in which $v = v(z)$. Only weak lateral changes in velocity are allowed. Three widespread methods exist to accomplish time migration: Kirchhoff (an integral or summation approach), finite difference, and frequency–wave number. Depth migration performs image reconstruction in a more arbitrary world; i.e., the lateral velocity variation restriction of time migration has been relaxed. Digitized reflection segments are cheaply migrated by use of ray theory in event migration. Three-dimensional migration is a time or depth migration performed upon 3-D data.

Time Migration (Post-Stack)   Time migration yields optimal results in stratified media or in weakly laterally changing velocity fields. The input CMP stack is assumed to be the zero-offset section containing all primaries and diffractions and no multiples. The accuracy of the velocities used to migrate the data governs the accuracy of the output. Velocity errors up to 10 percent can often be tolerated however, since a 10 percent change in velocities usually has little effect on the imaging of the data and displaces the results only minimally. Migration velocities come from seismically determined rms velocities, check-shot surveys, vertical seismic profiles (VSPs), sonic information, and/or diffraction hyperbolas on the input stack. The input seismic line is assumed to be a dip line. If the line is not along true dip, the migration velocities are calculated by dividing the rms velocities by the cosine of the angle the seismic line makes with true dips, as discussed by French.[34]

Kirchhoff or Summation Migration Kirchhoff migration is conceptually the simplest of migration approaches. This discussion will follow Johnson and French.[32] A reflector may be visualized as made up of many closely spaced point scatterers. The impulse response in the time domain to a point scatterer in the subsurface z is a hyperbola whose curvature is a function of the overlying velocity. Therefore, summation over the hyperbola appropriate for each time sample of the input data set will add in-phase all diffraction hyperbolas, and image all the reflectors. The velocity field $v = v(x, t)$ is used to determine the hyperbolic summation curves (portrayed earlier on the diffraction overlay chart). The summation operator is weighted so as to honor the wave equation. The method is based on Kirchhoff's theorem for a point-source integral solution to the wave equation. Schneider[35] describes a 2-D operator which requires time-domain convolution beneath hyperbolic apertures, then spatial summation, then differentiation to correct the phase.

Aperture size is a key concept in seismic-data acquisition and processing (see Fig. 10-11 and its discussion in the text). Aperture size in Kirchhoff migration refers to the number of traces forming, or the width of, the summing (hyperbolic) operator. Energy cannot move farther than half the aperture width: the larger the aperture, the longer the run time. The aperture should therefore be carefully chosen to handle the maximum dips of interest. With a proper aperture size, steep dips can be handled well. Weighting schemes can easily be applied to decrease noise. The Kirchhoff technique has been adapted to migration before stack and 3-D migration.

Finite-Difference Techniques The widely used wave equation migration method pioneered by Claerbout and Johnson[33] used a finite-difference solution to the one-way acoustic wave equation to describe and manipulate propagating waves. Operating in the time domain, finite-difference operators "push" or propagate the wavefronts through the earth. Due to certain approximations, dips up to about 15° were migrated properly. Subsequent formulations of the migration operators allowed dips to 45° or more to be properly migrated.

The CMP stack is the customary input for migration programs. "Perfect processing" has transformed (stacked) the multioffset data collected in the field into the zero-offset section required in migration. The zero-offset section is the simplest conceptual description of the end product of CMP stack. By definition, the zero-offset section is the wave field that would be recorded if each source on the line used only one collocated receiver to record the reflected energy (see Fig. 7-44).

The exploding reflector model (ERM) is currently the mathematical model of the zero-offset section from which the finite-difference treatment of seismic

Zero-offset Section   *Exploding Reflectors*

FIGURE 7-44   The zero-offset section is the section recorded when the source *s* and geophone *g* (receiver) are collocated. Processing attempts to turn the offset-recorded field data into the zero-offset section. The exploding reflector model (ERM) is diagrammed on the right: the sources arc on the reflector, and the strength of the source is scaled by the reflection coefficient. (From Claerbout.[14])

data is derived. The "zero-offset field experiment" concept is replaced by one in which the sources arc on the reflectors, and the strength and sign of the source are determined by the reflection coefficient of the reflector. At time zero, the sources are activated, following which the receivers, located on the surface of the earth, record the upgoing wave field. The recorded wave field is considered to be "the zero-offset section," as generated by the ERM. The travel time in the ERM, which is one-way time, would be half that of the zero-offset section, which is two-way time. In practice, the velocities are halved, so that the time axis is unchanged.

There are, however, at least three situations in which the ERM fails to mimic the zero-offset section (Claerbout[14]): (1) Travel paths in which the downgoing path is not the same as the upgoing path are present on the zero-offset section and not in the ERM (see Fig. 7-45*a*). (2) Multiple reflections are incorrectly predicted. On the zero-offset section, a flat seafloor reflection at t s has multiples at $2t$, $3t$, etc. In the ERM, the seafloor reflection arriving at t s has its multiples arriving at $3t$, $5t$, $7t$, etc. (3) In real data, reflections can exist from both sides of an interface, e.g., the sides of salt domes, or salt swells, etc. (see Fig. 7-45*b*). By the definition of a reflection coefficient, the two reflections will have opposite signs. The ERM will require the boundary to be assigned one reflection coefficient, with the result that the waves radiating from both sides of the boundary have the same sign. Another limitation of the ERM is related more generally to the wave fields recorded in seismic exploration: the ERM does not address the problem of how to migrate non-zero-offset data.

Downward Continuation   The closer the receivers are to the reflecting horizon, i.e., the sources in the ERM, the truer and less complicated the reflected representation is. This is especially obvious in the case of a syncline with a buried focus (see Fig. 8-18). Wave propagation operators, based on the one-way equation, are used to calculate the wave field that would be recorded if the receivers were closer to the reflectors. This treatment of the seismic data, termed *downward continuation*, is the effective movement of the recording

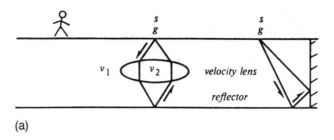

(a)

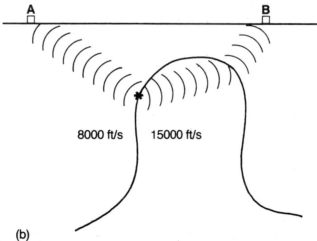

(b)

FIGURE 7-45   Real earth situations in which the exploding reflector model fails to predict the zero offset section. (a) The down-going path is not the same as the up-going path. (*Claerbout*.[14]) (b) Reflections from both sides of an interface. Location A would record a positive reflection (peak); location B, a negative reflection (trough). The ERM would predict the same sign reflection for locations A and B.

surface downward into the earth. The size of the Fresnel zone (discussed in Sec. 9-1), the area of the reflecting surface contributing the major portion of the reflected wave, depends upon the travel time of the wavefront [see Eq. (9-1)]. The shorter the effective travel time, the smaller the effective Fresnel zone, and the better the reflector is imaged. The virtual movement of receivers into the earth shortens the travel time, thus having the effect of decreasing the Fresnel zone and increasing the spatial resolution.

Downward continuation uses the stacked section as the initial wave field. This data set, recorded at the surface of the earth, $z = 0$, is the wave field $P(x, 0, t)$, where $P(x, z, t)$ is the pressure amplitude of a traveling acoustic disturbance at (x, z, t) (Johnson and French[32]). The propagating wave field is described by the 2-D scalar wave equation

$$\frac{\partial^2 P}{\partial x^2} + \frac{\partial^2 P}{\partial z^2} = \frac{1}{v^2} \frac{\partial^2 P}{\partial t^2}$$

The one-way wave equation is used for simplicity of formulation and speed of computation, so only waves propagating down (or up) are handled. The receivers are downward extrapolated, and at each depth the wave field is evaluated for $t = 0$. If there is energy at $t = 0$, the receiver must be on a source, i.e., on a reflector. The wave field for each $t = 0$ as the receivers are pushed Δz steps into the earth is stripped off as the migrated data set. The final section of time migrated data is $P(x, z, 0)$. At $t = 0$ in the ERM one has a "snapshot" of the reflectors before the complicated effects of wave propagation begin.

Cascaded Migration A recent innovation is the sequential or multistep migration of data using the inexpensive 15° finite-difference operator to obtain superior migrated results at no additional cost (Larner and Beasley[36]). Since the time dip of an event is related to its earth dip by the overlying velocity, a fraction of the true migration velocity, when used to migrate the data, will cause the time dips to be seen as a fraction of their true dip. Thus the effective dip of the event will usually be well under the 15° limitation, so minimal error or dispersion will ensue with each migration. A possible division of stages in this type of cascaded migration is to perform N migrations with a velocity function that is the true migration velocity divided by $\sqrt{N}$. The cost of multistage migration when the multiplexed (Sec. 7-1) output is input each time to the next migration step is no greater than one-step (conventional), 15° finite-difference migration.

Frequency-Domain Techniques Frequency-wave-number-domain techniques were introduced in 1978 by Stolt.[37] The data are transformed ("stretched") into a pseudo-depth domain to approximate a constant-velocity earth. The data are then 2-D Fourier transformed. The migration is accomplished by a repositioning of the energy in the frequency–wave-number domain by means of the wave equation. The data are inverse Fourier transformed and stretched back into normal travel time. The algorithm is formulated for a constant-velocity earth; the "stretch" allows for a stratified-velocity earth $v = v(z)$. Slow lateral changes in velocity can be handled by changing the stretching function along the line. Rapid or large changes in velocity produce effects on the seismic data that are not treated properly. In theory, frequency–wave-number migration can migrate dips up to 90°.

Relative Costs Frequency-domain migration is generally the fastest, and hence cheapest, way to migrate data. Kirchhoff migration takes longer but suffers less from spatial aliasing effects, performing well in steep-dip areas.

Finite-difference approaches are relatively expensive. Dispersion due to the approximations used in calculating derivatives creates noise on the output sections, but sections after migration do not appear mixed (a complaint of other migration techniques) due partly to the dispersion noise and partly to the dip limitation of the operator which avoids smoothing of noise.

Depth Migration (Post-Stack)

Normal Rays and Image Rays   For unmigrated CMP stacks, the travel times to the events are associated with normal incident-ray paths, also termed normal rays. These are rays that leave the source and hit the reflector at 90° and so return to the surface along exactly the same ray path, the zero-offset ray path. For time-migrated sections, the travel time to any event is associated with an image-ray path. These are rays that leave the surface perpendicularly and hit the reflectors at arbitrary angles (see Figs. 7-46 and 7-47). Image rays have a particular use in identifying the severity of lateral-velocity variations. If the image rays do not deviate substantially from the vertical, they can be used to

FIGURE 7-46   Image-ray plot, based on the velocity model of Figure 7-47a. Crossing of image rays indicates the need for a depth-migration algorithm, not a time-migration algorithm. (*Western Geophysical.*)

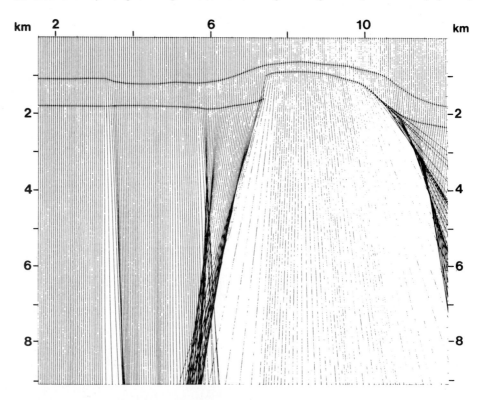

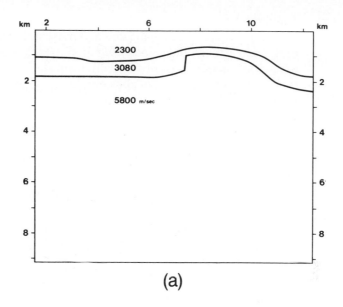

(a)

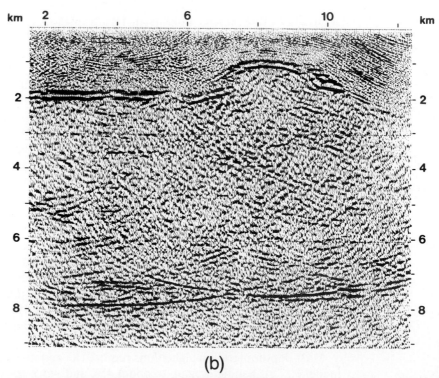

(b)

FIGURE 7-47 (a) Velocity model, used for the migrations of Fig. 7-36 (the input time section). A time migration of Fig. 7-36 was given in Fig. 7-37. (b) The depth migration (post-stack) using the input section of Fig. 7-36 and the velocity model in (a). (*Western Geophysical*.)

convert a time-migrated section to a depth section. This type of time-to-depth conversion is more sophisticated and more accurate than the simple stretching of the time axis by the velocity function (which is often the method used). If the image rays do deviate substantially from the vertical, especially if they cross, time migration is not an appropriate imaging tool and depth migration is necessary. If the image rays should cross, energy from each crossing point is displayed at two different spatial positions on the time-migrated section—a situation which makes interpretation more difficult. Interpreters prefer energy from a given subsurface reflecting horizon to be manifest only once on a migrated section and placed correctly in space. Figure 7-46 illustrates the image rays for the velocity plot of Fig. 7-47a, and for the time migration shown in Fig. 7-37a. A further discussion of image rays and normal rays is in Hubral and Krey.[38]

Depth migration is designed to migrate data in the presence of strong lateral-velocity variation. An example of this is shown in Fig. 7-47a, and the depth-migrated data are shown in Fig. 7-47b. These figures should be compared to Figs. 7-36 and 7-37. For these data, depth migration is clearly the more correct imaging procedure, due to the radical lateral-velocity variation. The input CMP stack is assumed to be the zero-offset section with no multiples. The output-migrated section is in depth, and its appearance is quite sensitive to the accuracy of the velocity field used. Depth migrations are more sensitive than time migrations to the accuracy of the velocity-depth model.

Sometimes a geophysicist has just the CMP stack, not accompanied by an image-ray plot, with which to decide whether to time migrate or depth migrate. The presence of significant velocity anomalies (pull-ups, push-downs, etc.) on the CMP stack are tipoffs that depth migration is the required choice. Velocity anomalies stand out when the seismic rms velocities are color plotted on the wiggle traces or contoured upon an overlay sheet to the stacked section. A time migration would migrate the "spurious" (velocity-induced) dips just like "true" structural dips, thus causing further, and more complicated, distortion on the output (time-migrated) section. When the distorting velocity layers (or lenses) are accurately described in the input velocity field to the depth-migration program, the output, depth-migrated section will have the velocity anomaly removed and will portray an accurate image of the subsurface in depth. The accurately migrated depth section will match the input depth model.

Time migrations do not shift apexes of diffraction hyperbolas sideways. Depth migrations do. An important example of this necessary spatial shift is the circumstance of anticline(s) under dipping layers or under strong lateral-velocity contrasts. The crest of the anticline is incorrectly located in space on the stack, yet will be correctly located in space after depth migration with the correct velocity field.

Most depth-migration algorithms require the geophysicist to input a velocity model $v(x, z)$, handle dips up to about 45°, and work in (x, ω) space. The one-way, acoustic wave equation is used to design the operators, which means, among other things, that multiples are not handled properly. Depth migration is usually more expensive than time migration, but produces a superior (and more nearly correct) section when the correct velocity model is used.

Event Migration   In complex data areas, it can be difficult to construct, without computer assistance, the velocity model required for the depth migration. Iterative depth migrations, a desirable approach, may be prohibitively expensive. Event migration is the inexpensive tool used to build the velocity-depth model. The interpretable significant events on the time section are digitized and depth migrated by use of ray theory and the geophysicist's best guess for the velocity-depth model. The model is updated by the new depth

FIGURE 7-48   Model indicating structure of recumbent diapir and deformation of associated layers. Reflection-ray paths shown are to the deep side of the interface observed at a depth of 4000 ft along the left edge. (*Seiscom Delta, Inc.*)

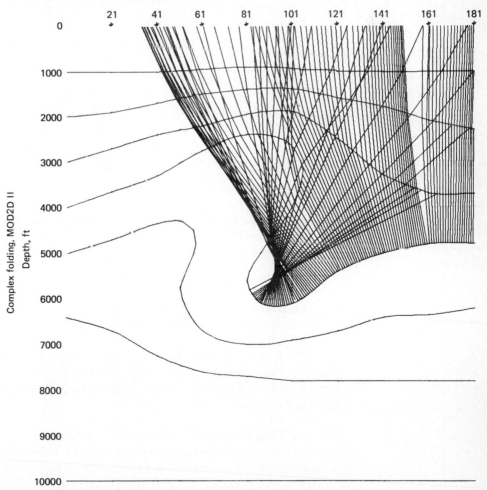

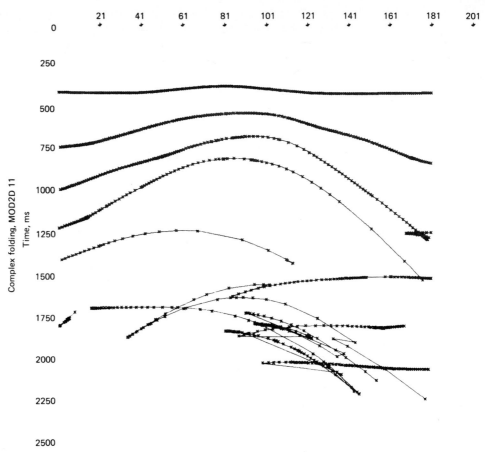

FIGURE 7-49 Computed time section based on ray paths and assumed velocities for structural model shown in Fig. 7-48. (*Seiscom Delta, Inc.*)

section in areas of discrepancy, and the digitized event, time section is remigrated. After several iterations, the model and the output depth section will agree. If it is so desired, a time section can be generated from the model, which is then compared to the real CMP stack (see Figs. 7-48 and 7-49). In Sec. 7-6 under horizon-event analysis, we noted the use of the earth model to generate offset (V_{st}) data for comparison with field data as a further test of the model's accuracy. Once a satisfactory model is constructed, the CMP stack can be migrated with confidence by means of the sophisticated but expensive depth-migration algorithm.

Reverse-Time Migration Whitmore[39] and Baysal et al.[40] have presented a depth-migration approach that allows an arbitrary velocity model and makes no approximations to the acoustic wave equation. It handles all dips as well as up-going and down-going waves. This algorithm is considerably more expensive to implement than are all of the others, but it is useful in complex data areas. As with all migration techniques, the accuracy of the output depends upon the accuracy of the input velocity model and the degree to which the CMP stack approximates the zero-offset section. Event migration can assist in the early stages of model construction, as discussed above, followed by a similarly iterative approach to migrate the CMP stack. As computers become faster and larger, the cost of this approach is expected to decrease.

Three-Dimensional Migration   Three-dimensional data sets are usually collected in areas of complex geology where the need for migration is the greatest as is the uncertainty in velocity. The Kirchhoff and frequency–wave-number migration techniques are usually chosen to expand to the 3-D case. The cost of 3-D migration is much higher than that of 2-D migration, but the results are significantly superior. Three-dimensional depth migration (post-stack) is available but even more expensive; it is a crucial step for securing the imaging power inherent in 3-D data. Chapter 10 will deal further with 3-D migration.

Time Migration before Stack   In the presence of dipping horizons, the sorting of traces into CMP gathers produces gathers composed of many subsurface depth points, not just one depth point. When the CMP stack is made, there is smearing in the subsurface coverage. Also, in conventional stacks, the steeply dipping tails of the diffractions usually cross flatter events, and are thus lost due to conventional moveout and stack. The quality of the migrated section suffers when all primary events and diffractions are not present on the input stack. As discussed earlier, this situation in which two or more events with different dips exist at the same time is the multivalued NMO problem. Migration before stack corrects these two problems and almost always produces better results than the conventional stack-migrate process. Currently most pre-stack migration algorithms are time migrations, using either a frequency–wave-number or Kirchhoff approach.

The drawbacks of migration before stack are, however, numerous. It is currently much more expensive. Common-offset sections are migrated, then stacked to form the output-migrated section. Usually several offsets are stacked together prior to migration to reduce the fold by 3 or 4. Thus the cost of pre-stack migration can be about 6 to 10 times the cost of post-stack migration. Migration before stack is much more sensitive to the accuracy of the velocity model than in post-stack migration. Small errors (<5 percent) in the velocity model can have visible, deleterious effects on the output. Finally, most interpreters need (or want) a CMP stack section as an intermediate output, as well as the final migrated section. (The CMP stack is often used as the mappable section, with the migrated section showing the locations of the faults and approximate positions of the crests of structures.) Migration before stack does not output such a section. Of course, as an added expense, the migrated output can be "diffracted" to yield a computed CMP stack. Diffraction in this sense is the inverse operator to migration.

Dip moveout (DMO), or partial migration before stack, as discussed earlier in Sec. 7-6, presents one solution to the problems we have outlined. It provides, at substantially less cost than pre-stack migration, a CMP stack in which all primary events, regardless of their dip, have been preserved (see Figs. 7-34 and 7-35). That section is subsequently migrated to obtain a section comparable to a pre-stack migration. Dip moveout is also significantly less sensitive to errors in the velocity field. The usual processing sequence is gain, sort, NMO, apply the DMO correction, restore the normal moveout, and reestimate the velocities. Now, the velocity analyses yield V_{rms} functions, not V_{st}, for the cosine dependence of V_{st} on the dip of the reflector has been removed. The new velocity functions are applied, followed by stack and migrate.

Migration before stack is justifiable in areas with severe lateral-velocity changes; i.e., a depth-migration problem is presented. A time migration either before or after stack will not satisfactorily image the earth in these situations. Therefore, a depth migration before stack should be considered.

Depth Migration before Stack and Elastic-Wave-Equation Migration   With a vector computer (supercomputer) these two types of migration can be performed, although the cost is high. As always, a velocity model of the earth is required for the migration, and the quality of the output depends upon the accuracy of the model. The elastic-wave equation unites the reflected P-wave, shear-wave, and converted-wave fields to yield an image of the earth with respect to the bulk modulus, shear modulus, and density. Elastic-wave-equation migration is, of course, less expensive to perform post-stack than pre-stack.

7-11   SPECIAL CONSIDERATIONS FOR SHEAR-WAVE PROCESSING

Shear-wave processing often proceeds along lines similar to P-wave processing. There are a few, perhaps obvious, differences that are standard.

The velocity of shear waves is approximately half that of P waves. The V_P/V_S ratio ranges from 1.5 to 1.76 for many sandstones, 1.78 to 1.98 for many carbonates (Domenico[41]), while shales appear to have V_P/V_S ratios from 1.6 to 2.2. The brute stack (first stack) can be made by applying half the P velocity at twice the P transit time; subsequent velocity analyses will then refine the moveout function.

The frequencies contained in shear-wave data are often half those of corresponding P-wave data. A fundamental equation is that frequency times wavelength equals velocity. The factor of approximately 2 that relates P velocity and shear velocity will also relate either frequencies or wavelengths. It usually relates frequencies. Field tests must be performed, though, in each new area to determine the frequency range of signals. If the P-frequency content equals that of the shear, the shear wavelength will be half that of P, and thus the shear data will have twice the resolution. Most shear-wave data use a vibroseis source, so the filters will be determined by the sweep used and the frequency content of the noise.

Statics can present a substantial problem. The low-velocity zone can have V_P/V_S ratios ranging from 2 to 5 or more. In many areas, the LVL for the shear wave is not the same LVL as for the P wave, so the two static fields are not coupled. If the shear static is caused by the same zone that caused the P static, the static values will be related by the V_P/V_S ratio of that zone. That ratio might well change along the line. In the "easier" to handle situation in which the two static value fields are related, if a coincident P-wave line has static values ranging from 5 to 20 ms, the shear-wave line could well have static values from 10 to 100 ms or more. Refraction static routines may provide a good estimate of weathering statics, and then automatic static routines may be able to refine the initial static estimates.

Time sections of shear-wave data are usually plotted at about half the vertical scale of P-wave data. This compression of the vertical axis allows an easier visual comparison of the two data sets. Final sections of shear-wave data may be plotted using either the best average $1/(V_P/V_S)$ ratio around the zone of interest to scale the shear-wave time axis, or the best average $1/(V_P/V_S)$ ratio of all the sedimentary reflectors, which achieves an approximate match of shear to P for the whole section.

In the real earth, V_P/V_S varies both with depth and laterally. Time-variant but space-invariant time-shift ("stretch-squeeze") programs can match shear to P reflectors for display purposes or for analysis purposes. Now, coplotting of the two data sets (in different colors) can highlight lateral changes in V_P/V_S. When the V_P/V_S ratio can be estimated, Poisson's ratio may then be calculated and displayed in color on the stacked data. Section 9-3 deals with the interpretation of P- and shear-wave data sets.

REFERENCES

1 Dragoset, W. H.: A Comprehensive Method for Evaluating the Design of Air Guns and Air Gun Arrays, *The Leading Edge*, vol. 3, pp. 52–61, October 1984.
2 Sheriff, R. E., and L. P. Geldart: "Exploration Seismology," vol. 2, "Data Processing and Interpretation," Cambridge University Press, New York, 1983.
3 Burg, J. P.: Maximum Entropy Spectral Analysis, Ph.D. thesis Stanford University, Stanford, California, 1975.
4 Wood, L. C.: Imaging the Subsurface, in K. C. Jain and R. J. P. de Figueiredo (eds.), "Concepts and Techniques in Oil and Gas Exploration," Society of Exploration Geophysicists, Tulsa, Okla., 1982.
5 Cassano, E., and F. Rocca: After-Stack Multichannel Filters without Mixing Effects, *Geophys. Prospec.*, vol. 22, no. 2, pp. 330–344, 1974.
6 Gelfand, V., and K. Larner: Seismic Lithologic Modeling, *The Leading Edge*, vol. 3, pp. 30–35, November 1984.
7 Slotnick, Morris M.: In Richard A. Geyer (ed.), "Lessons in Seismic Computing," Society of Exploration Geophysicists, Tulsa, Okla., 1959.

8 Waters, K. H.: "Reflection Seismology: A Tool for Energy Resource Exploration," John Wiley, New York, 1978.

9 A. W. Musgrave (ed.): "Seismic Refraction Prospecting," Society of Exploration Geophysicists, Banta, Menasha, Wis., 1967.

10 Savit, C. H.: Refraction Profiling Using Average Velocity to Near Horizontal Beds, pp. 330–336, in A. W. Musgrave (ed.), "Seismic Refraction Prospecting," Society of Exploration Geophysicists, Tulsa, Okla., 1967.

11 Hileman, J. A., P. Embree, and J. C. Pflueger: Automated Static Corrections, *Geophys. Prospec.*, vol. 16, pp. 326–358, 1968.

12 Berryhill, J. R.: Wave-Equation Datuming, *Geophysics*, vol. 44, pp. 1329–1344, 1979.

13 Berryhill, J. R.: Wave-Equation Datuming before Stack, *Exp. Abs. of the 54th Annual SEG Meeting*, pp. 397–399, 1984.

14 Claerbout, J. F.: "Imaging the Earth's Interior," Blackwell Scientific, Palo Alto, Calif., 1984.

15 Kleyn, A. H.: "Seismic Reflection Interpretation," Elsevier, New York, 1983.

16 Green, C. H.: Velocity Determination by Means of Reflection Profiles, *Geophysics*, vol. 3, pp. 295–305, 1938.

17 Dix, C. H.: Seismic Velocities from Surface Measurements, *Geophysics*, vol. 20, pp. 68–86, 1955.

18 Taner, M. Turhan, and Fulton Koehler: Velocity Spectra: Digital Computer Derivation and Applications of Velocity Functions, *Geophysics*, vol. 34, pp. 859–881, 1969.

19 Lynn, W. S., and J. F. Claerbout: Velocity Estimation in Laterally Varying Media, *Geophysics*, vol. 47, pp. 884–897, 1982.

20 Yilmaz, O., and J. F. Claerbout: Pre-Stack Partial Migration *Geophysics*, vol. 45, pp. 1753–1779, 1980.

21 Deregowski, S., and F. Rocca: Geometrical Optics and Wave Theory of Constant Offset Sections in Layered Media, *Geophys. Prospec.*, vol. 29, pp. 374–406, 1981.

22 Hale, D.: Dip-Moveout by Fourier Transform, *Geophysics*, vol. 49, pp. 741–757, 1984.

23 Strange, B. B.: U.S. Patent No. 3,262,095, Method and Apparatus for Signal Compositing and Recording, issued July 19, 1966. Re 26,574 issued April 29, 1969.

24 Savit, C. H.: U.S. Patent No. 4,319,347, Seismic Method and System of Improved Resolution and Discrimination, issued March 9, 1982.

25 Taner, M. T., and R. E. Sheriff: Application of Amplitude, Frequency, and Other Attributes to Stratigraphic and Hydrocarbon Determination, pp. 301–328, in C. E. Payton (ed.), "Seismic Stratigraphy—Applications to Hydrocarbon Exploration," AAPG Memoir 26, Tulsa, Okla.

26 Taner, M. T., F. Koehler, and R. E. Sheriff: Complex Seismic Trace Analysis, *Geophysics*, vol. 44, pp. 1041–1063, 1979.

27 Savit, C. H., and E. J. Mateker, Jr.: "From Where to What," *Proceedings of Eighth World Petroleum Congress*, pp. 95–104, 1971.

28 Brown, A. R., R. J. Graebner, and C. G. Dahm: Use of Horizontal Seismic Sections to Identify Subtle Traps, pp. 47–56, in "The Deliberate Search for the Subtle Trap," AAPG Memoir 32, Tulsa, Okla., 1982.

29 Sheriff, R. E., compiler: "Encyclopedic Dictionary of Exploration Geophysics," 2d ed., Society of Exploration Geophysicists 1984.

30 Jakosky, J. J.: "Exploration Geophysics," 2d ed., Trija, Los Angeles, 1950.

31 Hagedoorn, J. G.: A Process of Seismic Reflection Interpretation, *Geophys. Prospec.*, vol. 21, pp. 85–127, 1954.

32 Johnson, J. D., and W. S. French: Migration—The Inverse Method, in K. C. Jain and R. J. P. de Figueiredo (eds.), "Concepts and Techniques in Oil & Gas Exploration," Society of Exploration Geophysicists, Tulsa, Okla., 1982.

33 Claerbout, J. F., and A. G. Johnson: Extrapolation of Time Dependent Waveforms along Their Path of Propagation, *Geophysical J. Roy. Astr. Soc.*, vol. 26, pp. 285–293, 1971.

34 French, W. S.: Migration and 3-D Interpretation, in "Modeling and Migration," A symposium sponsored by the Dallas Geophysical Society, February 1977.

35 Schneider, W. A.: Integral Formulation for Migration in Two Dimensions, *Geophysics*, vol. 43, pp. 49–76, 1978.

36 Larner, K., and C. Beasley: Cascaded Migrations: A Way of Improving the Accuracy of Finite-Difference Migration, *Expanded Abs. of the 55th Annual SEG Meeting*, pp. 417–419, 1985.

37 Stolt, R. H.: Migration by Fourier Transform, *Geophysics*, vol. 43, pp. 23–48, 1978.

38 Hubral, P., and T. Krey: Interval Velocities from Seismic Reflection Time Measurements, Society of Exploration Geophysicists, Tulsa, Okla., 1980.

39 Whitmore, N. D.: Iterative Depth Migration by Backward Time Propagation, *Exp. Abs. of the 53rd Annual SEG meeting*, pp. 382 385, 1983,

40 Baysal, E., D. D. Kosloff, and J. W. C. Sherwood: A Two-Way Non-Reflecting Wave Equation, *Geophysics*, vol. 49, pp. 132–141, 1984.

41 Domenico, S. N.: Rock Lithology and Porosity Determination from Shear and Compressional Wave Velocity, *Geophysics*, vol. 49, pp. 1188–1195, 1984.

CHAPTER 8

STRUCTURAL GEOLOGICAL INTERPRETATION OF SEISMIC REFLECTION DATA

In preceding chapters we have considered how seismic reflection data are recorded in the field and enhanced by processing in the computer. We have also examined techniques for velocity determination, time-depth conversion, and adjustment for distortions caused by ray-path geometry. But there is still another aspect of the geophysicist's work which is perhaps the most important of all, and that is the translation of the seismic information into geological terms. This process, *geological interpretation*, calls for the greatest possible coordination between geology and geophysics if it is to be carried out successfully. It is in this area that the demands for technical competence are so stringent that it is hard for either geologists or geophysicists to meet them unless they work together.

The many technological developments in the seismic art that have virtually revolutionized geophysical exploration during the 1950s and 1960s did not often affect the interpretation of seismic data except peripherally. More recently, there has been an upsurge of interest in the application of sophisticated computer techniques, and more powerful and speedier computers to the solution of interpretation problems. The use of computer-driven, work stations for interpretation and mapping, especially in 3-D and large 2-D offshore areas, is becoming more and more important. The new uses of reflection data for identifying lithology and studying stratigraphy, as described by Vail and his colleagues[1] at Exxon, have triggered much debate and reinterpretation of existing data. The techniques of direct detection of hydrocarbons and associated interpretive modeling have given a profound stimulus to such activity. Direct detection and modeling will be discussed in Chap. 9.

8-1 THE MEANING OF INTERPRETATION

The word *interpretation* has been given many different meanings by geophysicists who deal directly with seismic sections and by the geologists and geophysicists who coordinate the geologic information with the seismic information. To some it is virtually equivalent to data processing and is tied inextricably to computer software. To others it consists of all of the operations we considered in the last chapter, such as the transformation of seismic reflection data into a structural picture by the application of corrections, migration, and time-depth conversion.

Seismic data have been interpreted in two modes, with gradations between the modes. The first is in areas of substantial well control, in which the well information is first tied to the seismic information, and the seismic then supplies the continuity between the wells for the zones of interest. The second mode is in areas of no well control ("frontier areas"), in which the seismic data provide both definition of structure and estimates of depositional environments. Seismic velocities and seismic stratigraphic concepts are used to define the lithology. Seismic reflection amplitudes help to detail velocities and serve as a guide to pore constituents. In frontier areas, gravity and magnetic data are usually acquired, so that the geophysicist can decide among various geologic interpretations (e.g., igneous plug or salt dome). The more information incorporated into the interpretation, the better the interpretation becomes. Integration of seismic data with the geological information, whether from satellite, surface, or subsurface sources (e.g., fault traces or geologic contacts) involves identifying reflections and making ties to wells or surface features. The extent to which this can be done depends on the amount of geologic information available.

Interpretation can incorporate all the above concepts, subject to the one inviolable condition that it involve some exercise of judgment based on geological criteria. By this conception, interpretation can begin with the planning and programming of a seismic reflection survey if the planners are guided by the geology of the area and by the economic or scientific objectives of the survey. It can involve the choice of field parameters, such as the kind of seismic source to be used, the geometry of source and receiver patterns, and the settings of the recording instruments, as long as such choices are governed by the geological information desired. The selection of processing procedures and parameters is also an important part of the interpretation if it is supported by the same considerations.

Any purely mechanical operations not requiring discretion on the part of the geophysicist would come under the category of data reduction, not interpretation. It is possible even to make a seismic map, particularly one in time, without carrying out any real interpretation at all if every stage of its preparation is routine or automatic and no decisions have to be made that involve geological considerations.

The computer has made it feasible to use previously unexploited characteristics of seismograms to obtain geological information. Under favorable circumstances, interval velocities can be determined from reflection records with enough precision to permit them to serve as a basis for identifying lithology (Sec. 9-2). Another property of seismic waves that has been employed for studying rock composition is attenuation of seismic-wave amplitudes between successive reflectors, a parameter that can now be measured because of the high dynamic range in modern recording equipment. Due to the power of modern computers, the selection of tools available for seismic interpretation has been greatly extended since the late 1960s.

8-2   CORRELATION OF REFLECTIONS

Before corrected record sections came into universal use, it was customary to place adjacent records edge to edge in the manner shown in Fig. 4-4 and to correlate reflections from the last trace of one record to the first of the next. Stacked record sections, which have almost entirely replaced the individual multitrace records, make it possible to follow events over long distances much more conveniently.

Even with stacked, migrated data displays correlation of reflections is not always as simple as it may appear. Often a reflection characterized on the record by a single trough evolves into two troughs over a very few traces, as illustrated in Fig. 8-1. There may then be some doubt as to which of the two events correlates with the one trough from which they branch. In the case shown, the interpreter may be guided by the pattern of an adjacent reflection of better quality like the one just above. Although such changes in waveform may be associated with the geology of the reflecting formation, too often the reason for them is noise of one type or another which causes distortion of the signal. Modern data-processing techniques are designed to suppress such noise and thus increase the reliability of correlation and interpretation. Even so, it often requires considerable experience and good judgment, particularly when the data are marginal, to make correct picks. An error of 1 cycle could mean that the predicted depth to a geological boundary is 100 to 200 ft higher or lower than it should be. Another situation in which the lateral correlation of reflections can be difficult is in crossing a fault. Sometimes it is simple to see which "leg" of the pulse correlates; other times, it is quite difficult. For example, to correlate a time horizon correctly across some growth faults in the offshore Gulf Coast can even require micropaleontological data from nearby (but scarce) wells.

8-3   RESOLUTION AND PRECISION OF SEISMIC REFLECTION MEASUREMENTS

Although current recording and processing techniques produce high-quality reflection data suitable for structural interpretation, the intrinsic limitations in the reflection process must be recognized. All these limitations are related to the basic physics of seismic reflection in a medium having the characteristics of earth materials.

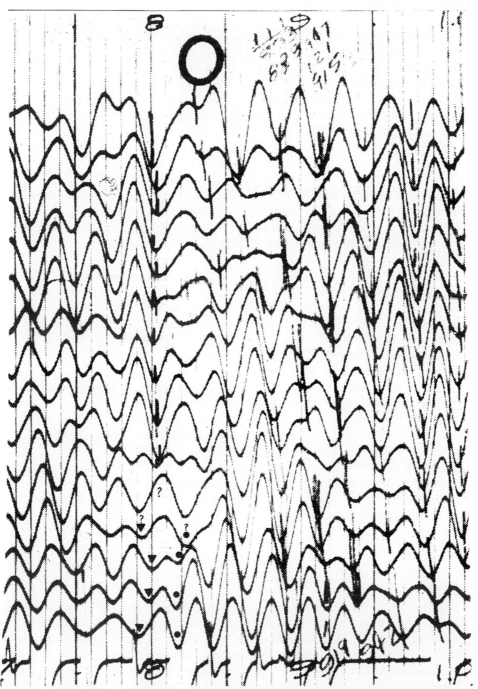

FIGURE 8-1   Break in continuity of reflection with attendant uncertainty in correlation. Event starting at top trace on time line marked 8 can be followed for nine more traces and then seems to terminate. Does continuation of event below this follow series of troughs marked by solid circles or that marked by solid triangles? The trend of other reflections suggests that the former is more likely.

Spatial Resolution

A reflecting horizon can change laterally, either in velocity, which will change the reflection coefficient, or stop laterally, as by faulting or by absence of deposition (e.g., channel sands). It is often necessary to map (in space) these certain phenomena from the seismic data. However, a reflection does not originate from a point on a reflector but from a zone on the reflector. The radial width of this zone, the *Fresnel zone*, is defined as

$$\text{Fr} = \frac{V}{4}\sqrt{\frac{t}{f}} \qquad (8\text{-}1)$$

where V is the average velocity to the reflector, t is the two-way time, and f is the dominant frequency content of the reflection. This equation can be derived by use of a point source, spherically radiating energy, and ray theory to calculate the width of the zone in which the reflected energy is in phase (all peaks or all troughs).

Neidell[2] has shown that as a reflecting body (e.g., a sand lens) becomes as small or smaller than the Fresnel zone, the amplitude of the reflection decreases, and diffractions from the sides become apparent. When a body occupies only 25 percent of the Fresnel zone, the amplitude is down 40 percent from the amplitude recorded when the body occupies 100 percent of the Fresnel zone. The effect of the Fresnel zone was graphically illustrated by Woods[3] in experiments with sound waves in air.

The attenuation of seismic signals at a rate which is proportional to frequency strongly affects the resolution (both spatial and vertical) that can be expected from such signals. Seismic waves are generated at their source as pulses of such short wavelength that they can be looked upon as spikes for all practical purposes. If the pulses could actually travel as spikes for large distances through the earth, there would be few problems in resolving reflections. But the continual removal by attenuation of higher-frequency components as the signals propagate through earth materials results in a continual broadening of the basic signal with increasing travel time. This effect has been discussed in Chap. 2 (pp. 47-49).

Compositing of Reflections

The basic seismic signal traveling through the earth is, as we have noted, a pulse with a breadth that increases with distance traveled. After the pulse has passed through 10,000 ft of section, its effective wavelength may be about 200 ft. At 15,000 or 20,000 ft it may be twice this magnitude. If a pair of reflecting surfaces are no closer together than the wavelength of the reflection pulse, they can easily be resolved on a reflection record. If, on the other hand, the surfaces are separated by less than a wavelength, the problem of resolution becomes more complex, the difficulty increasing as the separations become smaller.

Temporal Resolution   Figure 8-2 shows the reflected signal from a high-speed bed of finite thickness underlain and overlain by thick sections of lower-speed material. This earth model generates a two-term reflectivity spike log: one positive reflection coefficient followed after an interval by a negative reflection coefficient. The time separation of the two spikes is proportional to the thickness of the bed. The waves on the right are the reflections that would be expected for various ratios of bed thickness to wavelength. The waveforms have been synthesized by superposition of reflections from the top and bottom of the pinchout. The signal reflected by the lower surface is equal in amplitude to the signal reflected by the upper surface but 180° out of phase with it because there is a decrease in velocity below the deeper interface and an increase in velocity below the shallower one. When the thickness is about three-eighths of a wavelength or less, the two signals merge with so little separation between them that it is no longer possible to resolve the pulse by eye into two identifiable elements. The anomalously high amplitude reflections from bed thicknesses of around $\frac{1}{4}\lambda$ are attributable to a "tuning" phenomenon, in which constructive interference has caused amplification of this reflected signal. At an eighth of a wavelength, the amplitude begins to decrease rapidly because of cancellation,

FIGURE 8-2   Effect of varying bed thickness on reflection wave. R_1 is reflection from top, R_2 from bottom of bed. High-speed layer is sandwiched between beds of much lower speed, as shown on left. When thickness of high-speed layer reaches three-eighths of a wavelength, it is no longer possible to resolve reflections. (*Modified from Widess.*[4])

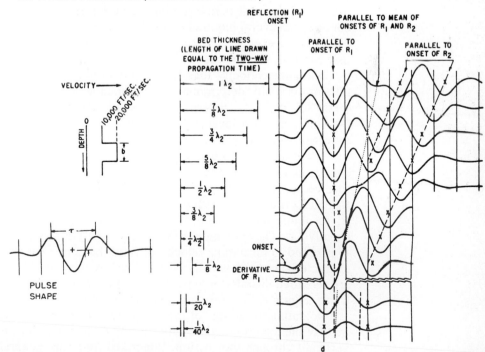

as the beginnings of the two out-of-phase reflections approach coincidence. The analysis leading to these conclusions was carried out by Widess.[4] A further discussion concerning amplitudes, bed thickness, resolution, and detection of thin beds is in Sec. 9-4.

This model, like most models that represent the earth by discrete layers, is oversimplified. It is quite likely that other reflecting interfaces would be located close enough to the surfaces bounding the high-speed layer for reflections from them to interfere with (and thus complicate) the reflection signals that are shown. Also, despite the success of modern field and processing techniques for suppressing noise, some interference from other sources would almost certainly be superimposed on the reflection signals, making it unlikely that the increasingly weak reflections generated as the high-speed bed gets thinner would stand out enough above the noise level to be observable on real records.

Actually, most sedimentary rocks are so highly stratified that there are many discontinuities in velocity within a vertical distance corresponding to a seismic wavelength. The continuous-velocity log introduced early in the 1950s first made this evident to geophysicists.

Continuous-Velocity Logs   *Continuous-velocity logs*, also called borehole-compensated, sonic logs, or simply sonics, show the interval velocities near the borehole of the formations penetrated by wells as functions of depth either for the entire well below the casing or for selected formations. The *sonde* is the tool used in the collection of sonic data. For seismic applications it is desirable that all of the well below the casing be logged and that drilling and logging continue to several hundred feet below the (deepest) target horizon. As will be discussed, deeper sonic data are necessary to generate a synthetic seismogram that correctly depicts the seismic response in and around the zone of interest.

Continuous-velocity logs have many applications, such as geological correlation, porosity determination, identification of formations, creation of synthetic seismograms, determination of migration velocities, and estimation of the time-depth relationship. It is the well log used more often than any other in reflection seismic work. The transit time of an acoustic pulse through the formation near the borehole is recorded as the sonde is pulled up the hole. As shown in Fig. 8-3a, the sonde contains two sources, S_1 and S_2, and four receivers, R_1 through R_4. The time difference between the arrivals from S_1 at R_4 and R_2 is averaged with the time difference of the arrivals from S_2 at R_3 and R_1 to obtain the estimate of the travel time through the span of the sonde, usually 2 ft. The *spacing* is either 8 ft or 4 ft. The longer spacing is more likely to respond to formation velocity beyond the zone near the well in which rock characteristics have usually been altered by the drilling process. Transit times are recorded digitally on tape or plotted continuously on a chart in the logging truck. Figure 8-3b shows a typical velocity log.

Integrating these logs of interval time with respect to depth yields an estimate of the total travel time between any two points for a seismic wave passing vertically through the section. Integrated times are generally shown, for constant intervals, on the log itself as pips along a vertical line near its edge.

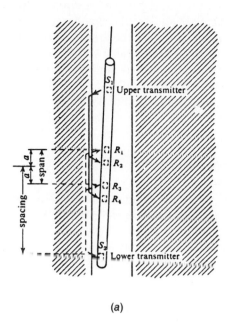

(a)

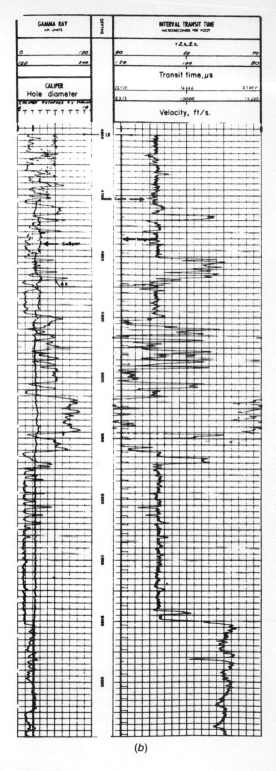

(b)

FIGURE 8-3 (a) Diagram of a borehole-compensated logging sonde. The span is 2 ft, the spacing is either 4 or 8 ft. (*From Sheriff and Geldart.*[25]) (b) Velocity–gamma-ray log from well in Michigan. Velocity log is on right side. Transit times between elements 1 ft apart are logged. Velocities (shown on nonlinear scale) are reciprocals of the transit times. (*John W. Mack, Jr.*)

If integrated times are desired from the surface to the logged portions of the well, additional steps must be taken. Because no signals can be recorded through surface casing (the first string of casing, run from the ground surface to a shallow depth in the well), it is necessary to record a near-surface shot by conventional means with a detector (ordinarily attached to the logging tool) at the bottom of the casing. The integrated time from the log is added to the time measured through the casing, and the sum (after correction to datum elevation) becomes the time from which velocity is calculated to any desired depth in the borehole. Shots of the same type are also recorded at a number of other depths in the borehole to check the integrated times from the logs and to correct for local irregularities in the velocity. This second type of velocity survey is called a *check-shot survey*, *well shot*, or simply a *velocity survey*.

Gretener[5] has compared vertical travel times obtained from well shooting with those determined by integrating velocity logs from 50 wells in the Alberta plains. A statistical analysis of the discrepancies showed an essentially gaussian distribution with a standard deviation of 1.8 ms/1000 ft in such a direction that the travel times based on the velocity logs were systematically less than those from the well shots. No plausible explanation could be found by Gretener for this shift, but Strick[6] has endeavored to explain the discrepancies on the basis of inelastic attenuation effects in the formations. Many geophysicists have encountered in different areas a time delay of seismic reflection time relative to integrated sonic travel time. In many cases, geophysicists attribute this effect to a pegleg multiple-delay phenomenon, in which the main portion of the energy of a propagating wavefront becomes progressively more and more delayed the longer its travel path, i.e., the more thin beds it encounters. Another possible cause is the different velocity of energy at different frequencies, a phenomenon known as *dispersion*. The frequency difference is significant since the sonic log operates at kilohertz frequencies while seismic reflection frequencies range from 5 to 100 Hz.

Many velocity logs, like that in Fig. 8-3, show contrasts that would give rise to reflections no more than a few tens of feet apart. Figure 8-4 shows how a simple down-traveling source pulse with a waveform comparable to that of a Ricker wavelet is altered when it is reflected from a sequence of boundaries a short distance apart as compared to the wavelength of the pulse. Each interface returns a pulse having the same waveform as the source pulse, but the amplitude and phase (whether or not reversed by a lower velocity below the boundary) are governed by the reflection coefficient across it. The sum of all the individual reflections is recorded by the geophones at the surface. The difference between the source pulse and reflected signal is quite pronounced, and it is not often possible to isolate the contribution made to the reflection waveform by any one of the individual boundaries.

This example shows how a typical seismic reflection should be looked upon as an interference pattern made up of impulses from many sources spread vertically over hundreds of feet rather than as a simple event originating from a single lithological interface. (See Fig. 8-5, which will be discussed shortly.)

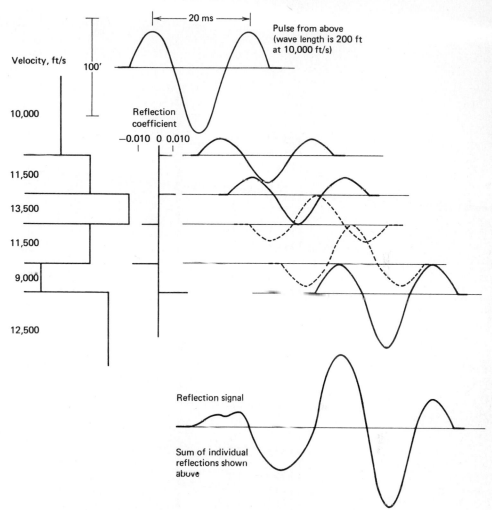

FIGURE 8-4   Composition of reflection from series of five interfaces with separations small in comparison to wavelength. Note change in waveform caused by reflection process. Waveforms indicated by dashed lines represent reflections with phase reversal.

When the separations (in time) or the relative strengths of the individual reflections change with lateral distance, we should expect the character of the resultant reflection event on the record to change also. Model experiments illustrating this process were carried out by Woods[3] to illustrate the composition of reflections from various stratigraphic configurations.

The reflection process in a case like that illustrated in Fig. 8-4 is entirely comparable to the action of a time-domain filter of the type discussed in Chap. 6. The down-going pulse is the input, and the reflectivity-versus-depth plot for the layering as shown on the diagram is equivalent to the impulse response. The

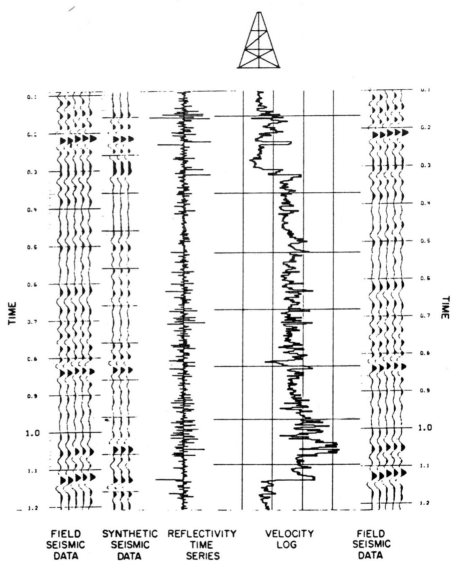

FIGURE 8-5 The visual relationship between seismic field data, synthetic seismic data, the reflectivity time series calculated from the velocity log, and the velocity log itself. The seismic field data are displayed again next to the velocity log. Some of the major velocity boundaries are clearly visible on the seismic field data (e.g., the start of the low velocity section at 1.15 s), while others are almost indistinct, and recourse is necessary to the synthetic for character identification (e.g., the velocity increase at 0.3 s). (*From Wood.*[10])

individual reflectivities act as weighting functions, and the travel times between the boundaries govern the time shifts between successive pulses returned to the surface. It is thus evident that a layered earth acts as a filter and that the shape of the reflected pulse depends on the reflectivity-versus-depth function. Sengbush et al.[7] have shown that the reflection waveform can be predicted, or a synthetic seismogram can be constructed, by convolving the source signal with the reflectivity function (of seismic travel time rather than of depth) associated with the earth. The convolutional model of a reflection seismogram is $r(t) * w(t) + n(t)$, where r is reflectivity, w is the wavelet, and n is the noise.[8]

Synthetic Seismograms   Synthetic seismograms of the type first described by Peterson et al.[9] are artificial reflection records made from velocity logs by conversion of the velocity log in depth to a reflectivity function in time and by convolution of this function with a presumed appropriate wavelet or source pulse. Figure 8-5 displays the velocity log, reflection coefficient log, and synthetic seismogram so generated as compared to the field seismic data (Wood[10]). The "reflectivity function" or "reflectivity series" is the series of reflection coefficients calculated by the equation

$$RC = \frac{\rho_2 v_2 - \rho_1 v_1}{\rho_2 v_2 + \rho_1 v_1} \tag{8-2}$$

where the densities of the upper and lower media are ρ_1 and ρ_2, respectively, and the velocities are v_1 and v_2 for a plane wave at normal incidence from medium 1 (see Chap. 2). The reflection coefficient is positive for an increase in acoustic impedance (ρv) and negative for a decrease in acoustic impedance. While velocity often plays the dominant role in the reflection coefficient calculations, density can, on occasion, also be important. The treatment of the density information is subject to variation. When both velocity and density logs are available, both are used to create the synthetic seismogram after log editing and matching procedures. Occasionally, the reflectivity function is calculated from the velocity function alone, which in effect holds density equal everywhere. In those areas where density does not seem to vary appreciably, the synthetic seismograms made using velocity only are similar "enough" to those created from acoustic impedance. Another widely used alternative is to supply the density as calculated by Gardner's equation (Sec. 9-2), i.e., density proportional to the one-fourth power of velocity.

For best results, the target horizon should not be the final interval logged (i.e., drilled). Since the wavelet (or presumed source pulse) convolved with the reflectivity series is usually 80 to 105 ms long, the contribution to the target's total waveform from deeper horizons should be considered, depending upon the phase of the wavelet of the data. Zero phase is generally preferred for the wavelet since it yields maximum resolution. Unfortunately, wavelets produced by impulsive sources are more nearly minimum phase than zero phase.

In Fig. 8-5 the match between the synthetic and the field data allows correlation of the reflection events with lithologic boundaries. The sonic log is not, however, obviously related to the seismic trace: the striking, large change in velocity at 0.3 is clearly visible on the synthetic as a broad, positive doublet, but is correlated with a much weaker positive doublet on the seismic field data. The synthetic seismogram gives clues to the interpretation of the seismic record, even though the absolute amplitudes of the events on the two data sets differ. The relationship between the seismic trace and the sonic log is complex and not open for simple or naive interpretation. The band-limited nature of the seismic data, the thin-bed interference or tuning effect (see Fig. 8-2 and Sec. 9-4), and other factors of noise, multiples, etc., combine to obscure the desired, simple relationship among seismic amplitude, reflection coefficient, and velocity (or acoustic-impedance) contrast.

The nature, or shape, of the wavelet convolved with the reflectivity function greatly affects the character of the output synthetic seismogram and the resultant quality of match with the field seismic data. The data that are easiest to interpret are data containing a zero-phase, white (within the band limits) wavelet. Such a wavelet comes the closest to allowing each peak on the wiggle trace to represent a positive reflection coefficient and each trough a negative reflection coefficient. Not all field seismic data are, however, zero-phase. If the synthetic generated with a zero-phase wavelet does not match the field data, a series of phase-rotated wavelets may be convolved with the reflectivity series for visual correlation with the field seismic data. Once the best visual match is determined, the times associated with the various formations can be identified, as well as the appearance of "the desired anomaly," as determined through modeling with the appropriate wavelet (see Sec. 9-2).

Wuenschel[11] was the first to describe a technique for obtaining synthetic seismograms that include multiple reflections. The same computer·programs used for time-domain filtering of reflection signals in routine seismic processing can be applied to generate synthetic seismograms with any assumed source waveform $f(t)$ or wavelet if the detailed velocity stratification of the subsurface is known from a velocity log.

Precision of Reflection Times

Another limitation associated with the seismic reflection process lies in the precision with which reflection times and depths of reflecting surfaces can be determined from events on seismic records.

The time assigned to a reflection event, in practice, is ordinarily that of the highest-amplitude trough (or sometimes peak) of the oscillatory signals. Such features are easiest to identify reliably and consistently, particularly in the presence of noise. Theoretically, for minimum-phase data (see Sec. 6-3), the time of the onset of each reflection should be recorded rather than the time of any trough or peak that follows the onset. The problem is complicated by the fact that the signals, having been recorded by velocity-sensitive geophones, show peaks or troughs where the particle displacement has its greatest rate of change rather than its greatest amplitude. Also, processing operations such as deconvolution usually cause further phase shifts which make it difficult to identify reflection onsets. Many filter programs are designed, when possible, for minimum phase shift so as to leave the greatest energy in the reflected wave as close to its onset as possible. Such manipulation can sometimes distort complex waveforms and obscure identification of events. Phase-shifting filters, which are central to some "wavelet processing" routines, will change the time of the maximum-amplitude peak or trough.

As a typical reflection signal will normally be the composite of several individual overlapping reflections from a series of interfaces extending over a depth range of a hundred feet or more, it is not often that any identifiable feature of the signal, such as a peak or trough, can be uniquely related to a specific geological boundary, as was pointed out in our discussion of Fig. 8-3. Many interpretation procedures, however, do correlate a given signal to a geologic boundary, and sometimes with no adverse consequences.

The filtering action of the earth causes time lags comparable to phase lags in electronic filters. The existence of such lags, as discussed previously in the chapter, has been well established by comparing field records with synthetic seismograms made from logs run in wells near the lines where the field records were shot. These lags range from 20 to 80 ms, but there is seldom any way to predict what the lag should be at a location near which there are no well ties.

It is thus more difficult to determine the absolute depth of a reflecting interface in the earth from a reflection signal than it is to measure relative depths of such a boundary between two points at which the same reflection has been recorded. Where all individual layers encompassed within the zone contributing to the reflection are conformable, the structural relief can be mapped with an accuracy of 1 or 2 ms if the reflection quality is good. Where velocities do not change laterally, absolute depths can be obtained with comparable accuracy if the lines are tied to at least one well at which the reflection event is related to a particular well top. The differences between the time for an event at the well tie and the times elsewhere on the line can readily be transformed into depth differences reliable to 10 or 20 ft if the reflections are good and the average velocity values are known precisely enough.

8-4 USE OF WELL DATA TO INTERPRET SEISMIC DATA

Three main types of data are collected in boreholes that bear significantly or primarily upon the interpretation of seismic data. These are the wireline logs, especially the sonic, density (FDC), and resistivity logs; the check-shot surveys; and vertical seismic profiling (VSP).

Wireline Logs

The most important wireline log is the sonic, at least for most geophysicists faced with interpreting seismic data with nearby well control. The sonic, or continuous-velocity log, was discussed in the previous section, in which the creation of the synthetic seismogram from the sonic, or from the sonic and density logs combined, was presented. Migration velocities can also be estimated from the elapsed (integrated) travel time calculated from the sonic. Once a time-depth chart is established, from the sonic log or another source, other logs, such as the SP or the resistivity, can be displayed to match the seismic time scale to aid the interpretation process. When many wells in an area contain sonics as well as density logs and resistivity logs, it is possible to derive a functional relationship that expresses the value of the sonic log in terms of the other two for specific formations or lithologies. After such a relationship has been established, a well with only a resistivity log or a density log or both can have a "pseudosonic" calculated from one of the other logs. A synthetic seismogram can then be made. In some cases, synthetics made from resistivity logs have aided in the identification of seismic events.

Check-Shot Surveys

A check-shot survey, discussed earlier, is an abbreviated form of VSP, which will be discussed in the next section. The typical check-shot survey involves lowering a geophone into a well to measure transit time of a seismic signal to each of a selected set of levels in the well.

The geophone is especially designed to withstand the extreme pressures and temperatures at great depths in a well. It is generally lowered to a point just slightly above the deepest point in the well (T.D., for total depth). A shot is taken on the surface near the top of the well, and a record is made of the geophone response. The record typically is run from the shot time until a half-second or so after the first seismic signal is received. The geophone is then raised to another level and the process is repeated. Shots are similarly taken at regular intervals of hundreds or thousands of feet. Often the known levels of particular marker horizons are chosen for additional check shots.

In an area with many check-shot surveys, the velocity information from surface to the zone of interest can be calculated and mapped to determine the amount of lateral velocity variation present (which affects the conversion to depth of the time maps), or to convert time-isopach maps to depth-isopach maps. Trends of major lithology changes can be followed by examining such velocity maps.

VSP (Vertical Seismic Profile)

Vertical seismic profiles also employ a surface seismic source and a downhole receiver. Recordings are, however, taken every 50 to 100 ft as the receiver travels up the hole. Unlike check-shot recordings, VSP recordings are long enough to include reflections from well below the T.D. of the well. The source can be impulsive or vibroseis and can be at or near the borehole for the zero-offset VSP or walked away from the borehole for a distance up to the depth of the target for an offset VSP. A significant amount of specialized processing is needed for VSPs, since they record a mixture of down-going and reflected seismic signals. Hardage and Toksoz[12] provide a comprehensive treatment of VSP.

A VSP yields the best synthetic seismogram information, both in timing relationships and in waveform character, since a surface seismic source is employed to record the wave field with a geophone down the borehole. The frequencies thus employed in the VSP are usually the same as those in surface seismic data. Multiples can be positively identified, as well as the layers generating them. From the downward propagating waveform, the attenuation of the seismic wave may be estimated, a process which often aids in the design of deconvolution filters. Since the reflected wave field from deeper than the phone is also recorded, a VSP yields seismic information from below the total depth of the well. Such data can frequently be tied to conventional surface seismic data and aids in determining whether the target has yet been reached. Figure 8-6*a* illustrates the match between a seismic profile, a VSP, and a synthetic seismogram.

Offset VSPs yield structural and stratigraphic information around the borehole. Modeling is required in the presence of dip to calculate the mapping operators that transform the offset VSP data to a CDP-type space display. This mapping is needed because a given offset VSP trace has several reflections from different CDP positions contained in one trace.

Salt-Proximity Surveys Borehole seismic surveys, using offset VSP techniques, can provide a more precise outline of the salt flank than can surface seismic profiles. The classic salt proximity survey, used since the 1940s, involves a transmission or refraction of the energy from the surface source

FIGURE 8-6   (a) Seismic profile with a zero-offset VSP and a synthetic seismogram inset at the well location. Here, the VSP appears to have a slightly higher frequency content than does the surface-seismic data. It is important to compare the VSP with the sonic-derived synthetic seismogram: the VSP gives a valid time-to-depth relationship and waveform shape, but the synthetic seismogram is often the only estimate available.

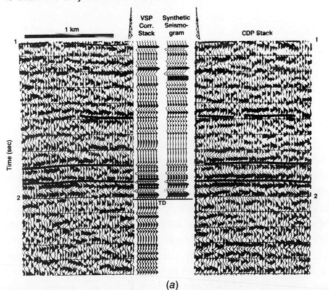

(a)

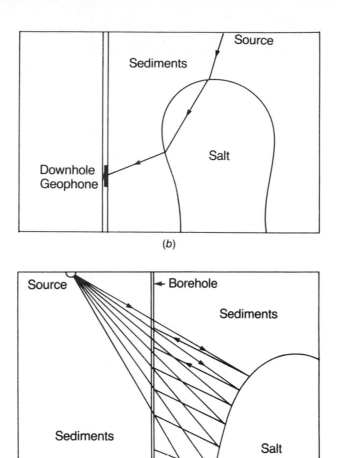

FIGURE 8-6 (b) Diagram of offset VSP technique: Salt proximity survey, transmission or refraction type. (c) Reflection type of salt proximity survey.

through the salt to the detector locations in the borehole, as shown in Fig. 8-6b. The newer type of borehole reflection survey uses the energy reflected from the salt face (Fig. 8-6c). Since the different salt-proximity techniques make different assumptions about what earth variables are known to the geophysicist, the technique(s) used depends upon the geologic problem and information at hand (Manzur[13]). Figures 8-6d and e show the ray-path determinations that lead to the interpretation of the salt-face location with a transmission survey. When salt overhangs mask, on surface seismic data, the nature of the underlying rocks, salt-proximity surveys are sometimes the only seismic technique that can reveal potential hydrocarbon traps and guide drilling operations.

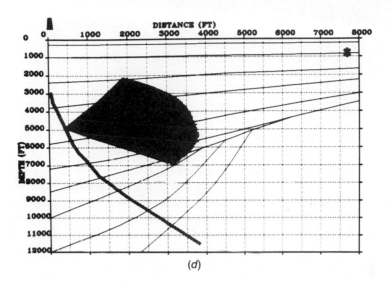

(d)

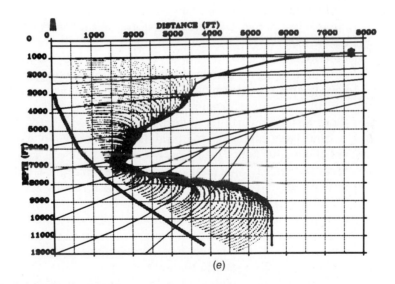

(e)

FIGURE 8-6 (d) For a refraction salt-proximity survey, ray tracing is carried out from each downhole geo-phone location towards the salt face to determine the equi-travel-time or aplanatic curve which provides an estimate of the location of the salt boundary. (*Western Geophysical.*)

(e) Family of aplanatic curves along which the salt-sediment interface is located by the geo-physicist. The envelope of a set of such curves describes the shape of the salt face. (*Western Geophysical.*)

8-5 REFLECTION DATA OVER GEOLOGIC STRUCTURES SOUGHT IN OIL EXPLORATION

Over the period of more than four decades during which the reflection method has been used in exploration, it has been possible to obtain detailed, useful information on many types of structural features that could entrap hydrocarbons. Stacked seismic sections, particularly those presenting data obtained with modern field and processing techniques, often make the presence of such structures obvious to the eye.

In 1983, a landmark publication in seismic interpretation became available to the earth sciences community. Bally,[14] at Rice University, in collaboration with AAPG and many geophysicists and geologists, collected and edited three volumes of seismic profiles from all over the world that illustrate the structures found in sedimentary basins, extensional provinces, compressional provinces, and strike-slip regimes. The seismic profiles are usually displayed with and without migration, and with and without interpretation. The text provides excellent discussions on the general structural styles, commentaries on the particular seismic examples and locales, and a bibliography for each seismic example. The visual training in seismic interpretation provided by these volumes is invaluable.

Additional, worthwhile publications that link seismic interpretation to drilling results are the seismic case histories in the journals *Geophysics*, *Geophysical Prospecting*, and the Expanded Abstracts of the International SEG Meetings (1982 and following years). The case histories document complex structural imaging problems, interpretation techniques and aids, and stratigraphic-play developments in both clastic and carbonate regimes. The pitfalls and the rewards of seismic interpretation in specific areas make the study of these histories worth the interpreter's time.

The most common structural targets associated with oil entrapment are anticlines and faults (see Fig. 8-7). Anticlines are generally easy to see on record sections, and faults of more than marginal displacement should be discernible, although some types are more readily recognizable than others. Structural deformations caused by salt domes and other intrusives can usually be mapped as well. In the paragraphs to follow we shall consider the interpretation of many such structural features and present examples illustrating their appearance on seismic sections. Stratigraphic traps (like the ones in Fig. 8-7*f*, *g*, *h*) will be discussed in the next chapter.

Correctly migrated record sections almost invariably improve the definition of complicated structures from areas where there has been major tectonic disturbance. They are particularly helpful in resolving complex fault patterns.

Anticlines

Anticlines can easily be mapped by reflection if the data are of good quality and if the closure (the elevation difference between the crest and the lowest closed contour line) is greater than spurious irregularities in apparent structure such as

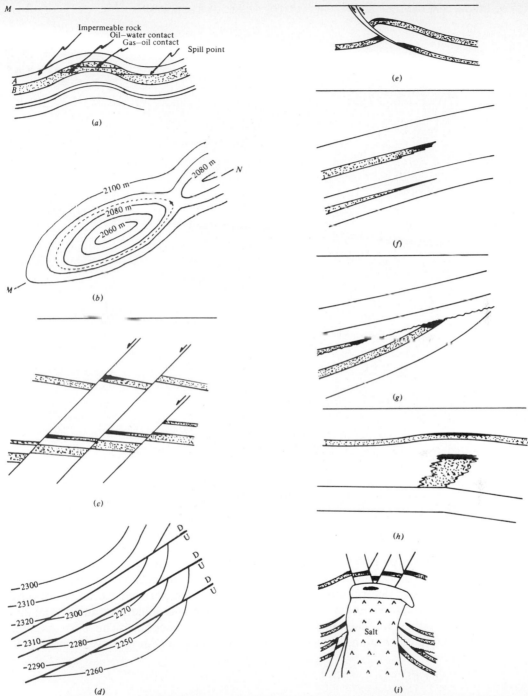

FIGURE 8-7 Hydrocarbon traps in layered sediments. The dotted formations are permeable, and when filled with hydrocarbons (areas shaded black), are the reservoirs. (*a*) Vertical section through anticline along line MN in (*b*); (*b*) contour map of the top of the reservoir bed in (*a*), with the spill-point contour dashed; (*c*) en-echelon, normal faults and (*d*) the mapped representation of the middle reservoir bed of (*c*); (*e*) possible traps caused by thrust faulting; (*f*) stratigraphic traps due to pinchout and lithologic change; (*g*) unconformity traps; (*h*) trap in a reef and draping over the reef; (*i*) traps around a salt dome. (*From Sheriff and Geldart.*[25])

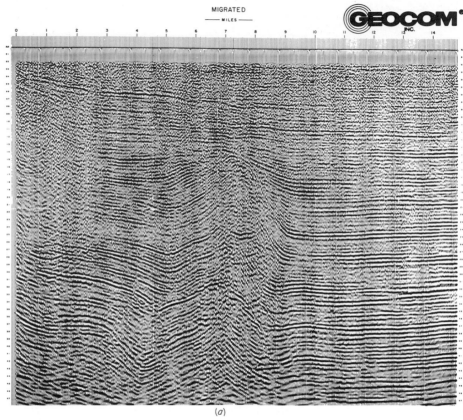

(a)

FIGURE 8-8 Anticline from San Joaquin Valley, Calif. (a) Migrated. (b) Unmigrated. The migration has collapsed the many diffraction patterns that concealed the actual structure and has moved the dipping energy back to a more correct location. The result is that the structure is much more clearly interpretable.

are caused by lateral velocity changes or near-surface irregularities. Oil-bearing, anticlinal structures may be associated with compressive tectonic forces as well as with deformations due to the upward push of rising salt domes or other diapiric features underneath (Fig. 8-7i). Figure 8-8a illustrates an unusual kind of anticline as displayed on a migrated record section. The corresponding unmigrated section, shown in Fig. 8-8b, does not show a very meaningful picture.

Faults

The detection of faulting on seismic sections can be quite easy under favorable circumstances. Often, however, the indications are subtle, and the identification and delineation of such features can be quite challenging. Because of the role faults often play in the entrapment of hydrocarbons, the techniques for finding and mapping faults have considerable practical importance.

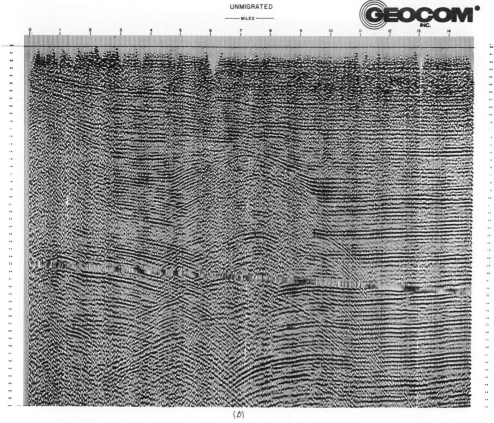

UNMIGRATED
—— MILES ——

(b)

FIGURE 8-8   continued

The principal indications of faulting on reflection sections are the following:

1 Discontinuities in reflections falling along an essentially linear pattern
2 Misclosures in tying reflections around loops
3 Divergences in dip not related to stratigraphy
4 Diffraction patterns, particularly those with vertexes that line up in a manner consistent with local faulting
5 Distortion or disappearance of reflections below suspected fault lines

Where discontinuities are well defined, the position of the fault trace may be highly evident on the record sections even to someone entirely inexperienced in seismic interpretation. Figure 8-9, an offshore 15-mi-long reflection section in the Gulf of Mexico, shows two systems of normal faults, one group dipping to the right, the other to the left. Throws, indicated quite clearly by the displacement of the more conspicuous reflections, are as great as 500 ft. The faulting is attributed to uplift of a salt mass (not visible on the section) as well as to subsidence of formations toward the center of the basin. The exceptional

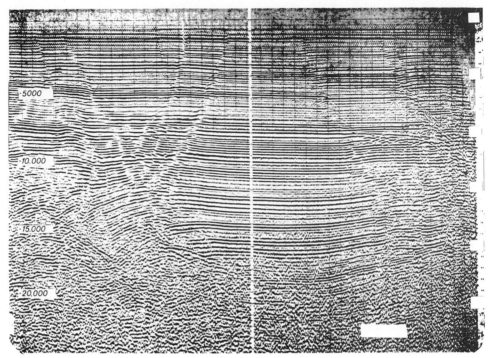

FIGURE 8-9 Pattern of normal faulting in the Gulf of Mexico. The faults appear to be associated with salt structures, indicated but not explicitly visible, at the lower right and lower left (*Exxon, Inc.*)

detail that can be observed in the faulting pattern indicates the success with which processing eliminated the noise that might otherwise have obscured the more marginal fault indications.

The detection and mapping of thrust faults is generally based on divergences between reflections as well as on the repetition of identifiable reflections above and below the thrust plane. A classic area for faulting of this kind is in the foothills of the Canadian rockies, where oil and gas are entrapped in allochthonous* limestone sheets at their updip termination against the underlying thrust plane. Another area where such faulting shows up well on seismic recordings is the Wind River Basin of Wyoming, where the section shown in Fig. 8-10 was obtained.

An important aid to identifying and tracing fault surfaces is the family of diffraction patterns that originate from the edges of beds disrupted by faulting. Such an edge can often act as a "point" source for returning seismic energy by diffraction of the type discussed in Chap. 2 (page 44). The resulting pattern will

---

* The term *allochthonous* is applied to rocks not formed in place, i.e., rocks that have been transported to their present location. *Autochthonous* is applied to the rocks that have been formed in place.

Wind River Basin, Wyoming, five fold,
45 to 8 Hz

West: offsets 1320 ft near, 4050 ft far

1 mi

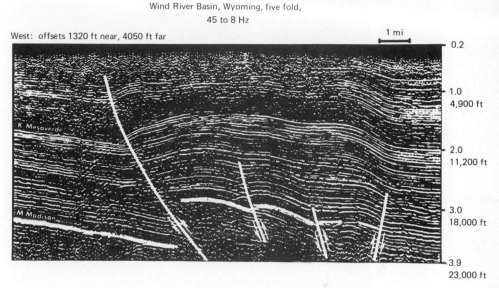

0.2

1.0
4,900 ft

2.0
11,200 ft

3.0
18,000 ft

3.9
23,000 ft

FIGURE 8-10
Overthrusting in the Wind River Basin of Wyoming as indicated on a vibroseis section. (*Continental Oil Co.*)

have an arcuate shape like the trace of a surface of maximum convexity discussed in the previous chapter. The vertex of the diffraction pattern shows the position of the diffracting edge on the section. A number of such patterns originating from different points along a fault should make it possible to locate the fault edge even in the absence of reflections yielding such information. Figure 8-11 shows diffractions which have vertexes that line up in way that supports the presence of fault trends independently indicated by patterns of displacement in the reflections.

Diffraction patterns need not be complete to be useful in this way. Sometimes fragmental portions of a pattern can be fitted to an appropriate curve of maximum convexity based on the known velocity for the area concerned, and the curve can be used to project the position of the vertex even when it is not actually observable on the sections.

Unless diffraction patterns are recognized as such, they might be interpreted by the unwary as reflections. A diffraction observed on both sides of its source can look deceptively like a reflection from a symmetrical anticline. The best way to determine whether a suspected feature on a section is a diffraction pattern or a true structure is to migrate the data. Another way is to calculate the time-versus-horizontal-distance relationship for a diffraction that would originate from the vertex of the feature based on the best velocity information available. Then one compares the predicted and observed patterns, preferably by the use of a transparent overlay. The closer the fit, the greater the likelihood that the feature is a diffraction. Interpretation is best accomplished through the use of both unmigrated and migrated data for each profile. Most modern sections are migrated as a matter of course but an unmigrated section is usually

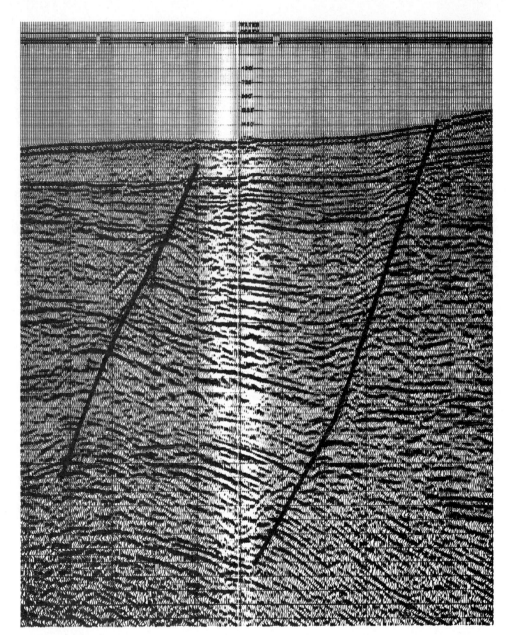

FIGURE 8-11
Tracing fault surfaces by following vertexes of diffraction patterns. (*Western Geophysical Co.*)

available. Faults, anticlines, and synclines are all far more clearly displayed after migration.

It is often possible to recognize faulting from divergences of reflections below the fault plane or from disturbances in the quality or character of reflections originating from beneath the suspected fault. Quarles[15] has shown how faults in the Gulf Coast are identified by divergences in the apparent dip of underlying reflectors, and Laubscher[16] has pointed out the diagnostic value of distortion and deterioration of reflections from below a fault, illustrating this criterion by an example from Venezuela.

A special type of anticline is one that overlies an increased sedimentary section or former graben (Harding[17]). This situation is termed *positive structural inversion* and is defined as a change in the polarity of structural relief, from a previous low to a high, and applied to a specific structure. In some instances, older faults have been reactivated: Due to a change in the tectonic stress field, the later sense of throw is the opposite of the original throw (see Fig. 8-15a for a schematic representation). In other situations, flexural arching of earlier sedimentary thicks (lows) has occurred, and the positive inversion has not relied upon fault slip for its development. On a large scale, this type of deformation has been referred to as *basin inversion* by some workers (Bodenhausen and Ott[18]). Harding[17] illustrates this type of feature with a seismic section from the South Sumatra Basin, in which normal faulting accompanied the basin's initial subsidence, but subsequent basement-involved compression reversed the movement on the faults and produced surface anticlines over formerly deep grabens.

Figure 8-12 illustrates this type of anticline. Deeper than 1.5 s, on the left of the section, is a complex of growth faults. These normal faults, which formed in an extensional stress regime, were concurrent with deposition, with the result that the sedimentary section on the down-dropped blocks is thickened (see, for example, the Lias and the Dogger). Over this feature, between 1.0 to 1.4 s, the lower Cretaceous and the early upper Cretaceous section is clearly folded into a rather tight anticline. An unconformity divides the Jurassic from the Cretaceous section, as evidenced by the truncation within the upper Jurassic (see the Dogger, for example). The practically equal thickness of the originally flat-lying lower Cretaceous section indicates that by that time, growth faulting had ceased, and a quasi-equilibrium had been reached. Late in the upper Cretaceous there was a burst of compressive stress that arched the strata into the anticline. It appears likely that the original normal faults were reactivated as reverse faults, based upon the appearance of the tight anticline over the former depocenter. The Tertiary section appears to rest upon an unconformity. There is, however, some varying degree of rather subtle, long-wavelength structural relief still present in the Tertiary section over the deeper-seated anticline.

Basement Structure

Before common-depth-point recording and digital processing, it was seldom possible to identify the surface of the basement from reflection records because of multiple reflections and other noise dominating the deeper portions of the records. While it is still not always feasible to recognize the basement on record sections, particularly when it is very deep, the removal of noise and multiples may make its surface readily observable. Irregularities on the top of the

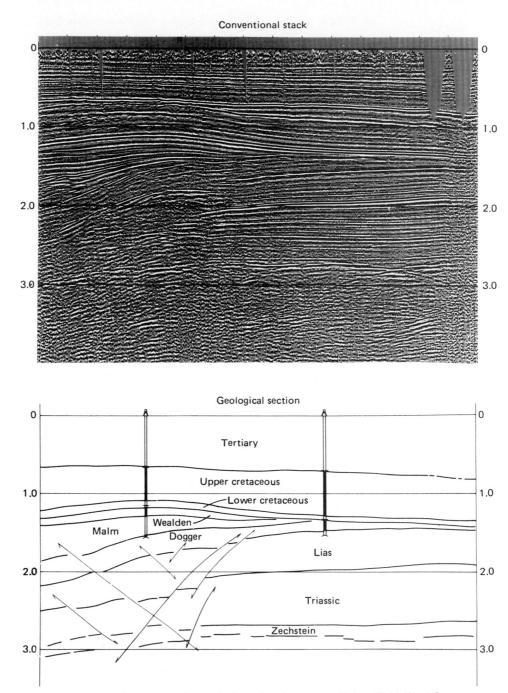

FIGURE 8-12   Record section and corresponding geologic section through the Hohne Field, West Germany. Production is in the Dogger subcrop below a Jurassic-Cretaceous unconformity. (*Prakla-Seismos.*)

basement often generate diffraction patterns which give a series of closely spaced arcs on the section having an envelope that can define the convolutions of the basement quite closely. Figure 8-13 illustrates this effect in a deep-sea area. The absence of reflection events below this envelope makes the identification all the more likely, even though there has been no drilling along the line to verify it.

Many explorationists categorize faulting and structures as either basement involved, or basement detached (Harding and Lowell[19]) as shown in Fig. 8-14. The structures in strike-slip faulted locales can appear puzzling on seismic sections. Pure strike-slip movement juxtaposes sedimentary sequences from different areas. The detection on seismic sections of such movement rests upon the dissimilarity of the two sedimentary sequences, or upon foreknowledge of the fault from surface geologic maps. For further discussion of seismic interpretation in strike-slip regimes, see Harding[17] and Bally.[14]

Strike-slip, or wrench, movement with components of compression or extension give rise to flower structures. A positive flower structure is defined as a "linear antiform (possessing the overall shape of an anticline) that is bounded longitudinally along its flanks by the upward and outward diverging strands of a wrench fault that show mostly reverse separation" (p. 586 in Harding[17]) A negative flower structure is defined as a synform (possessing the overall shape of a syncline) bounded by the upward and outward diverging strands of a wrench fault that show mostly normal separation. Positive flower structures are found in zones of convergence (compression) along strike-slip faults, in association with en echelon folds on either side of the wrench fault. The strain ellipsoid can be used in strike-slip locales to work out the major directions of compression and of extension. Negative flower structures occur where blocks have diverged or moved parallel to each other. Associated with such structures are flanking, en echelon normal faulting, some reverse faulting, and paralleling monoclines. Figure 8-15 illustrates these structures. Harding has pointed out that "the differentiation of structural styles (Fig. 8-14) by using seismic data is frequently difficult and imprecise. [However,] explorationists must have a working familiarity with all structural categories. It is also necessary that such analysis always consider both profile and map characteristics" (p. 599 in Harding[17]).

Salt Domes and Other Diapirs

Salt domes can show up quite conspicuously on reflection sections. Figure 8-16 shows an example of such a feature. The rim syncline formed around the dome stands out conspicuously on the left side; also the formations show a rise on each side of the figure, indicating other salt features in both directions. It is rare that the salt surface itself yields a clearly defined reflection. More generally, the distortion of reflecting formations above the dome and alongside it, as well as the apparent absence of reflections within the apparent salt mass itself, are used to delineate the approximate location of the salt face. Salt overhangs mask

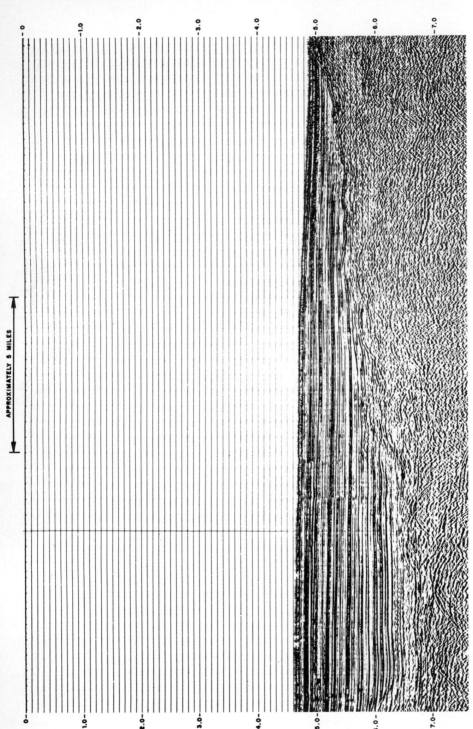

FIGURE 8-13 Identification of basement surface from diffraction patterns on section along traverse in deep water. (*United Geophysical Corp. proprietary data.*)

Structural style	Characteristics	Dominant deformational stress	Plate-tectonic habitat	Typical profile
BASEMENT-INVOLVED STYLES				
Pull-apart zones	Fairly high-angle normal faults dipping 60–70° in either direction Rotated fault blocks	Extension	Divergent boundaries (1) at spreading centers (2) aborted rifts Intraplate rifts Transform boundaries with component of divergence Secondary at convergent boundaries: (1) Trench outer slope (2) Arc massif (3) Stable flank of foreland and fore-arc basin (4) Back-arc marginal seas	
Compressive faults and basement thrusts	High-angle reverse faults, upward imbricating of faults	Compression	Convergent boundaries (1) Foreland basins (mostly) (2) Orogenic belt cores (3) Trench inner slopes and outer highs Transform boundaries with component of convergence	
Wrench-fault assemblages	Strike-slip faulting is primary, secondary features at about 30° angle to main trend Fairly narrow trend Faults generally steepen with depth	Couple	Transform boundaries Convergent boundaries at an angle: (1) Foreland basins (2) Orogenic belts (3) Arc massifs Divergent boundaries with offset spreading centers	
Basement warps	Gentle structure: domes, arches, sags	Isostatic adjustment Heat-flow	Plate interiors Passive boundaries Other areas	
BASEMENT-DETACHED STYLES				
Thrust assemblages	Faults sole out at décollement in incompetent rocks	Compression	Convergent boundaries (1) Inner slopes of trenches and outer highs (2) Mobile flank of forelands (orogenic belts) Transform boundaries with component of convergence	
Growth faults and other normal fault assemblages	Downthrown toward basin or toward center of uplift Dip often lessens with depth (for growth faults) Often contemporaneous with deposition	Extension	Passive boundaries Secondary to uplifts (folds, saltdomes)	
Salt structures	Pillows, domes, salt walls	Plastic flow Solution	Divergent boundaries (rifts provide venue for salt deposition)	
Shale structures		Plastic flow (often involving overpressuring produced by rapid burial)	Passive boundaries	
Drape features		Differential compaction	Subsiding basins Over reefs	
Volcanic plugs		Igneous intrusions		

FIGURE 8-14 Structural styles and plate-tectonic habitats. (*Harding and Lowell*[19], *and Sheriff and Geldart.*[25])

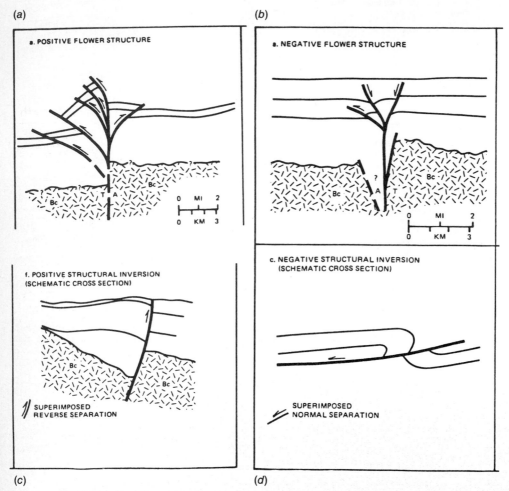

FIGURE 8-15 Illustration of various structures (*from Harding*[17]). (*a*) and (*b*) are from strike-slip zones with different components of compressive force (*a*), or extensive force (*b*). (*c*) is from the Malay basin (*after Eubank and Makki*[28]), (*d*) is from the Idaho-Wyoming thrust belt (*after Sprinkel*[29]).

the existence and attitudes of underlying rocks. Salt-proximity surveys, used in these situations, were discussed in Sec. 8-4 in connection with VSPs. Migration of the steeply dipping reflections from beds close to the dome that have been tilted upward by it habitually improves the precision with which one can map the flank positions of the salt. Faulting of sedimentary formations caused by uplift of the salt can sometimes be observed in the reflections. Structures in sedimentary rocks resulting from the uplift of other diapiric bodies such as igneous plugs often have an appearance on record sections that is identical to that caused by the uplift of salt domes. In areas such as previously unexplored offshore shelves where the geology is little known, it would generally require gravity or magnetic data to identify the nature of the diapir causing a pattern of disruption in the reflections.

Pitfalls in Structural Interpretation

The basis for seismic interpretation is the association of specific reflections with specific acoustic-impedance contrasts or series of contrasts in the earth. The impedance contrasts usually are linked to given formation or bed boundaries, usually through well control (such as velocity surveys, sonic information, or VSP) but occasionally by outcrop. Lateral continuity in the reflection is attributed to lateral continuity in the bed or physical cause of the reflection.

Reflections occur that do not arise from a change in lithology, i.e., a formation boundary. Impedance contrasts produced by a change in pore constituents (fluid to gas) can give rise to reflections termed "flat spots" that cross-cut bedding plane reflections (Backus[20]). (See Sec. 9-4.) A phase change, from solid to gas, of the pore constituents decreases the velocity of the medium at the phase-change boundary and so can also give rise to a reflection. In marine data, some of the bottom-simulating reflections (BSRs), which parallel the sea floor and cut across lithologic reflectors, are attributed to "the base of a zone cemented by a natural-gas hydrate below the sea floor. Natural-gas hydrates are solids composed mainly of methane and water. Gas hydrates form under certain pressure and temperature conditions when there is an adequate supply of methane" (Field and Kvenvolden[21]). When bottom water temperatures approach 0°C, natural-gas hydrates can form in sediments at water depths greater than about 300 m. The gas hydrates present on the northern California continental margin occur in water depths between about 500 and 2600 m (2000 and 8500 ft). The temperature increase due to deeper burial, which depends upon the area's geothermal gradient, will cause the gas hydrate to melt at a certain depth below the sea floor. "The base of the gas hydrate follows a pressure-temperature surface that defines that maximum depth at which the gas hydrate is stable" (Field and Kvenvolden[21]). Velocities within the hydrates have been reported from 1.6 to 2.2 km/s. If there is sufficient recoverable gas under the hydrate zone, exploitation of such gas as an energy resource may occur in the future as deep-water drilling technology advances.

Other BSRs have been attributed to changes in acoustic velocity that occur at diagenetic boundaries, e.g., a change from biogenic (opal-A) to crystalline (opal-CT) silica (Hein et al.[22]). Distinguishing between the two different causes for BSRs is usually accomplished by analyzing the temperature-pressure regimes present at the BSR as it mimics the sea floor. Furthermore, a gas-hydrate BSR should become deeper in sediment with increasing water depth; a diagenetic BSR often becomes shallower in sediment with increasing water depth (Field and Kvenvolden[21]).

The next fundamental assumption in seismic interpretation is that after correct processing, the seismic waveshape is governed primarily by the geology within the reflection zone (the Fresnel zone) such that changes in lithology

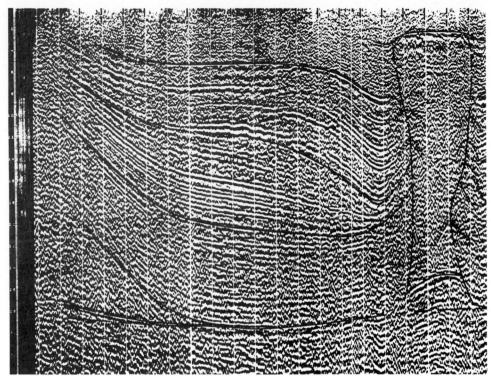

FIGURE 8-16 Distortion of sedimentary layers due to forces associated with salt-dome buoyancy. Some of the structures shown, e.g., those below the piercement-type salt dome and salt pillows (like the deep one on the right) are not real but result from velocity effects. (*Exxon, Inc.*)

(stratigraphy), pore constituents, pore space, or termination of a bed affect the waveshape in a manner that can be modeled.

The conventional representation of a single channel of seismic reflection information is a plot of signal amplitude versus time on a trace corresponding in its position on the section to that of the receiving geophone group represented by the channel. Since normal-moveout-stack maps offset seismic data to the zero-offset, where source and receiver are collocated, modern stack displays show the common-midpoint data at the zero-offset. The record section shows an assemblage of such traces side by side. Such a presentation should not be looked upon as a geological cross section because it can distort the actual geometry of the subsurface in two ways: (1) Any variations in velocity, either vertical or lateral, will cause the time section to have a configuration different from that of the actual geological section plotted in depth. (2) Geometric bending of the ray paths away from the vertical will have the same effect as pointed out in our discussion of migration in the preceding section.

Migrated sections and sections plotted in depth rather than time (see Figs. 7-38, 7-39, and 7-49) are designed to minimize the distortion present on conven-

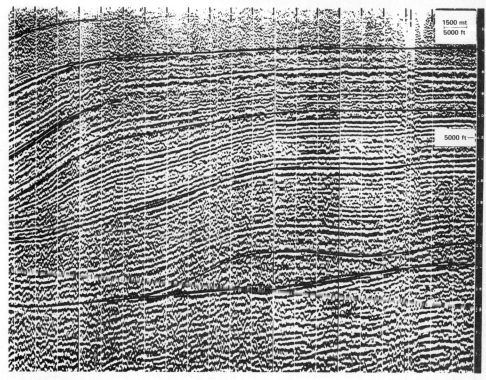

1500 mt / 5000 ft

5000 ft —

FIGURE 8-16   continued

tional (time-CDP-stack) record sections. But a large majority of the sections actually used in exploration are of the conventional type, and it is important that all geophysicists recognize the errors that these distortions can lead to in seismic interpretation. Moreover, many migrated sections display incorrect structural indications because of out-of-the-plane events which are inherently not migrated correctly, and because of uncertainties, errors, or complexities in the velocity distribution.

Another common pitfall in structural interpretation can result from erroneously chosen processing parameters (e.g., an incorrect stacking velocity).

All these types of hazards have been reported by Tucker and Yorston.[23] A few of the examples they present will be discussed here to illustrate the consequences that result when some of the pitfalls they point out are not taken into account.

Velocity Pitfalls   Let us take another look at Fig. 8-16, which illustrates spurious structures attributable to velocity anomalies in overlying salt bodies. A strong reflection is observed under the large salt dome that is about 150 ms higher at its shallowest point than are the correlative events on either side of the dome. Yet there is no real structural uplift below the salt. The fact that the

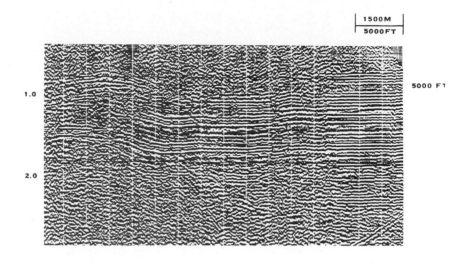

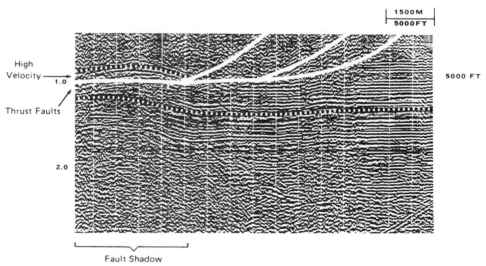

FIGURE 8-17 "Anticline" caused by thrusting of high-velocity material over monoclinal layers. Markings on lower section indicate interpreted structure. (*From Tucker and Yorston.*[23])

velocity in the salt column is higher than that in the surrounding material can account completely for the apparent structure of the subsalt formation. The observed dropoff in the same reflection near the right-hand edge of the section is explainable by a salt pillow just above it, which happens to have a lower velocity than that of the surrounding formation, an effect often observed when salt is unusually deep.

Another example from Tucker and Yorston[23] is related to overthrusting. Figure 8-17 shows a section that would lead one to the conclusion that there is an anticlinal feature between 1.0 and 2.0 s. But the authors' interpretation is quite different, as one sees from the marked section in the lower portion of the figure. A low-angle overthrust fault has a high-velocity allochthonous tongue (presumably limestone) on the left side of the section. This tongue causes the flat autochthonous beds below to appear arched upward because of velocity pull-up. Such effects are frequently observed in the foothills of Alberta, Canada, particularly in the area around Turner Valley where the Mississippian Rundle limestone is thrust at a low angle over lower-velocity Cretaceous formations.

The presence of gas similarly affects P-wave velocity, slowing it down measurably. A shallow gas accumulation, if thick enough, can mask the true structural picture of the deeper horizons, even to the point of concealing a field. Detailed velocity (and amplitude) work can yield the information necessary to compensate for this gas effect, either through depth migration or through (manual) interpretation steps, and thus a more accurate structural picture can be derived.

Geometrical Pitfalls   A common type of geometrical pitfall is illustrated by Fig. 8-18. Crossing dip segments are observed over a syncline with a "buried focus", i.e., such a sharp curvature that the reflection ray paths cross one another on their way to and from the surface. Figure 8-19 shows the ray-path geometry resulting in the "bow tie" that is observed on the section at depths

FIGURE 8-18   Bow-tie effect observed over sharp syncline in the Adriatic Sea. Apparent anticline is actually a diffraction feature. (*Geocom, Inc.*)

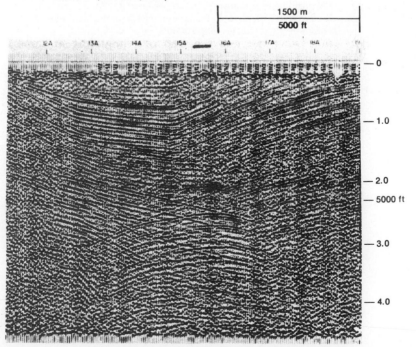

FIGURE 8-19   "Bow-tie" effect. Wave paths and pattern on record section for reflections from syncline with curvature greater than that of approaching wavefronts, producing a buried focus.

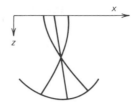
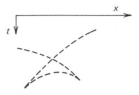

below 1.0 s. The two reflections dipping steeply in opposite directions are reflections from respective sides of the synclinal structure that cross one another on their way to the surface; the arcuate feature below is a diffraction from a point at the bottom of the syncline, the shortest time of the diffraction being observed over the deepest point of the syncline. Migration with the correct (earth) velocities would collapse the diffraction arc to a point and would shift the flank reflections to their true positions, but even in the absence of such migration the bow-tie pattern should enable the knowledgeable geophysicist or geologist to recognize the true nature of the source.

Processing Pitfalls   Figure 8-20 illustrates a processing pitfall. It is an example of how different choices of stacking velocity can lead to greatly different interpretations. On the left the deeper structure appears to be a gently warped monocline. On the right it appears to be a sharp anticline with a strong

FIGURE 8-20   Which structure is correct? Each represents a different stacking velocity. As gently dipping events on the left have all the characteristics of multiple reflections, the structure on the right is preferred. (*From Tucker and Yorston.*[23])

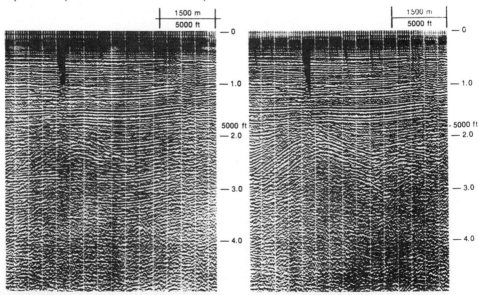

suggestion of faulting on one side. A careful comparison of the deeper dipping events on the section at the left with shallower ones at half their time makes the deeper events look like multiples. This correspondence favors the likelihood that the stacking velocity yielding the anticlinal structure is the correct one.

Presentation of Reflection Data on Maps

The transfer of seismic data from record sections to a map involves a transformation from a 2-D to a 3-D representation. Ordinarily the data are presented on the map in the form of contours representing actual reflection times, or depths. Sometimes the reflections are not continuous; where this is the case, it may be desirable to construct a phantom horizon, which is kept parallel to whatever reflections are nearest it along the section. The phantom horizons must close around loops like continuous reflections. If they do not, previously unsuspected faulting could account for the misclosure.

Times or depths are ordinarily entered on maps at convenient intervals along the shooting lines, often at those shot points that fall approximately $\frac{1}{4}$ mi apart. The positions of the reflections will be displaced from the shot points if the reflectors have appreciable dip, and the time map should be migrated to correct for such lateral and vertical displacement. Kleyn[24] and Sheriff and Geldart[25] discuss this topic. An average-velocity map from the seismic-datum plane to the selected reflector is constructed based on the best available information. The map migration can be acomplished through the computer or by hand. If done by hand, dip segments taken along true dip of the structures are manually repositioned by use of Eqs. (7-10) or similar equations.

If information on intermediate velocity surfaces is available, computer techniques allow the input of this information along with the digitized time contour map to perform a more sophisticated map migration. A ray-tracing migration is performed with the rays bending according to Snell's law as they encounter the intermediate velocity surfaces. The average-velocity field may then be used to convert the time map to depth.

After conversion of times to depths based on the best available velocity information, the reflection map should ideally be equivalent to a structure map for the geological horizon that is represented. The reliability of the map as an indicator of true geological structure depends on the quality of the reflections, the extent to which adequate information on seismic velocities is available over the area, and the density of well ties. Faulting or lithology changes may also affect the accuracy of seismic structure maps.

Time Versus Depth in Structural Mapping

An important consideration that must be taken into account in evaluating maps and sections in depth is the reliability of the velocity information on which the time-depth conversion was made. Closely spaced velocity surveys provide good time-to-depth conversion information. However, with the computer programs available today for determining velocity analytically from the 48- to 96-fold (or more) reflection data, we are no longer forced to rely solely on well-velocity surveys for trustworthy information on reflection depths. Many areas lack deep enough or closely spaced well-velocity surveys, and so high-quality surface seismic velocity determinations guide the time-to-depth conversions. Yet the precision of conversion velocities obtained from moveout times alone is subject to certain limitations. Accuracy depends on reflection quality, which is not always good in spite of computer-based data-enhancement techniques. Moreover, velocities determined by computers are generally based on slant-ray paths and uniformly dipping reflectors. Because of anisotropy and other reasons, computer-derived velocities usually differ from the vertical velocities that should be used for time-depth conversions. (See Sec. 7-6.)

For many years there has been a difference of opinion among geophysicists over whether seismic results should be presented in time or in depth. Some have preferred cross sections and maps in time rather than in depth because they are based only on objective data and are not subject to change as new velocity information is acquired. Such a preference is hardly justified now that automatic computer programs like that for the velocity spectrum allow the determination of velocities directly from the reflection data and thus make it much easier to obtain detailed velocity information than was possible before such programs became available. It is also possible, as demonstrated in Fig. 7-49, to plot record sections directly in depth by use of the velocity information obtained with such programs.

The final presentation of seismic structures in terms of reflection times must often be looked upon as an evasion of the geophysicist's responsibility, which is to convert his data into a form that is as geologically meaningful as possible. Well tops and isopachs are expressed in units of distance, not time, and geophysical information, to be coordinated properly, must be presented in the same way. Maps in time do not incorporate the effect of lateral velocity changes, which in drastic cases could even account for reversals in the directon of dip with respect to those indicated by time contours. Even admittedly imperfect and incomplete velocity control can prevent grossly erroneous conclusions in geological interpretation that might be made on the basis of time sections and time maps alone. The geologist and exploration manager must rely on the geophysicist to provide the best possible interpretation the geophysical art allows. The geophysicist is not taking his professional responsibilities seriously enough if he or she presents only objective information and leaves it to others, often less qualified, to convert that information into geologically meaningful terms.

Seismic Work Stations

Seismic work stations have been discussed in the processing chapter for their usefulness in interactive trace processing. Various types of seismic work stations have been designed also to accomplish interpretation tasks. Some are specialized for 3-D interpretation, and others can handle either 2-D or 3-D data equally well.

Two-Dimensional Work Stations Even for "interpretive work stations," trace-processing capability is important. Different stacking velocities, filters, deconvolution parameters, migration velocities, and other processing parameters can be tested in order to enhance the critical areas on a line. Color display of the seismic information can aid greatly in the interpretation. Long before the mapping stage, a new line can be previewed by animating (making a movie of) the constant-offset sections. This step, prior to standard processing, can quickly and easily focus the geophysicists's attention on possible problem areas, and give an overview of the geology.

The specific interpretive tasks in which a work station can assist are:

Manual or automated picking (once the geophysicist has started picking) of reflection events for mapping, posting the times and grades
Overlay the digitized picks on the seismic data
Time shift, to tie from one vintage (vintage usually refers to the year of an item, but here also means the acquisition parameters, recording system, and/or processing flow used on the given data set from that year) to another; design and apply match filters to shape different vintages of seismic data to match a (zero-phase) standard in the mapping area
Post misties at intersections
Computer contouring, input of manual contours, and editing of all contours
Correlation of reflectors across faults
Horizon flattening to illustrate growth history
2-D modeling (zero-offset, non-zero-offset)
Computation, posting, and contouring of isotimes (isochrons)
Digitize velocity maps, create and edit the velocity maps from the seismic velocity data base
Map migration; map conversion from time to depth
Integraton of geologic database (well depths) with the seismic datums
3-D view of contoured surface

The geologic database is an important part of an interpretive work station. The well locations, names, API or other identifying numbers, total depths, and the depths of the important formations in all the wells in an area constitute part of the geologic database. The digitized well logs themselves constitute the other part. Obviously, the software should allow retrieval from the database of any or any combination of the above categories. Once the geologic database is in place, the following specific tasks may be carried out at the work station:

Creation of synthetic seismograms from digitized well logs; plotting of any log or suite of logs in time or depth
Tieing the synthetics to the seismic; insertion of a synthetic seismogram or any well log curve onto a seismic stack;

1-D modeling (building hypothetical geologic columns to determine the seismic response)

2-D modeling (computing the zero-offset seismic response to a given 2-D geologic model)

The ability to input, modify, and update the base map is an obvious necessity. The locations of all wells, all seismic lines (of different vintages, entered from base maps of different scales), and all types of geographic entities (rivers, towns, pipelines, etc.) need to exist in the database in such a way that additions or corrections are easily performed. Hard copy from the database should be available at any scale (within reason) and with annotation of whatever type of information desired from the databases.

Three-Dimensional Interpretation   A 3-D interpretive work station should offer all of the above capabilities, with specific attention paid to facilitating the three basic 3-D interpreting modes: data preview, data interpretation, and map generation. Data preview usually means animation of dip-line sections, followed by strike-line sections in order to gain an overall perspective on the geology of the area. Chapter 10 deals with 3-D interpretation at length. The specific tasks that a 3-D work station needs to perform are:

Retrieval of sections along any azimuth (post-stack, and usually post–3-D migration) as well as retrieval of profiles connecting multiple wells in an area ("random profile") and subsequent picking of horizons and faults

Display of time slices from the data and subsequent picking of horizons and faults

Concurrent display of base map with the location of the seismic profile currently being viewed highlighted

Post-stack processing (change filters, gain, etc.)

Movable windows for correlation from line to line or across faults; and correlation across faults by cutting the seismic display along the fault and setting two edges together by means of time shifts

Stretchable correlation windows especially useful across growth faults

Scaling, zooming, editing of displays, generating hard copy, both black and white and color

Animation (rapid display of parallel seismic lines or time slices, also known as a "movie")

Timely completion of mapping in 3-D projects is the best accomplished with work-station assistance. Estimates of the time spent in computer-assisted interpretation, compared to standard manual interpretation with paper records, range from one-fifth to one-tenth (Cole et al.[26]). "Letting the computer manage and retrieve the data gives the interpreter more time to recognize geology and prepare results and presentation materials such as contour maps" (Cole et al.[26]). With 3-D data, work-station assistance in the tasks listed above under 2-D work-stations tasks becomes even more important for timely completion of 3-D mapping.

8-6 THE USE OF SEISMIC DATA TO DETECT DRILLING HAZARDS

In marine settings, the seismic data over the proposed rig location are analyzed to determine if there are hazards to the rig or to drilling. If such hazards are detected, usually a dense grid of high-resolution seismic will be collected to determine where the rig and drilling may safely be located. Some hazards that high-resolution seismic reflection surveying can detect include hydrocarbon seeps on the sea floor; buried river channels, which mean less stable sediments, unsuitable for rig anchoring; gas pockets within the sedimentary section, often detected by their high-amplitude reflections, which can cause blowouts if not properly anticipated and handled in the drilling program. Gassy mud sediments, often of anomalously high attenuation and/or slow velocity, have low shear strength and are not appropriate for the anchoring of structures. Many of the above-mentioned hazards can be properly identified and studied by means of constant-offset panels, as described by Fulton and Darr.[27]

An overpressured section, often shale masses, if not properly anticipated, can also cause blowouts. Overpressured shale masses can be detected in many cases by detailed moveout-velocity analyses because they have a velocity lower than that of the surrounding sediments. To perform this type of analysis requires, of course, that there be at least one sub-shale-mass, high-quality, primary reflection on all offsets, so that there will be reflected energy that has traveled through the low-velocity zone. The mass also tends to be internally reflection free and is therefore visually different from the other parts of the seismic section.

REFERENCES

1 Vail, P. R., R. G. Todd, and J. B. Sangree: Chronostratigraphic Significance of Seismic Reflections, pp. 99–116, in C. E. Payton (ed.), "Seismic Stratigraphy—Applications to Hydrocarbon Exploration," *Am. Assoc. Petrol. Geol. Mem. 26,* 1977.

2 Neidell, N. S.: Stratigraphic Modeling and Interpretation Geophysical Principles and Techniques, Am. Assoc. Petrol. Geol. Continuing Education Course Note Series #13, p. 145, 1979.

3 Woods, J. P.: The Composition of Reflections, *Geophysics,* vol. 21, pp. 261–276, 1956.

4 Widess, M. B.: How Thin Is a Thin Bed?, *Geophysics,* vol. 38, pp. 1176–1180, 1973.

5 Gretener, P. E. F.: An Analysis of the Observed Time Discrepancies between Continuous and Conventional Well Velocity Surveys, *Geophysics,* vol. 26, pp. 1–11, 1961.

6 Strick, E.: An Explanation of Observed Time Discrepancies between Continuous and Conventional Well Velocity Surveys, *Geophysics,* vol. 36, pp. 285–295, 1971.

7 Sengbush, R. L., P. L. Lawrence, and F. J. McDonal: Interpretation of Synthetic Seismograms, *Geophysics,* vol. 26, pp. 138–157, 1961.

8 Neidell, N. S. (ed): The Convolutional Model, course notes from SEG school, Soc. Explor. Geophys., Tulsa, Okla.

9 Peterson, R. A., W. R. Fillippone, and F. B. Coker: The Synthesis of Seismograms from Well Log Data, *Geophysics,* vol. 20, pp. 516–638, 1955.

10 Wood, L.: Imaging the Subsurface, pp. 45–90, in K. C. Jain and R. J. P. de Figueiredo (eds.) "Concepts and Techniques in Oil and Gas Exploration," Soc. Explor. Geophys., Tulsa, Okla., 1982.

11 Wuenschel, P. C.: Seismogram Synthesis Including Multiples and Transmission Coefficients, *Geophysics*, vol. 25, pp. 106–129, 1960.

12 Hardage, B. A., and M. N. Toksoz: "Vertical Seismic Profiling Parts A, B," Geophysical Press, Netherlands, 1983.

13 Manzur, A.: Delineation of Salt Masses Using Borehole Seismics, *Oil and Gas J.*, pp. 147–149, Oct. 7, 1985.

14 Bally, A. W. (ed.): "Seismic Expression of Structural Styles, A Picture and Work Atlas," vols. 1–3, *Am. Assoc. Petrol. Geol. Studies in Geology Series #15*, Am. Assoc. Petrol. Geol. Tulsa, Okla., 1983.

15 Quarles, Miller, Jr.: Fault Interpretation in Southwest Texas, *Geophysics*, vol. 15, pp. 462–470, 1950.

16 Laubscher, Hans P.: Structural and Seismic Deformation along Normal Faults in the Eastern Venezuelan Basin, *Geophysics*, vol. 21, pp. 368–387, 1956.

17 Harding, T. P.: "Seismic Characteristics and Identification of Negative Flower Structures, Positive Flower Structures, and Positive Structural Inversion," *Am. Assoc. Petrol. Geol.*, vol. 69, pp. 582–600, 1985.

18 Bodenhausen, J. W. A., and W. F. Ott: Habitat of the Rijswijk Oil Province, Onshore, The Netherlands, pp. 301–309, in L. V. Illing and G. D. Hobson (eds.), "Petroleum Geology of the Continental Shelf of Northwest Europe," Hayden and Son (for Institute of Petroleum), London, 1981.

19 Harding, T. P., and J. D. Lowell: Structural Styles, Their Plate-Tectonic Habitats, and Hydrocarbon Traps in Petroleum Provinces, *Am. Assoc. Petrol. Geol.*, vol. 63, pp. 1016–1058, 1979.

20 Backus, M. M., and R. L. Chen: Flat Spot Exploration, *Geophys. Prospec.*, vol. 23, pp. 533–577, 1975.

21 Field, M. E., and K. A. Kvenvolden: Gas Hydrates on the Northern California Continental Margin, *Geology*, vol. 13, pp. 517–520, 1985.

22 Hein, J. R., D. W. Scholl, J. A. Barron, M. G. Jones, and J. Miller: Diagenesis of Late Cenozoic Diatomaceous Deposits and Formation of the Bottom Simulating Reflector in the Southern Bering Sea, *Sedimentology*, vol. 25, pp. 155–181, 1978.

23 Tucker, Paul M., and Howard J. Yorston: "Pitfalls in Seismic Interpretation," *Soc. Explor. Geophys. Monogr. Ser. 2*, 1973.

24 Kleyn, A. H.: "Seismic Reflection Interpretation," Applied Science, London; Elsevier, New York, 1983.

25 Sheriff, R. E., and L. P. Geldart: Data Processing and Interpretation, "Exploration Seismology," vol. 2, Cambridge Univ. Press, 1983.

26 Cole, R. A., and H. R. Nelson, Jr.: Interactive Computer Graphics and Interpretation of Three-Dimensional Seismic Surveys, *54th Ann. Int. SEG Meeting*, Expanded Abstracts, pp. 412–413, 1984.

27 Fulton, T. K., and K. M. Darr: Offset Panel, *Geophysics*, vol. 49, pp. 1140–1152, 1984.

28 Eubank, R. T., and A. C. Makki: Structural Geology of the Central Sumatra Back-Arc Basin, Jakarta, Indonesian Petrol. Assoc., 10th Ann. Convention, p. 53, 1981.

29 Sprinkel, D. A.: Apparent Reverse Movement on Previous Thrust Faults along the Eastern Margin of the Basin and Range Province, North-Central Utah, pp. 135–143, in G. W. Newman and H. D. Goode (eds.), *Basin and Range Symp. and Great Basin Field Conf.* Rocky Mountain Assoc. Geol., 1979.

CHAPTER 9

SEISMIC STRATIGRAPHY, MODELING AND INVERSION, AND HYDROCARBON INDICATORS

The use of the geometry (or character) of reflections, their amplitudes, and their velocities to determine the stratigraphic setting, the depositional history, the lithology, and hydrocarbon presence is the area of seismic interpretation that has experienced the most rapid expansion since the mid-1970s. In the early 1970s, geophysicists began to discuss interpretation methods that used the character of reflections to discern and map seismic sequences and facies and to relate the appearance of a seismic facies to its depositional environment. This appears to have been the start of what is now termed *seismic stratigraphy*. At about the same time, it was acknowledged that in recent, unconsolidated sediments, the presence of gas was often directly indicated by anomalously high amplitude reflections. These phenomena became known as *bright spots*, in reference to their startlingly prominent appearance on sections processed to preserve relative amplitudes. The modern era of "direct hydrocarbon detection" is generally considered to have been started by the bright-spot technique of gas exploration. More recently, the combined study of detailed velocity information, derived from moveout curves and reflection amplitudes, the geometry (or times) of seismic reflections, and the amplitudes of painstakingly processed seismic stacks, yields a wealth of stratigraphic, lithologic, and pore-constituent information. Such information can only be validated when carefully and correctly set in the local geologic context through model studies. This chapter will address these and related interpretation techniques. For example, the pre-stack, nonnormal incidence amplitudes of carefully processed data contain information concerning the partitioning of energy between P- and shear-wave modes and, as such, shed light upon the ratio of P- and shear velocities at the boundary. This ratio, in turn, can be used to distinguish among a variety of modeled geologic scenarios. P- and shear-wave reflection data can be interpreted jointly to extract more information on lithology and hydrocarbon presence.

The subtle post-stack features of waveshape and phase of the reflection are being used in conjunction with extensive, sophisticated seismic modeling studies to extract lithologic and pore-constituent information. All of these methods of seismic stratigraphic interpretation are seen as growing areas of expertise, in which radical and widespread changes are expected over the next 20 years with respect to processing, seismic display, and, of course, additional interpretation techniques. Meticulous processing is critically important to the use of such interpretation techniques.

9-1 REFLECTION AS A TOOL FOR STRATIGRAPHIC STUDIES

Throughout the history of the reflection method, its performance in locating hydrocarbons in stratigraphic traps has been much less favorable than in finding structurally entrapped oil and gas. Only one type of stratigraphic feature associated with hydrocarbon entrapment has been discovered and mapped by reflection with consistent success, and that is the carbonate reef. Contrasting lithological characteristics of reefs and the shales they replace have made them favorable targets for seismic location ever since the Leduc Field in Alberta was found by reflection in 1947. The physical limitations of the seismic technique have made it less successful in exploring for other kinds of stratigraphic traps, which generally have lithologic characteristics giving a less diagnostic response to seismic waves.

Let us consider some examples of the results obtained in actual exploration to illustrate the varying degrees of success for the different types of stratigraphic entrapment. Many of the examples to be reviewed appear in Ref. 1. The general problems encountered in exploring for stratigraphic traps with the seismograph are discussed by Lyons and Dobrin[2] in the same publication. Key sources for seis-strat case histories and the techniques of seis-strat interpretation are AAPG Memoirs 26,[3] 32,[4] and 39.[5]

Stratigraphic oil traps can result from reefs, pinchouts, or other features associated with erosional truncation, facies transitions, and sand lenses associated with buried channels, lakes, or similar sources. (Some of these traps are illustrated in Fig. 8-7.) Levorsen[6] extensively reviews the geological considerations for the formation of stratigraphic traps. The tremendous variety of geologic situations giving rise to such entrapment makes it difficult to reduce the problem of finding them seismically to as small a number of basic elements as we would like.

The principal factors for the poor success of seismic methods heretofore in detecting stratigraphic features other than reefs are (1) the limited resolution of the seismic survey, and (2) inadequate displays of final stacks and coarse processing. The first factor is a physical restraint and depends on the frequencies inserted into and transmitted through the earth and to the density of coverage of the prospect. The second factor can be rectified, as is discussed and illustrated in Sec. 9-4. Structural traps generally involve deformations in beds that remain conformable over at least a few hundred feet of section. In most types of stratigraphic traps, however, there is a variation in lithology that is often confined to a depth interval much shorter than a wavelength, so that resolution becomes a major problem. And it is evident from our discussion of the composition of reflections that any change in stratification could result in the alteration, or even the destruction by interference effects, of reflection signals associated with the beds above and below the point where the layering characteristics change.

Use of Reflection Data to Reconstruct Depositional History

The greatest success of the seismic method in stratigraphic studies has not been related directly to the discovery of hydrocarbons but more indirectly in casting light upon the depositional environment and history of deposition in the areas where exploration is being carried out. Change in the depositional environment, lithology, and sea level can be identified by character and geometry on the seismic section. In the words of Vail and his colleagues,[7] "whereas all the rocks above a stratal unconformity surface are younger than those below it, the resulting seismic section is a record of chronostratigraphic (time-stratigraphic) depositional and structural patterns and not a record of the time-transgressive lithostratigraphy (rock-stratigraphy)" (p. 51). Seismic sequence analysis identifies the major depositional sequences based upon internally conformable reflections and upon the bounding reflections, or reflection character (onlap, downlap, toplap, truncation). (See Fig. 9-1.) Again, according to Vail[7] (p. 51):

> Analysis of seismic facies is the delineation and interpretation of reflection geometry, continuity, amplitude, frequency, and interval velocity, as well as the external form and associations of seismic facies units within the framework of depositional sequences. Analysis of relative changes of sea level consists of constructing chronostratigraphic correlation charts and charts of cycles of relative changes of sea level on a regional basis and comparing them with global data. A prediction of age, time of unconformities, paleoenvironments, and lithofacies may be attempted when the local sea-level changes are similar to those found in global sea-level change studies. There is some controversy concerning whether or not the sea-level changes determined by seismic stratigraphic techniques are caused more often by local structuring or are global in nature.

The patterns shown by reflections often make it possible to understand how the deposition took place in the areas under investigation. Interval-velocity studies often enable the explorationist to identify gross lithological features and allow a more complete reconstruction of the depositional environment.

The various movements of a shore line, progressive and regressive, are associated with geometrical patterns on the seismic data that are indicative of the types of deposition that took place at various periods of geological history.

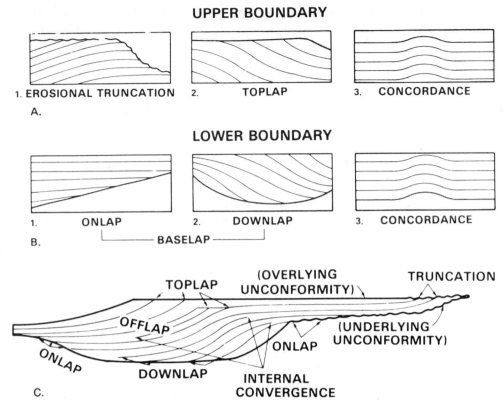

FIGURE 9-1 Pattern of reflections within a sequence unit, related to the unit boundaries. (*a*) Pattern at the top of a sequence unit. (*b*) Pattern at the base of a sequence unit. (*c*) Reflection relationships within an idealized unit. (*From Mitchum, Vail, and Thompson[80]; reprinted by permission of The American Association of Petroleum Geologists.*)

A knowledge of such history enables the explorationist to predict the most favorable areas for oil accumulation, and more detailed exploration (e.g., by means of a detailed 3-D survey and by stratigraphic drilling) over such areas should lead to the most expeditious location of stratigraphically entrapped hydrocarbons.

Some patterns on seismic sections that should make it possible to reconstruct depositional history are illustrated in Fig. 9-2. Parallel bedding (one of the seismic facies present) indicates deep-water deposition on a stable surface. The arrows on the section indicate whether the basin was rising or sinking during each phase of deposition. A rising basin hinged at the shoreline leaves a wedge that thins in the seaward direction, while a sinking basin so hinged is associated with a wedge that thickens seaward. Onlap deposition and prograding as in deltaic fans can be deduced from characteristic patterns of cycle termination on seismic records.

Unconformities can also be mapped from the divergent pattern of reflections on a seismic section. The presence of unconformable contacts on a seismic

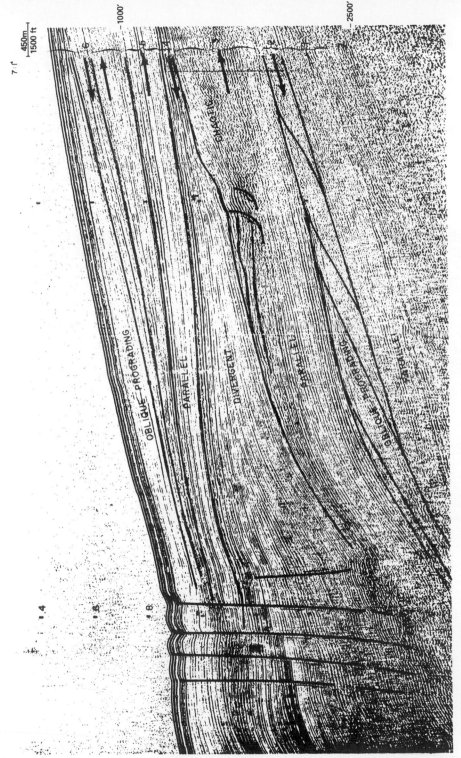

FIGURE 9-2 Section showing successive periods of transgressive and regressive deposition. Divergences and convergences indicate shore-line movements or sinking of basins. Oblique prograding sequences denoted by pattern of updip termination of dipping reflections. (*Exxon, Inc.*)

333

section can often cast important light on the depositional and erosional history of an area and on the environment existing during the time when the movements took place.

Figure 9-3a shows a rather unusual pair of unconformities with large divergences in structure across each discontinuity. The complexity of the geological history is increased even more by folding and possible faulting in the portion of the section lying between the unconformities. In offshore areas where information from exploratory drilling is not available, seismic patterns like this may provide the only basis for reconstructing depositional as well as tectonic

FIGURE 9-3
Unconformities at two levels indicated by seismic layering pattern: (a) complete section; (b) detail of central portion. (Prakla-Seismos.)

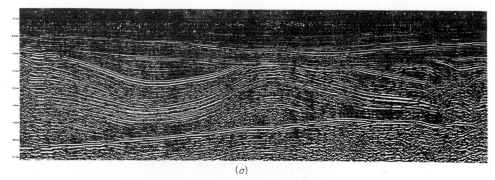

(a)

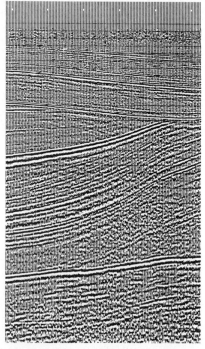

(b)

history. Figure 9-3*b* is a closeup of a portion of the section illustrating the depositional pattern in greater detail.

Classification of Stratigraphic Traps

The success of the seismic reflection method in finding stratigraphic traps varies with the type of trap involved. Most such entrapment features fall within four categories:

1 Carbonate reefs
2 Permeability barriers associated with erosional truncation
3 Sand bodies, such as lenses or stream channels, surrounded by impermeable materials
4 Facies changes from permeable to impermeable lithology

Seismic exploration for each type of entrapment is discussed in the following paragraphs.

Reefs Reefs consist of the skeletal remains of coral, algae, or similar shallow-water organisms, the buildups generally occurring on shoals or islands surrounded by deeper water. The porous reef material originally deposited is surrounded and overlain by muds, which are subsequently consolidated into shale, resulting in ideal conditions for generation and entrapment of hydrocarbons. Since the discovery by seismic means of oil in the Leduc reef of Alberta, reflection techniques have been successful in finding productive limestone reefs in west Texas, Alberta, Illinois, Michigan, Libya, and other petroliferous areas.

Reefs are manifested in numerous ways on seismic sections. Some common ones are shown in Fig. 9-4. Two characteristics of reefs facilitate their location by the seismic method. The more widely used one is the contrast between the velocity in reef limestone and that in the shale that often surrounds it at the same stratigraphic level. This contrast causes the reef to act as a lens which can give rise to apparent time structures in underlying reflectors. (See Fig. 9-4*f*.) The other characteristic is draping, which frequently occurs in the overlying sediments due to differential compaction over the reef and over the shale (Fig. 9-4*e*). Structures caused by draping effects can, of course, be mapped in the same way as other structures.

The velocity differential between reef carbonate and off-reef shale affects the times of the reflections from below the reef level, as demonstated by Skeels.[8] Figure 9-5 illustrates the respective electric logs and the interval-velocity distributions in a well (*B*) penetrating a thick Devonian reef as well as in another well (*A*) off the reef about 3 mi away. The seismic velocity through the reef averages about 18,500 ft/s, while the normal velocity through the shale and limestone in the same stratigraphic interval averages about 13,000 ft/s. So large a velocity contrast would lead us to expect a substantial shortening of the time interval between a reflection from below the reef zone and one from above

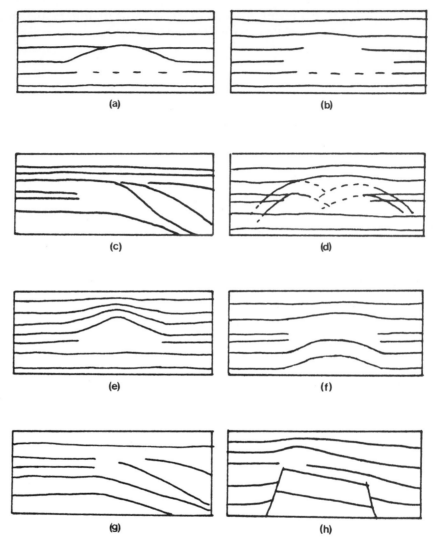

FIGURE 9-4 Criteria on seismic data for reef identification: (*a*) reef outline by reflections; (*b*) reef indicated by reflection void; (*c*) change in reflection pattern on opposite sides of reef; (*d*) diffractions from reef edges; (*e*) differential compaction over reef; (*f*) velocity anomaly underneath reef; (*g*) reef located on hingeline of a basin; and (*h*) reef located on a structural uplift. (*After Bubb and Hatlelid[81]; reprinted by permission of The American Association of Petroleum Geologists.*)

it as the maximum reef buildup is approached from the area outside of the reef (see Fig. 9-4*f*).

Reefs are sometimes revealed on seismic records by subtle changes in reflection quality, including the interruption of reflections and possibly by diffraction effects (Fig. 9-4*d*). Occasionally reefs can show up very conspicuously on record sections, as in Fig. 9-6 over the North Knox City Field in west

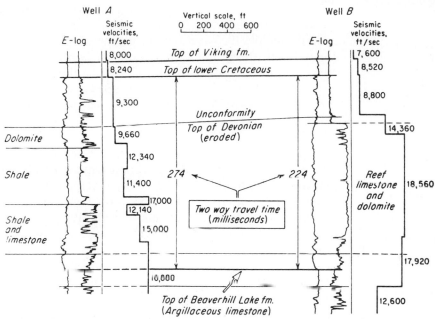

FIGURE 9-5 Electric logs and seismic interval velocities in corresponding portions of nearby off-reef (*A*) and reef (*B*) wells in Alberta. (*From Skeels.*[8])

Texas (see Harwell and Rector[9]). Below the reef buildup in the Canyon Formation, a "structure" is shown in the underlying Caddo, which is entirely the result of velocity pull-up in the reef limestone.

A somewhat different approach to reef exploration, proposed by Fitton and Dobrin[10] for areas of poor reflection quality, involves measuring changes in

FIGURE 9-6 Seismic section showing reef buildup in North Knox City Field, west Texas. (*From Harwell and Rector.*[9])

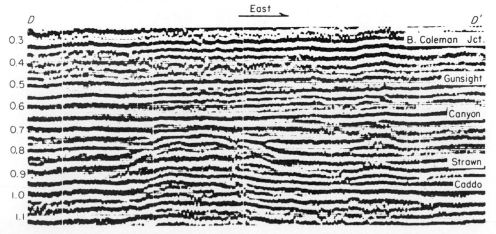

reflection frequency in the zone above the reef where differential compaction might be expected.

In the middle 1960s, oil-bearing pinnacle reefs were discovered in the middle Devonian in the Rainbow Lake area in northwestern Alberta. Evans[11] discusses the seismic exploration for reefs of this type which occur in the Keg River Formation. He shows sections displaying conspicuous draping effects in the overlying Slave Point as well as irregularities in the reflections from the Keg River zone.

Pinchouts and Erosional Truncations When a stratum becomes thinner and thinner as it is traced in any direction, until it finally disappears, it is said to pinch out, or thin out. A stratum may pinch out due to depositional causes or erosional causes, or a combination of the two. It is generally difficult to detail erosional surfaces and pinchouts with the reflection seismograph because of the limitations in resolution inherent in the seismic method. Most reflections observed on records, as pointed out in Chap. 8, are a composite of returns from individual boundaries that arrive at such a time that they interfere constructively. A single boundary, such as an uncomformable surface which is not parallel to other interfaces above or below, would not be expected to generate a phase-constant reflection with the lateral persistence that is necessary if it is to be useful in reflection mapping. Nevertheless, the presence of higher-frequency energy will improve the ability to detect pinchouts by improving resolution. As early as 1959 Seelis[12] showed the benefits of enhanced high frequencies in tracing a horizon to pinchout. Figure 9-7 illustrates how an erosional unconformity associated with a pinchout would cause the character of a reflection to change continually in the lateral direction because of progressive shifts in the phase relation between constituent signals from different lithological boundaries encompassed by a single seismic wavelength.

Such unconformities have considerable practical significance in oil exploration. This is because oil is often entrapped in the updip wedge that is left when a dipping, porous sand is eroded and the erosional surface makes an angle with the base of the sand, eventually truncating it as shown in Fig. 9-7. When this surface is covered by impermeable material in subsequent deposition, we have conditions favorable for oil accumulation. The East Texas Field, one of the world's greatest, had its origin in the updip wedging by erosion of the Woodbine sand and the subsequent deposition of the Eagle Ford shale, which acted as a seal for hydrocarbon entrapment. Other traps associated with unconformities are the sands often deposited on an erosional surface.

To locate such features precisely by seismic reflection would be a most desirable objective, and sometimes it can be done. More generally, however, the limitations in resolution we have discussed make it difficult to do more than narrow the range of uncertainty in where to look for this type of entrapment. Figure 9-8 from a paper by Robinson[13] illustrates the problems that occur when one is looking for such pinchouts by combining geological and seismic information. At 1.1 s there are three peaks on the left side of the section which correlate

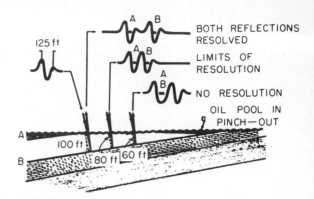

FIGURE 9-7 Following a converging bed toward its termination using seismic reflections from its top and bottom surfaces. (*From Lyons and Dobrin.*[2])

on the basis of velocity information with a water-bearing sand 290 ft thick at well 1. Following this event in the updip direction, which is to the right, we see that the three peaks soon converge into two peaks near the center of the section, which as they approach the extreme right lose their coherence. This change in waveform should indicate that the reflecting formation has changed character or disappeared. The second well to be drilled, well 2, encountered no sand at all, and when well 3 was drilled downdip from well 2, the sand was

FIGURE 9-8 Pinchout of sand body as seen on seismic section. Sand is indicated by arrows along left edge of section where well 1 showed it to be 290 ft thick. It is missing in well 2. In well 3 it was water-bearing, suggesting no oil in pinchout. (*From Robinson.*[13])

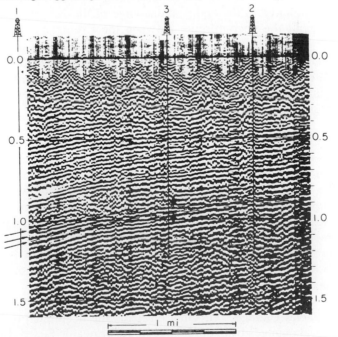

found, higher and thinner but water-bearing. No further drilling has been done on the feature. Of course, a sand pinching out updip can be saturated with water all the way to the edge of the wedge just as an anticline can be water-bearing at its highest point.

Better resolution of the reflections from this level might have made it possible to predict the position of the pinchout more closely and to locate the third well where it might have brought in oil rather than water, if oil is indeed present farther updip in the sand than well 3. More up-to-date shooting and processing procedures might obtain such resolution. In general, however, one has had to expect more dry holes before bringing in a stratigraphic oil pool than would usually be required for structural discoveries. This example illustrates why greater risks are perceived to be involved in drilling for stratigraphic oil than for structural oil. The newer techniques we describe in these chapters will tend to redress this imbalance.

One of the greatest accumulations of oil in the world, Prudhoe Bay on the Alaska North Slope, is entrapped on one side by a truncational surface between the impermeable Cretaceous and the productive Jurassic-Mississippian zone. The unconformity responsible for the entrapment shows up clearly on the seismic section, published by Morgridge and Smith,[14] that crosses the field from southwest to northwest.

Productive truncation traps of a somewhat different type have been found by seismic reflection in the Gifhorn Basin of northwestern Germany. Here the oil-bearing Dogger Beta sand (Jurassic) subcrops below the unconformity at the base of the Albian (Cretaceous). Along the line illustrated in Fig. 8-12, oil has accumulated in the updip wedge-edge of the Jurassic Dogger sand that termi-nates at the unconformity between the Cretaceous and the Jurassic. A con-vergence indicative of such wedging was observed on early seismic records, leading to the discovery of Dogger production in the Hohne Field. A case history of this discovery has been published by Hedemann and Lorenz.[15] The seismic section shown in the upper part of Fig. 8-12 is from shooting carried out after the field was developed.

Channel-Sand Deposits and other Sand Lenses   Where a buried stream chan-nel is covered with an impermeable material, it can entrap oil under favorable source and reservoir conditions. Lyons and Dobrin[2] show how an extension to the South Ceres Field in Noble County, Oklahoma, where oil is entrapped in a channel sand of this type, was located on the basis of seismic reflection data. Figure 9-9 is a cross section through the sand which illustrates how the lens was traced by careful measurement of the differential times between a reflection directly above the sand zone and one directly below it. The isochron pattern shows how the position, where this time is a maximum, coincides with the maximum thickness of the sand body.

Facies Changes   In some oil fields the accumulation of oil is governed by lateral changes from permeable to impermeable facies. It is difficult to observe such a transition directly by the seismograph, but it was possible to do this over

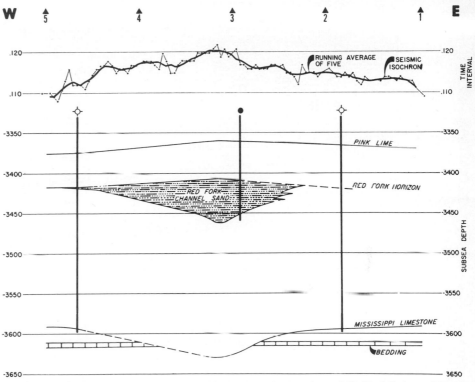

FIGURE 9-9 Cross section made from seismic records defining productive channel-fill (Red Fork sandstone) on basis of anomalies in time interval between two reflections (Pink lime and Mississippi-limestone) straddling sand. (*From Lyons and Dobrin.*[2])

the Bramberge Field of West Germany, discussed by Roll.[16] The Bentheim Formation changes from sand to shale, the facies change making possible the updip entrapment of the oil in the field. The contours in the original seismic map indicated an updip structural closure against a fault, but the discovery well, drilled to meet an obligation rather than on technical grounds, found oil outside the closure and suggested that the accumulation was actually due to a change in facies from sand to shale. A later experimental seismic survey showed a clear-cut character change between the Bentheim sand surface and the shale surface on the other side of the facies boundary that could have been used to outline the field's boundaries if its significance had been appreciated at the proper time.

The San Emidio Nose Field of California, reported by Bazeley,[17] has a complicated discovery history. Twenty-four years elapsed between the initiation of seismic work and the drilling of the discovery well. During this period more and more subsurface information was obtained, mainly from dry holes, that made it possible to close in on the productive area. The oil is entrapped in tongues of sand interfingering and terminating updip in shale. The boundaries were not detectable on seismic records, but the existence of a structural nose

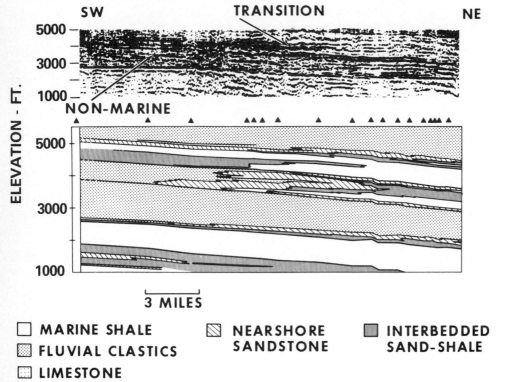

FIGURE 9-10 Comparison of geological and seismic cross sections over area in San Juan Basin, where sand and shale facies interfinger. Black triangles show well locations. (*From Sangree and Widmeier.*[19])

could be determined, and this information helped in the search for a successful drill site. This discovery may reflect one of the most thorough efforts to integrate geology and geophysics that has ever been described in the literature. The estimated reserves are greater than 50 million barrels of oil, and so it appears that the effort ultimately paid off.

Recent developments in seismic-data acquisition and processing have made it possible to trace sand-shale interfingering more successfully in favorable areas than in earlier times (Neidell and Beard[18]). Figure 9-10, from a paper by Sangree and Widmeier,[19] shows how a transition from marine shale (on the right) to fluvial near-shore sandstone (on the left) could be traced on a reflection record section. The section is plotted in depth, facilitating the comparison with the geologic section, which was based on 18 closely spaced wells. The increased density of reflections in the middle of the section indicates the greater number of alternations between sands and shales along this part of the line and shows how the density of reflection events can give information on the location of such transitions.

9-2 EXTRACTING LITHOLOGIC INFORMATION FROM REFLECTION DATA: MODELING AND INVERSION

The identification of lithology in potentially productive strata is an important step in stratigraphic exploration. In the past, there was little that could be learned from seismic reflection records that would help with such identification, but modern field techniques and processing procedures now make it possible, under favorable conditions, to estimate such lithological parameters as local (interval) velocity, porosity (assuming a given lithology), or relative acoustic impedance.

Seismic Lithologic Modeling

Seismic modeling is the vehicle by which seismic correlations with geology may be verified in complicated stratigraphic settings. Although few recent publications describing modeling techniques and applications have appeared (see Taner et al.,[20] Shah,[21] and Neidell[22]), the technology has reached a rather sophisticated level, as illustrated through study of exhibits and talks at the annual SEG convention. Two dimensional zero-offset modeling or 2-D offset-modeling is used to calculate travel times and/or amplitudes of reflections through various anomalous geologic scenarios. Three-dimensional modeling, both zero-offset and non-zero-offset, is also available. Two-dimensional algorithms usually view the subsurface as having perfect lateral continuity and homogeneity outside the plane of the subsurface location. Geometry of virtually any complexity in the plane of the line may be treated. The seismic parameters (velocity, density, Poisson's ratio, bed thickness, etc.) are permitted to vary both vertically and laterally to represent lithologic transitions, pore constituent changes, and similar subtle stratigraphic effects. Models may test qualitative concepts or determine quantitatively the porosity, oil/gas reserves, bed thicknesses, and/or areal (3-D) or spatial (2-D) extent of the reservoir. Quantitative models can be used with quantitative measures of consistency and so can offer scales of comparisons by which alternative (geologic) possibilities are weighed.

Modeling can employ wave theory or ray theory, as first discussed in Sec. 7-5. The approach chosen depends upon the type of information desired. The key to model applicability rests on two considerations: First, the physical elements of wave propagation must be adequate to describe the observations. Next, the input parameters to describe the model must also approximate in good measure the real physical circumstance of the subsurface. Well-conceived model studies can guide interpretation. Cost is always a factor: The type of modeling studies that an explorationist can undertake depends upon the hardware, software, and funds available. For example, in 1985, non-zero-offset modeling using a wave-theoretical approach and a large, complex, multilayered model required a vector (or super) computer, which were available only in a few major oil company research departments and at the processing centers of even fewer major contractors.

Thin-Bed Modeling In many seismic stratigraphic studies, the number and constituent lithology of the thin beds in and around the target zone need to be determined in order to locate the optimum well site. A thin-layer interpretation of seismic data usually is accompanied by seismic modeling studies showing the effect of different geologic situations on the seismic section. A given two-dimensional interpretation ideally employs and is consistent with all the information (geologic, borehole, and seismic). When a synthetic seismic section, generated from the interpreter's model, does not match the seismic data as well as might be hoped, it is customary to perturb the model in order to obtain a better match, since the believability of the interpretation rests upon the match of the model data with the field data.

Such parameter perturbations, in the acoustic impedance and the thickness of the layers, can be made systematically and implemented on the computer. Acceptance of any given perturbation would require that the sum-squared difference between the amplitudes of the stacked field data and synthetic based on the model has been reduced. All the geologic information available is used; the interpreter incorporates such into the initial model and constrains the allowed variations of the parameters to geologically reasonable values. The user specifies the wavelet, which can be held fixed, or the wavelet shape is one of the free parameters, which may be determined during the data fitting and allowed to vary along the profile. In the latter case, the wavelet is a modulated sinusoid, describable by dominant frequency, duration, and energy delay. Trade names for this general type of approach are SLIM (Gelfand and Larner[23]) and CNLPE (Kaman et al.[24]). Some geophysicists refer to this type of approach as *forward-modeling inverse techniques*.

The result of this type of approach is a 2-D earth model which generates synthetic data that has a high correlation coefficient (95 percent or more) with the field seismic data. Although the set of possible solutions, or earth models, that could have generated a given seismic trace is large, the subset of geologically acceptable solutions is quite small. When all local well log data and local geologic information are used to constrain the possible solutions, there is a high probability of determining an earth model very close to that which truly exists.

Migrated 3-D data offer superb input to this type of lithologic analysis: Out-of-the-plane effects are minimal to effectively nonexistent; the resulting high signal-to-noise ratio and the dense spatial sampling allow even complicated stratigraphic reservoirs to be studied and reserves estimated based on all the available seismic information.

An example of the power of 3-D data and seismic lithologic modeling to obtain detailed stratigraphic information is found in Gelfand et al.[25] The geologic setting, shown in Fig. 9-11, is the lower Cretaceous in southern Alberta, an area characterized by intermittent thick pods of excellent reservoir quality sand (the Glauconitic Formation in the Upper Mannville) at a depth of 3300 ft (1 km), postulated to be a river channel system. Abrupt transitions to higher-velocity siltstones and unproductive shales, and an entirely stratigraphic trap-

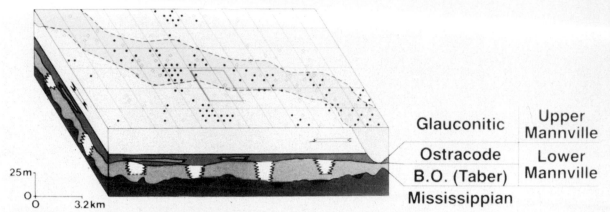

FIGURE 9-11   Geologic setting of the Mannville group, Taber/Turin area, Alberta. Box indicates location of the 3-D survey. The target reservoir is within the Glauconitic sandstone member of the basal Cretaceous Lower Mannville Formation. (*From Gelfand et al.*[25])

pling mechanism render successful exploration difficult. The Glauconitic Formation lies on thin formations, the Ostracode and Taber, which themselves lie on the top of the major unconformity, a regionally strong reflector between the clastics of the lower Cretaceous above and the Mississipian limestones below. The overlying and underlying beds to the Glauconitic Formation have velocities of about 14,760 ft/s (4500 m/s); the Glauconitic Formation averages about 15 percent porosity and has a velocity of about 12,630 ft/s (3850 m/s). Three-dimensional data were collected in order to delineate a reservoir. Gelfand et al.[25] state that

> The data were collected with a uniform bin size of 20 m by 20 m and processed for amplitude and phase compensation, spectral whitening, velocity and static corrections, and post-stack 3-D migration. The SLIM process was then applied to derive a thin-layer interpretation of the migrated data. The geologic parameters of velocity, allowable change in velocity for a given layer, and number of layers were loosely constrained by parameters from one of the six boreholes located within the survey area. The SLIM process determined the optimum wavelet shape at the borehole location and the other control points. The derived model (time-velocity) showed remarkable consistency with the remaining five boreholes and provided a reasonable basis for the estimation of gross reservoir pore volume, hydrocarbon distribution, and reserves in place. . . . The SLIM process was used to detect sands less than 12 m thick, and to quantify the interpretation for translation to reservoir variables such as gross pore volume and reserves in place.

Figures 9-12 and 9-13 are depth (meters)-velocity models output by the process. Figure 9-12 shows that the locations of two producers (black arrows) penetrate model-deduced low-velocity zones (shown as the lightest tone in the black-and-white reproduction, shown as yellow in the color-insert reproduction) that correspond with producing sands. The arrows in Fig. 9-13 are dry holes; the velocity model from the 3-D data reveals the relative absence of low-velocity

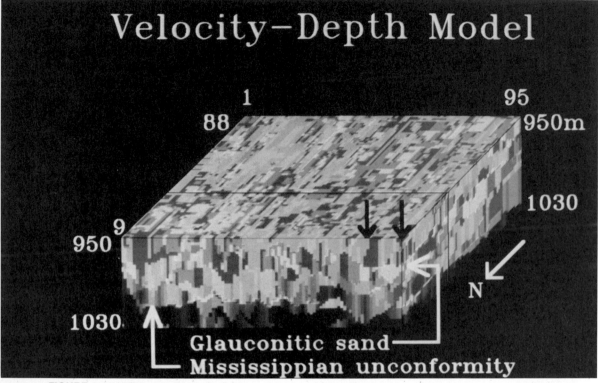

FIGURE 9-12 The velocity-depth model derived by the SLIM[26] process from the 3-D migrated seismic data. The findings in the five boreholes and two subsequent wells based on the SLIM model are all concordant with the 3-D SLIM interpretation. Shown here is the model-deduced, low-velocity zone [producing sand, lightest tone (yellow in the color-insert reproduction)] which was penetrated by two producers, located at the two black arrows. Note this figure also appears in the color insert. (*From Gelfand et al.[25]*)

productive sands. Time-slice analysis for the black arrow dry hole showed that the dry hole drilled "a localized zone of high velocity siltstone surrounded by low velocity sand. . . . The 3-D thin-layer model derived by the SLIM method was consistent with the results in all six previously drilled boreholes, although the information from only one borehole was used for the modeling." (Gelfand et al.[25]). Two wells drilled subsequent to the SLIM interpretation have been producers as predicted.

Another type of approach to extract lithologic information from seismic data is that often termed *direct inversion*, which will be discussed below. Commonly, this type of approach involves a 1-D transformation of each individual seismic trace into a pseudovelocity log or an acoustic-impedance log. Depth or time may be the vertical scale, and the input data to the inversion may or may not have been migrated. Waveshape processing to zero-phase before the inversion step is, however, a widespread practice. Trade names for this type of processing are synthetic sonic log, trace integration, instantaneous velocity section, seismic log, SHADCON,[26] SEISLOG (Lindseth[27]), VELOG,[28] or synthetic acoustic impedance log (SAIL or SAILE).

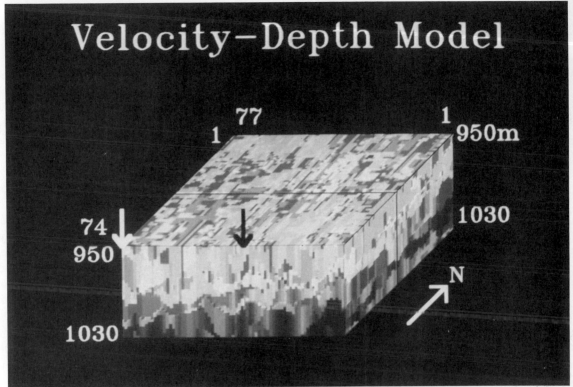

FIGURE 9-13 The velocity-depth model derived by the SLIM process from the 3-D migrated seismic data. Here, two dry holes are matched with a relative absence of the low-velocity zones associated with production. The black-arrow dry hole, on this 3-D view, appears as though the borehole was drilled just at the edge of the low-velocity reservoir. A clearer portrayal of the situation is achieved through depth-slice analysis through the velocity model, which indicates that the dry hole is located just inside a localized zone of high-velocity siltstone surrounded by the low-velocity sand. Note this figure also appears in the color insert. (*From Gelfand, et al.*[25])

Inversion, or the Inverse Problem

The inverse problem is defined as

> the determination of a distribution of parameters (velocity, acoustic impedance, etc.) whose calculated response matches observations (field seismic data) within given tolerance; . . .the direct, forward, or normal problem, (on the other hand) involves calculating what would have been observed from a given model

which is otherwise known as seismic modeling (Sheriff[29]). Standard "forward modeling" requires the interpreter to generate the initial model based on well logs or regional geology, and produces 1-D or 2-D synthetic seismic data. The model is updated, usually by hand, to a achieve a better match with the seismic data. Geologically acceptable solutions are always obtained since the modeling is user-controlled, but this approach is sometimes expensive and slow. Direct inversion techniques seek to automate, in a computationally efficient manner, the determination of a possible acoustic-impedance series. Depending upon the inversion technique and the constraints used, geologically acceptable solutions may or may not result.

Inversion, or inverse modeling, is the calculation of an impedance function which could have generated a given seismic trace. The previous sentence emphasizes the nonunique nature of the solution generated by most inversion techniques. An example of the nonuniqueness inherent in seismic data is taken from a Minnelusa sand play in the Powder River Basin, Wyoming (Raffalovich and Daw[30]). The Minnelusa contains abrupt lithology changes that provide many different hydrocarbon traps (and unwelcome surprises to the explorationist). Modeling determined that the seismic response to a thick (30 to 50 ft), porous productive Minnelusa sand unit is a peak at the top of the Minnelusa. Subsequent drilling based upon the presence of the desired seismic characteristic met with moderate success but also revealed that a relatively thick (greater than 80 ft) Opeche shale, overlying the Minnelusa, of slower than average velocity (less than 15,000 ft/s) also caused a seismic peak to occur at the top of the Minnelusa. The authors reported that their "attempts to distinguish (porous) Minnelusa sands from thick (slow) Opeche shale met with less success."

The well logs in the area provide the critical calibration of impedance (or velocity) to lithology since there is no worldwide relationship linking the two (Harris et al.[31]). Figure 9-14 provides a graph illustrating this fact: the dashed lines of constant acoustic impedance intersect different lithololologies. Thus there is no range of acoustic-impedance values uniquely associated with any one lithology. Study of Fig. 9-14 pinpoints the crux of the explorationist's problem with inversion: One may use any selected method to estimate the acoustic-impedance series that appears to have generated the observed field data; correctly determining the lithologic significance and hydrocarbon poten-

FIGURE 9-14 P-wave velocity-density relationships for different lithologies (the scale is log–log). The dotted line shows Gardner's equation. The dashed lines are lines of constant acoustic impedance [(kg/sm^2) × 10^6]. The fact that the dashed lines of constant impedance cross different lithologies illustrates one of the key ambiguities present in seismic data inversion. (*From Sheriff and Geldart.*[82])

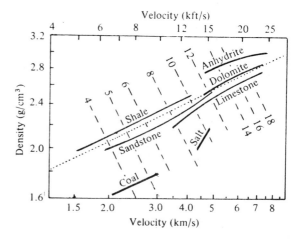

tial of the acoustic-impedance values nevertheless requires substantial knowledge of the local geologic conditions and variables.

Most inversion techniques assume that the seismic trace is the convolution of a wavelet (of describable bandwidth and phase) with the reflectivity series underlying the ground location of the seismic trace. The seismic trace is considered to be noise-free, multiple-free, and zero-offset. The amplitudes of the seismic trace are taken as proportional to the reflection coefficients of the subsurface. The common violations of the assumptions include out-of-the-plane effects, improper scaling of the data, amplitude changes due to tuning effects, and residual phase effects either left in the data after processing, or, regrettably, introduced by the processing. In some key situations, amplitude varies with offset so that after stack, the amplitude of the event is not the zero-offset value, but some mid-offset value. (See Sec. 9-4.)

Many inversion approaches use the sonic log in a well on (or near) the line to help start or guide the inversion. The reflectivity function from the sonic log can be used to determine the effective wavelet present on the seismic field data. This wavelet can then be used to estimate the reflectivity function of each trace, and from the latter the values of the acoustic-impedance function are estimated. In the presence of noise, some inversion techniques are unstable and all are inaccurate. The amount of user intervention required depends upon the algorithm and the approach used.

Acoustic-inversion techniques seek only the v_i's or the $\rho_i v_i$'s; elastic-inversion techniques seek the P and S velocities (or velocity contrasts) and the ρ_i's of the earth layers. Current elastic-inversion techniques work with multioffset P-wave data. As shear-wave data and three-component recording become more widespread, elastic-inversion techniques will probably evolve that will incorporate these reflected wave fields explicitly. Unless specified otherwise, the following discussion deals with acoustic-inversion techniques, since these are more common, more stable, and less expensive. Some techniques are recursive or iterative: they attempt to refine or better the initial inverse solution by perturbing the model, evaluating the improvement, or lack thereof, of the second solution compared to the first, and repeat this process to arrive at the best estimate of the earth parameters sought. Some approaches are post-stack and are therefore essentially zero-offset inversions; some are pre-stack and use either explicitly or implicitly the information contained in the hyperbolic moveouts (velocity) and the reflection amplitudes of the multioffset data.

Most post-stack inversion techniques produce a pseudosonic log from the seismic trace; some produce an acoustic-impedance log. The reflection coefficient R is taken as

$$R = \frac{v_2 - v_1}{v_2 + v_1} \tag{9-1}$$

which ignores the effect of density, or the reflection coefficient can be defined in terms of acoustic impedance (the product of velocity and density). In the latter case, density is usually a function of the velocity, as determined from well log suites in the area. Alternatively, density can be set proportional to the one-fourth power of velocity, an empirical relationship reported by Gardner et al.,[32]

$$\rho = av^{1/4} \tag{9-2}$$

where ρ is in g/cm^3 and v is in m/s when $a = 0.31$ and in ft/s when $a = 0.23$. This function is plotted as the dotted line in Fig. 9-14. Coal, salt, and anhydrite do not conform at all to this relationship, as is shown in Fig. 9-14. Neither velocity nor impedance uniquely correlates with a given lithology, unless local geologic input and well data constrain the relationships.

The terms from (9-1) may be reordered as

$$v_2 = v_1 \frac{1 + R}{1 - R} \tag{9-3}$$

The initial velocity (or acoustic impedance) is given by the user, and the program will calculate all subsequent v_2's from the reflection coefficient log derived from the data. Inversion of this type is a form of integration of the seismic section. The phase is lagged 90° and the slope of the amplitude spectrum is tilted, emphasizing the low-frequency end. This is why the frequency content of most integrated (inverted) sections appears lower than that of the input seismic section. A zero crossing on a seismic trace has become a peak on the pseudosonic log, and the seismic peaks represent changes of the shape of the integrated trace.

Due to the band-limited nature of the seismic reflections, a seismically derived, acoustic-impedance log will look like a high-cut filtered version of the well log acoustic-impedance function, as shown in Fig. 9-15. Here logs from a North Sea well were used to calculate the reflectivity series and an acoustic-impedance log. Log-editing procedures were applied first, as usual. A filtered version of the acoustic-impedance log is also shown, bandpass filtered to a frequency content comparable to that recoverable from a single seismic trace.

For a seismic trace to mimic the appearance of a sonic log, a low-frequency component (less than 8 Hz) must be present. Sometimes, this component is simply disregarded totally. Usually, this important, low-frequency interval-velocity information is estimated from the unstacked data by careful and detailed normal-moveout-velocity-analysis techniques. The high-quality velocity picks are then used for interval-velocity calculations. The interval-velocity curves can then be added trace by trace to the inverted, or integrated, seismic traces. In other cases, the low-frequency velocity information comes from low-pass filtered sonic logs in the area; the seismically derived interval-velocity information may or may not be blended in. In some areas there are significant variations of the low-frequency velocities among wells; in others the low-frequency velocities are consistent. The seismically derived low-fre-

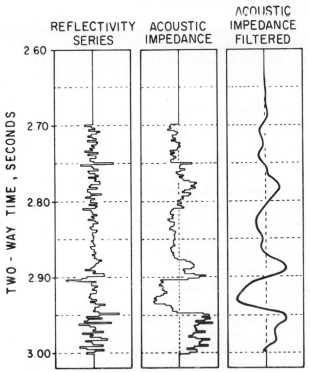

FIGURE 9-15   Acoustic-impedance log calculated from a North Sea well and reflectivity series calculated from this acoustic-impedance log. The bandpass filtered acoustic-impedance trace has a frequency content comparable to that recoverable from a single seismic trace. Usual log-editing procedures were applied prior to all of these calculations. (*From Neidell and Beard.*[83])

quency, interval-velocity curve(s) can be compared at the appropriate location to the low-pass filtered sonic curve, to determine the degree of similarity. In most areas, the seismic-moveout velocity information must be incorporated to achieve exploration success.

In addition to the missing but important low frequencies, the high frequencies of a sonic (greater than 100 Hz) are lacking from the seismic. Quality of resolution and detail of the inverted traces depend upon the presence of high frequencies and a broad, seismic-signal bandwidth.

The Born inverse method treats changes in velocity or density as perturbations of a known (constant) background velocity. These perturbations are related to the recorded wave-field response to obtain the inverse solution. Good results are obtained when only small velocity variations occur. Clayton and Stolt[33] refined the Born inverse method by recommending a variable background velocity so that the perturbations can remain small. There is an accuracy trade-off between locating the reflective interfaces (the boundaries) and estimating the velocity (Carrion and Foster[34]). Errors in velocity estimation and reflector location accumulate with depth. The Born approximation has been used to retrieve separate density and bulk-modulus depth profiles from multioffset reflection data (Clayton and Stolt[33]; Le Bras and Clayton[35]).

Other inversion techniques, such as described by Cohen and Bleistein,[36] Cohen and Hagin,[37] and Coen,[38, 39] have also been proposed.

Elastic-inverse approaches require multioffset P-wave data, sometimes out to nearly critical angle (Morley[40]) or beyond. This type of reflection data may not be available to the depths of all targets, although for some targets it could be collected with current field capabilities. Not all of the theory has been worked out for complete elastic inversion of multioffset P- and shear-wave reflected wave fields. Nonuniqueness, inadequate true-amplitude corrections, potentially long run time, and the necessity for a good initial model are the customary handicaps for the current (somewhat limited) approaches in elastic inversion. P and S velocity contrasts across the target layer and the densities are typical desired quantities from the inversion. When the P and shear velocities (or velocity contrasts) and the densities are determined, lithologic identification becomes easier. The V_P/V_S values as lithologic discriminants are discussed later in this chapter.

Use of Stacking-Velocity Information for Stratigraphic Studies Interval velocities as determined from stacking velocities have been used to estimate sand-shale ratios or shale-limestone ratios. Long spreads and high-quality data can yield reasonably accurate results in the "simple" cases of two-lithology systems. The length of the time interval between the events chosen as input to the Dix equation governs the amount of averaging over an interval that will occur. For best results, only high-quality, primary events should be used in this analysis. The presence of (undetected) multiples can seriously deteriorate the quality of the results from an interval-velocity–lithology study. As mentioned before, interval-velocity information is color plotted on top of the seismic stack (wiggle trace plot) for ease of interpretation and for a striking display of this critically important information. This technique for stratigraphic studies is a subset of the direct inversion approaches that use both the amplitude information and the velocity information derived from the hyperbolic moveout.

Another approach to the identification of lithology within a portion of the geologic section is to measure the attenuation of seismic waves passing through the section. Using data recorded with systems of adequate dynamic range, one can determine changes in relative amplitude between successive reflections that can be interpreted in terms of transitions from sand to shale within the stratigraphic interval that is represented. Figure 9-16 illustrates a case where sand bodies were mapped from attenuation data, the predictions having been verified by well information.

As pointed out by Savit and Mateker,[41] a combination of velocity and attenuation data should yield more reliable lithological information than either kind alone. Modern recording and processing techniques appear to be bringing us closer to the goal of being able to identify subsurface formations as well as to

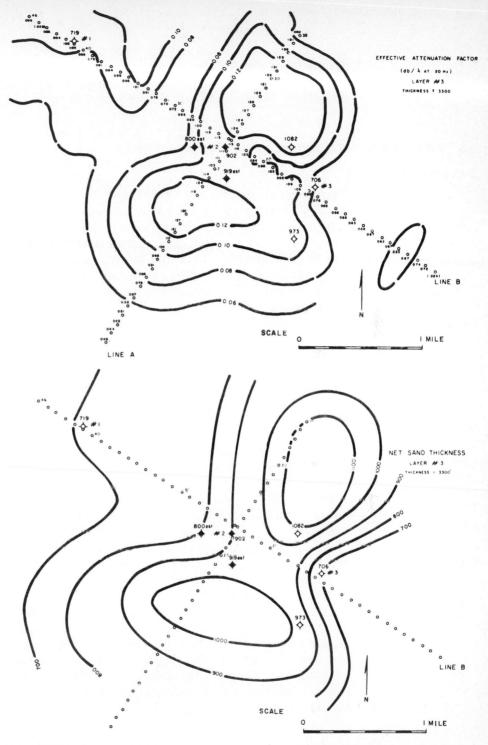

FIGURE 9-16 Comparison of attenuation and net sand thickness in Beer Nose Field, Calif. (*From Savit and Mateker.*[41])

describe their geometry from seismic reflection data. At the present state of the art, a considerable amount of well data usually needs to be incorporated before the seismic data can be properly interpreted in terms of lithology.

9-3 SHEAR-WAVE DATA AND LITHOLOGIC INFORMATION

Sources of Shear Data

There are two sources of reflection shear-wave information: ''pure'' shear-wave reflection (shear source and recording through shear-wave or horizontal phones), and converted waves (P-wave source recorded into P and/or shear phones, or at sea into hydrophones with subsequent processing done in addition to conventional P processing to enhance the converted arrivals). Shear-wave sources and phones may be oriented so that oscillation transverse to the profile direction (SH) or oscillation parallel to line direction (SV) are generated and recorded.

In a flat-layered isotropic medium, mode conversions from P to SV and SV to P are expected with increasing offset; mode conversions from pure SH to P are not expected. The extent to which mode conversion occurs is generally seen as a further complication to the exploration problem and, as such, tends to be treated as an undesirable phenomenon to be avoided as much as possible, except in those cases in which the converted waves are explicitly sought, processed, and interpreted. Thus, SH has been preferred to SV for ''pure'' shear-wave hydrocarbon exploration purposes.

The shear information available from typical shear-wave data (SH sources into SH phones, and SV into SV) is the amplitude of the shear reflectors, the two-way travel time to the reflectors, and, with high-quality data, the moveout velocity to the different reflectors. Sriram et al.[42] and Seriff[43] have pointed out that in the presence of transverse isotropy, the horizontal shear-wave velocity is greater (measurably) than the vertical velocity. Typical magnitudes of this ''apparent anisotropy'' ($V_{horizontal} / V_{vertical}$) are about 1.2 to 1.4. A medium that is transversely isotropic is one ''having properties which are the same in two orthogonal directions but different in the third orthogonal direction'' (Seriff[29]). The third orthogonal direction contains the axis of symmetry. This is the situation in thinly bedded, contrasting lithologies and within shale units in which the clay platelets are much the same along a bedding plane, but perpendicular to the bedding plane the properties of the medium vary. The axis of symmetry is vertical. This situation is to be contrasted with ''azimuthal anisotropy'' (Crampin[44]), in which the axis of symmetry is horizontal and is related to the presence of oriented cracks or fractures. (The axis of symmetry is taken normal to the crack faces.)

Shales and Transverse Isotropy

Winterstein[45] uses the anisotropic effect caused by shales (transverse isotropy) to correlate lithology (shale) to the magnitude of the anisotropic effect. He determined the shear interval velocities from the shear stacking velocities, and then a layer thickness; the thickness is compared to that so calculated from collocated P-wave data. Significant differences in layer thicknesses were interpreted to indicate anisotropy (transverse isotropy), and the predominance of shale within the unit. The effect was slight or missing in sandstone and massive carbonate sequences. As a diagnostic for a (measurably thick) shale unit, this tool can be effective.

The other two methods now documented for extracting hydrocarbon or lithologic information from P and shear data are in comparative reflection-amplitude studies performed upon CDP stacks (P and shear) and in the use of V_P/V_S ratios.

Direct Detection Verification

The comparison of amplitudes on P-wave and shear-wave stacks to distinguish between an HCI (hydrocarbon indicator or bright spot) and an LCI (lithologic change indicator) has been documented by Ensley[46] and Robertson and Pritchett.[47] Briefly, the P wave is affected by the gas in the pore space and travels at a slower velocity, while the shear wave is unaffected by the gas in the pore space. (See Sec. 9-4 for further treatment of the effect of gas on P-wave velocity.) Thus a change in pore constituent (water or oil to gas) can cause a high-amplitude P-wave reflection (HCI or bright spot) while effectively no change of shear-wave reflection amplitude will be detected. (This assumes that there is no concurrent or additional change in lithology or porosity.) A reflection generated by a lithologic change (LCI) is indicated by a significant amplitude change on both P- and shear-wave stacks. An example of an LCI is a facies change from a thin sandstone bed to a coal bed, limestone streak, shell layer, etc.

V_P/V_S and Lithology

The use of V_P/V_S ratios to determine lithology requires collocated P- and shear-wave stacks, both with good S/N. Reflection events are correlated from P to shear, based on (preferably) check-shot information or visual similarity. Once correlative times for a given formation top are established, the ratio V_P/V_S equals $\Delta t_S/\Delta t_P$. Correlative interval-transit times from shear and P stacks are noted, divided, and posted within layers to detect lateral variations. This information is suitable for color encoding. Well log and laboratory data tie the seismic values to given lithologic changes in an area.

This method has been used to track sands versus shales, due to their distinct V_P/V_S ratios (McCormack et al.[48]). Predominantly shale units had V_P/V_S ratios seismically measured as 2.1 to 2.4 in the Morrow Formation, New Mexico; predominantly sand units had V_P/V_S ratios between 1.5 and 1.9. The sands constituted the pay zones.

The Clearfork facies change in the Midland Basin from carbonate to clastic has been mapped based on V_P/V_S ratios (Benzing et al.[49]). Both in the seismic measurements and in the lab data, the sandstones had smaller V_P/V_S ratios than did the carbonates. The absolute magnitude of the two kinds of measurements did not however agree precisely. The lab data indicated a V_P/V_S ratio for sandstone of 1.72 to 1.96, for carbonates, 2.00 to 2.38. The seismic V_P/V_S ratios for the sandstones varied between 1.66 to 1.81; for the carbonates, 1.81 to 1.88. In all of the above case histories, well control and laboratory velocity measurements played an important role in interpreting the seismic V_P/V_S data.

Robertson[50] detected and tracked changing amounts of carbonate porosity in the Hunton of the Anadarko Basin. The shape of the pores (round or penny shaped) affected the relationship of the V_P/V_S ratio to porosity.

Use of converted waves in hydrocarbon exploration is still relatively new. Converted waves have been studied in offshore areas, especially those with a hard sea-floor bottom, since such a bottom facilitates mode conversion from P to shear (Tatham and Goolsbee[51]). The data are processed once for P and once for converted shear (SV) energy. The converted shear-wave section provides an independent estimate of the structure present, and the opportunity to do $\Delta t_S/\Delta t_P$ (V_P/V_S) interpretation for lithologic identification and gas detection, as discussed above. Mode-converted wave experiments have been recorded on land; typical methods use P sources into three-component recording systems (one vertical phone and two horizontal phones).

9-4 DIRECT DETECTION OF HYDROCARBONS: COMBINING SEISMIC STRATIGRAPHIC AND LITHOLOGIC TECHNIQUES

The acknowledged use of amplitude information and the geometry of the reflections to detect directly the presence of hydrocarbons is a method of seismic interpretation that had its publicized beginnings in the early 1970s. The current state of direct detection is that with "sufficient" knowledge concerning the area under exploration, the explorationist is able to identify "the anomaly" and the associated likelihood of hydrocarbon accumulation by carefully comparing the amplitudes, the geometry of the reflections, and the seismic velocities to the model studies. An illustration of this, as presented at length below, is that in young, unconsolidated sediments (Gulf Coast, Niger Delta, etc.), shallow gas accumulations are discernible by their anomalously high-amplitude reflections. This direct detection anomaly is the classic bright spot. The amount of geologic background that the interpreter needs to perform seismic stratigraphic interpretation and direct detection is substantial. The construction or the use of appropriate models requires the knowledge of the range of velocities and densities associated with the lithologies present, the depositional environment, and the geologic age of the rocks. (The knowledge of the depositional environments, and the suspected lithologies and geologic age, can in some areas be extracted from the seismic data by use of various interpretation techniques as set forth in Refs. 4, 5, and 7.)

In effect, the quest for direct indicators of hydrocarbons has caused an intensive reexamination of the seismic method starting at basic theory. Following the lead of Peter Vail and his co-workers,[7] information in the form of reflector geometry, seismic character, and seismic velocities are related to depositional environment and lithology on a global basis. The costs associated with the extraction of this further information are in the meticulous processing needed, display, and in modeling studies; the benefits are in the reconstruction of the geologic history, the identification of subtle traps, and in reservoir development. With the required improvements in processing and display has come the indication that even the "mature" hydrocarbon provinces are in a sense underdeveloped. Most of the new exploration opportunities are, in the main, stratigraphic in nature. Hence the subject of direct indicators becomes strongly intertwined with methods for studying seismic stratigraphy and for lithology determination. The detailed information extracted is being used more and more in engineering and production applications.

The rest of this chapter will present the methods and considerations pertinent to the direct detection of hydrocarbons, and, inextricably, seismic stratigraphy. The physical nature of the reflection amplitude is reviewed, as well as the factors other than reflectivity that control the recorded and displayed amplitudes and waveshapes. Probably the most critical factor that affects the amplitudes and the waveshapes presented for interpretation is processing. In fact, high-quality data acquisition and processing are taken as the given prerequisites for any seismic stratigraphic or direct detection work. Since the interpreter relies on plots to construct the interpretation, the plot must contain all relevant information in a format easily used. While this may sound trivial, the current practice of black-and-white, variable-area wiggle plots not only restricts the observable amplitudes to a woefully inadequate range of values but also throws away at least two major dimensions of information: the moveout curve as a function of lateral space and depth, and the amplitude as a function of offset. Earlier editions of this book stressed that conventional black-and-white wiggle trace plots were "virtually useless" for displaying the type of amplitude variations sought in direct detection techniques. It is therefore, inevitable that radical and widespread changes in display and processing will be effected so that interpreters will have easy and routine access to this and other information. The conclusion of this chapter addresses the long-term potential of direct detection techniques.

Reflection Amplitude as an Indicator of Hydrocarbons in Porous Sands

The amplitude of a seismic wave reflected from an interface between two materials is governed by the reflection coefficient R, which, as noted on page 40, is expressed for normal incidence by the relation

$$R = \frac{\rho_2 V_2 - \rho_1 V_1}{\rho_2 V_2 + \rho_1 V_1} \tag{9-4}$$

where ρ_1 and ρ_2 are the respective densities on the near (incident) and far sides of the boundary and V_1 and V_2 are the respective velocities for the two sides. The product of ρ and V is the acoustic impedance; it is evident that the reflection coefficient and hence the reflection amplitude depend on the contrast in acoustic impedance across the reflecting interface. Any lateral change in the velocity or density of one or both of the materials separated by the interface should cause the amplitude of the reflection from this boundary to vary.

Figure 9-17 shows a cross section of velocities across a hypothetical oil and gas entrapment. Reflections would be expected from the five interfaces, A to E, shown in the diagram, across which there are distinctive contrasts in acoustic impedance. Because V_g, V_o, and V_w as well as ρ_g, ρ_o, and ρ_w differ along the base of the overlying shale, one would expect lateral variations in the amplitudes of the reflection from this boundary.

The dependence of seismic velocity of a porous material upon the fluid contained in the pore spaces (see Gassmann[52] and Geertsma and Smit[53]) have been studied both theoretically and experimentally for several decades (see Wyllie et al.[54, 55]; Domenico[56–58]). These investigations have shown, as might be expected intuitively, that a sand saturated with gas will have a lower velocity than the same sand saturated with oil or water. A paper by Gardner et al.[32] is particularly pertinent to the problem of predicting velocity as a function of porosity for different pore fillers; by combining Gassmann's theory with experimental observation, these authors have computed the respective velocity-depth relations for a sand saturated with gas, oil, or brine in an unconsolidated section in recent basins (recent to lower Eocene). Figure 9-18 presents the results of their study. From the curves that are shown, it is evident that the contrast between the respective velocities decreases with depth. At depths less than about 5000 ft, the difference between the velocity in the gas sand and that in the oil sands is rather large, being more than 20 percent at 4000 ft. The contrast, on the other hand, between the velocity for brine-saturated and for oil-saturated sand at that depth is only 6 percent. At 10,000 ft the velocity contrast between the gas sand and the oil sand is 6 percent, while that between oil and saltwater sands is only about 1 percent. It would appear from

FIGURE 9-17   Anticlinal entrapment of hydrocarbons in porous sand by shale layer. Interfaces separating different materials designated by letters A to E. Velocities and densities for each layer indicated by appropriate symbols.

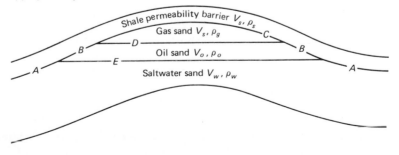

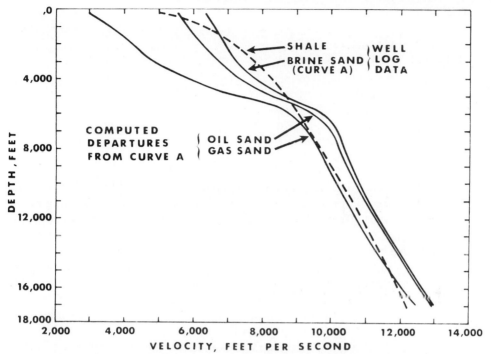

FIGURE 9-18   Variation, predicted from Gassmann's theory, of velocity with depth in shale and in sand saturated with oil, gas, and brine, respectively. (*Gardner et al.*[32])

the curves that detection of gas-saturated sands is quite easy at shallower depths but becomes increasingly difficult at greater depths. In different geologic settings, though, the contrast between gas sands and water sands is different. A starting place to analyze the effect of gas on the velocity of a given formation must be well founded in the petrophysics of the area under study. Engelmark et al.[59] presented results from the petrophysical analyses of over 750 wells in the offshore Gulf Coast Pleistocene to Miocene. The authors related the geologic age, geopressure, and depth of burial of a given lithology (sand or shale) to the velocity and density usually encountered. To calculate reflection coefficients accurately, especially for studies of offset-dependent amplitudes and subsequent lithology determination, good values for both velocity and density are needed. The authors recommended that the contribution of density to the total reflection coefficient should not be disregarded.

Let us assume the velocities and densities shown in Table 9-1 for the various materials making up the section shown in Fig. 9-17. The reflection coefficients for each interface are indicated in Fig. 9-19. The reflectivity contrast between the water-saturated sand and the gas-saturated sand is considerably greater than that between the water-saturated sand and the oil-saturated sand. The interpreter therefore wants the amplitudes of the reflections on the seismic

TABLE 9-1

Material	Velocity V, ft/s	Density ρ, g/cm³
Shale	8500	2.50
Gas sand	5700	2.025
Oil sand	7300	2.270
Water sand	7700	2.277

section to be related closely to the true subsurface reflection coefficients. To achieve this, careful processing is needed, along with an understanding of the other factors that affect reflection amplitudes, which will be discussed in the next section.

The above model study, however, has several key assumptions and simplifications. Reflection coefficients as shown are for normal-incidence ray paths, a circumstance which cannot reasonably be achieved with real-life seismic surveys. The zero-offset trace is thus synthesized by the CDP method (pp. 107–111). Hence, the role of processing is critically important, since it is in processing that the zero-offset trace is constructed. The simple models indicated in Figs. 9-17 and 9-19 have no wavelets nor a scale in depth or equivalent reflection time. The wavelet affects the interpretability of the data. The depth of the anomaly affects the pressures, the velocities, and the frequencies (the resolution) recorded at the surface, that is, our perception of "the anomaly." It is further obvious that model studies usually have no noise, no multiples, and a given, stable wavelet of known phase, in contrast to the observed data in which noise and multiples are present and in which the wavelet is often both variable and usually unknown.

The relationships portrayed by Fig. 9-18 have been found valid in portions of the Gulf Coast (onshore and offshore) and Niger Delta in young, unconsolidated sediments. Overgeneralizing from theoretical models is a serious hazard of seismic interpretation. For other environments, the depth-versus-velocity relationship must be carefully worked out for the different lithologies. For example, in a certain geologic setting, the gas reservoir could be a low-amplitude dimout, not a high-amplitude bright spot.

FIGURE 9-19   Reflection coefficients at interfaces marked in Fig. 9-17.

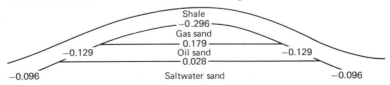

Factors Other Than Reflectivity That Control Reflection Amplitude

Reflection amplitudes on stacked data cannot be used as a means of identifying porosity or hydrocarbons unless corrections are made pre-stack for the other effects that govern the amplitudes of reflections, some of which are predictable. Factors affecting amplitude include spherical spreading, attenuation, interference effects (constructive or destructive) between reflections from interfaces that are close together, distortions due to focusing effects, and processing operations. Sheriff[60] has summarized many factors affecting reflection amplitudes which must be taken into account in the interpretation of amplitude anomalies on seismic records.

Spherical Spreading   The amplitude of any elastic wave traveling through a homogeneous, nonabsorptive medium will be inversely proportional to the distance from the source of the wave. This is because the energy of the disturbance is uniformly distributed over the area of the spherical shell which it occupies at any instant of time. This area is proportional to the square of the radius so that the energy density at any point on the spherical surface is inversely proportional to the square of the radius, which is the distance from the source. But as the amplitude is proportional to the square root of the energy, it should bear an inverse first-power relation to the distance.

Absorption   In Chap. 2 we showed that materials in which seismic waves propagate absorb some of the energy of the wave by viscoelastic drag or internal friction. In general this effect causes amplitude A to fall off with distance x from its initial value A_0 according to the relation (for a plane wave)

$$A = A_0 e^{-\alpha x} \tag{9-5}$$

where α is the attenuation coefficient, which varies with the material in which the wave travels as indicated in Table 2-2. The attenuation coefficient appears to be proportional to the frequency of the wave; i.e., if the frequency doubles, so does the value of α.

The amplitude of a reflection will obviously be affected by the absorptive properties of all the material through which the reflected wave passes along its path from the source to the reflector and back to the receiver. If the absorption coefficient varies laterally along any part of the path, one would expect the amplitude of a reflection signal from an interface of uniform reflectivity to show variations that are related to the lithologic changes affecting the absorption. Sand generally has a higher absorption coefficient than does shale. Thus a change of facies within a layer from sand to shale could give rise to a corresponding variation in the amplitude of a reflection signal passing through the layer from an interface below. Such variations in amplitude are sometimes put to use for identifying lithology, as pointed out earlier in this chapter (page 356).

Interference Effects   If two or more reflecting surfaces are close together relative to a wavelength, the pulses reflected from them will be superimposed and the waveform of the resulting reflection signal will have an amplitude that depends to some extent on the separation between the respective reflectors (see Fig. 9-20). This effect was first considered in Chap. 8. The individual reflection coefficients may be positive or negative, depending on whether the acoustic impedance of the lower medium is greater or less than that above. Figure 9-20 shows the resolution and detection graphs for two 2-termed reflectivity spike (top and bottom of a bed) models (from Wood[61]). Resolution is the discernment of two separate events, the top and the bottom of the thin bed. Detection is the determination of the presence of a thin bed, without separate events from the top and bottom, by use of amplitude information. A 12.5- to 50-Hz sinc wavelet was used in the calculations for Fig. 9-20. For beds significantly thicker than the tuning thickness, the true thickness of the thin bed is correctly determined by using the apparent time separation of the two events

FIGURE 9-20   Resolution and detection graphs for two-termed reflectivity spike models consisting of a wedge of material bounded above and below by dissimilar material. These curves show tuning thickness and temporal resolution limits for a 12.5 to 50-Hz sinc wavelet. (*From Wood.*[61])

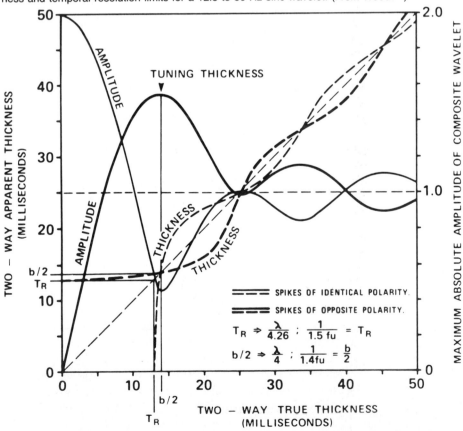

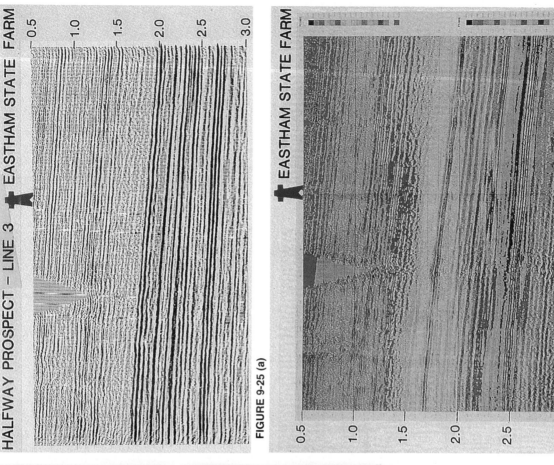

HALFWAY PROSPECT – LINE 3   EASTHAM STATE FARM

FIGURE 9-25 (a)

EASTHAM STATE FARM

FIGURE 9-25 (b)

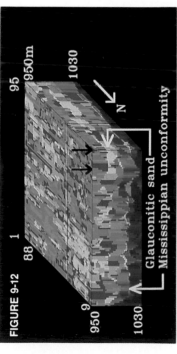

FIGURE 9-12

950m

95

1

88

9

950

1030

Glauconitic sand
Mississippian unconformity

N

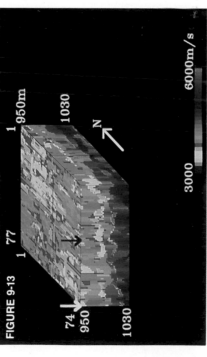

FIGURE 9-13

950m

1

77

1

74

950

1030

N

3000   6000m/s

FIGURE 9-12   Color version. See p. 346 for complete description.
(*From Gelfand et al*[25])

FIGURE 9-13   Color version. See p. 347 for complete description.
(*From Gelfand et al*[25])

FIGURE 9-25   The preservation and display of the velocity information contained in all modern seismic data has dramatically increased
the visibility of a carbonate bank sequence (Houston County, Texas).
(a) The upper data panel is a conventional black and white seismic
section on which the carbonate bank would be missed. (b) The lower
data panel is a color display of the integrated (or postinversion) data, in
which the colors are keyed to the interval velocity estimates (1000 ft/s
increments). A trend function developed from the moveout velocity
estimates has been applied to produce the background color.
(*From Neidell and Beard*[18])

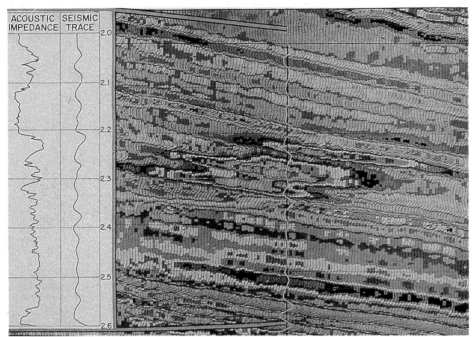

FIGURE 9-26 A closeup of the carbonate bank sequence shown in Fig. 9-25. The color scale is interval velocity in 400 ft/s steps. The moveout velocity estimates provided a trend function in the calculations of interval velocities. The integrated trace nearest the wellbore agrees well with the filtered acoustic impedance function as scaled in time. (*From Neidell and Beard.*[18])

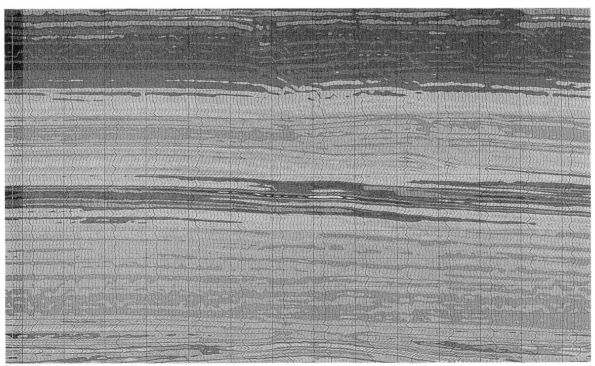

FIGURE 9-31 Color display of acoustic impedance (approximating velocities). Transgressive sequence of Bunter sandstones is clearly visible as is possible gas accumulation (lowest of velocity shades) in the sands to the left of the crest in Platten dolomite. The moveout velocities supplied the trend function for the interval velocities. (*From Neidell and Beard.*[18])

and the correct interval velocity of the bed. As the tuning thickness is approached, the two separate events begin to merge. At the tuning thickness, the time separation of the two spikes is such that a maximum, or minimum, amplitude is created. In the situation in which only one event is observed from a two-spike model event, if one knows the polarity of the two spikes expected, and that a two-spike model is appropriate, the amplitude information can yield the time separation of the two spikes This type of information is useful for reservoir-pay thickness and areal-extent calculations.

A greater number of interfaces gives rise to a larger potential range of variation in the amplitude. This kind of amplitude effect depends both on geometric and on lithologic factors, the lithology governing the actual amount of time shift between reflectors because of the dependence of velocity upon rock characteristics.

Geometric Effects   Curvature of a reflecting interface can have a significant effect upon the amplitudes of the reflections that are recorded from it. If the reflecting surface is convex upward, the reflected rays are spread out because of the defocusing effect of a convex mirror and the energy density at any point above it is decreased. The amplitude should therefore be lower for reflections recorded above the structure than for those recorded from flat areas on either side. If the surface is concave upward, as in a syncline, the rays are concentrated by the focusing effect of a concave mirror and the energy density is increased over the structure so that the reflection amplitudes are anomalously high. The effects of such focusing on reflection amplitudes are discussed by Dix.[62] A simple technique to estimate the effects of curvature and diffraction on seismic amplitudes was proposed by Hilterman.[63] Post-stack wave-equation migration alleviates most of the amplitude problems associated with geometric effects for zero-offset data.

Effects of Processing and Display   The CDP stack trace presents amplitude information that has been constructed by seismic-data processing. Any amplitude gaining, filtering, or processing step that manipulates in any way the seismic waveform (deconvolution, migration, normal moveout, stack, etc.) has affected the amplitudes of the reflections. Any uncorrected trace-to-trace time shifts left in the data, either in statics or in moveout, will introduce amplitude error into the final stack. Since dipping seismic reflections are not correctly located in space on a stack (see Sec. 7-11, Migration), the amplitude relations can properly represent subsurface lithologic changes only after migration, especially if the particular area has nonuniform, nonplanar structural elements or even subtle faults or lateral changes of lithology.

Gain   As discussed in Sec. 7-4, there are two major types of gain: AGC or structural gain and relative-true-amplitude-preservation gain. The latter is usually some type of a smooth exponential gain curve applied to the data.

The range of variation in the absolute amplitudes encountered in a typical seismic record is large—10^6 or more. A black-and-white variable-area, wiggle trace plot has a total dynamic range no greater than a factor of 20 (26 dB). For structural mapping, AGC, which restricts the amplitudes of all reflections to a very limited range, is acceptable. This equalization of amplitudes by expansion, suppression, and AGC for structural mapping and conventional plotting, however, defeats attempts to discern amplitude variations associated with changes in gas/water saturation or lithology.

The dynamic range afforded in color displays makes it possible to present the true-amplitude data needed to discern the amplitude variations that indicate changes in subsurface reflectivity. One practical procedure is to determine, either theoretically or empirically, the normal variation of amplitude with record time due to all causes other than reflectivity changes and to correct the observed amplitudes accordingly. If the normal amplitude thus determined is subtracted from the observed amplitude, the residual variations should be primarily attributable to differences in reflection coefficients.

The simplest model that might be used for the correction is one that takes only spherical spreading into account. As the record is plotted versus time rather than distance, it is necessary to make use of the best available, detailed, velocity information and convert time to distance in order to make such a spreading correction. On the other hand, variation in velocity destroys the geometric relationship upon which the inverse-distance formula is based. There is thus some justification for assuming that the normal variation of amplitude is linear in time rather than distance. The two assumptions are, of course, equivalent for a constant velocity.

Another common procedure is to fit an appropriate smooth curve to the observed amplitude decay-versus-time function. This is done by averaging amplitudes of successive samples over a moving window many cycles long and expressing the smoothed ampltude-versus-time function thus obtained as a low-order polynomial. The curve so calculated may be offset dependent or offset independent. The value for the resultant polynomial at each sampling time is subtracted from the observed amplitude of the sample. It is the difference between the two that is ultimately plotted on the record section. The polynomial accounts for changes caused by spherical spreading and absorption, but it is not of high enough order to incorporate variation in reflection coefficients at individual boundaries.

Amplitude effects due to interference between events from individual reflecting surfaces in close proximity cannot be taken into account in developing the polynomial. Such effects are studied by constructing models of a type considered in Sec. 9-2.

A variable-area or variable-density record section processed to preserve relative true amplitudes should register higher-amplitude events from interfaces with a larger reflection coefficient as a thicker or "heavier" lineation than that associated with adjacent boundaries where the reflectivity is lower. The stripe or doublet of stripes that indicates a particular reflection event becomes more prominent or "blacker" over a limited horizontal region than it is on either side. This high-amplitude portion of the reflection is referred to as a bright spot, although it usually looks more like a "black band." (See Fig. 9-21.)

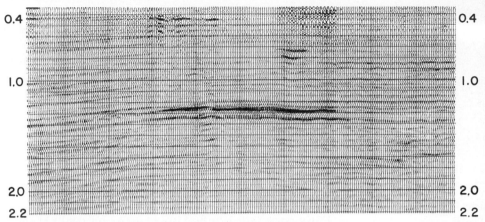

FIGURE 9-21   Record section processed to bring out relative amplitudes. Bright spot at center shows known gas accumulation. (*Western Geophysical Co. of America.*)

When the reflection coefficient from the top or bottom surface of a gas sand is greater than that from the corresponding surface of a water- or oil-bearing sand, as for a "classic" bright spot, the presence of the gas sand should be indicated on the section as a high-amplitude reflection event. Figure 9-21 shows a reflection section processed to preserve relative amplitudes. The strong reflection event at about 1.24 s stands out above the level of the rest of the record. This event comes at a time correlative with a known gas-saturated sand, and its lateral boundaries correspond to the known limits of gas accumulation. The same section conventionally processed with AGC is shown in Fig. 9-22.

The principal evidence that bright spots can indicate the presence of gaseous hydrocarbons comes from processed sections of reflection lines over known

FIGURE 9-22   Same section as in Fig. 9-21 processed by conventional techniques designed to equalize amplitudes. Reflections from the gas zone do not stand out as they do when the special processing is employed. (*Western Geophysical Co. of America.*)

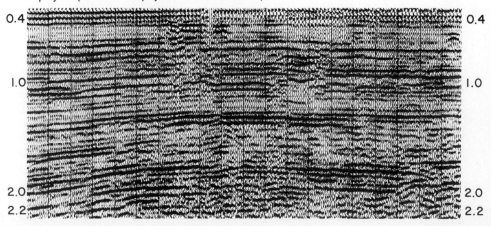

gas accumulations. Laboratory studies and theory support the existence of this phenomenon. High-amplitude events are, however, also observed at levels where it is known that no hydrocarbons are present. Other causes, such as facies changes, geometric focusing effects, or lithologically related acoustic-impedance contrasts (e.g., as at a limestone-shale, or shale-overpressured shale, boundary) probably account for these amplitude anomalies. In Sec. 9-3 and later in this section, various seismic methods to verify a gas accumulation as associated with high-amplitude reflections are discussed.

The model of Fig. 9-17, which represents one family of geologic circumstances, portrays bright-spot reflection coefficients that typically range from 3 to 5 times as large as what would be considered the "norm," i.e., those reflection amplitudes found laterally adjacent. Hence, recognition is clearly expected, given proper processing and display.

Early work failed to find bright spots on land except in areas in the Sacramento Valley, Alberta, and in Yugoslavia. The reasons for such failures are now attributed to the poor dynamic range of normal displays, the limitations of "standard" data processing and display, and an increased state of knowledge now concerning the effect of gas upon velocities and densities of well indurated rocks of various ages at different depths of burial.

Waveform Shaping   Ability to capture, manipulate, and generally transform seismic waveforms is needed in order to facilitate the geologic correlations and calculations that must be made. Such techniques and their effects on waveform polarities, shapes, and amplitude must be used and studied (respectively) as a prerequisite to any seis-strat work.

The following example of relative true-amplitude-processed data illustrates the improvement in resolution and interpretability obtainable through manipulation of the waveform. Closeup panels of differently processed seismic data in the vicinity of a partially gas-filled sand in the Gulf Coast are shown in Fig. 9-23; the larger data set, although with different processing, in Fig. 9-24. The comparison (Fig. 9-23) shows true-amplitude processing with the original wavelet and with the transformed wavelet. In both cases, the gas-sand is noted as a bright spot. However, the wavelet-processed data denotes the onset of the low-acoustic-impedance, gas-filled sand as a white trough, as predicted by theory and models, and the gas-water contact as a black peak. Conventional polarity is that a negative reflection coefficient indicates a change to a lower-impedance medium, and is represented by a trough (negative deflection) on the seismic section. The peak-to-trough time separation from the second figure used with an estimate of seismic velocities in similar gas sands gives quite an accurate estimate of the gas-saturated thickness, which in this case is about 65 ft (Schramm et al.[64]). Wavelet processing, which is supposed to convert the waveshapes to zero phase, has transformed the data so that the geologically significant peak-trough separation will now yield the time equivalent of the thickness of the gas zone. This data example illustrates successful extracton of important information by means of the following controversial interpretation assumptions. (1) Each trace of the section represents only primary reflections

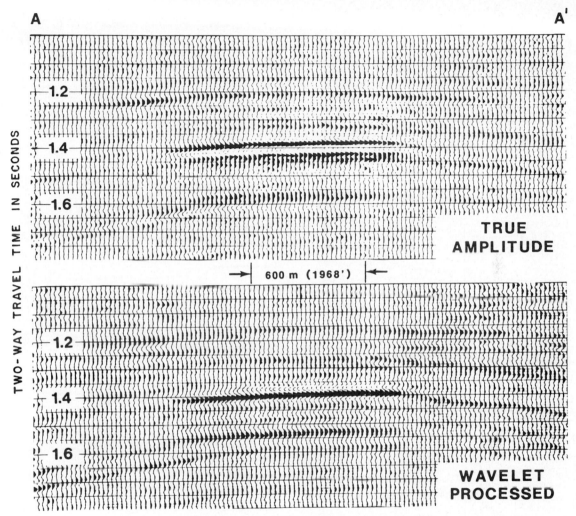

FIGURE 9-23   Comparison of conventional and wavelet processing, relative true amplitude preserved. These windows of data are from Fig. 9-24. These data are without the AGC that was applied in Fig. 9-24. (*From Schramm et al.*[64])

from the subsurface having a location immediately below its plotted location. (2) Individual reflection events on the wavelet processed data (peak, trough) can be identified, and the amplitude is diagnostic of the step in acoustic impedance across the boundary causing such reflection. Each contrast in acoustic impedance will be marked by a reflection event having a similar waveform. The polarity of the reflection and its size will indicate the nature of the contrasts.

Dedman et al.[65] interpreted the wavelet-processed data equivalent to Figs. 9-23 and 9-24 between 1.0 and 1.8 s, using the above procedure. They were able to identify the major shale units and the major sand units, as compared to the

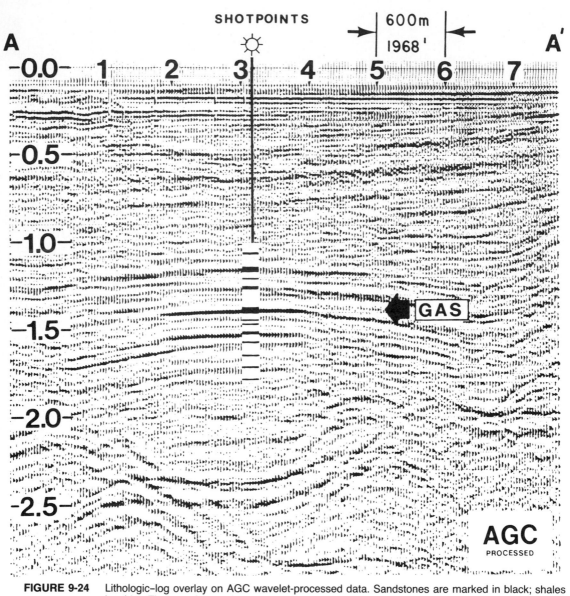

FIGURE 9-24 Lithologic–log overlay on AGC wavelet-processed data. Sandstones are marked in black; shales in white. The top of a sand corresponds to a trough or white event. (*From Schramm et al.*[64])

''independent'' information provided by the well data, given the resolution afforded by the bandwidth of the signal. The well-data information, shown in Fig. 9-24, is the lithologic log, plotted in time based on the appropriate time-to-depth function, overlain on the AGC wavelet-processed data. Sands are colored black, shales are colored white on the lithology-log inscrt. The top of a sand on the lith-log corresponds to a seismic trough or white event, while the top of a shale on the lith-log corresponds to a seismic peak or black event. In this illustration, the waveforms present in the seismic data were manipulated and transformed to simpler waveforms which were more amenable to interpretation. The transformations can be made based on sonic information, as discussed in Sec. 9-2, or by classical deconvolution approaches, as presented in Sec. 7-2.

The differences between the conventional waveform section and the wavelet-processed section go far beyond a simple reversal of display polarity as might be suggested at first glance. In the wavelet-processed data, waveshape as well as amplitude is a most significant interpretive diagnostic.

Current methods almost always yield acceptable control of the seismic waveform. By this is meant the transformation of the "raw" undesirable wavelet into a stable, zero-phase wavelet. Now the other steps in seismic processing become paramount in preserving the information contained in the seismic amplitude. In particular, velocity and static corrections come under scrutiny.

Velocity and Static Corrections   In order to utilize fully the velocity information inherent in moveout curves and minimize coarseness, it is necessary to optimize all parameters and procedures. Starting with wavelet-processed land data, a velocity analysis may be computed as frequently as from every shot point to perhaps every four shot points. In the marine case in which data quality is usually superior owing to more uniform coupling conditions and less static error, six to eight analyses per mile are computed. Frequent velocity analyses make it possible to minimize the residual normal moveout and hence to improve the accuracy of the residual static calculations. Dip moveout (DMO) corrections, as discussed in Secs. 7-6 and 7-10, can improve the quality of the velocity estimation, the final stack, and the migrated stack.

Localized velocity information in spatial terms is desired. The stacking velocity represents the "raw" data extracted. The interval velocity is the derived quantity that is useful for local stratigraphic studies, but it is bounded by larger error bars than is the stacking velocity. As discussed in Sec. 7-6, stacking velocities may exhibit spatial anomalies that are artifacts of the hyperbola-fitting, velocity estimation technique. As target depth (or time) increases, the size of the Fresnel zone increases, the frequencies become lower (and hence the resolution becomes less), the S/N of the target reflection often decreases, and below about 3 or 4 s, velocity discrimination through normal-moveout analysis becomes increasingly coarser. All these factors work together to decrease the velocity resolution with increased travel time. The optimum zone in which reflection seismic affords the best resolution of both velocity and frequencies, is a depth between about $\frac{1}{2}$ to $1\frac{1}{2}$ cable lengths.

Residual static solutions for seismic data of particular elegance and great promise have been developed by Taner et al.[66] and Wiggins et al.[67] Yet in practice, the quality of results promised by theory are rarely achieved. These static methods have in common the decomposition of time delays among four components, one component always relating to the error in moveout velocity (or residual normal moveout), as discussed in Sec. 7-4. Typical practice of one or two velocity analyses per mile undersamples the velocity variation of interest in stratigraphic studies, and so, since a residual moveout error is left in the data, the benefits of these static programs are diminished. Tight velocity control will minimize the moveout component in the static shift, thus affording better residual static computations. Wave equation migration techniques yield additional velocity information and so produce even more reliable amplitude information. The benefits of this careful and expensive processing can be largely lost through the poor dynamic range of conventional seismic displays, and the lack of velocity-display information. Color display of both seismic amplitude and velocity is therefore recommended.

Trace-by-Trace Inversion The transformation of a stacked seismic trace into a pseudovelocity log, or a band-limited acoustic-impedance log, a final step in processing, should incorporate both seismic-amplitude and moveout-velocity information. After appropriate processing, especially with respect to the seismic waveform, integration of the seismic traces enables one to estimate the acoustic impedance trace by trace, as discussed in Sec. 9-2. The color scale should be used to approximate interval velocities rather than arbitrary magnitudes. Lavergne and Willm[68] and Lindseth[69] are among the earliest proponents of this technology. In a final display, color can present information that would otherwise be lost or overlooked. Loper[70] used color to represent velocity and its first two derivatives, which was the first patented use of color for seismic-data display. The modulation of color by assigning to two or more different seismic attributes different colors to produce a unique, resulting color was patented by Savit.[71]

Figures 9-25 and 9-26 (see color insert) illustrate this type of improved integrated trace display technique. Figure 9-26 provides the closeup display of a carbonate bank sequence in the Cretaceous section in Houston County, Texas.[18] The entire bank sequence is not seismically perceptible on the conventional display (in Fig. 9-25). The background color display for each trace is a trend function developed from the moveout-velocity estimation. The trend supplied the low frequencies not recorded in the single seismic traces.

The en echelon sequence of carbonate banks is classic in terms of structure and velocities measured. The two most prominent members of the sequence, upper and lower Edwards cycles, have much in common with the bull's-eye of a target in terms of visibility. The banks are shelfal developments which relate to the East Texas Basin north of the profile. They formed at a time when the section dipped into this basin. The big Edwards member is at least 300 ft thick and is some 12,000 ft deep. It has a reflection coefficient of about 0.1.

In Fig. 9-26, the integrated trace nearest the well bore agrees quite well with the filtered acoustic-impedance function derived from well data and scaled in time.

Gardner's relation (see Sec. 9-2) was used to recover velocity information, rather than acoustic impedance, from the seismic, trace-amplitude data. The velocity increment is 400 ft/s in Fig. 9-26; the display of velocity information in a format easily interpretable is an important component in the seis-strat interpretation. At all times, however, velocity information derived from seismic-trace amplitudes must contain an unknown but significant component of error and uncertainty, especially for land data, for reasons already mentioned, and reviewed later in this section.

Seismic visibility of anomalies is increased manyfold by color plotting of the moveout-velocity information in conjunction with the amplitude information, as shown in Figs. 9-25 and 9-26. In Fig. 9-25, the colors are keyed to velocity estimates, with a 1000-ft/s increment. Both amplitude and moveout information were used to calculate the local interval velocity.

Figure 9-25 contains certain features in the color display that increase the seismic visibility of the anomaly. The color scale employed emphasizes the visibility of a change in velocity, even where the geometries entail great subtlety, as is usually the case with stratigraphic developments. These plots had trend or low-frequency velocity information measured at each SP. In general, plots designed for seis-strat interpretation should have indications at the top of the plot as to where the low-frequency velocity information (well or moveout curve) was determined.

The display is derived entirely from seismic information. No well logs have been incorporated. Crossing profiles must tie not only in reflection time but in rms velocity as well. The stacking velocities depend not only on the earth velocities but also upon the dip of the reflector and the azimuthal angle the line makes with the true dip direction. To achieve velocity ties on crossing lines, the stacking velocities are adjusted for these effects (see Sec. 10-3 for the development of this topic). However, the interpretation of spatial stacking velocities, in the presence of lateral velocity variations may contain a pitfall, which was discussed in Sec. 7-6.

The conventional black-and-white variable-area, wiggle trace display of the seismic data (Fig. 9-25) has thrown away the diagnostic information to detect the bank sequence. Subsequent study of this feature and others like it, and in several basins, has led to the conclusion that a large number of the shelfal carbonate buildups are not visible through standard seismic processing and display methods. Bank sequences, patch-type reefs, or pinnacles positionally analogous to the formation shown in Fig. 9-25 are considered to be quite common spatially and throughout geologic time. Many basins have had regimes present over long periods of geologic time that are conducive to the development of shelfal carbonate buildups. Without the newer tools suggested here or some equivalent technology, perhaps 60 to 80 percent of these potential exploration targets are not found because they are not visible in the conventional displays.

Reserve Estimates

It is of economic importance to be able to map the geometry and lithology of the hydrocarbon reservoirs and to estimate the total reserves in such accumulations. The extraction of such information on the hydrocarbon zones is best initiated by modeling the rock formations associated with them as well as the fluids filling the pore spaces involved.

The basic procedure is to construct a cross section on which interfaces corresponding to observed reflections are drawn and appropriate trial velocities are introduced between the interfaces. Adjustments are made in the geometry of the boundaries initially postulated as well as in the velocities assumed for the spaces between them until a synthetic record is obtained for a model that gives the closest resemblance to the actual processed section. Such adjustments may be made manually or by computer, as discussed in Sec. 9-2. The variables of greatest practical significance are the geometry of the gas sand, the porosity, and the degree of gas saturation in the sand. Such information gives a basis for estimating the total amount of gas in the sand body.

Figure 9-27 shows the portion of a seismic section recorded in offshore

FIGURE 9-27 Model based on actual record (*top*) of a single gas sand with synthetic section (*center*) based on model parameters shown at bottom. (*Geocom, Inc.*)

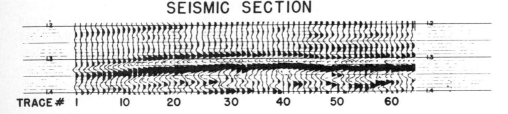

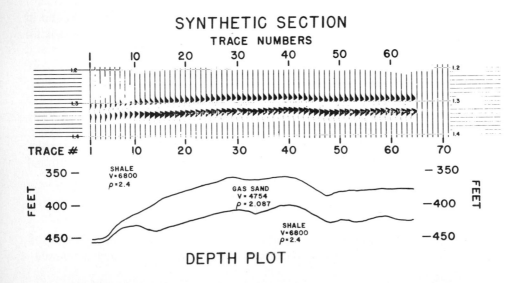

Louisiana and processed for preservation of relative amplitude that exhibits a bright spot indicating the presence of gas. Assuming that the gas thus postulated is entrapped in a sand body sandwiched between two shale layers, we would like to determine the size and shape of the body and its gas content. The velocity of seismic waves in the same body depends both on porosity and gas saturation. If a set of velocities assumed for the respective elements of the model results in a synthetic section giving a good agreement with the actual section (both in the time interval between the reflections from its upper and lower boundaries and in relative amplitudes), it should be possible to determine the porosity of the sand and/or the extent to which it is saturated with gas.

The lower portion of Fig. 9-27 shows the structural and lithologic configuration of the subsurface that gives the optimum agreement with the seismic record section that has been recorded and processed. The synthetic section resulting from the particular model parameters indicated on the geological section seems to show a good similarity to the actual record section at the top of the figure.

Some modeling can be applied for other purposes, often to examine different hypothetical patterns of hydrocarbon entrapment in actual producing zones such as those modeled in the example just considered. An example of this type of model, reproduced in Fig. 9-28, is for a sand 100 ft thick at the left, embedded in shale which wedges out updip on the right side of the model. On

FIGURE 9-28
Modeling of reservoir containing oil and gas entrapped in a pinchout. (*Teledyne Exploration Co.*)

UPDIP PINCHOUT

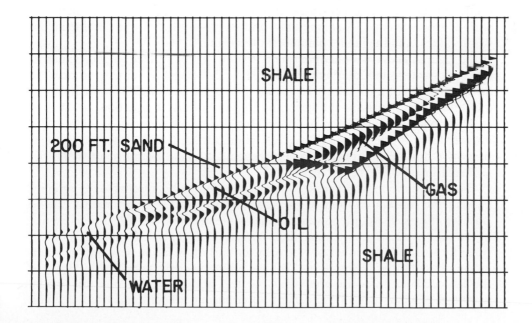

its left side the sand contains water, in its central part oil, and in the wedge itself gas. The gas-liquid contact is indicated by the fragmental horizontal reflection segment near the center of the figure. Such segments, termed *flat spots*, are often observed on field data, as illustrated in Fig. 9-34 (from Backus and Chen[72]), and will be discussed later. The velocities of the sand(s) depend on the porosity, the liquid and/or gas filling the pore spaces, and the degree of saturation for each constituent. The amplitudes depend on both the velocity contrasts at the interfaces and on interference effects between individual reflections when the reflecting interfaces are close together. Modeling makes it possible to vary all these parameters independently and to arrive at combinations that match results obtained by appropriate processing of the field data. The ambiguities inherent in such procedures and the inability of the technique to model fine changes on a scale smaller than the seismic resolution allows must inevitably limit the precision of reserves estimates made in this way.

A companion model-study to the data shown in Fig. 9-23 will be presented next (from Schramm et al.[64]). The geologic situation is a partially gas-filled sand. This particular sand body under consideration is a schematic representation of the bright-spot gas sand discussed earlier in connection with wavelet processing, and the seismic responses for the model should be compared with the data panels presented earlier. The two data panels showed the effect of two different wavelets; now the model study using two different wavelets is presented.

The model, Fig. 9-29, is a mildly structurally closed sand unit of relatively uniform thickness. The upper 60 ft of this 120-ft sand is gas saturated. Field seismic data (Figs. 9-23, 9-24) exhibited a bright spot of about the amplitude contrast shown in Fig. 9-29. This model was originally created with the theoretically derived rock velocities and densities for the sands and shales as derived from well logs. An amplitude contrast of only 1.25:1 was obtained from these values, and the model parameters were altered to have the values shown in the figure. These were derived by assigning a 0.04 reflection coefficient to the shale–water-sand interface and adjusting the gas-sand velocity to provide the amplitude contrast shown on the seismic data. Densities were included in the reflection calculation and generally follow Gardner's equation.

The model was run with two different but documented marine wavelets. It is apparent that the seismic sections look quite different, and if they were members of a grid of data on the same prospect, it would be diffficult to tie the different lines.

For conventionally processed data, it is generally unreliable to attempt picking the top and bottom of the gas-sand for thickness estimates, due to wavelet effects. It would, however, be possible to detect the probable presence of the sand and to place it on the map. Wavelet B might be interpreted as one or possibly two sands, while wavelet A looks fairly low frequency, and as such, lacking in detail. Wavelets A and B have a bandwidth approximately equal to the 8- to 32-Hz response shown at the top of Fig. 9-29. Thus this model response is what each of the other two could have been converted to, with

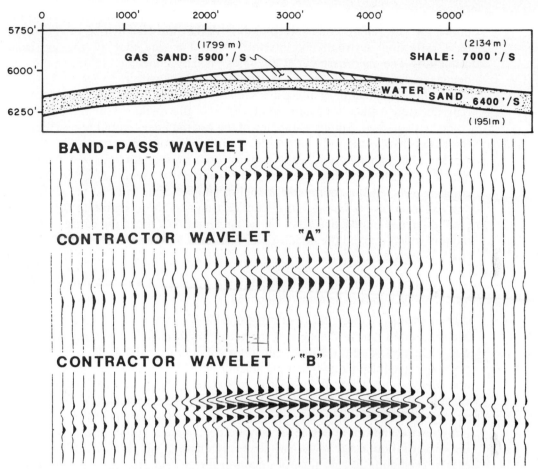

FIGURE 9-29   Model seismic data, with three different wavelets, using the model shown at the top: a sandstone with a gas cap encased in shale. (*From Schramm et al.*[64])

appropriate processing. No problems of tieing data between the two different shoots (or contractors) would then exist.

The symmetric (zero-phase) waveform response at the top of Fig. 9-29 exhibits the great advantage of having the top (the seismic trough) and the bottom (the peak) of the gas portion of the sand clearly visible. The interpretive procedure used here is that every peak indicates a positive reflection coefficient at the time of maximum deflection, and every trough a negative reflection coefficient at the time of maximum deflection. Next, the water-sand interfaces are visible in this noise-free example, and sometimes this is true for actual data. Some intriguing phasing appears at the base of the gas on either side of the structure. Since we already know the depth cross section, one might dismiss this effect by postulating that the phasing is the transition from a reflection at the base of the gas to one from the base of the sand. But the base of the sand is physically present across the entire structure, and yet it is only seen out from under the gas. The correct interpretation is that the center lobe of the sand-base reflection destructively interferes with the side lobe of the gas-base reflection. The sand-base event becomes visually undetectable under the gas becauase the gas-liquid contact reflection interferes with it.

An additional matter of interest is seen in the model response. Given reasonably accurate values for water-sand velocity, the thickness of the sand unit could be estimated. Similar estimates of the gas thickness would reveal less gas thickness than total sand—hence the reservoir is not full.

Thin-bed interpretation relies heavily upon model studies, and matching model responses with the real data, as discussed in Sec. 9-2. Even the Dix equation (Sec. 7-6) is an inverse model of simple form. Interval velocities are derived from rms velocities and reflection times on the assumption that a 2-D, parallel-layered model describes the actual situation. One of the earliest inverse models which relaxed the condition of parallel layers was described by Taner, Cook, and Neidell.[20]

Facies Analysis, Seismic Visibility, and Stratigraphic Objectives

Earlier in this chapter, the work of Peter Vail et al.[7] was noted as an interpretive tool of extraordinary power. Recapping briefly, a seismic sequence is established by noting, within a unit, internally conformable reflections and the generally unconformable bounding seismic reflections. The seismic sequences are seen as the major depositional sequences. The geometry and all other seismic information of the reflections within the seismic sequence, termed the *seismic facies*, cast light upon the depositional environment of that unit. The relative rise and fall of sea level may be determined within an area and such information compared to global sea-level changes so that, when similarity exists, prediction of age, time of unconformities, and paleoenvironments may be attempted. Further discussion of these seismic stratigraphic concepts is found in Sheriff.[73] One of the controversial statements made by Vail et al.[7] is that the seismic section is a chronostratigraphic record, not a lithostratigraphic record.

In many cases, borehole tests confirm the lithologic and other type predictions made by the seis-strat interpretation. In other cases, the seis-strat interpretation is inconsistent with the well log data. Scholarly debates have arisen as to whether seismic reflections followed lines of equal geologic time or changing lithology. The situation appears confused.

Seismic theory, of course, indicates that seismic reflections must follow changes in the acoustic impedance as in Eq. (9-4). Why then the controversy? Reconciliation of the two viewpoints is related to the issue of seismic visibility and can be illustrated by an example from the North Sea. A North Sea line is shown in conventional seismic display in Fig. 9-30. The zone of interest is the Bunter Sandstone. Faulting above the Bunter is believed to be related to evaporite dissolution. The color acoustic-impedance display of the data is

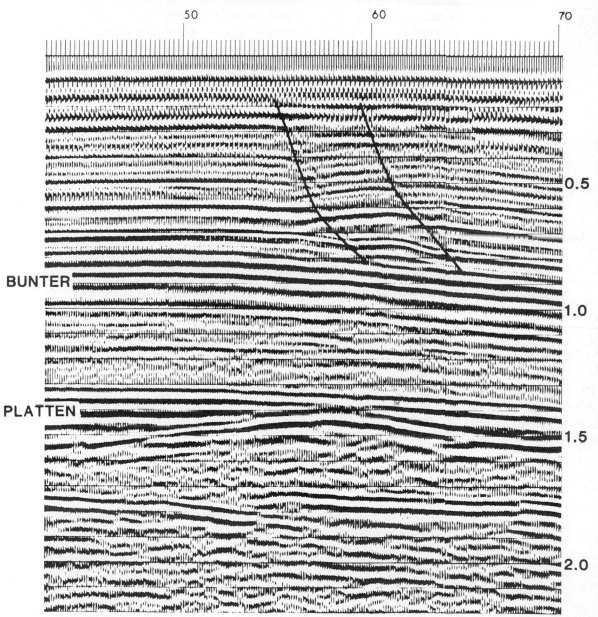

1960 VINTAGE AQUISITION

NORTH SEA LINE 12

FIGURE 9-30 North Sea Line 12, 48-fold data shot in 1960, conventional black and white display. To be compared with Fig. 9-31, a color acoustic-impedance plot of the same field data set. (*From Neidell and Beard.*[18])

shown in Fig. 9-31 (see color insert). Here the Bunter Sandstone is clearly seen to be a transgressive sequence of lower-velocity rocks than the adjacent formations. Two of the sand barriers, in particular, appear to have hydrocarbon potential in terms of their velocity reduction. One shows a small white streak inside a dark blue streak denoting lowest velocity, while the second shows a dark blue (one velocity increment higher), but still a relative low. The low acoustic impedance is related to porosity and/or the presence of hydrocarbons. Improved visibility of all the seismic information can deflate the arguments concerning whether reflections mark equal time or changing lithology boundaries. The power of the facies and sequence analysis interpretive approach is effectively magnified by interpreting seismic patterns, geometry, and velocity information. Depositional environments, lithology, and hydrocarbons can often be indicated along with individual suspected traps, placed in the context of a geologic setting. Seis-strat approaches can be used also in basinwide studies; one example of this is the seis-strat study of the west Sumatra Forearc Basin (Beaudry and Moore[74]).

Amplitudes and Nonnormal Incidence

Amplitude variation with offset, a pre-stack amplitude analysis technique, became a serious topic of investigation in the early 1980s for determining hydrocarbon potential and lithologic information. Early works by Bortfeld[75] and Koefoed[76] presented various possible approximations to the Knot-Zoeppritz equations (see Chap. 2).

When P-wave energy impinges upon an acoustic-impedance boundary at an angle other than normal incidence, shear-wave motion is induced. The amplitudes of transmitted and reflected P waves can show significant variation with incidence angle due to the fact that differing amounts of energy from the incident P-wave mode convert to shear-wave propagation. The partitioning of energy as a function of incidence angle is discussed in Sec. 2-4. A good treatment of the partitioning of energy is found in Telford et al.[77]

In many circumstances, the reflection coefficients are small (0.001 to 0.01), and the incident angles represented by the offsets present in the seismic data are between 0 and 15°. In such circumstances, there appear to be negligible amounts of mode conversion and amplitude variation with offset. Mode conversion from P to shear is greater at the farther offsets (larger theta) and for greater contrasts in P and shear velocities. Significant mode-converted energy has been recorded where large acoustic-impedance contrasts exist. Some examples are in relatively shallow-water hard-bottom (carbonate) settings, where the P-wave energy incident on the sea floor generates significant shear-wave energy propagating downward. The shear reflections that return to the surface, mode convert to P at the sea floor and are recorded as P-wave reflections by the hydrophones. Onshore, mode-converted energy has been recorded on the farther offsets; significantly more mode-converted energy is received in areas of large reflection coefficients (e.g., in places where a massive carbonate section is overlain by an unusually low-velocity section, like shales or other clastics).

The primary data inputs to offset-amplitude analyses are amplitude values as functions of offset, but variation in the subsurface P and shear velocities and densities are not the sole parameters that can cause such changes. Other factors include source directivity and array effects, near-surface velocity variations, geometrical spreading, loss through propagation of the high frequencies, dispersive phase distortion, velocity anisotropy, thin-bed interference effects, short-period multiple interference, reflector curvature, and undesirable processing effects. For land data, one of the variables that is least known but most important is the lateral variability in coupling between source and earth, and receiver and earth, as well as variation in the near-surface Q (quality factor, see Sec. 2-6). Some adequate accounting or control must be given for each of these effects in order to relate the remaining amplitude variation to reflectivity change effects. This requirement often leads to model studies as a key element.

Gas Detection Using Amplitude Variation with Offset

Backus et al.[78] have published theoretical studies concerning the offset-amplitude variation. Ostrander[79] has published field-data results. Both make extensive use of models. One of Ostrander's models is shown in Fig. 9-32, which represents a rather thick gas-filled sand in which the seismic parameters are reasonable for Tertiary sediments of moderate depth. From the graph we see that

> the top-of-sand reflection coefficient changes from about -0.16 to -0.28 over a range of 40 degrees, while the base-of-sand reflection coefficient changes from $+0.16$ to $+0.26$ over the same range. Thus, the amplitude of the complex seismic reflection resulting from this hypothetical model would increase about 70% over the 40 degrees. By perturbing the variables in this three-layer model, even greater amplitude increases can be generated (p. 216).

Ostrander states that a medium with an abnormally low Poisson's ratio (like a gas sand) embedded within media with "normal" Poisson's ratios tends to give rise to a reflection that increases in energy with angle of incidence. Poisson's ratio is a function of the V_P/V_S ratio, as is discussed in Chap. 2. To investigate particular hydrocarbon traps in different areas would require non-zero-offset amplitude modeling based on appropriate velocities, densities, and Poisson's ratios so that erroneous conclusions are not drawn from overgeneralizations.

The thickness of the sand unit plays an important role in determining the offset behavior. Figure 9-33 shows field data contrasting the amplitude variation with offset for gas-filled and gas-free zones. In order to improve the S/N conditions, 10 adjacent, moveout-corrected CDP gathers representing the two cases are noted. Near offsets are displayed to the right in each gather. The high amplitudes of the stacked reflections from SP 80-120 are associated with gas. Beyond SP 120, the high-amplitude events are not attributed to gas. The gas-

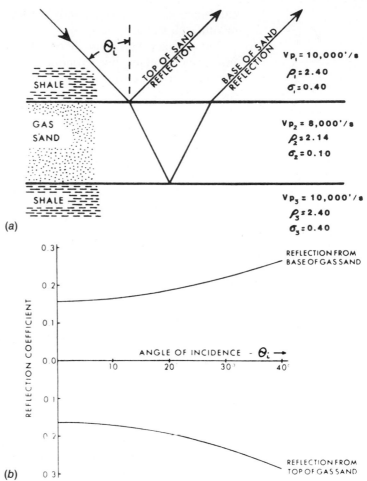

FIGURE 9-32 Model (a) and reflection coefficient graph (b) for a moderately thick gas sand encased in shale. The reflection coefficients for the top and base of the gas sand are plotted against angle of incidence (or increasing offset). (*From Ostrander.*[79])

filled zones give rise to reflections brighter at far offsets; the gas-free zones to reflections brighter at near offsets.

Two conclusions are drawn from Ostrander's[79] work.

First, Poisson's ratio has a strong influence on changes in reflection coefficient as a function of angle of incidence. Secondly, analysis of seismic reflection amplitude versus offset can, in many cases, distinguish between gas-related amplitude anomalies and other types of amplitude anomalies [i.e., lithologic-change anomalies]. Numerous analyses of this type have been performed on seismic data recorded over known gas sands in California, Alaska, Canada, and the Gulf Coast. Additionally, analyses have been performed on amplitude anomalies recorded over high-velocity volcanics, basalts, and conglomerates. Results have been very encouraging (p.218),

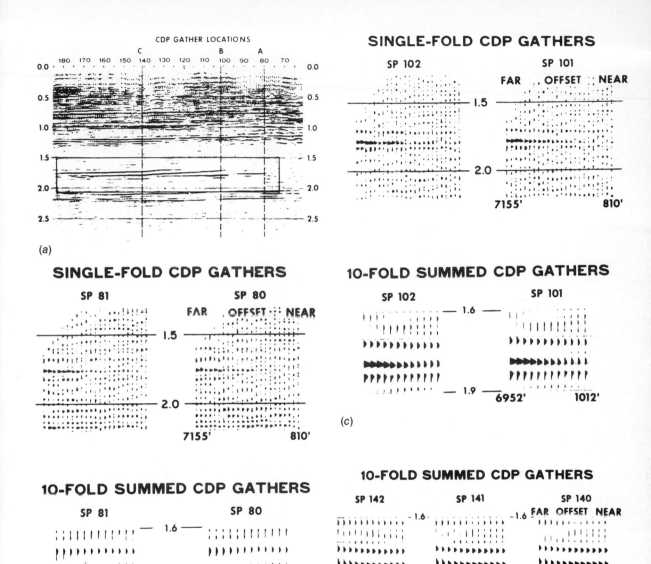

FIGURE 9-33   (a) Field data showing offset–amplitude relations for high-amplitude reflection events correlative with gas sands (SP-80-120, locations A and B) and nongas sands (beyond SP 120, location C). Near offsets are displayed to the right in each gather. In order to improve the S/N, ten adjacent, moveout-corrected CDP gathers are displayed beneath the single-fold CDP gathers. (b) CDP gathers at location A. (c) CDP gathers at location B. (d) CDP gathers at location C. The gas sands display increasing amplitude with increasing offset, as predicted in the model study shown in Fig. 9-32. This effect is missing in the high-amplitude events not associated with gas. (*From Ostrander.*[79])

which probably means that discrimination between LCI (lithologic-change indicator) and HCI (hydrocarbon indicator) can be accomplished a significant percentage of the time. Thus, the exploration risks can be reduced on prospects exhibiting amplitude anomalies.

The behavior of the amplitudes with offset in different geologic scenarios is modeled, thus allowing the geophysicist to discriminate among possible interpretations. The slope of the amplitude variation with offset may be color encoded (for example: blue, decrease; red, increase; intensity of color keyed to rate of amplitude change) so that the wiggle trace, stack plot is overlain with the information concerning amplitudes and offset. The interpreter uses model studies to confirm and understand the origin of the anomalies presented in the field data. The distinguishing of HCIs from LCIs based on P- and shear-wave data was discussed in Sec. 9-3.

Flat Spots and Other Seismic Indications of Hydrocarbons

A key diagnostic for the presence of hydrocarbons is a flat spot: a situation in which "the hydrocarbon-brine contact produces a flat [horizontal] reflection, unconformable with the lithologic reflections from the trap boundaries, and over a limited area bounded by structural contours. Where it can be reliably detected and mapped, the flat spot can provide a reasonably unambiguous indication and areal extent of a reservoir and an estimate of reservoir thickness" (Backus and Chen,[72] p. 533). It is evident that a horizontal interface in nonhorizontal lithology can only arise from an interface between two fluids. Thus a flat spot can indicate a gas-oil, gas-water, or oil-water interface with the reflection coefficient for the last interface being substantially lower than that of each of the others. A field-data example of a flat spot is given in Fig. 9-34. A model study showing a flat spot is Fig. 9-28.

Early in the era of direct detection in the Gulf Coast area, peripheral clues qualified as additional indicators of hydrocarbons. These clues, such as pull-downs, sags, diffraction patterns, polarity reversals at the edges of gas sands, or dimouts (attenuation effects with the selective absorption of the higher-frequency components) indicated abrupt changes in acoustic parameters. Some of these additional indicators were the result of not changing the processing parameters (velocities, etc.) fast enough. When 8 to 16 stacking-velocity analyses are performed per mile and the results are encoded upon the final stack plot, some of the earlier peripheral clues will reveal themselves as direct detection phenomena.

Long-Term Potential of Direct Detection Techniques

It is always hazardous to make predictions of future technological developments, particularly in books designed to be current over a longer time than more ephemeral publications. Direct detection by its very nature will always be a forefront technology, and hence any discussion will represent an earlier stage

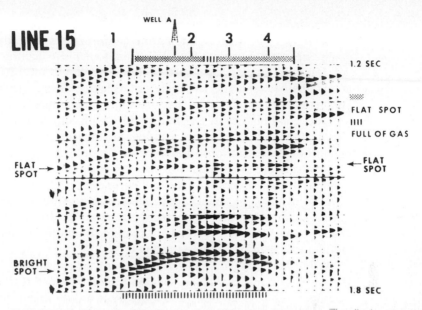

FIGURE 9-34 Field data displaying the "flat-spot" and "bright-spot" phenomena. The display is dual polarity (solid black deflections are peaks, grey deflections are rectified troughs). Formation dip is to the left. The flat-spot reflection is from the horizontal gas–water interface. Arrows at the left denote the top sand of reservoir 1 (upper arrow) and the tuned thin sand of reservoir 3 (lower arrow). Upper-side margin marks indicate level of the flat, unconformable gas–brine contact reflection in the upper reservoir. At the top of the figure, the flat-spot, lateral extent is shown (for reservoir 1). The "full of gas" mark indicates the starting point at which the sand reservoir is interpreted to be full of gas. Lower-side margin marks indicate level of reflection dimming point in reservoir 3, interpreted as the gas–brine contact. (*From Backus and Chen.*[72])

of development than the one in current practice, which is usually proprietary. Also, owing to the economics involved and competitive factors, "hard" information and statistics on exploration success ratios, in which direct detection techniques were employed, will always be difficult to come by. Most of the time, a geophysical textbook is in a position to record only what is well known and even mundane. The power of the most advanced methods will only be suggested by the scant data that are released.

As our understanding broadens due to an expanding catalogue of laboratory data values, case-history documentations, and experience, we become better able to define limitations and areas that are amenable to the existing state-of-the-art technology. For example, the initial work of Domenico[56] suggested that small amounts of gas in sands could give exaggerated reductions in velocity. It was recognized later that this situation was generally only true for young and unconsolidated sands. When rocks of early Miocene age or older are involved, absence of consolidation is rarely the case. In fact the patchy results available suggest a direct relationship between the amount of gas and the velocity reduction, given a fixed porosity.

The industry's collective ability to measure velocities by seismic methods is improving at great speed. In marine environments, amplitude-derived interval velocities from inversion have been said to achieve accuracies in relative terms of 150 ft/s. Investigation into deriving lithologic information from the relationships between the two types of velocity measurements (amplitudes and moveout curves) is in progress (personal communication, Neidell).

The coordination of seismic results with subsurface information derived from other sources such as well logging measurements is another avenue for important investigations. Early studies employing synthetic seismograms or matching filtered, acoustic-impedance measurements from well logs to inverted seismic traces suggested excellent agreements. Under more careful scrutiny, and particularly in quantitative terms, some of these correlations have been found lacking. It is now being recognized that the disparity of each result will in fact provide yet a new level of information about the subsurface of even greater refinement than previously imagined.

With the increasing power to define the subsurface, traditional barriers between disciplines can be seen to fall. It is clear that exploration seismic methods will be used more and more by reservoir or production engineers and geologists. A new field of development or exploitation geophysics is emerging in which reservoir parameters and field extensions are defined first in advance of the drill and later improved with subsurface information. The next chapter will present the 3-D seismic techniques used so often in exploitation and sometimes in exploration.

There is little question that the success obtained thus far with direct detection by seismic methods will have a great effect on the future course of geophysical technology. Investigation in this area will dominate the development of exploration geophysics for a long time to come. The possibility of expanding present capabilities to the point of directly locating both oil and gas onshore and offshore offers a tremendous incentive for accelerating research and development in this field. Inherent in this quest is the research effort to extract the lithologic parameters, like P velocity, shear velocity, density, Poisson's ratio, the various elastic constants, and bed thickness. These efforts, in view of the extent of the world's inevitable energy shortfall, are not likely to diminish until their objectives are achieved or until a long-continued lack of success in meeting them leads to a major reduction in such activity. The problems to be faced are formidable, but so are the technical resources available, especially through the rapid increase in computer power and capacity. Continued breakthroughs in the art are seen as necessary.

REFERENCES

1 King, Robert E. (ed.): "Stratigraphic Oil and Gas Fields: Classification, Exploration, and Case Histories," *Am. Assoc. Petrol. Geol. Mem. 16*, and *Soc. Explor. Geophys. Spec. Pub. 10*, 1972.

2 Lyons, Paul L., and M. B. Dobrin: Seismic Exploration for Stratigraphic Traps, pp. 225–243, in Ref. 1.

3 Payton, C. E. (ed.): "Seismic Stratigraphy—Applications to Hydrocarbon Exploration," *Am. Assoc. Petrol. Geol. Mem. 26*, Tulsa, Okla., 1977.

4 Halbouty, M. T. (ed.): "The Deliberate Search for the Subtle Trap," *Am. Assoc. Petrol. Geol. Mem. 32*, Tulsa, Okla., 1982.

5 Berg, O. R., and D. G. Woolverton (eds.): "Seismic Stratigraphy II: An Integrated Approach to Hydrocarbon Exploration," *Am. Assoc. Petrol. Geol. Mem. 39*, Tulsa, Okla., 1985.

6 Levorsen, A. I.: "Geology of Petroleum," 2d ed., Freeman, San Francisco, 1967.

7 Vail, P. R., R. M. Mitchum, Jr., R. G. Todd, J. M. Widmier, S. Thompsom, III, J. B. Sangree, J. N. Bubb, and W. G. Hatlelid: Seismic Stratigraphy and Global Changes of Sea Level, pp. 49–212, in C. E. Payton (ed.), "Seismic Stratigraphy—Applications to Hydrocarbon Exploration," *Am. Assoc. Petrol. Geol. Mem. 26*, Tulsa, Okla., 1977.

8 Skeels, D. C.: Correlation of Geological and Geophysical Data, *Proc. 4th World Petrol. Congr.*, sec. I, pp. 665–673, Geology and Geophysics, Brill, Leiden, Netherlands, 1955.

9 Harwell, J. C., and W. R. Rector: North Knox City Field, Knox County, pp. 453–459, in Ref. 1.

10 Fitton, John C., and Milton B. Dobrin: Optical Processing and Interpretation, *Geophysics*, vol. 32, pp. 801–818, 1967.

11 Evans, Hugh: Zama: A Geophysical Case History, pp. 440–452, in Ref. 1.

12 Seelis, Karl-Heinz: Das Reflexionsseismiche Bild des Bentheimer Sandsteines in Raum von Meppen, *Erdöl und Kohle*, vol. 12, pp. 953–957, 1959.

13 Robinson, W. B.: Geophysics Is Here to Stay, *Bull. Am. Assoc. Petrol. Geol.*, vol. 55, pp. 2107–2115, 1971.

14 Morgridge, Dean L., and William B. Smith, Jr.: Geology and Discovery of Prudhoe Bay Field, Eastern Arctic Slope, Alaska, pp. 489–501, in Ref. 1.

15 Hedemann, H. A., and H. Lorenz: Truncation Traps on Northwest Border of Gifhorn Trough, East Hannover, Germany, pp. 532–547, in Ref. 1.

16 Roll, A.: Bramberge Field, Federal Republic of Germany, pp. 286–296, in Ref. 1.

17 Bazeley, William: San Emidio Nose Oil Field, California, pp. 297–312, in Ref. 1

18 Neidell, N. S., and J. H. Beard: Seismic Visibility of Stratigraphic Objectives, presented at 60th Annual Conference of Soc. Petrol. Engineers, Las Vegas, Nev., Sept. 1985. Preprint, 14 pp. SPE, P. O. Box 833836, Richardson, TX 75083-3836.

19 Sangree, J. B., and J. M. Widmeier: Interpretation of Depositional Facies from Seismic Data, Soc. Explor. Geophys. Convention, Dallas, Tex., November 1974.

20 Taner, M. T., E. E. Cook, and N. S. Neidell: Limitations of the Reflection Seismic Method—Lessons from Computer Simulations, *Geophysics*, vol. 35, pp. 551–573, 1970.

21 Shah, P. M.: Ray Tracing in Three Dimensions, *Geophysics*, vol. 38, pp. 600–604, 1974.

22 Neidell, N. S.: What Are the Limits in Specifying Seismic Models? *Oil Gas J.*, pp. 144–147, Feb. 17, 1975.

23 Gelfand, V., and K. Larner: Seismic Lithologic Modeling, *The Leading Edge,* vol. 3, pp. 30–35, Nov. 1984.

24 Kaman, E. J., P. van Riel, and A. J. W. Duyndam: Detailed Inversion of Reservoir

Data by Constrained Parameter Estimation and Resolution Analysis, Expanded Abstracts, *54th Ann. Int. Soc. Explor. Geophys. Meeting*, pp. 652–655, 1984.

25 Gelfand, V., G. Taylor, J. Tessman, and K. Larner: 3-D Seismic Lithologic Modeling to Delineate Rapidly Changing Reservoir Facies: A Case History from Alberta, Canada, Expanded Abstracts, *55th Int. Soc. Explor. Geophys. Meeting*, pp. 343–345, 1985.

26 Trademark, Western Geophysical.

27 Lindseth, R. O.: Seislog Process Uses Seismic Reflection Traces, *Oil Gas J.*, pp. 67–71, Oct. 25, 1976.

28 Trademark, Companie Generale de Geophysique (CGG).

29 Sheriff, R. E. (compiler): "Encyclopedic Dictionary of Exploration Geophysics," 2d ed., Soc. Explor. Geophys., Tulsa, Okla., 1984.

30 Raffalovich, F. D., and R. E. Daw: Use of Seismic Stratigraphy for Minnelusa Exploration, Northeastern Wyoming, Expanded abstracts of the *52nd International SEG Meeting*, pp. 24–26, 1982.

31 Harris, D. G., J. F. Sang, P. R. Vail, and F. Branisa: Use of Seismic Stratigraphic Procedures in the Interpretation of Trace Inversion Sections, Expanded Abstracts, *52nd Int. Soc. Explor. Geophys. Meeting*, pp. 22–23, 1982.

32 Gardner, G. H. F., L. W. Gardner, and A. R. Gregory: Formation Velocity and Density—The Diagnostic Basics for Stratigraphic Traps, *Geophysics*, vol. 39, pp. 770–780, 1974.

33 Clayton, R. W., and R. Stolt: A Born-WKBJ Inversion Method for Acoustic Reflection Data, *Geophysics*, vol. 46, pp. 1559–1567, 1981.

34 Carrion, P., and D. Foster: Limits of the Born Inversion, Expanded Abstracts, *53rd Int. Soc. Explor. Geophys. Meeting*, pp. 492–493, 1983.

35 Le Bras, R., and R. W. Clayton: Presentation of a Born Inversion for Multioffset Reflection Data: Tests on Synthetic Seismograms, Expanded Abstracts, *54th Int. Soc. Explor. Geophys. Meeting*, pp. 572–575, 1984.

36 Cohen, J. K., and N. Bleistein: Velocity Inversion Procedure for Acoustic Waves, *Geophysics*, vol. 44, pp. 1077–1087, 1979.

37 Cohen, J. K., and F. G. Hagin: Computational and Asymptotic Aspects of Velocity Inversion, *Geophysics*, vol. 50, pp. 1253–1265, 1985.

38 Coen, S.: Velocity and Density Profiles of a Layered Acoustic Medium from Common Source-Point Data, *Geophysics*, vol. 47, pp. 898–905, 1982.

39 Coen, S.: On the Elastic Profiles of a Layered Medium from Reflection Data. Part I: Plane-Wave Sources, *J. Acoust. Soc. Am.*, vol. 70, pp. 172–175, 1981. Part II: Impulsive Point Source, *J. Acoust. Soc. Am.*, vol. 70, pp. 1473–1479, 1981.

40 Morley, L. C.: Invertibility of Elastic Layered Earth Parameters from Precritical P-Wave Reflection Amplitudes, Expanded Abstracts, *54th Int. Soc. Explor. Geophys. Meeting*, pp. 641–643, 1984.

41 Savit, C. H., and E. J. Mateker, Jr.: From "Where?" to "What?," *Proc. 8th World Petrol. Congr.*, vol. 3, pp. 95–104, Applied Science, London, 1971.

42 Sriram, K. P., T. W. Fulton, J. J. Nooteboom, and A. J. Seriff: Velocity Anisotropy of Seismic Waves: Field Observations, Expanded Abstracts, *54th Int. Soc. Explor. Geophys. Meeting*, pp. 596–598, 1984.

43 Seriff, A. J.: Anisotropy, Shear Waves, and Shales, Expanded Abstracts, *54th Int. Soc. Explor. Geophys. Meeting*, p. 854, 1984.

44 Crampin, S: Evaluation of Anisotropy by Shear-Wave Splitting, *Geophysics*, vol. 50, pp. 142–152, 1985.

45 Winterstein, D. F. Anisotropy Effects in P and SH-Wave Stacking Velocities Contain Information on Lithology, Expanded Abstracts, *54th Int. Soc. Explor. Geophys. Meeting*, pp. 852–853, 1984.

46 Ensley, R. A.: Evaluation of Direct Hydrocarbon Indicators through Comparison of Compressional and Shear-Wave Data: A Case Study of the Myrnam Gas Field, Alberta, *Geophysics*, vol. 50, pp. 37–48, 1985.

47 Robertson, J. D., and W. C. Pritchett: Direct Hydrocarbon Detection Using Comparative P-Wave and S-Wave Seismic Sections, *Geophysics*, vol. 50, pp. 383–393, 1985.

48 McCormack, M. D., J. A. Dunbar, and W. W. Sharp: A Case Study of Stratigraphic Interpretation Using Shear and Compressional Seismic Data, Expanded Abstracts, *52nd Int. Soc. Explor. Geophys. Meeting*, pp. 21–22, 1982.

49 Benzing, W. M., P. E. Byerly, and J. R. Hopkins: Shear and Compressional Wave Data Interpretation—Midland Basin, Texas, Expanded Abstracts, *53rd Int. Soc. Explor. Geophys. Meeting*, pp. 358–359, 1983.

50 Robertson, J. D.: Carbonate Porosity from S/P Traveltime Ratios, Expanded Abstracts, *53rd Int. Soc. Explor. Geophys. Meeting*, pp. 356–358, 1983.

51 Tatham, R. H., and D. V. Goolsbee: Separation of Shear-Wave and P-Wave Reflections Offshore Western Florida, Expanded Abstracts, *53rd Int. Soc. Explor. Geophys. Meeting*, pp. 421–422, 1983.

52 Gassmann, F.: Elastic Waves through a Packing of Spheres, *Geophysics*, vol. 16, pp. 673–685, 1951.

53 Geertsma, J., and D. C. Smit: Some Aspects of Elastic Wave Propagation in Fluid-Saturated Porous Solids, *Geophysics*, vol. 26, pp. 169–181, 1961.

54 Wyllie, M. R. J., A. R. Gregory, and L. W. Gardner: Elastic Wave Velocities in Heterogeneous and Porous Media, *Geophysics*, vol. 21, pp. 41–70, 1956.

55 Wyllie, M. R. J., A. R. Gregory, and G. H. F. Gardner: An Experimental Investigation of Factors Affecting Elastic Wave Velocities in Porous Media, *Geophysics*, vol. 23, pp. 459–493, 1958.

56 Domenico, S. N.: Effect of Water Saturation on Seismic Reflectivity of Sand Reservoirs Encased in Shale, *Geophysics*, vol. 39, pp. 759–769, 1974.

57 Domenico, S. N.: Effect of Brine-Gas Mixture on Velocity in an Unconsolidated Sand Reservoir, *Geophysics*, vol. 41, pp. 882–894, 1976.

58 Domenico, S. N.: Elastic Properties of Unconsolidated Porous Sand Reservoirs, *Geophysics*, vol. 42, pp. 1339–1368, 1977.

59 Engelmark, F., F. Hilterman, L. C. Liang, and C. S. Burns: Relating Seismic Lithology to Gulf Coast Petrophysics, Expanded Abstracts, *Soc. Explor. Geophys., 55th Ann. Meeting*, pp. 442–446, 1985.

60 Sheriff, R. E.: Factors Affecting Seismic Amplitudes, *Geophys. Prospect.*, vol. 23, pp. 125–138, 1975.

61 Wood, L. C.: Imaging the Subsurface, in K. C. Jain and R. J. P. de Figueiredo (eds.), "Concepts and Techniques in Oil and Gas Exploration," Soc. Explor. Geophys., 1982.

62 Dix, C. H.: "Seismic Prospecting for Oil," Harper, New York, 1952.

63 Hilterman, Fred J.: Amplitudes of Seismic Waves—A Quick Look, *Geophysics*, vol. 40, pp. 745–762, 1975.

64 Schramm, M. W., Jr., E. V. Dedman, and J. P. Lindsey: Practical Stratigraphic Modeling and Interpretation, in Seismic Stratigraphy—Applications to Hydrocarbon Exploration, *Am. Assoc. Petrol. Geol. Mem. 26*, pp. 477–502, Tulsa, Okla., 1977.

65 Dedman, E. V., J. P. Lindsey, and M. W. Schramm, Jr.: Stratigraphic Modeling: A Step Beyond Bright Spot, *World Oil*, vol. 180, no. 6, pp. 61–65, 1975.

66 Taner, M. T., F. Koehler, and K. A. Alhilali: Estimation and Correction of Near-Surface Time Anomalies, *Geophysics*, vol. 39, pp. 441–463, 1974.

67 Wiggins, R. A., K. L. Larner, and R. D. Wisecup: Residual Static Analysis as a General Linear Inverse Problem, *Geophysics*, vol. 41, pp. 922–938, 1976.

68 Lavergne, M. and C. Willm: Inversion of Seismograms and Pseudo Velocity Logs, *Geophys. Prospect.* vol. 25, no. 2, pp. 231–250, 1977.

69 Lindseth, R. O.: Synthetic Sonic Logs—A Process for Stratigraphic Interpretation, *Geophysics*, vol. 44, pp. 3–26, 1979.

70 Loper, G. B.: Seismic Display System, U. S. Patent No. 2,991,446, July 4, 1961.

71 Savit, C. H.: Method of Displaying Seismic Data, U.S. Patent No. 3,662,325, May 9, 1972.

72 Backus, M. M., and R. L. Chen: Flat Spot Exploration, *Geophys. Prospect.*, vol. 23, pp. 533–577, 1975.

73 Sheriff, R. E.: "Seismic Stratigraphy," International Human Resources Development Corp., Boston, 1980.

74 Beaudry, D., and G. F. Moore: Seismic Stratigraphy and Cenozoic Evolution of West Sumatra Forearc Basin, *Am. Assoc. Petrol. Geol.*, vol. 69, pp. 742–759, 1985.

75 Bortfeld, R.: Reflection and Refraction of Spherical Compressional Waves at Arbitrary Plane Interfaces, *Geophys. Prospect.*, vol. 10, pp. 517–538, 1962.

76 Koefoed, O.: Reflection and Transmission Coefficients for Plane Longitudinal Incident Waves, *Geophys. Prospect.*, vol. 10, pp. 304–351, 1962.

77 Telford, W. M., L. P. Geldart, R. E. Sheriff, and D. A. Keys: "Applied Geophysics," Cambridge Univ. Press, New York, 1982.

78 Backus, M. M., F. Nepomuceno, and J. Cao: The Reflection Seismogram in a Solid Layered Earth, Expanded Abstracts, *52nd Ann. Soc. Explor. Geophys. Meeting*, pp. 218–220, 1982.

79 Ostrander, W. J.: Plane Wave Reflection Coefficients for Gas Sands at Non-Normal Angles of Incidence, Expanded Abstracts, *52nd Ann. Soc. Explor. Geophys. Meeting*, pp. 216–218, 1982.

80 Mitchum, R. M., Jr., P. R. Vail, and S. Thompson, III: Seismic Stratigraphy and Global Changes of Sea Level. Part 2: The Depositional Sequence as a Basic Unit for Stratigraphic Analysis, pp. 53–62, in Ref. 64.

81 Bubb, J. N., and W. G. Hatlelid: Seismic Stratigraphy and Global Changes of Sea Level. Part 10: Seismic Recognition of Carbonate Buildups, pp. 185–204, in Ref. 64.

82 Sheriff, R. E., and L. P. Geldart: "Exploration Seismology. vol. 2: Data Processing and Interpretation," Cambridge Univ. Press, Cambridge, 1983.

83 Neidell, N. S., and J. H. Beard: Progress in Stratigraphic Seismic Exploration and the Definition of Reservoir, Distinguished Authors Series, Soc. Petrol. Engineers of AIME, pp. 709–726, May, 1984.

CHAPTER 10

3-D SEISMIC EXPLORATION

Many geological features in the subsurface that are of interest in hydrocarbon exploration are 3-D in nature: for example, salt diapirs, overthrust and folded belts, major unconformities, and deltaic sands. The 2-D seismic section is, in reality, a cross section of the 3-D seismic wave field. It contains signals coming from all directions, including out of the plane of the profile, although the latter is usually assumed to be part of the signal that comes from the plane of the profile itself. Although out-of-plane reflections are often recognizable by the experienced seismic interpreter, a well-known problem is that the out-of-plane signal gives rise to misties of 2-D migrated sections from a survey. The problem of misties can be viewed as inadequate imaging of the subsurface when 2-D migration is used as a substitute for 3-D migration of seismic data. Three-dimensional migration requires a much denser spatial sampling of the subsurface than is required for 2-D surveys. Having a detailed image of the subsurface certainly makes the interpretation more reliable. In geologically complex areas, 3-D seismic is essential to effective exploration for hydrocarbons. Many 3-D surveys are performed after the discovery well has proved a reservoir exists. In a complicated structural or stratigraphic setting, the field development well locations are chosen after interpreting the 3-D seismic survey.

Special attention must be given to 3-D survey design and acquisition. A typical marine 3-D survey is carried out by shooting parallel lines that are closely spaced (line shooting). A typical land 3-D survey, on the other hand, is carried out by laying out a number of receiver lines parallel to one another and placing the shot points along a line perpendicular to the receiver lines (swath shooting).

In marine 3-D surveys, the shooting direction (boat track) is called the *in-line* direction, whereas in land 3-D surveys the receiver cable is along the in-line direction. The direction perpendicular to the in-line direction is called the *cross-line* direction. In contrast to 2-D surveys in which the line spacing can be 10 km or more, line spacing in 3-D surveys is as small as 50 m. Such a dense coverage requires highly accurate knowledge of shot and receiver locations. The size of the survey area is not only dictated by the areal extent of the target zone in the subsurface but also the aperture size required for adequate migration of the 3-D seismic-data volume for imaging of that target zone. This increases the areal extent of a 3-D survey. Normally, a few million traces are collected during a 3-D survey.

The basic principles of 2-D seismic-data processing still apply to 3-D—particularly hyperbolic moveout and zero-offset migration. In 2-D seismic data processing, traces are sorted into common-midpoint gathers. In 3-D data processing, traces are sorted into common-cell gathers. A cell is a rectangular area on the earth's surface and constitutes the basic element of a grid that covers the entire area of the 3-D survey. A common-cell gather coincides with the common-midpoint gather for swath shooting. Typical cell size is 25 × 25 m for land, and 12.5 × 37.5 m for marine surveys. These gathers are then used in velocity analyses, and common-cell stacks are generated. A particular problem of travel-time deviations from a hyperbolic moveout within a common-cell gather occurs in marine 3-D surveys due to the cable feathering (deviation of the cable from the survey line) in the presence of dipping events. Moreover, in land 3-D surveys, one has to take into account the azimuth-dependent moveout within a common-cell gather. Following the stacking, the 3-D data volume often is migrated in two stages. First, a 2-D migration is applied along the in-line direction. Then the data are sorted, and a second pass of 2-D migration is applied along the cross-line direction. Normally, prior to the second pass of migration, data need to be trace-interpolated along the cross-line direction in order to avoid spatial aliasing of high frequencies at steep dips. [Spatial aliasing is the equivalent of frequency (i.e., time) aliasing along a spatial direction.] (See Secs. 6-3 and 7-2.)

The 3-D data volume is then made available to the interpreter in the form of vertical sections, in both in-line and cross-line directions, as well as horizontal sections, usually called *time slices*. Time slices allow the interpreter to generate contour maps for marker horizons with considerable ease and accuracy. Fault correlations, horizon tracking, map making, horizon flattening, and some image-processing techniques can be accomplished in the interactive environment. An interactive environment enables the geophysicist to interpret effectively and efficiently the large volume of 3-D migrated seismic data.

10-1   WHY 3-D?

Consider the earth model in Fig. 10-1, consisting of a dipping plane interface in a homogeneous medium. Let us examine a line along the dip direction, line *A*.

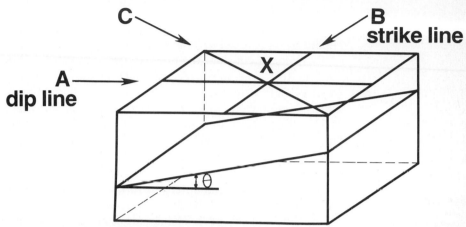

FIGURE 10-1 A simple subsurface model consisting of a single dipping plane interface in a homogeneous medium. Line *A* is in the dip direction, line *B* is in the strike direction, and line *C* is at an arbitrary direction. Data recorded at the intersection point, *X*, will migrate to different subsurface locations as a result of migration of these three lines. Schematic illustrations of the migrations are shown in Figs. 10-2 and 10-3. (*Adapted from Workman.*[1]).

If the survey consisted of lines just in the dip-line direction, the 2-D assumption about the subsurface is adequate. No out-of-plane signal would be recorded, and therefore 2-D migration of these dip lines would be adequate, as shown in Fig. 10-2*a*. Prior to migration, the dipping event is mispositioned, but the lines

FIGURE 10-2 (*a*) Migration along the dip line, *A*, and (*b*) along the strike line, *B*, over the depth model shown in Fig. 10-1. Point *D* after migration is moved updip to *D'* along line *A*, whereas it does not move after migration along the strike line, *B*. A mistie as indicated between the two migrated sections is the result.

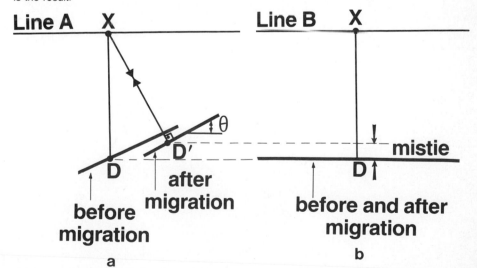

tie; i.e., the reflection *D* arrives at the same time on both the dip and strike lines. Following the 2-D migration, point *D* beneath surface point *X* moves updip to its true subsurface position, *D'*.

Now let us consider the line parallel to the strike direction, line *B*, as shown in Fig. 10-1. The subsurface point *D'* in Fig. 10-2*a* is observed on this line as well as on the dip line just beneath the intersection point *X*. On the strike line, the reflection from the dipping interface would show no dip, as depicted in Fig. 10-2*b*. Since migration does not alter the position of flat, horizontal events, the migrated section along the strike line would be identical to the unmigrated section. If we attempt to tie the dip line *A* with the strike line *B* after migrating both sections, we find a mistie, as indicated in Fig. 10-2*b*.

In general, we encounter subsurface dips in all directions, and the in-line direction is neither in the dip nor the strike direction. Such is the case for line *C*, as shown in Fig. 10-1. The apparent dip perceived by this line is less than the true dip of the plane interface as correctly perceived along the dip line. Let us examine the positioning after migration of point *D* beneath the intersection point *X* for all three lines in a plan view, as shown in Fig. 10-3. Point *D* is moved to the true subsurface position, *D'*, along dip line *A*. The same point does not move after migration along strike line *B*. On the other hand, it is moved to *D''*

FIGURE 10-3   Plan view of the migrations at the intersection point along the three lines indicated in Fig. 10-1. Point *D* moves to *D'*, its true subsurface position, along the dip line, *A*. It does not move on the strike line, *B*. The same point moves to *D''* along line *C*, which is at an arbitrary direction; complete imaging can be achieved by migrating the data once more along the direction perpendicular to *C* so as to move the energy from *D''* to *D'*.

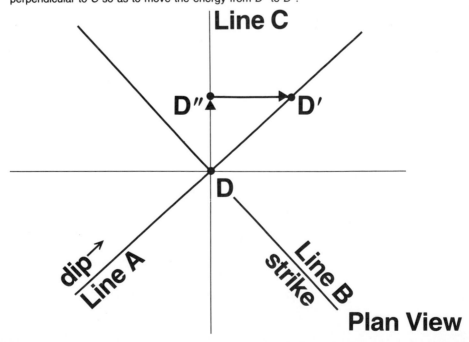

along line C. Note that a second migration pass seems to be needed in the direction perpendicular to line C to move the already migrated energy from D'' to its true subsurface position D'. Before the advent of modern 3-D migration techniques, simple geometrical corrections were used during mapping to tie seismic sections at corners by displacing section lines from their surface locations (Dix, Ref. 17, Chapter 7, p. 284).

Although principles of 3-D migration will be discussed later in the chapter, let us examine some field data in order to assess the interpretational differences between 2-D and 3-D migration. Figure 10-4 shows a stack section and its 2-D and 3-D migrations from a marine 3-D survey. Note the better delineation of the two salt domes and the basin between them after 3-D migration. Often 3-D migration produces sections surprisingly different from those produced by 2-D migration. The example in Fig. 10-5 shows a no-reflection zone on the 2-D migrated section while the same zone contains a series of continuous reflections on the 3-D migrated section that are easily correlated with the reflections away from that zone. The 3-D migration has moved energy into the section from the cross-line direction, with the result that the subsurface structure is more clearly imaged.

We have demonstrated on a number of field-data examples that 3-D migration provides a complete imaging of a 3-D subsurface structural geometry; in contrast, 2-D migration yields inadequate results. Also, 2-D migration introduces misties between the in-line and cross-line directions in the presence of dipping events. Three-dimensional migration eliminates these misties by completing the imaging process. The main difference that affects the interpretation between 2-D seismic and 3-D seismic is the migration procedure. In other words, dense control on top of the target zone, say 25-m trace spacing in the in-line direction and 25-m trace spacing in the cross-line direction, does not itself provide an adequate imaging of the subsurface. It is only when 3-D migration is performed that the complexity of the reflected wave field is reduced, yielding a focused, highly interpretable data set. Adequate spatial sampling is essential, however, for the 3-D migration to yield results free of spatial aliasing effects. In Fig. 10-6 we see the increasingly improved interpretation made from seismic data obtained from increasingly detailed surveying carried out over the years. Three-dimensional surveying is the ultimate in achieving a high degree of accuracy and reliability in the interpretation from an area. Since the 3-D data volume minimizes the amount of interpretational extrapolation, the resulting interpretations tend to increase the success ratio in hydrocarbon exploration or development.

We may summarize advantages of 3-D exploration as follows:

1 The subsurface is real 3-D; the more complex the subsurface—i.e., the greater the degree of three-dimensionality of the subsurface—the more necessary is 3-D exploration. Even in moderate complexity, 2-D migration is inadequate; complete imaging of the subsurface can only be achieved by 3-D migration.

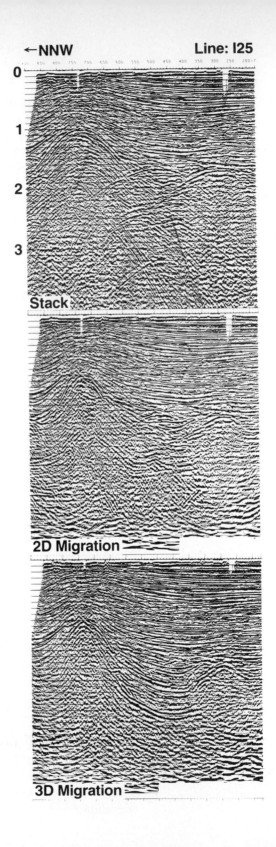

← NNW   Line: I25

Stack

2D Migration

3D Migration

FIGURE 10-4 (a) An in-line stack section from a marine 3-D survey, (b) 2-D migration, (c) 3-D migration. (*Amoco*.)

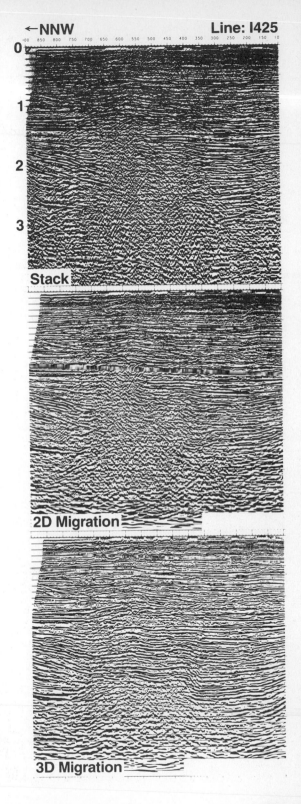

Stack

2D Migration

3D Migration

FIGURE 10-5 (*a*) Another in-line stack section from the same marine 3-D survey as in Fig. 10-4, (*b*) 2-D migration, (*c*) 3-D migration. (*Amoco*.)

Evolution of basal Zechstein structural map

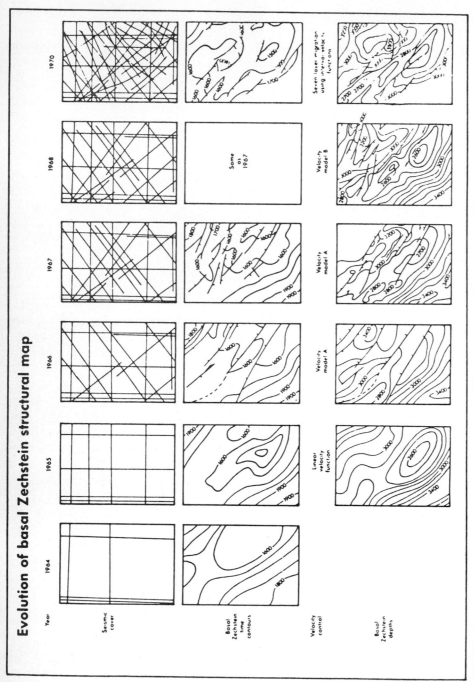

FIGURE 10-6 Progress of seismic exploration over a North Sea structure between the years 1964–1970. As more data were acquired, interpretation has become more detailed and more accurate. (*Homabrook.*[2])

2 Since migration requires adequate spatial sampling of the seismic wave field, 3-D surveys are carried out such that the data to be migrated are contained in a 3-D volume with closely spaced traces in both in-line and cross-line directions. Such detailed coverage in turn provides a more detailed and reliable interpretation of target zones.

10-2   3-D SURVEY DESIGN AND ACQUISITION

The general considerations for land and marine acquisition were discussed in Chaps. 4 and 5. Now we will address the specific considerations for 3-D acquisition. The ultimate goal from a 3-D survey is to obtain a 3-D migrated wave field. The success of the migration depends upon the stack quality as well as the accuracy in velocity estimation. Moreover, there are two other factors that control the fidelity of migration, and they are tied to the design of the field survey.

Migraton Aperture

Figure 10-7a is a depth model that contains a dipping reflector segment CD buried in a homogeneous medium. Zero-offset modeling using normal incidence rays yields the time section depicted in Fig. 10-7b. Although not shown in the figure, the time section would also include diffractions from the edges of the reflecting segment. Migration, while collapsing the diffractions, moves the event $C'D'$ on the time section to its true subsurface position, CD, which is overlaid on the time section for comparison. The horizontal extent of the zone of interest is OA. If we were to confine the profile length during recording to OA, obviously the time section would be blank. If, on the other hand, we were to confine the recording to the profile segment AB, there would be no place for the event $C'D'$ after migration. So, although the target is entirely contained in profile segment OA, the field recording must be over the longer segment, OB. The profile must also be sufficiently long to include most of the diffractions. Additionally, the recording must be sufficiently long to include diffraction tails and dipping events in their entirety. If we were to record only OE, the recorded segment would be $C'D''$, which would only yield part of the true image CD. The length of line (spatial recording length) and maximum recording time (temporal recording length) required to image a given dipping target depends upon the medium velocity and the dip and depth of the target events. The surveyed area and its position on the surface must be carefully chosen based on the migration aperture required to adequately image the target zone of interest.

Shown in Fig. 10-8 is the depth contour map to the top of a fictitious structural trap. The subsurface extent of the structure is indicated by the smaller rectangle. Using the principles discussed above, we can define the actual survey size, namely the recording area shown as the larger rectangle. It is important to note that the survey area does not have to be extended equally

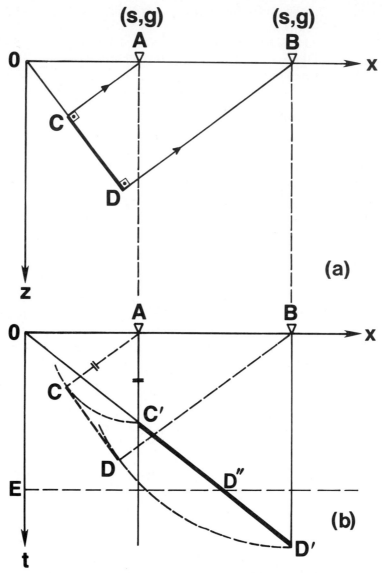

FIGURE 10-7 (a) A depth model consisting of a single dipping reflector segment in a homogeneous medium. (b) Zero-offset time model obtained from normal-incidence rays such as *ACA* and *BDA* using two collocated shot and geophone pairs (s,g). Migration moves the event *C'D'* seen on the time section to its true subsurface position *CD*. (*Modified from Chun and Jacewitz.*[3])

in all directions. The northern flank of the structure is the steepest part and therefore the survey area must be extended most greatly in that direction. Extensions in other directions must be determined similarly. Another consideration in extending the survey area is the required additional length of profile to achieve full coverage over the already extended survey area. So, a typical

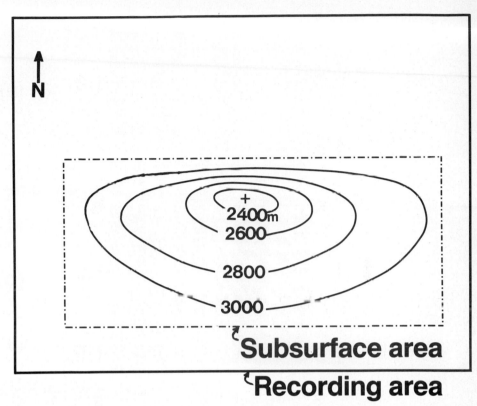

FIGURE 10-8   Size of a 3-D survey over a subsurface structure is normally greater than that of the structure in order to provide for the migration aperture.

subsurface anomaly with a lateral extent of say 3 × 3 km might require a 3-D survey over an area as much as 9 × 9 km.

Spatial Sampling

Consider the synthetic section in Fig. 10-9a, which contains dipping events ranging from 0 to 45° with an increment of 5°. Two narrow bandpass-filtered versions of this section are shown in Fig. 10-9b and c, with passbands 8.75 to 10 Hz and 35 to 40 Hz, respectively. In the low-frequency passband, Fig. 10-9b, the true dips of all the events are easily inferred (the dip directions in Fig. 10-9a and b are in agreement). In the high-frequency passband, however, shown in Fig. 10-9c, events to the right of the arrow do not indicate true dip directions. The dips that the migration process would sense are those in Fig. 10-9c for this frequency band. We see that high frequencies at steep dips are in danger of being migrated to wrong positions, since migration moves events in the apparent updip direction. Spatial aliasing will be further discussed in connection with 3-D migration in Sec. 10-4. However, the problem of spatial aliasing is due to

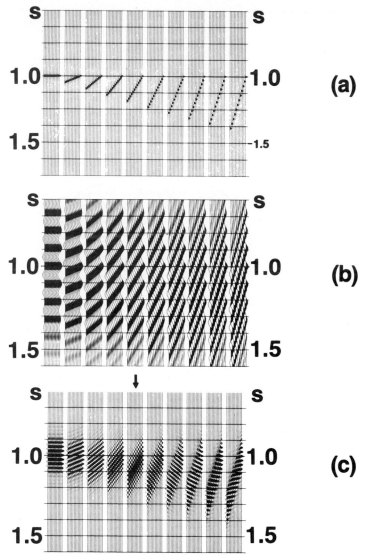

FIGURE 10-9 (a) Broadband dipping events, from 0° to 45°, at 5° increments, (b) narrow bandpass filtering, 8.75 to 10 Hz, and (c) 35 to 40 Hz. No frequencies within the passband 8.75 to 10 Hz are aliased, whereas frequencies within the passband 35 to 40 Hz are aliased for the dips to the right of the arrow. (*Rothman et al.*[6])

too coarse spatial sampling of the wave field to be migrated, namely the stack section. Therefore, care must be given to the choice of receiver spacing in the field as well as the spacing between shot lines, namely the cross-line direction.

From the diagram in Fig. 10-10, we can derive a relationship between trace spacing on a stack section (zero-offset section), dip, and frequency. If we follow normal-incident rays in a constant-velocity earth to two receivers, A and B, we see that the angle between the surface and the wavefront is the true dip of

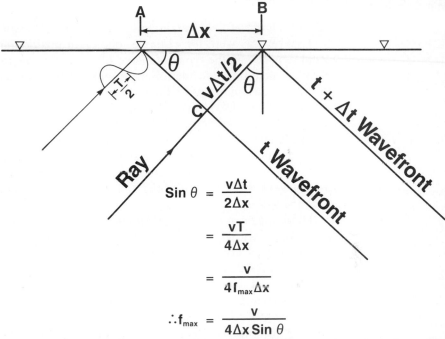

$$\text{Sin } \theta = \frac{v\Delta t}{2\Delta x}$$

$$= \frac{vT}{4\Delta x}$$

$$= \frac{v}{4f_{max}\Delta x}$$

$$\therefore f_{max} = \frac{v}{4\Delta x \, \text{Sin } \theta}$$

FIGURE 10-10   Ray diagram for deriving the threshold frequency for spatial aliasing. For a given dip, θ, velocity, v, and trace spacing Δx, the maximum frequency that is not aliased is f_{max}.

the reflector from which these rays emerged. There will be a time delay Δt equivalent to the travel path CB between the receivers at A and B. Sampling theory requires a minimum of two samples per cycle in order to record the original signal adequately. If the time delay between the arrival at A and at B is half the period T of a given frequency component f of the signal arriving at the receivers, that frequency is at the threshold of being aliased. From the relationship indicated in Fig. 10-10, we note that the maximum frequency that is not aliased gets smaller at increasingly steep dips, lower velocities, and coarser trace spacing (the trace spacing in Fig. 10-10 refers to that on a stack section).

From the relationship indicated in Fig. 10-10, we can derive an optimum trace spacing in the in-line and cross-line directions in the field if we have a regional knowledge of the velocity field and of dip in the subsurface. Typical trace spacings in the in-line and cross-line directions in marine 3-D surveys are between 12.5 and 25 m and 50 and 100 m, respectively. Even if trace spacing in the cross-line direction is chosen as small as possible, it is usually greater than that in the in-line direction for economic reasons. Marine 3-D surveys therefore usually require trace interpolation along the cross-line direction after stack and before 3-D migration. Typical trace spacings in the in-line and cross-line directions in land 3-D surveys are between 12.5 and 25 m and 25 and 50 m, respectively. Therefore, trace interpolation may not be required for some land 3-D surveys.

Other Considerations

Almost all of the field operational aspects of 2-D acquisition are applicable to 3-D surveys as well, for example, choice of positioning and recording equipment depends on the type of field conditions. The operating environment must also be taken into consideration. In marine environments, water depth, tides, currents, sea conditions, fishing and shipping activity, obstacles such as drilling platforms, wrecks, reefs, fish traps, and on land, environmental restrictions, accessibility, topography, cultivation, and demographic restrictions are some factors that affect the survey design and acquisition. In some parts of a survey area, because of such restrictions, one does not achieve the desired fold of coverage or the shot and receiver spacing planned. Positioning is important for 3-D surveys, since data are collected with dense spatial sampling as opposed to reconnaisance 2-D surveys.

Three-dimensional surveys require a relatively dense coverage of an entire area in contrast to 2-D surveys, which require only linear traverses. It follows that increased efficiency will be obtained in 3-D surveying by increasing the areal extent of data obtained at one time. In land operations efficiency is sought by laying out a number of parallel receiver lines at one time so that a wide swath is covered.

Similarly in marine surveying, two-ship operations in which both ships tow sources and receivers while traversing parallel tracks are sometimes used (see Fig. 5-11). Since the early to mid-1980s operations have been conducted in which one ship tows two source arrays displaced on either side of the ship's track by paravanes. Firing of the two arrays must necessarily be alternated to prevent interference. More efficiency is obtained when two receiver arrays are towed with the source in the middle.

Marine Acquisition Geometry

A marine 3-D survey involves shooting a number of closely spaced, parallel 2-D lines (line shooting). (In the shallow water environment, the swath shooting technique that is used in land acquisition is preferred.) The direction that the ship sails is called the in-line direction and the direction perpendicular to it is called the cross-line direction. The receiver cable is subject to a certain amount of sideways drift (*feathering*), from the ideal streamer line due to crosscurrents. Cable feathering is illustrated in Fig. 10-11, and cable shapes associated with a selected set of shot points from a marine 3-D survey are shown in Fig. 10-12. The angle between the actual cable position and the shot-line direction (the ship track) is called the *feathering angle*. As can be seen from the actual cable shapes in Fig. 10-12, this angle is not always constant, even along the cable associated with a single shot. Assuming the simplistic cable shape shown in Fig. 10-11, we see that although we may be shooting along line 2, we are actually recording data at midpoints associated with the neighboring lines. For a typical feathering angle of 10° and a cable length of 2400 m, the midpoint

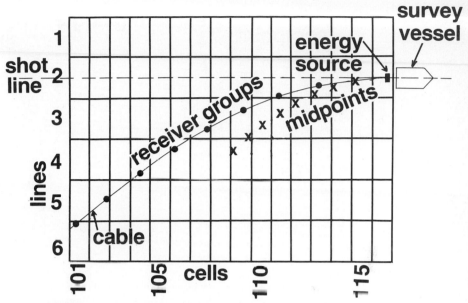

FIGURE 10-11   Crosscurrents cause feathering of the marine cable, deflecting it from the shot-line direction. This, in turn, causes spreading of midpoints in the cross-line direction. Data are sorted into common-cell gathers; within each cell, normally there are midpoints associated with more than one line. (*Adapted from Workman.*[1])

associated with the far receiver is offset more than 200 m from the shot line. Such an offset represents a four-line displacement at a 50-m line spacing.

Clearly, the midpoint distribution in the cross-line direction will not be as regular as implied by Fig. 10-11 due to the significant variations in the cable shape during recording, as shown in Fig. 10-12. It is then extremely important to know not only the shot location but exactly where each of the receivers is located along the cable. Navigation data collected aboard the survey vessel normally includes such information as the ship location, the source location, and cable compass locations. Along a typical marine cable, there are 8 to 12 digital compasses. Readings of bearings from these devices allow the computation of the cable shape based on a curve-fitting procedure that takes into account any anomalous measurements. By precise determination of the shot and receiver coordinates, we are able to determine the midpoint locations and therefore are able to gather them into cells during acquisition, as shown in Fig. 10-11, for determining the subsurface coverage. Navigation data are also analyzed during the processing stage, and an extensive quality control is carried out in deriving the final shot-receiver locations. Cable shapes and source locations from a 3-D survey are shown in Fig. 10-13 in their entirety. Note the nice illustration of cable feathering especially apparent at the edges of the survey. Midpoint locations associated with the source-receiver locations given in this figure are plotted in Fig. 10-14. We see that there are some "holes" in

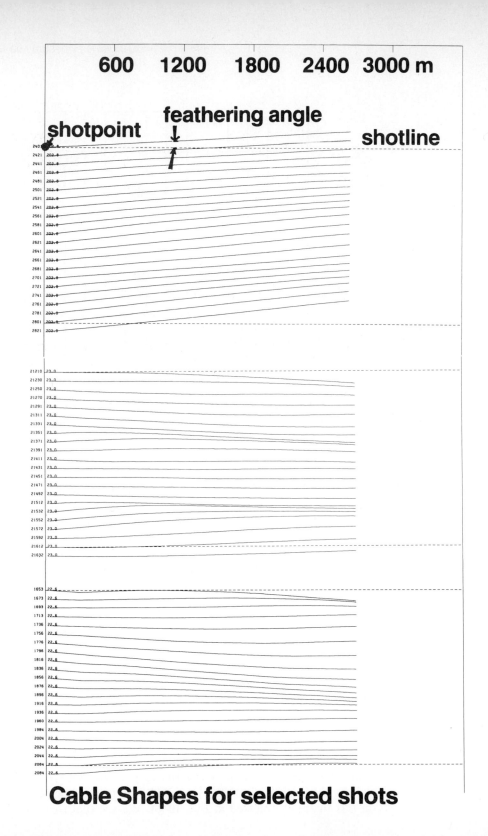

Cable Shapes for selected shots

the coverage over the survey area. It is important to discover these low-fold areas during the acquisition stage. More lines can then be collected at appropriate locations. Otherwise, when such deficiencies are discovered in the processing stage, it is far more costly to send the vessel back for further acquisition. If the ship does not return to collect data for the "holes," the success of the entire costly project is risked. The cost-benefit economics of 3-D surveys demand that every effort be made to ensure adequate data collection in the first stage. Quality control work is thus performed onboard during acquisition in order to monitor the coverage.

Land Acquisition Geometry

Depending upon terrain, recording system, various logistical considerations processing software demands, and other constraints, a variety of 3-D land acquisition schemes has been used. The data order required by the processing center's software must be accommodated so that reasonably quick turnaround time can be achieved. Through the years, however, more and more land 3-D surveys are acquired with the *swath shooting* technique. In swath shooting, the receiver cables are laid out in parallel lines and shots are positioned in the perpendicular direction. An example is provided in Fig. 10-15. In this particular case, six receiver cables were laid out, each with 80 receiver groups, 50 m apart. The distances between receiver cables from left to right were 100, 200, 100, 200, and 100 m. Shooting was in the perpendicular direction to the swath starting from far left, moving in and away to the right of the swath. This pattern of shooting provides a wide range of azimuthal coverage, which is a matter of concern during velocity analysis (as will be discussed in Sec. 10-3). The main advantage of swath shooting is its economic benefit. As the shooting progresses, the receiver cable sections are moved up from the rear of the swath to the forward end while shooting continues. The shooting geometry shown in Fig. 10-15 provided a common-cell gather in cells measuring 25×25 m. Once one swath is completed, another one parallel to it is recorded, and this procedure is repeated over the entire survey area. The complete survey plan including the 12 swaths of receivers and shot locations is shown in Fig. 10-16. Due to operating conditions, a uniform coverage was not achievable over the whole of the survey. For the most part, the average fold for the survey shown in Fig. 10-16 was 12 increasing to 24 toward the bottom right-hand side of the area.

FIGURE 10-12   Cable shapes for selected shots. Note the change in the cable shape varying from shot to shot, making the feathering angle nonuniform. Variations in the cable shape then cause variations in the distribution of midpoints within cells. (*Western Geophysical*.)

FIGURE 10-13 Cable shapes and source locations for an entire marine 3-D survey. (*Western Geophysical.*)

FIGURE 10-14 Midpoint locations derived from the cable shapes shown in Fig. 10-13 This type of plot is useful in the acquisition stage to verify complete coverage of survey area. Holes are filled in during the acquisition stage. (*Western Geophysical.*)

Lines

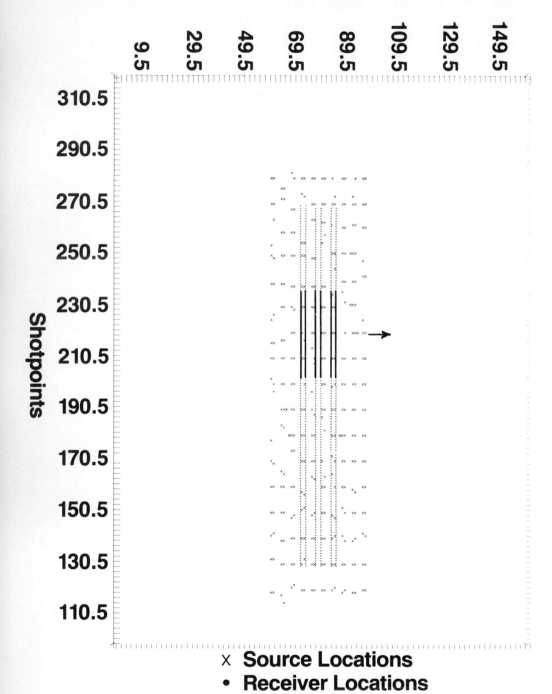

X **Source Locations**
• **Receiver Locations**

FIGURE 10-15 Swath shooting geometry used in a land 3-D survey. Solid lines indicate the actual receiver cables for a particular shot line aligned with the arrow indicated. Receiver cables (80 groups each)
and shots are moved up along the swath. When the end of the swath is reached, the next one is
started until all of the survey area is covered. (*Western Geophysical.*)

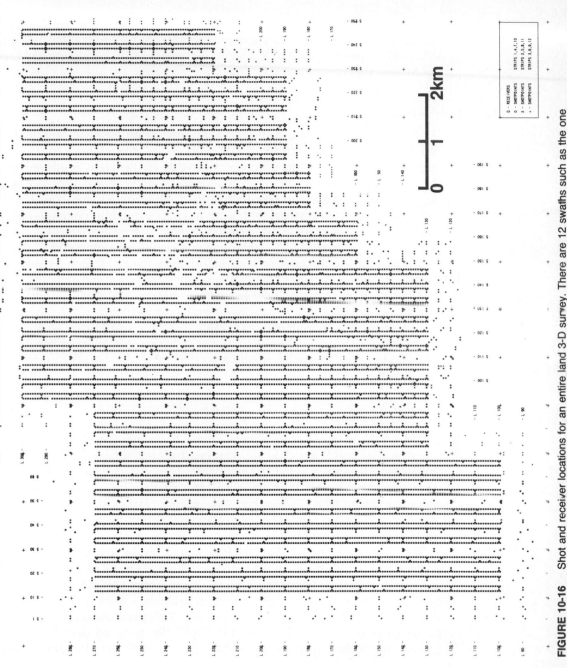

FIGURE 10-16 Shot and receiver locations for an entire land 3-D survey. There are 12 swaths such as the one shown in Fig. 10-15. Coverage varies over the survey from 12- to 24-fold. (NAM.)

Swath shooting may not always be possible due to environmental and topographic restrictions. For example, coverage over a topographic high can be achieved by shooting around it, making a complete loop with shots and receivers located on the loop.

10-3 PROCESSING OF 3-D DATA

Undoubtedly, almost all aspects of 2-D seismic-data processing are applicable in 3-D data processing with additional effort on velocity analysis, stacking, and migration. Performed in the preprocessing stage are the steps of editing the bad traces containing high-level noise, geometric spreading correction, deconvolution and trace balancing, and field statics applications (for land data). In conventional 2-D processing, traces are next collected into common-midpoint (CMP) gathers, whereas in 3-D processing traces are collected into common-cell gathers. A common-cell gather coincides with a common-midpoint gather in the case of swath shooting. Sorting into common-cell gathers introduces special problems, such as azimuthal variations of the normal moveout (NMO) within the cell in the case of land geometry, and travel-time deviations from the hyperbolic moveout due to scatter of midpoints within a cell in the case of marine geometry. After NMO and residual statics, CMP stack is performed. Migration of 3-D data involves a first-pass 2-D migration in the in-line direction followed by trace interpolation and a second-pass 2-D migration in the cross-line direction.

Marine Processing

Following the preprocessing, data are ready for common-cell sorting. As illustrated in Fig. 10-11, a grid is superimposed on the survey area consisting of cells whose dimension in the in-line direction is half the receiver group spacing (equivalent to the CMP spacing in 2-D processing), and the dimension in the cross-line direction is the nominal line spacing. Traces that fall within a cell make up a common-cell gather, and they are not all from the same shot line because of cable feathering.

Shown on the right of Fig. 10-17 is a single cell associated with the field geometry depicted on the left of the same figure. The cell size is 12.5 m in the in-line (shot-line) direction and 50 m in the cross-line direction. Different symbols in the cell on the right represent midpoints associated with different shot lines and illustrate *cross-line smearing*. This particular cell contains midpoints from six different lines. In Fig. 10-17 the midpoint distribution corresponds to the ideal case of constant feathering angle over the entire survey.

FIGURE 10-17 A marine recording geometry on the left (line shooting) and an individual cell with midpoint locations indicated on the right. The latter illustrates the midpoint scattering in cells. (*Bentley and Yang*.[7]) The different symbols in the individual cell represent different shot lines.

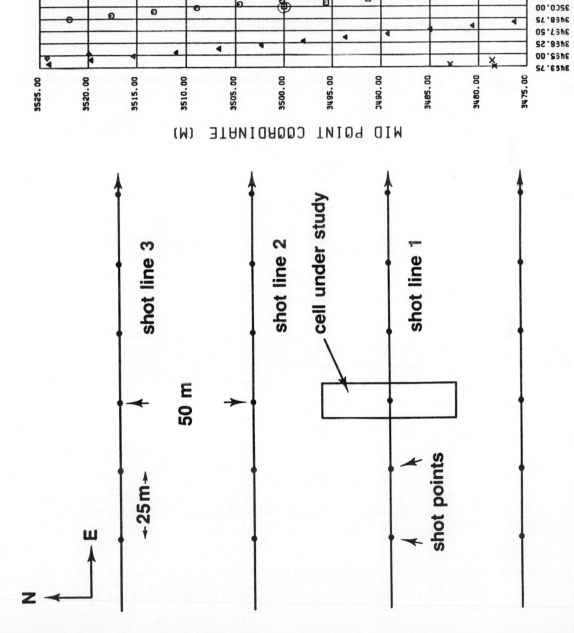

MID POINT COORDINATE (M)

MID POINT COORDINATE (M)

411

Moreover, the shooting direction is assumed to be the same for all the shot lines that contribute midpoints to this cell. In reality, midpoint distribution within a cell is not necessarily uniform because cable shape can vary from shot to shot and line to line (Fig. 10-12). Sometimes, midpoints may be clustered at one part of the cell; that is, the centroid of midpoints may not necessarily be at the center of the cell. Moreover, fold and midpoint distribution can vary from cell to cell: Some cells may contain more traces than others, and some cells may have a less uniform distribution of midpoints than others. Figure 10-18 is the plot of cell midpoint multiplicity (fold) for the midpoint locations of Fig. 10-14 and the cable shapes of Fig. 10-13. Note that the fold of coverage is not uniform over the survey area. Such irregularity could produce a lack of consistency in the degree of accuracy in velocity estimation and variations in the stacked amplitudes. We must consider some modifications to the way we do the common-cell sorting.

Sometimes, a slight translation and rotation of the grid imposed on the survey area may remedy the problem. Such a grid optimization may yield a more uniform midpoint distribution within each cell and even improve the uniformity of the fold of coverage over the survey. A common practice is to permit cells to be of unequal size. Expanding the size of the cell in the cross-line direction as needed can yield a uniform fold of coverage. Expanding in this fashion allows including more midpoints into the cell from the neighboring cells. Although the same midpoint may be used in more than one cell, one can impose restrictions on the offset range and multiplicity to prevent the number of such midpoints from being excessive.

The problem with common-cell sorting is not solved by restoring only uniformity in the fold of coverage. As mentioned earlier, the centroid of midpoints may not necessarily coincide with the center of the cell. If the centroid departs significantly from the center, we may consider stacking onto the centroid rather than to the cell center. Such irregular stack points will, of course, produce irregular spacing of the stack traces in the cross-line direction. Trace interpolation can, however, create equally spaced data in the cross-line direction. The result is a valid simulation of stacking with respect to cell centers. The required trace interpolation does not normally cost extra since it is a routine step in 3-D migration.

Finally, with common-cell sorting, there is the problem of travel-time deviations from hyperbolic moveout resulting from cable feathering. Let us assume that the cable is straight with constant feathering angle. Consider the single cell and the field geometry shown in Fig. 10-17. The midpoint distribution within this cell corresponds to a constant feathering angle of 10°. We will work with a

---

FIGURE 10-18   Midpoints whose locations are shown in Fig. 10-14 after sorting into common-cell gathers yield the fold of coverage shown here. A thin line indicates a cell containing 1 to 48 midpoints; a thick line, more than 48 midpoints. Note the nonuniformity of the fold in several parts of the survey. (*Western Geophysical.*)

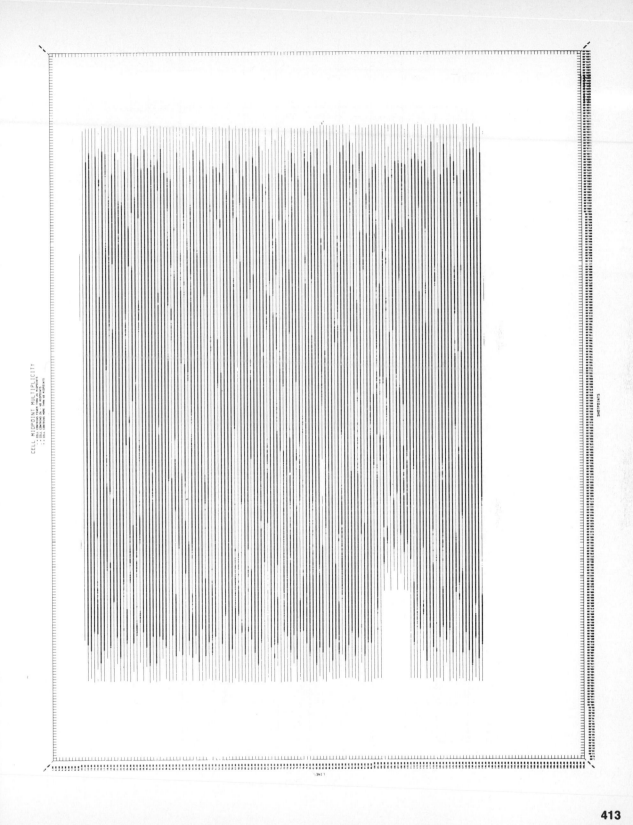

CELL MIDPOINT MULTIPLICITY

SHOTPOINTS

413

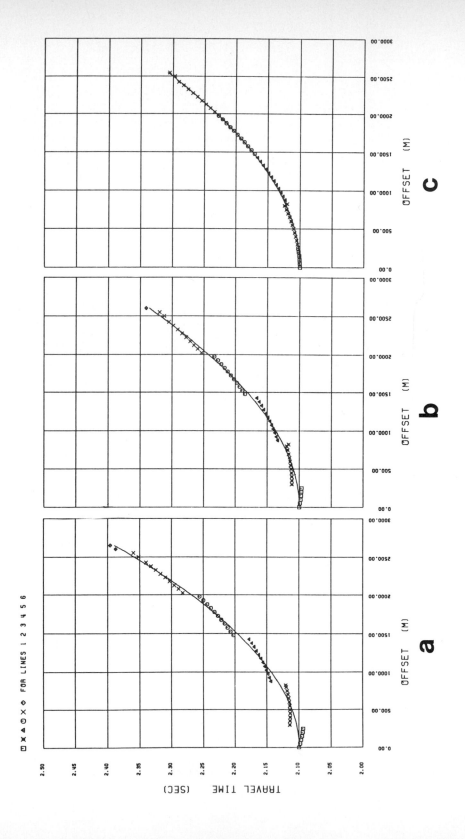

simple earth model containing a single dipping event with a dip angle of 30° and a constant-velocity medium above the dipping interface.

Shown in Fig. 10-19 are travel-time curves for three different shooting directions: (*a*) strike-line shooting, that is, no dip along the in-line direction, but a maximum amount of cross-dip, (*b*) shot line at 45° azimuth with respect to the dip direction, and (*c*) dip-line shooting—that is, no dip perceived along the cross-line direction. The various symbols represent the reflection arrival times from different lines. The solid curve corresponds to the "ideal" hyperbolic moveout expected when all midpoints in the cell coincide with the cell center (i.e., no cable feathering). Note that different lines contribute to different portions of the travel-time curves. Normally, for a single dipping event, 2-D recording geometry would yield a hyperbolic moveout curve. It is important to realize that as the cross-dip increases and the cable feathers, travel times deviate more and more from the ideal hyperbolic moveout curve. The worst case occurs when shooting in the strike direction, as shown in Fig. 10-19*a*. For this idealized case with constant feathering angle, straight cable shape, and a single dipping event in a homogeneous medium, travel-time deviation increases with increasing feathering angle, cross-dip, and cross-line dimension of the cell. Moreover, it is more significant at lower velocities and shallow depths.

If we do a common-cell stack along the best-fit hyperbolic path as shown in Fig. 10-19*a*, we should expect loss of high frequencies. The question is how significant is this high-cut action due to scatter of midpoints in the cross-line direction in a cell. By measuring the time differences between the ideal hyperbolic path and the actual moveout curve in Fig. 10-19*a*, we can derive the time-shift histogram plotted in Fig. 10-20*a* along with the amplitude spectrum that results from stacking with those time shifts (Fig. 10-20*b*). Note the high-cut action of the misaligned stacking; the -6-dB amplitude level is at about 70 Hz.

In summary, when there are crosscurrents, they give rise to cable feathering. The resulting deviation of the receiver positions from the line of survey results in scattering of midpoints within a cell in the cross-line direction. If the shooting direction is such that a dipping interface has a cross-dip component, the travel times associated with that interface from a common-cell gather deviate from the ideal hyperbolic moveout. This, in turn, causes smearing of the data during stacking and acts as a high-cut filter. The cutoff frequency is primarily a function of the amount of cross-dip, reflection time, and velocity.

Although there are different approaches for minimizing the cross-line smear, it often does not have a significant impact on the frequency content of the stacked traces. From the amplitude spectrum of the histogram in Fig. 10-20*b*, it

FIGURE 10-19   Travel-time deviations from hyperbolic moveout caused by cable feathering. Travel times and the least-squares fitted hyperbolic moveout curves associated with (*a*) strike-line shooting, (*b*) shooting in the direction of downdip azimuth of 45°, and (*c*) dip-line shooting. These travel times were derived from a single planar interface with a dip of 30° in a homogeneous medium. Feathering angle is 10° and midpoint distribution in the cell is shown in Fig. 10-17. (*Bentley and Yang.*[7])

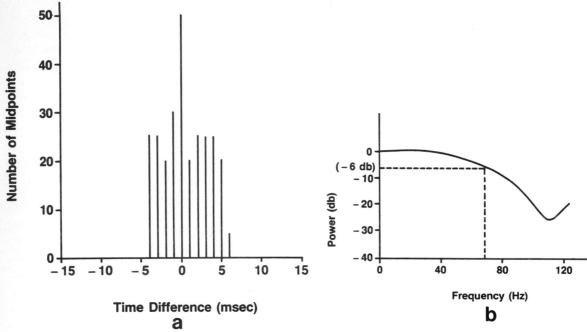

Time Difference (msec)

a

Frequency (Hz)

b

FIGURE 10-20   (*a*) The time-difference histogram associated with the scatter of midpoints along the cross-line direction. This distribution of time shifts was derived from the travel-time deviations from the hyperbolic moveout curves shown in Fig. 10-19*a*. (*b*) The resulting amplitude spectrum suggests that high frequencies are attenuated due to the midpoint scattering (cross-line smearing). (*Bentley and Yang*.[7])

is apparent that the cutoff frequency may be beyond the signal bandwidth, so that within the signal bandwidth not much attenuation takes place. If the problem of cross-line smearing is serious, a CMP location correction may be required. That correction involves mapping travel times associated with all the midpoints onto a specified midpoint location, normally the cell center (Meinardus and McMahon[8]). The procedure requires dip information derived from a velocity model from the survey area; and it essentially involves a linear moveout correction. We will not concern outselves with details of the procedure; we shall, however, demonstrate the use of such a correction using the model example from the above reference. Shown in Fig. 10-21*a* is a single cell

FIGURE 10-21   (*a*) A common-cell gather containing midpoints from five different shot lines in the same direction; (*b*) common-cell gather data for a dipping reflector with a nonzero cross-dip angle. Segments *A, B, C, D,* and *E* come from midpoints 1–4, 5–16, 17–28, 29–41, and 42–48, respectively. Travel times can be fitted to a hyperbola and moveout correction applied as in (*c*). Stacking of these traces would cause loss of high frequencies as illustrated in Fig. 10-20 (cross-line smear). After midpoint-location correction, all midpoints shown in (*a*) are mapped onto the cell center and the moveout curve is simpler (*d*). Stacking of the traces after the midpoint-location and moveout correction (*e*) preserves all useful frequencies. (*Meinardus and McMahon*.[8])

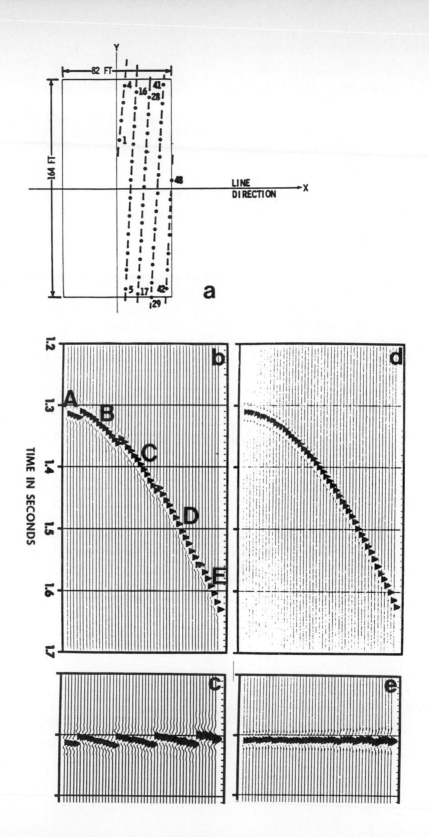

containing 48 midpoints from five different shot lines in the same direction. The earth model consists of a single dipping reflector with cross-line dip of 30° and in-line dip of 45°. Note the discontinuities along the travel-time curve shown in the common-cell gather data in Fig. 10-21b. Each of the five lines contributes to different parts of the moveout curve, A, B, C, D, and E. Fitting the best hyperbolic moveout curve to this gather and applying the appropriate moveout correction yield the gather in Fig. 10-21c. Stacking these traces would clearly cause attenuation of high frequencies, as illustrated in Fig. 10-20. To make the midpoint location correction is to map the travel times in Fig. 10-21b to those in Fig. 10-21d. Following the NMO correction, a better-quality stack trace results (Fig. 10-21e) because there is no cross-line smearing.

The problem of cross-line smearing may be compounded by a large azimuthal range of shots and receivers. Such is the case in Fig. 10-22 where the cell contains midpoints from five lines—two shot in one direction (traces 29 through 48), and the other three shot in the other directon (traces 1 through 28). Shooting in opposite directions would make the effective azimuth range twice the feathering angle. Although we can correct for the midpoint scattering, there is still a discontinuity along the corrected moveout curve (Fig. 10-22d) due to the source-receiver azimuthal variation. As shown later in this section (Fig. 10-24), the NMO depends not only on dip but also on source-receiver azimuth measured from the dip-line direction. One may use different velocities to do the NMO correction for segments A and B in Fig. 10-22d; the result is shown in Fig. 10-22e.

After the data are sorted into common-cell gathers, the velocities are determined. In this respect, there is no difference between 2-D and 3-D data processing. In 2-D, several neighboring CMP gathers are included in the velocity analysis for increasing S/N. Similarly, a number of common-cell gathers, say five in the in-line and five in the cross-line direction making a total of 25 common-cell gathers, are included into the velocity analysis. As in the 2-D case, velocity analyses are performed at certain intervals, typically half a kilometer, along selected in-lines that may be as much as half a kilometer apart. Geologic structure variations signal the need to perform velocity analyses to account for the dip dependency of stacking velocities. Results of the velocity analyses at selected control points are then used to derive the 3-D velocity field for all of the common-cell gathers over the entire survey. Three-dimensional

---

FIGURE 10-22   (a) A common-cell gather containing midpoints from five different shots. Traces 1 to 28 come from lines shot in one direction and traces 29 to 48 come from lines shot in the opposite direction. (b) Common-cell gather data for a dipping reflector with nonzero cross-dip angle; (c) the same gather after NMO correction; (d) the gather in (b) after midpoint-location correction; (e) the gather in (d) after NMO correction based on azimuth-dependent velocities (one velocity for segment A and another one for segment B). Note that even after midpoint-location correction, the moveout curve is composed of two segments, A and B, associated with two shooting directions opposite to one another. (*Meinardus and McMahon.*[8])

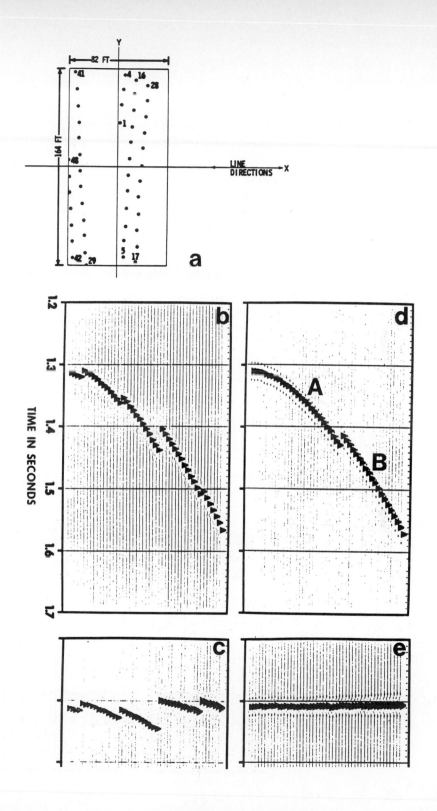

interpolation of the velocity functions between the control points usually yields a satisfactory velocity field.

Land Processing

Land 3-D surveys are commonly acquired by swath shooting and produce common-cell gathers in which all midpoints coincide with the cell center. Large variations in the source-receiver azimuths, however, create travel-time deviations similar to those caused by midpoint scattering in marine surveys. Shown in Fig. 10-23a is a recording geometry comprising a range of shot-receiver azimuths. The reflections from a dipping interface do not align along a hyperbolic moveout (Fig. 10-23b). Using a single velocity for NMO correction (Fig.

FIGURE 10-23 (a) Recording geometry with a range (Δθ) of shot-receiver azimuths commonly encountered in swath shooting. (b) Common-midpoint gather consisting of 10 traces. (c) Moveout correction based on the velocity derived from the best-fit hyperbola. (d) Moveout correction based on azimuth-dependent velocities. (*Meinardus and McMahon.*[8])

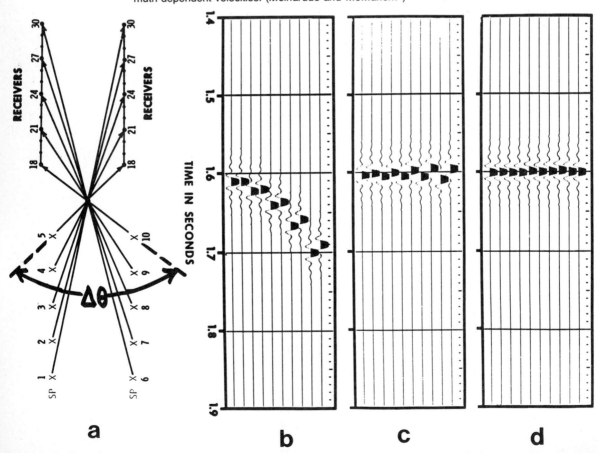

10-23c) would yield a stack trace with high frequencies attenuated in a manner similar to that encountered in cable feathering. Stack attenuation increases with increasing shot-receiver azimuth range (Meinardus and McMahon[8]). If this attenuation is serious, one would have to correct for the shot-receiver azimuth (Fig. 10-23d) before stacking. Levin[9] showed that the moveout velocity for a dipping reflector is not only dip dependent but is also a function of source-receiver azimuth. Shown in Fig. 10-24 is the 3-D geometry for a dipping event and the expression for the moveout velocity. Azimuth is measured from the dip-line direction. Figure 10-22d suggests a way of correcting for the source-receiver azimuth. One may group the midpoints into different ranges of azimuths and use different velocities for moveout correction. Levin's relation is the equation of an ellipse in polar coordinates. The radial coordinate is the NMO velocity, and the polar angle is the azimuth. The velocity ellipse can be constructed based on moveout velocities measured in three different directions (Fig. 10-25). Lehmann and Houba[10] discuss several practical aspects of such

FIGURE 10-24   Geometry for deriving Levin's[9] relation for the NMO velocity associated with a dipping reflecting interface with an arbitrary orientation in the subsurface.

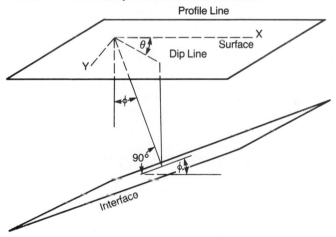

$$V_{NMO} = V/(1 - \sin^2\phi\cos^2\theta)^{1/2}$$
$$\phi = \text{Dip Angle}$$
$$\theta = \text{Azimuth Angle}$$
$$\text{Special Case: } \theta = 0$$
$$V_{NMO} = V/\cos\phi$$

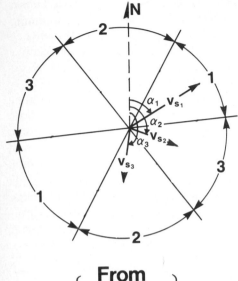

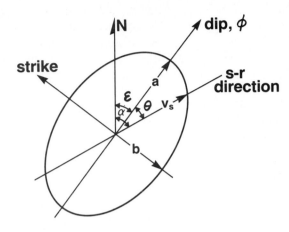

From
$$V_{s_1}, V_{s_2}, V_{s_3}$$
$$\alpha_1, \alpha_2, \alpha_3$$
find
a, b

From a, b:

$$v = b$$

$$\phi = \cos^{-1}(b/a)$$

$$\varepsilon = \text{down dip azimuth} = \alpha - \theta$$

$$v_s = v/(1 - \sin^2\phi \cos^2\theta)^{1/2}$$

FIGURE 10-25 The NMO–velocity relationship derived from the geometry in Fig. 10-24 is the equation of an ellipse in polar coordinates. The radial coordinate represents the NMO velocity at a given azimuth which is the polar angle. By subgrouping traces from a common-midpoint gather into three different azimuths ($\alpha_1, \alpha_2, \alpha_3$), one can estimate the stacking velocities (V_{s1}, V_{s2}, V_{s3}) along those azimuths. Knowing the stacking velocities in three different directions enables one to construct the ellipse (i.e., to define a and b, the major and minor axes, respectively), and thereby to use the proper stacking velocity for each individual trace in the gather.

measurement. Once the velocity ellipse is determined, each trace in the CMP gather is moveout-corrected with the velocity along the shot-receiver azimuth associated with that midpoint. Although azimuthal variations in velocity may be observable on velocity spectra, it may not make a significant impact on stacking. Moreover, one may not have enough azimuth range of shots and receivers to be able to define the velocity ellipse with sufficient accuracy.

Both cable feathering and shot-receiver azimuth problems need to be examined for a given survey to assess their significance prior to making corrections for them. The problems of cable feathering and source-receiver azimuth are significant only in the presence of dipping events or lateral velocity variations.

10-4 3-D MIGRATION

In order to gain a basic understanding of 3-D migration, we consider a point scatterer buried in a constant-velocity medium. The travel-time curve from the point scatterer in 2-D is a hyperbola. One can visualize the 3-D response to be the hyperboloid as shown in Fig. 10-26a. Migration in 2-D amounts to summing amplitudes along the diffraction hyperbola and placing the result at the apex of the hyperbola. The same idea can be extended to 3-D; migration in 3-D should amount to summing amplitudes over the surface of the hyperboloid and placing the result at the apex of the hyperboloid as illustrated in Fig. 10-26a. Typically, in the case of 2-D migration, data values from the intersections of the hyperbola with as many as 300 traces may be summed to produce the migrated data point. This implies that in 3-D as many as 70,000 data values may have to be included in each summation.

Fortunately, there is a much more practical alternative to brute force summing over the hyperboloidal surface. As shown in Fig. 10-26b, first we may sum along hyperbolic cross sections in the y direction, say the in-line direction, and place the resulting amplitudes at the local apexes, such as A_0, A_1, A_2, A_3. The resulting partial sums collapse the hyperboloid to a hyperbola in the plane perpendicular to the direction of the first summations. This hyperbola consists of the local apexes and is contained in the cross-line section. The second step involves summing the energy along the hyperbola of local apexes and placing the result at its apex, A_0; A_0, also the apex of the hyperboloid, is the correct position for the final sum as shown in Fig. 10-26a.

Actually, this two-step approach is supported by theory described in several publications (Claerbout,[11] Gibson et al.,[12] Jacubowicz and Levin[13]). Computationally efficient, it consists of two successive 2-D migrations: (1) migration in the in-line direction, (2) transposing the results from the first step and migrating in the cross-line direction.

Although two field-data examples were used to emphasize the importance of 3-D migration as far as complete imaging of the subsurface (Figs. 10-4 and 10-5), the point is worth a further discussion based on model data. Shown in Fig. 10-27 is an earth model consisting of two interfaces; the shallow interface contains a normal fault while the deep interface contains a tight syncline and an equally tight anticline. Although this model is 2-D, if the shooting direction is not the same as the dip direction (EW), the stack section would contain some energy reflecting from out of the plane of recording. Consider a 3-D seismic survey over this structural model where the shooting direction is at a 45° azimuthal angle from the dip direction (NE, SW). Let us further consider one of these parallel lines that coincides with the subsurface cross section in Fig. 10-27b. The resulting zero-offset section is shown in Fig. 10-28a. The 2-D migration in Fig. 10-28b has neither delineated the normal fault nor resolved the synclinal and anticlinal features; imaging of the subsurface is inadequate. Complete imaging is achieved by 3-D migration as shown in Fig. 10-28c.

There is one practical problem requiring our attention in 3-D migration. A typical 3-D survey has a line spacing (which is equivalent to trace spacing in the cross-line direction) that is normally coarser than the trace spacing in the in-line direction, perhaps as much as four times as great. Such coarse spacing gives rise to spatial aliasing in the cross-line direction. Trace interpolation must be

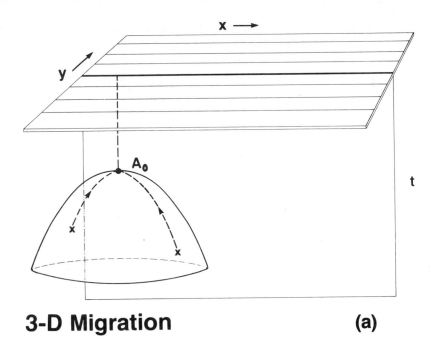

3-D Migration

(a)

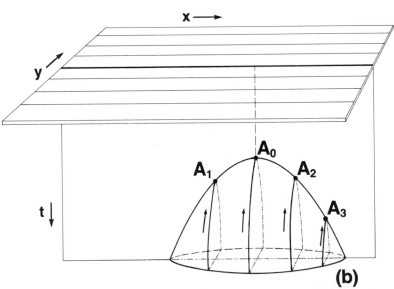

(b)

FIGURE 10-26   (a) The three-dimensional, zero-offset response of a point scatterer is a hyperboloid, (b) two-pass 2-D migration is an efficient method of 3-D migration. First, amplitudes are summed along the hyperbolic paths parallel to the y axis and placed at their apexes, such as A_0, A_1, A_2, A_3. The apexes make up a hyperbola in the perpendicular direction, the x axis. The second step in 3-D migration is summing these amplitudes along the indicated hyperbola and placing the amplitude at the apex, A_0. (*Gibson et al.*[12])

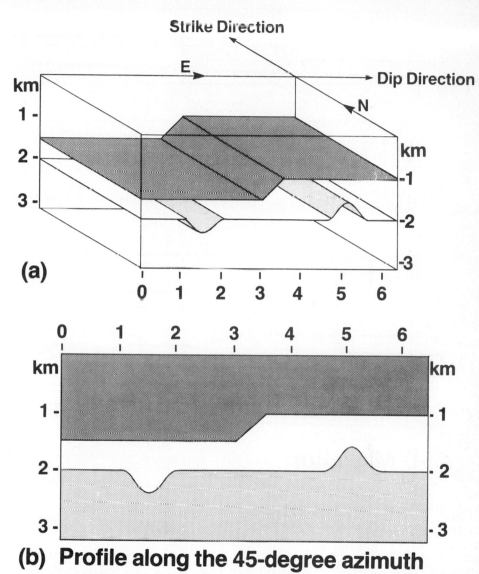

(b) Profile along the 45-degree azimuth

FIGURE 10-27   (a) An earth model consisting of two layers, (b) profile along the 45° azimuth. (*Gibson et al.*[12])

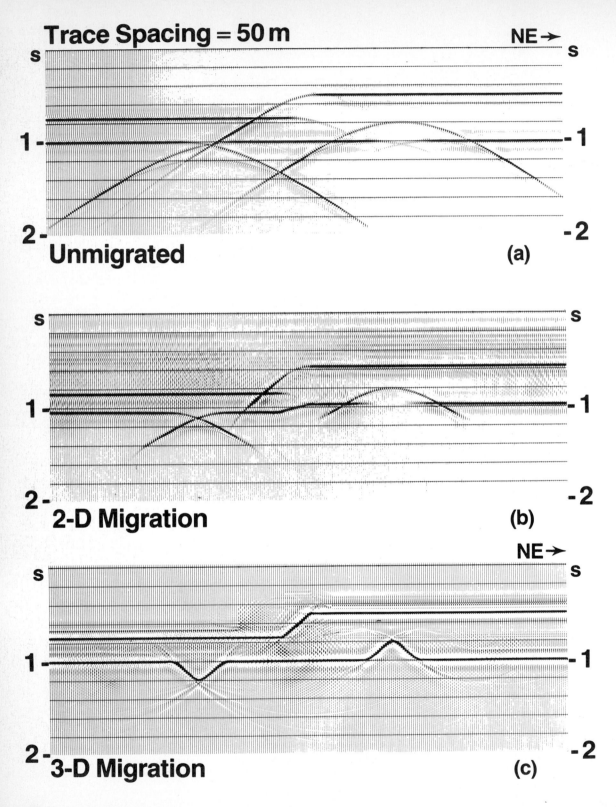

Trace Spacing = 50 m

NE→

Unmigrated (a)

2-D Migration (b)

NE→

3-D Migration (c)

incorporated into the 3-D migration procedure to overcome this problem. A flow graph is shown below:

3-D stack data

↓

2-D migration in the in-line direction

↓

Sort data into cross lines

↓

Trace interpolation

↓

2-D migration in the cross-line direction

↓

3-D migration completed

Trace Interpolation

The problem of spatial aliasing was reviewed in Sec. 10-2. Trace interpolation yields a finer spatial sampling, which in turn prevents high frequencies from being aliased at steep dips. If the trace spacing is 75 m in the cross line direction, one may have to do a 3:1 interpolation to obtain sufficient spatial sampling within the signal bandwidth. Although the number of traces input to the second-pass migration is increased, and hence the migration becomes more costly, trace interpolation is necessary to preserve the information originally present in the 3-D seismic data.

Shown in Fig. 10-29a is a synthetic zero-offset section created from dipping-reflector segments. The trace spacing is 48 m. Much of the high-frequency part of the steeper events is spatially aliased. Migration will perceive these frequency components with dip directions that are different from the actual dips of these events and therefore will produce what may be called "migration noise," as shown in Fig. 10-29b. One might propose to do high-cut filtering to eliminate this undesirable noise as is shown in Fig. 10-29c. Such filtering can, however, only be done at the expense of loss of signal resolution. The more effective solution to avoid the migration noise shown in Fig. 10-29b is first to interpolate the input section (Fig. 10-29a) to yield data with smaller trace spacing (in this case 12 m) and then migrate. The result is shown in Fig. 10-29d, and it is clear that the aliasing noise is avoided and wavelet character is preserved.

A typical trace interpolation procedure involves determining dominant dip directions in the data by cross-correlating data from a few consecutive traces.

FIGURE 10-28   (a) The zero-offset section along the depth profile shown in Fig. 10-27b, a 45° azimuth to true dip direction, (b) 2-D migration, (c) 3-D migration. Note the inadequate imaging with 2-D migration, whereas the 3-D migrated section closely resembles the depth profile (Fig. 10-27b). (Gibson et al.[12])

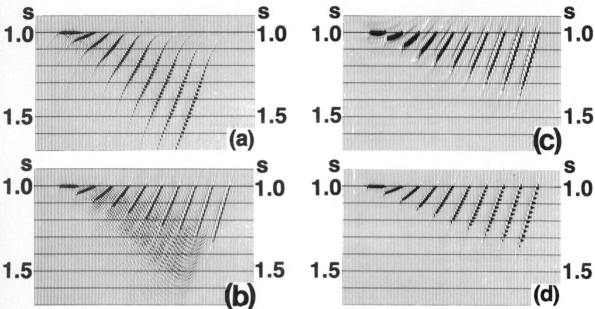

FIGURE 10-29   (a) Synthetic zero-offset section with trace spacing of 48 m, (b) its migration, (c) high-cut filtering applied to (b) to remove the aliasing noise, (d) migration of the data in (a) after a 4:1 trace interpolation, so that trace spacing is 12 m. (*Rothman et al.*[6])

Trace-to-trace time delays are selected to correspond to the range of expected dips. Maximum sums or cross-correlation peaks are taken to indicate that their corresponding per-trace time delays represent dipping reflections in the data. Simple linear interpolation of trace amplitudes along the dips corresponding to the calculated maxima yields suitable interpolated traces. Usually average values of dip are taken over geologically plausible zones. Noise, variations in the waveform, and complexity of structure nevertheless affect the quality of the output from the interpolation procedure. Note that trace interpolation does not create data; it only unwraps the spectrum such that aliased frequencies are mapped to the correct quadrant in the frequency–wave-number plane. The reason that one is able to eliminate spatial aliasing by trace interpolation of a stack section is that the interpolation procedure provides additional information—namely the amount and direction of dominant dip.

Shown in Fig. 10-30a is a migrated stack section in which the trace spacing is 33 m. By omitting every other trace in the stack section and migrating it, we get the section in Fig. 10-30b. Note that the quality of migration has suffered due to coarser trace spacing (67 m). We can improve the migration of the stack section with coarser trace spacing by first trace interpolating it. This is followed by the migration shown in Fig. 10-30c, which should be compared with the migration of the original data (Fig. 10-30a). Finally, it should be pointed out that trace interpolation must precede migration in order to prevent spatial aliasing; if done after migration (Fig. 10-30d), trace interpolation only provides a more

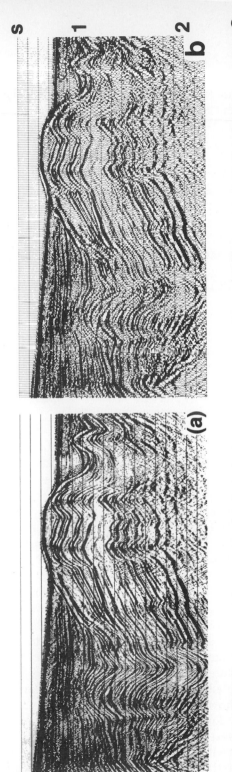

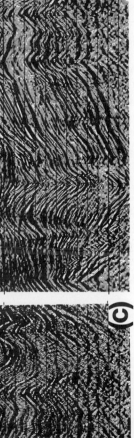

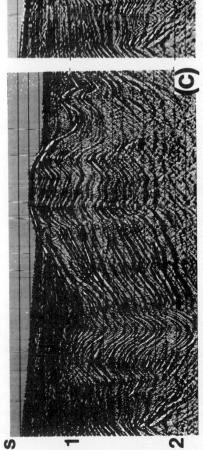

FIGURE 10-30 (a) A migrated CMP stack section (trace spacing is 33 m), (b) migration of data consisting of every other trace from the input used in (a) (trace spacing is 67 m), (c) migration of interpolated data which should be compared with (a), (d) trace interpolation of the migrated data shown in (b). A comparison of (c) and (d) makes it clear that interpolation must be performed before migration. (*Rothman et al.*[6])

aesthetically pleasing section in comparison to a section with coarser trace spacing (Fig. 10-30*b*). The result nevertheless lacks the detail in the steeply dipping parts of the section that is present in Fig. 10-30*a* and *c*.

10-5   INTERPRETATION OF 3-D SEISMIC DATA

A 3-D migrated data volume is ready for the interpreter to derive the 3-D subsurface geological model. Because of the completeness of data within that volume, relatively more information is available, as compared to a 2-D reconnaisance type of data set. Although more information leads to less uncertainty in deriving the geological model, the interpretation of such abundant data may be quite exhausting. An interactive environment is most suitable for handling the large volume of data. Moreover, such an environment provides versatility in viewing the 3-D data volume. For example, one can examine not only vertical sections in in-line, cross-line, or any arbitrary direction, but also horizontal sections, called *time slices*. An interactive environment can also provide capabilities to improve upon interpretation, for example, real-time horizon flattening, correlation of marker horizons across faults, and the enhancement of certain features within the data volume through some image-processing tools.

3-D Interpretation Session

A 3-D interpretation session may begin with viewing selected in-line and cross-line sections so as to acquire a regional understanding of the subsurface geology. One may have to resort to other orientations, such as vertical sections along the dominant dip direction, in order to be able to ascertain the structural pattern. Time slices may then be studied to check on the structural model. This preview may also be made dynamic (or "animated") in an interactive environment; vertical or horizontal sections can be viewed in rapid succession just as for a film strip from a motion picture. Any change in structure in space and time can be grasped quite effectively.

Shown in Fig. 10-31 is a reference base map of a 3-D land survey, and in Fig. 10-32 are selected cross-lines from that survey (in-lines are not shown because regional geology was best inferred from cross-lines). Every twenty-fourth line is displayed, starting from the south side of the survey and moving to north. As we move from south to north, starting at the bottom of Fig. 10-32, a model for the regional setting begins to emerge; there is an elongated basin SW-to-NE confined between two salt domes situated at the northwest and southeast corners of the survey area. Time slices shown in Fig. 10-33 verify the presence of a basin confined between the two salt domes. Moreover, note the presence of a small synclinal feature at the southwest half of the basin (on time slices at 1180 through 1500 ms), and another one situated at the northeast half of the basin. Note that as we move deeper in time, the internal geometry of the basin becomes increasingly complex.

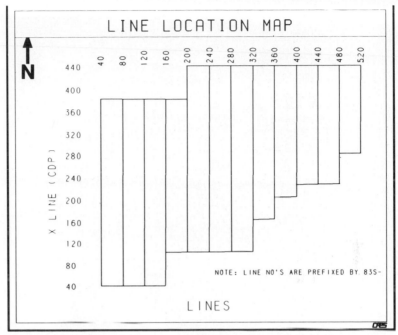

FIGURE 10-31   Line location map for the land 3-D data shown in Figs. 10-32 and 10-33.

The next step in 3-D interpretation is to mark the main structural features, such as faults, synclinal and anticlinal axes, on the base map and cross-check these on time slices. This is followed by a preliminary contouring of the marker horizons based on time slices.

A time slice at any one time value contains more than one horizon. Time slices are used to generate structural contour maps. Referring to the time slices at 1300 and 1340 ms shown in Fig. 10-33, one may infer steep dips (such as A) from the high-frequency character of the events, and gentle dips (such as B) from the low-frequency character of the events. A high-frequency event on a time slice is either a steeply dipping event or a high-frequency event in time. If contours contract upon themselves with increasing time, the feature is a syncline (observe the closure C in Fig. 10-33 on time slices from 1340 to 1460 ms). If contours expand with increasing time, the feature is an anticline (D on Fig. 10-33). An extensive discussion on the use of time slices in 3-D interpretation is provided by Bone et al.[14] and Brown et al.[15]

Shown in Fig. 10-34 are selected cross-lines (every fiftieth) from a 3-D marine survey. At the center of the survey area, there exists a structural high which has been subject to extensive tensional faulting. Structural configuration was best inferred from cross-lines; therefore, only these are included. Time slices shown in Fig. 10-35 confirm the existence of the structural high. The tensional faulting is also quite apparent on the time slices. Cross-lines run

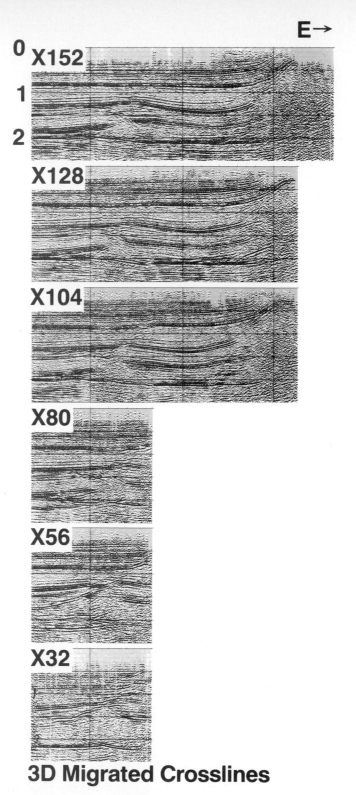

E→

0 **X152**
1
2

X128

X104

X80

X56

X32

3D Migrated Crosslines

FIGURE 10-32
Selected cross-lines from a land 3-D survey starting from the south side and moving up to the northern edge. For reference use the location map shown in Fig. 10-31. (*NAM.*)

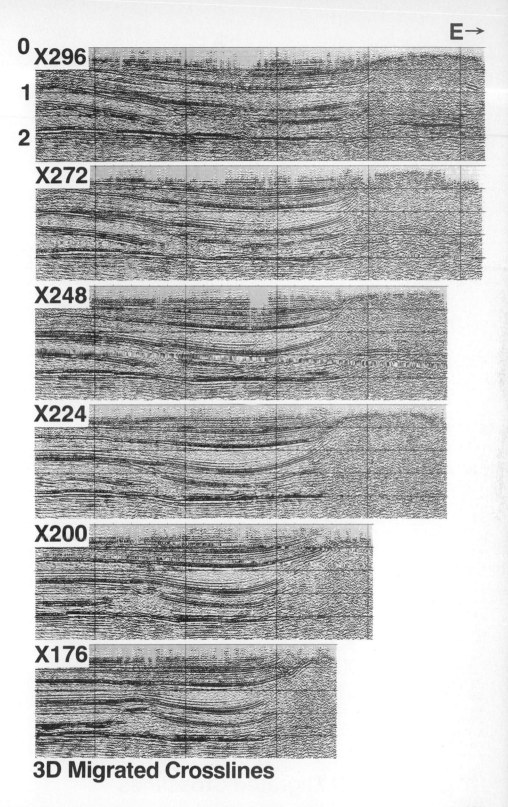

E→

0
X296
1
2

X272

X248

X224

X200

X176

FIGURE 10-32
continued

3D Migrated Crosslines

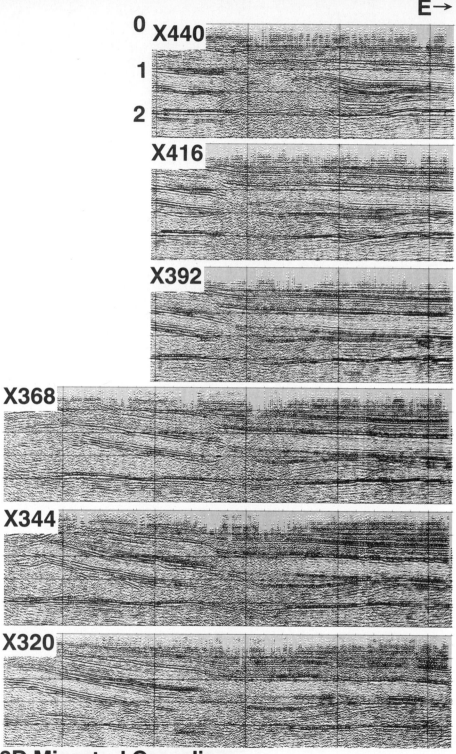

E→

0 X440
1
2

X416

X392

X368

X344

X320

FIGURE 10-32
continued

434

3D Migrated Crosslines

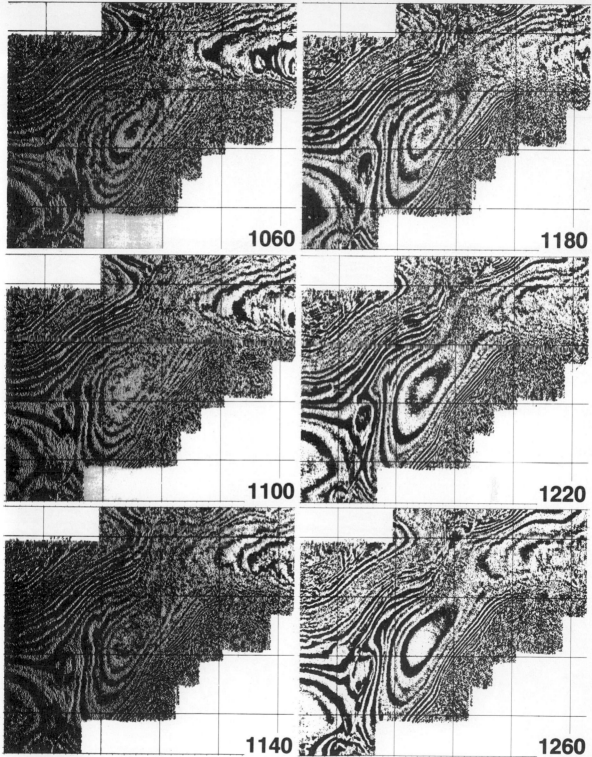

FIGURE 10-33 Selected time slices from a land 3-D survey starting from 1060 ms and moving down to 1740 ms at an interval of 40 ms. For reference, use the location map shown in Fig. 10-31. Vertical sections from this survey are shown in Fig. 10-32. (*NAM.*)

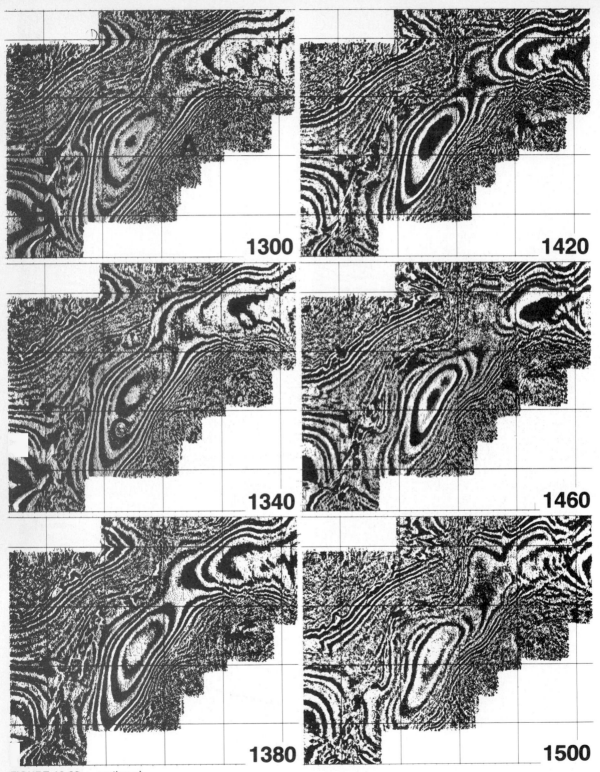

FIGURE 10-33 continued

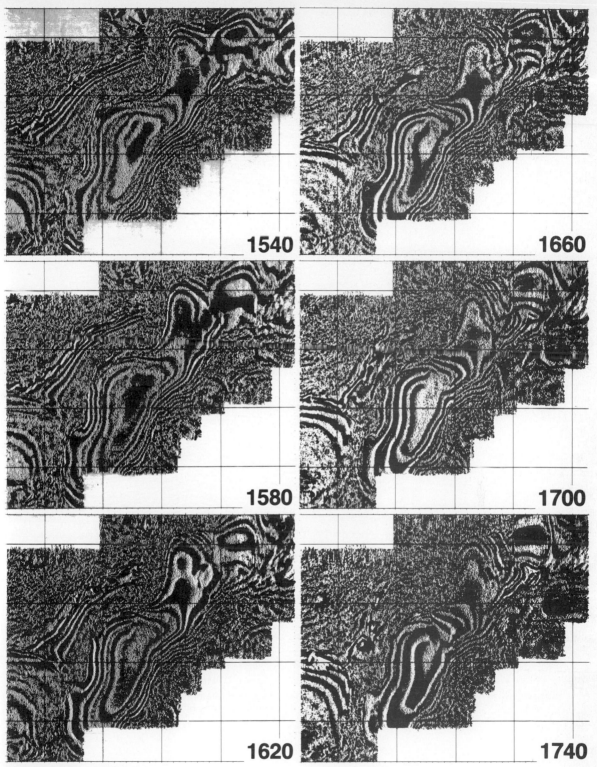

1540

1660

1580

1700

1620

1740

FIGURE 10-33 continued

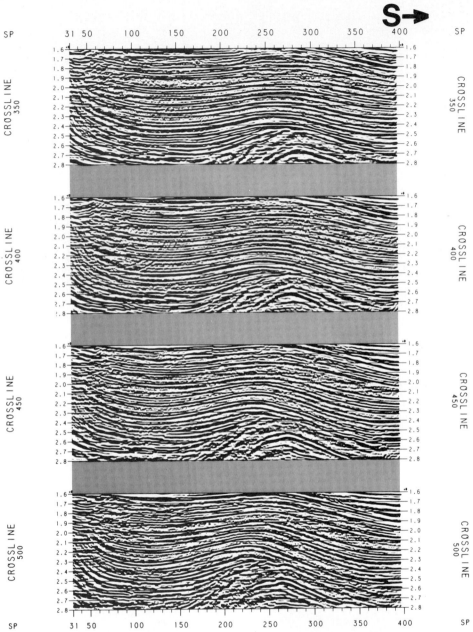

FIGURE 10-34 Selected cross-lines from a marine 3-D survey. For reference use the time slice annotation in Fig. 10-35. Line 350 is on the left and line 900 is on the right-hand side of the time slices. (*Amoco*.)

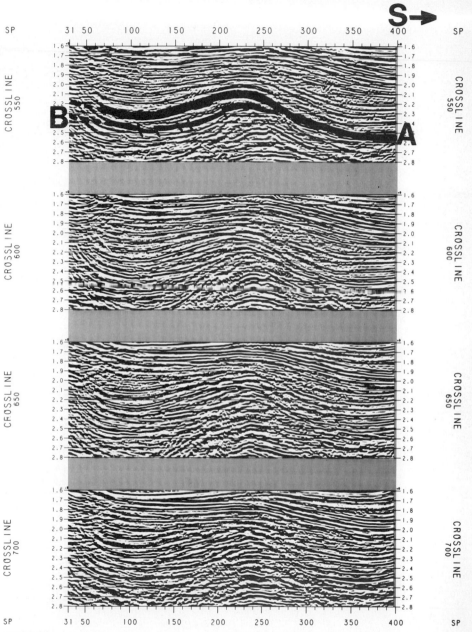

FIGURE 10-34   continued

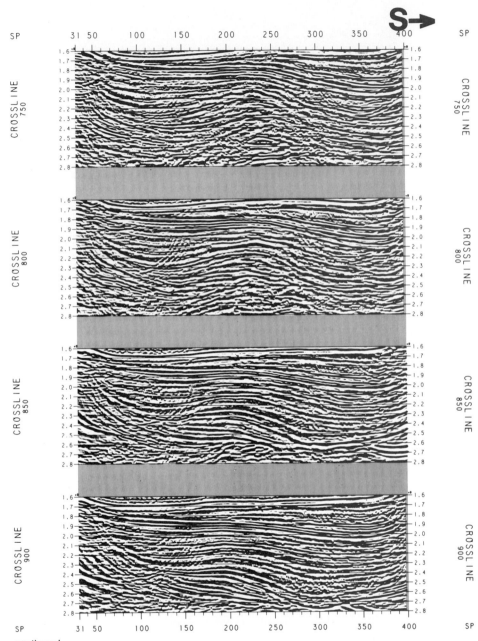

FIGURE 10-34 continued

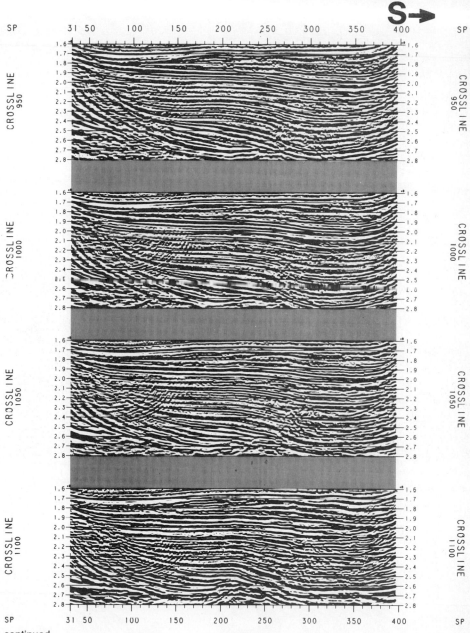

FIGURE 10-34   continued

FIGURE 10-35 Selected time slices from a marine 3-D survey starting from 2008 ms and moving down to 2752 ms at an interval of 24 ms. (*Amoco.*)

TIMESLICE TIME 2200 MS LINE NUMBERS
TIMESLICE TIME 2224 MS LINE NUMBERS
TIMESLICE TIME 2248 MS LINE NUMBERS
TIMESLICE TIME 2272 MS LINE NUMBERS
TIMESLICE TIME 2296 MS LINE NUMBERS
TIMESLICE TIME 2320 MS LINE NUMBERS
TIMESLICE TIME 2344 MS LINE NUMBERS
TIMESLICE TIME 2368 MS LINE NUMBERS

N

FIGURE 10-35   continued

443

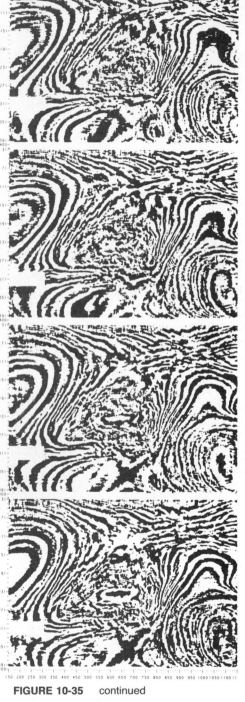
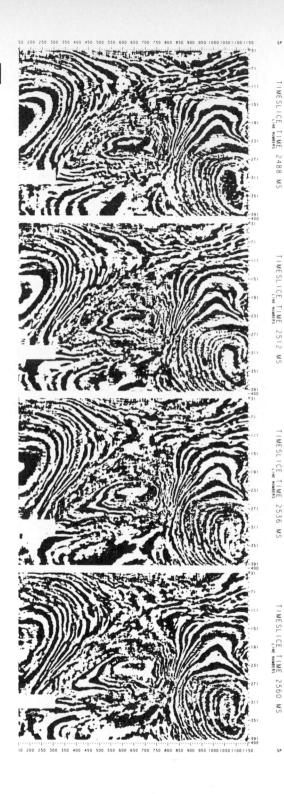

FIGURE 10-35 continued

FIGURE 10-35 continued

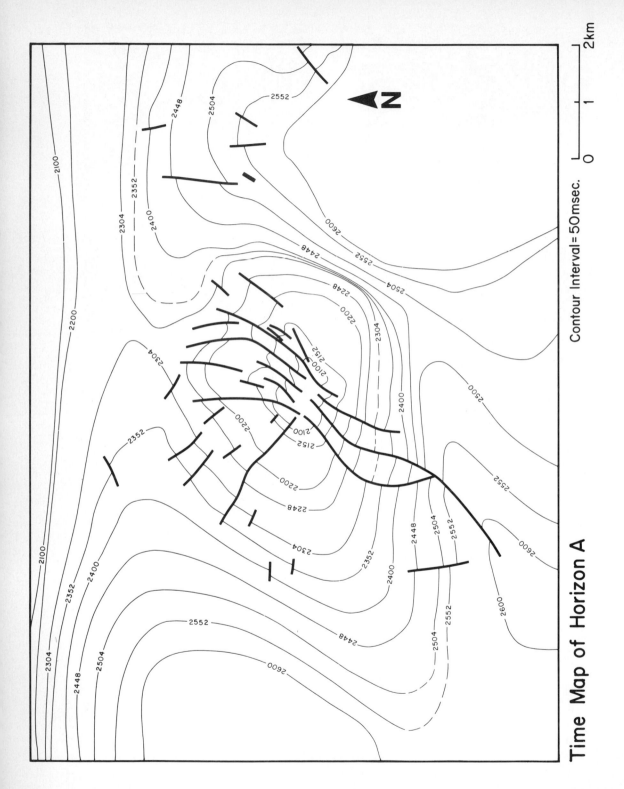

Time Map of Horizon A

Contour Interval = 50 msec.

2km

446

Time Map of Horizon B

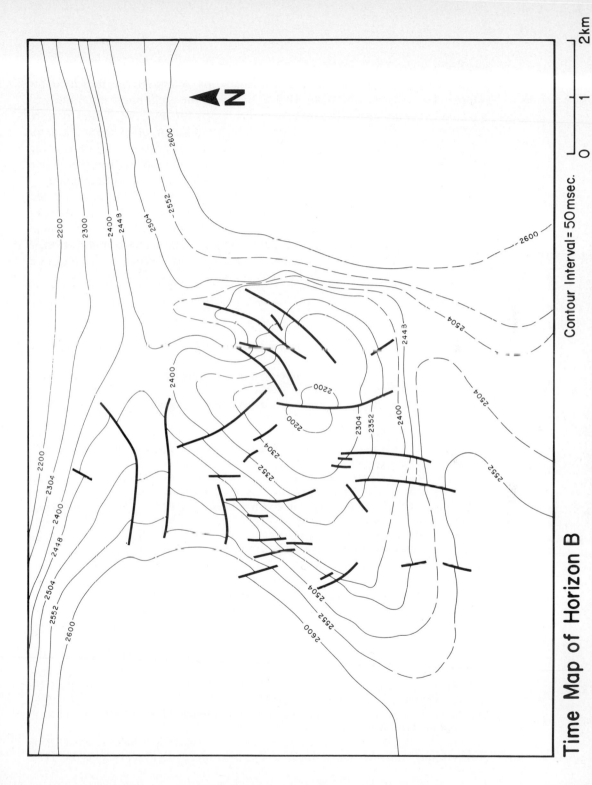

Contour Interval = 50 msec.

FIGURE 10-36 Preliminary structural contour maps of two horizons from the marine survey (vertical and horizontal sections are shown in Figs. 10-34 and 10-35, respectively).

vertically across the time slices. Two marker horizons were interpreted from both vertical and horizontal sections. Horizons A and B are indicated for reference on cross-line 550 (Fig. 10-34). Based on the preliminary contouring of time slices 50 ms apart, the time structure maps for horizons A and B were obtained (Fig. 10-36). The final stage of interpretation involves the tracking of marker horizons continuously along all of the vertical sections and correlating across faults. The interpreted horizon and fault information are then stored in a database and retrieved later to construct a complete 3-D subsurface image.

There are several publications on 3-D case histories. For the interested reader, a modest list of references is provided (Blake et al.,[16] Bone,[17] Bone et al.,[14] Brown,[18] Brown et al,[19] Brown et al.,[15] Brown and McBeath,[20] Dahm and Graebner,[21] French,[22] Galbraith and Brown,[23] Hautefeuille and Cotton,[24] Johnson and Bone,[25] Kurfess et al.,[26] Leflaive and Paturet,[27] Saeland and Simpson,[28] Sanders and Steel,[29] and Tegland[30]).

REFERENCES

1 Workman, R.: Marine 3-D Acquisition and Processing, Western Geophysical Technical Document, TD 84.01-13.01, 1984.

2 Homabrook, J. T.: Seismic Re-interpretation Clarifies North Sea Structures, *Petroleum International*, April-May, 1974.

3 Chun J. H., and C. A. Jacewitz: Fundamentals of Frequency Domain Migration, *Geophysics*, vol. 46, pp. 717–733, 1981.

4 Lynn, H. B., and S. Deregowski: Dip Limitations on Migrated Sections as a Function of Line Length and Recording Time, *Geophysics*, vol. 46, pp. 1392–1397, 1981.

5 Sheriff, R. E.: "Encyclopedic Dictionary of Exploration Geophysics," 2d ed., Society of Exploration Geophysicists, Tulsa, Okla., 1984.

6 Rothman, D., K. L. Larner, and R. Chambers: Trace Interpolation, *39th Annu. Meet. EAEG,* Venice, May 23–27, 1981.

7 Bentley, L., and M. Yang: Scatter of Midpoints Grouped in Cells and its Effects on Stacking, Western Geophysical Technical Document, TD 82.11-01.01, 1982.

8 Meinardus, H. A., and I. T. McMahon: Velocity Modeling for 3-D NMO and Stack, *51st SEG Annu. Int. Meet.*, Los Angeles, October 12–15, 1981.

9 Levin, F. K.: Apparent Velocities from Dipping Interface Reflections, *Geophysics*, vol. 36, pp. 510–516, 1971.

10 Lehmann, H. J., and W. Houba: Practical Aspects of Determination of 3-D Stacking Velocities, *Geophys. Prospect.*, vol. 33, pp. 34–51, 1985.

11 Claerbout, J. F.: "Fundamentals of Geophysical Data Processing," McGraw-Hill, New York, 1976.

12 Gibson, B., K. Larner, and S. Levin: Efficient 3-D Migration in Two Steps, *Geophys. Prospect.*, vol. 31, pp. 1–33, 1983.

13 Jacubowicz, H., and S. Levin: A Simple Exact Method of 3-D Migration—Theory, *Geophys. Prospect.*, vol. 31, pp. 34–56, 1983.

14 Bone, M. R., B. F. Giles, and E. R. Tegland: Analysis of Seismic Data Using Horizontal Cross-Sections, *45th Ann. Int. SEG Meet.*, Denver, October 14, 1975.

15 Brown, A. R., R. J. Graebner, and C. G. Dahm: Use of Horizontal Seismic Sections to Identify Subtle Traps, pp. 47–56, in "The Deliberate Search for the Subtle Trap," *Am. Assoc. Petrol. Geol. Mem. 32*, 1982.

16 Blake, B. A., J. B. Jennings, M. P. Curtis, and R. M. Philipson: Three-Dimensional Seismic Data Reveals the Finer Structural Details of a Piercement Salt Dome, OTC paper 4258, pp. 403–406, 1982.

17 Bone, M. R.: A Case History of 3-D Seismic Application in the Gulf of Mexico, OTC paper 3176, pp. 1109–1118, 1978.

18 Brown, A. R.: 3-D Seismic Interpretation Methods, *48th Annu. Int. SEG Meet.*, San Francisco, November 1, 1978.

19 Brown, A. R., C. G. Dahm, and R. J. Graebner: A Stratigraphic Case History Using Three-Dimensional Seismic Data in the Gulf of Thailand, *Geophys. Prospect.*, vol. 29, pp. 327–349, 1981.

20 Brown, A. R., and R. G. McBeath: Three-D Seismic Surveying for Field Development Comes of Age, *Oil Gas J.*, vol. 78, pp. 63–65, 1980.

21 Dahm, C. G., and R. J. Graebner: Field Development with Three-Dimensional Seismic Methods in the Gulf of Thailand—A Case History, *Geophysics*, vol. 47, pp. 149–176, 1982.

22 French, W. S.: Two-Dimensional and Three-Dimensional Migration of Model-Experiment Reflection Profiles, *Geophysics*, vol. 39, pp. 265–277, 1974.

23 Galbraith, R. M., and A. R. Brown: Field Appraisal with Three-Dimensional Seismic Surveys Offshore Trinidad, *Geophysics*, vol. 47, pp. 177–195, 1982.

24 Hautefeuille, A., and W. R. Cotton: Three-Dimensional Seismic Surveying Aids Exploration in the North Sea, *Oil Gas J.*, vol. 77, pp. 72–79, 1979.

25 Johnson, J. P., and M. R. Bone: Understanding Field Development History Utilizing 3-D Seismic, OTC paper 3849, pp. 473–475, 1980.

26 Kurfess, J. A., B. F. Giles, and M. R. Bone: Field Development with 3-D Seismic Methods: A Case History, *47th Annu. Int. SEG Meet.*, Calgary, September 21, 1977.

27 Leflaive, R., and D. Paturet: Three-Dimensional Seismic: Structural Interpretation of Parentis Oil Field, France, *51st Annu. Int. SEG Meet.*, Los Angeles, October 14, 1981.

28 Saeland, G. T., and G. S. Simpson: Interpretation of 3-D Data in Delineating a Subunconformity Trap in Block 34/10, Norwegian North Sea, in "The Deliberate Search for the Subtle Trap," *Am. Assoc. Petrol. Geol. Mem. 32*, pp. 217–235, 1982.

29 Sanders, J. I., and G. Steel: Improved Structural Resolution from 3D Surveys in Australia, *The APEA J.*, vol. 22, pp. 17–41, 1982.

30 Tegland, E. R.: 3-D Seismic Techniques Boost Field Development, *Oil Gas J.*, vol. 75, pp. 79–82, 1977.

CHAPTER 11

SEISMIC REFRACTION PROSPECTING

The first seismic technique to be used in petroleum prospecting was the refraction method. As early as 1923 refraction shooting was introduced for oil exploration in Mexico. Over the following 7 years, it was responsible (along with the torsion balance) for the spectacular success of geophysics in finding a great number of shallow Gulf Coast salt domes, many of them associated with large accumulations of oil.

Before the seismic refraction method was introduced as a tool for oil exploration, its principles had been applied for some time by earthquake seismologists in determining the structure of the earth's interior from records of earthquakes. The times at which the initial signals from earthquakes were recorded at a number of seismological observatories provided a basis for locating the epicenters and times of origin for the earthquakes. Such information made it possible to plot the distribution of seismic-wave velocities as a function of depth and thus obtain clues to the earth's internal constitution. In 1912 Gutenberg had discovered the earth's core and had calculated its depth (about 3000 km) by refraction techniques. This discovery and Mohorovičić's identification, also made with refraction data from earthquakes, of the boundary which has been given his name at the base of the earth's crust are among the most important contributions ever made to our knowledge of the earth's deep interior.

11-1 REFRACTION VERSUS REFLECTION

The principal difference between the geometry of the refraction and that of the reflection methods is in the interaction that takes place between the seismic waves and the lithological boundaries they encounter in the course of their propagation. The waves reflected by the boundaries travel along paths which are quite easy to visualize. Refracted waves of the type used in exploration work follow a somewhat more complicated trajectory that may not be as obvious to one's intuition. Refraction paths cross boundaries between materials having different velocities in such a way that energy travels from source to receiver in the shortest possible time, as required by Fermat's principle. Most refraction prospecting involves the use of waves having trajectories along the tops of layers with speeds that are appreciably greater than those of any overlying formations. The speeds and depths of such layers are determined from the times required for the refracted waves to travel between sources at the surface and receivers which are also on the surface. The distances between the two are almost always several times as great as the depths of the boundaries along which the waves travel.

The wave path geometry associated with refraction prospecting requires a considerably different source-geophone geometry in the field than is used for reflection surveys. In mapping structures at any particular depth, the shot and geophones must be farther apart for refraction than they would be for reflection. In most refraction work only the initial arrival of seismic energy is recorded, although later arrivals are sometimes used if conditions are favorable. Because of the greater distances traveled, the frequency of refraction signals tends to be lower than that of reflections. The recording requirements are thus different, and the instruments employed are likely to have different characteristics.

Applications Refraction had historically been used as a reconnaissance tool in newly explored areas. It was most useful where there was at least one high-speed bed having geological interest that extended without significant change over a wide area. To be mappable by refraction such a bed must be overlain by formations which have a lower speed. The method had been extensively used for structural mapping in the Alberta foothills, where the productive Rundle limestone, with a velocity around 20,000 ft/s, underlies Cretaceous sands and shales having speeds which are seldom greater than 12,000 ft/s.

The formations within many sedimentary basins have slower speeds than the basement rocks below them. Where this is the case, refraction was useful for mapping the basement top and thus determining the thickness of the sedimentary section.

Since the conclusion of the early fan-shooting campaign in the Gulf Coast in the 1920s, refraction has been used much less frequently than reflection. Since the 1970s, refraction surveys have largely disappeared from oil exploration but have continued to be used for groundwater and engineering surveys. Refraction calculations are nevertheless applied to land reflection data to determine the thickness and velocity of the weathered layer.

The proper interpretation of refraction data may require a higher degree of skill and ingenuity than is generally needed for interpreting reflection data. The techniques are not only more complex but call for a greater exercise of judgment. Thus refraction interpretation offers a greater potential challenge to the geophysicist and affords a greater degree of satisfaction when a solution is found that fits all the data.

Literature on Refraction In 1967, the Society of Exploration Geophysicists[1] published a volume of papers on refraction prospecting that covers many significant aspects of the subject. Among these are field techniques, fundamental principles, interpretation techniques, and case histories. The papers in the volume were all prepared specifically for it and generally do not cover material previously published; thus the book cannot be looked upon as a comprehensive reference work covering the field. But an extensive bibliography is provided to guide readers through the large body of literature on the subject that appeared before 1967.

The geometrical optics of refraction prospecting is covered in considerable detail by Slotnick.[2] Although his book is intended for the beginning student, it is recommended for all who want to learn the fundamentals of refraction from the ground down.

11-2 WAVE PATHS AND TIME-DISTANCE RELATIONS FOR HORIZONTAL LAYERS

Mechanism for Transmission of Refracted Waves

Refraction ray paths are not always as easy to predict as reflection paths. It may not be obvious that in a layered earth rays refracted along the tops of high-speed layers travel down to them from their source along slant paths, approach them at the critical angle, and return to the surface along a critical-angle path rather than along some other path, e.g., at normal incidence. The physical mechanism involved in this type of propagation was first treated mathematically by Muskat.[3] Dix[4] has summarized Muskat's treatment without using any mathematics, and his explanation will be reproduced here.

Let us consider a hypothetical subsurface consisting of two media, each with uniform elastic properties, the upper separated from the lower by a horizontal interface at depth z (Fig. 11-1). The velocity (longitudinal) of seismic waves in the upper layer is V_0 and in the lower V_1 with $V_1 > V_0$. A seismic wave is generated at point S on the surface, and the energy travels out from it in hemispherical wavefronts. A receiving instrument is located at point D a

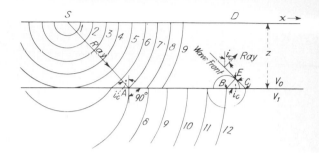

FIGURE 11-1 Mechanism for transmission of refracted waves in two-layered earth. (*After Dix.*[4])

distance x from S. If x is small, the first wave to arrive at D will be the one that travels horizontally at a speed V_0. At greater distance, the wave that took an indirect path, traveling down to, along, and up from the V_1 layer will arrive first because the time gained in travel through the higher-speed material makes up for the longer path.

When the spherical wavefronts from S strike the interface where the velocity changes, the energy will be refracted into the lower medium according to Snell's law. The process is demonstrated in the diagram for the time corresponding to wavefront 7. At point A on wavefront 7 the tangent to the sphere in the lower medium becomes perpendicular to the boundary. The ray passing through this point now begins to travel along the boundary with the speed of the lower medium. Thus, by definition, the ray SA strikes the interface at the critical angle. To the right of A the wavefronts below the boundary travel faster than those above.

The material on the upper side of the interface is subjected to oscillating stress from below which, as the wave travels, generates new disturbances along the boundary. These disturbances themselves spread out spherically in the upper medium with a speed of V_0. The wave originating at point B in the lower medium will travel a distance BC during the time in which the one spreading out in the upper medium will attain a radius of BE. The resultant wavefront above the interface will follow the line CE, which makes an angle i_c with the boundary. From the diagram, it is seen that

$$\sin i_c = \frac{BE}{BC} = \frac{V_0 t}{V_1 t} = \frac{V_0}{V_1}$$

The angle which the wavefront makes with the horizontal is the same as that which the ray perpendicular to it makes with the vertical, so that the ray will return to the surface at the critical angle $[\sin^{-1}(V_0/V_1)]$ with a line perpendicular to the interface.

As with reflection, the simplest and most useful way to represent refraction data is to plot the first-arrival time T versus the shot-detector distance x. In the

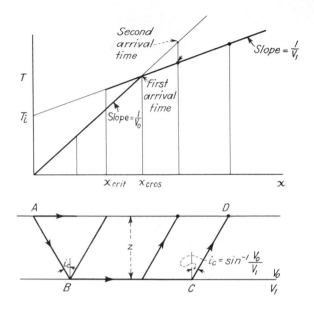

FIGURE 11-2 Ray paths of least time and time-distance curve for a layer separated from its substratum by horizontal interface; x_{crit} is critical distance; x_{cros} is crossover distance.

case of a subsurface consisting of discrete homogeneous layers, as in Fig. 11-2, this type of plot consists of linear segments.

Two-Media Case

Let us determine the time-distance relations for the case, illustrated in Fig. 11-2, of two media with respective speeds of V_0 and V_1, separated by a horizontal discontinuity at depth z.

Intercept Time The direct wave travels from shot to detector near the earth's surface at a speed of V_0, so that $T = x/V_0$. This is represented on the plot of T versus x as a straight line which passes through the origin and has a slope of $1/V_0$. The wave refracted along the interface at depth z, reaching it and leaving it at the critical angle i_c, takes a path consisting of three legs, AB, BC, and CD. To determine the time in terms of horizontal distance traveled we make use of the three relations

$$\sin i_c = \frac{V_0}{V_1} \qquad \cos i_c = \left(1 - \frac{V_0^2}{V_1^2}\right)^{1/2}$$

and

$$\tan i_c = \frac{\sin i_c}{\cos i_c} = \frac{V_0}{\sqrt{V_1^2 - V_0^2}}$$

The total time along the refraction path $ABCD$ is

$$T = T_{AB} + T_{BC} + T_{CD} \tag{11-1}$$

One can write Eq. (11-1) in the form

$$T = \frac{z}{V_0 \cos i_c} + \frac{x - 2z \tan i_c}{V_1} + \frac{z}{V_0 \cos i_c} \tag{11-2}$$

$$= \frac{2z}{V_0 \cos i_c} - \frac{2z \sin i_c}{V_1 \cos i_c} + \frac{x}{V_1} \tag{11-3}$$

This can be readily transformed into

$$T = \frac{2z}{V_0 \cos i_c}(1 - \sin^2 i_c) + \frac{x}{V_1} \tag{11-4}$$

$$= \frac{x}{V_1} + \frac{2z \cos i_c}{V_0}$$

$$= \frac{x}{V_1} + \frac{2z \sqrt{1 - (V_0/V_1)^2}}{V_0} \tag{11-5}$$

so that finally

$$T = \frac{x}{V_1} + \frac{2z \sqrt{V_1^2 - V_0^2}}{V_1 V_0} \tag{11-6}$$

On a plot of T versus x, this is the equation of a straight line which has a slope of $1/V_1$ and which intercepts the T axis ($x = 0$) at a time

$$T_i = 2z \frac{\sqrt{V_1^2 - V_0^2}}{V_1 V_0} \tag{11-7}$$

T_i is known as the *intercept time*.

Crossover Distance   At a distance x_{cros} (see Fig. 11-2), the two linear segments cross. At distances less than this, the direct wave traveling along the top of the V_0 layer reaches the detector first. At greater distances, the wave refracted by the interface arrives before the direct wave. For this reason, x_{cros} is called the *crossover distance*.

Depth Calculation   The depth z to the interface can be calculated from the intercept time by use of Eq. (11-7). This equation can be solved for z to obtain

$$z = \frac{T_i}{2} \frac{V_1 V_0}{\sqrt{V_1{}^2 - V_0{}^2}} \tag{11-8}$$

T_i can be determined graphically as shown in Fig. 11-2 or numerically from the relation $T_i = T - x/V_1$.

The depth can also be expressed in terms of x_{cros}, the crossover distance, making use of the fact that the times

$$T_0 = \frac{x}{V_0} \quad \text{and} \quad T_1 = \frac{x}{V_1} + \frac{2z \sqrt{V_1{}^2 - V_0{}^2}}{V_1 V_0}$$

are equal at x_{cros}. Then

$$\frac{x_{cros}}{V_0} = \frac{x_{cros}}{V_1} + \frac{2z \sqrt{V_1{}^2 - V_0{}^2}}{V_1 V_0} \tag{11-9}$$

and

$$z = \frac{1}{2} \frac{V_0 V_1 x_{cros}}{\sqrt{V_1{}^2 - V_0{}^2}} \left(\frac{1}{V_0} - \frac{1}{V_1} \right) \tag{11-10}$$

This simplifies to

$$z = \frac{1}{2} \sqrt{\frac{V_1 - V_0}{V_1 + V_0}} x_{cros} \tag{11-11}$$

Three-Media Case

For three formations with velocities V_0, V_1, and V_2 ($V_2 > V_1 > V_0$), the treatment is similar but somewhat more complicated. Figure 11-3 shows the

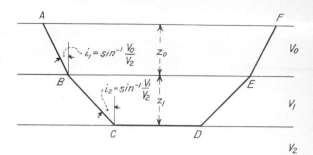

FIGURE 11-3   Ray paths of least time for two layers and a substratum separated by two horizontal interfaces.

wave paths. The ray corresponding to the least travel time makes an angle $i_1 = \sin^{-1}(V_0/V_2)$ with the vertical in the uppermost layer and an angle $i_2 = \sin^{-1}(V_1/V_2)$ with the vertical in the second layer, i_2 being the critical angle for the lower interface. The time along each of the two slant paths AB and EF through the uppermost layer is

$$T_{AB} = \frac{AB}{V_0} = \frac{z_0}{V_0 \cos i_1} = \frac{z_0}{V_0 \sqrt{1 - (V_0/V_2)^2}} = T_{EF} \qquad (11\text{-}12)$$

while that through each of the legs BC and DE crossing the middle layer is

$$T_{BC} = \frac{BC}{V_1} = \frac{z_1}{V_1 \cos i_2} = \frac{z_1}{V_1 \sqrt{1 - (V_1/V_2)^2}} = T_{DE} \qquad (11\text{-}13)$$

The time for the segment of path CD at the top of the V_2 layer is CD/V_2. The expression for the total travel time from A to F is

$$T = T_{AB} + T_{BC} + T_{CD} + T_{DE} + T_{EF}$$

$$= \frac{2z_0}{V_0 \sqrt{1 - (V_0/V_2)^2}} + \frac{2z_1}{V_1 \sqrt{1 - (V_1/V_2)^2}} + \frac{CD}{V_2} \qquad (11\text{-}14)$$

where $CD = x - 2z_0 \tan i_1 - 2z_1 \tan i_2$

$$= x - 2z_0 \frac{V_0}{V_2 \sqrt{1 - (V_0/V_2)^2}} - 2z_1 \frac{V_1}{V_2 \sqrt{1 - (V_1/V_2)^2}} \qquad (11\text{-}15)$$

Rearranging terms, one obtains

$$T = \frac{x}{V_2} + \frac{2z_0\sqrt{V_2{}^2 - V_0{}^2}}{V_2 V_0} + \frac{2z_1\sqrt{V_2{}^2 - V_1{}^2}}{V_2 V_1} \qquad (11\text{-}16)$$

for the overall travel time of the wave refracted along the top of the V_2 zone. The portion of the time-distance curve corresponding to the first arrival of this wave is a straight line with a slope $1/V_2$ and an intercept time

$$T_{i2} = T - \frac{x}{V_2} = \frac{2z_0\sqrt{V_2{}^2 - V_0{}^2}}{V_2 V_0} + \frac{2z_1\sqrt{V_2{}^2 - V_1{}^2}}{V_2 V_1} \qquad (11\text{-}17)$$

Solving for z_1, one obtains

$$z_1 = \frac{1}{2}\left(T_{i2} - 2z_0\frac{\sqrt{V_2{}^2 - V_0{}^2}}{V_2 V_0}\right)\frac{V_2 V_1}{\sqrt{V_2{}^2 - V_1{}^2}} \qquad (11\text{-}18)$$

The depth to the lower interface is the sum of z_1 and z_0, where z_0 is computed by the two-media formula [Eq. (11-8)] using the slopes of the first two segments of the time-distance curve and the intercept of the second segment.

Figure 11-4 shows time-distance-depth relations for a refraction profile over two subsurface discontinuities (two layers and a substratum). The arrival times for the first five detector positions are measured on the record shown schematically at the right side of the block. The first arrival on each trace appears as a

FIGURE 11-4 Wave paths, schematic record, and time-distance curve for subsurface consisting of two horizontal layers overlying a substratum.

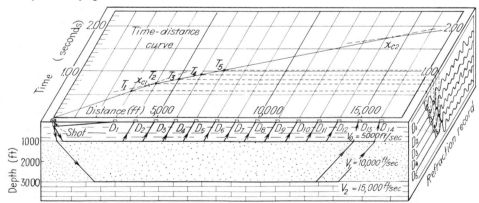

sharp upward displacement from the baseline representing an undisturbed earth. The three segments of time-distance curve represent paths along the tops of the respective media. The two breaks in the slope of the time-distance curve occur at the crossover distances x_{c1} and x_{c2} for the respective interfaces.

Multilayer Case

The time-depth relations just derived for the two- and three-media cases can be readily extrapolated to apply to a larger number of layers as long as the speed in each layer is higher than in the one just above it. This is illustrated by Fig. 11-5, which shows ray paths and time-distance plots for six media, the lowermost designated for generality as the nth. Each segment on the plot represents first arrivals from the top of one of these subsurface layers, the horizontal ray paths corresponding to the respective segments being designated by the letters b to f. The deeper the layer, the greater the shot-detector distance at which arrivals from it become the first to be observed. In other words, the crossover distance for each layer increases with its depth. The slope of each segment is simply the reciprocal of the speed in the layer if the wave has traveled along it horizontally. The intercept time of each segment depends on the depth of the interface at the bottom of the corresponding wave path as well as on the depths of all those interfaces that lie above it in the section.

FIGURE 11-5   Ray paths, time-distance curve, and critical distances for multilayered earth. x_{c1}, x_{c2}, etc. are crossover distances for successively deeper interfaces.

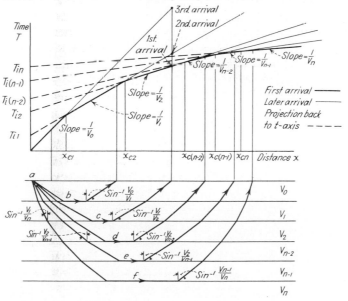

Low-Speed Layer

To calculate depths for additional layers by extending Eq. (11-18) to apply to more than two refracting interfaces would be valid only in cases where successively deeper layers have successively higher speeds. If any bed in the sequence has a lower speed than the one above it, it will not be detectable by refraction shooting at all. This is because the rays entering such a bed from above are always deflected in the downward direction, as shown for the interface between the V_0 and V_1 layers in Fig. 11-6, and thus can never travel horizontally through the layer. Consequently there will be no segment of inverse slope V_1 on the time-distance curve. The presence of such an undetected low-speed layer will result in the computation of erroneous depths to all interfaces below it if only observed segments are used in the calculations.

Blind Zone

A similar kind of error may occur if the thickness of a layer with a speed intermediate between that of the layer overlying it and the one below it is small and/or the velocity contrast between it and the layer that underlies it is inadequate. If only first arrivals can be observed on the records, the refracted waves from the intermediate layer will not be discernible because they will always reach the surface at a later time than from either a shallower or a deeper bed, depending on the shot-detector distance. Figure 11-7 shows the relation of the

FIGURE 11-6 Ray paths of least time and time-distance curve where low-speed layer V_1 lies below higher-speed layer V_0. $V_3 > V_2 > V_1$.

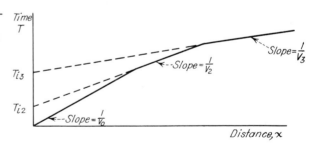

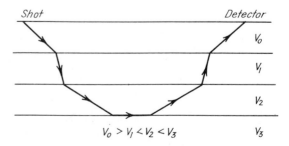

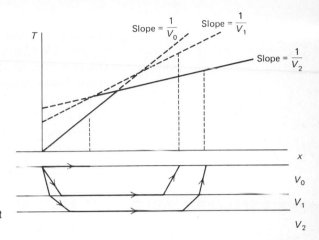

FIGURE 11-7   The blind zone in refraction shooting. It is not possible to observe a first arrival from the top of the V_2 layer because arrivals from either V_3 or V_1 are earlier at all receiving distances.

time-distance segments from the respective layers when there is a *blind zone*, as an intermediate layer of this type is called.

Soske[5] has pointed out the importance of taking such zones into account for proper accuracy in shallow refraction investigations, particularly for engineering purposes. Unless second events can be identified on the records it is not possible to recognize the existence of blind zones from seismic data alone. But if a test borehole in the area of the survey reveals a layer undetectable by refraction, its effect can be taken into account in calculating depths to high-speed beds. A paper by Savit in the 1967 SEG volume[1] presents a practical means to determine depths to refractors if vertical velocities can be estimated by logging a borehole or from reflection measurements. Soske's technique for doing this makes use of the wavefront method of Thornburgh,[6] which will be discussed in more detail later in this chapter. Hawkins and Maggs[7] have developed a nomogram that yields the limiting thickness of a blind zone having any assumed velocity on the basis of observed arrival times.

A related problem occurs when a high-speed layer on the surface or at shallow depths masks a deeper marker of equal or only slightly greater velocity which it is desired to map by refraction. This difficulty is sometimes encountered when surface volcanic layers, e.g., the basalts in the Parana Basin of Brazil, cover a sedimentary section which contains deeper high-speed layers such as the basement surface or sheets of dense limestone that could be mapped by refraction if the volcanic cover were not present. When the speed of the volcanic material is approximately equal to or greater than that of the marker to be mapped, rays that could be returned to the surface by refraction should not penetrate below the near-surface material. But if the shallow high-speed layer is thin compared with the wavelength of the seismic impulse, it will be "transparent" to the seismic energy and will not mask arrivals from the deeper horizon. As the distance from source to detector becomes greater, the wavelength naturally increases because of selective absorption of high frequencies. Thus it is possible to overcome masking effects of surface or near-surface high-speed layers if they are thin enough by operating at large shot-geophone distances. Trostle[8] describes an experiment in the Delaware Basin of west Texas where interference from such layers was overcome by recording at distances greater than 100,000 ft from the shot. Dense Devonian limestones at depths of 15,000 ft were mapped through anhydrites of almost the same speed with tops as shallow as 3500 ft.

11-3   DIPPING BEDS WITH DISCRETE VELOCITIES

When the top surface of a refracting marker bed is not horizontal, the angle of dip can be determined from the time-distance data. Consider (as shown in Fig. 11-8) a boundary between two beds having respective speeds of V_0 and V_1 which dips at an angle α. We define z_d as the perpendicular distance from the shot to the interface at the end of the line at which one shoots downdip, and z_u as this distance at the end from which the ray refracted downdip originates.

As with the horizontal interface, the ray path for the first refracted arrival consists of three linear segments. One of these extends along the sloping interface and corresponds to wave travel at speed V_1. The other two, in the upper medium, make an angle of i_c with the normal to this boundary and the wave travels along them at speed V_0.

FIGURE 11-8   Refraction along an interface dipping at an angle α. Respective shots are at updip and downdip ends of profile.

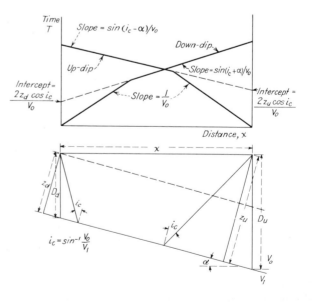

Shooting downdip, the total time from shot to detector is

$$T_d = \frac{z_d}{V_0 \cos i_c} + \frac{x \cos \alpha - z_d \tan i_c - (z_d + x \sin \alpha) \tan i_c}{V_1} + \frac{z_d + x \sin \alpha}{V_0 \cos i_c} \tag{11-19}$$

Making the same transformation used in deriving the formula for a single layer and substratum separated by a horizontal interface, one obtains

$$T_d = \frac{2z_d \cos i_c}{V_0} + \frac{x}{V_0} \sin (i_c + \alpha) \tag{11-20}$$

Similarly, the time for shooting updip is

$$T_u = \frac{2z_u \cos i_c}{V_0} + \frac{x}{V_0} \sin (i_c - \alpha) \tag{11-21}$$

where z_u is the perpendicular distance to the interface from the shot from which arrivals are received at the updip end of the line.

Time-distance relations for both trajectories are shown in Fig. 11-8. The respective slopes of the two linear segments for each are used to determine the true speeds, V_0 and V_1, of the two media and the dip α of the sloping interface.

To obtain V_1 and α, one makes use of the fact that the slope m_d of the downdip segment is $[\sin (i_c + \alpha)]/V_0$ while the slope m_u of the updip segment is $[\sin (i_c - \alpha)]/V_0$, so that

$$V_0 m_d = \sin (i_c + \alpha) \tag{11-22}$$
$$V_0 m_u = \sin (i_c - \alpha) \tag{11-23}$$
$$i_c + \alpha = \sin^{-1} V_0 m_d \tag{11-24}$$
$$i_c - \alpha = \sin^{-1} V_0 m_u \tag{11-25}$$

Solving for i_c, one adds and obtains

$$i_c = \tfrac{1}{2}(\sin^{-1} V_0 m_d + \sin^{-1} V_0 m_u) \tag{11-26}$$

To solve for α, one subtracts, obtaining

$$\alpha = \tfrac{1}{2}(\sin^{-1} V_0 m_d - \sin^{-1} V_0 m_u) \tag{11-27}$$

With i_c determined, V_1 is readily obtained from the relation

$$V_1 = \frac{V_0}{\sin i_c} \tag{11-28}$$

The perpendicular distance z_u to the interface comes from the intercept time

$$T_{iu} = \frac{2z_u \cos i_c}{V_0} \qquad (11\text{-}29)$$

and is

$$z_u = \frac{V_0 T_{iu}}{2 \cos i_c} \qquad (11\text{-}30)$$

A similar expression is obtained for z_d in terms of T_{id}. The depth D_u is $z_u/(\cos \alpha)$, while D_d is $z_d/(\cos \alpha)$, as is evident from Fig. 11-8. When there is more than one dipping layer, the formulas for depth and dip are derived by use of the same principle but the computations are more complex. Mota[9] has published formulas which apply this approach to a large number of layers.

11-4 REFRACTION SHOOTING ACROSS A FAULT

If a high-speed bed (velocity V_1) situated under a low-speed overburden (velocity V_0) is faulted vertically, a refraction profile across the fault should make it possible to locate the faulting and measure its throw. When the source is on the upthrown side of the fault, as shown in Fig. 11-9a, the rays that are refracted along this high side will be received as first arrivals over the portion of the recording profile from B to D. Diffractions from the corner of the fault taking paths like DF will be observed as first arrivals from D to G, at which point they will be overtaken by refracted events from the downthrown side of the fault. The refracted arrivals for each direction of shooting are plotted along two parallel but displaced linear segments on the time-distance curves. These have an inverse slope equal to the speed in the faulted formation. The two segments correspond to rays refracted respectively from the upthrown and downthrown sides of the fault. The amount of throw z_t can be determined from the difference $T_{i2} - T_{i1}$ between the intercept times corresponding to these segments.

The case where the shot is on the downthrown side of the fault is illustrated in Fig. 11-9b. Any waves from the shot received by detectors to the left of point C' cannot emerge at the critical angle because they cannot have traveled along the interface at grazing incidence. But at a large distance from it, such as at F', the path from the base of the fault Q becomes so nearly parallel with the interface that a critical angle with the high-speed surface can be assumed and the intercept time for arrivals on the upthrown side can be determined from the limiting position on the left of the curved segment between C' and F'. Here also the throw can be determined from the difference between the intercept times T_{i2} and T_{i1}.

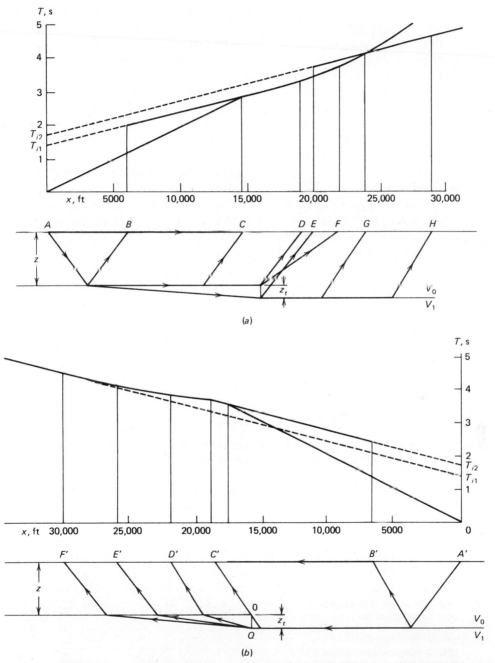

FIGURE 11-9   Refraction across a fault with a throw z_t. Depth to the high-speed surface on its upthrown side is z: (a) shooting from the upthrown side; (b) shooting from the downthrown side. Discontinuities in times and slopes on both time-distance curves are diagnostic of the faulting.

11-5 REFRACTION IN A MEDIUM HAVING CONTINUOUS CHANGE OF SPEED WITH DEPTH

In many areas, e.g., the Gulf Coast of the United States, the lithology tends to change gradually with depth of burial rather than in discrete steps at boundaries of the type we have been considering. In most clastic formations the velocity increases continuously with depth because of differential compaction effects. To visualize the paths of refracted waves through a section with this kind of lithology, we can assume a series of thin layers, each of higher speed than the one above, as in Fig. 11-10, and pass to the limit of an infinite number of infinitesimally thin members. Such a limit corresponds to a section having a continuous increase of velocity with depth. The ray path would then have the form of a smooth curve which is convex downward, and the time-distance curve, also smooth, would be convex upward. In many cases, as Ewing and Leet[10] have pointed out, it is a matter of choice whether a set of observed time-distance points should be connected by linear segments each representing a discrete layer or by a smooth curve representing a continuous increase of speed with depth.

The actual ray trajectory, as well as the form of the time-distance curve, depends on just how the velocity varies with depth. Where the relation between velocity and depth is linear, the ray paths are circles. More complex velocity-depth functions, e.g., those involving a velocity proportional to the square or square root of depth, also give mathematically expressible ray-path trajectories and time-distance relationships. Kaufman[11] has published a useful set of tables relating ray-path geometry and time for a large number of velocity functions.

Time-Distance Relations for Linear Increase of Velocity with Depth

Because of its simplicity and its close correspondence to the actual velocity-depth relationship in most clastic materials, the function

$$v = V_0 + kz \qquad (11\text{-}31)$$

where v = speed at depth z
V_0 = speed at zero depth
k = constant

FIGURE 11-10   Ray path on the side toward the shot for series of thin layers with small increments of velocity between them. Ray refracted along bottom interface approaches it at the critical angle i_c which is $\sin^{-1}(V_{n+2}/V_{max})$.

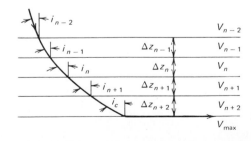

have historically been employed to represent the velocity variation in sedimentary basins. The geometry and time-distance relations for reflection paths in a medium with this type of velocity function were discussed in previous editions of this text.

To demonstrate in an intuitive way how the time-distance and time-depth relationships are derived for this velocity function, we can trace a ray through a sequence of layers each with a thickness Δz and a velocity $v = V_0 + kz_n$, where z_n is the depth to the center of the nth layer. For any particular ray there will be a layer having a speed V_{max} in which the path becomes horizontal. V_{max} is actually a parameter that itself identifies the particular ray under consideration. A ray passing through the nth layer will be bent as shown in Fig. 11-10. The time ΔT_n required for the ray to travel through this layer is

$$\Delta T_n = \frac{\Delta z_n}{V_n \cos i_n} = \frac{\Delta z_n}{V_n \sqrt{1 - \sin^2 i_n}} \tag{11-32}$$

But $i_n = \sin^{-1}(V_n/V_{max})$, where V_{max} is the velocity of the layer in which the ray travels horizontally, so that

$$\Delta T_n = \frac{\Delta z}{V_n \sqrt{1 - (V_n/V_{max})^2}} \tag{11-33}$$

Δx_n, which is the horizontal distance traversed by the ray as it passes through the nth layer, can be expressed as

$$\Delta x_n = \Delta z_n \tan i_n = \Delta z_n \frac{V_n/V_{max}}{\sqrt{1 - V_n^2/V_{max}^2}} \tag{11-34}$$

The total time for a wave to travel through N such layers is

$$t = \sum_{n=1}^{N} \frac{\Delta z_n}{V_n \sqrt{1 - (V_n/V_{max})^2}} \tag{11-35}$$

and the net horizontal distance is

$$x = \sum_{n=1}^{N} \frac{\Delta z_n \, V_n/V_{max}}{\sqrt{1 - (V_n/V_{max})^2}} \tag{11-36}$$

According to Snell's law,

$$\frac{\sin i_n}{\sin 90°} = \frac{V_n}{V_{max}}$$

so that

$$\frac{1}{V_{max}} = \frac{\sin i_n}{V_n}$$

The ratio $(\sin i_c)/V_{n-1} = (\sin i_0)/V_0$ is a parameter that is constant for any particular ray with a given initial angle of penetration into the earth. This constant, which we designate as the *ray parameter p*, thus describes each ray in terms of the surface velocity V_0 and the emergence angle i_0.

As the number of beds increases and the thickness Δz_n of each becomes smaller, the limit is approached of a continuous increase of velocity with depth, where the velocity at any depth z can be expressed as a continuous function of z. V_n becomes v, and $1/V_{max}$ becomes p. The time and net horizontal displacement can then be expressed for each ray corresponding to a given p as

$$t = \int_0^{z_{max}} \frac{dz}{v \sqrt{1 - p^2 v^2}} \tag{11-37}$$

and

$$x = \int_0^{z_{max}} \frac{pv \, dz}{\sqrt{1 - p^2 v^2}} \tag{11-38}$$

In the case where v is a linear function of depth having the form

$$v = V_0 + kz$$

then

$$t = \int_0^{z_{max}} \frac{dz}{(V_0 + kz) \sqrt{1 - p^2(V_0 + kz)^2}} \tag{11-39}$$

and

$$x = \int_0^{z_{max}} \frac{p(V_0 + kz) \, dz}{\sqrt{1 - p^2(V_0 + kz)^2}} \tag{11-40}$$

Evaluation of these integrals is straightforward if p is constant. The reader is referred to Slotnick[2] (pp. 206–208) for the details. The resultant expressions are

$$x = \frac{1}{kp} \{(1 - p^2 V_0^2)^{1/2} - [1 - p^2(V_0 + kz)^2]^{1/2}\} \tag{11-41}$$

$$t = \frac{1}{k} \ln \frac{(V_0 + kz)[1 + (1 - p^2 V_0^2)]^{1/2}}{V_0\{1 + [1 - p^2(V_0 + kz)^2]^{1/2}\}} \tag{11-42}$$

Equation (11-41) can be rewritten

$$\left[x - \frac{(1 - p^2 V_0^2)^{1/2}}{kp} \right]^2 + \left(z + \frac{V_0}{k} \right)^2 = \frac{1}{k^2 p^2} \tag{11-43}$$

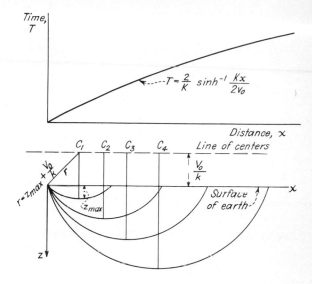

FIGURE 11-11 Ray paths and time-distance curve for linear increase of speed with depth.

This is the equation of a circle having a radius $1/kp$ and a center along a horizontal line a distance V_0/k above the surface and to the right of the origin a distance $(1 - p^2V_0^2)^{1/2}/kp$. Figure 11-11 illustrates a family of such circles for a number of rays having different angles of immergence into the earth.

The time-distance relation for such a circular ray path between entry into and emergence from the earth can be found by eliminating p and z from Eqs. (11-41) and (11-42). This can be expressed in the form*

$$T = \frac{2}{k} \sinh^{-1} \frac{kx}{2V_0} \tag{11-44}$$

Also the formula for the depth of maximum penetration for a ray with an initial angle of i_0 is

$$z_{max} = \frac{V_0}{k} (\csc i_0 - 1) \tag{11-45}$$

The time-distance curve applying for a linear increase of speed with depth is plotted in the upper part of Fig. 11-11. The inverse slope of the time-distance curve at any point is equal to the velocity at the depth of maximum penetration for the ray reaching the surface at that point.

---

* The notation $\sinh^{-1} u$ means the angle whose hyperbolic sine is u. Hyperbolic functions can be found in most books of mathematical tables, where they are tabulated in the same way as trigonometric functions.

TABLE 11-1   CURVED-PATH TIME-DEPTH DATA
k = 0.6 ft/(s)(ft) V_0 = 6000 ft/s

Shot-detector distance x, ft	Arrival time T, s	Depth of maximum penetration, ft
1,000	0.167	12
2,000	0.333	50
5,000	0.827	310
10,000	1.602	1,180
20,000	2.935	4,140
30,000	3.983	8,028
40,000	4.82	12,360

Application of Curved-Path Theory to Refraction Exploration

In most areas where linear relationships exist between speed and depth, k is of the order of 1 ft/(s)(ft). In the Gulf Coast of the United States it is usually around 0.6. Table 11-1 shows travel times and depths of maximum penetration as a function of shot-detector distance x for V_0 = 6000 ft/s and k = 0.6.

Increase of Velocity to Indefinite Depths   For these constants, it appears that the penetration is less than 1000 ft if the detector is within about 9000 ft of the shot. At a distance of 10,000 ft, the first arrival time is only about 3.5 percent less for a wave along the curved path than it would be for a wave following the earth's surface at a speed of V_0. At a distance of 40,000 ft, the gain in time is 27.5 percent. The penetrations indicated in the table are greater than those actually observed in the Gulf Coast because the true increase in velocity does not continue downward indefinitely but levels off at depths where compaction no longer increases.

Section with Linear Variation Underlain by High-Speed Marker   A geologic section in which the velocity increases continuously with depth for an indefinite distance below the surface would probably be of little practical interest. Refraction surveys would be more likely to be useful in areas where there is some definite discontinuity in velocity associated with discrete changes in lithology. Such discontinuities could be mapped by refraction if the underlying material had a higher velocity than anything above it.

Often a horizontal high-speed marker* bed lies at the base of a section in which there is a linear increase of speed with depth having constants V_0 and k, as shown in Fig. 11-12. At a depth H, the velocity changes discontinuously to V_m and remains constant at this value from here on downward. The path of

---

* A *marker horizon* is the top surface of a bed with a high enough velocity compared with formations above it to permit waves refracted along it to be observed at the surface.

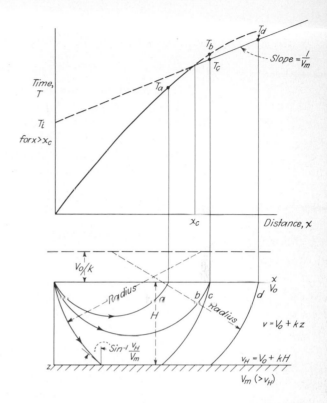

FIGURE 11-12   Time-distance curve and ray paths for high-speed marker below overburden with linear velocity-depth relation.

least time to the marker is the arc of a circle, with center V_0/k above the surface, whose tangent at the velocity break makes the angle $i_c = \sin^{-1}(v_H/V_m)$ with the vertical. Here $v_H = V_0 + kH$. The path along the marker follows the horizontal interface, and the return path to the surface follows an arc which is identical to that for the downward trajectory. Barry[12] has presented the derivation of an expression first developed by Gardner[13] for the total travel time of refracted rays for this velocity configuration:

$$
T = \frac{x}{V_m} + \frac{2}{k}\left[\cosh^{-1}\frac{V_m}{V_0} - \cosh^{-1}\frac{V_m}{v_H} - \sqrt{1 - \left(\frac{V_0}{V_m}\right)^2} + \sqrt{1 - \left(\frac{v_H}{V_m}\right)^2}\right]
$$

$$(11\text{-}46)$$

The time-distance curve (T versus x) obtained from this equation is shown in the upper part of Fig. 11-12. The intercept time T_i can be obtained by subtracting x/V_m from the righthand side of the equation.

To put this relationship into useful form it is necessary to express T, in terms of the depth H. If the velocity v_H is written as $V_0 + kH$, we have

$$T = \frac{2}{k} \left[\cosh^{-1} \frac{V_m}{V_0} - \cosh^{-1} \frac{V_m}{V_0 + kH} - \sqrt{1 - \left(\frac{V_0}{V_m}\right)^2} + \sqrt{1 - \left(\frac{V_0 + kH}{V_m}\right)^2} \right]$$

(11-47)

This equation shows the functional relationship between T_i and H, but it cannot be solved explicitly for H. To determine H, one can plot Eq. (11-47) using the marker depth H as the independent variable and introduce appropriate values for V_0, V_m, and k. The depth can be determined implicitly from such a plot when the intercept time is known. An equation like this involving a trial-and-error solution is particularly adaptable for handling by digital computers.

11-6 DELAY TIMES

Refraction interpretation is intrinsically ambiguous because the depths computed from intercept times represent the sum of the respective depths to the marker below the shot and below the detector. If the refracting interface is horizontal, the actual depths are equal at each end and formulas like those in Eq. (11-8) or (11-18) apply. If the interface is an inclined plane, solutions like those developed for this case in a preceding section can be used. Generally, however, the refractor is neither horizontal nor uniformly dipping, as is the case in Fig. 11-13, so that separating the depths at the two ends of the trajectory will require special interpretation techniques.

The concept of *delay time*, introduced by Gardner,[14,15] is convenient for carrying out this separation. The intercept time $T - x/V_1$ may be considered to be made up of two *delay times*: D_1, associated with the shot end of the trajectory, and D_2, associated with the detector end. The principle underlying the separation of the intercept time into its component delay times is illustrated in Fig. 11-13.

The interface shown in the diagram lies at depths of z_1 below the shot and z_2 below the geophone. Immediately below the shot and geophone, the interface is horizontal; between these flat portions the interface slopes so gently that the horizontal distance deviates only negligibly from the actual slant distance.

The intercept time is the difference between the actual travel time of the wave and the time that would be required if the wave traveled horizontally between shot and detector at the highest speed encountered along the refrac-

FIGURE 11-13 Separation of intercept times into delay times where depth is different under shot O than that under receiver at D.

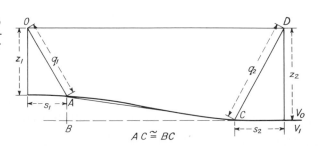

tion path. The portion of the path along the refractor will not enter into the calculation as long as its dip is so small that AC can be considered equal to BC. Virtually all the intercept time is associated with the slant paths q_1 and q_2.

In the case shown, the delay time D_1 for the shot end is simply $q_1/V_0 - s_1/V_1$, while the delay time D_2 for the detector end is $q_2/V_0 - s_2/V_1$. Expressed in terms of depths and velocities,

$$D_1 = z_1 \frac{\sqrt{V_1{}^2 - V_0{}^2}}{V_1 V_0} = \frac{z_1 \cos i_c}{V_0} \tag{11-48}$$

and

$$D_2 = z_2 \frac{\sqrt{V_1{}^2 - V_0{}^2}}{V_1 V_0} = \frac{z_2 \cos i_c}{V_0} \tag{11-49}$$

Thus the depths at each end can be determined if the intercept time can be separated into component delay times. If the interface is horizontal, each of the two delay times is half the intercept time.

Since delay times are never measurable directly, it is necessary to separate the observed intercept time into its component delay times by indirect means. Some techniques for accomplishing this separation will be discussed in Sec. 9-8.

11-7 REFRACTION OPERATIONS IN THE FIELD

There is little difference between the organization of refraction and reflection parties. Most crews can shift with ease from one type of operation to the other by making some minor changes in their equipment, usually by substituting lower-frequency for higher-frequency geophones. Normally a refraction crew needs more surveyors than a reflection crew, and it may be most efficient for two shooting units to operate at the same time. Radio communication is essential in refraction although it is not always used in reflection shooting.

It is generally desirable to use lower-frequency instruments in refraction recording than in reflection work because refracted signals travel much greater distances than reflections. In early refraction work in Iran, where recording distances were particularly great, the first arrivals had exceptionally low frequencies, often less than 5 Hz, and detectors as large as wastebaskets were employed. In most refraction shooting, however, the distances are such that the first arrivals seldom have frequencies lower than 10 Hz. Many geophones used in reflection recording can handle refraction signals of 10 Hz or less. Thus there is an overlap between the frequency bands in which reflection and refraction geophones are sensitive that often makes it possible to use reflection phones for refraction surveys with good results, especially where recording distances are not much greater than 10 mi.

For reconnaissance surveys in new areas, profiles are usually shot in reverse directions with progressively increasing shot-detector distances in order to obtain a complete set of time-distance curves. These curves provide the ve-

FIGURE 11-14 Typical time-distance curves obtained on refraction profile in west Texas. Numbers on time-distance segments are inverse slopes or apparent speeds. Average speed of zone just below uppermost low-speed layer is 8200 ft/s; of next layer, 15,200 ft/s; and of deepest layer, 19,000 ft/s. Thickness of each zone can be determined from intercept times. (*After Harris and Peabody.*[16])

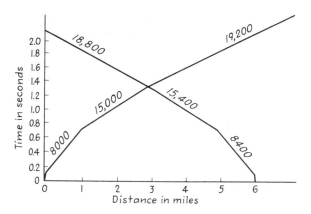

locity information needed for calculating depths from refraction times. They also establish the range of shot-detector distances that should be used over the area when any particular marker horizon is to be mapped. Figure 11-14 illustrates the type of information obtained from such profiles. The two shot locations are fixed, and the geophone spreads are moved progressively to obtain complete two-way coverage over the line between the shots. Each zone of discrete speed in the earth is represented by a pair of linear segments on the time-distance plot. Suppose, for example, that the top of the second zone, with an average speed of 15,200 ft/s, is being mapped. We see from the time-distance plot that the shot-detector distances should be confined to the range between 1 and 3 mi if this is the only marker of interest in the area.

11-8 REFRACTION RECORDS; FIRST AND SECOND EVENTS

Figure 11-15 shows two typical refraction records from the foothills of western Canada which were shot from opposite directions, each being recorded with a spread of 22 detectors spaced 300 ft apart along a profile in line with the shots. It is evident from the times marked on each record that the shot moments, not shown, occurred about 1.75 s before the first signals from each shot arrived at the nearest detectors. The first arrival at each detector is indicated on the corresponding trace by a pronounced rise in amplitude above the background level, after which the level of ground motion decreases somewhat but still remains much more active than before. On the records shown, each arrival is characterized by an "upkick" followed by a trough and a subsequent peak. The troughs, which are blacked in, are easier to correlate from trace to trace across the records than the actual first breaks are. From the moveouts of about 0.440 s across each of the 6300-ft spreads, it is apparent that the first arrival has an apparent speed of about 14,200 ft/s.

At times 0.2 to 0.3 s later on the upper record and at 0.4 to 0.5 s later on the lower record a similar set of events is observed These are *second arrivals*. Their apparent velocity is observed to be much higher, as is evident from the

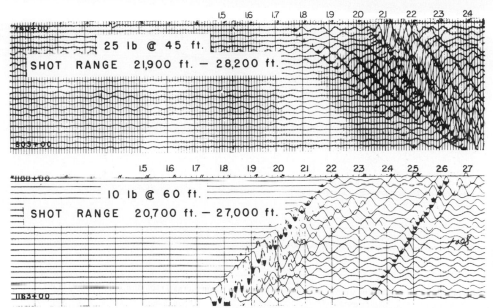

FIGURE 11-15   Two typical refraction records, shot in opposite directions, from foothills of Canadian Rockies. Earliest events on the respective records are from marker with speed of about 14,000 ft/s. Second events are from higher-speed and deeper refractor, in this case the Rundle limestone. (*After Blundun*.[17])

shorter times needed for the events from the respective shooting directions to cross the records. The speed turns out to be about 21,000 ft/s, which identifies the second arrivals as coming from the high-speed Rundle limestone.

In the first decade or so of refraction shooting, it was seldom possible to identify any arrival later than the first on the records, and operational and interpretation techniques were based almost entirely on use of first-arrival times. Subsequent instrumental improvements have made detection and resolution of later arrivals feasible in many areas, particularly in marine recording of refractions using sonobuoys. For reasons which are not well understood, second arrivals are not generally distinguishable on seismic traces, even when the background noise level is low at the time on the record when such events would be expected. The foothills area east of the Canadian Rockies, where the records in Fig. 11-15 were shot, appears to be a classic location for good reception of second arrivals, and most of the refraction work carried out there since the middle 1950s has been designed for recording such events.

The earliest description of second-event refraction work was published by Gamburtsev,[18] who discussed techniques used in the U.S.S.R. around 1940. The earliest account of North American refraction work using second arrivals is by Gillin and Alcock.[19]

For second-event shooting the range of shot-detector distances is kept within the crossover distance for the refractor to be mapped, as shown in Fig.

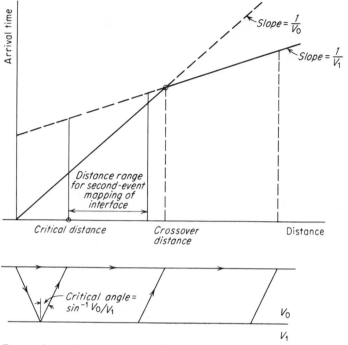

FIGURE 11-16 Range of shot-detector distances for second-event mapping of interface at base of V_0 layer. The range does not extend to the crossover distance because second arrivals become difficult to pick at too short a time after the first arrival.

11-16. Because this distance range is shorter than would be necessary for first-event mapping, the field operations can be carried out more economically and efficiently, and the interpretation of the data is generally not so subject to ambiguity. Less dynamite is necessary for the shorter receiving distances, and radio communication is less subject to interference. Logistics can also be simplified. With the shot-detector distances shorter, the refracting points at the shot and geophone ends of the trajectory may be so close together that the depths corresponding to each will not generally be much different. Thus the problem of converting intercept times into delay times becomes simpler.

Second and even later arrivals are often readily discernible on record sections obtained directly on drum recorders or, after processing, in playback centers from signals received by, and transmitted from, sonobuoys in marine refraction operations. The sections thus obtained are effectively time-distance plots which by preserving a record of the waveforms contain information that can be more useful for interpretation than conventionally plotted time-distance data.

Figure 11-17 is a typical section from a sonobuoy survey covering a distance of about 50,000 ft. The water-wave arrival serves to calibrate the distance scale, as the velocity of sound in water is deduced from the water temperature

FIGURE 11-17   Typical sonobouy refraction profile made in processing center from digital tape recording on ship. First arrivals observable to a distance of about 40,000 ft from source. (*Petty-Ray Geophysical Division, Geosource Inc.*)

and salinity. First, second, and later arrivals, as well as some reflections (identified by their characteristic curvature), are readily distinguished by inspection.

The presentation of the data on such record sections makes it easier to recognize refraction arrivals from thin beds, i.e., beds having thicknesses less than a wavelength. Arrivals from such beds lose amplitude more rapidly with distance than those from formations which are at least a wavelength thick, and the loss of energy thus observed on the sections could identify the refractors as thin layers.

11-9   INTERPRETATION FOR COMMON SHOOTING ARRANGEMENTS

In planning refraction surveys in the field, the arrangement of shots and detectors is determined by a number of factors such as the geologic problem involved, the terrain, and the facilities available. Most of the standard arrangements are designed to facilitate the separation of intercept times into delay times. For this reason, different interpretation techniques have been developed for different shooting configurations. In this section, a number of widely used field arrangements and the interpretation methods designed for them will be discussed together.

Profile Shooting

In profile shooting, the most widely used of all field techniques for refraction work, the shots and detectors are laid out on long lines. Successive shots are taken at uniform or almost uniform intervals along each line, and successive detector spreads are shifted about the same distance as the corresponding shot points in order to keep the range of shot-detector distances approximately the same for all shots. Shots are generally received from opposite directions on each detector spread. Figure 11-18 illustrates a typical arrangement.

The distance range is chosen so that the first (or, where desired, the second) arrivals will be refracted from formations of interest such as the basement or a high-speed limestone marker. The proper distance is usually determined from a time-distance plot like that illustrated in Fig. 11-14, which is based on experimental shooting carried out early in the program.

The principal problem in profile interpretation is to convert the intercept times into delay times which represent the respective depths to the marker under shot and receiver. Several techniques for determining the individual delay times from the intercept times have been reported in the literature and will be reviewed here.

FIGURE 11-18
Typical shooting and receiving arrangement along refraction profile. Shots A and A', fired successively, are picked up by detectors 1A to 12A, etc.

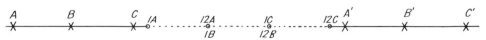

Barthelmes' Procedure   One of the simplest methods has been described by Barthelmes.[20] It requires that the depth to the mapped horizon be known at one point on the profile, as would be the case if the profile were tied to a well. To determine the depths at other points along the profile, it is only necessary to know the differences between intercept times at the other points and that at the known point.

The relation between the difference in depth Δz and the differential intercept time ΔT_i at two detectors a distance x apart is evident from the relation (for the two-layer case)

$$z = \frac{V_0 V_1}{2 \sqrt{V_1{}^2 - V_0{}^2}} T_i \qquad (11\text{-}50)$$

so that

$$\Delta z = \frac{V_0 V_1}{2 \sqrt{V_1{}^2 - V_0{}^2}} \Delta T_i \qquad (11\text{-}51)$$

In applying this method, one must bear in mind that the point at which the depth applies is not directly under the shot or detector but is offset either toward the shot or toward the detector, as shown in Fig. 11-19, by a distance

$$q = z \tan i_c \qquad (11\text{-}52)$$

in the single-layer case or

$$q = z_0 \tan i_0 + z_1 \tan i_1 + z_2 \tan i_2 \qquad (11\text{-}53)$$

in the case where the ray path has three slanting segments. The angles are determined by Snell's law from the speeds of the successive layers.

The relative dip curve is actually made up from intercept times computed at

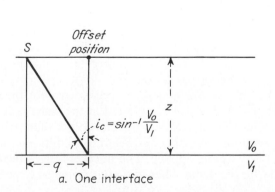

a. One interface

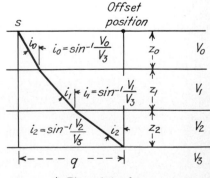

b. Three interfaces

all detector positions along the profile. The intercept-time curves for adjacent surface spreads where different shot points have been used will not appear as continuous segments, but the dips, averaged for opposite directions of shooting after the shifts for offset have been made, can be followed to make up a continuous line which is a kind of "phantom" dip horizon. It is this line which is tied to the well or other point where the depth is known.

Wyrobek-Gardner Method Where continuous two-way subsurface coverage is available along the profile over the marker to be mapped and where the marker has dips no greater than 10°, the separation of the intercept times into delay times is fairly unambiguous. Continuous coverage makes it possible to determine the *differences* in delay time (and hence in depth) between the offset positions along the refractor corresponding to the shots and those corresponding to the various receiving stations. The intercept time observed at each geophone station gives the *sums* of the two delay times corresponding respectively to the shot and geophone positions. As both the sums and differences are thus known, it is a simple matter to compute their values along the profile and to map depths uniquely.

Wyrobek[21] and Gardner[14] have independently developed interpretational techniques for two-way continuous coverage over gently dipping markers. The techniques differ more in details of execution than in principle. The Wyrobek method makes use of special graphical aids designed to facilitate routine computations and it may be more handy for routine use. Being based on the same principle, both methods should yield about the same information.

As previously noted, the dip of the marker bed must be small (less than 10°), and the structure of overlying formations must be sufficiently uniform for the section above the marker to be represented as a single homogeneous layer. Continuous control is necessary, preferably two-way, but if the shooting pattern is properly designed, and if the marker velocity has been well established, shooting from a single direction will yield data suitable for interpretation by this method.

Figure 11-20 illustrates the steps employed in the Wyrobek approach, starting with a plot of arrival time T versus detector position for all receiving stations along the profile. These steps are:

1 From the slopes, averaged in both directions, of numerous characteristic segments on the time-distance plot corresponding to the horizon to be mapped, an average marker velocity V_2 is determined for intercept-time calculations.

2 The values for the intercept time, $T - x/V_2$, are computed for all arrivals and are plotted at the respective detector positions along the profile. Values for opposite directions of shooting are plotted at the same receiving positions.

3 It is important to guard against the possibility that arrivals received from the opposite directions have been refracted from different marker horizons. A reciprocity test is therefore applied. The intercept times between any shot and receiver should be the same when the shot point and receiver positions are

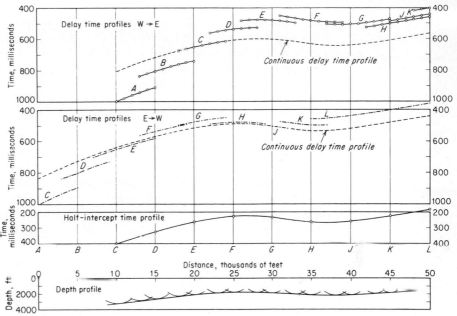

FIGURE 11-20 Steps in conversion of delay-time profiles shot from opposite directions to final depth using Wyrobek method. (*After Wyrobek.*[21])

interchanged. For example, the intercept time for a receiver at shot point *K* from a source at shot point *H* should be the same as the intercept time for a receiver at shot point *H* from a source at shot point *K*. If it is not, the events picked on the respective records do not correspond to equivalent wave paths in the earth and a new cycle must be picked on one of the records.

4 On the intercept-time plots, continuous lines are drawn having the slopes of the successive intercept-time segments along the profile. These are designated as *relative curves*. The vertical positions of these curves are chosen arbitrarily.

5 Intercept times are now determined at the shot points for the opposite directions of shooting. The respective values at each shot point are averaged, and the averages are divided by 2 and plotted at the shot-point positions as *half-intercept times*. The points thus plotted are used, on a best-fit basis, to provide an absolute reference for the relative delay-time curves.

6 The two relative curves for the respective direction of shooting are transferred to separate pieces of transparent paper or acetate which can be superimposed on the original plot. The lines are then shifted from their original horizontal positions in the directions of the respective shot points for each curve. This shifting takes care of the horizontal offset between refracting point and surface receiver. The proper amount of shift is considered to be that for which the curves come closest to coinciding in shape. If there is a systematic divergence between the curves after the lateral shifting, they are tilted by an equal angle in opposite directions until the best coincidence is observed. Such tilting will be necessary if the velocity chosen for the intercept-time determination is not equal to the actual velocity over the profile. The amount of tilt, incidentally, gives measure of a true average velocity which can be applied in the initial determination of intercept times.

7 After the two relative curves are offset and tilted where necessary, a relative curve averaging the dips of the individual curves is drawn to represent the true dip along the profile. The average curve is fitted to the half-intercept times plotted at the shot points by vertical shifting and by further tilting when required. This represents the delay-time curve for the profile.

8 Values of the delay time D picked at each shot from the final profile thus plotted are multiplied by an appropriate factor F for conversion to depth. For a homogeneous overburden with a velocity V_1, this factor is $V_1 V_2 / \sqrt{V_2^2 - V_1^2}$, where V_2 is the marker speed. Arcs with a radius equal to FD are drawn at regular intervals on a vertical cross section with a 1:1 distance scale. A smooth-line tangent to these arcs gives the depth profile.

The procedure outlined above is applicable only to relatively shallow horizons where there is no appreciable change in dip over a horizontal distance equal to the offset distance. Computerized versions of similar methods are often used for weathering determination in reflection shooting. For deep refractors, Wyrobek outlines a more complex technique.

In Gardner's variation upon this technique, delay times are obtained from the averaged relative curve and the observed intercept time at each detector position. The following relation is used to separate the intercept time into a delay time D_1 under the shot and delay time D_2 under the receiver:

$$D_1 - D_2 = \Delta D$$

along the composite relative curve between the respective ends of the wave trajectory.

$$D_1 + D_2 = T_i = \text{intercept time}$$

Since ΔD and T_i are known, D_1 and D_2 can readily be determined.

Slotnick Method   A graphical technique has been developed by Slotnick[22] for interpreting refraction data where successively deeper marker beds have dips that differ from one another. It is quite useful where the beds maintain their identities without change of velocity over appreciable distances along the profile. The method involves the optical tracing of rays from the surface downward through the various layers in the subsurface and back up to the detector. This is done by applying the laws of refraction to velocities observed

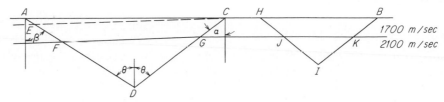

FIGURE 11-21 Construction for applying Slotnick method to two-layer problem. (*After Slotnick.*[22])

for opposite directions of shooting along the profile. The depths and dips of successively deeper interfaces are determined by working downward one layer at a time from an arrival time corresponding to wave travel along the top of that layer.

In the Slotnick method the slopes of the various segments of the time-distance curves are used to determine the angle of approach at the surface for the waves refracted along the interfaces corresponding to the respective segments. With the angle of approach to the surface known, a ray can be traced to the marker along which it travels by using Snell's law at each interface. The total travel time is used to calculate the depth of the marker.

The method can be illustrated by a simple example, taken from Slotnick's paper, which is for a two-layer earth with a dipping interface between the layers (Fig. 11-21). From other work in the area it has been established that the true velocities of the two layers represented here are 1700 and 2100 m/s, respectively. The critical angle θ is thus $\sin^{-1}(1700/2100) = 54°$. At point C the emergence angle α is $\sin^{-1}(1700/2130) = 53°$, where 2130 m/s is the apparent speed at C. At point A, the emergence angle β can be obtained from the relation

$$\beta = 2\theta - \alpha = 108° - 53° = 55°$$

We then draw CD so that $\alpha = 53°$ and AD so that $\beta = 55°$. The point E is then located so that DE will equal DC. AE is scaled off and found to be 85 m. The travel time recorded for the trajectory $AFGC$ is 1.588 s while the time from A to E is

$$t_{AE} = \frac{85 \text{ m}}{1700 \text{ m/s}} = 0.05 \text{ s}$$

The remaining time t along the path EDC is $1.588 - 0.050 = 1.538$ s. This must be separated into two portions, one corresponding to slant-path travel through the upper layer at 1700 m/s and the other corresponding to travel along the interface at 2100 m/s. The distance CE is scaled off and found to be 2930 m.

The slant distance a, which is equal to CG or EF, is determined from the observed time t, the velocities, and the distance CE (here designated as d) from the formula

$$a = \frac{V_1 t - d}{2(V_1/V_0 - V_0/V_1)} \qquad (11\text{-}54)$$

where V_1 and V_0 are the respective velocities for the upper and lower media. Applying this to the calculation of CG or EF, we find that

$$a = \frac{2100 \times 1.538 - 2930}{2(2100/1700 - 1700/2100)} = 350 \text{ m}$$

The points G and F are scaled off on CD and AD, respectively, so that $CG = EF = a = 350$ m. The line FG, which is located by connecting F and G, is the required refracting surface.

A similar calculation at B and H for the ray path $BKJH$ on the right-hand side of the profile gives the line JK as the refracting surface in the neighborhood of shot point B. These lines may be joined as shown.

The same approach can be applied to map deeper interfaces, each boundary being used progressively in tracing rays to the next lower surface of velocity discontinuity. In the example for which the beginning step is shown above, Slotnick maps four interfaces separating five layers with different velocities.

Wavefront Method Although the wavefront technique was first demonstrated as early as 1930 by Thornburgh,[23] it did not take its place as an established method of refraction interpretation until more recently. Rockwell[24] has published a comprehensive survey of this method which presents more complicated applications than will be discussed here.

Figure 11-22 should be helpful in visualizing how the method works. This diagram shows that as successive individual wavefronts reach the first interface, the ray corresponding to the point of contact is bent in accordance with Snell's law as it passes into the second layer. The wavefront perpendicular to it

FIGURE 11-22 Wavefront travel in two-interface case. Each continuous line represents position of wavefront at successive tenths of second after shot. Crossover distances are SC and SD. (*After Thornburgh.*[23])

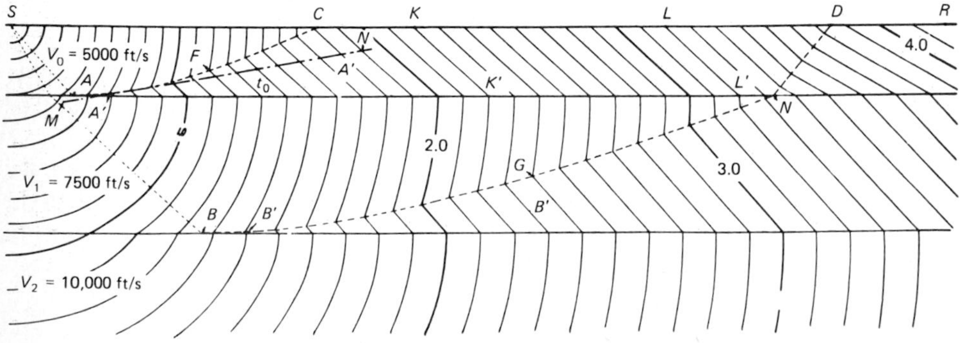

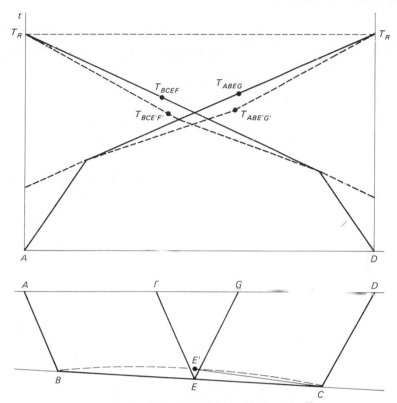

FIGURE 11-23   Use of reciprocal times to locate points along a refracting surface.

is also bent, as shown. Just below the deepest interface, the wavefront is oriented vertically until it peels off and returns to the surface at the critical angle, as illustrated in Fig. 11-1. Every wavefront is labeled by the time it represents.

The times for intersecting wavefronts from sources in opposite directions can be used to map structures of refracting interfaces by use of the relation demonstrated in Fig. 11-23. This shows two shot points, A and D, with recording positions laid out between them along the surface. As the time from A to D will be the same regardless of which point is the source and which the receiver, we can designate the equivalent times T_{ABCD} and T_{DCBA} as the reciprocal time T_R.

At a refracting point E from which the respective rays EF and EG leave the boundary at the critical angle in opposite directions, it is easy to see from the diagram that

$$T_R = T_{ABEG} + T_{DCEF} - T_{EF} - T_{EG}$$

or

$$T_R = T_{ABE} + T_{DCE} \qquad (11\text{-}55)$$

if E lies along a straight line connecting B and C.

If the marker does not have excessive relief, E can depart appreciably from such a line without introducing an unacceptable amount of error in the depth determination. As a rule of thumb, convolutions of the marker surface (as illustrated by the dashed line $BE'C$) can be accommodated up to the point where the angle $E'CE$ is as great as $10°$.

If wavefronts are constructed from both shot points, any point where the two wavefronts for respective times which add up to T_R intersect will lie along the surface of the refractor. The wavefronts for each shot point can be constructed by starting from the source as was done by Thornburgh (Fig. 11-22). It is more convenient, however, to work backwards from the receiving point, as illustrated by Fig. 11-24. We need to know the velocity V_0 of the material above the refracting surface, and this can be obtained from the time-distance curve.

Consider the segment of the time-distance curve for arrivals from shot A at a distance of 27,000 ft. As the arrival time at this distance is 3.0 s, the surface trace of the wavefront for a travel time of 3.0 s must pass through this point. At 23,000 ft, the 2.5-s wavefront intersects the surface. Now if the velocity V_0 is 6000 ft/s, the 2.5-s wavefront will also pass through a point below the surface from which the time of travel to the 3.0-s emergence point P is 0.5 s. This subsurface point can be located by striking an arc centered at P having a radius of $0.5V_0$ or 3000 ft. A line through Q tangent to this arc defines the course of the 2.5-s wavefront as it approaches the earth's surface. By the same mechanism, the emerging wavefront corresponding to 2.0 s can be constructed by drawing a line from R that is tangent to an arc 3000 ft in radius corresponding to a travel time from Q of 0.5 s and also tangent to a second arc centered at P with a 6000-ft radius corresponding to a travel time from P of 1.0 s. Applying this procedure, one can draw a family of wavefronts for refracted events from A corresponding to any desired time interval. These are the full lines which are inclined to the right.

The same method can be employed to construct wavefronts for the arrivals from shot point B and a family of such waves at 0.5-s intervals is also shown, being indicated on the diagram by the dotted lines inclined to the left.

According to the time-distance plot in the upper part of Fig. 11-24, the reciprocal time for shot poins A and B is 4.8 s, and the marker surface is located wherever the *sum* of the times for crossing wavefronts from the respective shot points equals 4.8 s. A series of intersections where the times conform to this condition is indicated on the cross section of Fig. 11-24, and the smooth curve connecting them is the desired marker surface in the plane of the profile.

The wavefront technique can be used for a multilayered subsurface if the velocity of each layer is known. Once the structure of the shallowest boundary

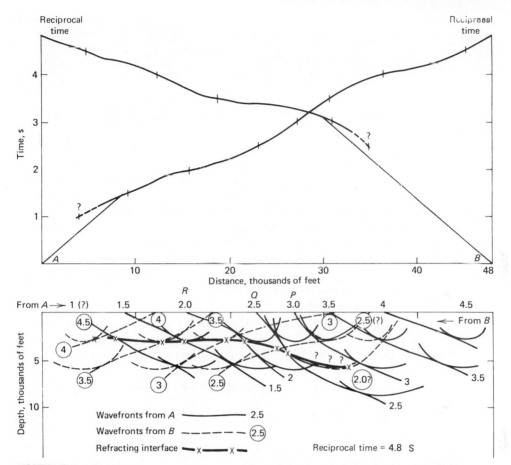

FIGURE 11-24
Example of how wavefront method can be applied to obtain structure from reversed time-distance curves.

has been determined by the method we have illustrated, the next interface is constructed by extending the wavefronts downward from points along the boundary and repeating the process, using such points as the source of new arcs, drawn with proper radii, for tracing the wavefronts into the lower medium. Deeper interfaces can be mapped in the same way by peeling off successive layers as their bases are mapped. It is only necessary that the velocities of the layers be known, and they can generally be determined from the two-way time-distance segments for the respective layers.

Tarrant Method The Tarrant method[25] was designed for cases where the subsurface marker is so irregular that it is difficult or impossible to select segments from the time-distance curves for the respective directions of shooting that correspond to the same part of the refractor.

Going back to the definition of delay time as given on page 472, we see from Fig. 11-13 that

$$D_1 = \frac{q_1}{V_0} - \frac{s_1}{V_1} = \frac{q_1}{V_0} - \frac{q_1 \cos \phi}{V_1} \qquad (11\text{-}56)$$

where ϕ is the angle made by OA with the horizontal. As $V_0/V_1 = \sin i_c$, it follows that

$$q_1 = \frac{V_0 D_1}{1 - \sin i_c \cos \phi} \qquad (11\text{-}57)$$

This is the equation of an ellipse with one focus at the origin having a semi-minor axis of $V_1 D_1 \tan i_c$ and a semimajor axis of $V_0 D_1/(\cos^2 i_c)$. The center of the ellipse is displaced horizontally from the focus by a distance $V_1 D_1 \tan^2 i_c$.

In applying this method, V_0 and V_1 are determined from time-distance relations over the area or from well-velocity information. Intercept times are separated into delay times by some technique appropriate to the type of data available. An ellipse is then constructed for each detector station using the constants given above. The envelope of the family of ellipses thus obtained is the desired refracting surface.

When the dips are not large, it is often permissible to approximate the ellipses by circular arcs, which are much simpler to draw. The radius R of the circle having the same curvature as the ellipse just below its center is

$$R = V_1 D_1 (\tan i_c + \tan^3 i_c) \qquad (11\text{-}58)$$

Hales' Method   This graphical technique, devised by Hales[26] for interpreting refracton profiles, is particularly applicable to high-relief structures. With the Hales method, it is only necessary to identify the sections of time-distance curves for opposite directions of shooting that correspond to arrivals from the marker horizon to be mapped. The geometrical relations involved in the method are illustrated in Fig. 11-25.

The technique is designed to locate the position of a refracting point such as F by determining the distance between the two points at which refracted rays originating from shot points A and D, respectively, and traveling upward from F in opposite directions reach the surface. If an arbitrary point C is chosen along the time-distance curve for shot point A, a simple construction is used to locate the point B, at which the ray originating from shot point D and leaving the marker surface at F reaches the surface.

The distance X_R is obtained by drawing a line on the time-distance plot from point P (a distance AC from A and a time T_{AEFC} below the reciprocal time) with a slope equal to $V_1 \sin i_c$, where i_c, the critical angle, is $\sin^{-1}(V_0/V_1)$, and noting the intersection at Q of this diagonal line with the segment of the time-distance

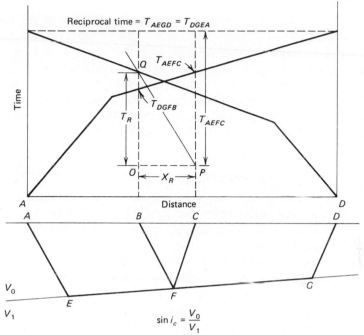

FIGURE 11-25 Finding T_R and X_R from reversed time-distance curves by Hales' method.

plot from shot point D. The time T_R is found graphically as shown in the figure. The horizontal distance PO is equal to X_R.

With T_R and X_R known, the refractor position is determined by a construction of the type shown in Fig. 11-26. B and C are located a distance X_R apart

FIGURE 11-26 Use of Hales' method for locating position of refractor using data from time-distance curves representing shots from opposite directions.

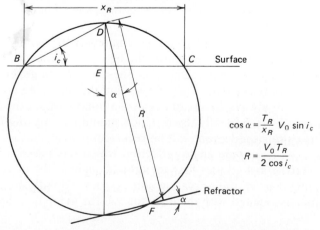

along a horizontal line. Then a line is drawn from B at an angle i_c with BC and its intersection with the perpendicular bisector of BC becomes the point from which line DF, having a length R (the formula for which is indicated), is drawn at an angle α (also defined) with the vertical. The perpendicular to DF at F gives the position of the refracting surface through point F.

A series of constructions like this are made at intervals along the time-distance curve, and the refractor is mapped over the entire range where arrivals from it are received. Derivation of the relations used in the reductions are presented in detail by Musgrave[27](p. 268).

General Discussion of Profile Interpretation Methods

It is evident that there is a wide variety of techniques available for interpreting data from in-line refraction profiles. Most of them are designed primarily for two-layer problems, although many can be adapted to multilayered configurations. The Slotnick method is most suitable for a multiplicity of layers with the boundaries between them having different dips. Many of the methods, such as the Wyrobek and wavefront techniques, are accurate when the dip of the refractor is gentle (say less than 10°), while others, such as the Hales and Tarrant methods, can be applied where refractor dips are steep. The nature of the subsurface and the type of data available will ordinarily govern the choice of the interpretation method to be employed.

Broadside Shooting

In some areas it is not feasible to use profile shooting techniques to determine the structure across strike. As an alternative, broadside shooting may provide a convenient and economical method of getting the desired information. The broadside lines are often laid out in conjunction with conventional profiles that run along strike. In the Alberta foothills, for example, the steep dips in the high-speed Rundle limestone, which is the refraction marker, make it difficult to get useful information from profile shooting perpendicular to geological and topographic strike.

The field setup is illustrated schematically in Fig. 11-27, and a typical group of correlated records is shown in Fig. 11-28. The shot points and detector spreads are laid out along parallel lines, which are generally across strike. The distance between each line of shots and the receiving line should be chosen so that it will always be greater than the double offset distance for the refractor being followed. Ideally the distance should be only slightly greater so that the primary refracted event will be received as a second arrival or, as Richards[28] suggests, as a wide-angle reflection which has taken a path making an angle equal to or just greater than the critical angle at the marker surface. When this spacing is used, the refracting point associated with the shot will be very close to that associated with the detector and the delay time for each will be approx-

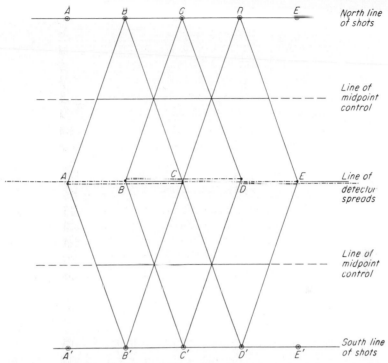

FIGURE 11-27   Shot and geophone pattern for broadside shooting. Adjacent spreads overlap 50 percent, so that subsurface midpoint control is continuous along indicated lines on both sides of the receiving line.

imately half the intercept time. A single depth point (based on half the intercept time) is then plotted midway between shot and receiver. All depth points can thus be plotted along the *control lines* which are located halfway between the shooting line and the receiving line. For shot-detector distances much greater than the critical distance, such plotting can lead to some error in mapping the structure of the marker.

Whenever possible, the broadsides should be tied to an in-line profile where delay times and depths have been determined at the subsurface tie point by one of the profiling methods. In second-event work, it is particularly desirable to have such a tie, since it is often difficult to identify the correct peak or trough on the broadside records. Where the broadside is tied to an in-line, the respective records at the tie point can be correlated and the apparent speed on the in-line record can be used to identify the proper pick on the broadside. If the same cycle is not followed on all broadsides and in-lines, the final map will be in error.

Blundun[17] has described broadside refraction operations in the Alberta foothills, where this kind of shooting had provided the most economical

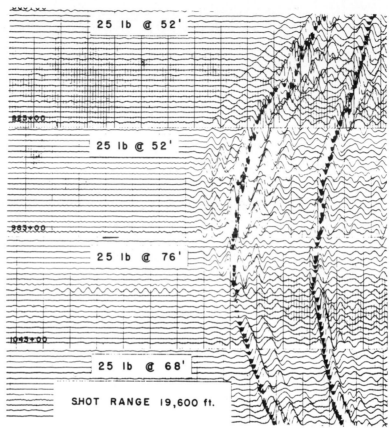

FIGURE 11-28 Four refraction records made in the foothills of Alberta from a single shot point with adjacent geophone spreads along a broadside. Second and later events are marked. (*After Blundun.*[17])

method for obtaining structural information on a reconnaissance basis. This method made it possible to observe faults in the high-speed limestone directly on the records and thus to map their location without having to wait for completion of the interpretation over the entire area of the survey.

11-10 CORRECTIONS USED IN REFRACTION ANALYSIS

Refraction times must be corrected for elevation and for changes in the thickness of the weathered layer. The former correction removes differences in travel times due only to variations in the surface elevation of the shots and detector stations. The weathering correction, like the comparable reduction in reflection work, removes differences in travel time through the near-surface zone of unconsolidated, low-speed sediments which may vary in thickness from place to place. Similar corrections are made in reducing reflection times, but the slant paths along which most refraction ray paths leave and approach the surface and the common use of intercept or delay times in refraction interpretation create a need for somewhat more complex correction procedures.

Elevation Correction   The most usual computational procedure is to put both the shot and the detector on the same imaginary datum plane by subtracting the times that would be required for the wave to travel from the datum to the respective shot or detector locations if they are higher than the datum or by adding the times that would be required if they are lower.

Figure 11-29 demonstrates how this transformation is accomplished. Assume that both the shot and the detector are above the datum plane. We wish to place the shot point at P on the datum plane directly below the shot hole and the detector at point Q on the datum plane below E. The hypothetical ray path after the correction is shown by the dotted line The difference between the time from A to D along the actual path and that from P to D along the hypothetical path is

$$\frac{AB}{V_0} \quad \frac{CD}{V_1} - \frac{AB}{V_0} - \frac{PB}{V_1} \equiv D_s \qquad (11\text{-}59)$$

which is, by definition, the delay time associated with the layer between the bottom of the shot at elevation $e - h$ and the datum plane at elevation d. This material constitutes a horizontal slab of thickness $e - h - d$. In this case the delay time is

$$D_s = \frac{(e - h - d)\cos i_c}{V_0} = \frac{(e - h - d)\sqrt{V_1^2 - V_0^2}}{V_1 V_0} \qquad (11\text{-}60)$$

Similarly, at the detector end, where the elevation is E, the delay time associated with the path from the surface to the datum is

$$D_d = \frac{(E - d)\sqrt{V_1^2 - V_0^2}}{V_1 V_0} \qquad (11\text{-}61)$$

The sum of these corrections in delay time should be subtracted from the

FIGURE 11-29   Elevation correction for two-layer case; e is shot elevation, E the detector elevation above sea level.

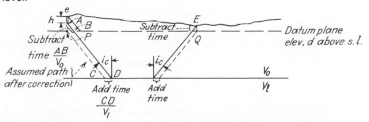

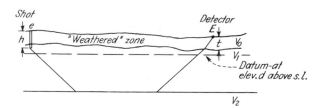

FIGURE 11-30   Correction of refraction times for weathering and elevation.

observed intercept time in order to place both shot and detector effectively in the datum plane. The elevation of the shot is actually the surface elevation at the top of the shothole e minus the depth of the charge in the hole h, so that the final elevation correction to be applied to the intercept time is

$$\text{Elevation corr.} = \frac{(e - h + E - 2d)\sqrt{V_1^2 - V_0^2}}{V_1 V_0} \qquad (11\text{-}62)$$

Weathering Corrections   As with reflection work, uncorrected variations in the thickness of the weathered zone near the surface could easily lead to fictitious structures on horizons mapped from refraction data. There are several methods of correcting for the effect of the weathered layer by determining its speed and thickness and then subtracting the delay time associated with it from the observed intercept time. Because no arrivals from the base of the weathering are ever observed on long-offset refraction records, it is necessary to correct for weathering by shooting with short shot-geophone distances. The thickness t of the low-speed material above the first velocity discontinuity (Fig. 11-30) is calculated from the intercept times using the two-layer depth-intercept-time formula. The delay time associated with this low-speed layer can now be removed from the intercept time for the regular refraction shot recorded at the same position. Elevation corrections are then made from the base of the weathered layer at the detector end of the trajectory and from the bottom of the shot hole (which usually penetrates the weathered layer). Thus the total correction (weathering plus elevation), to be subtracted from the intercept time, is the delay time associated with the weathered zone plus the delay time for the layer between weathered zone and datum plane, plus the delay time from the bottom of the shot hole to the datum. Adding these times together, we obtain a total correction

$$\text{Total corr.} = [(e - h - d) + (E - t - d)]\frac{\sqrt{V_2^2 - V_1^2}}{V_1 V_2} + \frac{t\sqrt{V_2^2 - V_0^2}}{V_2 V_0}$$

$$(11\text{-}63)$$

The term in brackets can of course be simplified to $e + E - h - t - 2d$.

11-11 DETAILING SALT DOMES BY REFRACTION

Although the fan-shooting technique was highly successful during the 1920s in discovering shallow salt domes, it was not suitable for locating domes with tops many thousands of feet deep because of limited penetration in the Gulf Coast sedimentary section. McCollum and LaRue[29] proposed a variation on the technique in which the fans would center around a detector located in a deep well, radiating outward to a group of near-surface shot points placed at intervals around a ring. Any time leads noted from such a three-dimensional fan would suggest the presence of a deep salt dome which might not be detectable using a conventional fan consisting of phones on the surface. They suggested that the time differences at various detector depths in the well could be used to define the shape of such a dome as well as to determine the presence and extent of overhang.

Gardner[30] described a similar technique for detailing the boundaries of a salt dome by using a detector in a deep well which penetrates or flanks the dome. Shots were fired from points near the surface so chosen that the vertical planes determined by the well and the respective shot points will cut the salt dome at well-distributed angles. Since part of the total time from shot to well detector is through the sediments and part through the higher-speed salt, the problem is to determine how much of the trajectory lies in each medium. The locus of the salt boundary must satisfy the condition that the sum of the two times equals the observed time for each shot-detection combination. The envelope of these loci should correspond to the boundary between the salt and the sediments.

Gardner's method has been applied by Musgrave et al.[31] to the delineation of shale bodies as well as salt. In mapping salt domes these authors also made use of careful surface-to-surface profiling to define the top surface of the diapiric body and the upper portion of the flanks.

11-12 PRESENTATION OF REFRACTION DATA

The practice, common since 1960, of recording refraction signals on analog or digital tape makes it a simple matter to present refraction data in variable-density or variable-area modes. Such a presentation can often facilitate interpretation. A series of refraction records made from a common shot point with tying geophone spreads at progressively greater distances can be easily plotted in the form of a variable-area section. This will give all the information obtainable from a time-distance plot plus additional data, such as amplitudes, waveforms, and indications of possible second arrivals that are not observable on conventionally plotted time-distance curves.

The section shown in Fig. 11-17 from a sonobuoy profile illustrates the appearance of a refraction record or a series of records from the same shot point after conversion into variable-area form.

By appropriate time shifting it is possible to present refraction signals on sections as plots of intercept time (absolute or relative) versus distance, which, as in the case of broadsides, give structural information very similar to that on a geological cross section. As the intercept time is simply $T - x/V$, it is only necessary to shift the arrival time by an interval equal to the distance x over the marker velocity V to obtain a direct plot of this quantity on the final section.

REFERENCES

1 Society of Exploration Geophysicists: "Seismic Refractoin Prospecting," Albert W. Musgrave (ed.), Banta, Menasha, Wis., 1967.

2 Slotnick, Morris M.: "Lessons in Seismic Computing," Richard A. Geyer (ed.), Society of Exploration Geophysicists, Tulsa, Okla., 1959.

3 Muskat, Morris: The Theory of Refraction Shooting, *Physics*, vol. 4, pp. 14–38, 1933.

4 Dix, C. H.: Refraction and Reflection of Seismic Waves, II: Discussion of the Physics of Refraction Prospecting, *Geophysics*, vol. 4, pp. 238–241, 1939.

5 Soske, Joshua L.: Discussion on the Blind Zone Problem in Engineering Geophysics, *Geophysics*, vol. 24, pp. 359–416, 1959.

6 Thornburgh, H. R.: Wave-Front Diagrams in Seismic Interpretation, *Bull. Am. Assoc. Petrol. Geol.*, vol. 14, pp. 185–200, 1930.

7 Hawkins, L. V., and D. Maggs: Nomograms for Determining Maximum Errors and Limiting Conditions in Seismic Refraction Survey with a Blind Zone Problem, *Geophys. Prospect.*, vol. 9, pp. 526–533, 1961.

8 Trostle, M. E.: Some Aspects of Refraction Shooting through Screening Layers, pp. 469–481 in Ref. 1.

9 Mota, L.: Determination of Dips and Depths of Geological Layers by the Seismic Refraction Method, *Geophysics*, vol. 19, pp. 242–254, 1954.

10 Ewing, Maurice, and L. D. Let: Seismic Propagation Paths, *Trans. Am. Inst. Min. Met. Eng.*, *Geophysical Prospecting*, pp. 245–262, 1932.

11 Kaufman, H.: Velocity Functions in Seismic Prospecting, *Geophysics*, vol. 18, pp. 289–297, 1953.

12 Barry, K. M.: Delay Time and Its Application to Refraction Profile Interpretation, pp. 348–361 in Ref. 1.

13 Gardner, L. W.: Seismograph Prospecting, U.S. Patent 2,153,920, Apr. 11, 1939.

14 Gardner, L. W.: An Areal Plan of Mapping Subsurface Structure by Refraction Shooting, *Geophysics*, vol. 4, pp. 247–259, 1939.

15 Gardner, L. W.: Refraction Seismograph Profile Interpretation, pp. 338–347 in Ref. 1.

16 Harris, Sidon, and Gwendolyn Peabody: Refraction Exploration in West Texas, *Geophysics*, vol. 11, pp. 52–58, 1946.

17 Blundun, G. J.: The Refraction Seismograph in the Alberta Foothills, *Geophysics*, vol. 21, pp. 828–838, 1956.

18 Gamburtsev, G. A.: Correlation Refraction Shooting (condensed by L. W. Gardner), *Geophysics*, vol. 11, pp. 59–65, 1946.

19 Gillin, J. A., and E. D. Alcock: The Correlation Refraction Method of Seismic Surveying, *Geophysics*, vol. 11, pp. 43–51, 1946.

20 Barthelmes, A. J.: Application of Continuous Profiling to Refraction Shooting, *Geophysics*, vol. 11, pp. 24–42, 1946.

21 Wyrobek, S. M.: Application of Delay and Intercept Times in the Interpretation of Multilayer Time-Distance Curves, *Geophys. Prospec.*, vol. 4, pp. 112–130, 1956.

22 Slotnick, M. M.: A Graphical Method for the Interpretation of Refraction Profile Data, *Geophysics*, vol. 15, pp. 163–180, 1950.

23 Thornburgh, H. R.: Wave-Front Diagrams in Seismic Interpretation, *Bull. Am. Assoc. Petrol. Geologists*, vol. 14, pp. 185–200, 1930.

24 Rockwell, Donald W.: General Wavefront Method, pp. 363–415 in Ref. 1.

25 Tarrant, L. H.: A Rapid Method of Determining the Form of a Seismic Refractor from Line Profile Results, *Geophys. Prospect.*, vol. 4, pp. 131–139, 1956.

26 Hales, F. W.: An Accurate Graphical Method for Interpreting Seismic Refraction Lines, *Geophys. Prospect.*, vol. 6, pp. 285–294, 1958.

27 Woolley, W. C., A. W. Musgrave, and Helen Gray: A Method of In-Line Refraction Profiling, p. 287 in Ref. 1.

28 Richards, T. C.: Wide Angle Reflections and Their Application to Finding Limestone Structures in the Foothills of Western Canada, *Geophysics*, vol. 25, pp. 385–407, 1960.

29 McCollum, B., and W. W. LaRue: Utilization of Existing Wells in Seismograph Work, *Bull. Am. Assoc. Petrol. Geol.*, vol. 15, pp. 1409–1417, 1931.

30 Gardner, L. W.: Seismograph Determination of Salt-Dome Boundary Using Well Detector Deep on Dome Flank, *Geophysics*, vol. 14, pp. 29–38, 1949.

31 Musgrave, A. W., W. C. Woolley, and H. Gray: Outlining of Salt Masses by Refraction Methods, *Geophysics*, vol. 25, pp. 141–167, 1960.

CHAPTER 12

GRAVITY PROSPECTING: PRINCIPLES AND INSTRUMENTS

Seismic prospecting, discussed in Chaps. 2 to 11, requires introducing elastic-wave energy (generally artificial) into the earth and recording the energy returned to the surface from buried interfaces. The gravity method, on the other hand, involves measuring a field of force in the earth that is neither generated by the observer nor influenced by anything the observer does. The magnetic method and some electrical techniques involve passive observations of the same kind. All such methods of exploration make use of natural potential fields.

The type of information obtainable from gravity or magnetics is quite different from that which seismic prospecting, especially the seismic reflection method, can yield. Whereas seismic reflection records give a picture of the subsurface that shows detailed structure at many levels at once, the field observed in gravitational or magnetic prospecting is a composite of contributions from all depths within the usual range of exploration interest, and such contributions can be individually resolved only in special cases. Hence one cannot expect to obtain the detailed and relatively precise structural picture from gravity or other potential data that is generally obtainable by seismic methods.

In most gravity surveys the quantity actually observed is not the earth's true gravitational attraction but its variation from one point to another, usually at positions along the earth's surface that are close together. Such lateral differences can be measured more easily than the total gravitational field, and field instruments are designed to measure differences in gravity rather than its actual magnitude.

After appropriate reductions, the variations in gravity observed through such measurements depend only upon lateral changes in the *density* of earth materials in the vicinity of the measuring point. Many types of rocks have characteristic ranges of density which may differ from those of other types that are laterally adjacent. Thus an anomaly in the earth's gravitational attraction can often be related to a buried geological feature, e.g., a salt dome or other diapir, which has limited horizontal extent.

12-1 THE PLACE OF GRAVITY IN OIL AND MINERAL EXPLORATION

The gravity method was initially used in oil exploration for locating salt domes in the Gulf Coast of the United States and Mexico and later for finding anticlinal structures in the midcontinent area. Even now special types of structures in which hydrocarbons are entrapped exhibit such large contrasts in density with respect to surrounding formations that gravity data alone can be used to decide on drilling locations. In northwestern Peru, for example, oil entrapped by block faulting in shallow indurated formations has been found with drilling guided by appropriate anomalies on gravity maps.

Most gravity surveys currently carried out in the search for oil are designed for reconnaissance of large, previously unexplored areas. Where little or no geological information is available in a region, the first question that must be answered is whether a sedimentary basin large enough and thick enough to justify further investigation is present. If the geology is suitable, the gravity method can provide this kind of information rapidly and economically. Most sedimentary rocks have densities lower than basement rocks, and where this condition is met, the density contrast makes it possible to map the boundaries and determine the approximate depth distribution of the sedimentary basins.

Gravity surveys can be particularly useful in the initial exploration of water-covered shelf areas, where no geological information may be available at all. The introduction in the late 1960s of shipborne gravity meters has led to an increased amount of gravity prospecting over continental shelves. Gravity recording can be carried out simultaneously with seismic shooting for only a small incremental cost. The combined gravity and seismic data frequently enable the geophysicist to identify and detail geologic features such as diapiric structures more reliably than would be possible with either method alone.

In analyzing potential fields it is desirable, but not always feasible, to separate effects from different subsurface sources. The greater the difference between the lateral dimensions of the individual sources, the easier it should be to isolate the field associated with each. Techniques have been developed for discriminating between gravity effects from large regional features and those from smaller, generally shallower features having more limited horizontal dimensions. These will be discussed further in Chap. 14.

Gravity appears to have more limited applicability in mineral prospecting. Some ores, such as chromites, have such a high density compared with the material that surrounds them that they can be located directly by detailed gravity surveys. Buried channels that might contain gold or uranium minerals can frequently be located by gravity because the channel fill is less dense than the rock in which the channel has been cut. Regional studies making use of gravity surveys may make it possible to detail major structural features such as faults or lineaments where mineral accumulations are likely to be found.

Gravity surveys are employed in base-metal exploration for a number of purposes. In the southwestern United States they have been used to find shallow bedrock features such as pediments under alluvial cover. In the Canadian Shield they have been carried out to differentiate electromagnetic anomalies caused by massive sulfides from those caused by low-density graphites. Such surveys have also been useful for estimating tonnages in sulfide or iron deposits detected by drilling.

12-2   GRAVITATIONAL FORCE, ACCELERATION, AND POTENTIAL

The expression of gravitational attraction in a form most useful for application to exploration requires an understanding of the basic physical concepts relating force, acceleration, and potential.

Gravitational Force   The theory behind gravitational prospecting is based on Newton's law expressing the force of mutual attraction between two particles in terms of their masses and separation. This law states that two particles of mass m_1 and m_2, respectively, each with dimensions very small compared with the separation r of their centers of mass, will be attracted to one another with a force

$$F = \gamma \frac{m_1 m_2}{r^2} \tag{12-1}$$

where γ, known as the universal gravitational constant, depends on the system of units employed.

In SI (International System) units, the value of γ is approximately 6.67×10^{-11} N·m^2/kg^2. This gives the force in newtons that will be exerted between two masses of 1 kg each with centers 1 m apart. Although the law of gravitational attraction was deduced by Newton from astronomical observations, the constant γ cannot be determined astronomically but must be measured in the laboratory. The earliest measurement was by Cavendish in 1797. His apparatus consisted of a horizontal beam with an equal weight at each end suspended at the center by a sensitive torsion fiber. Large external weights were placed alongside the ends of the beam in such a way that their attraction would cause it to rotate. The restoring torque of the fiber, increasing linearly with the rotation, balanced the turning moment of the weights. Nettleton[1] presents an interesting graphical history of the changes in the best value for γ since Cavendish's original determination of 6.754×10^{-11} N·m²/kg².

Consider the attraction between two billiard balls touching one another so that their centers are about 7.5×10^{-2} m (3 in) apart. If we assume each ball to have a mass of 0.225 kg (about $\frac{1}{2}$ lb), we can compute the attractive force F in newtons.

$$F = \frac{(6.67 \times 10^{-11})(0.225)^2}{(7.5 \times 10^{-2})^2} \cong 6 \times 10^{-10} \text{ N} \qquad (12\text{-}2)$$

This force is less than 3×10^{-10} times the force exerted on one of the balls by the earth's gravitational field.

Gravitational Acceleration   The acceleration of a point mass m_2 due to the attraction of a point mass m_1 a distance r away can be obtained simply by dividing the attracting force F by the mass m_2 (since force is mass times acceleration), whereupon

$$a = \frac{F}{m_2} = \gamma \frac{m_1}{r^2} \qquad (12\text{-}3)$$

Because the acceleration is independent of the mass on which it acts, it is the conventional quantity used to measure the gravitational field acting at any point. In the SI system, the dimension of acceleration is meters per second per second (m/s²). Among geophysicists an acceleration of 1 cm/s² is referred to as the Gal (in honor of Galileo, who conducted pioneering research on the earth's gravity). The gravitational acceleration at the earth's surface is about 9.8 m/s² or 980 Gal, but in exploration work we are likely to be measuring differences in acceleration one-ten-millionth or less of the earth's field. For convenience in working with gravity data obtained for geological and geodetic studies, the milliGal (mGal, $\frac{1}{1000}$ Gal) has come to be the common unit for expressing gravitational accelerations. Another unit, less commonly used, is the gravity unit, gu = 10^{-6} m/s² = 0.1 mGal.

Gravitational Potential   The analysis of certain kinds of force fields, such as gravitational, magnetic, or electric, can often be simplified by using the concept of potential. The potential at a point in a given field is defined as the work done by the force in moving a unit mass from an arbitrary reference point (usually at an infinite distance) to the point in question.

Let us assume, as illustrated in Fig. 12-1, that two masses, one of unit magnitude and the other of magnitude m_1, are initially an infinite distance apart; the unit mass is moved until it reaches point O a distance R from m_1, which has remained at P. Let r, which is a variable, be the separation of the two

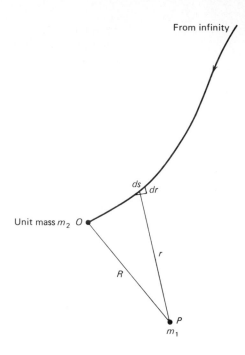

FIGURE 12-1 Gravitational potential is the work done by the attractive force of m_1 on m_2 as it moves to 0 from infinity.

masses at any point along the path taken by the unit mass between its initial position at infinity and its final position O.

The force per unit mass, or acceleration, at a distance r from P, is $\gamma m_1/r^2$, and the work necessary to move the unit mass a distance ds having a component dr in the direction of P is $\gamma m_1\, dr/r^2$. The work v done in moving the mass from infinity to O in the gravitational field of m_1 is

$$v = \gamma m_1 \int_{\infty}^{R} \frac{dr}{r^2} = \gamma m_1 \left.\frac{1}{r}\right|_{\infty}^{R} = \frac{\gamma m_1}{R} \tag{12-4}$$

It can easily be shown that this result will be obtained regardless of the path taken by m_2 in traveling from its starting point an infinite distance from m_1 to its end position at O. The quantity $\gamma m_1/R$ is the gravitational *potential* and depends only on R, the distance from the point source m_1. The gravitational acceleration is the derivative of the potential with respect to r. Any component of the force can be obtained by differentiating the potential with respect to distance in the direction along which the force is desired.

Any surface along which the potential is constant is referred to as an *equipotential surface*. No work need be done by or against gravity in bringing a body from one point on an equipotential surface to another. Sea level, for example, is an equipotential surface even though the actual force of gravity varies along the sea surface by more than 0.5 percent between the equator and either of the poles.

12-3   APPLICATION OF NEWTON'S LAW TO MASSES WITH LARGE DIMENSIONS

The theory thus far has considered only masses with infinitesimally small dimensions compared with the distance at which the attraction is measured. When the dimensions of the source are large, it is necessary to extend the theory. The procedure is to divide the mass into many small elements, each of infinitesimal dimensions, and to add the effects of each of the elements. Because force or acceleration is a vector having both magnitude and direction, it is necessary to resolve the force from each element of mass into its three components (most generally its vertical component and its north-south and east-west components in a horizontal plane) before the attraction of the body at any point can be determined.

To illustrate this principle let us consider the attraction of an irregular laminar body (part of a two-dimensional sheet) in the xz plane at an external point P also in the xz plane (Fig. 12-2). We must first determine the x (horizontal) and z (vertical) components of acceleration at P associated with this attraction. To do this we divide the plate into N small elements of mass, each of area ΔS as shown. If the density (mass per unit area) σ_n is uniform within the nth element, we can express the x component of acceleration at point P due to the attraction of this element as

$$a_{xn} = \gamma \frac{\sigma_n \Delta S}{r_n^2} \cos \theta = \gamma \frac{\sigma_n \Delta S}{r_n^2} \frac{x}{r_n} = \gamma \frac{x}{r_n^3} \sigma_n \Delta S \qquad (12\text{-}5)$$

and the z component as

$$a_{zn} = \gamma \frac{\sigma_n \Delta S}{r_n^2} \sin \theta = \gamma \frac{\sigma_n \Delta S}{r_n^2} \frac{z}{r_n} = \gamma \frac{z}{r_n^3} \sigma_n \Delta S \qquad (12\text{-}6)$$

FIGURE 12-2   Determining gravitational acceleration caused by irregular two-dimensional sheet. ΔS is element of area.

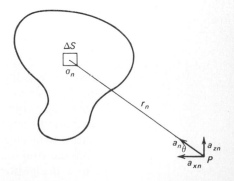

Adding the accelerations for these elements, we obtain the respective accelerations

$$a_x = \sum_{}^{N} \gamma \frac{x\sigma_n}{r_n^{\ 3}} \Delta S \tag{12-7}$$

and

$$a_z = \sum_{}^{N} \gamma \frac{z\sigma_n}{r_n^{\ 3}} \Delta S \tag{12-8}$$

As the elements become smaller and smaller, ΔS approaches the limit dS and we can express the two components of acceleration at P by the respective integrals.

$$a_x = \int^{S} \gamma \frac{\sigma x}{r^3} \, dS \tag{12-9}$$

and

$$a_z = \int^{S} \gamma \frac{\sigma z}{r^3} \, dS \tag{12-10}$$

where S is the area of the body and σ is the mass per unit area.

We now apply the same approach to a three-dimensional body with a density (in this case the mass per unit volume) of ρ. It is easy to show by extending the reasoning for a two-dimensional body to one of three dimensions that the components of acceleration in the x, y, and z directions, respectively, become

$$a_x = \int^{V} \gamma \frac{\rho x}{r^3} \, dV \tag{12-11}$$

$$a_y = \int^{V} \gamma \frac{\rho y}{r^3} \, dV \tag{12-12}$$

and

$$a_z = \int^{V} \gamma \frac{\rho z}{r^3} \, dV \tag{12-13}$$

where V is the volume of the body.

In gravity exploration, only vertical force is measured, so that we are normally concerned only with a_z in determining the attraction at the surface of a buried body. Later in this chapter, it will be shown how Eq. (12-13) can be used to derive the components of the accelerations caused by several bodies having simplified geometrical forms for which the integration can be carried out in a straightforward way.

12-4 THE EARTH'S GRAVITATIONAL FIELD AND ITS RELATION TO GRAVITY EXPLORATION

As gravity measurements made in exploration work show only *differences* in gravity from one place to another, the attraction of the earth itself is significant only insofar as it varies laterally over the earth's surface. Such variation must be taken into account in evaluating the gravity effect of buried bodies having geological or exploration significance.

If the earth were made up of homogeneous spherical shells and did not rotate, the attraction at the surface of the earth would be the same everywhere and it would not affect the readings of gravity meters, which measure only *differences* in acceleration between one place and another. Actually, the earth rotates (so that centrifugal forces are superimposed on gravitational attractions), is spheroidal (being flattened at the poles), and has lateral irregularities in density. The observed value of gravity depends on latitude, elevation, topography, and tidal movements as well as on lateral changes in density distribution that are sometimes of economic interest. Variations in gravitational attraction not associated with anomalous geological features have different degrees of predictability. For further information on the relationship between the earth's shape and its gravity field, the reader is referred to a condensed discussion of these topics in Garland[2] or a more detailed one in Heiskanen and Moritz.[3]

Global Variations in Gravity

To predict the gravitational field of the earth precisely at any point, we must know its shape and density distribution with the greatest possible accuracy. Because of its rotation, the earth is not actually spherical. Its shape can be approximated as an oblate spheroid (a surface generated by revolving an ellipse around its minor axis) with an eccentricity of approximately $\frac{1}{298}$. Both its departure from sphericity and its rotation (because of associated centrifugal forces) cause the earth's gravitational acceleration to have a maximum value at the poles and a minimum at the equator. The actual difference in gravity between the equator and poles is about 5.3 Gal, or 5300 mGal, although a theoretical calculation based only on the earth's rotational characteristics and the difference in distance from the earth's center at the two positions would lead one to expect about twice the contrast that is actually observed between pole and equator. Hammer[4] has shown that the discrepancy can be resolved by considering the attracting effect of the material that exists between a sphere having the polar radius and the actual earth surface which has its maximum radius at the equator.

For the purpose of predicting the variations in gravitational attraction caused by the rotation and the nonspherical shape of the earth, it has proved convenient to agree upon a theoretical formula for the gravitational attraction on the surface of an idealized reference model of the earth. For many years, the International Gravity Formula established in 1930 was used to predict gravity values in the reduction of gravity data. At present, many surveys are reduced using the Gravity Formula 1967 based upon the Geodetic Reference System 1967[5]. This formula in closed form is

$$g = g_e \frac{1 + k \sin^2 \phi}{\sqrt{1 - e^2 \sin^2 \phi}} \tag{12-14}$$

where ϕ = latitude
g_e = 978.031 845 58   Gal
k = 0.001 931 663 383 21
e^2 = 0.006 694 605 328 56

and g represents the normal acceleration of gravity in Gal on the surface of the reference ellipsoid. This reference ellipsoid is an ellipsoid of revolution defined by numerical values that specify the earth's equatorial radius, coefficient of flattening, and total mass and by the requirement that the surface of the ellipsoid be an equipotential surface. Interestingly, the gravitational formula for this ideal body can be derived without any additional assumptions about the distribution of mass within the reference ellipsoid.[6]

The Gravity Formula 1967 gives the normal value of gravity on the smooth surface of the reference ellipsoid. Commonly, gravity surveys are reduced using not the surface of the ellipsoid, but sea level as the reference elevation. This sea-level surface has bulges and hollows of the order of hundreds of miles in diameter and up to several hundred feet in elevation (Fig. 12-3). Their presence is related to density irregularities in the earth's interior comparable to those on the moon (although not as large in gravitational effect). Off the tip of Ceylon, for example, there is an area where a ship could sail along a parallel of latitude and climb 250 ft in a day without having to do any work against gravity.

The actual equipotential surface of the earth that corresponds to sea level is called the *geoid*, which is defined under land areas as the surface that would be assumed by the top of the water in a narrow sea-level canal if it were extended inland across a continent to connect one ocean with another. The geoid is by definition everywhere perpendicular to the direction of the plumb line. Elevations "above sea level" on topographic maps are actually distances above the geoid.

The discrepancies between the geoid and the reference ellipsoid can be expressed by maps like that in Fig. 12-3. As more precise information on the figure of the earth is obtained from gravity and satellite observations, such maps are periodically revised.

Isostasy

If mountains had to be supported by an entirely rigid earth, the higher ones would collapse because their weight would give rise to pressure variations at great depths that exceed the crushing strength of rock materials. It is much

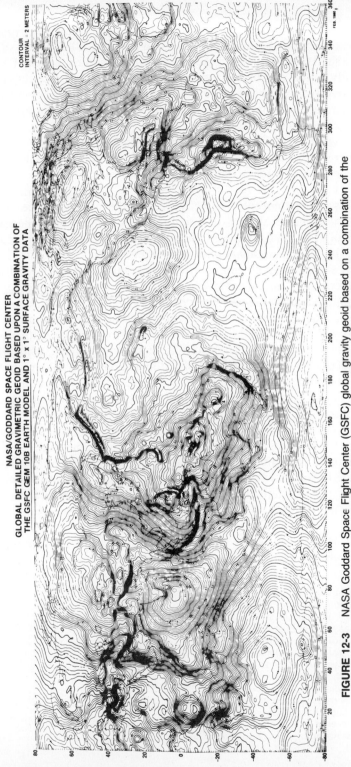

FIGURE 12-3   NASA Goddard Space Flight Center (GSFC) global gravity geoid based on a combination of the GSFC GEM 10B earth model and 1° × 1° surface gravity data. Contour interval is 2 m. Longitude is given east from Greenwich. (*From Taylor et al. EOS, vol. 64, no. 43, p. 610: Oct 25, 1983; derived in accordance with J. G. Marsh and E. S. Chang: Global Detailed Gravimetric Geoid, Marine Geodesy, vol. 2, p. 145, 1979.*)

easier to account for the persistence of topographic relief over long periods of geologic time if one assumes that the rigid portion (lithosphere) of the earth is an outer shell that is thin compared to the earth's radius, and that it *floats* on an effectively liquid and highly viscous interior. This concept requires that any mass above sea level be compensated by a deficit of mass below sea level, and any ocean basin, being abnormally light, must be underlain by a mass that is greater than normal. If this were not so, the mountains would sink and the basin bottoms would rise. The total weight per unit area at any depth below the lithosphere must be uniform everywhere if equilibrium is to be sustained. Dutton designated such a state of equilibrium by the term *isostasy.*

Origins of the Concept   In the middle of the nineteenth century, a highly precise triangulation survey of India brought to light a discrepancy of about 5 seconds of arc (500 ft) between the separation of two stations, Kalianpur and Kaliana (about 375 mi apart on a north-south line), as measured geodetically and their separation as computed from astronomical readings. Although 500 ft would seem to be an almost trivial error out of a total distance of 375 mi, the precision and internal consistency of the triangulation had been too great for even this small a difference to be disregarded as a geodetic mistie.

Figure 12-4 indicates the positions of the two stations with respect to the Himalayas. Kaliana is in the foothills of the mountains, while Kalianpur is surrounded by hundreds of miles of flat lands. Seeking to explain the discrepancy in the distance between the two stations, J. H. Pratt conceived that the mass of the Himalayas would tend to deflect the plumb line northward at each station but more at Kaliana than at Kalianpur. Such deflection would lead to errors in the astronomic survey, which is based on angles of stars with the vertical. Calculating the discrepancy that would be expected because of the horizontal attraction of the Himalayas, Pratt[7] was surprised to find that the difference in separation should have been about 15 seconds of latitude instead of the 5 seconds actually found. In his paper presenting the results of his calculations he made no attempt to account for this discrepancy.

Airy's Hypothesis   Less than 2 months after Pratt's paper was delivered, G. B. Airy[8] submitted his solution to the puzzle. The earth's crust, he said, is a

FIGURE 12-4   Pratt's explanation for discrepancy between astronomically and geodetically determined distances measured in Everest's survey of India. The apparent angle of the star with the plumb line differs between two stations by amount α, the angle by which the Himalayas deflect the plumb line at Kaliana (deflection at Kalianpur assumed zero). This leads to an error in astronomical latitude for Kaliana.

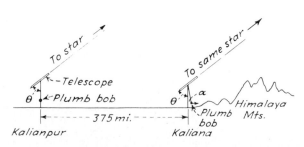

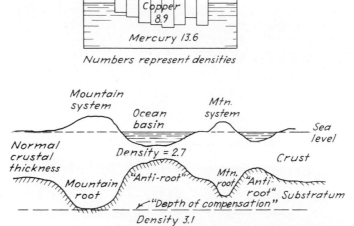

FIGURE 12-5 Airy's theory of compensation. Mountains overlie regions of greater crustal thickness (roots), while ocean basins overlie sections where crust is thin (anti-roots). The mechanism is illustrated by copper blocks of various heights and density of 8.9 g/cm³ floating on mercury with a density of 13.6 g/cm³. The *depth of compensation* is the shallowest depth at which pressure is everywhere equal.

rigid shell floating on a liquid substratum of greater density. Under mountains the base of the crust would have penetrated farther into the substratum than under land at sea level. Figure 12-5 illustrates this principle. He pointed out that the hydrostatic state of the earth's crust supported by a denser liquid substratum (the mantle) is like that of a raft made of logs having different diameters floating upon the water. If the upper surface of one log rises to a higher level than any of the upper surfaces of the others, we can be certain that its lower surface lies deeper in the water than the lower surfaces of the others. Similarly, the crust under ocean deeps would be thinner than under land surfaces at or near sea level.

When this concept is applied to the Himalayas, it follows that mountain roots of relatively light crustal material penetrating into a heavier substratum would account for a deficiency of mass below the mountains. The roots of the Himalayas, lighter than the surrounding substratum, would deflect the plumb line in a direction opposite to that of the mountains themselves.

Pratt's Hypothesis Four years later Pratt[9], admitting that the compensation effects are not entirely complete, proposed a somewhat different although equally plausible explanation for his observations. He acknowledged that, as Airy had pointed out, the excess mass of the mountains above sea level had to be compensated by a deficit below sea level, but he hypothesized a crust having a uniform thickness (below sea level) with its base everywhere supporting a uniform weight per unit area. Under the mountains these conditions would call for a deficiency in density of the crustal rocks. The subcrustal density, although

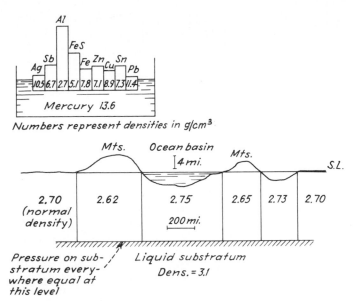

FIGURE 12-6 Pratt's theory of compensation. Elevated blocks such as mountains are underlain by crustal material of less than normal density. Ocean deeps are underlain by greater than normal density. Densities are such that weight per unit area is same at base of each column. Upper diagram illustrates analogy to metals having different densities floating on mercury.

variable, should always be such that the total weight of the mountains and crustal material below them is equal to the weight of the crustal rocks alone in an area where the earth's solid surface is flat and at sea level. Under the oceans, the density of the rocks must be greater than average to compensate for the less than normal weight of the ocean water. Figure 12-6 illustrates this hypothesis.

For almost a century the Pratt and Airy hypotheses on the mechanism of compensation were the subject of controversy. Seismological evidence generally appeared to substantiate the Airy theory of roots under mountains and a thinner than average crust under the ocean basins, yet some kinds of seismological data favored Pratt and suggested that the crustal thickness is the same under some mountains as it is under the coastal plains. The choice between the competing hypotheses is complicated by the strength of the earth's lithosphere: Compensating masses that support topographic loads need not lie directly under the loads, because the crust and lithosphere can bend elastically, thereby distributing the compensation over a broader area. But plate tectonic theory has put this controversy in a new perspective, for it predicts a mobile earth.

Today we have a far better appreciation of how mountain belts are formed and how major density contrasts within the crust evolve than we did just two decades ago. Regions of the fluid substratum, on which the crust was imagined to float passively in classical isostasy, are now known to be moving as part of the whole plate-tectonic flow—upwelling at oceanic ridges and hotspots, descending at subduction zones near the down-going slabs. As a result, it is now clear that in certain tectonic contexts the question of equilibrium needs to be framed (at least for some wavelengths of the gravity field) in more dynamic terms than the classical concept of isostasy allows. It is also apparent that both the Airy and Pratt models are far too simple to describe the detailed density distributions of an ever evolving crust, and that they should perhaps be regarded as simplified end-member models.

Nevertheless, isostatic models continue to be useful for geodesists and geophysicists, because worldwide gravity measurements have established that some form of isostatic compensation exists over most of the earth's surface, even though the mechanism probably varies considerably from place to place and is generally more complicated than any of the classical models. One factor that continues to make isostatic calculations feasible in the face of such complexity is the smoothing effect of distance—the details of the distribution of the compensating masses make only small differences in the gravity field observed at the earth's surface because of the depths of these masses.

Anomalies Based on Absolute Gravity Determination

In exploration work, any variation in gravity from that predicted either theoretically or empirically from surrounding values is referred to as a positive gravity anomaly when higher and a negative gravity anomaly when lower. The determination of what is anomalous and what is normal is not always obvious, and later we shall consider methods of identifying localized anomalies of interest in exploration by separating them from variations which are more likely to be of regional extent. This concept of a local gravity anomaly applies where interest is confined to areas of relatively limited dimensions, e.g., those involved in most surveys where oil-bearing structures are sought.

The concept of a gravity anomaly in geodetic applications made its appearance long before gravity was used as a prospecting tool and has considerable value to geologists studying tectonics on a large scale. It is based on departures of observed gravity from the gravity predicted from an earth model that attempts to incorporate the known elements causing variations in the gravity field. Typically, the predicted value includes the theoretical gravity on some reference surface (such as that calculated from the Gravity Formula 1967 for points on the 1967 reference ellipsoid), which accounts for the latitudinal variations produced by the earth's rotation and shape. Some combination of additional terms then attempts to take into account other known elements, such as the elevation difference between the observation point and the reference surface, the effect of masses above the reference surface, and the effect of known lateral density changes below the reference surface. Any difference between the observed gravity and the predicted gravity is called a *gravity anomaly*.

Certain models for predicting gravity are so widely used that special names have been given to the gravity anomalies they produce. A model that includes a prediction of theoretical gravity on a reference surface and that also compensates for the fact that the gravitational attraction decreases as observations are made at heights above the reference surface (actually the height above the geoid is commonly used in the prediction) produces the *free-air anomaly*. A model that also accounts for the mass distribution between the earth's surface and the reference surface (actually the geoid surface is again commonly used) produces the *Bouguer anomaly*, named for Pierre Bouguer who made pioneering geodetic observations in the Andes during the eighteenth century. Formulas for computing the free-air and Bouguer corrections are presented in Chap. 13.

In both these predictive models the gravity values calculated from the Gravity Formula are for locations on the surface of the reference ellipsoid, whereas for practical reasons the elevations of gravity observations used in the free-air and Bouguer corrections generally are given with respect to sea level (which defines the geoid surface). The choice of which surface is used can be incorporated into the definition of the anomalies.[3] The important point is that the interpreter must be aware of the choice that has been made. For gravity studies confined to sufficiently small regions, the difference in elevation between the two surfaces (reference ellipsoid and geoid) may be nearly constant. For studies encompassing broader regions, the undulations of the geoid relative to the reference ellipsoid can become sufficiently large so that failure to consider this effect can seriously hinder the comparison of observed gravity values with predicted values or the interpretation of long-wavelength anomalies in terms of anomalous subsurface masses. In such cases, as has been pointed out by Chapman and Bodine[10] and many others, correction must be made for this so-called *indirect effect*.

The Gravity Formula makes no allowance for lateral density changes within the earth, yet where topographic masses are present, the existence of isostatic compensation implies that there must be lateral changes in subsurface density produced by the presence of compensating masses. To reduce the discrepancy between observed and predicted gravity values produced by these compensating masses, an additional term can be added to the Bouguer prediction model. The value of this term is determined from surface elevation data describing the topography and from an assumed isostatic model (e.g., Pratt, Airy). The value obtained will depend to some degree upon the choice of isostatic model, but generally the differences between models are less than a few percent of the total magnitude of the correction. With this extra term, the difference between observed and predicted gravity is called the *isostatic anomaly*.

Certain misconceptions regarding isostatic anomalies need to be clarified. It must be emphasized that for a crust containing lateral density variations, there will, in general, be sizable isostatic anomalies even in the presence of complete isostatic equilibrium as can be seen in Fig. 12-7. Often these anomalies are of considerable geologic interest. The temptation to regard positive or negative isostatic anomalies as indicative of undercompensation or overcompensation must be avoided, at least in the absence of other evidence. Commonly, isostatic anomalies up to several hundred kilometers in width are caused by density contrasts associated with geologic bodies in the crust. Such bodies could be in

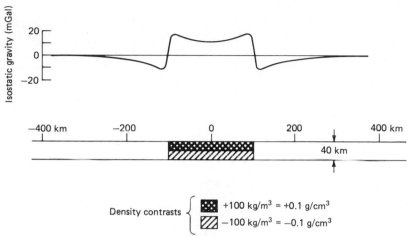

FIGURE 12-7 Simplified model showing that isostatic gravity anomalies can exist over different "kinds" of crust, perhaps juxtaposed by plate tectonic processes, but all in complete local isostatic equilibrium. Density contrasts are deviations from an average density value.

complete isostatic equilibrium, but would still exhibit large isostatic anomalies because the deeper compensating masses will tend to produce a broader, lower-amplitude anomaly of opposite sign that cannot cancel the anomaly produced by the body itself (Fig. 12-8). In principle, the resulting composite anomaly—for example, a positive anomaly surrounded by negative anomalies on all sides—could reveal the presence of isostatic equilibrium. In practice, the anomalies produced by neighboring geologic features may tend to interfere with or completely obscure the lower-amplitude negative anomalies surrounding the central positive anomaly. The most useful approach to interpreting many isostatic anomaly maps may be to assume the existence of isostatic equilibrium, unless other evidence argues against that state, and to interpret the resulting isostatic anomalies in terms of density contrasts produced by geologic bodies within the crust. Presumably, departures from isostatic equilibrium will become more evident in the modeling process, especially if other sources of information on subsurface geometries can be used to constrain the model.

An area where isostatic anomalies seem to indicate departure from isostatic equilibrium occurs around the eastern Baltic Sea where Norway, Sweden, and Finland come closest together. There an extensive negative isostatic anomaly appears to result from the recent melting of the Pleistocene glaciers that covered the area. Such an anomaly would be produced if the compensation developed during the glaciation is greater than what is actually necessary to balance the land mass that extends above sea level after melting of the ice. Careful geodetic observations over a long period of time, as well as the present elevations of ancient structures on the waterfront, indicate that the entire area is rising at a rate of more than 0.5 cm/year in a rebound following its depression during glacial times. In the portion of the region where the anomaly has its

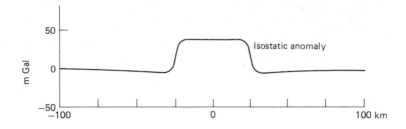

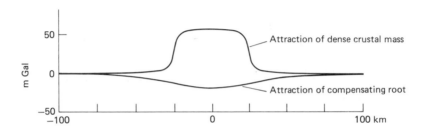

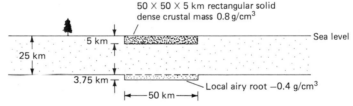

FIGURE 12-8 The attraction of the compensating masses to bodies within the crust cannot cancel the attraction of the bodies themselves because of the smoothing effect of depth.

greatest negative value it is expected that there will be a further rise of nearly 200 m before equilibrium is reached.

Earth Tides

Gravity-measuring instruments for geophysical prospecting are so sensitive that they respond to the gravitational attraction of the sun and moon and register the periodic variations in the attraction caused by movements of the earth with respect to these bodies. The waters of the earth, having no rigidity, are regularly raised and lowered by such forces in predictable tidal cycles. The earth itself is also acted upon by these tidal forces, and since it is not infinitely rigid, the surface of its solid portion is deformed somewhat in the same way as the free water surface, although not of course to the same extent. The actual tidal movement of a point on the land surface is much smaller than the corresponding fluctuation in water level, being only a matter of a few centimeters. This displacement in itself causes small but measurable changes in gravity as the distance from the center of the earth is altered and the masses within the earth are redistributed. Such changes are, of course, superimposed on changes in gravity caused by the attractive forces of the two celestial bodies. The magnitude of these changes varies with latitude, time of month, and time of year, but the complete tidal cycle is accompanied by a gravity change of only 0.2 to 0.3 mGal.

Heiland[11] has derived the formula for the vertical component of the tidal force Δg caused by the sun (mass M_s, distance from the earth D_s) and the moon (mass M_m, distance from the earth D_m) at any point on a perfectly rigid earth of radius r when the respective celestial bodies make geocentric angles of a_s and a_m with the observation station:

$$\Delta g = \frac{3\gamma r M_m}{2D_m{}^3} (\cos 2a_m + \tfrac{1}{3}) - \frac{3\gamma r M_s}{2D_s{}^3} (\cos 2a_s + \tfrac{1}{3}) \qquad (12\text{-}15)$$

Here γ is the gravitational constant. Evaluation of the respective coefficients of the terms in parentheses indicates that the moon's attraction is more than twice that of the sun. A comparison of theoretically predicted and observed tidal variations is shown in Fig. 12-9.

Worldwide observations of tidal gravity compiled by Melchior[12] indicate that the distortion of the earth due to the tidal forces increases the effective gravitational pull of the sun and moon about 16 percent. The exact percentage increase varies from place to place, mainly as a result of indirect effects due to ocean tides. Because these variations are small, tidal gravity values calculated

FIGURE 12-9 Comparison of theoretical and observed curves of tidal gravity variation: (A) Gravity-meter readings; (B) drift curve; (C) observed variation of gravity from drift curve; (D) calculated gravity variation. (*After Wolf.*[29])

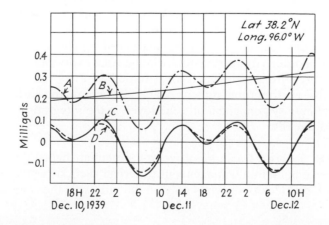

for a rigid earth and magnified by a factor of 1.16 will approximate actual tidal gravity values within a few percent at most worldwide locations. Formulas for tidal accelerations given by Longman[13] can be readily programmed for the purpose of applying a tidal correction to gravity observations.

12-5 GRAVITATIONAL EFFECTS OVER SUBSURFACE BODIES HAVING DISCRETE SHAPES

Long before gravity prospecting came into existence, relationships had been worked out for the gravitational attraction of bodies having various analytically describable shapes. Exploration applications always involve measurement of differences in the vertical component of gravity fields which are associated with buried geologic features. The fact that the attraction of the earth is superimposed upon the attraction of a body buried beneath its surface does not affect these differences as long as any lateral changes in the earth's field (such as those associated with latitude variation) are taken into account. If all other sources of attraction can be considered constant over the area of the survey, the effective density to be used in such calculations is the *contrast* between the density of the body in question and that of the material surrounding it. Only the *vertical* component of the attraction need be taken into account, as all gravity meters are designed to respond to vertical forces alone.

One can determine a body's attractive force (or a component of it) at any desired point in space either by direct application of Newton's law or by differentiation of its potential field. The function so computed for geometrical forms having different shapes and depths of burial can be compared with variations of gravitational acceleration actually observed along profiles or on contour maps. Such comparisons with different theoretical models can be used to deduce the shape, depth, and other characteristics of the geological feature responsible for the gravity anomaly.

It is not generally possible to calculate the gravitational fields of bodies having arbitrary or irregular shapes by using simple analytical formulas. Computer programs and graphical devices designed for such a problem will be described in a later chapter. It is relatively easy, however, to calculate fields from generalized geometrical forms such as spheres, sheets having circular or rectangular shapes, and rectangular parallelepipeds. The computation of such fields is ordinarily carried out by integrating expressions for the vertical attraction force from two-dimensional buried sources on a horizontal plane [Eq. (12-10)] or from three-dimensional bodies below the surface [Eq. (12-13)]. The coordinate system and limits employed in the integration depend on the shapes of the bodies.

The Sphere It can be proved by potential theory that the attraction at an external point of a homogeneous spherical shell, as well as of a solid sphere, in which the density depends only on the radius, is the same as though the entire

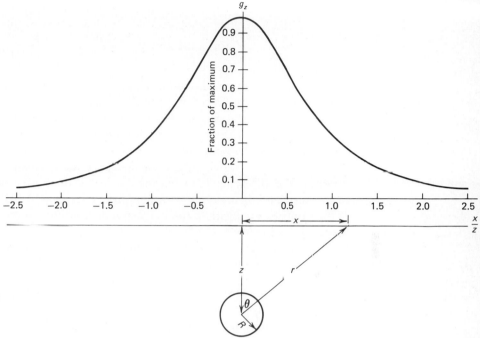

FIGURE 12-10
Gravitational field over
sphere. Vertical gravity
is plotted versus hori-
zontal distance from
center.

mass were concentrated at the center of the sphere. The mass M of a sphere
having a radius R and a density (mass per unit volume*) ρ is the volume times
density or $\frac{4}{3}\pi R^3\rho$. If the center is at a depth z below the surface, as shown in
Fig. 12-10, the total gravitational attraction of the equivalent mass at the center
upon a unit mass on the surface a horizontal distance x from the center will be

$$g = \gamma\,\frac{M}{r^2} = \frac{4\pi\gamma R^3\rho}{3(z^2 + x^2)} \tag{12-16}$$

Since

$$r = \sqrt{z^2 + x^2}$$

the vertical component g_z, which is simply $g\cos\theta$ or gz/r, will be

$$g_z = \gamma\,\frac{M}{r^2}\,\frac{z}{r} = \frac{4}{3}\,\pi\gamma R^3\rho\,\frac{z}{(z^2 + x^2)^{3/2}} \tag{12-17}$$

* The correct unit of density in SI units is kg/m³. One kg/m³ equals 10^{-3} g/cm³.

Nettleton[14] has rearranged this equation in the form

$$g_z \text{ (in milliGals)} = \frac{8.52\rho R^3}{z^2} \frac{1}{[1 + (x^2/z^2)]^{3/2}} \tag{12-18}$$

when R, x, and z are measured in kilofeet and ρ in grams per cubic centimeter. This is a convenient form for calculation since g can be found at any distance x by multiplying the peak value at $x = 0$, which is $8.52\rho R^3/z^2$, by a factor dependent only on the ratio x/z. The falloff of gravity along the surface at a distance x from the point directly over the center is plotted in Fig. 12-10.

For any mass buried in the earth, the effective density ρ, as previously noted, is the difference between the density of the buried object itself and that of the surrounding material. This quantity is designated as the *density contrast*. If the contrast is negative, the corresponding gravity anomaly will be negative also.

The magnitude of the gravity anomaly that might be expected over a roughly spherical salt dome can be estimated from Eq. (12-18). If the dome can be represented by a sphere 2000 ft in radius, with a density contrast of -0.25 g/cm^3 and with its center 4000 ft below the surface, the anomaly should have a maximum value of -1.07 mGals. The effect is thus only about one-millionth the total gravitational acceleration of the earth itself, yet is easily measurable.

Horizontal Cylinder   It is shown in an appendix to this chapter (Sec. 12-9) that the vertical component of attracton of an infinite wire with mass λ per unit length buried at a depth z will be

$$g_z = 2\gamma\lambda \frac{z}{z^2 + x^2} \tag{12-19}$$

where x is the perpendicular distance of the measuring point on the surface from the trace of the vertical plane containing the wire on the earth's surface.

If the wire is expanded to a cylinder of radius R, λ can be expressed as the volume density ρ times the area, or $\pi R^2 \rho$, so that the formula now becomes

$$g_z = 2\pi\gamma R^2 \rho \frac{z}{z^2 + x^2} \tag{12-20}$$

If all distances are expressed in thousands of feet and the density in grams per cubic centimeter, this can be written

$$g_z \text{ (in milliGals)} = \frac{12.77\rho^2}{z} \frac{1}{1 + x^2/z^2} \tag{12-21}$$

The falloff of the gravity field of a horizontal cylinder with horizontal distance from the point on the surface directly over its center is plotted in Fig.

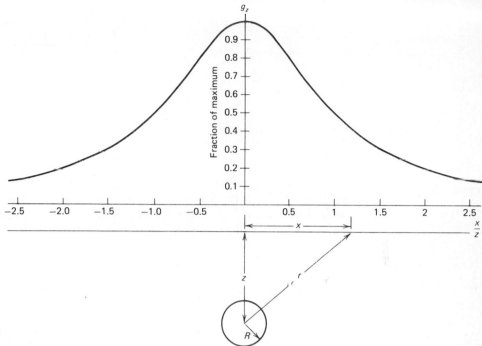

FIGURE 12-11
Gravitational field over horizontal cylinder. Gravity is plotted versus horizontal distance from the center.

12-11. The anomaly is not so sharp as that from a sphere at the same depth, since the term involving the horizontal distance x, which is in the denominator, is taken to a lower power for the cylinder. It is seen by comparing the respective equations that a horizontal cylinder will have a maximum gravitational effect about $1.5z/R$ times as great as a sphere of the same radius, depth, and density. This should be expected in view of the much greater mass contained in the cylinder.

Buried Vertical Cylinder An equally interesting case from a geological viewpoint is that of a buried vertical cylinder. This form is often convenient for computing gravity anomalies from salt domes and volcanic plugs. Consider the cylinder illustrated in Fig. 12-12 having a radius r and height L, with its top surface buried at a depth d. The distance from the point where the axis intersects the earth's surface to the top edge of the cylinder is s_2, and that to the bottom edge is s_1, as shown in the diagram. The formula for the vertical gravitational effect of the cylinder where the axis intersects the measuring surface is shown in Sec. 12-9 to be

$$g_z = 2\pi\gamma\rho(L - s_1 + s_2)$$

or
$$g_z \text{ (in milliGals)} = 12.77\rho(L - s_1 + s_2) \tag{12-22}$$

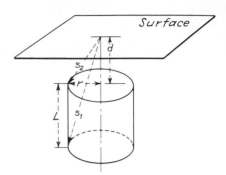

FIGURE 12-12   Definition of quantities used in calculating gravity effects from buried vertical cylinder.

where ρ is the density contrast in grams per cubic centimeter and all distances are in thousands of feet. If the cylinder is infinitely long, s_1 becomes $L + d$ and the gravity effect along the axis becomes

$$g_z = 12.77\rho(s_2 - d) \qquad (12\text{-}23)$$

Bowie[15] has prepared some convenient tables for computing the gravity effects of vertical cylinders at the centers of their upper surfaces.

Buried Slab   If our vertical cylinder is so extended horizontally that its radius becomes very large compared with its height, s_2 approaches s_1 and Eq. (12-22) becomes

$$g_z = 2\pi\gamma\rho L = 12.77\rho L \qquad (12\text{-}24)$$

if L is in thousands of feet and ρ in grams per cubic centimeter. This is of course equivalent to an infinite horizontal slab of thickness L. It should be noted that the gravity effect depends only on the thickness of the slab, not on its depth of burial.

Attraction of a Buried Vertical Cylinder at a Point off Its Axis   Returning to the buried vertical cylinder, let us consider the gravitational field on the surface at a point off the cylinder's axis. This is a considerably more complex case than that where the field is computed on the axis, but Bowie[15] has developed a simple approximation for the case where the top of the cylinder is at the earth's surface. If the radius of the cylinder having a height L is r and the distance of the measuring point from its axis is x, the vertical gravitational attraction is

$$g_z \cong 2\pi\gamma\rho[\sqrt{L^2 + (x - r)^2} - \sqrt{L^2 + (x + r)^2} - 2r]\frac{r}{4x} \qquad (12\text{-}25)$$

A case having greater practical interest is that of a cylinder having a top buried a given depth below the surface. An exact formula for this case can be derived but has not found practical use. When the height of the cylinder is smaller than the depth of its top, it can be approximated by a circular disk and its attraction determined by using the solid angle subtended by the disk at the measuring point. The principle involved will be discussed later in this section. Figure 12-13 shows a chart for ascertaining the subtended solid angle ω in terms of the radius and height of the cylinder, the depth to which its top is buried, and the horizontal distance x of its axis from the measuring point. Using quantities defined in the figure the formula is

$$g_z = 2.03\omega\rho t$$

where t is in thousands of feet.

FIGURE 12-13   Chart for calculating gravity at a point on the surface a distance x off the axis of a vertical cylinder of height t with center buried at depth z. Curves give solid angles. (*After Nettleton.*[14])

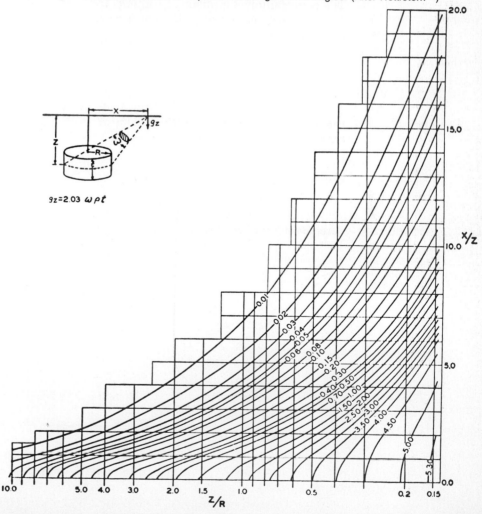

Attraction of Plates and Thin Slabs Many geological features can be modeled by a sheet or thin slab of anomalous (although not necessarily constant) density having boundaries that can be specified in various ways. The gravity effects of such forms can be determined analytically without great difficulty. Initially we shall consider bodies with densities contrasting with those of surrounding materials that can be represented by a plane surface (one with thickness small compared to its other dimensions) such as ancient salt-lake beds (now bounded slabs of evaporite), volcanic sills of limited extent, or thin faulted limestone beds.

Infinitely Long Horizontal Strip with Boundaries Perpendicular to Plane of Profile Figure 12-14 shows the edge of a sheet extending to infinity in a horizontal plane perpendicular to the page. The boundaries are perpendicular to the x direction. The density contrast of the sheet is σ (mass per unit area). The contribution of a ribbon of width dx to the vertical component of gravity at P is the same as that of an infinite wire perpendicular to the line of measurement. We can write it as

$$dg_z = 2\,\frac{\gamma\sigma\,\sin\phi\,dx}{r}$$

$\sigma\,dx$, the mass per unit length of the strip, is equivalent to λ in Eq. (12-19) for the wire, and r is the shortest distance from P to the ribbon. Integrating between the limits x_1 and x_2, we obtain

$$g_z = 2\gamma\sigma \int_{x_2}^{x_1} \frac{\sin\phi\,dx}{r} \qquad (12\text{-}26)$$

FIGURE 12-14 Attraction at P of a thin sheet of finite width but of infinite length in direction perpendicular to page.

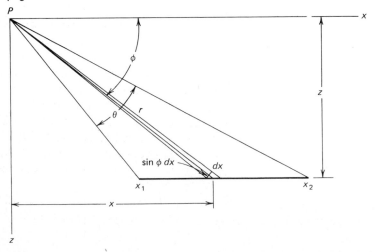

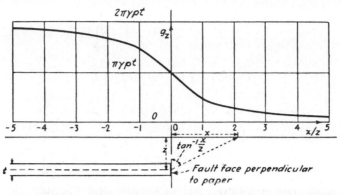

FIGURE 12-15   Gravity profile over thin faulted slab, downthrown side assumed infinitely deep.

But $\sin \phi \, dx/r$ is the angle subtended by dx at P, and the summation (or integral) of this quantity over all elements dx from x_1 to x_2 is simply the total angle θ subtended by the strip, so that

$$g_z = 2\gamma\sigma\theta \tag{12-27}$$

If the sheet extends to infinity in the x direction, the line from P to the far edge becomes horizontal and θ can be expressed as $\tan^{-1}(z/x)$ or $\pi/2 - \tan^{-1}(x/z)$.

If the sheet is a thin slab of thickness t which is faulted at $x = 0$ with the right side downthrown an infinite distance, as shown at the bottom of Fig. 12-15, we can write $\sigma = \rho t$ and

$$g_z = 2\gamma\rho t\left(\frac{\pi}{2} - \tan^{-1}\frac{x}{z}\right) \tag{12-28}$$

Far to the left of the fault edge, $x = -\infty$, and here the expression for the attraction of an infinite slab, $2\pi\gamma\rho t$, applies because $\tan^{-1}(-\infty/z) = -\pi/2$. If $x = \infty$, the arc tangent becomes $\pi/2$ and the gravitational effect is zero. Over the fault edge the vertical gravity field is half that of the slab itself. The gravity profile at the top of Fig. 12-15 illustrates these relations.

If the thickness of the faulted slab t is expressed in thousands of feet and the density contrast $\sigma = \rho t$, where ρ is in grams per cubic centimeter, we can write Eq. (12-28) in the form

$$g_z \text{ (in milliGals)} = 4.05\rho t\left(\frac{\pi}{2} - \tan^{-1}\frac{x}{z}\right) \tag{12-29}$$

Attraction of Thin Horizontal Plate of Finite Dimensions   Figure 12-16 shows a bounded thin horizontal plate of irregular shape, for which the attraction at

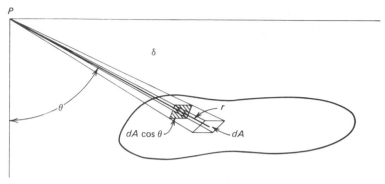

FIGURE 12-16 Determining attraction at P of a thin horizontal plate of irregular shape.

point P can be determined by summing up the effect of all elements of area on the plate. Consider the element of area dA shown in the figure having a density σ per unit area. The mass is then $\sigma\,dA$. The contribution of this element to the vertical gravity at P is

$$\frac{\gamma\sigma\,\cos\theta\,dA}{r^2} = \gamma\sigma\,d\Omega \qquad (12\text{-}30)$$

where Ω is the solid angle subtended by dA. The quantity of $dA\,\cos\theta$ is the component of the area perpendicular to R.

Integrating over the entire plate gives

$$g_z = \gamma\sigma\Omega \qquad (12\text{-}31)$$

which indicates that the depth of the sheet is not a unique factor in determining the attraction, the subtended angle Ω being all that counts. Nettleton[14] has published tables for determining the gravity from circular plates as a function of depth, radius, and horizontal distance from the observing point to the center of the circle.

Attraction of a Two-Dimensional Body with Rectangular Cross Section in Vertical Plane   Many tabular geological features that give rise to gravity anomalies can be approximated as three-dimensional slabs having elongated plane sides with upper and lower surfaces that are horizontal. The gravity effect of such a form can be readily determined by integrating contributions from a series of thin horizontal laminae, each of the kind shown in Fig. 12-14, which put together make up the slab. The effect of each lamina is given by Eq. (12-27).

The integration is tedious and will not be carried out here. The attraction of the body at a point P on the surface along a profile perpendicular to its horizontal axis can be expressed in terms of the depth of its top and its dimensions as well as by the positions of its corners with respect to P. Heiland[16] develops the formula for a slablike body with plane sides that are not

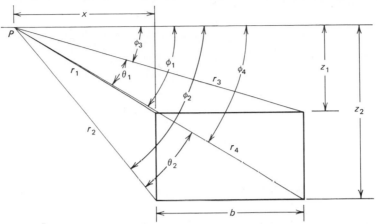

FIGURE 12-17   Determining attraction at P of a "two-dimensional" rectangular parallelepiped having infinite length in direction perpendicular to paper.

necessarily vertical. He shows how the formula can be applied to a number of geometrical forms that might be used as models for geologic features.

The relation for the case of a rectangular parallepiped expressed in terms of the variables defined in Fig. 12-17 is shown by Garland[2] to be

$$g_z = 2\gamma\rho\left(z_2\theta_2 - z_1\theta_1 + x \ln\frac{r_1 r_4}{r_2 r_3} + b \ln\frac{r_4}{r_3}\right) \tag{12-32}$$

This formula is applicable to the case of a rectangular bed bounded by vertical sides which is much longer than its width b and which has a density that is anomalous with respect to surrounding formations. Certain igneous intrusives as well as salt stocks can be represented by such a model. If the width b approaches infinity, then θ_1 approaches ϕ_1, θ_2 approaches ϕ_2, and r_3 approaches r_4, whereupon Eq. (12-32) becomes

$$g_z = 2\gamma\rho\left(z_2\phi_2 - z_1\phi_1 + x \ln\frac{r_1}{r_2}\right) \tag{12-33}$$

This is the formula for a thick vertically faulted slab with such a large throw that the downthrown side makes no contribution to the gravitational force. As the thickness becomes smaller, we can show that the attraction becomes identical to that expressed by Eq. (12-28) for a thin faulted slab of the type illustrated in Fig. 12-15.

Consider a faulted slab having a finite throw, as shown in Fig. 12-18. At large distances on either side of the fault, the gravity effect is associated only with the thickness of the slab, so that the gravity would be the same at large distances on either side of the fault, as the faulting is assumed to cause no

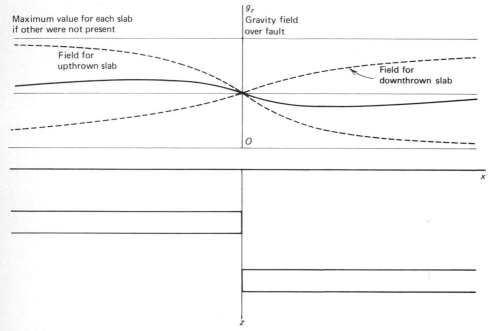

FIGURE 12-18 Attraction of a faulted slab having a finite throw.

change in the thickness. If we consider the gravity anomalies from the upper and lower slabs separately, we find the only difference, except for the reversal in directions of the high and low sides, is in the gradient across the fault, being steeper for the shallower slab than for the deeper one. Adding the two fields, we obtain a net gravity effect having the form of a doublet with a maximum on the upthrown side and a minimum on the downthrown side. The magnitudes of the positive and negative peaks depend upon the thickness of the faulted slab, the depth of the upthrown side, and the throw of the fault.

If the vertical dimension of a slab is large compared with its horizontal extent and the depth of the bottom is great compared both with its width and with the depth of its top, θ_1 and θ_2 approach zero. Also ϕ_1 approaches ϕ_3, and ϕ_2 approaches ϕ_4. We can then write the expression for the vertical component of gravity as

$$g_z = 2\gamma\rho b \ln \frac{r_2}{r_1} \tag{12-34}$$

Figure 12-19 shows the gravity field for this case as a function of distance from the center of the slab. This formula should give a good approximation in many cases to the field from a dike with its top and bottom both at finite depths or from thin vertically elongated salt stocks.

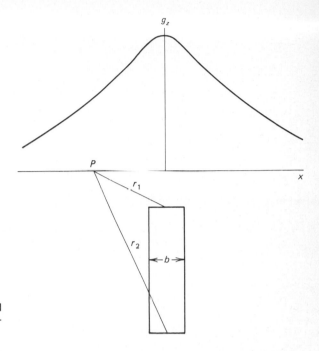

FIGURE 12-19   Attraction at P of a "two dimensional" rectangular parallelepiped with greater vertical than horizontal dimensions.

Gradients of Gravity   The rate of change of gravity with distance, designated as the *gradient*, has applications to exploration which are likely to assume increasing importance as the precision of gravity-measuring instruments is improved. Actually, the earliest use of gravity in exploration (and the first use of geophysics in prospecting for oil) involved direct measurement of gradient (along with a more complex parameter, the curvature) rather than of gravitational attraction itself. The Eötvös torsion balance, which was employed with great success in the mid-1920s for locating piercement type salt domes in the Gulf Coast area of the United States and Mexico, was used to map the gradient of gravity. The deepening of the Gulf Coast geosyncline to the south results in a normal gradient that is negative toward the Gulf of Mexico. The anomalous gradient resulting from the density deficit associated with a salt dome turned out to be diagnostic of the shallow domes sought in the area. A further discussion of the principles behind the operation of torsion balances and the interpretation of data obtained with them will be found in earlier editions of this book. Since the introduction of modern gravity meters in the early 1930s, it has been easier to observe gradients by measuring gravity values directly at appropriate intervals along a traverse line. As will be shown in some detail in Chap. 14, the direct interpretation of gravity maps often involves at least a mental scanning of contours for anomalous gradients. A steeper than normal horizontal gradient having a linear trend is often diagnostic of faulting.

In recent years the *vertical gradient* has been looked upon as a promising parameter for direct measurement by gravity meters. The normal vertical

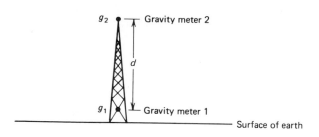

FIGURE 12-20 Proposed arrangement for measuring vertical gradient of gravity from top and bottom of tower.

Observed gradient $= \dfrac{g_1 - g_2}{d}$

Theoretical gradient $= .3086\ \text{mGals/m}$

gradient is readily obtained by differentiating the expression for the attraction of the earth (considered to be a sphere so that its mass can be treated as if it were concentrated at its center) in terms of its radius r to the measuring point. If we write $g = \gamma M/r^2$, where M is the mass of the earth, then

$$\frac{dg}{dr} = -2\,\frac{\gamma M}{r^3} = -\frac{2g}{r} \qquad (12\text{-}35)$$

At sea level the normal vertical gradient of gravity is 0.3086 mGal/m. The maximum deviation from this value at any latitude is -0.0002 mGal/m, a differential that is negligible for all practical purposes. Any deviation of the vertical gradient from its normal value could be associated with anomalous buried masses. A direct measurement of gradient might make it possible to detect such masses with fewer observations than would be needed in conventional gravity measurement. Hammer[17] discusses a number of cases of interest in exploration where it would be advantageous to work with vertical gradients. Such gradients can be measured directly by taking readings at two elevations at the same position and taking the difference between the readings. From a practical standpoint, this can best be done by using two gravity meters, one above the other, on a tower mounted on a truck or by a single meter used for successive readings at the two heights as shown in Fig. 12-20. The practical problems involved are discussed by Thyssen-Bornemisza and Stackler.[18] Thyssen-Bornemisza[19] has proposed a design for a gravity gradiometer that would make it possible to observe the gradients with a single instrument.

12-6 INSTRUMENTS FOR MEASURING GRAVITY ON LAND

Gravity measurements for exploration purposes have been made with three kinds of instruments, each quite different from the others. These are the torsion balance, the pendulum, and the gravity meter. The first two are obsolete, hardly having been used at all for exploration since the middle 1930s.

Many types of gravity meters have been used in exploration work over the past several decades. Only a few of these are in current use for land operations, but since the middle 1960s several special kinds of meters have been put into service for measuring gravity on board ship or in boreholes. The availability of shipborne gravity meters has led to a resurgence in gravity activity after conventional land work had declined to a small fraction of its activity level in earlier decades.

Gravity Meters for Use on Land

The requirements for precision in gravity exploration are so demanding that few measuring instruments of any kind have specifications which are more difficult to meet. The earth's gravitational field is about 10^4 mGal; yet many anomalies of interest in exploration have a maximum value of 1 mGal or less. To detail such anomalies with the accuracy needed for meaningful interpretation requires readings that are valid to at least 0.05 mGal. Modern land meters have a nominal precision as great as 0.01 mGal when readings are taken with extreme care; i.e., they are responsive to changes of this very small magnitude in the earth's gravitational field. It would be much more difficult and probably impossible to measure absolute gravity that precisely under any conditions, let alone in the field. The precision is attainable because we are measuring *differences* in gravity over a total range of gravity values of only tens to hundreds of milliGals.

There are two basic types of gravity meters, the stable and the unstable. A stable meter contains a responsive element (such as a spring) with a change in displacement proportional or approximately proportional to the change in gravity. Since such displacements are always extremely small, they must be greatly magnified by optical, mechanical, or electrical means. Unstable gravimeters are so designed that any change in gravity from its equilibrium value brings other forces into play which increase the displacement caused by the gravity change alone and hence the sensitivity of the instrument. How this is accomplished in practice will be illustrated when specific instruments are discussed. Most current gravity surveying is done with meters of the unstable type.

Stable Type   All stable gravimeters have a single element to balance the force of gravity with another force measurable by a displacement (linear, angular, or electrical) which can be magnified and read directly. Any change in gravity is accompanied by a corresponding change in this displacement. For a simple spring this change would be in its length. The usual formula for the restoring force of a weighted spring is

$$F = k(x - x_0) = mg \qquad (12\text{-}36)$$

where x = length of spring
$\quad x_0$ = original length before weight was hung from it
$\quad k$ = spring constant

Since the mass m is constant, any change in g causes a proportionate change in elongation.

The only type of gravity meter designed on this principle which has had extensive use on land is the Gulf gravimeter,[20] the sensing element of which is a flat spring wound in the form of a helix with the flat surface always parallel to the axis. A weight is suspended at the lower end. Any change in the gravitational pull on the weight causes the spring to rotate as well as elongate. In fact, the rotary motion of the bottom end of the spring is greater and hence easier to measure than the vertical displacement. A mirror attached rigidly to the bottom of the helix makes it possible to measure this rotation by deflecting a light beam. The Gulf instrument has not been used in exploration for several decades.

The Askania Gss3 Seagravimeter, for shipboard use, is also a stable type of meter. It will be discussed on pages 539–540.

Unstable Type   In unstable gravimeters, sometimes referred to as *labilized* or *astatized*, the force of gravity is kept in unstable equilibrium with the restoring force. The instability is provided by a third force which intensifies the effect of any change in gravity from its equilibrium value. For small changes of gravity the force called into play by a departure from equilibrium is proportional to the magnitude of change and acts, of course, in the same direction.

It is easy to show that a gravity meter operates like a seismometer except that the displacement is stationary instead of oscillatory. A vertical spring that is elongated by the gravitational pull mg of a mass m will oscillate with a period $T = 2\pi\sqrt{m/k}$, where k is the spring constant. From Eq. (12-36) it is evident that

$$x - x_0 = \frac{mg}{k} = \frac{T^2}{4\pi^2} g \qquad (12\text{-}37)$$

The elongation is thus proportional to g, and a change in gravity Δg will result in an elongation Δx which is dependent on it according to the formula

$$\Delta x = \frac{T^2}{4\pi^2} \Delta g \qquad (12\text{-}38)$$

Thus the sensitivity of a meter is proportional to the square of the period of the equivalent seismometer. For a weight hanging from a spring, the ratio of the elongation to the length of the spring would be the same as the ratio of the change in gravity to the earth's gravitational attraction. At the maximum desired sensitivity, this ratio, being of the order of 10^{-7} to 10^{-8}, would require much too long a spring to be practical; this explains why stable meters that have had practical use in the field, like the Gulf gravimeter, do not operate by measuring spring elongation directly.

It follows from Eq. (12-38) that any oscillating system can be adapted by proper damping for use as a gravity meter. A long-period vertical Galitzen-type seismograph developed by LaCoste[21] in 1934 turned out to be the basis for the design of the LaCoste and Romberg gravity meter, which is still widely used, as well as a number of other meters of the same type.

LaCoste and Romberg Gravity Meter   The LaCoste and Romberg instrument has a design typical of unstable gravity meters in general. Any change in the force of gravity acting on a weight at the end of a nearly horizontal beam supported by an inclined spring (Fig. 12-21) causes a motion which changes the angle between the beam and the spring (and hence the moment of the spring's pull on the beam), thereby accentuating the moment associated with the gravity increment or decrement, whichever it may be. This reinforcement provides the necessary instability to magnify the effect of the gravity variation. In practice the motion is nulled by an adjustable screw which varies the point at which the mainspring is supported. The angle through which this screw must be turned to restore a light beam, reflected by a mirror on the arm, to its null position is used as a measure of the change in gravity.

An important innovation introduced with the LaCoste and Romberg instrument is the *zero-length spring*. With it the displacement of the spring from equilibrium caused by the weight of the beam in zero position is effectively counteracted by an opposing tension put into the spring when it is wound. It is only with this arrangement that the elongation of the spring caused by any given increment in gravity will be actually proportional to the increment itself. In addition, the deflection will be symmetrical about the equilibrium position; i.e., the positive reading for an increase in gravity over its equilibrium value will be equal to the negative reading for a gravity decrease of the same magnitude.

The LaCoste and Romberg instrument, like the Gulf gravimeter, requires heating elements, a thermostatic regulator, and an insulated case to maintain the temperature sufficiently uniform to avoid significant errors in the gravity readings caused by thermal effects. A change in temperature of 0.002°C will result in a deflection equivalent to a gravity change of 0.02 mGal, which represents the limit of precision for most surveys. To keep the temperature constant, the meter is enclosed in an insulated housing, and a small electric

FIGURE 12-21   Operation of LaCoste and Romberg gravimeter (schematic).

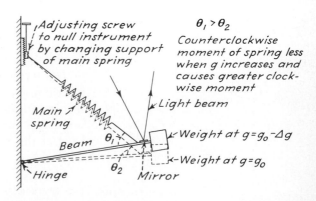

FIGURE 12-22   Worden gravity meter. (*Texas Instruments, Inc.*)

oven powered by a storage battery is regulated by a highly sensitive thermostat.

Worden Gravity* Meter   This extensively used instrument, provided with internal temperature compensation, has the advantage of exceptional portability because no storage battery is required for its operation. Instead of a heavy insulated case, the instrument is housed in a Thermos flask less than 1 ft high (Fig. 12-22). The flask is sealed and evacuated to eliminate the effect of changes in barometric pressure. The weight of the instrument is less than 6 lb, and the tripod and carrying case add only 8 lb to the total. In the Worden meter a number of torsion fibers are used to balance the torque of gravity upon a mass weighing only 5 mg at the end of the arm attached to a beam around which moments are balanced.

* Trademark, Texas Instruments, Inc.

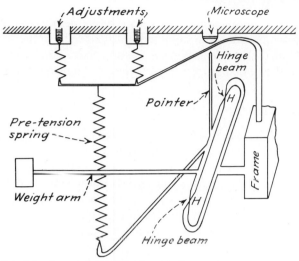

FIGURE 12-23   Principle of operation of Worden gravity meter.

Figure 12-23 illustrates the operation of this meter. The system is in unstable equilibrium around axis *HH*. Any increase in gravitational pull on the mass at the end of the weight arm causes counterclockwise rotation which can be nulled by tightening the pretension spring with an adjusting knob. The amount of rotation of the knob necessary to restore the pointer to its null position provides a measure of gravitational change. The instrument can be read to 0.01 mGal, and the model used for most petroleum exploration work has a dial range of about 60 mGal. A special model is available for geodetic work which has a range of 5500 mGal. Whatever the range may be, the actual values of gravity it covers may have to be set to fit the area of the survey.

Temperature compensation is achieved through the arrangement shown in Fig. 12-24. The two long arms are made of materials having different thermal-expansion coefficients and are connected by a spacing bar at one end. When

FIGURE 12-24   Temperature-compensation system for Worden gravimeter. (*Adapted by permission from Heiskanen and Vening Meinesz, "The Earth and Its Gravity Field," McGraw-Hill Book Company, New York, 1958.*)

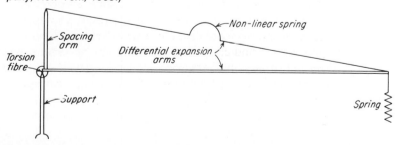

the temperature changes, the relative lengths of the arms change in such a way that there is an upward or downward movement at the end of the spring which largely compensates for any temperature effects in the spring itself. The curved portion of the upper arm represents a short nonlinear spring element which extends the temperature range of the compensation movement.

Calibration of Land Gravity Meters

All readings of gravity meters are in arbitrary scale divisions, and calibration is necessary to express them in milliGals. Calibration may be done by tilting the meter or by taking measurements on it at two points where either the absolute or relative values of gravity are known precisely. A pair of locations at which absolute gravity has been established by pendulum observations is often convenient for this purpose. If the absolute gravities differ by an appreciable fraction of the total range of the instrument, it is usually safe to assume linear response and to calibrate the whole scale on the basis of the two readings alone. Greater precision will of course be obtained from a larger number of reference stations. Hammer[22] describes some attempts to calibrate a gravimeter by taking readings at the top and bottom of a tall building and making use of the theoretical difference in gravity between two points at different elevations after correcting for the attraction of the building itself. He concludes that this method is impractical because of variations in vertical gradient and limitations in the precision of the building corrections. A much greater difference in gravity can be obtained between two points at a substantially different latitude. Kuo et al.[23] report some more recent measurements in tall buildings in New York City and its surroundings.

Drift of Gravimeters

If a gravimeter is left undisturbed for an hour or so after a reading and a second observation is taken, the gravity value will apparently have changed by an amount as great as several hundredths of a milligal. If additional readings are taken over a period of hours and the observed gravity is plotted against time, it will be found that the points tend to fall on a smooth curve. This continual variation of the gravity readings with time is known as *drift* and has a number of causes. One is the fact that the gravimeter springs or torsion fibers are not perfectly elastic but are subject to a slow creep over long periods. Another cause is earth tides, and still another is related to uncompensated temperature effects. A sample set of drift curves is reproduced in Fig. 12-25. The drift during the course of a day may be greater than the maximum gravity variation actually observed during the same period. Drift curves are obtained by repeated occupation of a single field station at intervals during the day. Adjustment of readings at other stations is made by recording departures from the drift curves using techniques to be described in the next chapter.

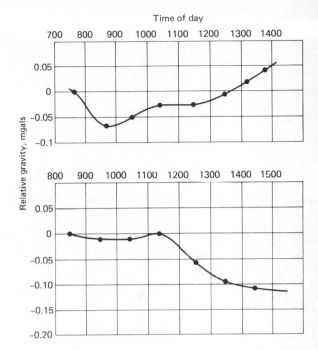

FIGURE 12-25 Typical drift curves for gravity meter. The total excursion in the course of a working day is not much more than 1 mGal. (*Tide-lands Geophysical Co.*)

12-7 INSTRUMENTS FOR MEASURING GRAVITY AT SEA

Two types of meters are used for measuring gravity in water-covered areas. One is lowered from a ship to the water bottom in a waterproof housing, whereupon it is leveled and read on board ship. The other measures the gravity on board a ship, being mounted on a platform stabilized by accessory equipment in order to minimize the effect of the ship's motion on the observed acceleration. The first type, for a long time the only one available for marine observations, is still used where an anomaly of small areal extent (such as from a salt dome) must be mapped with the highest possible precision. The ship-borne meter is intended for reconnaissance surveys over large areas where the anomalies of interest are so large that high resolution in following lateral variations is not needed.

Bottom Meters

As early as 1941, the Gulf gravimeter was adapted for underwater use by Pepper.[24] The meter was enclosed in a waterproof housing and operated on the water bottom by remote control through cables from a ship. Leveling was accomplished by motor-driven gimbals so designed that the level was controlled independently in two perpendicular directions. The underwater meter now most widely used in exploration work is the LaCoste and Romberg[25] type.

FIGURE 12-26 A LaCoste and Romberg water-bottom meter being lowered into the water from a ship. (*LaCoste and Romberg, Inc.*)

Figure 12-26 shows this meter being lowered into the water from a ship by a boom that swings it from the deck.

The LaCoste and Romberg instrument is equipped with a servo system to compensate for vertical motion. It also reads gravity automatically and presents it digitally on a shipboard display unit.

The basic gravity-measuring element operates on the same principle as the LaCoste and Romberg land meter discussed in Sec. 12-6, and the precision is about the same. A light beam from a source attached to the case is directed against the movable arm of the meter in such a way that a photocell is actuated when it moves vertically. The cell controls a servomotor which raises or lowers the meter in a direction opposing the motion of the case. Accuracy of the system under reasonably good sea conditions is 0.1 mGal.

Shipborne Meters

The advantages of measuring gravity on a moving ship are quite evident. With bottom meters, the ship must stop for at least several minutes at each location where an observation is made. Any instrumental system that allows readings without such stops should make it possible to obtain the gravity data much more economically and efficiently.

The principal obstacle to obtaining useful gravity information from an instrument on a ship is the fact that motions of the ship (such as pitch, roll, and heave) are accompanied by accelerations which are themselves much greater than the gravity differences to be measured. For a shipborne gravity meter to work at all, it is necessary to neutralize (by compensation or averaging) the accelerations associated with the motion of the ship itself. These accelerations may be 100,000 mGal or more, depending on the type of ship and the sea state, and they have both horizontal and vertical components. The horizontal motion is from pitch and roll and the vertical motion is from heave. All these motions have periods of only a few seconds.

Effects of pitch and roll are generally eliminated with a gyroscopically stabilized platform using accelerometers to actuate servomotors which keep the platform horizontal within a few seconds of arc. Vertical motion of the ship is removed by averaging many cycles of acceleration over an extended period. This can be done by introducing a damping that results in a long time constant for the meter; in one type of meter it is as great as 5 min. This means that about 100 vertical oscillations would have to be averaged for each observation. Such a long time constant limits the response of the instrument to gravity anomalies which appear to have a long period when recorded on a moving chart. For example, a shallow high-density buried mass 1000 ft wide would be crossed in 1 min by a ship traveling at 10 knots. If an instrument with a 5-min time constant were used, the gravity effect of this mass would be reduced fivefold by the averaging. The damping thus has the effect of a low-pass filter, suppressing frequencies associated with the ship's motion but passing frequencies associated with subsurface sources that generate fairly broad gravity anomalies. The type of damping that is employed varies with the instrument.

The LaCoste and Romberg Shipborne Meter   The shipborne gravity-measuring system most widely used in exploration work is the LaCoste and Romberg meter[25] mounted on a gyroscopically stabilized platform. Like the underwater instrument made by the same firm, the basic gravity-measuring system is that originally used in the LaCoste and Romberg meter designed for use on land. This consists of a weight at the end of a nearly horizontal beam supported by a spring making an acute angle with the beam. Because of the need for filtering out short-period vertical accelerations associated with the ship's motion, the damping must be much greater than with a conventional instrument. The damping mechanism consists of cylinders (one set on the beam and another on the frame) interweaving in such a way as to resist the flow of air during motion.

The heavy damping makes it impractical to read gravity directly from the displacement of the beam, as is done with gravity meters designed for use on land, but the rate of change in the deflection of the beam is responsive to changes in effective gravity (earth's gravity plus other vertical accelerations) regardless of the damping. This follows from the basic equation of motion of the system:

$$m\left(g + \frac{d^2z}{dt^2}\right) = kS - F\frac{dB}{dt} - \frac{d^2B}{dt^2} \tag{12-39}$$

where g = acceleration of gravity
$\qquad m$ = mass
$\qquad z$ = vertical position of point on meter case
$\qquad B$ = displacement of mass with respect to its null position in case
$\qquad F$ = damping coefficient
$\qquad k$ = spring constant
$\qquad S$ = displacement of spring

S can be taken as the length of the spring when it is the zero-length type used in the LaCoste land meter. The term d^2B/dt^2 can be neglected in comparison with the other terms because the time constant is much smaller than the time over which the gravity readings are to be averaged. When this term is removed, the equation can be written

$$g + \frac{d^2z}{dt^2} = \frac{k}{m}S - \frac{F}{m}\frac{dB}{dt} \tag{12-40}$$

The left-hand side is the effective gravity acting on the instrument.

As with the LaCoste and Romberg land meter, the beam is kept in balance by continual automatic adjustment of the spring tension, which is carried out by a servo system that changes the position where the end of the spring pivots. For a given total acceleration, Eq. (12-40) shows that this position varies as the rate of change of the displacement. A beam of light is reflected into a photocell by a mirror on the gravity meter beam. A chopper is used to give an ac output from the cell when the beam deviates from the null position, the magnitude depending on the *rate* of its motion away from null. A rectifier is used to convert this output to the signal, which is recorded as a measure of gravity.

Most of the horizontal acceleration associated with the ship's motion is removed by the action of the stabilized platform, but there will be some residual effects. Translational horizontal accelerations, for example, will not be removed even when the platform holds the instrument in a level position. The most serious effect, however, of residual horizontal accelerations, is *cross-coupling* between the horizontal and the vertical accelerations. When the beam, hinged around a horizontal axis, makes an angle β with the horizontal as in Fig. 12-27, there will be a horizontal torque on the beam of $mgD \sin \beta \, d^2x/dt^2$, where D is the length of the beam. It can be shown (see

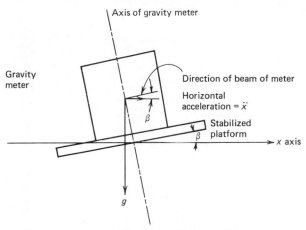

FIGURE 12-27   Cross-coupling in the LaCoste and Romberg shipborne meter.

LaCoste[25]) that the cross-coupling error in the gravity reading caused by this torque will be

$$e = \frac{d^2x}{dt^2} \tan \beta \cong \frac{d^2x}{dt^2} \beta \qquad (12\text{-}41)$$

This is the horizontal acceleration times the angle of inclination of the beam.

The angle of the beam β varies periodically with the motion of the ship according to the relation $\beta = \beta_0 + \beta_1 \sin(\omega t + \psi)$, where ω is the frequency of the ship's motion and ψ is the phase difference between the horizontal and vertical accelerations. A cross-coupling error e as great as 50 mGals is possible for the largest horizontal accelerations that are likely to be observed during recording. This is known as *inherent cross-coupling*.

In the LaCoste and Romberg instrument the cross-coupling error is evaluated internally by a computer into which data on β and the horizontal acceleration are continually being fed. The error is then removed electrically from the output of the gravity-sensing element.

Askania Seagravimeter   The first shipborne meter to go into service was designed by Graf and manufactured by the Askania Werke of West Berlin.[26] This instrument, the Gss2, which has a horizontal beam as the responsive element and a very strong magnet for damping, has seen extensive use in academic and governmental surveys but has seldom been employed in oil exploration.

In 1971, the Askania Seagravity meter Gss3 was introduced. It differs in principle from the Gss2 in that the sensing element has only vertical motion, eliminating cross-coupling effects. Figure 12-28 illustrates the design. The sensor is a vertically oriented tubular mass held in place by five fiber ligatures.

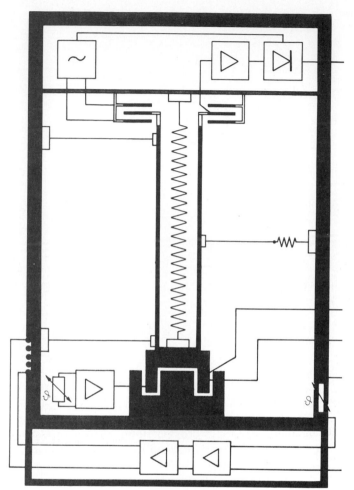

FIGURE 12-28   Principle of operation of Askania Seagravity meter Gss3. (*Bodenseewerk Gerätetechnik GMBH.*)

A vertical spring compensates for the weight of the sensing element. A capacitive transducer is used as a pickup, the signal from it being amplified and rectified. A feedback loop reduces the displacement of the system attributable to ship motion. A filter system is included which is designed to separate the components of voltage due to gravity changes from those caused by accelerations of the ship. The digital output of a voltmeter is fed into a recorder chart and optionally into magnetic tape and punched-tape recorders. An accuracy of 0.5 mGal is claimed for ship accelerations of 0.2 *g* or less.

Bell Ship Gravity Meter   Although this instrument, first employed for geophysical measurements in 1967, is no longer manufactured, it offers a number

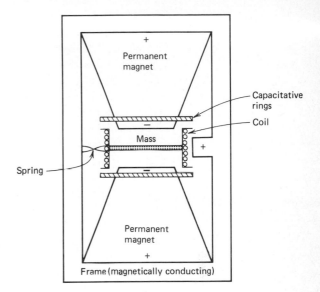

FIGURE 12-29 Principle of operation of Bell shipborne gravity meter.

of features worthy of note. The sensor, instead of being a pivoted beam kept horizontal by a spring, is a disklike mass less than $\frac{3}{16}$ in in diameter surrounded by a coil of wire and attached to the case by three light-guide springs (Fig. 12-29). The mass and coil are located between the poles of a pair of conical, permanent magnets which are oppositely polarized. The entire system is contained in a cylinder about $1\frac{3}{4}$ in high and $\frac{3}{4}$ in in diameter.

A variable current passes through the coil, and it is adjusted to keep the coil in a null position. If the gravitational force on the coil changes, the mass will move from its equilibrium position and the amount the current must be varied to bring it back to this position gives a measure of the change in acceleration. A pair of capacitive rings attached to the respective pole pieces is used to detect movement of the coil. The change in capacitance brought about by such motion unbalances a bridge, generating a signal that brings the mass back to equilibrium position. The electric signal used to obtain this balance, which is proportional to the change in gravity, is digitized and converted to gravity units for final shipboard presentation. Cross-coupling effects are negligible, as the sensing element is very small.

The sensor in the Bell instrument was originally designed for inertial navigation. A number of units have been used in government-sponsored surveys as well as in worldwide geophysical surveys carried out by oil companies.

12-8 BOREHOLE GRAVITY METERS

After more than a decade of development efforts in the United States, the U.S.S.R., and England, the first instruments for precise and reliable measurement of gravity in boreholes became available in the middle 1960s. Two types of meters came into use at this time. One, the Esso borehole gravity meter,[27] makes use of a vibrating filament; the frequency is related to the tension on the filament and changes as gravity varies. The other, developed jointly by the U.S. Geological Survey and LaCoste and Romberg, Inc.,[28] has as its basic sensing element a LaCoste and Romberg gravimeter especially adapted for the space available in a borehole and for the temperatures encountered at the maximum depths where gravity values are to be measured. Both instruments yield gravity measurements with a precision of 0.01 mGal.

The Esso meter has a platinum mass which hangs from a tungsten fiber in a vacuum. It is housed in a cylindrical case with dimensions that allow it to remain vertical in boreholes that deviate from the vertical as much as 4°. The outer diameter of the instrument is 10.2 cm. A thermostat keeps the temperature at 125°C, a value higher than the ambient temperature expected at any depth in the hole.

Gravity variations are measured by determining the precise times required for a specified number of oscillations, actually 10^5, 2×10^5, 3×10^5, etc., cycles. The longer the period of measurement the greater the precision of the gravity value. It takes 20 min to obtain a gravity reading good to 0.01 mGal.

The USGS–LaCoste and Romberg gravity meter is designed according to the same principle as the land and shipborne meters developed by its manufacturer. The sensor, with a zero-length spring and a special adjusting screw to allow a wide range of readings, is mounted on gimbals and can be leveled when the hole deviates as much as 6.5° from the vertical. The outside diameter of the instrument ranges from 15 to 17 cm. Temperature is maintained by a thermostat at 101°C.

Gravity is measured by nulling the beam, as with other LaCoste and Romberg instruments. It requires 5 min to obtain a reading with a precision of 0.01 mGal. Drift is low, and the thermostat keeps the gravity reading from varying more than 0.04 mGal when the temperature changes from 25 to 95°C. As the increase in temperature with instrument depth is smooth, this effect can be incorporated in the drift and can be eliminated in the same way as other drift effects.

Use of data from borehole gravity meters in determining density will be considered in a subsequent chapter (page 560).

12-9 APPENDIX

Attraction of Horizontal Cylinder at Point on the Surface along a Line Perpendicular to Its Axis

Figure 12-30 shows a buried mass distributed along an infinitely long horizontal line (such as a straight wire) at depth z with a linear density of λ g/cm. Assume that gravity measurements are made on a horizontal surface along the x axis which is perpendicular to the buried line. If a measurement of the *vertical*

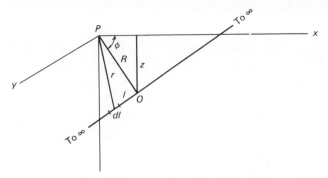

FIGURE 12-30   Gravity at P from infinitely long horizontal wire buried at depth z and parallel to y axis.

component of attraction of the line is made at point P, we can define distance R as the perpendicular distance PO from the measuring point P, ϕ as the angle between OP and the x axis, and r as the distance from P to an element of length dl, where l is the distance from O [with coordinates (x, R, z)] to the element of mass.

The vertical component of attraction from the element dl may be written

$$dg_z = \frac{\gamma\,dm\,\sin\,\phi}{r^2}\frac{R}{r} = \gamma\lambda\,\sin\,\phi\,R\frac{dl}{(R^2 + l^2)^{3/2}} \qquad (12\text{-}42)$$

and the total vertical attraction, obtained by integration, is

$$g_z = \gamma\lambda\,\sin\,\phi\,R\int_{-\infty}^{\infty}\frac{dl}{(R^2 + l^2)^{3/2}} \qquad (12\text{-}43)$$

$$= \gamma\lambda\,\sin\,\phi\,R\left[\frac{l}{R^2\,\sqrt{R^2 + l^2}}\right]_{-\infty}^{\infty} \qquad (12\text{-}44)$$

$$= 2\frac{\gamma\lambda\,\sin\,\phi}{R} = \frac{2\gamma\lambda z}{R^2} = 2\gamma\lambda\frac{z}{x_{\bullet}^2 + z^2} \qquad (12\text{-}45)$$

If the line is expanded into a cylinder of radius A and density ρ, the mass per unit length becomes $\pi A^2\rho$ and the attraction becomes

$$g_z = 2\pi\gamma A^2\rho\frac{z}{x^2 + z^2} \qquad (12\text{-}46)$$

Attraction over the Center of a Buried Cylinder with a Vertical Axis

Figure 12-31 shows a vertical cylinder with upper and lower surfaces at depths d and f, respectively. Its attraction is the difference between the fields of two

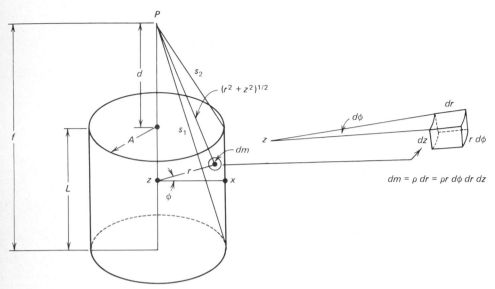

FIGURE 12-31
Quantities used in deriving formula for attraction along axis of buried vertical sphere.

infinitely deep cylinders of radius A with top surfaces at depths of d and f. The density of each cylinder is ρ.

Consider the upper cylinder of infinite depth. We see that the slant distance from P (on the axis at the surface) to its top edge is s_2. Its gravity effect can be computed by summing fields from mass elements dm, which are approximate cubes with edges of dimensions dz, $r\,d\phi$, and dr as defined on the right side of the figure. The attraction at P is obtained from the triple integral

$$g_z = \gamma\rho \int_d^\infty \int_0^A \int_0^{2\pi} \frac{d\phi\; r\; dr\; dz}{(r^2 + z^2)^{3/2}} \qquad (12\text{-}47)$$

Integration over the cylinder yields

$$g_z = 2\pi\gamma\rho[(d^2 + A^2)^{1/2} - d] = 2\pi\gamma\rho(s_2 - d) \qquad (12\text{-}48)$$

The lower infinitely deep cylinder with its top edge a distance s_1 from P has vertical attraction $2\pi\gamma\rho(s_1 - d)$. We find the field of a cylinder of height L (equal to $f - d$) by subtracting the effect of the deeper cylinder from that of the shallower. The difference is

$$\begin{aligned}
g_z &= 2\pi\gamma\rho[(s_2 - d) - (s_1 - f)] \\
&= 2\pi\gamma\rho(s_2 - s_1 - d + f) \\
&= 2\pi\gamma\rho(s_2 - s_1 + L) \qquad (12\text{-}49)
\end{aligned}$$

REFERENCES

1 Nettleton, L. L.: "Gravity and Magnetics in Oil Prospecting," pp. 10–13, McGraw-Hill, New York, 1976.

2 Garland, G. D.: "The Earth's Shape and Gravity," Pergamon, Oxford, 1965.

3 Heiskanen, W. A., and Helmut Moritz: "Physical Geodesy," W. H. Freeman, San Francisco, 1967.

4 Hammer, Sigmund: Note on the Variation from the Equator to the Pole of the Earth's Gravity, *Geophysics*, vol. 8, pp. 57–60, 1943.

5 International Association of Geodesy: Geodetic Reference System 1967, *Int. Asso. Geodesy Spec. Pub.* 3, 1971.

6 Chovitz, B. H.: Modern Geodetic Earth Reference Models, *EOS Trans. Am. Geophys. Union*, vol. 62, pp. 65–67, 1981.

7 Pratt, J. H.: On the Attraction of the Himalaya Mountains and of the Elevated Regions Beyond upon the Plumb-Line in India; On the Computations of the Effect of the Attraction of the Mountain Masses as Disturbing the Apparent Astronomical Latitude of Stations in Geodetic Surveys, *Phil. Trans. R. Soc. Lond.*, vol. 145, pp. 53–55, 1855.

8 Airy, G. B.: *Phil. Trans. R. Soc. Lond.*, vol. 145, pp. 101–104, 1855.

9 Pratt, J. H.: *Phil. Trans. R. Soc. Lond.*, vol. 149, pp. 747–763, 1859.

10 Chapman, M. E., and J. H. Bodine: Considerations of the Indirect Effect in Marine Gravity Modelling, *J. Geophys. Res.*, vol. 84, pp. 3889–3896, 1979.

11 Heiland, C. A.: "Geophysical Exploration," p. 163, Prentice-Hall, Englewood Cliffs, N. J., 1940.

12 Melchior, P. J.: "The Tides of the Planet Earth," Pergamon, New York, 1978.

13 Longman, I. M.: Formulas for the Tidal Acceleration of Gravity, *J. Geophys. Res.*, vol. 64, pp. 2351–2355, 1959.

14 Nettleton, L. L.: Gravity and Magnetic Calculations, *Geophysics*, vol. 7, pp. 293–310, 1942.

15 Bowie, William: "Isostasy," p. 69, Dutton, New York, 1927.

16 Heiland, C.: "Geophysical Exploration," pp. 151–153, Prentice-Hall, Englewood Cliffs, N.J., 1940.

17 Hammer, Sigmund: The Anomalous Vertical Gradient of Gravity, *Geophysics*, vol. 35, pp. 153–157, 1970.

18 Thyssen-Bornemisza, Stephen, and W. F. Stackler: Observation of the Vertical Gradient of Gravity in the Field, *Geophysics*, vol. 21, pp. 771–779, 1956.

19 Thyssen-Bornemisza, Stephen: Instrumental Arrangement to Measure Gravity with Gradients, *Geophysics*, vol. 35, pp. 713–715, 1970.

20 Wyckoff, R. D.: The Gulf Gravimeter, *Geophysics*, vol. 6, pp. 13–33, 1941.

21 LaCoste, L. J. B., Jr.: A New Type Long Period Vertical Seismograph, *Physics*, vol. 5, pp. 178–180, 1934; also see L. J. B. LaCoste and A. Romberg, U. S. Patent 2,293,437, issued Aug. 18, 1942.

22 Hammer, Sigmund: Investigation of the Vertical Gradient of Gravity, *Trans. Am. Geophys. Union, 19th Annu. Meet.*, pp. 72–82, 1938.

23 Kuo, John T., Mario Ottaviani, and Shri K. Singh: Variations of Vertical Gravity Gradient in New York City and Alpine, New Jersey, *Geophysics*, vol. 34, pp. 235–248, 1969.

24 Pepper, T. B.: The Gulf Underwater Gravimeter, *Geophysics*, vol. 6, pp. 34–44, 1941.

25 LaCoste, L.: The Measurement of Gravity at Sea and in the Air, *Rev. Geophys.*, vol. 5, pp. 477–526, 1967.

26 Anonymous: First Sea Surface Gravimeter, IGY Bull. 8, *Trans. Am. Geophys. Union*, vol. 39, pp. 175–178, 1958.

27 Howell, Lynn G., K. O. Heintz, and A. Barry: The Development and Use of a High-Precision Downhole Gravity Meter, *Geophysics*, vol. 31, pp. 764–772, 1966.

28 McCulloh, Thane H.: Borehole Gravimetry: New Developments and Applications, *Proc. 7th. World Petrol. Congr.*, vol. 2, pp. 734–739, Elsevier, London, 1967.

29 Wolf, Alfred: Tidal Force Observations, *Geophysics*, vol. 5, pp. 317–320, 1940.

CHAPTER 13

GRAVITY FIELD MEASUREMENTS AND REDUCTIONS

We shall now consider the techniques by which gravity data are obtained in land and marine surveys and converted into a form suitable for interpretation. Chapter 14 will deal with the final stage of gravity exploration, the extraction of geological information from the reduced gravity data.

The development of the equipment and techniques used for making gravity observations in the field has required a rare combination of engineering skill and operational efficiency. The instruments have been designed for ruggedness so that they can operate reliably under difficult field conditions, and the procedures used in obtaining data with them have been designed for maximizing the speed with which traverses can be covered.

The operational techniques employed for surveys on land are different in many respects from those used in marine surveys. Since the early 1950s the level of activity in gravity exploration on land (based on the number of crews operating) has dropped substantially in the United States; the fractional decrease since the period of peak activity has been considerably greater than that for seismic work. Yet the total number of miles of gravity coverage obtained per year has been much greater since the late 1960s than in previous years. The introduction of shipborne gravity meters has made it possible to record gravity at sea simultaneously with seismic reflection surveys, and a great deal of gravity data has been obtained in the course of such combined surveys.

The cost of making gravity observations and of acquiring seismic reflection data at the same time is only marginally greater than that of carrying out a seismic survey alone because the ship constitutes by far the largest item of expense in any kind of marine geophysical work.

13-1 GRAVITY MEASUREMENTS ON LAND

Determining Positions for Stations The placement of stations in a gravity survey depends on three factors: (1) feasibility of access, (2) spacing pattern necessary to detail the features which the survey was designed to locate and map, and (3) availability of precise elevations for the station locations.

Access depends on the nature of the terrain and the distribution of roads or other thoroughfares (such as streams) through the area being surveyed. Even when portable instruments like the Worden gravimeter are used, the rate of progress is seriously impeded if motorized transportation is not available between stations. In some surveys, the objectives can be achieved if gravity stations are confined to existing roads or (in jungle areas) to waterways. This is of course the most economical approach.

The pattern of the stations is generally designed so that they will come as close to forming a rectangular grid as access conditions allow. The spacing within the grid is governed by the depth and lateral extent of the geological features being sought. To obtain the necessary detail on the gravity field of a salt dome 1 km in diameter and 1 km deep at its top surface, one might set up a grid $\frac{1}{2}$ km on the side, although a spacing of 1 km between stations would probably be adequate for establishing the existence and approximate location of the dome. For small targets such as ore bodies, much closer spacing is in order. A gravity survey in Cuba, where chromite bodies several hundred feet or less in width were sought, is described by Hammer et al.[1] Here the grid spacing, 20 m, was particularly small.

It is often desirable to shift the stations from their position on a uniform grid to avoid topographic features that would distort the gravity readings so greatly that the usual correction procedures for topographic irregularities (discussed on page 566) could not yield sufficiently precise results. A gravity reading, for example, on the summit of a small knoll would be affected much more by the mass of the knoll itself than would readings a short distance to the side, where the uncertainty in the exact shape and density of the knoll would not be likely to contribute nearly as much error. Hubbert[2] has prepared a series of charts showing the magnitude of the correction required at various distances from various kinds of topographic features. These charts were designed for field operators who might need guidance in deciding how far to shift gravity stations from the centers of such features.

Surveying Surveying expense is the largest item in the budgets of most gravity parties. Both elevation and geographical position must be known accurately. Spirit leveling is usually necessary, but in some cases barometric leveling is adequate. The methods of surveying and the cost involved vary greatly, depending on the ease of transportation and on the scale and quality of existing maps and level nets. The degree of necessary precision is established by the sensitivity of observed gravity to elevation and latitude. An error in elevation of 1 ft should change the gravity value at a station by about 0.06 mGal, and an error of 100 ft in the north-south coordinate of position should result in an error of 0.03 mGal at middle latitudes. An accuracy of 0.1 ft in elevation and of less than 100 ft in horizontal control is thus required in surveying for gravity stations from which high precision is expected. Such accuracy can be achieved only by close spacing of transit positions and short chain lengths on slopes or by careful adjustment of theodolite data. The cost of such surveying is necessarily higher than that of topographic surveys made for most other kinds of geophysical work.

In regional or academically oriented surveys, where speed and economy are more important than the utmost attainable precision, it is often acceptable to determine elevations barometrically rather than geodetically. Instruments are available that measure differences in barometric pressure with much higher precision than the standard barometers used in geological surveys. Under favorable conditions they can respond to changes in atmospheric pressure equivalent to elevation differences as small as 0.1 ft. The precision of barometric measurements can be increased by comparing readings at field stations with *simultaneous* readings at bases of known elevation located on corners of a triangle covering the area of operation. Lateral gradients thus observed can be interpolated for individual stations inside the triangle. Variations in barometric pressure can be removed in the same way that drift is removed from gravity readings. In mountainous areas, errors in elevation caused primarily by local barometric pressure variations are difficult to control. Resultant elevation errors of 15 to 30 ft are common, particularly when the survey area is large.

Inertial surveying systems came into wide use in the late 1970s and were first used extensively in the Rocky Mountains of Utah and Wyoming. As Seibert[3] describes it:

> The inertial surveying system is basically a stable element containing three orthogonally mounted accelerometers which are maintained in north, east, and vertical alignment by a complex gyro control system. By double integration of the accelerometer outputs, displacement along each axis is determined. The inertial surveying system is primarily an interpolater.

The control points of the survey, from which are determined the interpolated values, are usually those established by various government agencies (National Ocean Survey, Bureau of Land Management, etc.) and/or satellite doppler control points. "Intertial system drift and misalignment cause closure errors at the traverse termination point. The closure error at the end point is distributed through the traverse as a function of time and distance."[3] Horizontal and vertical survey accuracies better than 3 ft have been routinely achieved. Close spacing of primary survey control points can result in accuracies relative to control of less than 1 ft. Inertial surveying enables accurate surveying without the limitations of conventional line-of-sight surveying. The inertial surveying system is transported from station to station by helicopter or any convenient land vehicle. The time required to establish survey coordinates is about 20 s, where the time required to read the gravity meter is about 2 min. Depending on travel time between stations, it is often possible to read as many as a dozen stations in an hour.

When the U.S. Global Positioning System is fully operational (Chap. 5, p. 150), it will be possible to determine precise elevations (and positions) in a few seconds with a portable receiver. If proper clearances are available, those elevations can be obtained without reference to a base station. If not, the equipment will have to be operated in a differential mode, that is, with a known base station at which a second receiver is operated.

Transportation and Operation of the Instrument   The heavier types of gravimeter, which generally use storage batteries for temperature regulation, are set up inside a truck or passenger automobile on a tripod which is lowered to the ground through holes in the floor. The heaters for thermostatic control required by such instruments are connected by cable to the vehicle's battery and operate continuously. There are many localities, however, where other means of transportation are required due to special terrain conditions. In the North Slope of Alaska, gravimeters are flown from station to station in light airplanes on skis or pontoons. In the desert areas of Australia, transportation is by airplane and helicopter. On a gravity survey in the foothills of Alberta, described by Hastings,[4] a Gulf party transported its instruments by pack horses. For the marsh country of southern Louisiana, where wheeled vehicles cannot travel at all, the

FIGURE 13-1
Marsh buggy used for gravity operations in swampy areas. (*Ardco.*)

problem of transporting gravimeters and other geophysical equipment has been solved for more than four decades by marsh buggies like the one shown in Fig. 13-1. In some areas, finally, there seems to be no effective substitute for carrying gravimeters on foot. The close station spacing required in the Cuban chromite survey just described made this the only practical means of locomotion. A light instrument like the Worden gravimeter, which does not use batteries for temperature control, is especially suitable for such transport.

Use of helicopters for transporting gravity meters initially encountered serious problems in determining station positions with the requisite degree of accuracy, particularly elevation accuracy. In general, barometric altimeters have been found to be accurate enough only for regional surveys. Conventional line-of-sight surveying provides sufficiently accurate coordinates. Survey efficiency suffers significantly where line-of-sight surveying is not possible.

The limitations of line-of-sight surveying in conjunction with helicopter transport of a gravity meter are eliminated by the use of an inertial surveying system. Horizontal and vertical coordinates are established relative to existing survey benchmark control at the beginning and end of each survey traverse. If insufficient benchmark control is available in the survey area, additional control can be established by satellite observations. Typically, helicopter-supported gravity surveys with inertial surveying achieve survey accuracies of 1 to 3 ft in both horizontal and vertical coordinates and gravity anomaly accuracies between 0.1 and 0.5 mGal. As many as 150 stations may be read in a single day, even with stations spaced a mile or more apart.

Adjustment for Drift   The instrumental readings as made in the field require a correction for the drift of the gravimeter (including earth-tide effects). All gravity values observed during the course of a given day's operations, including those obtained in reoccupations of stations, are plotted against time. In surveys where high precision is desired, each station is reoccupied several times during the course of a day, and thus the instrument must be moved along the profile in a zigzag trajectory. Figure 13-2 shows a drift curve for a typical survey made over the portion of a day in which stations were occupied. The curve, a straight line, was drawn to pass through the points plotted for the original occupation and two reoccupations of station 1. If the gravity difference between station 1 and any other station is wanted, one simply reads the vertical displacement of the plotted point from the drift curve at the time when the station of interest was occupied. The drift of the instrument used for the observations plotted in Fig. 13-2 was small relative to the change in gravity between stations. The drift curve plotted in Fig. 12-25 is plotted at nearly 10 times the vertical scale of Fig. 13-2.

For surveys where drift is large or irregular with respect to the precision desired, more complicated field techniques are necessary to eliminate its influence. In such cases an oscillating sequence of stations is established. A method proposed by Roman[5] requires four readings at each station. In the intervals between them, readings are taken at other nearby stations.

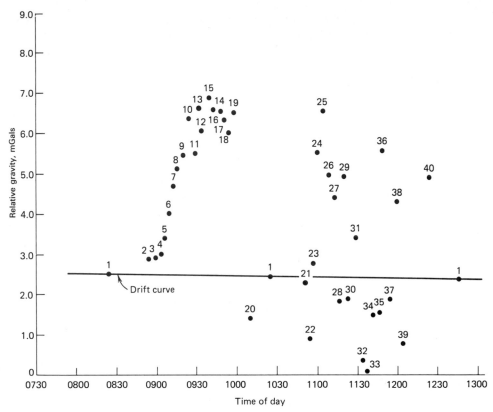

FIGURE 13-2 Typical plot for drift adjustment on day when 40 stations are occupied. Station 1, as base station, is reoccupied twice during the day. Drift curve based on readings at station 1. (*Petty-Ray Geophysical Division, Geosource Inc.*)

If stations lie along a profile in the order *a, b, c,* etc., they would be observed in the order *ab, abc, abcd, abcde, cdef, defg,* etc. Numerical adjustment by standard methods such as least squares is then used to reduce the error resulting from drift to a minimum.

Regional Gravity Surveys with Gravimeters Ever since the 1870s, when pendulums were used for gravity measurements, regional gravity surveys, in which station spacings are measured in tens or even hundreds of kilometers, have been conducted in many parts of the world for studying the figure of the earth as well as its large-scale geologic features. From such studies valuable information has been obtained which has improved our understanding of plate tectonics and crustal spreading. The early surveys with pendulums were cumbersome and only allowed a precision of several milliGals. In recent years, the gravimeter has been used for regional surveys, giving readings that are much more precise and convenient to obtain. Often specially designed geodetic gravimeters with a more extended range than those used in detailed exploration are employed for regional studies.

Gravity measurements well distributed around the world provide information that can be used to determine the vertical separation of the geoid and the reference ellipsoid at any desired point and, hence, the true shape of the earth. Stokes developed the theory for this type of analysis, which is summarized by Garland.[6] The denser and more widely distributed the gravity data, the better the precision of the geoidal shape thus obtained. Regional gravity studies have been conducted on land and sea by various geodetic institutes with this objective in view. The introduction of ballistic missiles has given military motivation to the acquisition of precise information on the gravity field and shape of the earth.

Academically oriented surveys are also carried out to gain a better understanding of regional geology than is obtainable from surface observations alone. Such surveys have been conducted in all parts of the world. The methods are similar to those used in oil exploration, but the spacing of stations is ordinarily greater and the elevation control is usually obtained either from existing benchmarks or from barometric measurements. Several typical surveys carried out for purposes of this kind are described later in this chapter (pages 576 to 578).

Such gravity surveys, whether run for geodetic or geological purposes, are most useful when tied to reference stations where absolute gravity is established. The determination of absolute gravity by standard pendulum observations is cumbersome in the field, and for a long time there was a serious shortage of reference points established by this means. In the late 1940s, however, Woollard,[7] at the University of Wisconsin, initiated a project to set up a worldwide network of stations by flying long loops with specially designed Worden gravimeters having a total range of 5400 mGal. These provided ties to established pendulum stations where absolute gravity is known to a high degree of precision. Drift effects were eliminated by returning to the reference station after closing loops sometimes as much as 20,000 mi long. Woollard and Rose[8] have catalogued the stations for which gravity values were established during the course of this project.

13-2 MEASUREMENT OF GRAVITY AT SEA

The earliest measurements of gravity in water-covered areas were in the shallow protected bays and bayous of Louisiana. Tripods and platforms were initially constructed so that readings could be taken above the water level using land meters. For a while gravity meters and their operators were lowered to the water bottom (as much as 125 ft deep) in diving bells.

Since 1941, remote-controlled bottom meters have been employed for work both in protected and open waters. Shipborne meters, first introduced in the late 1950s, have been employed for most marine gravity measurements since the later 1960s. The precision obtainable from shipborne meters is not generally as great as that from bottom meters, but for most regional or reconnaissance surveys the accuracy of 1 mGal or better that can be obtained from shipborne surveys is quite adequate.

Observations with Bottom Meters   The LaCoste and Romberg bottom meter (LaCoste[9]) is by far the most widely used instrument of this type. As shown in Fig. 12-26, it is lowered into position at the water bottom from the deck of the ship by a boom which holds it far enough out from the ship's side to protect it from banging when it is lowered to or raised from the bottom. When the meter reaches the bottom, it is leveled by a built-in servo system, and the reading is displayed digitally on a panel installed on board the ship.

The principal limitation in the accuracy of a bottom meter is from motion on the sea floor, usually from water waves. The wave motion gives rise to a pressure change at the water bottom, which at long periods (such as those of tides), approaches the difference in the static pressure between highest and lowest water elevations. Within the usual range of periods for waves and swell, however, the pressure is much attenuated, the effect decreasing with increasing depth and decreasing wave period. Thus wave effects should not be of concern except in shallow water. A soft bottom will transmit more of the wave motion to the meter than a hard one; thus a lower accuracy can be expected when the meter is standing in mud.

It is important to have accurate measurements of water depth at the point where the bottom meter is situated so that corrections will be as precise as possible. A pressure gauge built into the gravimeter case is designed to give digital readings of water depth on the same indicator panel on which gravity is read.

The speed with which observations can be made and the time between successive station occupations depend on the water depth and the grid spacing. If good handling equipment is available, it should be possible to make as many observations in a day as can be obtained on land under ordinary operating conditions. Accuracy of gravity readings is generally no better than 0.1 milliGal for a bottom meter, compared with a few hundredths of a milliGal in a land meter.

Observations with Shipborne Meters   There are a number of important differences, many of them obvious, between marine gravity surveys with bottom meters and those with meters on board ship. In the first type of survey, discrete readings are made at the individual stations at which the ship stops, just as in land operations. In shipborne surveys, continuous gravity readings are obtained while the ship is under way. Surveying and positioning techniques for offshore gravity measurements, whether with shipborne or water-bottom meters, are the same as those used for seismic surveys. The techniques involved were described in Chap. 5. The positioning requirements of shipborne gravity meters are somewhat different than for other offshore geophysical surveys because the need for precision in determining *speed* is greater than that in mapping the location where a reading was taken. This occurs because of the Eötvös effect, which occurs because the east-west component of the ship's speed causes an increase or decrease in the earth's centrifugal acceleration, depending on whether the motion is with or against the direction in which the earth rotates. The Eötvös effect on gravity Δg_E depends on the velocity V of the ship, its latitude ϕ, and its heading α with respect to the north-south direction in accordance with the relation

$$\Delta g_E = 7.487V \cos \phi \sin \alpha + 0.004V^2 \tag{13-1}$$

the constant applying when V is in knots and Δg_E in milliGals.

This formula is used to compute the Eötvös correction, which compensates for the effect. The correction is positive when the ship is moving to the east (because when it moves with the earth, centrifugal acceleration is increased, and the downward pull is decreased) and negative when its motion is westward. An error of 1 knot in measuring the ship's speed when it is moving in the east-west direction at the equator results in an error of 7.5 mGal in gravity, which would be entirely unacceptable for most exploration purposes. Since current speed-measuring techniques, such as those using continuous-wave electronic systems and doppler Sonar, have an accuracy that is seldom better than 0.1 knot under ideal conditions, it is evident that the precision obtainable in measuring the ship's speed can be the principal limitation in the accuracy of shipborne gravity work.

Herring[10] presented the results of a high-resolution field test that collected shipborne gravity data and GPS (global positioning system) navigation data. A previous underwater gravity meter survey had located a sharp anomaly with a half-width of about 1 km and an amplitude of about 2 mGal. This anomaly was resurveyed to test the performance of GPS and shipborne gravity: The anomaly was clearly and sharply identified. The author stated that this same anomaly probably would not have been recognized with any of the other currently available marine navigation systems. The success of the shipborne gravity survey to locate the anomaly was attributed to the accuracy of the GPS marine navigation system, which allowed the precise determination of the Eötvös correction.

The precision that can be expected in shipborne gravity measurements also depends upon the state of the sea.[10] In very calm seas, agreement at crossing points where the traverse lines are laid out in rectangular grids has been as good as 0.5 mGal. In heavier seas the agreement is in the range 0.7 to 1.0 mGal, but when the sea state is 4 or greater, it may be necessary to shut down gravity-measuring operations altogether if high accuracy is desired. The question of whether to continue gravity observations in rough seas can become complicated in combined seismic and gravity surveys. Seismic recording can be carried out successfully under sea conditions that will not allow high-accuracy gravity measurement. When this happens during such combined surveys, the decision must be made whether to do without gravity data over the traverse involved and continue the seismic recording or whether to shut down altogether. The importance of the gravity data in the overall exploration picture will usually determine which course is followed.

The output readings of the gravity system may be registered both on a pen-writing chart recorder and on digital tape. The visible chart record allows monitoring of results and gives an instantaneous check on how well the various

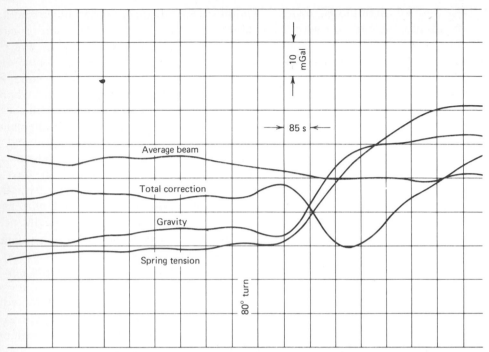

FIGURE 13-3 Typical chart made by pen recorder on board ship to monitor operation of LaCoste and Romberg gravity meter. The *average-beam* trace is used to get the slope correction, which is simply the derivative of the beam deflection. The *total correction* is the cross-coupling correction plus the slope correction. The *gravity* is the *spring tension* (bottom trace) minus the total correction. Filtering of the correction curves results in time lags that must be taken into account when the corrections are applied. (*Tidelands Geophysical Co.*)

components of the system are performing. Figure 13-3 shows a typical chart from a recorder used to monitor shipborne gravity measurements. It registers beam deflection, spring tension, total correction, and corrected gravity. Some shipborne charts record additional parameters, e.g., accelerometer outputs, cross-coupling, ship's speed, and water depth. Most systems record the data simultaneously on digital tape with formats designed for subsequent input into an electronic computer that will make all necessary corrections and present the corrected gravity values in a form suitable for mapping.

13-3 AIRBORNE GRAVITY SURVEYS

By the mid-1980s, airborne gravity surveys were being collected and reported. The data are usually downward continued to the ground surface (or sea level) for interpretation and/or comparison with conventionally recorded gravity data. As before, craft velocity and gravimeter altitude must be known precisely. The resolution attainable further depends upon the chosen flight speed, flight grid, elevation, sample rate, and type of filter used. Repeatability and accuracy of a few mGal were claimed for helicopter and fixed-wing surveys.[11] Airborne gravity surveys appear to be controversial; some geophysicists believe that for regional-type surveys, airborne gravity can yield usable results.[12] Other geophysicists have reported that inconsistent results were obtained when airborne and ground surveys were compared after allowance was made for elevation differences.[13] Errors of several mGals were found between the data sets. This magnitude of error was greater than the internal precision of most airborne gravity systems.

13-4 DETERMINATION OF DENSITIES

The terrain and Bouguer corrections made in the reduction of gravity data require a knowledge of the densities of the rocks near the surface. In many areas near-surface densities are sufficiently homogeneous for an average density value to be obtainable from a few well-spaced determinations. In others, there are such sharp local variations in lithology that use of an average density value can introduce considerable error. White[14] has described a gravity survey in Great Britain where three different densities had to be used for surface corrections within a small area.

When one wishes to determine density directly, representative samples of rock from surface outcrops, mines, or well cores and cuttings may be collected for measurement with a pyknometer or a Schwarz or Jolly balance.

Nettleton[15] has proposed an indirect means of density determination which may be more satisfactory for gravity reductions than direct measurements on small samples. It is illustrated in Fig. 13-4. A closely spaced gravity traverse is run over a topographic feature, such as a small hill or valley, with dimensions that have been measured accurately. When the profile of measured gravity is plotted, the predicted gravity field of the surface feature alone is calculated at each observation point along the profile and removed from the value observed at that point. The calculation is repeated a number of times, different densities being assumed for each computation. The density value at which the hill has the least observable effect on the gravity profile is considered to be most nearly correct. This method has the advantage of averaging the effect of density variations more accurately than can be done from surface samples. Even so, it gives information on densities only at relatively shallow depths and can be easily used only when the near-surface lithology is homogeneous. Since in many areas the topographic features owe their existence to outcrops with anomalous lithology, the density value so determined may not be correct.

The Density Logger   For some years, tools have been available for logging formation densities in boreholes (see Baker[16]). Logs thus obtained indicate back-scattered gamma radiation which is empirically related to formation den-

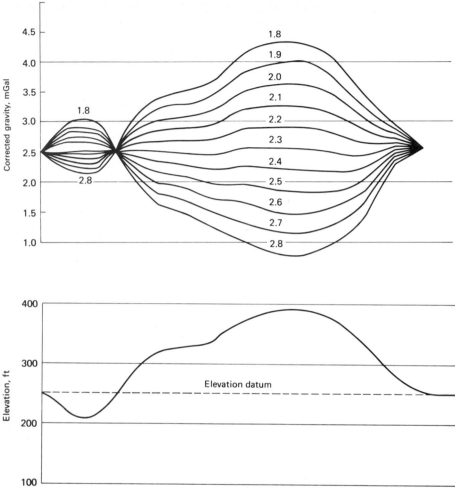

FIGURE 13-4   Nettleton method for determining density of near-surface formations by use of different densities in making Bouguer corrections over topographic feature. Corrections are referred to elevation of 250 ft. Correct density appears to be about 2.3 g cm^{-3}.

sity. The density logger consists of a radiation source, usually cobalt 60, at one end of the tool and a detector, generally a geiger counter, about 18 in away at the other end, as shown in Fig. 13-5. The outer wall of the tool is lined with lead shielding, which has two slits so positioned that the only radiation from the source which reaches the detector is that deflected back from the formation by Compton scattering. The principles of Compton scattering are reviewed by Faul and Tittle.[17] The amplitude of the scattered radiation depends on the electron concentration in the formation, and this in turn is roughly proportional to the density of the formation material. The energy is proportional to 1 −

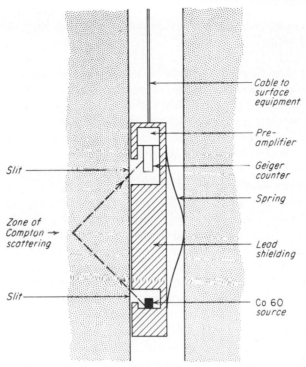

FIGURE 13-5   Schematic diagram of gamma-ray density logger.

$\cos \theta$, where θ is the angle between the incident ray and the scattered ray. This indicates that the maximum energy is at $\theta = 90°$, corresponding to emergent and returning rays which each make an angle of 45° with the borehole wall.

The maximum penetration of the gamma radiation into the borehole wall is 15 cm, and the effective sampling volume for each reading is about 0.03 m³. Close contact is maintained between the tool and one side of the hole by a spring on the other side. This may not be effective in zones where shale is washed out. Actually, comparisons of logged densities and densities measured from cores at the same level in the borehole generally show an agreement within several hundredths of a gram per cubic centimeter in all formations except shales, which are particularly subject to caving from washouts. The irregularity of the log itself is usually so great that it is necessary to smooth values by averaging over depth ranges of 100 ft or more to get results that are useful for gravity interpretation. In soft formations, frequent washing out of the borehole walls affects the reliability of the density readings. Thus, where there is any substantial amount of shale in the section, the integrated density would be of questionable accuracy. Moreover, the small volume of formation sampled in a single reading may not be representative of the much larger volume of rock contributing to the observed gravity. This hazard also holds for all density determinations made in the laboratory, whether from core samples or cuttings out of wells.

Borehole Gravity Readings The principal application of the borehole gravity meters described in the preceding chapter (see pages 541 to 542) is to determine density versus depth over a greater volume of the formation than is possible with the limited lateral penetration that a gamma-ray logger allows. There are a number of applications for the density information thus obtained. For production and reservoir studies, it is easy to determine porosity from the density if the fluid content and saturation are known or assumed. McCulloh[18] has shown how borehole density data can be used to determine zones of gas saturation. Most important for our purposes, the data can be used as an aid in the interpretation of gravity readings obtained at the earth's surface.

The density is computed from the differences between gravity readings at two depths (generally with separations of about 10 ft or more) in the borehole. After corrections are made for free-air, topographic, and other known effects that might account for some portion of the observed differential, the remaining gravity difference can be attributed to the attraction of a fictitious slab (considered to be infinite) of earth material respectively bounded at its top and bottom by horizontal planes in which the two readings are taken. The formula for the density ρ of the slab bounded by horizontal surfaces between the levels of boundaries Δh apart, as shown in Fig. 13-6, is expressed in terms of the difference Δg in gravity at those levels:

FIGURE 13-6 Determination of density of an "infinite" slab penetrated by a borehole by taking readings with a borehole gravity meter at its top and bottom surfaces.

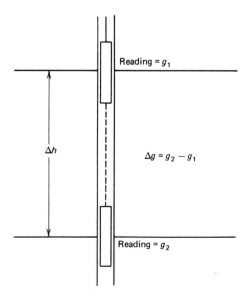

Reading = g_1

Δh

$\Delta g = g_2 - g_1$

Reading = g_2

$$\rho = 3.68237 - 0.005247 \sin^2 \phi + 0.000000524h - 39.1273 \frac{\Delta g}{\Delta h} \qquad (13\text{-}2)$$

where ρ is in g/cm^3, ϕ is latitude, h is elevation above sea level in feet, and Δg is in milliGals.

Densities obtained from borehole gravity measurements are representative of a much larger volume of rock than that sampled by the gamma-ray density logger and are less likely to be affected by the density of the formation near the wellbore which may have been altered during the drilling process. On the other hand, geologic structure in the vicinity of the wellbore may require corrections to the density obtained from the borehole gravity measurement and the slab assumption described above. LaFehr[19] discusses the concept of apparent density as measured by the borehole gravity meter.

13-5 REDUCTIONS OF GRAVITY DATA

In order to be most useful in prospecting, gravity data as obtained in the field must be corrected for elevation, the influence of nearby topography, and latitude. This concept has already been introduced and discussed in Sec. 12-4 (in Anomalies Based on Absolute Gravity Determination). There is no real difference in principle between the corrections discussed here and in the previous section. The computation of any gravity anomaly value (e.g., free-air anomaly, Bouguer anomaly, or isostatic anomaly) is based on the same fundamental principle: An anomaly value at a point on the earth is equal to the observed gravity value minus a predicted gravity value based on a given earth model; that is, the anomaly is the difference between what is measured and what is predicted.

The Bouguer Anomaly The Bouguer anomaly represents the most commonly used method of reducing gravity observations for exploration purposes. For computation of the Bouguer anomaly, there are just three elements of the earth model:

1 The expected increase in gravity with latitude.

2 The expected decrease in gravity with increasing elevation above sea level.

3 The expected increase in gravitational attraction due to the mass of rock between sea level and the observation point.

The first element is the latitude effect, $g(\text{lat})$. The second is the free-air effect $g(\text{fe})$, and the third is the Bouguer effect, $g(\text{Boug})$. Using these elements, we can write predicted gravity at a point as

$$g(\text{predicted}) = g(\text{lat}) + g(\text{fe}) + g(\text{Boug})$$

If we let observed gravity be g(obs), the Bouguer anomaly becomes

$$g(\text{BA}) = g(\text{obs}) - g(\text{predicted})$$

Observed Gravity   Observed gravity, as used here, refers to an absolute gravity determination. Most gravity instruments give readings of relative values of gravity. The following corrections are normally applied to an instrument reading in order to derive an absolute gravity value [g(obs) or observed gravity value]:

1 *Calibration*   Conversion from instrument units to milliGals.

2 *Tidal Correction*   As pointed out on pages 514 to 516, the normal value of gravity at any point will vary cyclically during the course of the day by as much as 0.3 mGal because of the tidal attraction of the sun and the moon. Many computer-based gravity reduction systems automatically compute and remove tidal effects based on the time of observation and the location (latitude, longitude, and elevation) of the station. In the past, tidal correction tables were used to compute the tidal correction. It is also possible to derive tidal corrections by observing a stationary gravity meter located close to the survey area; however, this is seldom done. More commonly, tidal corrections can be properly neglected as long as the observer is careful to return to the base station often enough that tidal effects will be adequately incorporated into the instrument drift curve by linear interpolation. Usually this means rereading the base station at intervals of about 2 h.

3 *Instrument Drift*   Instrument drift is corrected for by periodic reoccupation of established base stations. Small changes in the readings at these bases are attributed to instrument drift. A drift correction is applied to intervening observations by linear interpolation.

4 *Ties to Absolute Gravity Bases*   Absolute gravity bases have been established all over the world at most important airports, seaports, universities, and many other easily relocatable gravity station locations. Updated gravity base values are given in the International Gravity Standardization Net 1971 (IGSN71) (Morelli et al.[20]). Earlier nets were based upon a measurement of absolute gravity at Potsdam, which was discovered to be in error by approximately
14 mGal. Thus, IGSN71 base values differ from earlier values for the same locations by approximately this amount. The IGSN71 values should be used in conjunction with the Gravity Formula 1967, which is part of the Geodetic Reference System 1967.[21] Local gravity base net information is available in the publications of some states. The Defense Mapping Agency of the Department of Defense also maintains an extensive gravity base system in the United States. Tying gravity meter readings to such bases is good practice because it facilitates combining data from various surveys.

In most early exploration work, ties to absolute gravity bases and determinations of absolute observed gravity values were not made. For computational convenience, arbitrary anomaly datums were selected so that, for example, anomaly values in a prospect area would all be small positive numbers. It may have been this practice which has led to the widespread erroneous belief that gravity values are reduced to a topographic datum plane, either sea level or something else. On the contrary, anomaly values are relative to their surface of observation. Only by upward or downward continuation of the observed gravity field (as described, for example, by Henderson and Cordell[22]) can the anomaly field be inferred for other surfaces or datum planes.

Older gravity maps that were reduced relative to arbitrary datums can, in theory, be corrected to an absolute gravity datum by the simple addition of a constant to all of the anomaly values on the old map. Normally this constant will be between −300 and +300 mGal, which is about the range of Bouguer anomaly values over the world.

Latitude Effect

As has been discussed in Chap. 12, the gravitational effects of the earth's rotation and shape are usually predicted using the Gravity Formula 1967 given in Eq. (12-14). This formula gives the variation in normal gravity g in Gals as a function of latitude ϕ on the surface of the reference ellipsoid. A Chebychev approximation to Eq. (12-14) with a maximum error of 0.004 mGal may also be used:

$$g = (978.031\ 85)\ (1\ +\ 0.005\ 278\ 895\ \sin^2 \phi\ +\ 0.000\ 023\ 462\ \sin^4 \phi)\ \text{Gal}$$
$$(13\text{-}7)$$

At 45° latitude, the variation is about 0.1 mGal for each 400 ft of north-south displacement. Even for such a short distance, this large a gravity change could be significant in exploration surveys if no correction for it were made. It also indicates that positions must be known to better than 100 ft in the north-south direction where an ultimate precision of 0.02 mGal is desired. In early survey work, an arbitrary reference latitude was chosen in the vicinity of the survey area, and all readings were referenced to this latitude. If the actual latitude is within a degree or so of this reference, a uniform gradient was assumed and all stations were corrected simply by multiplication of the gradient computed for the reference latitude by the north-south distance of the station from the reference line. Most computer-based gravity reduction systems compute the latitude correction for each observation point using formulas derived from (12-4) or (13-7). Nagy[23] gives a form especially suited to rapid and accurate computer calculation.

We note again a slight discrepancy that was pointed out in Chap. 12. The value of theoretical gravity given by Eq. (12–14) and (13–7) is for points on the surface of the reference ellipsoid. The free-air and Bouguer effects are commonly calculated relative to sea level. The differences in elevation of these two reference surfaces is usually ignored in reducing gravity data, but must be included to properly model broad anomalies on profiles long enough to include significant geoid variations.

Free-Air Effect

The free-air correction is based on the fact that the attraction of the earth as a whole can be considered to be the same as if its mass were concentrated at its center. If the elevation of a gravity meter is changed, its distance from the center of the earth changes by the same amount. The inverse-square law enables us to predict how much the acceleration of gravity will change as a result.

If the radius of the earth (at sea level) is R, the height above sea level is h, and the value of gravity at sea level is g_0, then g, the gravity at h, can be expressed as

$$g = g_0 \frac{R^2}{(R + h)^2} = g_0 \frac{1}{(1 + h/R)^2} = g_0 \frac{1}{1 + 2h/R + h^2/R^2} \quad (13\text{-}8)$$

$$g \cong g_0 \frac{1}{1 + 2h/R} \quad \text{as} \quad \frac{h^2}{R^2} \ll \frac{2h}{R} \quad (13\text{-}9)$$

Using the first term of the binomial expansion

$$g \cong g_0 \left(1 - \frac{2h}{R}\right) \quad (13\text{-}10)$$

one obtains

$$g - g_0 \cong \Delta g \cong - \frac{2hg_0}{R} \quad (13\text{-}11)$$

If R, the radius of the earth, which is about 4000 mi, is expressed in feet and g_0, about 980 cm/s², in milliGals, it is easy to show that $\Delta g/h$ is 0.09406 mGal/ft.

This effect will be independent of whether or not there is any rock material between the sea-level datum and the station at elevation h. It is referred to for this reason as the *free-air effect*.

Bouguer Effect The expected increase in gravitational attraction due to the rock between the station and sea level is often modeled using the simplifying assumption that the rock can be approximated by a horizontally infinite slab of uniform density with a bottom surface at sea level and a top surface at the elevation of the station. If the material in this slab has a density of ρ, this attraction will be [according to the slab formula, Eq. (12-24)] $2\pi\gamma\rho h$ or $0.01277\rho h$ (with h in feet); for a density of 2.0 g/cm³, the correction will be 0.02554 mGal/ft. This is what is referred to as the *Bouguer effect*: It predicts an increase in gravity over what is predicted by the *latitude effect* and the *free-air effect* at the observation point. It is evident that this correction is very much dependent upon the density assumed for the material in the slab between the observing station and sea level.

For computational convenience, the corrections for the Bouguer and free-air effects are often combined and referred to as the "elevation correction." The elevation correction is commonly computed using an "elevation factor." For example, the elevation factor for an assumed Bouguer density of 2.0 g/cm^3 is 0.09406 − 0.02554, or 0.0685 mGal/ft (note that this is a predicted decrease in gravity with elevation). The commonly used Bouguer density of 2.67 g/cm^3 results in an elevation factor of 0.0600 mGal/ft, which happens to make this density convenient for manual computations.

The Bouguer Anomaly for Underwater and Surface Ship Gravity Measurements The elevation factors to be used for underwater and surface ship measurements are different from those used on land. Recall, however, that the Bouguer anomaly is the difference between observed and predicted gravity *at the observation point*.

The observation point for underwater gravity stations is on the water bottom, usually below sea level. Starting with a predicted value for gravity at sea level of g(lat), we expect an increase in gravity with depth due to the free-air effect of 0.09406 mGal/ft; the absence of rock between sea level and the water bottom leads to an expected decrease in predicted gravity; and finally, the upward attraction of the water leads to a further decrease in predicted gravity. Where depth is positive downward, the expected change in gravity with water depth d is

$$g(d) = +0.09406d - 0.01277\rho d - 0.01277\rho_w d \qquad (13\text{-}12)$$

Setting the rock density $\rho = 2.00$ g/cm^3 and the water density $\rho_w = 1.03$ g/cm^3 (for seawater), we get

$$g(d) = +0.09406d - 0.02554d - 0.01315d \qquad (13\text{-}13)$$
$$= 0.0554d \quad \text{or} \quad 0.0554 \text{ mGal/ft}$$

Terrain corrections for underwater gravity stations will be discussed later in this chapter.

Surface ship gravity measurements require a Bouguer correction using a different depth factor. The observation point for surface ship gravity measurements are assumed to be at sea level, so for surveys performed on the sea (as opposed to lakes with elevations other than sea level) the free-air effect is assumed to be zero.

Starting again with a predicted value of gravity of g(lat), we expect a decrease in gravity due to the absence of rock between sea level and the water bottom but a partly compensating increase in gravity due to the attraction of the water. Where depth is positive downward, the expected change in gravity caused by the presence of water of depth d is

$$g(d) = -0.01277\rho d + 0.01277\rho_w d$$

Setting $\rho = 2.00$ g/cm^3 and $\rho_w = 1.03$ g/cm^3 yields

$$\begin{aligned} g(d) &= -0.02554d + 0.01315d \\ &= -0.0124d \quad \text{or} \quad -0.0124 \text{ mGal/ft} \end{aligned} \tag{13-14}$$

Terrain Correction   In many gravity surveys, the terrain in the vicinity of a station is sufficiently flat for the elevation correction to provide adequate compensation for topographic effects. Nearby hills rising above the level of the station, however, give an upward component of gravitation attraction that counteracts a part of the downward pull exerted by the rest of the earth. Also, nearby valleys below the level of the station correspond to holes in the slab between station and datum level which are responsible for a smaller downward pull at the station than is accounted for by the Bouguer correction. It is necessary to compensate for such effects if the topographic features are causing distortions in the observed gravity large enough to affect the interpretation of anomalies from buried features of interest.

The usual procedure (Fig. 13-7) in making corrections for such distortions is to calculate the attraction of all the mass that would have to be added to the valleys below and all that would have to be removed from the hills above to give perfectly flat topography having the same elevation as the station. The terrain so reconstituted would then correspond to the slab assumed in making the Bouguer correction provided that it can be assumed that the hills are of uniform density. Either correction, whether from a hill or a valley, is added to the observed gravity. Calculation of the attraction of irregular topographic elements is greatly facilitated by the use of special templates and tables de-

FIGURE 13-7   Terrain correction removes effect of hill by adding its upward attraction at station and compensates for valley by adding attraction it would exert at station if filled in.

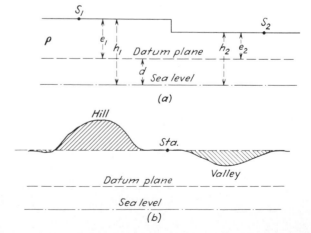

signed for the purpose. The first terrain-correction chart and set of tables published by Hammer[24] is still in widespread use. His chart, printed on transparent sheeting, is superimposed on a topographic map of the area around the gravity station and has the same scale as the map. It consists of a series of concentric circles with radial lines dividing the zones between the circles into compartments, as shown in Fig. 13-8. The center of the circles is placed over the gravity station on the map. Hammer's original tables have been extended by Douglas and Prahl[25] to allow corrections over a greater range of elevations in each zone.

Using the chart, a technician estimates from contours on a topographic map the average elevation of the land surface within each compartment and, taking the difference between this and the station elevation, determines the gravity effect of the prism of land within that compartment from Table 13-1, compiled by Hammer for the purpose. If, within a compartment, there are elevations both above and below the station elevation, the average of the elevation differences above and those below are added for that compartment. The correction is always added, regardless of the sign of the difference, except in the unusual circumstance where topographic corrections are made for features hundreds of miles from the gravity station and earth curvature enters into the computation of the terrain effect. Such corrections are well beyond the range of Hammer's tables and are not generally used in exploration surveys. The outermost circle of the chart corresponds to a distance on the map of about 14 mi, whereas the innermost circle (bounding zone E) represents a distance of only 558 ft. Topography closer to the station than this can be corrected for when necessary by using another chart constructed on the same principle but with a different scale.

FIGURE 13-8 Terrain correction-zone chart designed by Hammer,[24] used in conjunction with Table 12 1 for zones through J. Scale is $\frac{1}{175000}$. (*Gulf Research & Development Co.*)

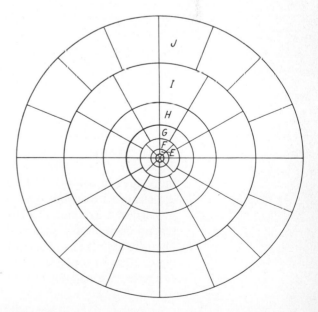

TABLE 13-1 TERRAIN-CORRECTION TABLES TO BE USED WITH FIG. 13-8*

Zone B, 4 compartments, radius 6.56–54.6 ft		Zone C, 6 compartments, radius 54.6–175 ft		Zone D, 6 compartments, radius 175–558 ft		Zone E, 8 compartments, radius 558–1280 ft		Zone F, 8 compartments, radius 1280–2936 ft		Zone G, 12 compartments, radius 2936–5018 ft	
± h, ft	T	± h, ft	T	± h, ft	T	± h, ft	T	± h, ft	T	± h, ft	T
0–1.1	0	0–4.3	0	0–7.7	0 .	0–18	0	0–27	0	0–58	0
1.1–1.9	0.1	4.3–7.5	0.1	7.7–13.4	0.1	18–30	0.1	27–46	0.1	58–100	0.1
1.9–2.5	0.2	7.5–9.7	0.2	13.4–17.3	0.2	30–39	0.2	46–60	0.2	100–129	0.2
2.5–2.9	0.3	9.7–11.5	0.3	17.3–20.5	0.3	39–47	0.3	60–71	0.3	129–153	0.3
2.9–3.4	0.4	11.5–13.1	0.4	20.5–23.2	0.4	47–53	0.4	71–80	0.4	153–173	0.4
3.4–3.7	0.5	13.1–14.5	0.5	23.2–25.7	0.5	53–58	0.5	80–88	0.5	173–191	0.5
3.7–7	1	14.5–24	1	25.7–43	1	58–97	1	88–146	1	191–317	1
7–9	2	24–32	2	43–56	2	97–126	2	146–189	2	317–410	2
9–12	3	32–39	3	56–66	3	126–148	3	189–224	3	410–486	3
12–14	4	39–45	4	66–76	4	148–170	4	224–255	4	486–552	4
14–16	5	45–51	5	76–84	5	170–189	5	255–282	5	552–611	5
16–19	6	51–57	6	84–92	6	189–206	6	282–308	6	611–666	6
19–21	7	57–63	7	92–100	7	206–222	7	308–331	7	666–716	7
21–24	8	63–68	8	100–107	8	222–238	8	331–353	8	716–764	8
24–27	9	68–74	9	107–114	9	238–252	9	353–374	9	764–809	9
27–30	10	74–80	10	114–120	10	252–266	10	374–394	10	809–852	10
		80–86	11	120–127	11	266–280	11	394–413	11	852–894	11
		86–91	12	127–133	12	280–293	12	413–431	12	894–933	12
		91–97	13	133–140	13	293–306	13	431–449	13	933–972	13
		97–104	14	140–146	14	306–318	14	449–466	14	972–1009	14
		104–110	15	146–152	15	318–331	15	466–483	15	1009–1046	15

* Each zone is a circular ring of given radius (in feet) divided into 4, 6, 8, 12, or 16 compartments of arbitrary azimuth. h is the mean topographic elevation in feet (without regard to sign) in each compartment with respect to the elevation of the station. The tables give the correction T for each compartment due to undulations of the terrain in units of $\frac{1}{100}$ mGal for density = 2.0 g/cm³. This correction, when applied to Bouguer anomaly values which have been calculated with the simple Bouguer correction, is always positive.

Often the terrain in the neighborhood of a gravity station has a systematic slope which can be approximated by an inclined plane. Where this is the case, the topographic correction will be more accurate if the blocks corresponding to the zones in Hammer's tables are assumed to have sloping instead of horizontal tops. Sandberg[26] has prepared a set of tables to be used with Hammer's chart which is computed for all integral slope angles from 1 to 30°, inclusive.

The Hammer tables have been computed for a Bouguer density of 2.00 g/cm³. These tables may be used with other Bouguer densities by changing the values in column T of the Hammer tables by a factor of $\rho/2.00$, where ρ is the assumed Bouguer density.

Terrain-correction algorithms for digital computers have replaced the use of terrain-correction charts in situations where a digital representation of topography is available or in surveys where the number and density of stations justifies digitization of topographic maps. Widely spaced gravity profile traverses, for example, are usually terrain-corrected by use of a chart. The advantages of

Zone H, 12 compartments, radius 5018–8578 ft		Zone I, 12 compartments, radius 8578–14,662 ft		Zone J, 16 compartments, radius 14,662–21,826 ft		Zone K, 16 compartments, radius 21,826–32,490 ft		Zone L, 16 compartments, radius 32,490–48,365 ft		Zone M, 16 compartments, radius 48,365–71,996 ft	
± h, ft	T	± h, ft	T	± h, ft	T	± h, ft	T	± h, ft	T	± h, ft	T
0–75	0	0–99	0	0–167	0	0–204	0	0–249	0	0–304	0
75–131	0.1	99–171	0.01	167–290	0.1	204–354	0.1	249–431	0.1	304–526	0.1
131–169	0.2	171–220	0.2	290–374	0.2	354–457	0.2	431–557	0.2	526–680	0.2
169–200	0.3	220–261	0.3	374–443	0.3	457–540	0.3	557–659	0.3	680–804	0.3
200–226	0.4	261–296	0.4	443–502	0.4	540–613	0.4	659–747	0.4	804–912	0.4
226–250	0.5	296–327	0.5	502–555	0.5	613–677	0.5	747–826	0.5	912–1008	0.5
250–414	1	327–540	1	555–918	1	677–1119	1	826–1365	1	1008–1665	1
414–535	2	540–698	2	918–1185	2	1119–1445	2	1365–1763	2	1665–2150	2
535–633	3	698–827	3	1185–1403	3	1445–1711	3	1763–2086	3	2150–2545	3
633–719	4	827–938	4	1403–1592	4	1711–1941	4	2086–2366	4	2545–2886	4
719–796	5	938–1038	5	1592–1762	5	1941–2146	5	2366–2617	5	2886–3191	5
796–866	6	1038–1129	6	1762–1917	6	2146–2335	6	2617–2846	6	3191–3470	6
866–931	7	1120–1213	7	1917–2060	7	2335–2509	7	2846–3058	7	3470–3728	7
931–992	8	1213–1292	8	2060–2195	8	2509–2672	8	3058–3257	8	3728–3970	8
992–1050	9	1292–1367	9	2195–2322	9	2672–2826	9	3257–3444	9	3970–4198	9
1050–1105	10	1367–1438	10	2322–2443	10	2826–2973	10	3444–3622	10	4198–4414	10
1105–1158	11	1438–1506	11	2443–2558	11						
1158–1209	12	1506–1571	12	2558–2669	12						
1209–1257	13	1571–1634	13	2669–2776	13						
1257–1305	14	1634–1694	14	2776–2879	14						
1305–1350	15	1694–1753	15	2879–2978	15						

Source: S. Hammer, *Geophysics,* vol. 4. pp. 190–191, 1939. Reproduced by permission of the Society of Exploration Geophysicists.

using the computer to make terrain corrections are that more accurate and detailed terrain models are practical and the results are more accurate than is practically achievable with a chart. Two widely used computer-based terrain-correction methods have been published by Plouff[27] and Krohn.[28]

The method of computing terrain corrections for underwater gravity stations is similar to that for land stations except that the density used in computing the terrain correction is the difference in density between rock and water. Using the rock and water densities cited earlier, the density difference would be 0.97 g/cm³. The values in the Hammer tables should be reduced by a factor of 0.97/2.00 so that appropriate underwater terrain-correction values will be computed.

For surface ship gravity measurements, the method generally followed to obtain terrain-corrected Bouguer anomaly values is to use a modeling program to compute the gravitational attraction, at sea level and along the ship tracks, of the mass defined by the volume between the water bottom and sea level with a density equal to the assumed rock density minus the water density. This value added to observed gravity yields the Bouguer anomaly.

Conclusions The object of all corrections is to obtain a picture of the variations in the earth's gravitational field that depends only on lateral departures from constancy in the densities of the subsurface rocks. The most likely source of error in the corrections usually lies in the choice of the near-surface density to employ in the Bouguer and terrain corrections, particularly where the lithology of the near-surface formations is not well known. Sometimes the terrain corrections are inadequate because of limited topographic data near the gravity stations in areas of high relief.

13-6 TYPICAL GRAVITY ANOMALIES FOR VARIOUS GEOLOGICAL FEATURES

After appropriate corrections are made, gravity data are generally presented on maps or cross sections. As the corrections generally do not involve any substantial exercise of judgment, presentations that incorporate only free-air, Bouguer, and latitude corrections are looked upon as objective. Interpretation enters in when regional effects are removed to point up residual anomalies associated with the subsurface sources of primary interest. Methods for doing this will be discussed in the next chapter. Bouguer maps are based on gravity data to which both the free-air and Bouguer correction have been applied. Such maps are commonly considered to represent "raw gravity." The information on them is used as the basis for separating anomalies by various analytical techniques which we shall consider later. All such techniques require a certain degree of interpretation, regardless of whether they involve graphical or computer-based methods.

In the presentation of gravity results it is desirable, where possible, to display the initial Bouguer map along with any residual maps derived from them so that the reader will be able to see the corrected data before the residual gravity was extracted from them.

In this section we shall examine gravity patterns over a number of typical geological features, both regional and local. These examples include maps and cross sections for which Bouguer, free-air, and latitude corrections have been made but from which regional effects have generally not been removed.

Salt Domes Figure 13-9 shows the gravity picture mapped by Nettleton[29] over a topographic mound in the Gulf of Mexico about 150 mi off Galveston and a short distance inside the edge of the continental shelf. The water depth on strike with the center of the mound is 400 ft, but pinnacles project from the mound to depths as little as 60 ft. The origin of the topographic feature was not established until the gravity survey indicated a large closed minimum coincident with the contours of the elevated mound that could be accounted for only

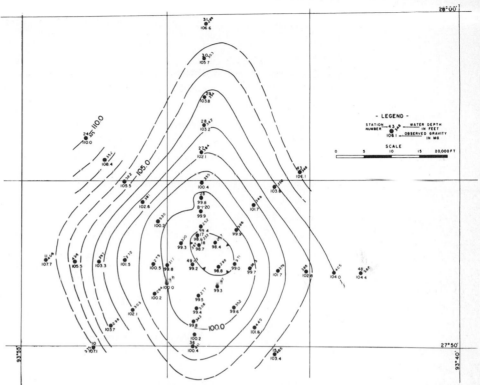

FIGURE 13-9   Gravity map obtained over inferred salt dome causing anomaly in water-bottom topography in Gulf of Mexico. Contours 1 mGal apart. (*After Nettleton.*[29])

by assuming a piercement-type salt dome. The survey was not extensive enough to define the gravity closure on all sides, but judicious extrapolation indicated the maximum negative anomaly to be about 9 mGal. Figure 13-10 shows Nettleton's interpretation of the salt structure giving rise to the anomaly. This is not strictly a "known" source for the anomaly, but the near-surface geology of the coast and continental shelf of the Gulf of Mexico is so well established from extensive drilling that no identification for such a gravity feature other than a salt dome would be geologically plausible. Because the top of the dome is so shallow, it is probable that the uppermost part of the salt (crosshatched in the figure) has a higher density than that of the surrounding sediments at the same level and hence gives rise to a positive anomaly above the center of the dome. This feature is referred to as the Way dome.

The Grand Saline salt dome in east Texas, with a top surface averaging only 250 ft in depth, has been mined extensively. Figure 13-11 shows observed gravity contours over the feature. The cap rock over Grand Saline is only 28 ft thick, so thin that no effects from it are observable on the gravity map.

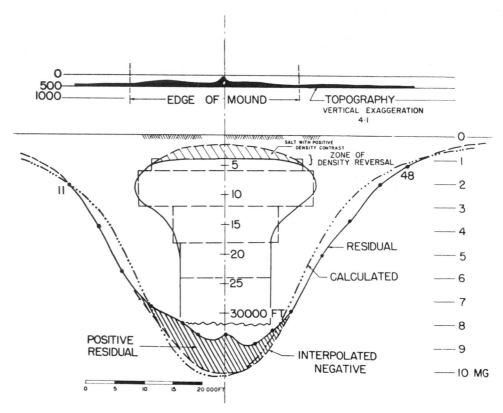

FIGURE 13-10   Assumed structure of salt dome believed to be causing offshore gravity anomaly of Fig. 13-9. Agreement between observed and calculated gravity profiles supports choice of model for structure. (*After Nettleton.*[29])

Anticlines   When the geologic section contains successive formations having appreciable contrasts in density, any major folding should be reflected in the gravity picture. If formations having greater than average density are brought nearer the surface at the crest of an anticline, its crest line should be the axis of a gravity maximum. If beds of less than normal density are uplifted, there should be a gravity minimum along the axis.

The Kettleman Hills–Lost Hills area of California (Fig. 13-12) shows both types of gravity feature over two parallel anticlines associated with the same structural trend. The Kettleman Hills trend has a prominent gravitational high along its entire length, which extends southward from the Fresno-Kings county line at the northwest of the map across the Kings-Kern county line, terminating about a township beyond. The Lost Hills structure, which begins only a few miles farther south, marks the axis of a pronounced gravity low, which is quite conspicuous in the southernmost two townships of the map. Boyd[30] explains the Kettleman Hills high as resulting from anomalously dense shales and sands of the 600- to 800-ft-thick Reef Ridge formation. The minimum over the Lost

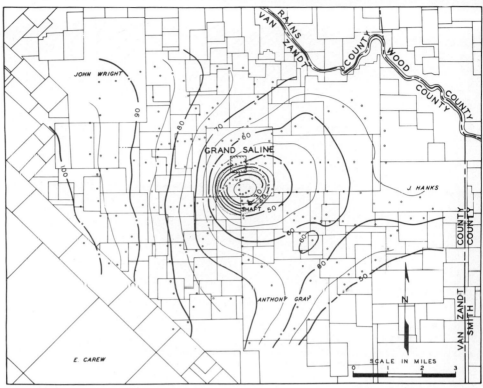

FIGURE 13-11   Gravity contours over Grand Saline salt dome. Free-air, Bouguer, and latitude corrections have been made, but there is no adjustment for regional trend. Each gravity unit is 0.1 mGal, so that contour interval is 1 mGal. Stippled area represents position of salt mass. (*After J. W. Peters and A. Dugan, "Geophysical Case Histories," vol. 1, Society of Exploration Geophysicists, Tulsa, Okla., 1949.*)

FIGURE 13-12   Contours from gravity survey, Kettleman Hills–Lost Hills area, Calif. Contour interval, 2 mGal. (*After L. H. Boyd, "Geophysical Case Histories," vol. 1, Society of Exploration Geophysicists, Tulsa, Okla., 1949.*)

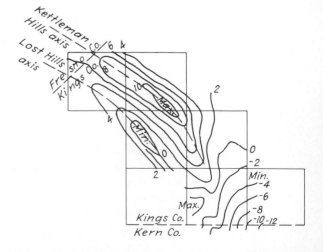

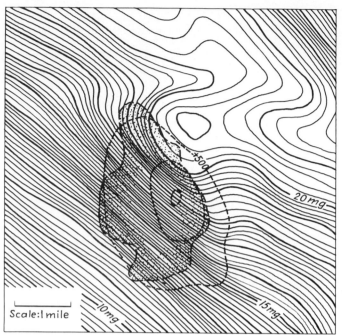

FIGURE 13-13   Observed gravity over Altus pool in Oklahoma. Note strong regional trend. Depth contours (*dashed*) show structure of top of Canyon Formation at 100-ft intervals. Stippling bounds area of production. (*After Coffin*.[31])

Hills is attributed to a considerable thickness of very light diatomaceous shale, which is found in the same formation at this point. Figure 13-12 illustrates the association between the structure and its gravity anomaly.

Often the gravity contours over an anticline do not show the closure characteristic of the structure because of regional gravity trends. Coffin[31] shows the gravity map obtained over the Altus Oil Field in Oklahoma. Here the gravity contours (Fig. 13-13) exhibit nosing instead of closure over the highest portion of the anticline in which oil is trapped. Means for removing such regional gravity variations, which can easily mask significant structures, will be discussed in the next chapter.

Limestone Reefs   When oil was first discovered in ancient carbonate reefs, it became desirable to determine whether such features could be located by gravity surveys. This would be possible only if there is a density contrast between the reef rock and the sedimentary formations that surround it. Unfortunately, the density and porosity of reef carbonate and the material it replaces can be so variable that it is not possible to specify what the contrast will generally be. Nevertheless, significant gravity patterns may be associated with reef masses in specific geological provinces. Brown[32] conducted an experimental gravity survey over the productive Jameson reef in Coke County, Texas.

The gravity effects he attributed to the reef limestone were so small as to be observable only with most stringent standards of accuracy in the surveying and instrumental operations. His residual contours indicated a high over the reef of about 0.3 to 0.5 mGal surrounded by an even smaller annular low.

Pohly[33] has reported on a gravity survey conducted in southwestern Ontario which resulted in the discovery of a productive reef. Here the reefs are exceptionally shallow (less than 2000 ft deep) and are surrounded by salt, which has a density much lower than that of reef limestone. The residual gravity high over the reef was 0.4 mGal. In the exploration program, five of the seven wildcat wells drilled on gravity anomalies found the desired reef objective. Ferris[34] and Nettleton[35] show examples of diagnostic gravity effects from reefs in many areas of the United States and Canada.

Ore Bodies During World War II the Gulf Oil Corporation carried out a gravity survey to locate chromite ores in the Camaguey district of Cuba. The high density of the mineral, averaging 3.99 g/cm^3, made it a particularly favorable prospect for gravity exploration. Preliminary calculations, which showed that anomalies having a relief as small as 0.05 mGal might be commerically significant, indicated that extremely stringent standards of accuracy would be necessary in the field work. A station spacing of 20 m was chosen, and particular pains were taken in both the gravity readings and surveying to secure the necessary resolution. The probable error of a single observation was 0.016 mGal. Figure 13-14 shows the gravity anomaly obtained during this survey over a known chromite deposit.

In prospecting for many minerals, gravity surveys are carried out in conjunction with other geophysical surveys such as magnetic or electrical. In a case history on the discovery of the Pyramid ore bodies in the Northwest Territories

FIGURE 13-14 Gravity anomaly over known chromite deposit. Contour interval 0.05 mGal. Open circles show locations of gravity stations; solid circles, of drill holes. (*After Hammer et al.*[1])

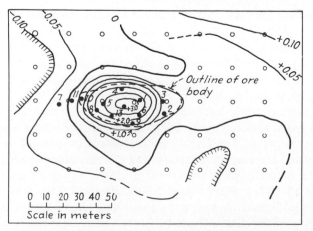

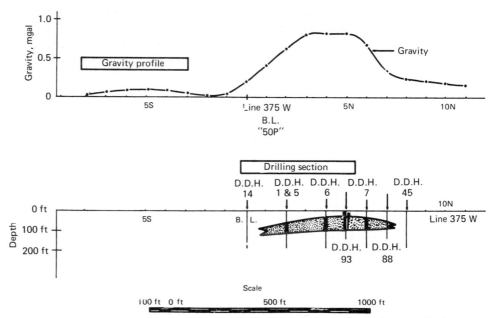

FIGURE 13-15   Cross section showing gravity anomaly over lead-zinc ore body in Pine Point area, Northwest Territories, Canada. (*After Seigel et al.*[36])

of Canada, Seigel et al.[36] show how gravity was used to obtain detailed information on the structure of a lead-zinc ore body which had initially been discovered by induced-polarization techniques. The density of the lead-zinc ore is 3.95 g/cm^3, while that of the surrounding limestones and dolomites is 2.65. The contrast resulted in a gravity picture quite diagnostic of the ore body's boundaries, as is indicated in Fig. 13-15. The depth to the top of the body is about 30 ft, and its maximum thickness is about 80 ft.

Regional Surveys   Many gravity surveys are undertaken to study regional geology rather than to detect or delineate individual features such as salt domes, anticlines, or reefs. Such surveys may be academically oriented, or they may have been designed to obtain reconnaissance information about little-explored areas of economic interest. Information of this kind can serve as the basis for planning subsequent geophysical or geological surveys that might yield more detailed information.

A typical regional study for which gravity provided useful data was carried out by Kane and Pakiser[37] in the southern part of the Owens Valley in California. Here again it was desired to determine the structure of the bedrock surface below a great thickness of clastic cover in an intermontane valley. Figure 13-16 is a gravity map over the valley. The contours show an unsymmetrical, closed low having its axis along the center of the valley. The interpretation of the data indicated that the valley bedrock is faulted and is covered

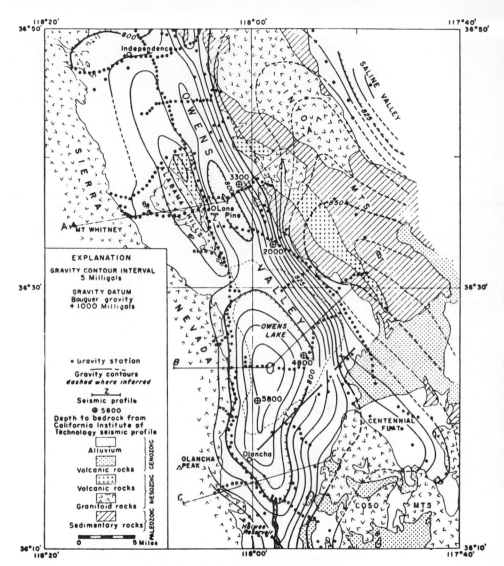

FIGURE 13-16 Bouguer gravity over southern Owens Valley of California and its relation to the geology of the area. Gravity low over alluvium-covered area interpreted as coming from thick sedimentary trough. (*After Kane and Pakiser.*[37])

with lower-density clastics which reach a maximum thickness of almost 10,000 ft.

Regional studies of gravity sometimes show major structural trends over large areas and make it possible to demonstrate relationships between major geological features where there are no exposures on the surface. Figure 13-17 shows a map of Bouguer gravity in western Washington. The contours indicate a low trend coincident with the Cascades, a high trend along the Coast Range,

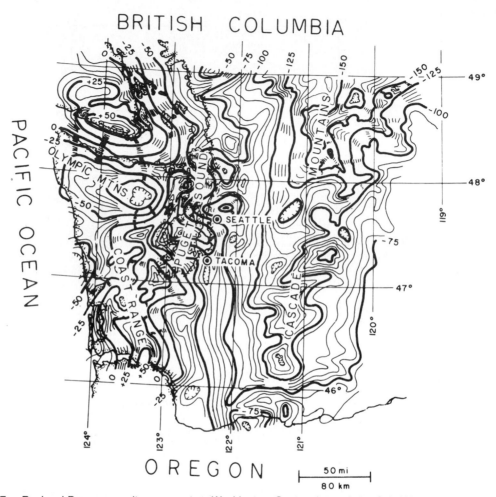

FIGURE 13-17   Regional Bouguer gravity over western Washington. Contour interval, 5 mGal. (*After Daneš.*[38])

and lows along Puget Sound and the Olympic Mountains. The gravity information makes it possible to distinguish the various geologic provinces associated with these features and to determine the relationships of faults and intrusives in the area. Combining such information with other data makes it possible to deduce the geologic history of the region with greater reliability.

REFERENCES

1 Hammer, Sigmund, L. L. Nettleton, and W. K. Hastings: Gravimeter Prospecting for Chromite in Cuba, *Geophysics*, vol. 10, pp. 34–39, 1945.

2 Hubbert, M. King: Gravitational Terrain Effects of Two-Dimensional Topographic Features, *Geophysics*, vol. 13, pp. 226–252, 1948.

3 Seibert, J. E.: Data Accuracies for Gravity Surveys Using Inertial Surveying, *Expanded Abstracts 54th Ann. SEG Convention*, pp. 228–231, 1984.

4 Hastings, W. K.: Gravimeter Observations in the Foothills Belt of Alberta, Canada, *Geophysics*, vol. 10, pp. 526–534, 1945.

5 Roman, Irwin: An Observational Method to Overcome Zero Drift Error in Field Instruments, *Geophysics*, vol. 13, pp. 466–490, 1946.

6 Garland, G. D.: "The Earth's Shape and Gravity," Pergamon, Oxford, 1965.

7 Woollard, G. P.: Recent Regional Gravity Surveys, *Trans. Am. Geophys. Union*, vol. 29, pp. 727–738, 1948.

8 Woollard, G. P., and J. C. Rose: "International Gravity Measurements," *Soc. Explor. Geophys. Spec. Pub.*, Tulsa, Okla., 1963.

9 LaCoste, L. J. B., Jr.: A New Type Long Period Vertical Seismograph, *Physics*, vol. 5, pp. 178–180, 1934; also see L.J.B. LaCoste and A. Romberg, U.S. Patent 2,293,437, 1900.

10 Herring, A. T.: Increased Resolution of Shipborne Gravity Measurements Using GPS, *Expanded Abstracts 55th Ann. SEG Convention*, pp. 218–219, 1985.

11 Paterson, N. R., and C. V. Reeves: Applications of Gravity and Magnetic Surveys: The State-of-the-Art in 1985, *Geophysics*, vol. 50, pp. 2558–2594, 1985.

12 Hammer, Sigmund: Airborne Gravity Is Here!, *Geophysics*, vol. 48, pp. 213–223, 1983.

13 Grumert, W. R., and T. Stanacato: Current Status of Airborne Gravity Surveys, *Expanded Abstracts 55th Ann. SEG Convention*, p. 199, 1985.

14 White, Peter H. N.: Gravity Data Obtained in Great Britain by the Anglo-American Oil Co., Ltd., *Q. J. Geol. Soc. Long.*, vol. 104, pp. 339–364, 1949.

15 Nettleton, L. L.: Determination of Density for Reduction Gravimeter Observations, *Geophysics*, vol. 4, pp. 176–183, 1939.

16 Baker, P. E.: Density Logging with Gamma Rays, *Trans. Am. Inst. Min. Met. Eng.*, Tech. Publ. 4654, *J. Petrol. Technol.*, vol. 9, 1957.

17 Faul, Henry, and C. W. Tittle: Logging of Drill Holes by the Neutron, Gamma Method, and Gamma Ray Scattering, *Geophysics*, vol. 16, pp. 260–276, 1951.

18 McCulloh, Thane H.: Borehole Gravimetry: New Developments and Applications, *Proc. 7th World Petrol. Congr.*, vol. 9, pp. 735–744, Elsevier, London, 1967.

19 LaFehr, T. R.: Rock Density from Borehole Gravity Surveys, *Geophysics*, vol. 48, pp. 341–356, 1983.

20 Morelli, C., C. Gantar, T. Honkasalo, R. K. McConnell, I. G. Tanner, B. Szabo, U. Uotila, and C. T. Whalen: "The International Gravity Standardization Net 1971," *Int. Assoc. Geodesy Spec. Publ. 4*, 1971.

21 International Association of Geodesy: "Geodetic Reference System 1967," *Int. Assoc. Geodesy Spec. Publ. 3*, 1971.

22 Henderson, R. G., and L. Cordell: Reduction of Unevenly Spaced Potential Field Data to a Horizontal Plane by Means of Finite Harmonic Series, *Geophysics*, vol. 36, pp. 856–866, 1971.

23 Nagy, Dezso: Direct Gravity Formula for the Geodetic Reference System, 1967, *Bull. Geod.*, vol. 52, pp. 159–164, 1978.

24 Hammer, Sigmund: Terrain Corrections for Gravimeter Stations, *Geophysics*, vol. 4, pp. 184–194, 1939.

25 Douglas, Jesse K., and Sidney R. Prahl: Extended Terrain Correction Tables for Gravity Reductions, *Geophysics*, vol. 37, pp. 377–379, 1972.

26 Sandberg, C. H.: Terrain Corrections for an Inclined Plane in Gravity Computations, *Geophysics*, vol. 23, pp. 701–711, 1958.

27 Plouff, D.: Digital Terrain Corrections based on Geographic Coordinates, *Geophysics* (Abstract), vol. 31, p. 1208, 1966.

28 Krohn, D. H.: Gravity Terrain Corrections Using Multiquadric Equations, *Geophysics*, vol. 41, pp. 266–275, 1976.

29 Nettleton, L. L.: Gravity Survey over a Gulf Coast Continental Shelf Mound, *Geophysics*, vol. 22, pp. 630–642, 1957.

30 Boyd, Lewis H.: Gravity-Meter Survey of the Kettleman Hills: Lost Hills Trend, California, *Geophysics*, vol. 11, pp. 121–127, 1946.

31 Coffin, R. Clare: Recent Trends in Geological-Geophysical Exploration, *Bull. Am. Assoc. Petrol. Geol.*, vol. 30, pp. 2013–2032, 1946.

32 Brown, Hart: A Precision Detail Gravity Survey, Jameson Area, Coke County, Texas, *Geophysics*, vol. 14, pp. 535–542, 1949.

33 Pohly, Richard A.: Gravity Case History: Dawn No. 156 Pool, Ontario, *Geophysics*, vol. 19, pp. 95–103, 1954.

34 Ferris, Craig: Use of Gravity Meter in Search for Stratigraphic Traps, pp. 252–267, in Robert E. King (ed.), "Stratigraphic Oil and Gas Fields," *Am. Assoc. Petrol. Geol. Mem. 16* and *Soc. Explor. Geophys. Spec. Pub. 10*, 1972.

35 Nettleton, L. L.: Use of Gravity, Magnetic and Electrical Methods in Stratigraphic-Trap Exploration, pp. 244–251, in Robert E. King (ed.), "Stratigraphic Oil and Gas Fields," *Am Assoc. Petrol. Geol. Mem. 16* and *Soc. Explor. Geophys. Spec. Pub. 10*, 1972.

36 Seigel, H. O., H. L. Hill, and J. G. Baird: Discovery Case History of the Pyramid Ore Bodies, Pine Point, Northwest Territories, Canada, *Geophysics*, vol. 33, pp. 645–656, 1968.

37 Kane, M. F., and L. C. Pakiser: Geophysical Study of Subsurface Structure in Southern Owens Valley, California, *Geophysics*, vol. 26, pp. 12–26, 1961.

38 Daneš, Zdenko F.: Gravity Results in Western Washington, *EOS Trans.*, vol. 50, pp. 548–550, 1969.

CHAPTER 14

THE INTERPRETATION OF GRAVITY DATA

To be carried out to best advantage, the acquisition, reduction, and mapping of gravity data require highly precise instrumentation, skill in planning and executing the field measurements, and expertise in proper correction of the data observed in the field. We shall now consider the final step, the most challenging of all, which is the deduction of geological structure from the corrected gravity observations.

The geological interpretation of gravity data is more difficult and involves more uncertainties than the interpretation of seismic records. Gravity maps have enough resemblance to structural maps that one can easily fall into the mental trap of identifying gravity contours as being indicative of structure. In evaluating gravity maps it is important that one keep in mind the true nature of the contours; specifically, one must not forget that they depict a potential field rather than a subsurface structure.

Two characteristics of potential fields in general and gravitational fields in particular make their interpretation more of an art than a science: (1) The field observed at any point represents the summation of the gravitational attractions of all subsurface sources detectable by the instrument employed. Yet our object in interpreting such a field is to obtain information on the individual sources contributing to it. Except in very simple cases, the separation of the observed field into its component parts is quite difficult and sometimes not possible at all. (2) The lack of uniqueness in the gravity field from a subsurface source means that an infinite number of different configurations can result in identical gravity data at the surface. To resolve such ambiguity, other information than that from gravity is needed. For this reason the value of gravity data usually depends on the amount of independent geological information available.

Thus interpretation of gravity data is not a clear-cut process but one which requires a great deal of intuition, both physical and geological, and which is most useful where other kinds of geophysical data or subsurface information, e.g., that obtained from wells or seismic shooting, are available. It is also worth emphasizing that the success of the process depends upon a number of interrelated steps that begin with the acquisition of data suitable for the interpretation desired. No amount of computer manipulation can compensate for a poorly designed survey. Once a good set of data has been obtained, the interpreter must (1) identify those parts of the observed field that are caused by geologic sources of interest; (2) separate the observed field into its component parts; (3) determine the geometries and densities of the geologic bodies that cause the isolated anomalies; and (4) analyze the geologic implications of the resulting model. Although in the end the interpreter may be only partially successful in accomplishing these various tasks, a number of tools are available that greatly enhance the possibility of a successful interpretation. A sampling of the more useful ones are discussed in the following sections in this chapter. The interested student may find many more with the help of bibliographies (Colorado School of Mines[1]), indices (Zwart[2]), and review articles (Paterson and Reeves[3]). Some of these interpretational tools are available as computer or hand-calculator programs, either through the Society of Exploration Geophysicists, the U.S. Geological Survey, or the National Technical Information Service.[4]

14-1 DESIGN OF SURVEYS

Interpretation of gravity data properly begins at the very earliest stages of survey planning, and surveys must be designed with the desired goals clearly in mind. Surveys meant to illuminate regional structural trends or to examine a large area for the presence of thick sediment-filled basins will generally require less accurate, more widely spaced data than surveys intended to determine the location and shape of specific features such as salt domes or buried faults. Accurate gravity data measured along a few well-placed and detailed profiles may be better suited for determining the important characteristics of a concealed body or structure than a larger data set spread uniformly over a wider area. Thus the two most critical factors of survey design are the *accuracy* and the *spatial distribution* of the data required. Other interpretational needs must also be foreseen, one of the most important being the availability of accurate density values for the rock units in the study area. Often, density samples are most easily collected from exposed units at the time of the survey itself—a useful approach may be to collect, where possible, a small hand sample from the vicinity of each gravity observation for later density determination in the lab. A rock specimen from a given gravity station can occasionally offer valuable clues later on that may aid in solving interpretational puzzles.

Deciding in advance what levels of accuracy and what station spacing are needed would seem to require a priori knowledge of the buried sources. This is not as difficult as it seems, because it usually is possible to predict from available geologic information what sizes and types of anomalies are likely to be found. Most gravity investigations are undertaken with specific goals in mind (e.g., detection of salt domes, determination of attitudes of faults, mapping of plutons, determination of thickness of sedimentary rocks, definition of the size and shape of ore bodies). Planners can consult case histories such as those presented in Chap. 13 to find the ranges of widths and amplitudes of gravity anomalies found over similar features in other places. Or gravity anomalies can be estimated for bodies or structures that are likely to be encountered by guessing their sizes, shapes, and density contrasts and approximating them with simple geometric shapes such as those given in Sec. 12-5. For example, anomalies over salt domes or plutons might reasonably be represented by the anomalies over spheres or vertical cylinders of appropriate size and density contrast. Similarly, anomalies over nearly vertical buried faults could be estimated from Eq. (12–28) or (12–33) which apply to a faulted slab. Once the likely anomalies are estimated, the survey can be designed in terms of accuracy and station spacing to maximize the chances of acquiring an adequate data set for the interpretational tasks at hand.

The accuracy of gravity data for geologic interpretations depends both on the accuracy of the gravity observations themselves and on the accuracy of the other quantities, namely station location, elevation, and density of the near-surface rocks, that must be used to reduce the gravity observations to a form suitable for interpretation. As discussed in Chap. 13, modern gravity meters are easily capable of yielding measurements of relative gravity accurate to about 0.1 mGal when suitable precautions are taken to determine the drift of the gravity meter during surveying. Even higher accuracies (about 0.02 mGal or better) are possible through the use of precisely calibrated gravity meters and special observing procedures employing many repeated measurements. Geologic interpretations seldom require accuracies greater than 0.1 mGal. Similarly, methods are available for determining station locations and elevations with accuracies sufficient for most interpretational purposes. Factors useful in planning are that a 100-ft error in north-south position will cause about a 0.03-mGal error, whereas a 1-ft error in elevation will cause about a 0.06-mGal error, depending on the density of near-surface materials. Note, however, that in areas with large gradients in the gravity field, the mislocation of a station can result in a mismatch of up to 0.5 mGal per 100 ft relative to neighboring stations. In general, in order to achieve an overall accuracy of a tenth of a milliGal in a gravity survey, the positions and elevations of the stations would probably have to be determined by surveying, whereas to achieve an overall accuracy of 5 mGal in a regional reconnaissance survey, station positions determined from topographic maps and elevations based on photogrammetric methods or barometric surveying may be adequate.

Once the expected shape of the anomalies is predicted from case histories or simple models, some general rules can be applied to determine optimal station spacing. In most cases, a minimum of four or five data points along a profile are required to define even the simplest anomaly. If the expected anomalies are two dimensional, i.e., they are much longer than they are wide, profiles across them should be oriented perpendicular to the long axis. For surveys designed to determine the attitude, shape, and extent of two-dimensional features such as buried faults, a few well-placed detailed profiles oriented perpendicular to the faults and supported by more widely spaced regional data may be more suitable for interpretation than data taken on a regular grid. In contrast, data taken on a regular grid probably are better suited for locating isolated salt domes or intrusions than are detailed profile data. For special problems such as estimating the total anomalous mass of an ore body, the lower-amplitude extensions surrounding the anomaly contain crucial information and must be defined with care. It should be clear from the discussion above that no single set of rules about data distribution apply in all situations. However, if the goals of the survey are kept clearly in mind, surveys can be designed in a way that will greatly facilitate the interpretation.

14-2 IDENTIFYING THE SIGNAL BY DISPLAYING AND ENHANCING ANOMALIES

The analysis of gravity data has been greatly aided over the past decade by the widespread use of digital computers and by the availability of continent-wide gravity and topographic data bases in computer-compatible form. Most interpreters now have available reliable and efficient gridding and contouring algorithms which open the door to many sorts of experimentation in the enhancement and display of data. Filtering techniques, in some cases originally designed for seismic processing or image enhancement, have been successfully applied to gravity data to reveal features and relations that were not obvious in original contoured presentations of the data. Needless to say, all such features require careful checking to verify that they truly exist in the original data set and are not simply artifacts introduced by the filtering or enhancement process. Nonetheless, experience has shown that before attempting any quantitative interpretation or modeling, it pays to examine the data set from as many different perspectives as possible, because this can often lead to a greater appreciation of the important elements present in the data set that deserve further quantitative analysis.

In Fig. 14-1, a series of maps derived from regional gravity data over the eastern Sierra Nevada of California are shown to illustrate some of the enhancements that are possible. The gravity low in the northeast corner of the area is caused by the presence of low-density volcaniclastic sedimentary rocks filling the Long Valley caldera. The strong west-sloping gradient evident in the western half of the Bouguer maps is caused by the attraction of low-density masses that are isostatically compensating the topography of the Sierras. The free-air map (Fig. 14-1a) and the simple Bouguer map (Fig. 14-1b), which has a Bouguer slab correction but no terrain corrections applied (see Sec. 13-4), are

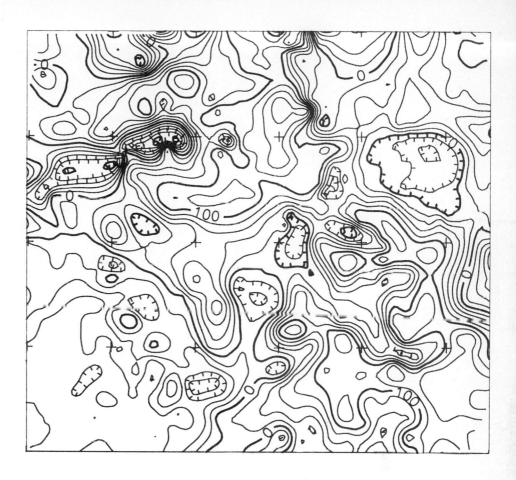

0   **50 km**

FIGURE 14-1a   Free-air gravity anomalies over a part of the eastern Sierra Nevada region of California. The Long Valley caldera coincides with the low anomaly in the northeast quadrant. Contour interval is 20 mGal. Hachures mark the low sides of closed contours. Latitude-longitude tic marks occur at 15-min interval.

included to illustrate that the gravity reduction process itself can be thought of as an enhancement technique. The usual starting point for most interpretations is the complete Bouguer map (*complete* implies that terrain corrections have been applied) shown in Fig. 14-1c.

We shall begin this section by reviewing the application of Fourier-transform techniques to gravity maps and by discussing briefly some of the simpler kinds of filters that commonly are applied to gravity data. We shall also discuss

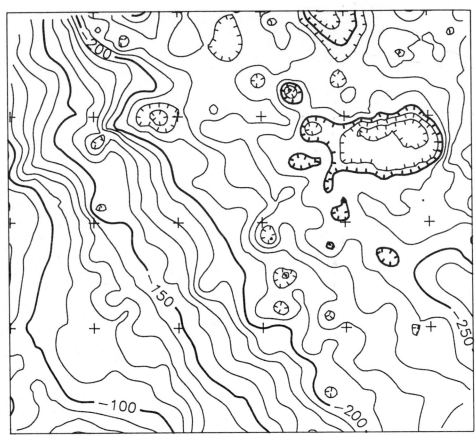

FIGURE 14-1*b*   Simple Bouguer gravity anomalies (i.e., no terrain corrections applied) for the same area as in Fig. 14-1*a*. Contour interval is 10 mGal.

briefly some of the other enhancement techniques that seem to work well on gravity data. There is every reason to believe that improvements in computer hardware and software will continue to provide the gravity interpreter with even more exciting and useful modes of examining the data.

Enhancement Based on Fourier Transforms

Introduction to Two-Dimensional Fourier Transforms   We learned in Chap. 6 that the Fourier transform is a powerful tool for analyzing a function of time $f(t)$. Efficient computer algorithms exist to calculate Fourier transforms and their inverses rapidly, and complicated filter operations in the time domain, for example, can become simple multiplications in the Fourier domain.

Fourier analysis has similar benefits for analyses and interpretations of gravity, magnetic, topographic, or other kinds of two-dimensional data dis-

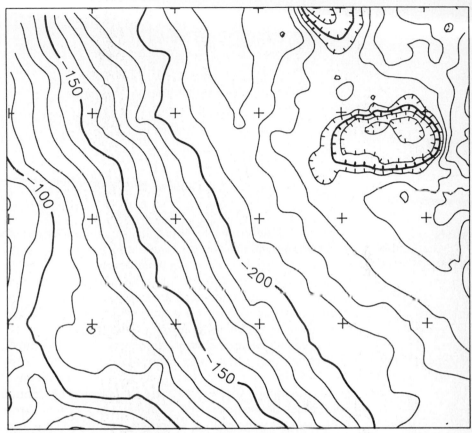

FIGURE 14-1c Complete Bouguer gravity anomalies for the same area as in Fig. 14-1a. Contour interval is 10 mGal.

tributed over horizontal surfaces. Such data can be represented by functions $f(x,y)$ of two cartesian coordinates, so the integral in Eq. (6-1) is applied twice to yield the Fourier transform

$$F(k_x,k_y) = \int_{-\infty}^{\infty} \int_{-\infty}^{\infty} f(x,y) \cos (k_x x + k_y y) \, dx \, dy$$

$$- i \int_{-\infty}^{\infty} \int_{-\infty}^{\infty} f(x,y) \sin (k_x x + k_y y) \, dx \, dy \qquad (14\text{-}1)$$

where k_x and k_y are called wave numbers with respect to the x and y axes, respectively, and have units of radians per kilometer if x and y are measured in kilometers. Wave numbers are the spatial counterparts of frequency (measured in radians per second) and are inversely proportional to wavelengths λ_x and λ_y:

$$k_x = \frac{2\pi}{\lambda_x} \quad \text{and} \quad k_y = \frac{2\pi}{\lambda_y}$$

The inverse Fourier transform for two-dimensional functions is

$$f(x,y) = \frac{1}{2\pi} \int_{-\infty}^{\infty} \int_{-\infty}^{\infty} F(k_x,k_y) \cos (k_x x + k_y y) \, dx \, dy$$

$$+ \frac{i}{2\pi} \int_{-\infty}^{\infty} \int_{-\infty}^{\infty} F(k_x,k_y) \sin (k_x x + k_y y) \, dx \, dy \qquad (14\text{-}2)$$

Bracewell[5] describes the two-dimensional Fourier transform in detail and gives various conditions which a general function $f(x,y)$ must satisfy in order for it to have a transform. One obvious difficulty in applying Eq.(14-1) to geophysical data is that all real data sets are of finite extent with large anomalies commonly truncated by the bounds of the survey, whereas the function $f(x,y)$ in (14-1) is implicitly defined over an infinite plane. In fact, the data, at this stage of the analysis, are often in the form of two-dimensional grids or arrays of numbers. The calculational tool most frequently used to transform such data is the discrete Fourier transform, for which efficient and speedy computer algorithms exist.[6] However, derivations and proofs are most conveniently carried out on the assumption that the data are represented by continuous functions of two variables defined over the xy plane, and theorems are commonly recast into discrete form by analogy for programming. Usually this approach works quite well, although there are certain assumptions built into the discrete formulation that can give rise to problems if the differences between the continuous and discrete formulations are forgotten.[7]

The Fourier transform $F(k_x,k_y)$ of the real-valued function $f(x,y)$ is a complex-valued, two-dimensional function. A function of two dimensions $f(x,y)$ represents an undulating surface with hills, ridges, and valleys. Equation (14-2) shows that $f(x,y)$ can be synthesized from a set of weighted sine and cosine terms, where the weights are given by the Fourier transform $F(k_x,k_y)$. Each sinusoid is a "corrugation" of the xy plane with a particular wavelength. Hence, two-dimensional Fourier analysis approximates the undulating shape of $f(x,y)$ by a summation of corrugations, each corrugation weighted according to its importance to $f(x,y)$. Bracewell[5] provides some graphical examples of two-dimensional functions and their Fourier transforms.

As in Chap. 6, the two-dimensional Fourier transform can greatly simplify filter operations. The convolution integral in two dimensions is defined to be

$$f(x,y) = \int_{-\infty}^{\infty} \int_{-\infty}^{\infty} f_1(u,v) \, f_2(x - u, y - v) \, du \, dv \qquad (14\text{-}3)$$

or

$$f(x,y) = f_1(x,y) * f_2(x,y)$$

and represents the output f that results when f_1 is filtered by f_2. In practice, f_1 and f_2 are digital functions with identical sample intervals. Evaluating the convolution integral in the spatial domain can be a time-consuming operation in practical applications, even with a computer. However, it can be shown[5] that in complete analogy with the one-dimensional case, the Fourier transform of both sides of Eq. (14-3) is

$$F(k_x,k_y) = F_1(k_x,k_y)\, F_2(k_x,k_y) \tag{14-4}$$

where F, F_1, and F_2 are Fourier transforms of f, f_1, and f_2, respectively. Equation (14-4) shows that the convolution operation can be accomplished in the Fourier domain by the multiplication of a pair of two-dimensional functions. Hence, in order to filter f_1 by f_2, we can either apply Eq. (14-3), or (1) Fourier transform f_1 and f_2 to F_1 and F_2, respectively; (2) multiply F_1 by F_2; and (3) inverse Fourier transform the product back to the space domain. Because of the speed of two-dimensional, discrete Fourier-transform algorithms, the three-step procedure is often more efficient than direct calculation with Eq. (14-3).

Wavelength Filters   As mentioned in the introduction, gravity maps are a composite of the gravity fields from all subsurface sources detectable by the instrument employed. Usually only a small subset of these sources are of interest in any specific study and, if one is lucky, these sources will cause anomalies whose characteristic width or wavelength is different from those of the other sources. In such cases, wavelength filtering can be used to emphasize or even reveal the existence of anomalies being sought. At regional scales, for example, Bouguer anomalies might include components with most of their energy at wavelengths less than 100 km caused by bodies of interest in the crust and components with wavelengths mostly greater than 200 km caused by deep compensating masses that support the regional topography. In an investigation of crustal geology, therefore, it might be desirable to eliminate the long-wavelength components as a means of highlighting the anomalies due to shallow crustal sources. This approach was used by Kane and Godson[8] to study the gravity field of the conterminous United States.

Similarly, long-wavelength anomalies caused by density variations within the basement might obscure shorter-wavelength anomalies due to bodies such as salt domes contained within the sedimentary section, and these long wavelengths might be suppressed by a suitable filter. At the other end of the spectrum, long wavelengths of the gravity field can be of interest in studies of isostasy or basement lithology, and they might be more clearly displayed if the short-wavelength anomalies were eliminated. Finally, data errors such as might arise from inaccurate terrain corrections may cause short-wavelength anoma-

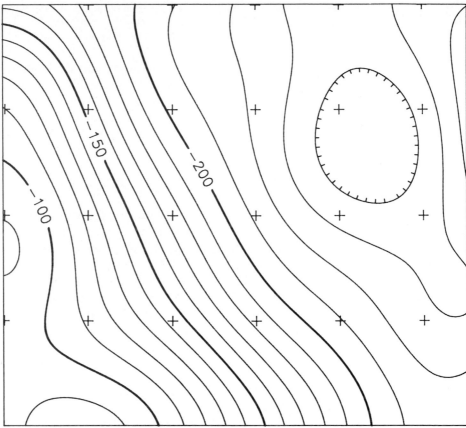

FIGURE 14-1d   Result of applying a *low-pass* filter to the complete Bouguer anomaly field in Fig. 14-1c. This map retains wavelengths longer than about 50 km. Contour interval is 10 mGal.

lies (noise) with wavelengths on the order of twice the typical station spacing. These anomalies can sometimes be smoothed by wavelength filtering. An example of wavelength filtering applied to a regional gravity survey is given in Fig. 14-1d and 14-1e.

The Fourier domain is a convenient place to apply filters that are designed to eliminate certain undesirable wavelengths. For example, if wavelengths less than $\lambda = \lambda_c$ are deemed undesirable in $f_1(x,y)$, we should design a filter $F_2(k_x,k_y)$ such that

$$F_2(k_x,k_y) = \begin{cases} 0 & \text{if } \sqrt{k_x^2 + k_y^2} > \frac{2\pi}{\lambda_c} \\ 1 & \text{elsewhere} \end{cases} \tag{14-5}$$

This type of filter is called a *low-pass* or *long-wavelength* filter because all wave numbers less than $2\pi/\lambda_c$ (or wavelengths greater than λ_c) are passed by

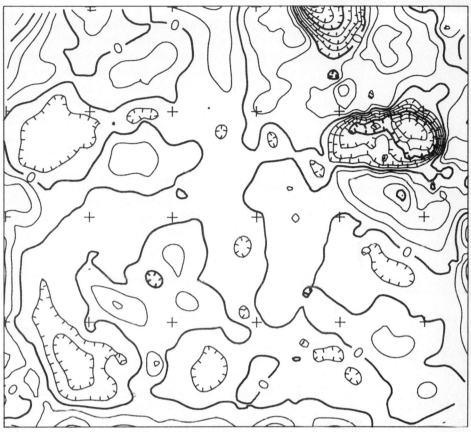

FIGURE 14-1e   Result of applying a *high-pass* filter to the complete Bouguer anomaly field in Fig. 14-1c. This map retains wavelengths shorter than about 50 km. Contour interval is 5 mGal.

the filter without modification. *High-pass* or *short-wavelength* filters, on the other hand, reject wavelengths longer than some threshold λ_c; for example

$$F_2(k_x,k_y) = \begin{cases} 0 & \text{if } \sqrt{k_x^2 + k_y^2} < \frac{2\pi}{\lambda_c} \\ 1 & \text{elsewhere} \end{cases} \qquad (14\text{-}6)$$

In spite of their conceptual simplicity, both of these filters work rather poorly in some applications because the abrupt and discontinuous change at wavelength λ_c can result in undesirable effects during inverse transformation. Most practical high-pass or low-pass filters allow for some sort of smoother transition across the step.

Although wavelength filtering has many advantages, such filtering can introduce artifacts into the data,[9] and it is often not possible to truly separate two sets of anomalies because most real source bodies will produce anomalies that have contributions from all wavelengths in the spectrum. The design of filters is a highly developed art, and the examples of this section are primarily intended to convey a concept of how the filters operate in the Fourier domain. For example, if geologic information is available to suggest that interfering sources are at rather different depths or that they possess rather different frequency attributes, then it may be possible to use the spectral characteristics of the gravity field to "design" a filter best suited to the separation task at hand. Some such filters have been called matched filters in the literature[10] and may sometimes provide both the best way of separating anomalies and a means of telling from the spectrum how inherently "separable" a set of anomalies may be.

Directional Filters   Another type of filter that can sometimes be used to advantage is one that selectively suppresses anomalies that have a preferred azimuthal orientation. For example, strong linear gravity lows over the north-trending sediment-filled basins of the Basin and Range province tend to dominate the gravity field in the region and mask the more subtle anomalies caused by variations in basement lithology. A suitable directional filter might be an effective tool for bringing out subtle east-west basement trends. Another use for directional filters might be in the processing of gravity data collected along parallel ship tracks. Errors in navigation, Eötvös corrections, and so forth can cause artificial anomalies that are linear and parallel to the ship tracks, and these anomalies can in some cases be usefully suppressed by a directional filter. Applied to a normal data set, the directional filter tends to exaggerate and enhance trends in some chosen direction (Fig. 14-1f). Trends and alinements that are "discovered" in the data set by the use of such filters must, of course, be verified by referring back to the original data set. If such trends cannot be seen, however subtly, in the original map, they are probably artifacts of the processing.

A property of the Fourier domain representation of two-dimensional data makes the design of such directional filters quite simple. Linear components in $f(x,y)$ that trend at an angle $\theta \pm \Delta\theta$ from the y axis will be located in the Fourier domain between angles $\theta + \Delta\theta$ and $\theta - \Delta\theta$ from the k_x axis. Filters can be designed to eliminate certain specific trends in the data by setting to zero all $F_2(k_x, k_y)$ values that lie within the pie-shaped segment of the $k_x k_y$ plane:

$$F_2(k_x, k_y) = \begin{cases} 0 & \text{if } \theta - \Delta\theta < \arctan \frac{k_y}{k_x} < \theta + \Delta\theta \\ 1 & \text{elsewhere} \end{cases} \tag{14-7}$$

This filter is called the *pie-slice* filter because of its characteristic shape in the Fourier domain. Real trends will also be eliminated by such a filter, of course, but in many cases they could not have been used in interpretation because they were obscured by the anomalies that the filter was designed to eliminate.

Upward Continuation of Gravity Data   The transformation of gravity data measured on one surface to some higher surface is called *upward continuation*.

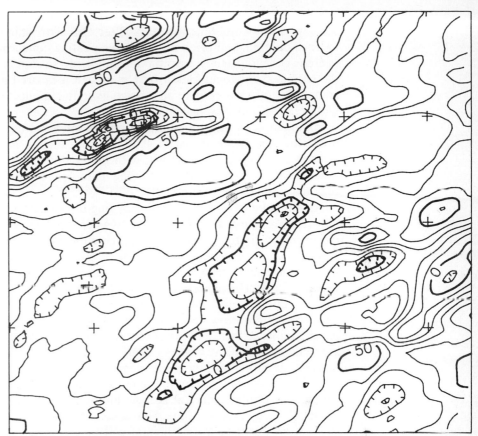

FIGURE 14-1f Result of applying a *directional* filter to the free-air anomaly field in Fig. 14-1a. Trends at an azimuth of N. 60°E. have been passed while perpendicular trends have been suppressed (Δθ was 45°) Contour interval is 10 mGal.

Upward continuation is a filter operation that tends to smooth the original data by attenuation of short-wavelength anomalies relative to their longer-wavelength counterparts, a logical consequence of the attenuation of anomaly amplitude with increasing distance from the source.

The upward-continuation filter $F_2(k_x,k_y)$ is elegantly simple for the special case of data measured on a flat surface:

$$F_2(k_x,k_y) = e^{-kz} \qquad (k = \sqrt{k_x^2 + k_y^2}) \qquad (14\text{-}8)$$

where z (>0) is the distance of upward continuation. Grant and West[11] provide a derivation of this result. Notice that upward continuation requires no knowledge about the actual shape of the masses or their density distributions. Equation (14-8) shows that as we move away from the sources, all wave numbers are attenuated by e^{-kz} and that the highest wave numbers (shortest wavelengths) are attenuated most rapidly. Hence, upward continuation can be seen as a very smooth, low-pass filter. As with standard low-pass filters, upward continuation often provides perspective concerning the large regional sources beneath a study area, but its simple physical interpretation (this is how the gravity data would look if they had been measured on the higher surface) sometimes offers a definite advantage over the application of low-pass filters with less obvious physical significances.

An example of upward continuation is shown in Fig. 14-1g. Notice that, as predicted, the anomalies with shortest wavelengths in the original data are attenuated relative to anomalies with larger dimensions by the upward-continuation filter. Many of the remaining features are caused by sources of more regional scale.

As might be expected, simply changing the sign of z turns Eq. (14-8) into a *downward-continuation* filter, which when applied to gravity data gets us closer to the sources. Practically, moving the observational surface nearer to sources is not a well-behaved problem,[11] however, because the shortest wavelengths, including data noise and numerical roundoff errors, are amplified exponentially. Hence, downward continuation should be used with extreme caution, although there are situations in which it can be a useful tool.

Vertical Derivatives   Second vertical derivatives have been traditionally used to enhance local anomalies obscured by broader regional trends and to aid in the definition of the edges of source bodies.[12] A shallow geologic feature of limited lateral extent (like a salt dome) will typically have a gravity anomaly with greater curvature than the regional field (which probably originates from deeper sources) on which it is superimposed. The second vertical derivative (which gives a measure of the difference of the gravity value at a point relative to its values at neighboring points) will be greater over the localized feature than over the more smoothly varying regional trend. Plotting a map of second-vertical-derivative values will have the effect of making the gravitational anomaly from the local feature stand out more conspicuously. Vertical derivatives can be regarded as types of high-pass filters that enhance anomalies caused by small features while suppressing longer-wavelength regional trends. An example is shown in Fig. 14-1h where the application of the vertical derivative emphasizes several local anomalies in the southwest quadrant that are obscured by the broad Bouguer regional gradient over the eastern Sierra Nevada. Numerous data problems in this regional data set are also marked by the small spotlike anomalies on the map, even though a somewhat arbitrary smoothing operator of the form $\exp(-\alpha k^2)$ was also applied to the data, where α is an adjustable smoothing parameter. (This added filter has the effect of suppressing the shortest wavelengths, and in essence turns the second vertical derivative filter into a *bandpass* filter, by which both the shortest and longest wavelengths are damped outside a band of "passed" wavelengths.)

First-vertical-derivative maps can serve many of the same purposes as second-vertical-derivative maps, and the noise amplification problem is not quite as severe. Moreover, a physical significance can be attached to the first

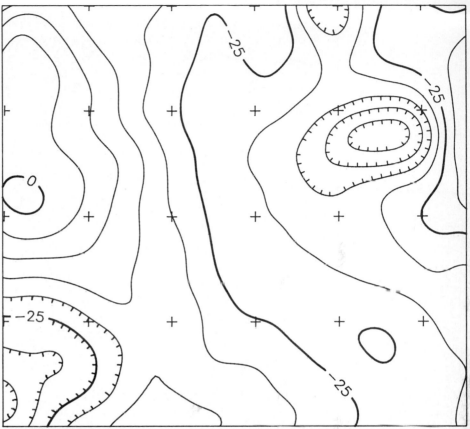

FIGURE 14-1g   Result of applying an *upward-continuation* filter to the isostatic anomaly field shown in Fig. 14-1*i*. Upward continued 5 km. Contour interval is 5 mGal.

vertical derivative. Because the force of gravity and the magnetic scalar potential are both proportional to $1/r^2$, a general relationship stated by Poisson exists between the two fields. If we know the gravitational field over a dense source body, we can predict, without knowing anything about the body itself, the magnetic field that would result if dense matter were replaced by magnetic material in constant proportion to the density and with known direction of magnetization. In the simple case where dense bodies are imagined to be replaced with magnetic material at the magnetic north pole (where induced magnetizations point straight downward), the magnetic field to be expected is equal to the first vertical derivative of the gravitational field multiplied by a suitable constant to convert from gravitational field units to units of magnetic field intensity.

Magnetic anomalies calculated from gravity data are called *pseudomagnetic anomalies*. They can be compared with measured magnetic data to learn if any gravity sources exist that are also magnetic and thereby draw some geologic

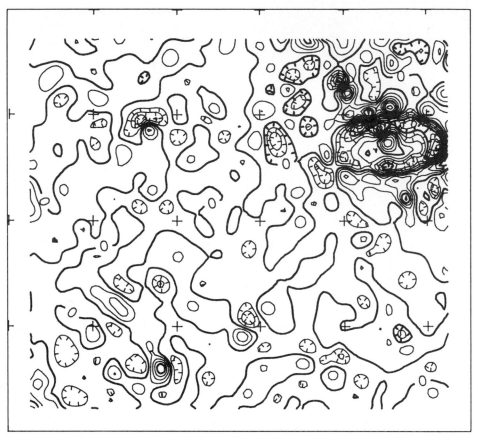

FIGURE 14-1h Result of applying a *second-vertical-derivative* filter to the complete Bouguer gravity anomaly field shown in Fig. 14-1c. A smoothing filter has also been applied ($\alpha = 1$) to dampen noise. Several small anomalies in the southwest quadrant obscured by the Bouguer gravity gradient over the Sierras are revealed, as are many data problems (small spotlike anomalies) in this regional data set. Contour interval is 0.5 mGal/km².

conclusions about the nature of the source. Mafic plutons, for example, often have high density and high magnetization; comparison of pseudomagnetic and measured magnetic maps may help distinguish mafic plutons from more silicic ones.

The nth vertical derivative of a gravity field can be expressed as a very simple form in the Fourier domain:

$$F_2(k_x, k_y) = (-k)^n \qquad (k = \sqrt{k_x^2 + k_y^2}) \tag{14-9}$$

Demonstration of this can be found in Gunn.[13] As with upward continuation, no information is required about the sources to calculate a vertical derivative. As with downward continuation, vertical derivatives greatly enhance short-wavelength noise and other defects in the data. The quality of a data set can sometimes be quickly assessed and the location of bad data points quickly spotted by the application of derivative filters to a grid constructed from the data.

Other Enhancement Techniques

The Isostatic Filter   Regional gravity data are uniquely suited to the application of a topography-driven "filter" that removes, to a first approximation, the gravitational effects of deep-seated density distributions that isostatically support the topography (see Chap. 12). These effects can be large in areas of extreme topographic relief, such as along continental margins and in mountain belts, and they tend to mask smaller anomalies due to near-surface sources of geologic interest. There are a variety of different approaches to producing

FIGURE 14-1*i*   Isostatic anomaly map of the same area as in Fig. 14-1*c*. Prepared using an Airy local compensation model. Density of topography, 2.67 g/cm³, density contrast across bottom of root, 0.4 g/cm³, depth of root for sea-level elevations, 25 km. Contour interval is 5 mGal.

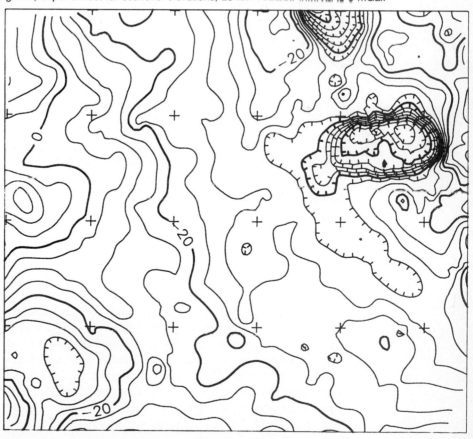

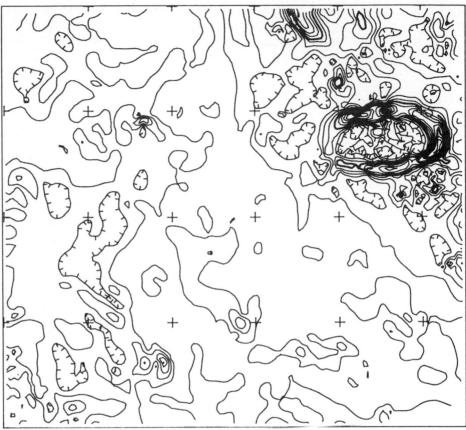

FIGURE 14-1j Values ot horizontal gradient are contoured for the isostatic anomaly map shown in Fig. 14-1*i*. Contour interval is 1 mGal/km.

isostatic anomaly maps and a variety of different isostatic models that can be chosen. Frequently the enhancement of anomalies produced by upper crustal sources is quite spectacular, regardless of the model used, especially in areas where changes in surface elevation are large. The isostatic "filter" is also fairly robust in the sense that despite the wide variety of different isostatic models possible, the isostatic anomalies produced by all of them are to first order quite similar—the filter is relatively insensitive to the details of the particular model. Examples of the isostatic filter applied to a continental data set in order to enhance the anomalies caused by upper crustal bodies of geologic interest are given by the maps of Jachens et al.[14] and Simpson et al.[15] Figure14-1*i* shows the isostatic residual anomaly calculated from Bouguer data over the eastern flank of the Sierra. It will be seen by comparison with the Bouguer map that a large gradient cause by compensating masses that support the topography has been removed to first order so that anomalies obscured by the gradient are more clearly defined.

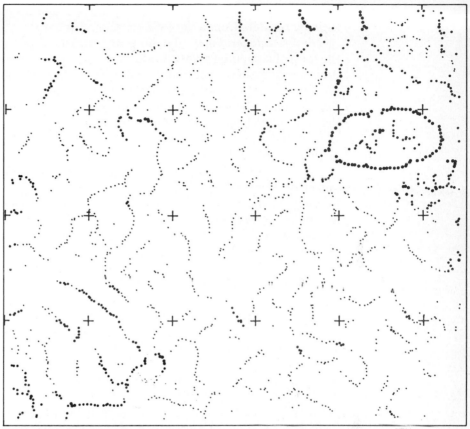

FIGURE 14-1k   Ridge crests on the horizontal gradient map (Fig. 14-1*j*) are picked by an automatic procedure and marked with spots. The smallest spots indicate horizontal gradient values from 0–2 mGal/km, the medium-size spots indicate values from 2–4 mGal/km, and the largest spots indicate values greater than 4 mGal/km.

The Maximum Horizontal Gradient   Gravity data are often useful in defining the lateral extent of geologic bodies such as plutons or sediment-filled valleys. Cordell and Grauch[16] have demonstrated that for near-surface bodies with near-vertical contacts, the maximum horizontal gradient of gravity as measured along a profile will occur nearly over the contact. In two dimensions, if a contour map (e.g., Fig. 14-1*j*) is made of the amplitude of the horizontal gradient (i.e., of the magnitude of the slope of the gravity field without regard to the direction of the slope), then lines drawn along "ridge tops" will approximately outline the density boundaries of the source bodies. This procedure has been automated (see Blakely and Simpson[17]) and can be applied with ease to any gridded data set to yield outlines such as those shown in Fig. 14-1*k*. The lines so obtained will not lie directly over contacts if the original assumptions are invalid, that is, if the contacts do not dip steeply or if the source body itself is too deep. However, the method usually provides a simple and rapid way of viewing the data from a very different perspective.

The Presentation Filter Traditionally, gravity data have been presented in the form of contoured maps. As alternative, usually computer-assisted, ways of presenting data have become available, it has become clear that complex data sets are best studied by displaying and examining them in many different ways. For example, contouring tends to emphasize the steep gradients in the data because of the high density of lines along gradients, whereas a color presentation of the same data makes it easier to grasp the relative amplitudes of anomalies and to detect subtle changes in base levels between different areas.

Shaded gray scales or color scales can be adjusted to some degree by trial and error or by techniques developed for the display of remote sensing images in order to enhance features of particular interest. Shaded relief maps, which are made by treating the gravity maps as if they were topographic maps and shading them according to the shadows that would be cast by the topography for various hypothetical sun positions, have the ability to bring short-wavelength features into greater prominence, or to emphasize trends in certain directions. Figure 14-2 shows a shaded relief rendition of the free-air gravity field over a large portion of the midcontinent region of the United States.

Perhaps some of the most interesting efforts involve the simultaneous presentation of multiple data sets such as gravity, aeromagnetic, topography, and geology. By judicious combinations of contours, colors, shading, and even stereo-optical presentation, two or more data sets can be examined in register. Such displays should greatly aid the interpretation of anomalies, because the human eye remains, in many ways, the best available integrator of complex patterns. Colored examples of the merging of gravity, topographic, and geologic data are given by Guinness et al.[18] Many other beautiful examples of the "presentation filter" are presented by Hinze[19] and by Paterson and Reeves.[3]

14-3 REGIONAL-RESIDUAL SEPARATION

Two types of problems are often encountered in gravity interpretation where anomalies must be separated from one another. The most usual one is where the lateral extent of one anomaly is much greater than the other. This generally occurs when the source with the larger dimensions is a regional geologic feature, such as a basin or geosyncline, and the smaller one is a local feature, such as an anticline or salt dome. In such a situation, the first anomaly can be considered to have a low spatial frequency (equivalent to a large lateral extent or a long wavelength) and the second a high spatial frequency (corresponding to a short lateral extent or wavelength). The most common objective in such cases is to isolate the anomaly from the smaller source, a process that involves high-pass spatial filtering. Techniques for carrying out such a separation were first developed some time before it was generally recognized that they were really filtering operations. The component of the gravity anomaly having the longer effective wavelength is usually referred to as the *regional*, while the narrower,

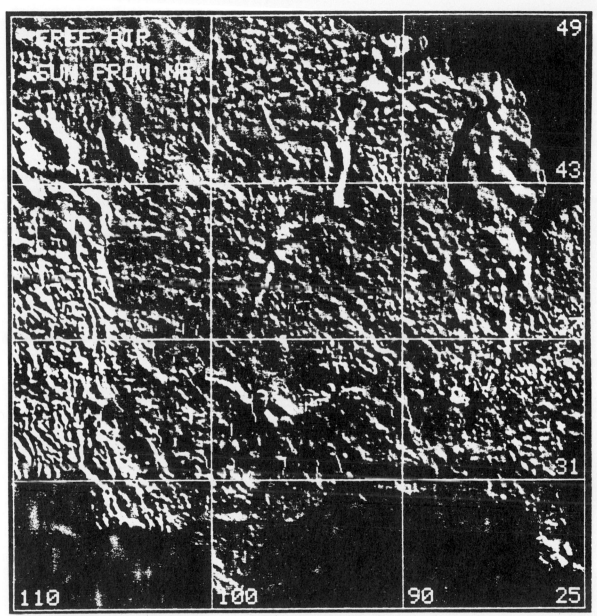

FIGURE 14-2 A shaded relief image depicting free-air anomalies as if they were hills and valleys illuminated by a sun located at 15° above the northeastern horizon. (*Guinness and others.*[18])

or shorter-wavelength, component having a more localized source is referred to as the *residual*. Extraction of residual from regional is done both by graphical and computational methods.

In regional studies, it may be desirable to remove anomalies from features of small lateral extent so as to bring out larger-scale structures more clearly. Techniques equivalent to low-pass filtering of the observed gravity field should achieve this objective.

A more complex type of filtering may be required when two sources of approximately the same size and buried at about the same depth are so close together that the field appears to come from a single source rather than from two separate ones. Resolution of such individual sources is not always possible, but when it is, rather sophisticated filtering techniques may sometimes be applicable with useful results.

The widespread use of electronic computers for filtering geophysical data of various kinds has led to the introduction of numerous programs for separating anomalies observed in measuring potential fields such as those from gravity.

Isolation of Residual Gravity Effects

There are numerous areas where large-scale, deep-seated structural features cause significant regional variations in the gravitational field. The Amarillo-Wichita uplift, a 200-mi-long basement trend crossing western Oklahoma and the Texas Panhandle, has a regional gradient along its southwestern flank of about 10 mGal/mi. In the Rio Grande Valley, there is a decrease in regional gravity of about 1 mGal/mi toward the Gulf of Mexico as one moves eastward from a point 70 mi inland. A comparable effect is generally observed as one approaches the Gulf anywhere along its periphery.

There are several sources of regional gravity variation. In addition to large-scale geologic structures, there are density effects caused by intrabasement lithologic changes as well as isostatic variations with sources that may often be indeterminate.

Regional gradients like these often distort or obscure the effects of structures, such as salt domes or buried ridges, that are sought in oil exploration. For this reason it is customary to remove the regional effects from the observed gravity in order to isolate more clearly the smaller structural features in which we are most interested. Both graphical and mathematical methods are employed for separating residual fields associated with the smaller geological features.

Regardless of the origin of the regional anomaly, and regardless of the method of calculating residuals, it is important to recognize that the basic criterion for separating regional and residuals is the area covered by each type of feature.

Graphical (Visual) Methods   In the graphical approach, the regional effect must be estimated from plotted profiles or contour maps of observed gravity; regional contours are interpolated more or less arbitrarily, being superimposed

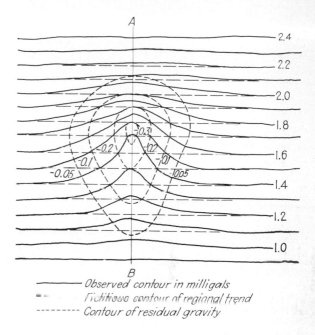

FIGURE 14-3 Determination of residual gravity by subtracting fictitious contours representing regional trend from observed contours.

——————— Observed contour in milligals
— — — Fictitious contour of regional trend
--------- Contour of residual gravity

over the original gravity field. A considerable amount of judgment and in many cases some geological information may be necessary to extract the regional properly from the observed data. The process is so subjective and empirical that one geologist has been quoted by Nettleton[20] as remarking that "the regional is what you take out in order to make what's left look like the structure."

Where the contours at a distance from a local anomaly are quite regular, it is possible to take out the regional trend by drawing lines which connect the undisturbed contours outside the area within which the anomaly is confined, as illustrated in Fig. 14-3. Where the smoothed contours cross contours of observed gravity, the differences between the two, which have discrete values at each intersection, are marked and themselves contoured. The resulting map gives residual gravity. In the example shown in Fig. 14-3, the removal of the regional converts an elongated gravity minimum into a closed low. The best results can usually be obtained if the smoothing is done on typical profiles rather than on contour maps. If a gravity cross section is drawn through the center of the anomaly on a map, the regional trend can be represented by the best straight line connecting the ends of the profiles on either side of the anomalous feature. Figure 14-4 illustrates this. The residual profile plotted below the observed cross section was obtained simply by subtracting the estimated regional value from the observed gravity at all points along the profile.

Often a series of profiles is drawn on the contour map as a network of intersecting lines. These lines may be profiles along which observations have been made, or they may be drawn arbitrarily across a gravity map with gravity

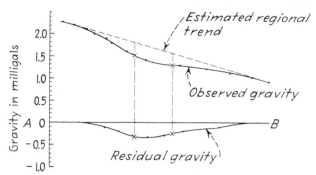

FIGURE 14-4 Gravity profile showing removal of regional trend across the anomaly shown in Fig. 14-3.

values picked off at intersections with contour lines. The regional is estimated for each profile as shown in Fig. 14-4, but there is additional control from the fact that the values on each pair of intersecting profiles must be adjusted to be the same at the points of intersection. Such additional control, although in a sense arbitrary, is particularly helpful when residuals have low relief.

The graphical methods have the advantage that all available geological information from an area can be put to use in drawing the regional. This is particularly important where the survey covers an area that is smaller than that of a major structural feature governing the regional trends. But experienced and highly trained personnel are required for good results. And even when such personnel are available, subjective processes involve the risk of erroneous geologic conceptions or mistakes in judgment.

Analytical Numerical Methods   With analytical methods of determining residual gravity, numerical operations on the observed data make it possible to isolate anomalies without such a great reliance upon the exercise of judgment in carrying out the separations. Such techniques generally require that gravity values be spaced in a regular array.

Most analytical methods are now based on computers, although initially many clever schemes were devised with templates that could be used directly on contour maps. Template methods have been described in earlier editions of this book, and although they are still of use in some special contexts, the discussion that follows will be confined to methods that are readily implemented on digital computers. The most straightforward and commonly used approaches are perhaps polynomial fitting and wavelength filtering. Several alternative methods which can be more adaptable to the geologic situation at hand are also discussed.

Polynomial Fitting   One of the most flexible of the analytical techniques for determining regional gravity is polynomial fitting. Here the observed data are used to compute, usually by least squares, the mathematically describable surface giving the closest fit to the gravity field that can be obtained within a specified degree of detail. This surface is considered to be the regional gravity, and the residual is the difference between the gravity field as actually mapped and the regional field thus determined.

In practice the surface is expressed mathematically as a two-dimensional polynomial of an order that depends on the complexity of the regional geology. If the regional field were a simple inclined plane, it would be a first-order surface of the form

$$z = Ax + By + C \qquad (14\text{-}10)$$

The coefficients A, B, and C are determined so as to minimize the variation of the residual. Agocs[21] provides a description of this technique.

The next stage of complexity would involve representation by a second-order polynomial

$$z = Ax^2 + By^2 + Cxy + Dx + Ey + F \qquad (14\text{-}11)$$

Polynomials of much higher order would probably be necessary for a large area over which the regional has numerous convolutions. The approach is quite similar to that used in trend-surface analysis, a technique that has seen increasing use in reconstructing geologic structures as they should have appeared before regional deformation took place.

Coons et al.[22] have used this technique to study a large midcontinent linear gravity high which extends for several hundred miles through Iowa and Minnesota. They computed residuals for a number of polynomial fits up to the thirteenth order. Figure 14-5 shows the Bouguer anomaly map for a portion of this area and the seventeenth- and thirteenth-order polynomial surfaces. The resemblance of the polynomial surface and the Bouguer map increases with the order of the polynomial. Residuals computed for the thirteenth-order polynomial show a number of closed features having apparent geological significance that were hardly discernible on maps of lower-order residuals such as those based on the tenth-order surface.

Wavelength Filtering   The use of wavelength filtering as a means of separating anomalies has already been discussed in Sec. 14-2. In the ideal case, the gravity data are gridded and transformed into the Fourier-transform domain, and the wavelengths (usually very long ones) corresponding to regional trends are removed by an appropriate high-pass filter, leaving the shorter-wavelength residual gravity anomalies. An example of such a regional-residual separation is provided by Figs. 14-1*d* and 14-1*e*. The fact that components of the regional field often cover a wide range of wavelengths may make it difficult to accomplish the separation satisfactorily in this way. In some cases, the short-wavelength components of the regional field cannot be removed without removing significant portions of the residual. Moreover, shallow features to be enhanced will have long-wavelength components of considerable significance in their spectra that produce an overlap with regional spectra that limits the usefulness of the technique. Thus, as Grant[23] points out, it is not as simple as it might seem

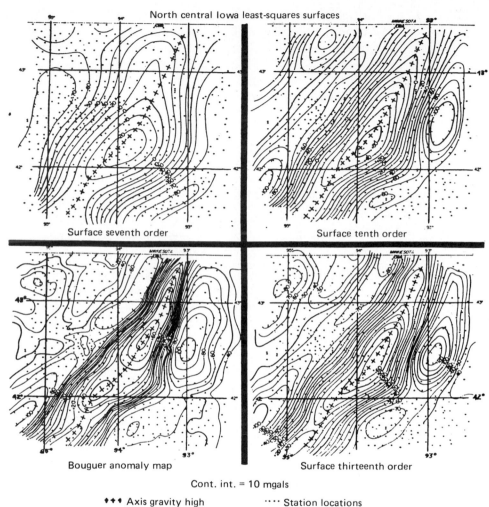

FIGURE 14-5 Bouguer anomaly and least-squares surfaces for three high-order polynomials over portion of north central Iowa. (*After Coons et al.*[22])

to design a spatial filter that will be effective in separating residual from regional fields.

The problems can be alleviated to some degree if one's goals are aimed toward the visual enhancement of anomalies rather than toward quantitative models, by preparing companion maps of both regional and residual fields and studying them together as a pair. Several choices of cutoff wavelength can also be instructive as in the maps of Hildenbrand et al.[24] because it is unlikely that a single choice of cutoff wavelength will serve equally well for all anomalies in a large area. Kane and Godson[8] discuss in more detail the utility and possible pitfalls of wavelength filtering as applied to the problem of interpreting anomalies in the Bouguer gravity field over the conterminous United States.

Calculation of Regional Fields by Interpolation In certain circumstances, it may be possible to remove from a data set the observations that are largely responsible for defining a local anomaly of interest and to use the remaining observations to prepare a regional field. This technique is implemented by computing two rectangular grids with identical grid intersections: one based on the entire data set and a second based only on the regional observations. The difference between the two grids provides a residual anomaly, that will, in favorable circumstances, be largely caused by the local source. The success of this approach depends critically on the ability of the gridding algorithm, which often uses either minimum-curvature or splines, to interpolate field values in the "hole" left behind by the missing data. Some gridding algorithms do very poorly at this indeed. Results must be examined critically by the interpreter in this regard.

This approach is perhaps the closest automatic analog to the graphical separation technique described earlier. It also could potentially allow the interpreter to insert some geologic constraints into the construction of a regional by using only stations observed on certain geologic units or on crystalline basement rather than on sedimentary deposits.

Geologic Regionals Polynomial fitting and wavelength filtering, in spite of their conceptual simplicity, both suffer from mathematical objectivity untempered by physical insight. These approaches will split the anomaly from a single source into regional and residual parts that have little interpretive significance. The use of these methods can result in the introduction of artifacts that severely impede quantitative modeling of source bodies.[9] Alternative methods that avoid some of these problems rely on regionals computed on the basis of some geologic or geophysical information about the deep density distributions. One such method was discussed in Sec. 14-1 under the name "isostatic filter." In the context of regional-residual separation, the isostatic anomaly map can be considered a residual map generated from the Bouguer anomaly map by removing a regional based on the principle of isostasy. Isostatic anomaly maps frequently require almost no further regional adjustments or datum shifts when used for the purpose of modeling anomalies due to local, near-surface sources. A somewhat similar form of regional extraction that is becoming more possible with the advent of new and better regional deep-seismic data consists of calculating the gravitational effects of deep density distributions inferred from seismic data. This is possible because seismic velocities in rocks are related to their densities, as was shown in Figs. 2-21 and 2-22. Information from other geophysical techniques can also contribute to the construction of a reasonable model for the deep structure of an area, and this model can then be used to predict a regional gravity field.

14-4   DETERMINATION OF DENSITY FOR GRAVITY INTERPRETATION

In the interpretation of gravity anomalies, it is necessary to estimate the densities of the subsurface rocks before one can postulate their structure. For this reason we shall give some attention to the densities of representative rocks

TABLE 14-1   BULK DENSITY OF SEDIMENTARY ROCKS

Formation	Age	Locality	Depth of sample, ft	Saturated bulk density (average), g/cm³
Sandstone				
Mount Simon	Cambrian	West Virginia, Wood County	13,005–13,065	2.70
Southern Potsdam	Cambrian	Wisconsin		2.41
Northern Potsdam	Cambrian	Wisconsin		2.32
St. Peter	Ordovician	Arkansas, Ozark Plateau		2.50
Bradford	Devonian	Pennsylvania	~600–~2300	2.40 *2.65
Chemung Formation	Devonian	Pennsylvania	~1700–~2300	2.51
Berea	Mississippian	Ohio, West Virginia	0–2160	2.39
Atoka Formation (and others)	Pennsylvanian	Arkansas:		
		Ozark Plateau		2.44
		Arkansas Valley		2.51
		Ouachita Mts.		2.56
Bartlesville sand	Pennsylvanian	Oklahoma	1570–2680	2.40
Bunter	Triassic	Great Britain		2.29
Keuper	Triassic	Great Britain		2.25
Woodbine sand	Cretaceous	Texas	2436–3701	2.25
Sandstones and siltstones	Cretaceous	Montana, eastern		2.17
Sandstones	Cretaceous	Wyoming	0–3187	2.32
Sandstones	Miocene	Switzerland		2.37
Limestone, Dolomite, Chalk, and Marble				
Ellenburger Group (limestone and dolomite)	Ordovician	Texas, Llano County		2.75
Beekmantown Group (dolomite)	Ordovician	West Virginia, Wood County		2.80
Black River (limestone)	Ordovician	Ontario		2.72
Niagara dolomite	Silurian	Wisconsin		2.77
Limestone	Carboniferous	Great Britain, Midlands		2.58
Marl	Carboniferous	Russia		2.63
Oolites	Jurassic	Great Britain		2.44
Limestones	Jurassic	Switzerland		2.66
Glen Rose limestone	Cretaceous	Texas	20.5–30.5	2.37
Chalk	Cretaceous	Great Britain		2.23
Limestone	Cretaceous	Switzerland		2.65
Green River Formation (marlstone)	Eocene	Colorado		2.26

TABLE 14-1   CONTINUED

Formation	Age	Locality	Depth of sample, ft	Saturated bulk density (average), g/cm³
Shale, Claystone, and Slate				
Shale	Pennsylvanian	Oklahoma	1000	2.42
			3000	2.59
			5000	2.66
Shales	Cretaceous	Wyoming, Montana		2.17
Shale, nearly horizontal and undisturbed	Oligocene and Miocene	Venezuela	~600	2.06
			~2500	2.25
			~3500	2.35
			~6100	2.52
Sand, Clay, Gravel, Alluvium, and Soils				
Cape May Formation (sand)	Pleistocene	New Jersey		1.93
Loess soil	Quaternary	Idaho		1.61
Fine sand	Quaternary	California		1.93
Very find sand				1.92
Sand-silt-clay				1.44
Mud	Quaternary	Hudson River		1.20†
Silt	Quaternary	Hudson River	50 ft below river	1.79†
Newly deposited material	Quaternary	Mississippi River delta		1.26†
Soft mud	Quaternary	Clyde Sea	0-2.5 cm in mud	1.31†
			22.5-25 cm in mud	1.43†
Miscellaneous				
Marble	?	U.S.A., Great Britain		2.75

Source: G. Edward Manger, in "Handbook of Physical Constants," rev. ed., *Geol. Soc. Am. Mem.* 97, 1966.
* Assumed grain density, g/cm³.
† Density computed from measured porosity.

in regions where gravity surveys are ordinarily made. For applications to interpretation, it is not the absolute densities but the density contrasts that are significant. In the sedimentary section, these contrasts are almost always small, seldom exceeding 0.25 g/cm³. Moreover, the variation in the possible densities of almost any type of rock sometimes makes it difficult to choose a suitable value to use in actual computations. Tables 14-1 to 14-3 illustrate the range of density values in a number of typical rock materials as well as the differences that can be expected between the different types. In addition,

TABLE 14-2   AVERAGE DENSITIES OF HOLOCRYSTALLINE IGNEOUS ROCKS

Rock	Number of samples	Mean density, g/cm³	Range of density, g/cm³
Granite	155	2.667	2.516–2.809
Granodiorite	11	2.716	2.668–2.785
Syenite	24	2.757	2.630–2.899
Quartz diorite	21	2.806	2.680–2.960
Diorite	13	2.839	2.721–2.960
Norite	11	2.984	2.720–3.020
Gabbro, including olivine gabbro	27	2.976	2.850–3.120
Diabase, fresh	40	2.965	2.804–3.110
Periodotite, fresh	3	3.234	3.152–3.276
Dunite*	15	3.277	3.204–3.314
Pyroxenite	8	3.231	3.10 –3.318
Anorthosite	12	2.734	2.640–2.920

Source: R. A. Daly, in "Handbook of Physical Constants," rev. ed., *Geol. Soc. Am. Mem.* 97, 1966.
* From Birch, *J. Geophys. Res.*, vol. 65, p. 1083, 1960.

TABLE 14-3   AVERAGE DENSITIES OF METAMORPHIC ROCKS

Rock	Number of samples	Mean density, g/cm³	Range of density, g/cm³
Gneiss, Chester, Vermont	7	2.69	2.66–2.73
Granite gneiss, Hohe Tauern, Austria	19	2.61	2.59–2.63
Gneiss, Grenville, Adirondack Mts., New York	25	2.84	2.70–3.06
Oligoclase gneiss, Middle Haddam area, Connecticut	28	2.67	
Quartz-mica schists, Littleton Formation, New Hampshire (high-grade metamorphism)	76	2.82	2.70–2.96
Muscovite-biotite schist, Middle Haddam area, Connecticut	32	2.76	
Staurolite-garnet and biotite-muscovite schists, Middle Haddam area, Connecticut	22	2.76	
Chlorite-sericite schists, Vermont	50	2.82	2.73–3.03
Slate, Taconic sequence, Vermont	17	2.81	2.72–2.84
Amphibolite, New Hampshire and Vermont	13	2.99	2.79–3.14
Granulite, Lapland:			
Hypersthene-bearing	7	2.93	2.67–3.10
Hypersthene-free	5	2.73	2.63–2.85
Eclogite	10	3.392	3.338–3.452

Source: Sydney P. Clark, Jr., in "Handbook of Physical Constants," rev. ed., *Geol. Soc. Am. Mem.* 97, 1966.

Johnson and Olhoeft[25] present a recent compilation of density data for rocks and minerals.

It is evident from these tables that each type of sedimentary rock covers a wide range of densities and that the ranges are quite similar for sandstones, shales, and limestones. Rocks containing massive sulfides often have densities around 4 g/cm³. Igneous rocks are generally denser than sedimentary formations. Even here, however, there is substantial overlap between the densities of sedimentary and igneous types as well as between those of the various kinds of igneous rocks themselves.

Because the densities of rocks within various groups are difficult to predict from a knowledge of the rock types alone, it is important to have direct measurements of the densities of rocks within a given survey whenever possible. This can be most easily accomplished by collecting samples from unweathered outcrops at the time the survey is performed and subsequently measuring their densities in the laboratory. Such procedures can be quite effective in areas where igneous, metamorphic, and well-consolidated sedimentary rocks are exposed at the surface or where they have beem sampled by drilling. Unfortunately, good exposures are not present in all areas.

In areas where the predominant rock types do not crop out and where they have not been sampled by drill holes, it is often necessary in gravity calculations to assume average densities based on a knowledge of the rock type present. Figure 14-6 indicates the average densities obtained from a large number of laboratory measurements on core and surface samples tabulated by J. W. Peters of Mobil Oil Company. The range of densities and the number of samples for each type rock are tabulated at the base of the diagram.

FIGURE 14-6 Average densities of surface samples and cores based on laboratory measurements. (*Mobil Oil Co.*)

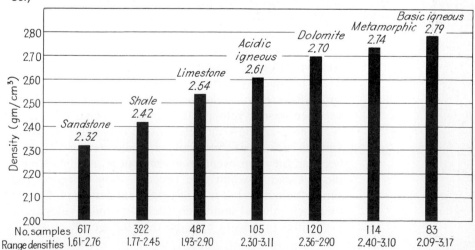

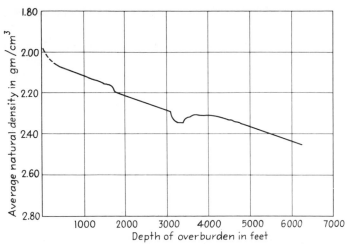

FIGURE 14-7　Natural density versus depth in a Venezuelan oil well penetrating into Tertiary shales. (*After Hedberg*[26])

In many areas there is a regular increase with depth in the density of the sedimentary section on account of compaction. Hedberg[26] has studied the density variation observed in a well penetrating more than 6000 ft of a shale formation in Venezuela (see Fig. 14-7). Nettleton[27] has made a study of the average variation with depth of the sedimentary rocks in the Texas Gulf Coast area by combining gravity data, density measurements, and Hedberg's compaction theory. Figure 14-8 shows the relationship of density to depth as determined from well samples in the Gulf Coast and in east Texas. Since the density of rock salt is about 2.15 g/cm³, the salt will generally be lighter than the surrounding sediments at depths greater than about 2500 ft in the Gulf Coast and at depths greater than about 2000 ft in east Texas.

An alternative approach to estimating densities of materials that have not been sampled directly or by borehole logging techniques is possible in areas where seismic information is available. Interpretations of seismic data often yield velocities of seismic waves in rocks that have not been sampled by drilling or are below a level that can even be reached by present drilling methods. If the subsurface seismic velocities are known in an area, then empirical relationships between seismic velocity and density can be used to estimate densities. Figures 2-21 and 2-22 show the relationship between P-wave velocity and density for various rock types. Such curves, while very useful, must be used with caution because they represent an average of many measurements that scatter about the average line and also because some different rock types may possess similar velocities but radically different densities. For example, Fig. 2-21 shows that rock salt and sandstone can have similar velocities of about 14,000 ft/s but may differ in density by more than 0.4 g/cm³.

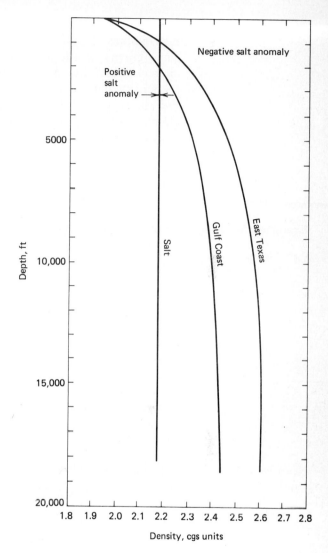

FIGURE 14-8 Density versus depth for sediments in Gulf Coast and east Texas. Note depths at which sediment densities are equal to density of salt. (*Exploration Techniques, Inc.*)

14.5 QUANTITATIVE INTERPRETATION

Ambiguity of Gravity Information

In Chap. 12 it was shown how one can predict the gravitational effect at any point on the surface from a given subsurface mass distribution by application of potential theory. In interpreting gravity data obtained in the field, one would like to reverse the procedure. Unfortunately, the process is not entirely reversible. Whereas a buried mass with a specified position, shape, and density distribution will give a predictable gravity field on the surface, any observed gravity profile could be produced by an infinite number of possible mass distributions. To consider a simple example, any buried sphere will give the same gravity profile as a point source having the same mass located at its center. Thus, if the mass and the position of the center of the sphere are fixed, its density and radius can have any combination that will yield this mass and there is no way of determining its true dimensions using the gravity anomaly alone. If we knew the density, we could then determine the radius, but even then we could not be certain that the body is a sphere just because the gravity profile has the form predicted for a sphere. Entirely different geometrical distributions of the subsurface mass can yield the same gravity field at the surface.

Examples Showing Lack of Uniqueness in Gravity Data

The limitations of the gravity method in defining subsurface structure follow from standard potential theory; they have been well illustrated in a much-quoted paper by Skeels[28] entitled Ambiguity in Gravity Interpretation. He shows how widely different subsurface mass distributions can give identical gravity pictures on the surface. In Fig. 14-9 we see a number of subsurface structures, each of which could account equally well for the indicated gravity anomaly if it were assumed that the anomaly results from undulations in the surface of a basement which has a fixed density contrast with the sediments above. The structure producing it could then have any of the shapes shown in the middle part of the figure. The lower part of the diagram shows an entirely different geological situation, a schist penetrated by an intrusive and overlain by sedimentary rock, and yet this could yield the same anomaly.

Need for Independent Geologic Information

It is seldom that a geological interpretation would be based on gravity data alone. Any independent control, like that obtained from borehole logs or seismic data, reduces the ambiguity in the interpretation. With such information the range of uncertainty is narrowed, and the number of variables can be reduced to the point where the gravity makes it possible to choose between alternative geological solutions (both lithological and structural) that fit all other kinds of observations. In the example shown in the upper part of Fig. 14-9, if a single well could be drilled to the basement somewhere along the profile, data would then be available on the densities of the sedimentary section and basement rocks as well as on the depth to the interface at one point. If the densities remain laterally uniform beneath the entire area, it should be possible to calculate the shape of the basement surface from the gravity data with considerable reliability.

It is often possible to use information obtained from surface geology to limit the possibilities and guide the assumptions upon which a gravity interpretation is based. Suppose, for example, that surface observations reveal an anticline

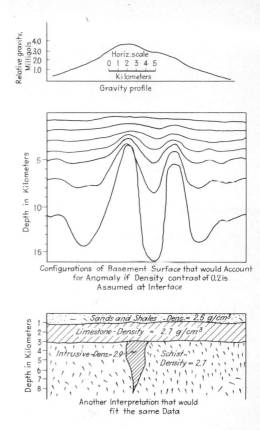

FIGURE 14-9   Alternative interpretations of a hypothetical gravity anomaly. (*After Skeels*.[28])

coincident with a gravity high, as in Fig. 14-10. From regional geology the surface feature is believed to result from a buried basement ridge. The shape of the ridge at each of several possible depths can be estimated from the surface dips. The only unknown is the depth of the basement, and this can be estimated from the gravity data by placing the ridge successively at a number of depths and computing each of the resulting gravity profiles. It is seen that one of these profiles gives a closer fit to the observed gravity profile than any of the others but does not coincide with it exactly. Although the geological control makes the final picture considerably less ambiguous than it would otherwise be, the structure so deduced is still not unique. Density inhomogeneities or structural features not reflected in the surface geology could make the interpretation quite unreliable.

Barton[29] has cautioned the interpreter on this point in the following words:

> Calculations in regard to the mass causing an observed anomaly are of great value in the interpretation of gravity data, but there are no panaceas for the uncertainties of interpretation. The geophysicist should keep the limitations and uncertainties constantly in mind and should see that the users of the results of the calculations are conscious of those limitations and uncertainties.

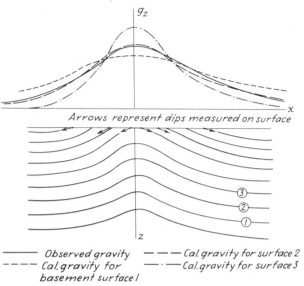

FIGURE 14-10 Estimating depth of buried igneous ridge by extrapolating surface structure downward and comparing calculated gravity for various assumed depths with that on the observed profile. Surface 2 appears to give the best fit.

He then points out that the chief value of such calculations is that they

> . . . definitely throw out possibilities that previously had looked plausible and bring to mind unthought-of new ones that are much more plausible.

This is why drilling locations are seldom selected on the basis of gravity indications alone. Gravity surveys are excellent for reconnaissance of previously unexplored areas, but anomalies thus obtained should be tested by applying other geophysical or geological information before the interpretations based on them are given much weight in decision making.

First-Cut Quantitative Methods

Comparison with Simple Bodies One straightforward approach to the interpretation of gravity anomalies is to approximate the geological feature considered to be the source by assigning it a simple geometrical form for which the gravity field can be computed mathematically. A salt dome, for example, might be approximated by a sphere or a vertical cylinder of specified dimensions. In Chap. 12, we derived formulas for the gravity effects of generalized forms as spheres, cylinders, laminae of various kinds, and faults with both inclined and vertical faces. Various values can be assigned to the parameters describing the geometry of these bodies, and the fields computed for such values are compared with measured anomalous fields. The parameters giving the best fit may be looked upon as plausible if they violate no constraints. Figure 14-11 tabu-

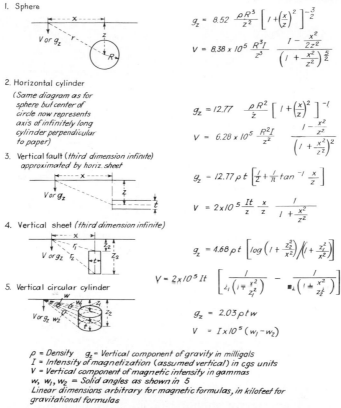

ρ = Density g_z = Vertical component of gravity in milligals
I = Intensity of magnetization (assumed vertical) in cgs units
V = Vertical component of magnetic intensity in gammas
w, w_1, w_2 = Solid angles as shown in 5
Linear dimensions arbitrary for magnetic formulas, in kilofeet for
gravitational formulas

FIGURE 14-11   Summary of formulas for vertical components of gravitational and magnetic fields from buried bodies having simple geometric forms. The magnetic formulas will be discussed in Chap. 16. (*L. L. Nettleton, Geophysics, vol. 7, 1942.*)

lates the formulas for the gravity fields from representative geometrical forms that often have geological significance.

Composite Forms   It is sometimes possible to fit together a number of simple geometric forms with different dimensions and (in some cases) different densities to simulate a presumed structure and to adjust the dimensions of the different component parts until the theoretical and observed gravity curves fit. Nettleton[30] accounted for the anomaly over the Minden salt dome in Louisiana by a salt and cap-rock configuration which he reduced to a number of equivalent cylinders, as shown in Fig. 14-12. The interpretation was facilitated by previous knowledge (from drilling) of the depth to the salt layer at the base of the dome. Here again the same gravity picture might have been matched just as well by an entirely different subsurface mass, but the well data made this picture the most plausible. A similar approach to detailing the structure of a salt dome is illustrated in Fig. 13-10. Unless the shape of the body is already well known to possess a high degree of symmetry or simplicity, however, greater

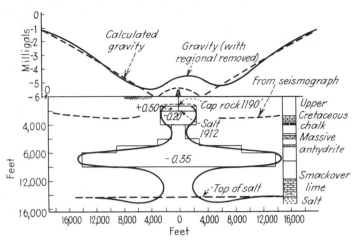

FIGURE 14-12 Comparison of observed gravity anomaly over Minden dome, Louisiana, with that predicted from salt dome having shape and density contrasts approximated by series of cylinders as shown. (*After Nettleton.*[30])

ultimate flexibility in the interpretation process is offered by the use of two-dimensional and three-dimensional forward computer modeling programs discussed in later sections of this chapter.

Gradients In the comparison of observed anomalies with those produced by simple geometric bodies, it is worth remembering that fitting only the general amplitude and width of the anomaly can lead to very poor estimates. In particular, careful attention ought to be paid to the steeper gradients of the observed anomalies, inasmuch as these gradients often offer the most explicit, least ambiguous insights into the depth of the source body and the location and dip of its edges. The estimation of depths is discussed in a following section. Figure 14-13 illustrates that in favorable circumstances, the asymmetry of gradients can yield useful information about the geometry of the source body, in this case a buried semi-infinite slab (or step model) with a dipping end. In this example, the steepest part of the gradient lies nearly over the end of the dipping contact nearest to the surface, and the position of the steepest gradient relative to the center of the entire gradient reveals the direction of dip. Grant and West[11] describe how quantitative estimates of dip and other parameters can be made from such a step model with the help of characteristic curves.

Depth Estimation Formulas for the gravity effect of various bodies may frequently be used to estimate the depth to the bodies to which they relate. Consider, for example, the gravity field over a long horizontal cylinder of radius R and density ρ along a line on the surface perpendicular to its axis. The formula for the gravity at a horizontal distance x from an axis buried at a depth z (Fig. 14-14) is

$$g_z = 12.77 \frac{\rho^2}{z}\left[1 + \left(\frac{x}{z}\right)^2\right]^{-1} \tag{14-12}$$

Case I. Contact vertical

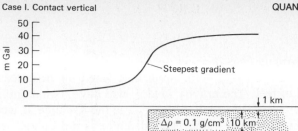

Case II. Contact dipping under body:

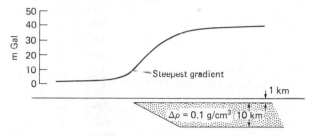

Case III. Contact dipping away from body:

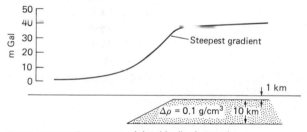

FIGURE 14-13 Gravity anomalies over a slab with dipping end.

FIGURE 14-14 Determining depth of horizontal cylinder from half-width $x_{1/2}$ on gravity profile.

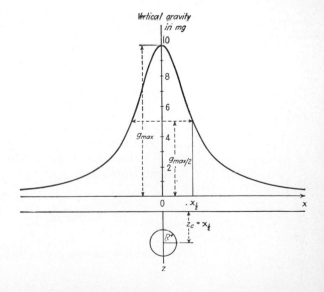

This formula was derived on page 518, where the terms in it are defined, the numerical constant being applicable when the distances involved are in thousands of feet. The gravity field g_z will have its maximum value over the axis, where $x = 0$. We shall define $x_{1/2}$ as the distance at which g_z has fallen off to half its maximum value. This distance is designated as the *half-width* of the anomaly. Taking 2 as the ratio of gravity at $x = 0$ to gravity at $x = x_{1/2}$, we can write

$$2 = 1 + \left(\frac{x_{1/2}}{z}\right)^2 \qquad (14\text{-}13)$$

whereupon

$$x_{1/2} = z \qquad (14\text{-}14)$$

The depth is equal to the half-width of the anomaly when measured along a line perpendicular to the axis. The radius of the cylinder can be determined from the maximum gravity value g_{max} and z using the formula

$$R = \sqrt{\frac{g_{max}^2 z}{12.77\rho}} \qquad (14\text{-}15)$$

It can be shown by a similar procedure that the half-width for a spherical source is

$$x_{1/2} = \frac{z}{1.305} \qquad (14\text{-}16)$$

$$z = 1.305 x_{1/2} \qquad (14\text{-}17)$$

The formula is applied in the same way as the corresponding relationship for a cylinder. It may be applicable to salt domes or knolls on the basement surface with heights and diameters that are approximately equal.

Sometimes, better estimates of the depth to a body can be made from gradient determinations than from amplitude and half-width information. This is especially true when the observed anomaly possesses gradients that are steeper than those on the anomaly over the simple geometric body being used to make the estimates. For example, in the case of a thin faulted layer, the depth to the center of the faulted slab can be estimated from the gradient of the gravity anomaly at the point where it is steepest.

The formula for the gravity of a thin faulted horizontal slab of thickness t and depth (to its center plane) z was shown on page 523 to be

$$g_z = 2\gamma\rho t \left(\frac{\pi}{2} - \tan^{-1}\frac{x}{z}\right) = 12.77\rho \left(\frac{t}{2} + \frac{t}{\pi} \tan^{-1}\frac{x}{z}\right) \qquad (14\text{-}18)$$

when all distances are in thousands of feet. The gradient is the derivative of g_z

with respect to x

$$\frac{dg_z}{dx} = 12.77\rho \, \frac{t}{\pi} \frac{1}{z} \frac{1}{1 + (x/z)^2} \tag{14-19}$$

and at $x = 0$, this becomes

$$\frac{dg_z}{dx} = \frac{12.77\rho t}{\pi z} \tag{14-20}$$

The required slope can be obtained by plotting g_z versus x on a profile perpendicular to the contours defining the linear fault trend and taking the tangent to the gravity curve at the point where the gradient is maximum.

Bowin, Scheer, and Smith[31] tabulate formulas for limiting depth estimates using amplitude and gradient information. In general, these estimates will yield depths that are as good as the assumptions that were used to derive the formulas—the quality of depth estimates can generally be much improved if the interpreter knows something about the geometry of the source body from other forms of geophysical data or from other considerations.

Forward Modeling

By far the most commonly used technique for quantitative interpretation of gravity data involves the direct calculation of the gravity effect of an assumed density distribution, and the comparison of the calculated values with those that were observed. The assumed density distribution is then modified by trial and error (usually with constraints imposed by geologic or other geophysical data) until satisfactory agreement is reached between observed and calculated values. A number of methods have been developed for the forward calculation of the gravity effect of assumed density distributions in two and three dimensions. Computer and hand-calculator programs employing certain of these methods are now widely available and make the calculation of forward models quick and easy.

Two-Dimensional Models   When it is reasonable to represent geological structure with a set of two-dimensional bodies (i.e., bodies that are much longer than they are wide), the method of Talwani et al.[32] provides an efficient means of calculation. In this method, the subsurface geology is described by a set of uniform density, n-sided polygons which represent the cross-sectional shapes of the two-dimensional structure.

An example of two-dimensional models along a profile across the Saline Range, California,[33] is shown in Fig. 14-15. Negative gravity anomalies of the adjacent Eureka Valley and the Saline Valley are connected by this negative gravity anomaly centered at the Saline Range. The Saline Range is a Pliocene basalt volcanic field, rising more than 1 km above the neighboring valleys. The volcanics in the Range have measured densities with a mean value of 2.66 g/cm^3

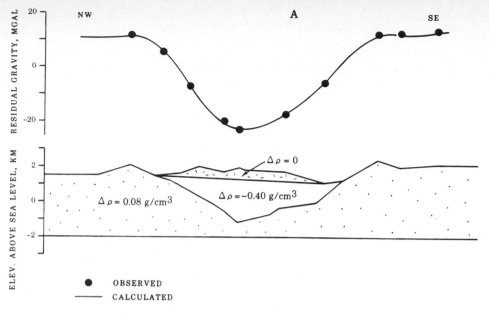

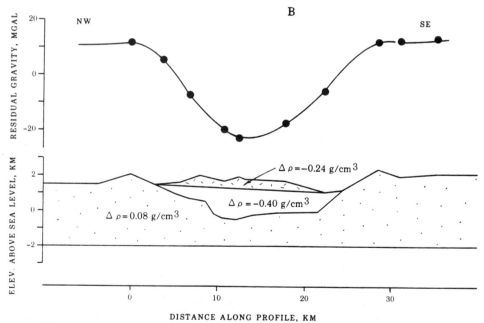

FIGURE 14-15 Observed gravity profile, exhibiting the pronounced gravity minimum centered over the Saline Range, California, and the density models used to calculate the hypothetical gravity responses shown by the straight lines. The sources are assumed to extend to large distances in directions perpendicular to profile. Note that for the two different models (the depths of the sediment-filled basin under the Range are different), the calculated gravity responses are just about equal. (*a*) Density of Saline Range is 2.67 g/cm³, the same density used for the Bouguer reduction and the terrain correction. (*b*) Density of the Saline Range is 2.43 g/cm³, which is a density decrease of 0.24 g/cm³ from the 2.67 g/cm³ used for the Bouguer reduction and the terrain correction. (*From Blakely and McKee.*[33])

and a median value of 2.68 g/cm³. Here the gravity modeling was used to demonstrate that low-density volcanic rocks cannot account for all of the observed gravity low and also to estimate the shape and thickness of the sedimentary deposits under the Range.

In many cases, the geologic bodies to be represented are only a few times longer than they are wide or thick and the assumption of two-dimensionality is not strictly valid. To handle these cases, Cady[34] modified the Talwani method by incorporating "end" corrections so that the gravity effect of bodies of finite strike length can be better approximated by calculation. The models thus produced are referred to as two-and-one-half-dimensional.

The speed and flexibility of computer programs that calculate the gravity effect of two- and two-and-one-half-dimensional polygons permit the construction of models of almost unlimited complexity.[35] Care must be taken, however, not to create models that are too complicated. While it may be tempting to add many vertices to each body until each observation point is matched exactly by the calculated curve, rarely does the accuracy of the gravity data, the validity of the two- or two-and-one-half-dimensional assumption, or the availability of good geologic constraints warrant such complexity. It is usually possible to fit observed gravity data "perfectly" with many very different models in the absence of additional constraints. Without additional information to constrain the geometry of the source bodies, it would usually be difficult to justify models using more than two or three bodies with perhaps two dozen vertices in all. Figure 14-16 shows a more complicated model by Zucca et al.[36] across Northern California that employed the results of a densely recorded seismic refraction survey. In the model the density interfaces were constrained by the seismic refraction depths at which velocities changed, and the densities were initially calculated from seismic velocities.

Often in the construction of a two-dimensional model, not enough attention is paid to achieving a satisfactory fit to observed steep gradients in the gravity field. Such gradients frequently provide powerful constraints to the depths of source bodies, and as much care should be exercised in matching the steeper gradients as is expended in fitting the amplitudes and general shapes of the anomalies, provided, of course, that the observed steepness of the gradient can be believed on the basis of the quality of the data set.

A computer program for the construction and calculation of two-and-one-half-dimensional models can be used to interpret profiles over models of a three-dimensional nature. Through the use of finite-length bodies offset from the profile and the option of placing the profile at an arbitrary angle to the bodies, almost any simple three-dimensional situation can be simulated. This can be quite useful, inasmuch as two- and two-and-one-half-dimensional programs are presently much simpler to operate and allow far more interactive flexibility for adding and altering bodies than do most three-dimensional forward modeling programs.

Three-Dimensional Models Interpretational situations arise where the geologic bodies of interest are nearly equidimensional and cannot be represented adequately by two- or two-and-one-half-dimensional polygons, yet are too

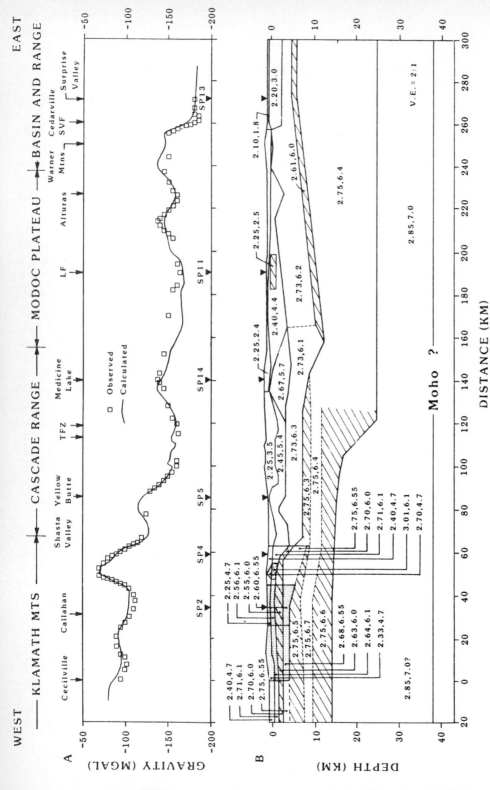

FIGURE 14-16 East-west gravity profile across northern California from the Klamath Mountains to the Basin and Range. The first number is density in g/cm³, the second is seismic velocities in km/s. Areas where density had to be changed significantly from initial values determined from velocity-density relation to match the observed gravity are indicated by shading. Densities are reduced in these areas by 0.07 g/cm³ (light shading), 0.15 g/cm³ (moderate shading), and 0.30 g/cm³ (heavy shading). Dashed lines separate layers with velocity differences, but no density differences. *(From Zucca and others.)*[36]

complex to be reasonably approximated by simple bodies such as spheres or vertical cylinders. In these cases a fully three-dimensional representation is required, and various methods have been developed for the rapid calculation of gravity effects from three-dimensional density distributions.

If a three-dimensional body is represented by contours of depth to its bounding surface, a technique developed by Talwani and Ewing[37] can be used to determine the field at any point on the surface. The contours can be looked upon as representing the edges of thin laminae bounded by horizontal planes above and below having elevations that correspond to the levels of the contours. A typical lamina is illustrated in Fig. 14-17. The outline is taken as that of the contour line defining its base.

The computation of the gravity effect is facilitated by a theorem of Green for transforming a surface integral over the top of a lamina into a line integral around the contour that bounds it.

Numerical computation of the line integral is simplified for purposes of computer programming if the contour generating the lamina is represented by a polygon instead of a curved loop. A sampling of points along the contour, expressed in terms of their *xy* coordinates, provides inputs for the corners of each polygon. The computer carries out the integration for each lamina and adds the gravity contributions for the laminae corresponding to each contour so as to yield the total effect from the buried body at any specified point on the surface.

Plouff[38] describes a method for calculating the gravity effect of a model composed of vertical right polygonal prisms of arbitrary shape and height. By superposing many such prisms, three-dimensional bodies of considerable com-

FIGURE 14-17   Principle of Talwani and Ewing method of determining gravity at *P* from a three-dimensional body of irregular shape that can be represented as a series of horizontal laminae bounded by contour lines on map. Computer carries out integration of elements of height *dz* as shown. Curved surface of lamina is approximated as polygon *ABCDEFGHI*. (*Talwani and Ewing* [37])

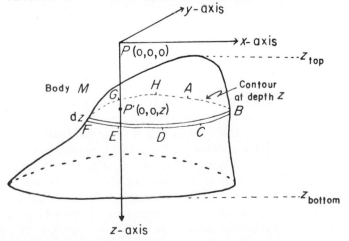

plexity can be represented. The usefulness of most three-dimensional techniques usually is limited by the practical difficulties involved in initially setting up and subsequently in changing the model. Chuchel[39] has prepared a program for the interactive creation and editing of polygon models on a color terminal using cursors driven by a mouse to define and move corners. This approach helps reduce much of the labor in constructing and altering three-dimensional models, but much work remains to be done along these lines.

As with all other methods of indirect interpretation, it is possible by use of three-dimensional modeling programs to modify the presumed shape or position of the subsurface source to improve the fit to the observed gravity on the surface. Even if a perfect fit were obtained, however, it would not be at all certain that the form hypothesized for the source is correct without other evidence.

Forward Models Using the Fourier Approach Under certain circumstances, it is possible to employ Fourier-transform techniques to calculate gravity anomalies due to hypothetical density distributions. Parker[40] described such an algorithm which can handle laterally varying density distributions. In particular, the density distribution can be bounded on the top with a topographic surface and on the bottom by a second undulating surface. The gravitational effects of the undulating boundaries are accounted for by summation of a convergent series; each element of the series is the Fourier transform of the density distribution multiplied by a power of the topographic surfaces. Because of the speed of fast Fourier-transform algorithms, these calculations are often more efficient for large or complex geometries than the forward algorithms discussed earlier.

Inverse Modeling

The preceding discussions have considered the calculation of anomalies due to hypothetical sources with known characteristics. Iterating upon this forward calculation process, the interpreter can modify the shape or density distribution of the sources until the calculated anomaly closely approximates the observed anomaly and all other available constraints are reasonably satisfied. It is also possible in favorable circumstances (and usually provided that certain assumptions hold) to infer directly and automatically from the observed gravity data certain information about the source. This direct inversion of data to yield parameters describing the source is known as solving the *inverse* problem. At first glance it may seem that the ambiguity inherent in gravity interpretations would preclude the existence of inverse methods that would yield realistic or even repeatable solutions. If any single gravity anomaly can be caused by an infinite number of different density distributions, how can we expect an inverse method to produce meaningful results? The answer lies in the fact that any successful inverse method places a sufficient number of constraints on the solution in addition to those posed by the gravity data themselves—that the number of possible answers is severely restricted. The constraints commonly occur as model assumptions: e.g., the body has a constant density, the top surface of the body corresponds to the land surface, the densities must increase with depth. Only by the application of such constraints can the inverse problem be made tractable.

Inverse methods have been applied to gravity data in a variety of ways by Pedersen,[41] Al-Chalabi,[42] Tanner,[43] Goodacre,[44] Oldenburg,[45] Bhattacharyya and Leu,[46] and Parker[47] to name a few. It is well beyond the scope of this text to describe these techniques in detail. Instead a few classic examples will be sketched and the interested reader is referred to bibliographies for further information.

One of the simplest inverse techniques makes use of the property that when the density ρ of a body is multiplied by a constant c, the gravity anomaly due to that body at each external point is also increased by the same factor c if the shape of the body is held fixed. Such a multiplicative relationship is termed *linear*, and the existence of linear relationships between variables usually leads to a relatively straightforward mathematical solution. Suppose that we divide a region beneath our gravity survey into individual compartments or bodies as in Fig. 14-18. Using the forward modeling techniques described in the previous section, we can compute the gravity anomaly B_{ij} at each observation point l that would be caused by each individual compartment j, assuming it has a density of 1 g/cm³. The total gravity anomaly g_i at each observation point i then can be expressed as the sum of the individual compartment anomalies, each multiplied by the appropriate density ρ_j:

$$g_i = \sum_{j=1}^{m} \rho_j B_{ij} \qquad i = 1, 2, \ldots, n \qquad (14\text{-}21)$$

FIGURE 14-18 The geometry used to derive Eq. (14-21). At the ith observation point, B_{ij} is the vertical component of the force of gravity caused by material of density $\rho = 1.0$ g/cm³ in compartment j of the body.

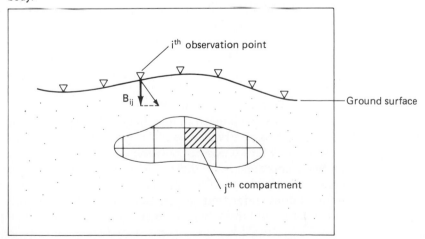

Because the gravity g_i has been measured at a number of locations, there will be as many equations as there are observations. Since the g_i are known from measurements and the B_{ij} are known from calculation, the densities ρ_j of each compartment can, in theory, be determined by standard methods for solving systems of linear equations. If, for example, $n > m$, then the system of equations (14-21) represents more equations than unknowns, and ρ_j can be solved by standard least-squares techniques. This method has had its greatest popularity with magnetic data.[48–50]

The procedure seems deceptively simple in principle, but should be used with caution if realistic results are to be obtained. Choices such as the locations, sizes, and number of compartments can be critical to the stability of the solution. If the size of the cell in Eq. (14-21) is too small compared with the separation of the gravity measurements or the distance between the observation points and the body, the calculated values of density will oscillate from cell to cell in an unrealistic manner, even though the agreement between calculated and observed gravity may be very close. Attempting to get more than the data allow, a topic related to "resolution," was discussed effectively in a series of papers by Bott and Hutton,[51] Van den Akker et al.,[52] and Emilia and Bodvarsson.[53]

Using a somewhat different approach, Bott[54] made an early attempt to solve the inverse problem automatically for single profiles of gravity data over sedimentary basins (Fig. 14-19). The thickness of the sedimentary basin beneath each point of the profile was estimated by assuming that the anomaly at that point is caused by a single infinite horizontal slab of density contrast equal to the contrast between the sedimentary basin and underlying basement rocks. Thicknesses thus estimated at each point of the profile provide a starting model. The residual between the anomaly calculated from this model and the observed anomaly is used in a subsequent adjustment of thicknesses. The procedure is continued until the residuals fall below an acceptable level.

This general procedure of iterative depth adjustment was extended to gridded data and three-dimensional sources by Cordell and Henderson.[55] The causative body in their method was assumed to be composed of a set of vertical-sided rectangular prisms with fixed density. Then, for example, by fixing the top of all the prisms, the vertical extent of each is adjusted iteratively until the discrepancy between calculated and observed anomalies is reduced satisfactorily.

Corbato[56] proposed an inverse method in which the cross-sectional shape of a dense body is changed automatically during successive iterations until the calculated and observed anomalies agree within certain tolerances. He gives an example in which a body of polygonal cross section is used as a starting model and the coordinates of the vertices that define this polygon are iteratively changed to better the fit. Although this method will work well in some situations, it does suffer from certain drawbacks. For one, different starting models can lead to different final models. Also the method can become computa-

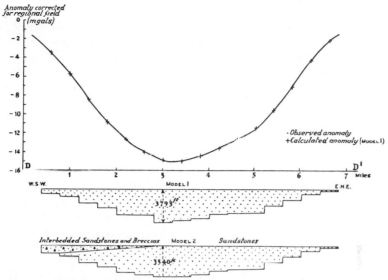

FIGURE 14-19 The interpretation of the gravity profile across the Dumfries New Red Sandstone basin. Model 1 has been calculated for an assumed uniform density contrast of 0.4 g/cm³ and the calculated anomalies are shown as crosses on the profile.

Model 2 takes into account certain denser breccias which are assumed to be distributed as shown and to have a density of 0.2 g/cm³ lower than the Silurian rocks. The residuals are negligible apart from one value of 0.3 mGal where convergence is poor. (*From Bott.*[54])

tionally unstable in the sense that very large changes in the positions of some vertices may result in small to negligible changes in the calculated anomaly.

The shape of the causative mass can also be estimated by an extension of the first inverse method described in this section. Last and Kubik,[57] for example, compartmentalize the subsurface region of interest by dividing its volume into a relatively large number of rectangular cells. They achieve stability by adding a special constraint. They constrain the density distribution to be one that minimizes the volume of the body and hence gives the most *compact* solution. The distribution of density thus determined yields a shape for the causative mass, which should approximate the true shape of the body at least insofar as nature is consistent with the assumed compactness constraint.

In general, inverse methods have found somewhat limited use in the everyday gravity interpretation process. However, given the great interest in such methods and the existence of large gravity data bases in need of more automatic interpretational aids, the field will continue to advance and will undoubtedly produce procedures having great practical applicability, at least as first-pass analysis tools. Such methods will make the interpreter's job easier, but they will not in the near future replace the human interpreter nor the forward calculation procedures that are in such widespread use today.

REFERENCES

1 Center for Potential Fields Studies: "Reduction, Analysis, and Interpretation of Gravity and Magnetic Survey Data—a Bibliography," Colorado School of Mines, Golden, Colo., 1984, 71 pp.
2 Zwart, W. J. (ed.): Cumulative Index of Geophysics: 1936–1982, *Geophysics*, vol. 51 *sup*, 636 pp., 1986.
3 Paterson, N. R., and C. V. Reeves: Applications of Gravity and Magnetic Surveys: The State of the Art in 1985, *Geophysics*, vol. 50, pp. 2558–2594, 1985.
4 National Technical Information Service, Springfield, Va. 22161. (202) 377-2000.
5 Bracewell, Ron: "The Fourier Transform and its Applications," McGraw-Hill, New York, 1965, 381 pp.
6 Singleton, R. C.: An Algorithm for Computing the Mixed Radix Fast Fourier Transform, *IEEE Trans. Audio Electroacoust.*, vol. AU-17, pp. 93–103, 1969.
7 Cordell, Lindrith, and V. J. S. Grauch: Reconciliation of the Discrete and Integral Fourier Transforms, *Geophysics*, vol. 47, pp. 237–243, 1982.
8 Kane, M. F., and R. H. Godson: Features of a Pair of Long-Wavelength (>250 km) and Short-Wavelength (<250 km) Bouguer Gravity Maps of the United States, pp. 46–61, in W. J. Hinze (ed.), "The Utility of Regional Gravity and Magnetic Anomaly Maps," Society of Exploration Geophysicists, Tulsa, Okla., 1985.
9 Ulrych, T. J.: Effect of Wavelength Filtering on the Shape of the Residual Anomaly, *Geophysics*, vol. 33, pp. 1015–1018, 1968.
10 Syberg, F. J. R.: A Fourier Method for the Regional-Residual Problem of Potential Fields, *Geophys. Prospect.*, vol. 20, pp. 47–75, 1972.
11 Grant, F. S., and G. S. West: "Interpretation Theory in Applied Geophysics," McGraw-Hill, New York, 1965, pp. 282–287.
12 Elkins, T. A.: The Second Derivative Method of Gravity Interpretation, *Geophysics*, vol. 16, pp. 29–50, 1951.
13 Gunn, P. J.: Linear Transformations of Gravity and Magnetic Fields, *Geophys. Prospect.*, vol. 23, pp. 300–312, 1975.
14 Jachens, R. C., R. W. Simpson, R. J. Blakely, and R. W. Saltus: Isostatic Residual Gravity Anomaly Map of the United States (exclusive of Alaska and Hawaii), *National Oceanic and Atmospheric Admin., Geophysical Data Center, Boulder, Colo.*, scale 1:2,500,000, 1985.
15 Simpson, R. W., R. C. Jachens, R. J. Blakely, and R. W. Saltus: Isostatic Residual Gravity, Topographic, and First-Vertical-Derivative Gravity Maps of the Conterminous United States, *U.S. Geological Survey Geophys. Inv. Map GP-975*, scale 1:7,500,000, 1986.
16 Cordell, L. E., and V. J. S. Grauch: Mapping Basement Magnetization Zones from Aeromagnetic Data in the San Juan Basin, New Mexico, pp. 181–197, in W. J. Hinze (ed.), "The Utility of Regional Gravity and Magnetic Anomaly Maps," Society of Exploration Geophysicists, Tulsa, Okla., 1985.
17 Blakely, R. J., and R. W. Simpson: Approximating Edges of Source Bodies from Magnetic or Gravity Anomalies, *Geophysics*, vol. 51, pp. 1494–1498, 1986.
18 Guinness, E. A., R. E. Arvidson, J. W. Strebeck, K. J. Schulz, G. F. Davies, and C. E. Leff: Identification of a Precambrian Rift through Missouri by Digital Image Processing of Geophysical and Geological Data, *J. Geophys. Res.*, vol. 87, pp. 8529–8545, 1982.
19 Hinze, W. J. (ed.): "The Utility of Regional Gravity and Magnetic Anomaly Maps," Society of Exploration Geophysicists, Tulsa, Okla., 1985, 454 pp.

20 Nettleton, L. L.: Regionals, Residuals, and Structures, *Geophysics*, vol. 19, pp. 1–22, 1954.

21 Agocs, W.B.: Least Squares Residual Anomaly Determination. *Geophysics*, vol. 16, pp. 686–696, 1951.

22 Coons, R. L., G. P. Woollard, and Garland Hershey: Structural Significance and Analysis of Mid-Continent Gravity High, *Bull. Am. Assoc. Petrol. Geol.*, vol. 51, pp. 2381–2399, 1967.

23 Grant, F. S.: Review of Data Processing and Interpretation Methods in Gravity and Magnetics, 1964–71, *Geophysics*, vol. 37, pp. 647–661, 1972.

24 Hildenbrand, T. G., R. W. Simpson, R. H. Godson, and M. F. Kane: Digital Colored Residual and Regional Bouguer Gravity Maps of the Conterminous United States with Cut-Off Wavelengths of 250 km and 1000 km, *U.S. Geological Survey Geophys. Inv. Map GP-953-A*, scale 1:7,500,000, 1982.

25 Johnson, G. R., and G. R. Olhoeft: Density of rocks and minerals, pp. 1–38, in R. S. Carmichael (ed.), "Handbook of Physical Properties of Rocks," vol. 3, CRC Press, Boca Raton, Fla., 1984.

26 Hedberg, H. D.: Gravitational Compaction of Clays and Shales, *Am. J. Sci.*, vol. 31, pp. 241–287, 1936.

27 Nettleton, L. L.: Fluid Mechanics of Salt Domes, *Bull. Am. Assoc. Petrol. Geol.*, vol. 18, pp. 1175–1204, 1934.

28 Skeels, D. C.: Ambiguity in Gravity Interpretation, *Geophysics*, vol. 12, pp. 43–56, 1947.

29 Barton, Donald C.: Case Histories and Quantitative Calculations in Gravimetric Prospecting, *Trans. Am. Inst. Min. Met. Eng.*, *Geophysics*, vol. 164, pp. 17–65, 1945.

30 Nettleton, L. L.: Recent Experimental and Geophysical Evidence of Mechanics of Salt-Dome Formation, *Bull. Am. Assoc. Petrol. Geol.*, vol. 27, pp. 51–63, 1943.

31 Bowin, Carl, Edward Scheer, and Woollcott Smith: Depth Estimates from Ratios of Gravity, Geoid, and Gravity Gradient Anomalies, *Geophysics*, vol. 51, pp. 123–136, 1986.

32 Talwani, M., J. L. Worzel, and M. Landisman: Rapid Gravity Computations for Two-Dimensional Bodies with Application to the Mendocino Submarine Fracture Zone, *J. Geophys. Res.*, vol. 64, pp. 49–59, 1959.

33 Blakely, R. J., and E. H. McKee: Subsurface Structural Features of the Saline Range and Adjacent Regions of Eastern California as Interpreted from Isostatic Residual Gravity Anomalies, *Geology*, vol. 13, pp. 781–785, 1985.

34 Cady, J. W.: Calculation of Gravity and Magnetic Anomalies of Finite-Length Right Polygonal Prisms, *Geophysics*, vol. 45, pp. 1507–1512, 1980.

35 Saltus, R. W., and R. J. Blakely: Hypermag—An Interactive, Two-Dimensional Gravity and Magnetic Modeling Program, *U.S. Geological Survey Open-File Report* 83-241, 1983.

36 Zucca, J. J., G. S. Fuis, Bernd Milkereit, W. D. Mooney, and R. D. Catchings: Crustal Structure of Northern California, *J. Geophys. Res.*, vol. 91, pp. 7359–7382, 1986.

37 Talwani, Manik, and Maurice Ewing: Rapid Computation of Gravitational Attraction of Three-Dimensional Bodies of Arbitrary Shape, *Geophysics*, vol. 25, pp. 203–225, 1960.

38 Plouff, Donald: Gravity and Magnetic Fields of Polygonal Prisms and Application to Magnetic Terrain Corrections, *Geophysics*, vol. 41, pp. 727–741, 1976.

39 Chuchel, B. A.: POLYGON—An Interactive Program for Constructing and Editing the Geometries of Polygons Using a Color Graphics Terminal, U.S. Geological Survey Open-File Report, 85-233-A, 38 pp., 1985.

40 Parker, R. L.: The Rapid Calculation of Potential Anomalies, *Geophys. J. Roy. Astronom. Soc.*, vol. 31, pp. 447–455, 1972.

41 Pedersen, L. B.: Interpretation of Potential Field Data—A Generalized Inverse Approach, *Geophys. Prospect.*, vol. 25, pp. 199–230, 1977.

42 Al-Chalabi, M.: Interpretation of Gravity Anomalies by Non-linear Optimisation, *Geophys. Prospect.*, vol. 20, pp. 1–16, 1972.

43 Tanner, J. G.: An Automated Method of Gravity Interpretation, *Geophysics*, vol. 13, pp. 339–347, 1967.

44 Goodacre, A. K.: Estimation of the Minimum Density Contrast of a Homogeneous Body as an Aid to the Interpretation of Gravity Anomalies, *Geophys. Prospect.*, vol. 28, pp. 408–414, 1980.

45 Oldenburg, D. W.: The Inversion and Interpretation of Gravity Anomalies, *Geophysics*, vol. 39, pp. 526–536, 1974.

46 Bhattacharyya, B. K., and L. K. Leu: Spectral Analysis of Gravity and Magnetic Anomalies due to Two-Dimensional Structures, *Geophysics*, vol. 40, pp. 993–1013, 1975.

47 Parker, R. L: The Theory of Ideal Bodies for Gravity Interpretation, *Geophys. J.*, vol. 42, pp. 315–334, 1975.

48 Bott, M. H. P.: Solution of the Linear Inverse Problem in Magnetic Interpretation with Application to Oceanic Magnetic Anomalies, *Geophys. J.*, vol. 13, p. 313, 1967.

49 Emilia, D. A., and G. Bodvarsson: Numerical Methods in the Direct Interpretation of Marine Magnetic Anomalies, *Earth Planet. Sci. Lett.*, vol. 7, pp. 194–200, 1969.

50 Bott, M. H. P., and M. A. Hutton: A Matrix Method for Interpreting Oceanic Magnetic Anomalies, *Geophys. J.*, vol. 20, p. 149, 1970.

51 Bott, M. H. P., and M. A. Hutton: Limitations on the Resolution Possible in the Direct Interpretation of Marine Magnetic Anomalies, *Earth Planet. Sci. Lett.*, vol. 8, pp. 317–319, 1970.

52 Van den Akker, F. B., C. G. A. Harrison, and J. D. Mudie: Even More on the Direct Interpretation of Magnetic Anomalies, *Earth Planet. Sci. Lett.*, vol. 9, p. 405, 1970.

53 Emilia, D. A., and G. Bodvarsson: More on the Direct Interpretation of Magnetic Anomalies, *Earth Planet. Sci. Lett.*, vol. 8, pp. 320–321, 1970.

54 Bott, M. H. P.: The Use of Rapid Digital Computing Methods for Direct Gravity Interpretation of Sedimentary Basins, *Geophys. J.*, vol. 3, pp. 63–67, 1960.

55 Cordell, L., and R. G. Henderson: Iterative Three-Dimensional Solution of Gravity Anomaly Data Using a Digital Computer, *Geophysics*, vol. 33, pp. 596–601, 1968.

56 Corbato, C. E.: A Least-Squares Procedure for Gravity Interpretation, *Geophysics*, vol. 30, pp. 228–233, 1965.

57 Last, B. J., and K. Kubik: Compact Gravity Inversion, *Geophysics*, vol. 48, pp. 713–721, 1983.

15

MAGNETIC PROSPECTING: FUNDAMENTAL PRINCIPLES AND INSTRUMENTS

Magnetic prospecting, the oldest method of geophysical exploration, is used to explore for oil, minerals, and even archaeological artifacts. In prospecting for oil, it gives information from which one can determine the depth to basement rocks and thus locate and define the extent of sedimentary basins. Such information is of particular value in previously unexplored areas such as continental shelves newly opened for prospecting. It is sometimes employed, although not always successfully, to map topographic features on the basement surface that might influence the structure of overlying sediments. Another application is the delineation of intrasedimentary magnetic sources, such as shallow volcanics or intrusives that disrupt the normal sedimentary sequence. Sedimentary rocks exert such a small magnetic effect compared with igneous rocks that most variations in magnetic intensity measurable at the surface result from topographic or lithologic changes associated with the basement or from igneous intrusives. Recent developments in instrumentation have, however, made possible the definition of small, high-frequency magnetic responses that may be related to very small changes in the magnetic character of the near-surface sedimentary rocks. "Very minor variations in magnetite concentration, causing anomalies as low as 0.1 nT (0.1 gamma), are now being correlated with diagenetic processes directly related to hydrocarbon accumulations." [Paterson and Reeves[1] (p. 2567)].

In mining exploration, the magnetometer is most often used to prospect for magnetic minerals directly, but it is also effective in the search for useful minerals that are not magnetic themselves but are associated with other minerals having magnetic effects detectable at the surface. Paterson and Reeves[1] have listed the following as some further important applications for mineral/

groundwater-oriented magnetic surveys. Large-scale aeromagnetic surveys have been conducted to locate faulting, shearing, and fracturing. Such zones can serve as potential hosts for a variety of minerals, and indirectly guide exploration for the epigenetic, stress-related mineralization in the surrounding rocks. Groundwater exploitation efforts are made more successful through the knowledge of fracture systems in crystalline rocks and bedrock aquifers under alluvial cover. Paleosurfaces and unconformities can be mapped as an aid to exploration for detrital minerals and/or unconformity-related uranium.

Until the middle 1940s all magnetic exploration was carried out on the ground by use of field methods similar to those in gravity surveys. Today, virtually all magnetic prospecting for oil is done from the air or from ships, as are most reconnaissance surveys for minerals. The speed, economy, and convenience of airborne and, to a lesser extent, marine techniques are responsible for this trend. In terms of line-kilometers surveyed annually, and in total line-kilometers, the magnetic method is by far the most widely used geophysical survey method (Paterson and Reeves[1]).

The magnetic method of prospecting has a great deal in common with the gravitational method. Both make use of potential fields. Both seek anomalies caused by changes in physical properties of subsurface rocks. Both gravity and magnetics have similar applications in oil exploration. While they are extensively used as reconnaissance tools, there has been an increasing recognition of their value for evaluating prospective areas by virtue of the unique information they provide. Seismic data make it possible to map an area structurally and, within certain limits, to determine seismic velocities. Gravity data make it possible to assign densities and magnetic data, magnetic susceptibilities or remanences to seismically defined features. The lithologic identifications that can be made by combining these different data have great value in evaluating possibilities for hydrocarbons over a prospective feature. Practically all marine magnetic surveys for hydrocarbon exploration are carried out in conjunction with seismic surveying.

Gravity and magnetics employ fundamentally similar interpretation techniques. The magnetic method, for a number of reasons, is more complicated both in principle and in practice. The intensity of magnetization, the characteristic of a rock that determines its magnetic effects, has both magnitude and direction and depends on the rock's susceptibility and permanent magnetization. The corresponding characteristic governing its gravitational pull, the mass, has magnitude only and depends on density. Magnetic force involves both attraction and repulsion, while all gravitational force is attractive. Also, magnetic effects from rocks may be greatly influenced by small traces of certain minerals, while gravitational effects originate mainly from the primary constituents of the rocks.

In magnetic surveys, the anomalies recorded in the field data are interpreted in terms of variations in magnetic susceptibility and/or remanent magnetism, the physical rock properties affecting the measurements. Both of these rock properties can exist only at temperatures cooler than the Curie point, which limits the sources of magnetic anomalies to a maximum depth of 30 to 40 km. In practice, however, the properties and concentrations of magnetite, a single accessory mineral, dominate almost all the magnetic properties of a bulk rock composition. Therefore, care and caution are exercised in relating the results of a magnetic survey to either surface or subsurface geology.

15-1 BASIC CONCEPTS AND DEFINITIONS

Understanding the magnetic effects associated with earth materials requires a knowledge of the basic principles of magnetism. In this section we shall review the elementary physical concepts that are fundamental to magnetic prospecting.

Magnetic Poles If one sprinkles iron filings at random on a sheet of paper which rests on a simple bar magnet, they will tend to line up as shown in Fig. 15-1. The lines along which the filings orient themselves are called *lines of force*. Each of these follows a curved path from a point near one end of the magnet designated as a *pole* to a corresponding pole near the other end. The filings have this orientation because each of them is itself a small magnet with an alignment determined by the force field coming from the bar magnet. The latter, if properly balanced, can be oriented by the magnetic lines of force of the earth, which itself acts as a great magnet. Thus if a simple magnet is pivoted at its center so that it can rotate freely in all directions, it will assume a direction governed by that of the magnetic force associated with the earth. One end will always point in the general direction of the North Pole. Near this end one will find the north-seeking, or positive, pole of the magnet. Near the other end is the south-seeking, or negative, pole.

Poles always exist in pairs, but in a very long magnet the lines of force around the positive pole will not be perceptibly affected by the presence of the negative one, and each can be considered to be isolated.

Magnetic Force If two poles of strength P_0 and P, respectively, are separated by a distance r, the force F between them will be

$$F = \frac{1}{\mu} \frac{P_0 P}{r^2} \tag{15-1}$$

FIGURE 15-1 Lines of force around bar magnet; *A* and *B* are poles.

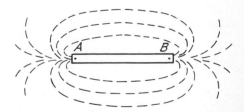

The constant μ, known as the *permeability*, depends upon the magnetic properties of the medium in which the poles are situated. The units of pole strength are determined by the specification that F is 1 dyne when two unit poles 1 cm apart are situated in a nonmagnetic medium such as air or vacuum (for which $\mu = 1$). Note the similarity between Eqs. (15-1) and (12-1), the latter expressing the gravitational attraction between two particles. If the poles are of like type, the force is repulsive; if they are unlike, it is attractive.

Magnetic Field The *magnetic field strength* at a point is defined as the force per unit of pole strength which would be exerted upon a small pole of strength P_0 if placed at that point. Thus, the field strength H due to a pole of strength P a distance r away is

$$ H = \frac{F}{P_0} = \frac{P}{\mu r^2} \tag{15-2} $$

The magnetic field strength is often expressed in terms of the density of the lines of force or flux representing the field. The unit of H is then expressed as one line of force per square centimeter. It may also be designated in the cgs system as one dyne per unit pole or as one oersted. In SI, the unit of flux density is the tesla, which is 10^4 Oe.

Magnetic Moment Since isolated poles have never been found, actual magnets are generally considered to be magnetic dipoles. A dipole consists of two poles of equal strength P and of opposite sign separated by a short distance L. We define the product PL of the pole strength by the separation as M, the magnetic moment of the dipole. The direction of the moment is along the line between the poles and by convention is toward the north-seeking pole.

Intensity of Magnetization (or Polarization) Any magnetic material placed in an external field will have magnetic poles induced upon its surface (Fig. 15-2). In the moderately magnetic materials and weak fields we are generally concerned with in geophysical work, this induced magnetization, sometimes called polarization, is in the direction of the applied field, and its strength is proportional to the strength of that field. The intensity of magnetization I may

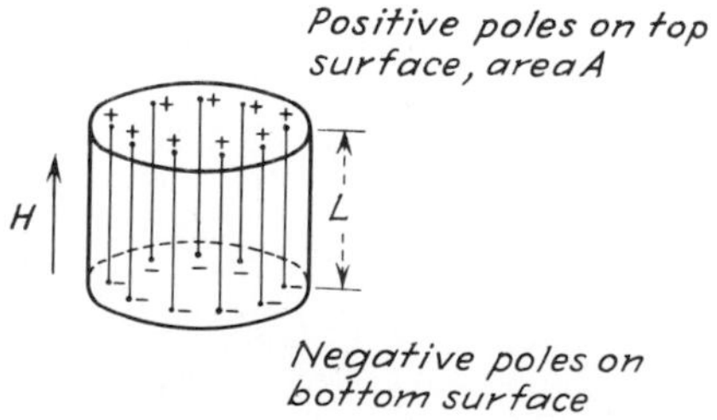

FIGURE 15-2 Polarization induced in cylindrical pillbox by field perpendicular to ends. Lines of length L represent separation of poles and are used in calculating effective magnetic moments for uniform field and homogeneous material within box.

Positive poles on top surface, area A

Negative poles on bottom surface

be considered to be the induced pole strength per unit area along a surface normal to the inducing field. It is also equivalent to the magnetic moment per unit volume. This type of magnetization may be looked upon as a lining up of elementary magnets or dipoles, which originally had random orientation, in the direction of the field. It is assumed that the number of magnets thus aligned depends on the strength of the magnetizing field.

Susceptibility   In the case of a homogeneous external field H which makes an angle θ with the normal to the surface of a material capable of being magnetized the induced pole strength per unit area is

$$I = kH \cos \theta \tag{15-3}$$

or for a field normal to the surface,

$$I = kH$$

where k, the proportionality constant, is called the *susceptibility*. For a vacuum, k is zero. *Ferromagnetic* materials have positive and relatively large susceptibilities. The interaction of the atoms and the coupling of the atomic magnetic moments result in the collective behavior of groups of atoms, termed *domains*. The domains orient in parallel configuration, with their long dimension in the direction of the external field, giving rise to the large susceptibility. Nearly all of the studies of rock magnetism are concerned with the effects of the ferromagnetic minerals. With a rise in the temperature to the Curie point, the atoms decouple, and the material behaves paramagnetically. *Paramagnetic* materials are weakly magnetic, characterized by small positive susceptibilities. The bulk of most rocks, for example, the common silicate minerals, are paramagnetic or diamagnetic, i.e., relatively magnetically inert. *Diamagnetic* substances are weakly magnetic, with negative susceptibilities; examples of such are rock salt and anhydrite. Salt domes can give rise to diamagnetic anomalies. Grains of paramagnetic and diamagnetic materials tend to line up with their long dimensions across the external field. Paramagnetic and diamagnetic effects can only be observed in the presence of an external field.

Magnetic Induction   The magnetic poles induced in a material by an external field H will produce a field of their own, H', which is related to the intensity of magnetization I by the formula

$$H' = 4\pi I \tag{15-4}$$

The total magnetic flux inside the material, as measured in a narrow cavity having an axis perpendicular to the field, is called the *magnetic induction B*. This is the sum of the external and the internal fields and is proportional to the external field strength in moderately magnetic materials, as shown by the relation

$$B = H + H' = H + 4\pi I = H + 4\pi kH$$
$$= (1 + 4\pi k)H = \mu H \tag{15-5}$$

Permeability   The proportionality constant $1 + 4\pi k$ is equivalent to the permeability μ introduced in Eq. (15-1). Equation (15-5) can thus be written

$$\mu = \frac{B}{H} = 1 + 4\pi k \tag{15-6}$$

The permeability is a measure of the modification by induction of the force of attraction or repulsion between two magnetic poles. Its magnitude depends on the magnetic properties of the medium in which the poles are immersed.

Remanent Magnetism   The direct proportionality between B and H indicated by Eq. (15-5) is at best an approximation, and it breaks down entirely in highly magnetic materials. The behavior of a ferromagnetic substance undergoing cyclic magnetization and demagnetization is illustrated in Fig. 15-3. An unmagnetized sample of magnetic material is placed between the poles of an electromagnet; it produces an external field H that can be controlled by increasing, decreasing, or reversing the current. Magnetization is begun by introducing a current in the coils of the magnet that will increase H from zero (step 1). The induction, which is measured by a ballistic galvanometer connected to a coil wound around the specimen, increases more or less linearly, following the relation $B = \mu H$, until the sample is magnetized to saturation, at which point the curve approaches a horizontal line. The external field is then brought back to zero (step 2), but B does not return to zero; instead it retains the value R, which we call the *remanent magnetization*. If the current and hence H are now reversed (step 3), B will decrease until it is also reversed, eventually approaching saturation in the negative direction. A decrease in the

FIGURE 15-3   Hysteresis loop for ferromagnetic material. R and R' are residual inductions.

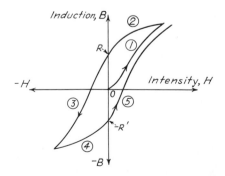

reversing field to zero (step 4) will bring B to $-R'$, while the application of a positive magnetizing field at this stage (step 5) will reverse the direction of B again and result in a second phase of positive saturation. This entire pattern of magnetization is called a *hysteresis loop*. The curve shows how a body with magnetic susceptibility can remain magnetized after the disappearance of the original magnetizing force.

Magnetization of Rocks   Magnetic rocks have almost always acquired their polarization from the earth's field, the exceptions being the rare cases where the magnetization has resulted from lightning. Often the polarization is of the induced type, and its magnitude and direction are determined entirely by the magnitude and direction of the earth's field as it is today. When the earth's field changes, this kind of magnetization changes accordingly. Other magnetic rocks display a remanent magnetization that is not related to the earth's present field but is governed instead by the field that existed when the rock was formed. If such a rock is igneous, its direction of magnetization will be that of the earth's field at some time after it solidified and before it reached the Curie point. This is called *thermoremanent magnetization*. If the rock is sedimentary, any orientation of its magnetic grains during deposition, generally in quiet water, would have been in alignment with the field that existed when the deposition occurred. This is *depositional remanent magnetization*.

The existence of such remanent magnetization in rocks gives earth scientists a powerful tool for studying the history of the earth's field and by inference the geologic history of the earth itself. This type of study is referred to as *paleomagnetism*.

The remanent magnetism of quickly cooled molten rocks (e.g., lava flows) is the record of the direction of the earth's field at the time of cooling, or solidification, due to the small grains of magnetite aligning with the direction of the earth's field. The study of the remanent magnetism of rocks has provided important evidence concerning plate tectonics, sea floor spreading, and the geomagnetic-reversal time scale (Cox[2]). The study of remanent magnetism also has applications for archaeological studies, as will be discussed at the end of Chap. 17. For further information on this application of magnetic data, the reader is referred to a nonmathematical discussion by Strangway.[3]

Units of Magnetic Intensity   In magnetic prospecting, one usually measures variations in the intensity, or some component of the intensity, of the earth's magnetic field. The conventional unit of field intensity is the oersted, although much of the geophysical literature uses the numerically equivalent gauss. The oersted is too large a unit for practical use in prospecting, since the variations in which we are interested are often less than a thousandth of this amount. The *gamma*, defined as 10^{-5} Oe, is more convenient and has become the most common unit of field intensity for geophysical work. The total magnetic field of the earth is normally about $\frac{1}{2}$ Oe or 50,000 gammas. The gamma is equivalent to the *nanotesla* of the SI.

The Total Field and Its Components   Any magnetic field associated with a buried source is of course superimposed on that of the earth. The resultant field observed on the surface is a vector which has both magnitude and direction. Early instruments for measuring the field on land like the magnetic balance were designed to read its horizontal or vertical components. Modern airborne and ship-towed instruments, on the other hand, measure the actual field, which is referred to as the *total field*. Interpretation of total fields, which can vary both in magnitude and direction, is necessarily more complex than that involving individual components, such as the vertical, which was the one generally recorded in most early measurements on land.

Electromagnetism   Every electric current generates a magnetic field in a plane perpendicular to it, as shown by the orientation of the compass needles around the wire in Fig. 15-4. The strength of the field is proportional to the current and in the case of a long, straight wire is inversely proportional to the distance from the wire. This principle is important in magnetic prospecting only insofar as it forms the basis for certain types of geomagnetic instruments and enables us to account for the earth's field on the basis of electric currents in its interior.

The Magnetic Potential and Poisson's Relation   Like the gravitational field, the magnetic field has a potential, which is simply the work necessary to bring a unit magnetic pole from infinity to a point a distance r from another source of magnetic polarity of strength P. The magnetic potential U can be expressed by the relation

$$U = \frac{1}{\mu} \frac{P}{r} \tag{15-7}$$

The magnetic field is the spatial derivative of the potential. The direction of the field is determined by the direction associated with the derivative. The x

FIGURE 15-4   Orientation of compass needles around straight wire (perpendicular to paper) carrying current. This experiment shows that the current creates a magnetic field with circular lines of force having their center at the wire.

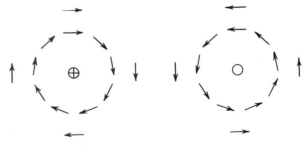

Current into paper— compasses take positions shown

Current out of paper— directions of compass needles reversed

component of the field is simply $\partial U/\partial x$, where x is in the direction of the resultant magnetic field.

The magnetic potential and hence the magnetic field strength associated with a magnetized body can be found at any point in terms of the gravitational potential by use of *Poisson's relation*. This is particularly valuable for predicting the magnetic effect of buried bodies. Magnetic fields from such bodies, even those with simple geometrical forms, are more difficult to derive directly than the corresponding gravitational fields. According to Poisson, the magnetic potential U can be expressed in the form

$$U = -\frac{I}{\gamma\rho}\frac{dV}{di} \tag{15-8}$$

where V = gravitational potential
i = direction of magnetic polarization
I = magnetization or polarization
ρ = density
γ = universal gravitational constant

The corresponding magnetic field component in any direction s is

$$H_s = -\frac{\partial U}{\partial s} = \frac{I}{\gamma\rho}\frac{\partial}{\partial s}\left(\frac{\partial V}{\partial i}\right) \tag{15-9}$$

If the body is polarized in the z (vertical) direction, and if the horizontal component H_x of the magnetic field is desired, it can be obtained from the equation

$$H_x = -\frac{\partial U}{\partial x} = \frac{I}{\gamma\rho}\frac{\partial}{\partial x}\left(\frac{\partial V}{\partial z}\right) \tag{15-10}$$

while the vertical component H_z will be

$$H_z = -\frac{\partial U}{\partial z} = \frac{I}{\gamma\rho}\frac{\partial^2 V}{\partial z^2} \tag{15-11}$$

These relations will be put to use later in this chapter to develop equations for the magnetic fields of polarized bodies having simple generalized forms for which gravitational fields have been computed in earlier chapters.

15-2 MAGNETISM OF THE EARTH

Recently trends have developed in magnetic surveying toward analyzing regional data to study large-scale geology as well as toward the use of more precision and detailing. With increased precision of field measurements, including precise geodetic control, adequate recognition of anomalies requires subtraction of the regional or background field. To determine what to subtract, familiarity with the earth's magnetism on a global scale is required. Fortunately, a large body of data of this kind has accumulated over the past century from magnetic observatories and field measurements.

In this section we shall summarize those aspects of the earth's magnetism that have the greatest bearing on magnetic prospecting. For more detailed information the reader is referred to Runcorn.[4]

The Magnetic Elements and Their Characteristics

At every point along the earth's surface, a magnetic needle free to orient itself in any direction around a pivot at its center will assume a position in space determined by the direction of the earth's magnetic field F at that point. Normally, this direction will be at an angle with the vertical, and its horizontal projection will make an angle with the north-south direction. Since measuring instruments conventionally installed in magnetic observatories respond only to the horizontal or vertical components of the actual field, it is customary to resolve the total field F into its horizontal component H (separated into X and Y projections) and its vertical component Z (see Fig. 15-5). The angle which F makes with its horizontal component H is the inclination I, and the angle between H and X (which by convention points north) is the declination D.

The quantities X, Y, Z, D, I, H, and F, known as *magnetic elements*, are related as follows:

$$H = F \cos I \qquad Z = F \sin I = H \tan I$$
$$X = H \cos D \qquad Y = H \sin D$$
$$X^2 + Y^2 = H^2 \qquad X^2 + Y^2 + Z^2 = H^2 + Z^2 = F^2 \qquad (15\text{-}12)$$

All these relations are derivable from the diagram. The vertical plane through F and H is called the *local magnetic meridian*.

FIGURE 15-5   The magnetic elements.

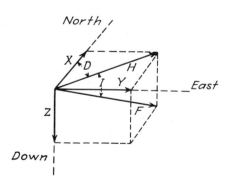

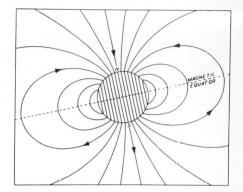

FIGURE 15-6   Magnetic field of an earth having characteristics of a homogeneous sphere. (*After S. Chapman and J. Bartels, Geomagnetism, Oxford, 1940.*)

If we take observations with our magnetic needle at various points over the earth, we shall find that in the magnetic northern hemisphere the north-seeking end of the needle will dip downward, while in the magnetic southern hemisphere the south-seeking end will be lowermost. In between, there will be a location along every meridian where the needle is horizontal; i.e., the inclination is zero. The curve around the earth connecting all such points is called the *magnetic equator*. It is rather irregular in shape and runs roughly (but not exactly) along the geographic equator. As one follows the compass needle north or south from the equator, the angle of inclination becomes increasingly larger until the point is reached, in Arctic or Antarctic regions, where the needle becomes vertical. These respective points are the earth's north and south magnetic dip poles. Both poles are displaced from the geographic poles by about 18° of latitude. They are not diametrically opposite one another, as the line that joins them passes about 750 mi from the earth's center.

As a first approximation the field of the earth might be looked upon as that of a homogeneous magnetized sphere, as illustrated in Fig. 15-6. Such a picture is much too idealized for practical applications, either in navigation or prospecting, because the earth is *not* a homogeneously magnetized sphere. The irregularities of the earth's field are quite evident on standard isomagnetic charts of the type used in navigation. Plotted on them are lines along which various magnetic elements are equal. They may be lines of equal declination, equal inclination, or equal horizontal or vertical intensity. World maps showing the variation of total intensity F and inclination I are reproduced in Figs. 15-7 and 15-8, respectively.

Variations with Time in the Earth's Magnetic Field

In the early days of navigation with the compass, it was recognized that the earth's magnetic intensity changes its direction slowly and irregularly. Later measurements at magnetic observatories showed many changes in the field that have shorter periods than those originally observed. The variations may be

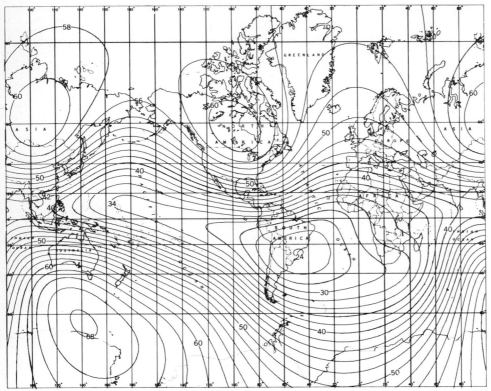

FIGURE 15-7 Total magnetic intensity over earth in 1965. Contour labels in thousands of gammas. [*After E. B. Fabiano and N. W. Peddie, National Oceanographic and Atmospheric Administration National Ocean Survey (formerly C&GS) Technical Report C&GS 38, April, 1969.*]

resolved into secular changes, solar-diurnal changes, lunar-diurnal changes, and changes resulting from magnetic storms.

Secular Variation Slow changes in the earth's field which take place progressively over decades or centuries are known as *secular variations*. Such changes are noted in all the magnetic elements at magnetic observatories everywhere in the world. The rates of change vary with time. In 1980, an annual change in declination of 7 min of arc was observed for the central United States, while at the same time the total magnetic intensity was decreasing by 80 gammas per year. Figure 15-9 shows the rate at which the total field changed around the world during 1965. Note the area of maximum change in the Southern Ocean. Figure 15-10 illustrates how declination and inclination have varied cyclically in London over the past four centuries.

The projection of current rates of secular variation is not a reliable means of determining past fields or predicting future ones. Paleomagnetic observations

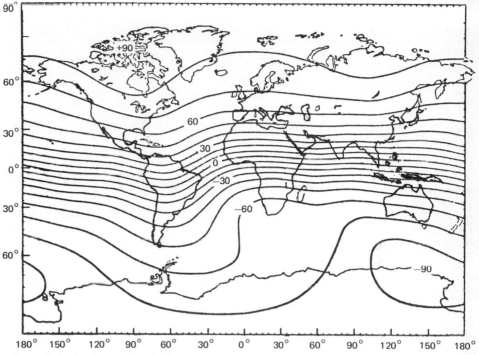

FIGURE 15-8   Magnetic inclination over earth. Contours labeled in degrees. (*Data from U.S. Naval Oceanographic Office Chart 1700, 8th ed., 1966.*)

show that there have been variations as well as repeated reversals of the earth's field over geological time, the most recent one having been about 700,000 years ago. Each reversal appears to have taken place in a very short time. The mechanism for the reversals is not well understood, although most theories associate it with changes in the flow of electric currents within the earth which are induced by conducting material in the earth's core set into motion by convection.

Diurnal Variation   Of more direct significance in magnetic prospecting are the smaller but more rapid oscillations in the earth's field which have a periodicity of about a day and an amplitude averaging about 25 gammas. *Diurnal variations,* as these are called, are regularly recorded at magnetic observatories. The records generally show two types of variations, the *quiet day* and the *disturbed day*. The quiet-day variation is smooth, regular, and low in amplitude; it can be separated into predictable components having both solar and lunar periodicities. The disturbed-day variation is less regular and is associated with magnetic storms. Figure 15-11 shows a magnetogram made on a quiet day

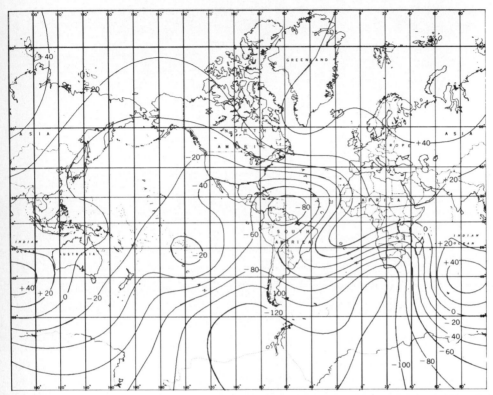

FIGURE 15-9   Annual change of total magnetic field in gammas/year for 1965. [*After E. B. Fabiano and N. W. Peddie, National Oceanographic and Atmospheric Administration National Ocean Survey (formerly C&GS) Technical Report C&GS 38, April, 1969.*]

at a magnetic observatory in Tucson, Ariz. Horizontal and vertical intensity and declination are shown on this record.

Analysis of variometer records on magnetically quiet days shows a definite 24-h periodicity that depends, to a close approximation, only on local time and geographic latitude. Because of its correlation with the period of the earth's rotation as referred to the sun, this portion of the variation is referred to as the *solar-diurnal variation*. The average range of this variation in magnetic inten-

FIGURE 15-10   Changes in declination and inclination at London since 1580.

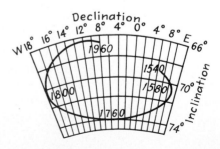

FIGURE 15-11 Magnetogram of typical quiet-day variation in horizontal and vertical intensities H and Z and in declination D at Tucson, Ariz., for Oct. 29, 1947. [*NOAA National Ocean Survey (formerly C&GS).*]

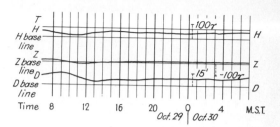

sity is of the order of 30 gammas, the amplitude being intensified in each hemisphere during the local summer. Most of the elements appear to vary simultaneously but in opposite phase in the Northern and Southern Hemispheres. The nature of the variation at different latitudes is illustrated in Fig. 15-12.

Another component in the periodic variation of the earth's magnetic elements has about one-fifteenth the amplitude of the solar-diurnal variation and a periodicity of approximately 25 h corresponding to the length of the lunar day. This component of the variation has been related to the earth's rotation with respect to the moon and is referred to as *lunar-diurnal variation*. Its low amplitude makes it less important as a source of disturbance in magnetic prospecting than the solar component.

Magnetic Storms In addition to the predictable short-term variations in the earth's field, there are transient disturbances which by analogy with their meteorological counterparts are called *magnetic storms*. Such storms cause considerable disruption in magnetic prospecting operations. The oscillations that take place while they are going on are so rapid and unpredictable that it usually is not feasible to correct for them as with diurnal variations. Magnetic surveys must generally be discontinued during storms of any severity. From the equator to latitudes of 60°, the oscillations during such storms may have

FIGURE 15-12 Solar-diurnal variation of four magnetic elements of latitudes 10° apart from 60°N to 60°S at the equinox. (*After S. Chapman and J. Bartels, Geomagnetism, Oxford, 1940.*)

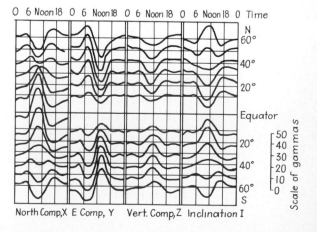

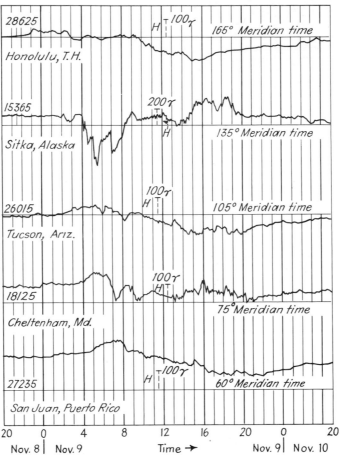

FIGURE 15-13 Magnetograms of horizontal magnetic field variations at five stations during magnetic storm starting on Nov. 9, 1947. Times are all for respective local time zones. [*Data from NOAA National Ocean Survey (formerly C&GS).*]

amplitudes as great as 1000 gammas. In polar regions, particularly during auroral displays, the storms may be accompanied by much greater amplitudes of magnetic variation. Their frequency correlates with the extent of sunspot activity. As the sun rotates, carrying sunspots away and toward the earth, some prediction of magnetic storms can be accomplished. The more intense storms begin suddenly, rage simultaneously all around the world, and usually last for several days.

Figure 15-13 shows magnetograms of the horizontal intensity at five well-separated magnetic observatories during the first day of a magnetic storm on Nov. 9, 1947. All records show considerable similarity except for the one from Sitka. The apparent time differences between onsets can be explained by the fact that the times indicated on the records are all local.

Corrections for Magnetic Variations

Secular Variation The need to tie different surveys, observed at different times, together and so compare individual magnetic responses in different areas has led to the development of models of the estimated value and the annual change of the main magnetic field of the earth. One such model is the International Geomagnetic Reference Field (IGRF).

The IGRF is a mathematical model of the earth's main field and its temporal variations and consists of a series of spherical harmonics based on worldwide magnetic observatory data. The model was developed in 1968 and is periodically updated. For more detailed information on the IGRF see the work by Peddie.[5]

It has become standard processing practice for magnetic surveys that the applicable IGRF (updated to the time of the survey) is subtracted from the observed values of the total magnetic intensity.

Diurnal Variation The correction for the observed diurnal variation is more problematical, because the daily variation of the earth's magnetic field is highly variable and cannot easily be approximated by a mathematical model. Diurnal variations are subject to amplitude and phase changes, depending on the geographic location of the observer, and can also be influenced by geological conditions, such as rock susceptibility, at the place of observation.

The necessary corrections are mostly attempted by the continuous observation of a base-station magnetometer located in or near the survey area. The measured magnetic field in the survey area is then corrected for the observed diurnal changes, either through a direct subtraction of the two data sets or through the manual removal of corresponding anomalies from the observed survey data.

For most marine magnetic surveys or airborne magnetic surveys in remote localities, the placement of a base magnetometer in or near the survey area can present a logistical problem. Significant phase and/or amplitude differences in the observed diurnal data from the base station and the survey area can be present and may require additional techniques, such as a cross-correlation method, to effectively remove the diurnal events in the observed total field. In some cases the effects of diurnal variation can be minimized by a tie-line analysis of the observed data set.

Magnetic gradiometers consisting of two magnetometers a fixed, short distance apart have been employed to obtain a derivative of the total magnetic field intensity, or a component thereof, free from diurnal events.

Magnetic Storms As mentioned, variations in the magnetic field due to magnetic storms can be so rapid, unpredictable, and of such large amplitude, that normally no corrections can be made. Magnetic surveying is therefore generally discontinued under these conditions.

15-3 MAGNETIC SUSCEPTIBILITY OF ROCKS

The most significant magnetic property of rocks is their susceptibility. This can be measured with the rocks in place by an induction balance of the type developed by Mooney.[6] Pulverized samples of rocks can be placed near a field magnetometer and the deflection of the magnetometer needle caused by the sample can be used to calculate the susceptibility. In situ measurements are preferable wherever it is feasible to make them.

In the laboratory, a number of instruments are employed to measure the susceptibility of rock samples. In one, primary and secondary coils are wound around the space where the sample is placed. When a known current is sent through the primary coil, the voltage induced in the secondary is measured and related to the susceptibility by appropriate calculations. Barret[7] describes an apparatus for measuring susceptibility that is based on this principle.

When an external magnetic field is used for measuring susceptibility, it is customary to specify the strength of this field in tabulating the results. The polarization that governs the response of the sample to the measuring field consists of two parts, the susceptibility polarization kH, dependent on the external field H and the susceptibility k, and the remanent polarization I_p, which governs the residual magnetism in the absence of an external field.

Table 15-1 gives some representative values of susceptibility for several different kinds of rocks and minerals. Note that many of the measurements were made with a field of 1 Oe, which is higher than that of the earth by a factor of around 2, while one (that on serpentine) was measured at a field of 30.15 Oe, about 50 times that of the earth. There is some question how applicable such

TABLE 15-1 MEASURED SUSCEPTIBILITIES OF ROCK MATERIALS

Material	$k \times 10^6$, cgs units	At H, Oe
Magnetite	300,000–800,000	0.6
Pyrrhotite	125,000	0.5
Ilmenite	135,000	1
Franklinite	36,000	
Dolomite	14	0.5
Sandstone	16.8	1
Serpentine	14,000	30.5
Granite	28–2700	1
Diorite	46.8	1
Gabbro	68.1–2370	1
Porphyry	47	1
Diabase	78–1050	1
Basalt	680	1
Olivine-diabase	2000	0.5
Peridotite	12,500	0.5–1.0

Source: C. A. Heiland, "Geophysical Exploration," Prentice-Hall, Inc., 1940, and L. B.Slichter, "Handbook of Physical Constants," *Geol. Soc. Am., Spec. Paper* 36, 1942.

TABLE 15-2   CALCULATED SUSCEPTIBILITIES OF ROCK MATERIALS

| Material | Magnetite Content and Susceptibility, cgs units | | | | | | Ilmenite, average | |
| | Minimum | | Maximum | | Average | | | |
	%	$k \times 10^6$	%	$k \times 10^6$	%	$k \times 10^6$	%	$k \times 10^6$
Quartz porphyries	0.0	0	1.4	4,200	0.82	2,500	0.3	410
Rhyolites	0.2	600	1.9	5,700	1.00	3,000	0.45	610
Granites	0.2	600	1.9	5,700	0.90	2,700	0.7	1000
Trachyte-syenites	0.0	0	4.6	14,000	2.04	6,100	0.7	1000
Eruptive nephelites	0.0	0	4.9	15,000	1.51	4,530	1.24	1700
Abyssal nephelites	0.0	0	6.6	20,000	2.71	8,100	0.85	1100
Pyroxenites	0.9	3000	8.4	25,000	3.51	10,500	0.40	5400
Gabbros	0.9	3000	3.9	12,000	2.40	7,200	1.76	2400
Monzonite-latites	1.4	4200	5.6	17,000	3.58	10,700	1.60	2200
Leucite rocks	0.0	0	7.4	22,000	3.27	9,800	1.94	2600
Dacite-quartz-diorite	1.6	4800	8.0	24,000	3.48	10,400	1.94	2600
Andesites	2.6	7800	5.8	17,000	4.50	13,500	1.16	1600
Diorites	1.2	3600	7.4	22,000	3.45	10,400	2.44	4200
Periodotites	1.6	4800	7.2	22,000	4.60	13,800	1.31	1800
Basalts	2.3	6900	8.6	26,000	4.76	14,300	1.91	2600
Diabases	2.3	6900	6.3	19,000	4.35	13,100	2.70	3600

Source: L. B. Slichter and H. H. Stearn, "Geophysical Prospecting," *Am. Inst. Mining Met. Engrs., Trans.,* 1929.

values are in predicting magnetic effects observable in the field. Susceptibilities determined by a method proposed by Slichter[8] are probably more reliable for such a purpose than those measured in fields greater than that of the earth, as were most of the values listed in Table 15-1. Assuming that the magnetism of most rocks is attributable to their magnetite content, he obtained the susceptibility of a rock type by multiplying the volume percentage of the magnetite in it by the susceptibility of magnetite (taken as 0.3 cgs unit). He found good agreement between values calculated in this manner and those measured directly in fields having the same strength as the earth's. Stearn[9] has tabulated the magnetite and ilmenite content of a large number of igneous rocks. Susceptibilities calculated on the basis of Stearn's data by Slichter's method are presented in Table 15-2, which shows the range of variation in susceptibility for any given type of rock.

Peters has prepared a bar graph (Fig. 15-14) showing rock susceptibilities from laboratory measurements on a large number of rock samples, igneous, metamorphic, and sedimentary. Igneous and some metamorphic rocks generally have higher susceptibilities than sedimentary rocks, but there is such a large range of variation that it is not possible to identify even the type of rock from magnetic information alone. Under exceptional circumstances sedimentary formations have a high enough magnetite content to be mappable by properly designed magnetic surveys, particularly when high-sensitivity instru-

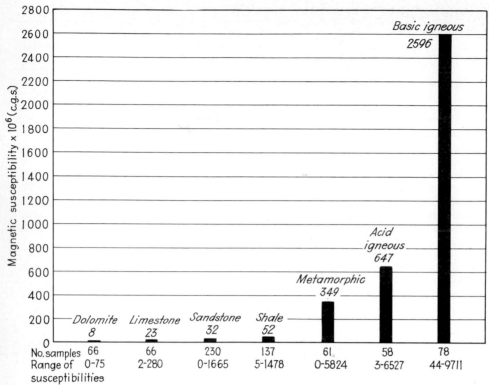

FIGURE 15-14 Average magnetic susceptibilities of surface samples and cores as measured in the laboratory. (*Compiled by J. W. Peters, Mobil Oil Corp.*)

ments are used. In general, however, the magnetization of sedimentary rocks is so small that structural features confined to the sedimentary section will seldom be reflected in magnetic profiles. A more recent statistical summary of data on rock susceptibility has been published by Lindsley et al.[10] It also shows substantial overlap between different rock types. Table 15-3 illustrates the distribution of susceptibility among samples of each type.

15-4 MAGNETIC EFFECTS FROM BURIED MAGNETIC BODIES

Analytical Methods of Computation: Forward Modeling

Magnetic effects at the earth's surface from buried bodies of a given shape and magnetization can be calculated from potential theory by methods similar to those used for determining the gravitational effects of density contrasts associated with the same bodies. The computations in the magnetic case are, however, considerably more complex. In the gravitational case, all elements of mass attract, whereas an element of magnetization, the dipole, has both attractive and repulsive components. Furthermore, gravity surveys nearly always

TABLE 15-3 RANGE OF MAGNETIC SUSCEPTIBILITY IN MAJOR ROCK TYPES IN CGS UNITS

Rock type	Number of samples	Percentage of samples with susceptibility $k - 10^6$			
		<100	100-1000	1000-4000	>4000
Mafic effusive rocks	97	5	29	47	19
Mafic plutonic rocks	53	24	27	28	21
Granites and allied rocks	74	60	23	16	1
Gneisses, schists, slates	45	71	22	7	0
Sedimentary rocks	48	73	19	4	4

Source: Data from Lindsley et al., "Handbook of Physical Constants," *Geol. Soc. Am. Mem.* 97, 1966.

measure the vertical component of gravity, whereas magnetic surveys usually measure the total field, which is the magnitude of the earth's field plus the anomalous field. Hence, the response of the buried bodies as measured in a total-field magnetic survey depends on the local direction of the earth's field, i.e., the location of the survey. Induced magnetization is parallel to the earth's field. Most interpretations assume that magnetizations of the subsurface sources are wholly induced. But in many areas, particularly where the anomalies are large, it is important to include the effects of remanent magnetization: for example, one of the basalts of the Columbia-River area have large reversed remanent magnetizations.

Previous editions of this book presented numerous equations to calculate the vertical magnetic field due to subsurface sources with various shapes, in addition to examples of vertical magnetic field anomalies due to simple source bodies. The vertical field of vertically polarized bodies can be described by relatively simple analytical formulas. In this edition, however, we shall concentrate on total-field measurements because the majority of surveys today use total-field instruments. Some simple total-field anomalies over bodies at different magnetic latitudes are shown in Fig. 17-6. Rough hand-drawn modeling can be performed by drawing the field lines around the body, as shown in the figure. When the field of the source reinforces the earth's field, a positive anomaly results; the anomaly is negative when the body's field opposes the earth's field. In this and all 2-D (two-dimensional) modeling, the strike dimension of the source (perpendicular to the page) is considered to be of infinite length.

Due to the complexity of the equations, numerical modeling of total-field data is usually done with the assistance of computers, ranging from small personal computers to large vector machines. Computer code for modeling magnetic and gravity anomalies is available in the literature and through the National Technology Information Service[11] (NTIS), the nationally used central clearing house.

Two-, two-and-a-half- (defined below), or three-dimensional modeling can be performed, the choice being determined by the geologic problem at hand, the available computer speed and size, and the available funds. Some algorithms work in the space domain, others in the Fourier domain. The two different approaches employ different assumptions or approximations.

Two-Dimensional, Space-Domain Modeling   Talwani's method[12,13] is probably the most widely used algorithm in potential-field interpretation. It calculates the anomaly due to a prism or set of prisms of polygonal cross section and infinite strike extent. The interpreter approximates the magnetic sources with prismatic shapes, compares the calculated anomaly with the measured anomaly, and adjusts the prismatic shapes by trial and error in order to improve agreement between the two anomalies. The magnetization may be induced, remanent, or mixed. Talwani and Heirtzler[12] point out that if the shape and size of the magnetic source are known, and if it possesses uniform magnetization, the anomaly calculations can be used to infer direction as well as the nature (remanent or induced) of the magnetization. Saltus and Blakely[13] have published computer code to perform interactive, 2-D magnetic and gravity modeling, in which Talwani's method is employed to calculate the magnetic response. Total-field anomalies over simple source bodies at different magnetic latitudes are shown in Figs. 15-15, 15-16, and 15-17. These figures illustrate the change in the shape of the magnetic anomaly as the orientation of the source body changes with respect to magnetic north.

A variation on Talwani's method allows the 2-D prism of polygonal cross section to be replaced with a prism of finite strike length.[13,14] Shuey and Pasquale[15] proposed that the finite strike-length effect could be handled by "end corrections." They defined 2-D modeling with end corrections as "$2\frac{1}{2}$-dimensional modeling." The profile is assumed to be midway between the two ends of the magnetic source body and to be perpendicular to strike. When trying to fit observed, total-field magnetic data with modeled data, Shuey and Pasquale[15] found that addition of the end corrections increases the inferred susceptibility, increases the inferred depth, and changes the magnitude (and

FIGURE 15-15   NEW Modeled total-field anomaly over a vertical dike (solid line) and 45° dipping dike (dashed line), with the magnetic field inclined 0° (magnetic equator), 60° (central United States), and 90° (magnetic North Pole). Trend is the trend of the infinite dimension of the source body and always points out of the page. A trend of 180° indicates that you are looking north and that the magnetic profile runs from west to east (left to right). (*Northwest Geophysical Associates.*)

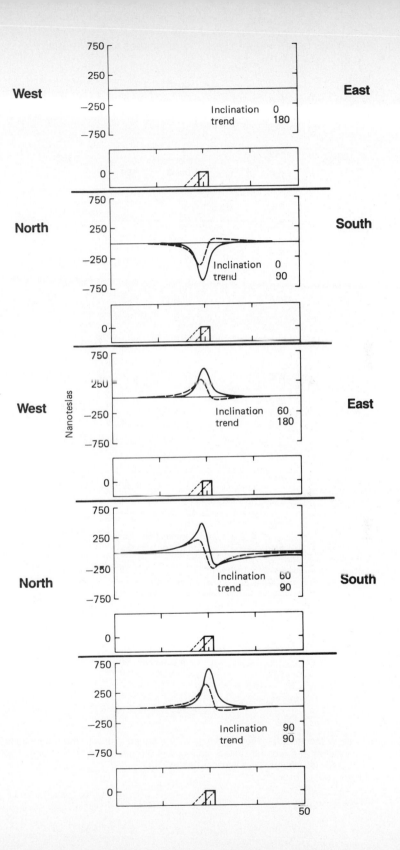

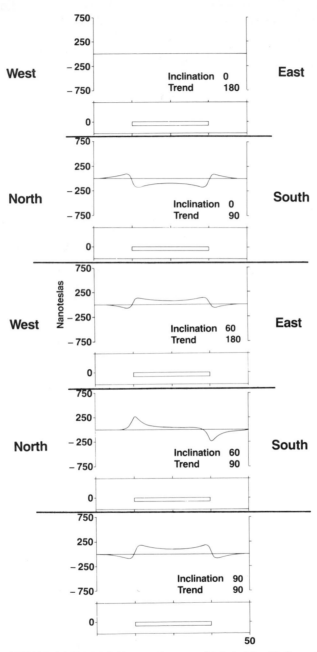

FIGURE 15-16 NEW Modeled total-field anomaly over a buried slab with the magnetic field inclined 0° (magnetic equator), 60° (central United States), and 90° (magnetic North Pole). Trend is as defined in Fig. 15-15. (*Northwest Geophysical Associates.*)

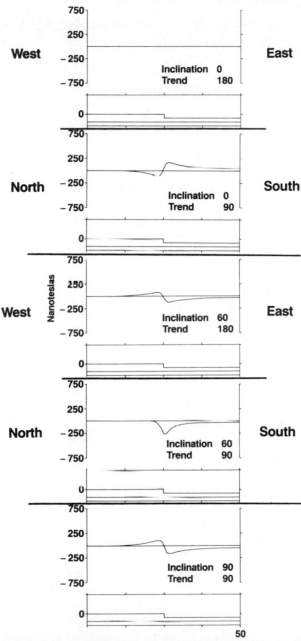

FIGURE 15-17   NEW Modeled total-field anomaly over a basement fault with the magnetic field inclined 0° (magnetic equator), 60° (central United States), and 90° (magnetic North Pole). (*Northwest Geophysical Associates.*)

sometimes the direction) of the inferred dip. The Saltus and Blakely[13] computer program, discussed above, incorporates the $2\frac{1}{2}$-D correction, and does not require the profile to be midway between the ends of the body.

Three-Dimensional, Space-Domain Modeling The 3-D Talwani method approximates the source by a set of thin laminae; each lamina is, in turn, approximated by a polygon in plan view. Talwani's method is especially amenable to topographic sources because the contours of topographic maps correspond to the boundaries of appropriate laminae.[16] In Talwani's formulation, the body is homogeneously magnetized in any specified direction. This algorithm is widely used. Its application to magnetic anomalies over seamounts was a critical step in the plate-tectonic revolution.

Plouff[17] described a generalization on Talwani's algorithm: Instead of a stack of laminae, he models the source with a stack of polygonal layers of finite thickness. He proposed integrating the laminar formulas in the direction of depth to give an exact solution for a 3-D polygonal prism (of finite thickness). Plouff stated that this method overcomes both the inaccuracy that results from the use of the laminar approximation and the inability to calculate the total magnetic field at the same level as the magnetic source body.

A third approach to 3-D modeling in the space domain is Bott's "geodesic dome," in which a 3-D source is approximated by a surface of polygonal facets.[18] It is useful for regular bodies whose depth is small in relation to areal extent.

Two-Dimensional, Fourier-Domain Modeling In this category some algorithms allow for the effects of topography, and others do not. When the topography does not provide a significant contribution to the magnetic field, models without topography can be used.[19-21]

Anomalies over magnetic sources that vary only with horizontal dimensions can be quickly computed in the Fourier domain. This is done by Fourier transforming the magnetization, multiplying by a filter (called the "earth filter" by Schouten[19,21]), and inverse Fourier transforming the product. The earth filter depends upon the depths to the top and bottom of the magnetic source layer, the direction of magnetization (assumed constant), and the direction of the earth's field. In certain circumstances, e.g., marine magnetic anomalies measured at the ocean surface, the geologic situation is adequately described by horizontal layers in which magnetization is a function of x only, and this method is especially applicable. This method is also discussed in Sec. 17-2.

Parker[22] extended the above approach to allow irregular topography and an irregular bottom surface. His algorithm involves the summation of a convergent series where each element of the series includes a Fourier transform of the magnetization times a power of the topography. Parker applied the tech-

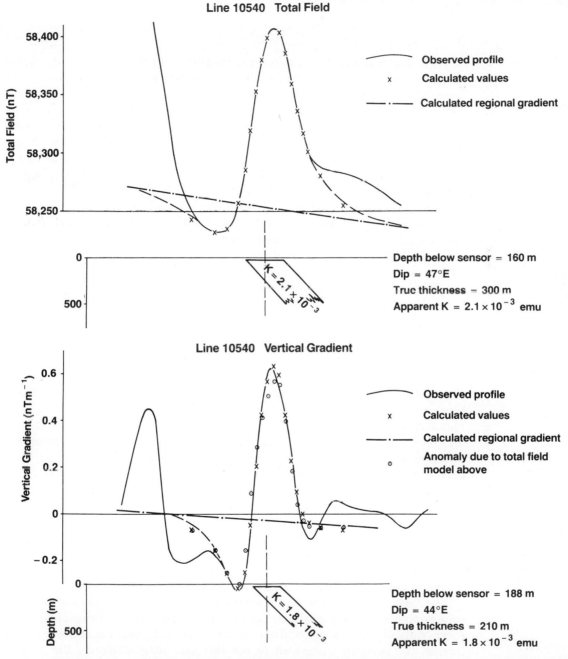

FIGURE 15-18   NEW Simultaneous modeling of total magnetic field and vertical gradient profile data. Note the reduction in interference between adjacent anomalies in the gradient profile, leading to a more accurate interpretation. (*From p. 2586, Paterson and Reeves.*[1])

nique to deeply towed marine magnetic surveys and assumed uniform thickness of the magnetic layer.

Three-Dimensional, Fourier-Domain Modeling   Parker's method described above is easily adapted to the 3-D case, and 2-D Fourier transforms of the topography are required. This algorithm is especially applicable to gridded terrain data. Blakely[23] published computer code which implements Parker's method. It calculates the total magnetic field on a horizontal plane from three gridded arrays that describe the body: its top surface, its bottom surface, and its magnetization. The inclinations and declinations of the magnetization and of the regional field are also user-specified, thus allowing for a wide range of applications.

The simultaneous modeling of the total magnetic field and the vertical magnetic gradient can lead to an improved estimate of the source body. Reeves and MacLeod[24,1] reported less ambiguity in the choice of base level and base slope and improved resolution of the anomalies through the use of this method. An example of their work is shown in Fig. 15-18.

15-5 INSTRUMENTS USED FOR MAGNETIC MEASUREMENTS

Instrument Use

The most common types of portable magnetometers today are proton-precession, alkali-vapor (or optical-pumping), and flux-gate magnetometers. Other types of instruments are also used in special-purpose applications. Magnetometers were initially mechanical devices, such as field balances or dip needles, but those were replaced after World War II by flux-gate magnetometers. These, in turn, are being replaced by the more sensitive and less cumbersome proton magnetometers. (See Fig. 15-19.) An alkali-vapor magnetometer, the most recently invented magnetometer in common use, is the preferred device when high precision is needed. If the magnetic relief is very small, or if the object of the survey is to observe magnetic effects from sedimentary rocks that are superimposed upon larger anomalies originating in the basement, the extra precision of the optical-pumping instrument can be most valuable. Such precision is critically needed in magnetic gradiometers, described later, in which the magnetic gradient is directly measured in the field.

The flux-gate magnetometer requires expensive mechanical controls. The proton-precession magnetometer does not require orientation or leveling and is more suitable for operation from or on a moving platform (vehicle, ship, aircraft, or person). Compared to the flux-gate magnetometer, the proton-precession and alkali-vapor magnetometers have greater sensitivity (0.1 gamma or better), absolute accuracy, no moving parts, and are free (or relatively free, respectively) from orientation errors. For borehole measurements though, flux-gate magnetometers are still common.

(a)

(b)

FIGURE 15-19   (a) Portable proton magnetometer. (*EG&G Geometrics.*) (b) Portable alkali vapor (cesium) magnetometer. (*SHE Corporation.*)

Total-Field Measurement

The total magnetic field intensity is simply the magnitude of the earth's field vector, independent of its direction. The total field is therefore a scalar quantity. Figure 15-7 illustrates the variation of the total field. In Fig. 15-20*a,* the magnitude of the regional earth's field vector, **F**, is shown to be 50,000 gammas. A local perturbation, **T**, of 10 gammas, is shown in Fig. 15-20*b* as a vector of arbitrary direction. This disturbance vector adds to the undisturbed field by vector addition (not shown to scale). A total-field magnetometer measures only the magnitude of the resultant vector whose direction is shown clearly from the

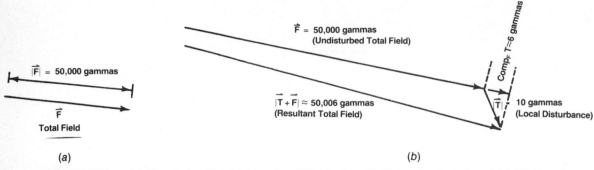

FIGURE 15-20   (a) Magnitude of total field vector. (*After Breiner.*[25]) (b) Local perturbation of total-field vector. (*After Breiner.*[25])

figure to be almost exactly parallel to the undisturbed total-field vector. As a result, the change in the measured quantity is very nearly the component of the disturbance vector in the direction of the original undisturbed total field. That is,

$$\mathbf{F} + \mathbf{T} \cong \mathbf{F} + \mathrm{comp_F T}$$

where $\mathbf{F} \gg \mathbf{T}$.

This condition almost always holds, except in the near field of large steel objects or in the vicinity of iron ore deposits or certain ultrabasic rocks that produce anomalies larger than 10,000 gammas. Thus, the change in total field, $\Delta\mathbf{F} = \mathrm{comp_F T}$, is the component of the anomalous field, $\mathbf{T}$, in the direction of $\mathbf{F}$. (Except where noted, $\mathrm{comp_F T}$ will be referred to simply as the anomaly $\mathbf{T}$.) The total-field magnetometer, for small perturbations, can therefore be considered to be an earth's field-determined component magnetometer.

The only limitation of such a scalar measurement, albeit a minor one, is the fact that the component of the anomalous field that is measured is not normally under the control of the observer but is determined by the local direction of the earth's magnetic field. This property of the total-field intensity measurement gives rise to asymmetric anomaly signatures which are important to recognize when interpreting anomalies.

Proton Magnetometer

The proton-precession magnetometer generates a measurement of the total magnetic field intensity. Sometimes called a proton, free-precession magnetometer, it is so named because it utilizes the precession of spinning protons or nuclei of the hydrogen atom in a hydrocarbon fluid to measure the total magnetic intensity. The protons in a sample of water, kerosene, alcohol, etc., behave as small, spinning magnetic dipoles. These magnets are temporarily aligned or polarized by application of a uniform magnetic field generated by a current in a coil of wire. When the current is removed, the spin of the protons causes them to precess about the direction of the ambient or earth's magnetic field, much as a spinning top precesses about the gravity field (see Fig. 15-21). The precessing protons then generate a small signal in the same coil used to polarize them, a signal whose frequency is precisely proportional to the total magnetic field intensity and independent of the orientation of the coil. The proportionality constant which relates frequency to field intensity is a well-known atomic constant: the gyromagnetic ratio of the proton, 23.4873826 gammas per Hz. In other words, a 1.0-Hz precession signal represents a total field of 23.4873826 gammas. The total field can then be expressed as $|\mathbf{F}| = \omega/\gamma$ where γ is the gyromagnetic ratio, ω is the precession frequency, and $|\mathbf{F}|$ is the external field strength.

The precession frequency, typically about 2000 Hz, is measured by digital counters as the absolute value of the total magnetic field intensity with an accuracy of 0.1 gamma (in special cases to 0.01 gamma) in the earth's field of approximately 50,000 gammas. A block diagram of a proton-precession magnetometer is shown in Fig. 15-22. Typically these systems can be sampled up to four times per second, depending upon sensitivity required. The sampling rate is limited both by the time required for polarizing the sensor and by the time interval necessary to obtain an accurate digital frequency measurement.

The two major limitations of the proton magnetometer are large gradients and ac power interference. A large magnetic field gradient, in excess of 300 to 1000 gammas per meter (depending upon the system), will cause a degradation of the proton precession signal due to the differences in the field within the volume of the sensor (usually sensors are 15 to 20 cm long and 8 cm in diameter). Under such circumstances, the magnetometer may lose precision in the least significant digit of its reading, or it may not be able to produce any valid reading. The loss of accuracy should not present a problem, since it occurs only in regions of very large field gradients. However, precision mapping of some very large anomalies, e.g., iron ore bodies, may be difficult.

FIGURE 15-21   Schematic of proton precession.

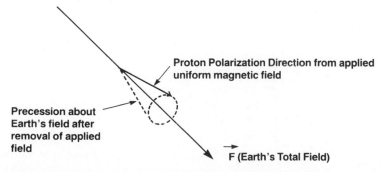

Proton Polarization Direction from applied uniform magnetic field

Precession about Earth's field after removal of applied field

F (Earth's Total Field)

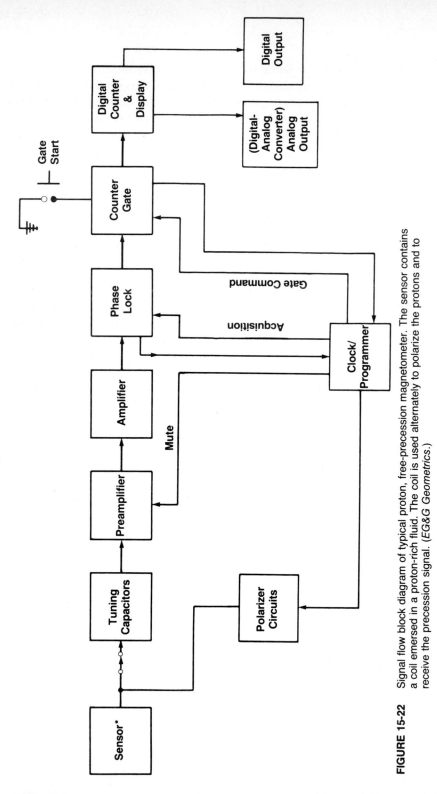

FIGURE 15-22 Signal flow block diagram of typical proton, free-precession magnetometer. The sensor contains a coil emersed in a proton-rich fluid. The coil is used alternately to polarize the protons and to receive the precession signal. (*EG&G Geometrics.*)

Overhauser-Effect Proton Magnetometer

The proton-precession magnetometer previously described is sometimes referred to as a free-precession magnetometer. Another type of proton-precession magnetometer utilizes the Overhauser effect to enhance the proton-precession signal. This system, developed in the early 1960s (Abragam and Borghini[26]), differs from the free-precession type in the following ways:

1 No polarizing field is applied; instead a radio-frequency, electromagnetic field is used to excite the system.

2 The proton-rich fluid is more complex, consisting of one or more added paramagnetic substances.

3 Proton precession is achieved by stimulation of paramagnetic resonances.

4 The precession signal output is continuous rather than discrete.

While magnetometers using the Overhauser effect produce a continuous output signal, a finite amount of time is still required to count the proton-precession frequency. The Overhauser effect does not change the proton gyromagnetic ratio; thus the overall accuracy of this magnetometer is no different than that of the free-precession type. The major advantages are slightly increased precession signal strength and the ability to sample more rapidly. Maximum sampling rates that can realistically be achieved are 8 to 10 per second, but at these rates the sensitivity is limited.

To explain the Overhauser effect in proton magnetometers requires quantum mechanics. There is, however, a mechanical analog similar to the one used to describe the standard proton magnetometer. In the free-precession magnetometer we used a magnetic field to polarize the protons. The Overhauser magnetometer uses a similar proton-rich fluid, but adds a solution rich in paramagnetic ions. These paramagnetic ions show a resonance at the so-called "free-electron" resonant frequency. This resonant frequency is in the VHF (very high frequency) radio-frequency range. When a saturating VHF signal is applied to the fluid (at the free-electron resonant frequency), a polarization of the nuclear spin in the proton occurs as a consequence of the interaction between the electrons and the nuclei. This is the equivalent of the magnetic polarization in the standard proton-precession magnetometer. In the case of the Overhauser effect, this polarization is continuous; thus the proton-precession signal changes instantaneously with the ambient magnetic field.

In addition to the continuous precession signal, this method increases the signal strength by as much as 100 to 1000. Thus the precession signal is about 1 to 10 mV instead of 10 μV. Thus there is a significant signal-to-noise improvement which, in turn, reduces the uncertainty in the measurement.

Optically Pumped Magnetometers

During the early 1960s, a type of magnetometer was introduced which was capable of measuring the earth's total field with a substantially greater precision than was possible with previous instruments. The principle on which it operates makes use of a development in radio-frequency spectroscopy called *optical pumping*. For a description of this process see Bloom[27,28] and Duffus.[29]

Optically pumped magnetometers consist basically of a cell of helium, cesium, or other alkali-metal vapor that is excited by a beam of light from a source of the same vapor. The most common alkali-vapor magnetometer in use today is the cesium type.

In its simplest form, the optically pumped sensor consists of the components shown in Fig. 15-23. The incoming light, generated from the same gas as the cell, is collimated through a circular polarizer before entering the vapor-absorption cell. The small amount of alkali-metal vapor in the cell is excited by this polarized light from its atomic ground-state energy level to various optical levels. Each of these levels (ground state and optical) are split into close magnetic (Zeeman) levels in the presence of a magnetic field (in this case, the earth's magnetic field).

Optical "pumping" results from the fact that the probabilities of transition out of the ground-state magnetic sublevels are not equal for each level of the circularly polarized pumping light, whereas the decay from the excited levels back to ground state is almost entirely the result of spontaneous emission, and decay occurs equally to all ground-state sublevels.

FIGURE 15-23 Alkali-vapor optical sensor. (*SHE Corp.*)

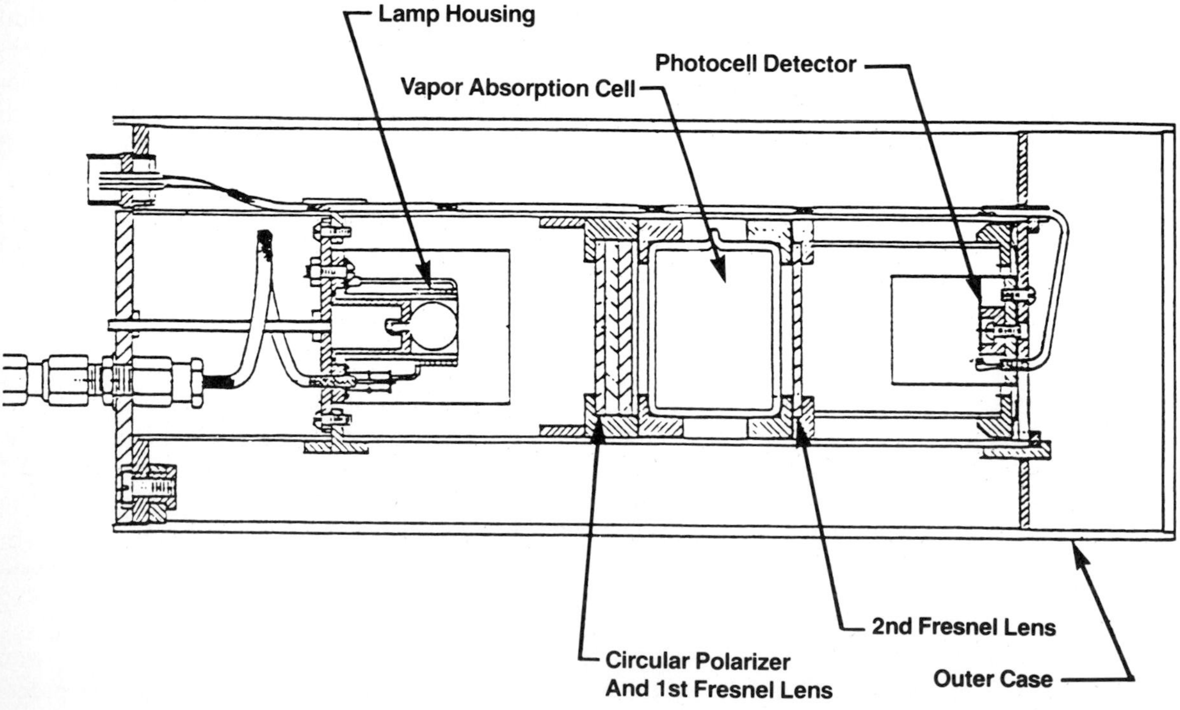

Since the ground-state sublevels are populated equally by decay but are depopulated by the absorption of pumping light at unequal rates, an unequal population of these sublevels will result. In this state, called the optically pumped state, the gas in the cell is more transparent to the pumping light than is the unpumped gas. It is the modulation of this transparency that is used to determine the ambient magnetic field.

Flux-Gate Magnetometer

Initially used for detecting submarines from aircraft during World War II, the flux-gate magnetometer was the first type of instrument to be used for magnetic measurements from a fixed-wing aircraft. It has also been employed, to a lesser extent, for magnetic surveys on the ground. Today, its major application lies in borehole measurements. This instrument uses a ferromagnetic element of such high permeability that the earth's field can induce a magnetization that is a substantial proportion of its saturation value. If the earth's field is superimposed upon a cyclic field induced by a sufficiently large alternating current in a coil around the magnet, the resultant field will saturate the core. The place in the energizing cycle at which saturation is reached is observed, and this gives a measure of the earth's ambient field.

Two types of flux-gate magnetometers are used in airborne systems. Both were employed for detection of submarines during World War II. One is the Gulf airborne magnetometer,[30,31] and the other is the type exemplified by the AN/ASQA-3A[32], designed by the Naval Ordnance Laboratory and the Bell Telephone Laboratories. Development of the Gulf instrument had already been started by Victor Vacquier as a tool for magnetic prospecting when the entry of the United States into World War II led him to adapt the device for submarine detection.

Sensitivity of flux-gate magnetometers is limited to about 0.5 to 1.0 gamma, which is adequate for some applications. In addition to its limited sensitivity, the flux-gate magnetometer is not an absolute instrument and is susceptible to drift. Where higher precision is required, proton-precession or cesium magnetometers must be used.

Characteristics of flux-gate magnetometers for ground surveys have been tabulated by Hood.[33] Precision of the readings from different instruments varies from 0.5 to 1.0 gamma, with most types in the 1.0-gamma range. These instruments have now almost completely been replaced by the portable proton magnetometer.

SQUID Magnetometers

SQUID is an acronym for superconducting quantum interference device. SQUID magnetometers are high-sensitivity vector devices. That is, they measure both direction and magnitude of the earth's field. In order to obtain total-field information, three such devices are required (measurements in *x, y,* and

FIGURE 15-24 SQUID magnetometer. (*SHE Corp.*)

z). These devices have sensitivities of 10^{-5} gammas. Figures 15-24 and 15-25 show a typical SQUID magnetometer capable of measuring one component of the earth's magnetic field.

Instruments based on SQUIDs operate at liquid helium temperatures and offer the greatest available sensitivity for magnetic field measurements. They are capable of responding to magnetic field variation from dc (static field measurement) to frequencies of thousands of hertz, thus making them applicable to a variety of geophysical problems. Due to their size and requirement for liquid helium, they are not normally suitable as portable instruments or for use

FIGURE 15-25 The flux transformer configuration used to measure a single component (B_s) of the earth's magnetic field (B) in a SQUID.

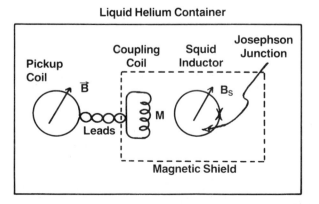

in airborne or marine platforms. Typical uses include magnetic sensors for magnetotelluric measurements, measurement of geomagnetic noise[34], the earth's magnetic field drift and micropulsation,[35] and as laboratory instruments for measurements of remanent and induced magnetization of rock samples.[36]

In general, a SQUID consists of a low-inductance superconducting ring in series with a Josephson junction. This ring is inductively coupled to a pickup coil, which is also superconducting. The pickup coil and superconducting ring are termed the *flux transformer*. (See Fig. 15-25 for a schematic of the flux transformer configuration.) This flux transformer circuit is completely superconducting, and therefore its resistance is zero. The Josephson junction is a very effective high-gain amplifier with practically no electronic noise to distort the signal. The frequency response is flat at all frequencies, including dc. The theory of operation of SQUIDs is described by Grivet and Malnur.[37]

Survey Systems

Magnetometer surveys are conducted on the ground, in the air, from satellites, and on ships. A ground system consists essentially of a magnetometer and some means of positioning. Airborne and shipborne systems are much more complex insofar as they require both analog and digital recording systems, sophisticated navigation systems (often creating digital records), and other support equipment. Chapter 16 discusses the magnetic surveying systems and techniques at length.

Airborne and marine systems can be operated either as total-field systems or as gradiometers. A gradiometer system measures not only the total earth's magnetic field but one or more of the earth's field gradients. In an aircraft the total field and the vertical gradient can be measured, or the total field and one or more components of the horizontal gradient can be measured. In marine systems the most commonly measured gradient is the longitudinal gradient, as will be discussed below. Measurements of gradients provide significant enhancement in the resultant data. Some advantages gained are isolation from magnetic diurnal variations and enhancement of near-surface magnetic sources. In some cases, time variations due to magnetic storms can be removed from the data via processing of the measured gradient data.

Figure 15-26 shows an aircraft equipped to collect high-sensitivity aeromagnetic data. A VLF (very low frequency) antenna is mounted in the nose stinger (Fig. 15-26a), and a six-cell cesium-vapor, optically pumped magnetometer is mounted under the aircraft (visible in Fig. 15-26b and c). Another configuration is to equip an aircraft with a magnetometer in the tail and to tow another one. Depending upon the requirements and terrain setting of the survey, usually one or the other is used as the measuring device. Thus, the craft can perform in a variety of different environments and geologic settings.

An airborne system to measure both the total-field and the horizontal gradients will typically have three magnetometers. One magnetometer is mounted in the stinger at the rear of the aircraft, and one magnetometer is mounted on

(a)

(b)

(c)

FIGURE 15-26   High-sensitivity magnetic survey craft equipped with six-cell cesium-vapor, optically pumped magnetometer. (*Aero Service*.)

FIGURE 15-27 Airborne equipment as installed in aircraft. (*EG&G Geometrics.*)

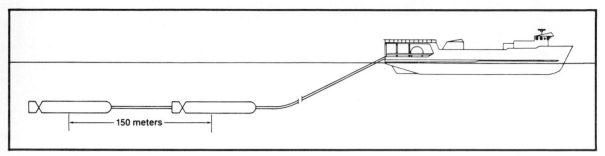

FIGURE 15-28 Schematic diagram of marine magnetic horizontal gradiometer system. The trailing sensor is usually termed the ''master'' sensor, the leading sensor the ''slave'' sensor. (*Aero Service*.)

each wingtip. With this configuration, the total-field and both the longitudinal and transverse gradients can be measured. This information can be used for interpolating the magnetic data on the map to produce improved magnetic detail for a given survey coverage.

An airborne equipment installation is shown in Fig. 15-27. Figures 15-26 and 15-27 represent virtually all of the airborne equipment, exclusive of navigation, required to perform a survey: the magnetometers, analog and digital recording system, and other support equipment. In addition to the airborne equipment, a base station to record the time variation in the earth's magnetic field is required. These ground data are used to remove such time variations from the field data.

A marine gradiometer system, such as shown schematically in Fig. 15-28, collects both total-field and longitudinal gradient data. The system consists of two magnetometers, towed one behind the other, separated by a distance of about 150 m. The forward sensor is usually towed about 300 m behind the ship. The use of the longitudinal gradient also allows elimination of time variations of the earth's magnetic field due to temporal disturbances (Fig. 15-29). Since in marine operations, nearby base-recording stations needed to define magnetic storm activity are not generally feasible, the marine longitudinal gradiometer provides the only practical means of removing time variations in the earth's magnetic field. This recent development has dramatically improved the applicability of marine magnetics in petroleum exploration.

REFERENCES

1 Paterson, J. R., and C. V. Reeves: Applications of Gravity and Magnetic Surveys: The State-of-the-Art in 1985, *Geophysics,* vol. 50, pp. 2558–2594, 1985.

2 Cox, Allan: ''Plate Tectonics and Geomagnetic Reversals,'' W. H. Freeman, New York, 1973.

3 Strangway, David W.: ''History of the Earth's Magnetic Field,'' McGraw-Hill, New York, 1970.

4 Runcorn, S. K.: The Magnetism of the Earth's Body, pp. 498–533, in J. Bartels (ed.), ''Handbuch der Physik,'' vol. 47, Springer, Berlin, 1956.

Marine Magnetic Horizontal Gradiometer

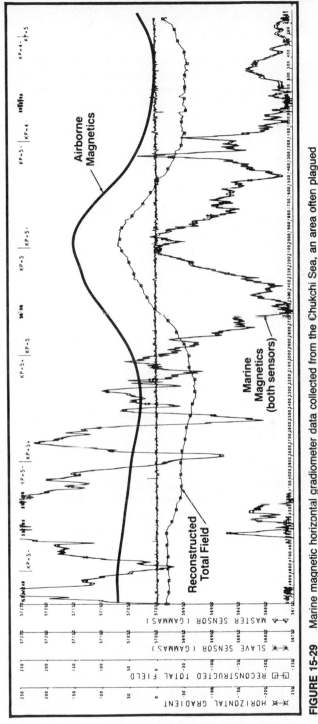

FIGURE 15-29 Marine magnetic horizontal gradiometer data collected from the Chukchi Sea, an area often plagued by extreme geomagnetic temporal disturbances. The reconstructed magnetic anomaly profile is the horizontal integration of the raw gradient data. Also shown is a profile from the aeromagnetic anomaly map. The correlation demonstrates the ability of the gradiometer software in removing the effect of severe external field contamination from the measured total magnetic intensity. (*Aero Service.*)

5 Peddie, Norman W.: International Geomagnetic Reference Field—Its Evaluation and the Difference in Total Field Intensity between New and Old Models for 1965-1980, *Geophysics,* vol. 48, pp. 1691-1696, 1983.

6 Mooney, H. M.: Magnetic Susceptibility Measurements in Minnesota. I: Technique of Measurement, *Geophysics,* vol. 17, pp. 531-543, 1952.

7 Barret, W. M.: A Semi-Portable A. C. Susceptibility Meter, pp. 17-24, in "Early Geophysical Papers," Society of Exploration Geophysicists, Tulsa, Okla., 1947.

8 Slichter, L. B.: Certain Aspects of Magnetic Surveying, *Trans. Am. Inst. Min. Met. Eng.,* vol. 81, Geophysical Prospecting, pp. 238-260, 1929.

9 Stearn, N. H.: A Background for the Application of Geomagnetics to Exploration, *Trans. Am. Inst. Min. Met. Eng.,* vol. 81, Geophysical Prospecting, pp. 315-344, 1929.

10 Lindsley, D. H., G. E. Andreasen, and J. R. Balsley: Magnetic Properties of Rocks and Minerals, pp. 543-552, in Sydney P. Clark, Jr. (ed.), "Handbook of Physical Constants," rev. ed., *Geol. Soc. Am. Mem. 97,* 1966.

11 National Technology Information Service (NTIS), Springfield, Va., 22161. Telephone: (703) 487-4600.

12 Talwani, Manik, and J. R. Heirtzler: Computation of Magnetic Anomalies Caused by Two-Dimensional Structures of Arbitrary Shape, pp. 464-480, in "Computers in the Mineral Industries," vol. 9, pt. 1, Stanford University Publications of the Geological Sciences, 1964.

13 Saltus, R. W., and R. J. Blakely: Hypermag: An Interactive, Two-Dimensional Gravity and Magnetic Modeling Program, U.S. Geological Survey Open-File Report 83-241, 91 pp., 1983.

14 Cady, J. W.: Calculation of Gravity and Magnetic Anomalies of Finite-Length Right Polygonal Prisms, *Geophysics,* vol. 45, pp. 1507-1512, 1980.

15 Shuey, R. T., and A. S. Pasquale: End Corrections in Magnetic Profile Interpretation, *Geophysics,* vol. 38, pp. 507-512, 1973.

16 Talwani, Manik: Computation with the Help of a Digital Computer of Magnetic Anomalies Caused by Bodies of Arbitrary Shape, *Geophysics,* vol. 30, pp. 797-817, 1965.

17 Plouff, Donald: Gravity and Magnetic Fields of Polygonal Prisms and Application to Magnetic Terrain Corrections, *Geophysics,* vol. 41, pp. 727-741, 1976.

18 Bott, M. H. P.: Two Methods Applicable to Computers for Evaluating Magnetic Anomalies due to Finite Three Dimensional Bodies, *Geophys. Prospect.,* vol. 11, pp. 292-299, 1963.

19 Schouten, J. A.: A Fundamental Analysis of Magnetic Anomalies over Oceanic Ridges, *Marine Geophys. Res.,* vol. 1, pp. 111-114, 1971.

20 Blakely, R. J., and Allan Cox: Identification of Short Polarity Events by Transforming Marine Profiles to the Pole, *J. Geophys. Res.,* vol. 77, pp. 4339-4349, 1972.

21 Shouten, Hans, and Keith McCamy: Filtering Marine Magnetic Anomalies, *J. Geophys. Res.,* vol. 77, pp. 7089-7099, 1972.

22 Parker, R. L.: The Rapid Calculation of Potential Anomalies, *Geophys. J. Roy. Astronom. Soc.,* vol. 31, pp. 447-455, 1973.

23 Blakely, R. J.: A Program for Rapidly Computing the Magnetic Anomaly over Digital Topography, U.S. Geological Survey Open-File Report 81-298, 46 pp., 1981.

24 Reeves, C. V., and I. N. MacLeod: Modelling of Potential Field Anomalies—Some Applications for the Microcomputer, *First Break,* vol. 1, pp. 18-24, 1983.

25 Breiner, S.: "Application Manual for Portable Magnetometers," EG&G Geometrics, 1973.

26 Abragam, A., and M. Borghini: "Dynamic Polarization of Nuclear Targets," vol. 4, chap. VIII, North-Holland, Amsterdam, 1964.

27 Bloom, A. L.: Optical Pumping, *Sci, Am.,* vol. 203, pp. 72–80, 1960.

28 Bloom, A. L.: Principles of Operation of the Rubidium Vapor Magnetometer, *Appl. Optics,* vol. 1, pp. 61–68, 1962.

29 Duffus, J. J.: Techniques for Measuring High-Frequency Components of the Geomagnetic Field, in S. K. Runcorn (ed.), "Methods and Techniques in Geophysics," vol. 2, Interscience, New York, 1966.

30 Muffly, Gary: The Airborne Magnetometer, *Geophysics,* vol. 11, pp. 321–334, 1946.

31 Wyckoff, R. D.: The Gulf Airborne Magnetometer, *Geophysics,* vol. 13, pp. 182–208, 1948.

32 Jensen, Homer: Geophysical Surveying with the Magnetic Airborne Detector, AN/ASQ-3A, U.S. Nav. Ordnance Lab. Rep. 937, 1945; L. H. Rumbaugh and L. R. Alldredge: Airborne Equipment for Geomagnetic Measurements, *Trans. Am. Geophys. Union,* vol. 30, pp. 836–849, 1949.

33 Hood, Peter: Magnetic Surveying Instrumentation: A Review of Recent Advances, pp. 3–31, in "Mining and Groundwater Geophysics/1967" *Geol. Surv. Can. Econ. Geol. Rep. 26,* Ottawa, 1970.

34 Buxton, J. L., and A. C. Frazer-Smith: A Superconducting System for High Sensitivity Measurements of PC 1 Geomagnetic Pulsations, *IEEE Trans. Geosci. Elec.,* vol. GE-12, p. 109, 1975.

35 Wolf, S. A., J. R. Davis, and M. Nisenoff: Superconducting Extremely Low Frequency "ELF" Magnetic Field Sensors for Submarine Communications, *IEEE Trans. Comm.,* vol. COM-22, p. 549, 1974.

36 Josephson, B. D.: Supercurrents through Barriers, *Adv. Phys.,* vol. 14, p. 419, 1965.

37 Grivet, P. A., and L. Malnur: Measurements of Weak Magnetic Fields by Magnetic Resonance, pp. 39–151, in "Advances in Electronics and Electron Physics," vol. 23, Academic Press, New York, 1967.

CHAPTER 16

MAGNETIC SURVEYING TECHNIQUES

Magnetic surveys are used in a wide variety of exploration programs. The interpretation and geologic application of magnetic data are the subjects of Chap. 17, but because the geologic targets determine the design of a survey, some of the more important applications will be discussed here.

In oil exploration, magnetic surveys are used as part of the geophysical mapping of basement structure and to delineate other magnetic structures, such as volcanics, which generally have large susceptibilities and often remanences. In addition, there has been considerable interest in mapping the intrasedimentary magnetite deposits believed to be associated with the upward migration of hydrocarbons from oil reservoirs. For this application high-resolution surveys are required.

Magnetic surveys have an important part in mineral exploration because many mineral deposits are associated with anomalous magnetite concentrations. Kimberlite pipes are often directly detected by magnetic surveys at close sample spacings. The alteration of hematite to magnetite by burning in coal seams is also easily detected by magnetic surveys.

Magnetics have also been used in a number of other ways. For example, the magnetic anomalies associated with hydrothermal alteration have been used in geothermal exploration, as has mapping of the magnetization contrast at the Curie transition.

Another interesting application is in archaeological exploration. Fire pits are easily detected by their magnetic anomalies; even the soil disturbances associated with building foundations and trenches can be mapped noninvasively by use of magnetic surveys.

There are three major types of magnetic survey: airborne, marine, and ground. Of these, airborne surveys are probably the most common for large areas (in the order of hundreds to thousands of square kilometers). They offer rapid coverage, generally high accuracy, and can be combined with radiometric, multispectral scanner, and other geophysical surveys. Although presently controversial, airborne gravity surveys combined with magnetics may be available and could be extremely useful.

However, airborne surveying is limited by flying speed, terrain clearance requirements, and navigational accuracy. For surveys requiring very close sampling (less than 10 m) or track spacings (less than 100 m) or extreme location accuracy, airborne platforms are unsuitable. In addition, lack of suitably precise navigation equipment has tended to limit the use of airborne surveys over water. The availability in the near future of the global positioning system (GPS) offers the opportunity to expand the use of aeromagnetic surveys over water. Aeromagnetic surveys as conventionally navigated can be successful over water if more than 100-m position precision can be tolerated.

While airborne surveys are used in near and limited offshore areas, marine surveys are the only currently practical method for magnetic-data acquisition at sea. They offer a good rate of coverage and generally more than adequate sampling rates. Marine magnetic data are often acquired in conjunction with marine seismic surveys at a low incremental cost. However, the inability to position a magnetic base station (or magnetic storm monitor) in the survey area creates potentially serious problems in removing temporal variations. Two-magnetometer systems—marine gradiometers—can be used to overcome this problem at least partially. Other problems include the fact that the ship is generally itself magnetic, requiring that the sensor be towed hundreds of meters astern. Finally, shipborne surveys are generally regarded as too expensive for magnetics alone. Therefore, magnetic-data acquisition is usually confined to lines planned for seismic study, which can lead to sparse and irregular coverage.

Land surveys are slow and often encounter problems with land access. Land surveys can, however, be positioned with great accuracy, and sample spacings as low as 1 m are perfectly feasible. Thus, land surveying is often used for detailed follow-up of areas identified as interesting in reconnaissance surveys. In archaeological studies, for example, because of the small size of the targets, land surveys are used almost exclusively.

In planning a magnetic survey, the choice of instrument, platform, sample rate, track orientation and spacing, and (for airborne surveys) altitude should be determined by the magnetic signal of the geological survey targets. The expected amplitude of the anomalies dictates accuracy requirements, both in instrument sensitivity and positioning tolerances (Jensen[1]).

The orientation of the anomalies determines the proper track orientation. Because the along-track sample distance is always smaller than the track separation, the survey tracks should always be oriented perpendicular to the predominant strike direction of the anomalies. This is generally the same as the predominant geological strike except near the magnetic equator, where east-west elongation of the anomalies may require north-south track directions and may create ambiguous interpretations.

The required sampling interval along track is determined by the expected along-track anomaly width. The track spacing necessary for adequate anomaly definition is determined by the cross-track anomaly dimensions, as is the flight altitude for airborne surveys (Reid[2]).

The following section outlines the instrumentation and operations for each survey type.

16-1   AIRBORNE DATA COLLECTION

Components of an Airborne System

Aircraft   Airborne surveys can be performed using either fixed-wing or rotary-wing (helicopter) aircraft. The major factor in choosing between the two vehicles is that helicopters are more suitable for semidetailed work and in rugged terrain. Under normal circumstances, fixed-wing aircraft are less expensive, cover an area faster, and produce higher-quality data, where quality in this case is defined as less noisy, higher-sensitivity results.

Two basic sensor configurations are used in airborne magnetic surveys: towed-bird and tail-stinger installations. In the towed-bird configuration, the sensor is housed in an aerodynamic bird attached by a cable to the aircraft (see Fig. 16-1). This type of installation places the sensor far enough away from the aircraft that the vehicle's magnetic field is negligible at the sensor. At the low speeds typical of helicopter surveys, the towed-bird configuration produces very good data, and this configuration is most commonly used in helicopter installations. At the relatively high speeds of fixed-wing aircraft (approximately 150 mi/h, or 240 km/h), however, the towed bird is subject to platform (bird) motion and tow cable vibrations. While towed-bird installations are sometimes used with fixed-wing aircraft, the most common configuration today is the tail-stinger mounting.

In a tail-stinger installation, the sensor is housed in a rigid boom at the rear of the aircraft (see Fig. 16-2). Occasionally, the sensor will be mounted in a wingtip pod instead. Similar considerations apply to a wingtip mounting as to a tail-stinger configuration.

At a distance of 6 to 10 m from the major components of the aircraft, the aircraft's magnetic field is not negligible. As changes in yaw, pitch, and roll occur, the magnetic field at the sensor changes. Additional effects from changing electric currents and from eddy currents in the aircraft skin may also be important. Coil systems and permalloy (Mumetal) strips located near the sensor are used to compensate for the major components of the aircraft's magnetic field. In high-sensitivity installations, it is essential to further reduce these effects by use of analog or digital compensation systems, either on board the

FIGURE 16-1   Helicopter magnetometer installation with towed bird.

FIGURE 16-2   Fixed-wing aircraft with tail-stinger-mounted sensor.

aircraft or in processing the data. With such compensation, excellent data can be obtained from tail-stinger installations in fixed-wing aircraft.

Stinger booms have also been used occasionally in helicopter systems. However, helicopters tend to be highly magnetic, so it is difficult to compensate a helicopter installation adequately.

Instrumentation

An airborne magnetic survey system usually includes the following basic equipment:

- *Magnetometer* Stinger-mounted or towed-bird sensor.
- *Digital Data Acquisition System* To record digitally magnetometer, altimeter, time, synchronization, navigation, and other pertinent survey data.
- *Analog Recorder* To record selected parameters, usually magnetics and altimeter data, for in-flight quality control and quick review after flight.
- *Doppler Navigation System* To provide spatially based sampling and navigation support.
- *Track Recovery System* Usually a vertically mounted video camera or 35mm film camera system to provide actual, visual track information to supplement the doppler navigation.
- *Recording Altimeters* Barometric and radar altimeters for vertical position information.
- *Magnetic Compensation Unit* (fixed-wing only) To compensate for the induced (both electrical and platform motion) and permanent magnetic fields of the aircraft.

Additional ancillary equipment may consist of:

- *Other Navigation Systems* Electronic or inertial systems.
- *Other Geophysical Instruments* Gamma-ray spectrometer, active or passive EM (electromagnetic) system, multispectral scanners, etc.
- *Ground Equipment* Base-station magnetometer and recording unit, and field computer system.

A typical airborne magnetic system block diagram is shown in Fig. 16-3.

Doppler Navigation

Many survey aircraft today use doppler systems to assist in navigation and provide spatial- (constant ground distance) based sampling. As a result, the doppler system is generally used as the central timing unit or master clock for the system.

The doppler system is a dead-reckoning (i.e., self-contained) navigation system. It provides information on actual ground speed and cross-track dis-

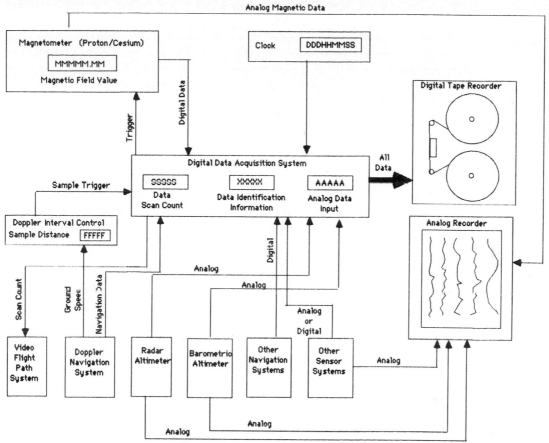

FIGURE 16-3   Survey system block diagram.

tance (distance left or right of desired track). Doppler systems generally use a magnetically slaved gyro compass as the inertial frame of reference from which all location information is derived.

By transmitting three or four precisely directed radar beams at the ground, the doppler system measures along-track (flight direction) and cross-track ground velocities. Using this information, the doppler interval controller can determine the actual distance traveled. Normally, aeromagnetic surveys use a sample interval of 50 to 160 ft (15 to 50 m), depending upon the survey objectives. The sample distance desired is manually selected at the doppler interval controller (Fig. 16-3). Each time the aircraft traverses the desired distance, a sample trigger is sent to the digital data acquisition system. The data acquisition system then samples all parameters, including a data scan count, the time of the sample, and all analog data (by analog-to-digital conversion).

After sampling, the data are written to digital magnetic tape. A typical 160-ft (50-m) sample interval in an aircraft traveling at 150 mi/h (250 km/h) is 0.8 s.

Simultaneously with the digital recording, selected data are recorded on an analog recorder for immediate viewing, both for quality checks and manual interpretation. With the advent of the field computer, the use of analog records for analysis has been significantly reduced. In these cases, analog data are considered useful only for in-flight data quality checks.

Other Navigation Systems

Navigation methods depend on the type of survey being conducted (i.e., target size, depth, location—land or water—and the availability of recent detailed topographic maps and/or photos). The techniques used can be classed as visual, dead-reckoning, inertial, or electronic. Visual navigation is done with maps or photomosaics as aids; flying the survey lines via visual reference; and performing photo flight-path recovery by use of vertical camera systems. Dead-reckoning systems are self-contained and are usually doppler systems. Inertial platforms are also dead-reckoning navigation systems but are not in common use due to drift problems. Electronic navigation can be either active or passive. Active systems require multiple transmitters on the ground and a transponder in the aircraft. Typical active systems are Syledis, Del Norte, and Mini-Ranger. Passive systems use a receiver in the aircraft and rely on existing networks such as Loran C, Omega, Decca, and satellite systems (i.e., SatNav and GPS).

Support Instrumentation

High-quality aeromagnetic data require not only a good airborne system but also that time variations in the earth's magnetic field be simultaneously recorded for later removal. This ground-data set is generally recorded both digitally and in analog form. In order to correlate these data sets, an accurate clock must also be recorded. This clock should be synchronized with the airborne system to within 1 s. Analog recording is necessary for immediate evaluation of the time variation in the earth's field that would cause interference in the airborne data and result in erroneous information.

Positioning of the base-station magnetometer is critical. It should be placed in an area free from cultural noise and other synthetic interference, such as vehicular traffic. As a rule of thumb, if corrections of the airborne data for time variations are to be about 1 to 10 gammas, the base station should be no more than 100 km from the survey area. In addition, there should be no major geological discontinuities between the survey area and the base station. Such occurrences cause phase and/or amplitude shifts in the time variations relative to the aircraft. These phase shifts can cause artificial anomalies in the corrected airborne data.

Another major support instrument is the field computer. This system is used to evaluate the quality of the airborne digital data at the end of each day's flying. Additionally, it can be used by field personnel to perform preliminary interpretation while on site in the field. Such results might be used for redirection of the airborne survey or other exploration crews.

Airborne Field Operations

A field crew for an airborne magnetic survey will, at a minimum, consist of a pilot, electronics technician, and a data person. The pilot flies the aircraft and is responsible for maintaining flying specifications. The pilot usually performs his or her own navigation. The electronics technician operates the instrumentation during flight, maintains the equipment as required, and is responsible for ensuring that good-quality data are recorded. The data person performs the flight planning, flight-path recovery, and, if a field computer is used, reviews the quality of digital data. The data person is also responsible for monitoring the base-station magnetometer and ensuring that all data are within specifications.

During a survey, the aircraft pilot endeavors to fly a course at a constant altitude above the terrain (mean terrain clearance, MTC), or above sea level (constant barometric altitude, CBA), dependent upon the type of survey being performed. The two types of altitude control will distort anomalies in different ways and will require some differences in both data reduction and interpretation. Flight direction and line spacing are maintained via visual navigation, doppler navigation, or other electronic navigation methods, using flight-path maps or photomosaics or combinations of these.

The region to be surveyed is covered by a series of parallel flight lines (traverse lines) at a specified horizontal separation and at a specified altitude (either MTC or CBA). These flight lines are crossed at regular intervals by tie lines, which are typically flown at right angles to the traverse lines. In general, the ratio between traverse lines and tie lines will be from 4:1 to 10:1. That is, if the traverse lines are spaced at 1 km, then the tie lines will be spaced from 4 to 10 km, depending upon the survey objectives.

The complete grid of flight lines (traverse and tie lines) is translated into a standard cartographic coordinate system by use of the data obtained from the navigation system. This then provides a mappable coordinate system to which the field data can be transformed.

In the past, airborne field operations that took place in remote locations could not perform data checks until the data were returned to the computer center. If data were not acceptable for some reason, the results from the survey would be delayed while the survey was reflown. To alleviate this burden, in-field computer systems are becoming common. These systems preprocess the digital data, verify the quality of the data, and provide a method of data backup during shipment of original tapes. Some field computer systems are powerful enough to perform limited interpretation at field sites.

When magnetics is used to guide seismic or other field methods, a geophysicist is usually present in the field. By use of a field computer, simple inversion techniques and 2-D or 3-D modeling methods may be applied to the data for structural analysis, thus providing preliminary results immediately. The analysis allows immediate redirection and any changes in survey parameters which may be required.

16-2 MARINE DATA COLLECTION

Marine magnetic surveys are generally conducted simultaneously with other surveys, such as seismic and gravity. When combined with gravity alone, the survey can be designed for these potential-field methods. When combined with seismic, magnetics becomes a secondary technique and must rely upon the design of the seismic survey, thus resulting in generally sparse coverage.

In general, the equipment is similar to that used in airborne surveys. The sensor is towed behind the vessel at a distance of up to 1500 ft (500 m), which is necessary to reduce the magnetic effects of the towing vessel. Data are simultaneously recorded in both analog and digital form. Sampling is usually time based rather than spatially based. Typical sample times are 4 to 20 s, producing sample intervals of between 25 to 50 ft (8 to 16 m) at a ship speed of 4 to 6 knots (7 to 12 km/h). Positioning systems typically include satellite navigation, Loran C, and Decca. In some cases, such as geohazard and archaeological surveys, positioning may require active systems such as Mini-Ranger.

Time variations in the earth's magnetic field produce problems similar to those encountered in aeromagnetic work. Unfortunately, the vessel is usually too far removed from land to use magnetic base stations effectively. Hence the magnetic data are often of questionable use. As a result of this problem, the marine longitudinal gradiometer was developed.

The principles underlying the marine gradiometer are simple. Two magnetometers are towed behind the ship on a single tow cable (see Fig. 15-33). The forward sensor is at a sufficient distance from the ship to minimize the effects of the ship's magnetic field, generally about 980 ft (300 m). The trailing sensor is placed far enough behind the forward sensor that the difference between the sensor readings is dominated by the geologic differences (rather than the noise), but close enough that the difference can be used to approximate the magnetic gradients due to geology. In practice, the sensor separation is usually about 500 ft (150 m).

The difference between the field values of the two sensors is essentially free of the effects of time variations in the earth's field. The difference reading reflects only magnetic gradients due to the geology differences between the sensors. By dividing the difference by the distance between the sensors, a good approximation to the geological gradient is then obtained. In theory, the anomalous total field (up to a constant of integration) may be recovered by numerical integration of the gradient along the tracks. In practice, the problem is somewhat more difficult, due to several types of errors which produce relatively small effects at the sensor but are amplified in the process of forming the gradient and integrating it. Several means of overcoming these problems have been developed and are in use today (see, for example, Hansen[4]).

16-3 MAGNETIC SURVEYS ON LAND

Field Procedures

Land magnetic surveys are often used for detailed follow-up in areas identified as interesting from reconnaissance surveys, in archaeological studies, and hazardous waste studies. Station spacing for these surveys can be as close as 1 m. In petroleum exploration, land magnetic and gravity surveys are often conducted in conjunction with land seismic surveys. Since the primary technique is seismic, station spacing will vary widely. In either case, positioning of the stations can be performed as precisely as desired—from visually spotting stations on a topographic map, to surveying in each station using highly accurate laser systems.

Regardless of the objective, stations should be set at safe distances from all magnetic interference such as power lines, bridges, and other cultural features. Typically, railroad tracks should be no closer than 360 ft (120 m), automobiles 75 ft (25 m), and wire fences 90 ft (30 m). The magnetometer operator should be relatively free of magnetic material. The importance of checking for such interference sources cannot be overemphasized if measurement accuracy on the order of 1 gamma is desired.

Two separate instruments should be used: a recording base-station magnetometer and the field unit itself. This allows direct subtraction of the time variation in the earth's field from the field data. If a base station is not used, then a "base" site must be chosen for periodic reoccupation during the survey. Reoccupation of the base site should be performed at least once per hour; if stations are of the order of meters apart, it should be performed every 10 to 15 min. Differences between the base readings are linearly interpolated for use in correction of the field data.

It is important to establish that the magnetometer is providing valid data. The simplest means of doing so is to take multiple readings at each station. Since present total-field magnetometers require no setup and can make measurements in seconds, multiple readings impose no delay in data collection. Once the operator is sure of a stable reading, then, and only then, should the measurement be recorded. Successive readings should be within one resolution element (e.g., for a 1-gamma resolution system, successive readings should be within ± 1 gamma).

16-4 DATA PROCESSING

Land Surveys

Prior to mapping the ground data, corrections for diurnal and other time variations must be applied. To further reduce the data for interpretation, a local regional field may be removed. In general, land surveys do not require the complex data-reduction procedures described later in the chapter for airborne surveys.

With the advent of microcomputers and data storage in field-portable magnetometers, processing of these data becomes greatly simplified. For example,

TABLE 16-1 SAMPLE REDUCTION CALCULATIONS USING DATA FROM A RECORDING BASE STATION

	Station				
	1	**2**	**3**	**4**	**5**
Time	0900:00	0905:00	0912:30	0917:15	0922:45
Field reading (gammas)	51325.1	51345.5	51350.8	51382.6	51380.4
Base-station reading (gammas)	51340.0	51340.2	51340.4	51340.6	51340.6
Residual total field	−14.9	5.3	10.4	42.0	39.8

using an IBM PC (trademark of IBM) microcomputer and an EG&G Geometrics Memory (trademark of EG&G), 300 stations of data can be read into the computer, corrected for time variations, and plotted in less than 2 h.

Performed manually, a similar reduction will require significantly more time. A sample of the manual procedure is shown in Table 16-1. The data shown use a separate recording base-station magnetometer, which is the preferred field procedure. Both magnetometers are total-field instruments of the proton-precession type. In this case, the base-station data are subtracted directly from the field data and the result is a residual field value with the dc components of the main field removed. The local regional field still remains.

Table 16-2 shows the method used when no base station is available. In this case we must take the values obtained in reoccupation of the base site and linearly interpolate between the two readings, taken 1 h apart. This produces an estimate of the rate of change in the main field over the time interval. These results are then used to correct the field readings. In this case, the results are slightly different due to a relatively large field change which occurred after our station readings. While the difference between the results is small, it can be

TABLE 16-2 SAMPLE REDUCTION CALCULATIONS USING DATA FROM REOCCUPATION OF A BASE SITE AND INTERPOLATING BETWEEN TIMES

	Station				
	1	**2**	**3**	**4**	**5**
Time	0900:00	0905:00	0912:30	0917:15	0922:45
Field reading (gammas)	51325.1	51345.5	51350.8	51382.6	51380.4
Interpolated base-station reading (gammas)	51340.0	51340.5	51341.8	51341.6	51342.0
Residual total field	−14.9	5.0	9.0	41.0	38.4

Reoccupation	*Time*	*Reading*
	0900:00	51340.0
	1000:00	51345.5

Linear interpolation gives 0.1 gammas/min

significant if measurements in the 1-gamma range are desired. On the other hand, if anomalies of about 10 gammas are to be resolved, these results would be adequate. Unfortunately, one does not know beforehand that the main field will shift only 5.5 gammas over the 1-h interval. It could have shifted 10 to 20 gammas or more, which would have hidden all useful information.

Airborne and Marine Surveys

In the early days of magnetic surveying, data from analog charts were often used directly for interpretation. Where surveys were made without continuous strip-chart recording, the data were plotted in profile form by hand. Contour maps, if required, were constructed by transferring the data values to plan map form and drawing contour lines between the plotted values.

These techniques can still be used when small quantities of data are involved and where accuracy is not a major consideration. This is often the case, for example, in land surveys for strongly magnetic minerals. However, airborne and shipborne surveys result in data sets too large to be handled practically without digital computer processing. Furthermore, the demand for more accurate results has led to increasingly elaborate treatment of both the magnetic measurements themselves and of the location data that accompanies them. Computer processing and plotting has therefore become an integral part of the magnetic survey and in some cases is actually performed in the field.

Figure 16-4 shows a generalized flow chart for processing magnetic survey data. Typically, the data consists of three sets: the magnetic field measurements, which are the primary data; the location recovery, generally in the form of station numbers transferred onto topographic maps or sets of aerial photographs; and the base-station data. The following sections describe the steps required to transform this information into final profile plots and contour maps.

Editing

The first step in processing is the removal of extraneous data. Surveys are normally organized into a series of profiles; the data are logically partitioned during the edit into blocks corresponding to these profiles, discarding the portions acquired during rapid turns in airborne or marine surveys. Lines which are broken for some reason during acquisition are treated as distinct segments.

The base-station data are treated in a similar manner. Since the base station is normally operated on a continuous basis during the survey, anywhere from 50 to 70 percent of these data are superfluous. The start and stop times for each survey track are used to edit the base-station data to correspond to the airborne data.

The next step is to remove from each line (including the base-station data), the spikes in each data variable. These erroneous values, introduced by record-

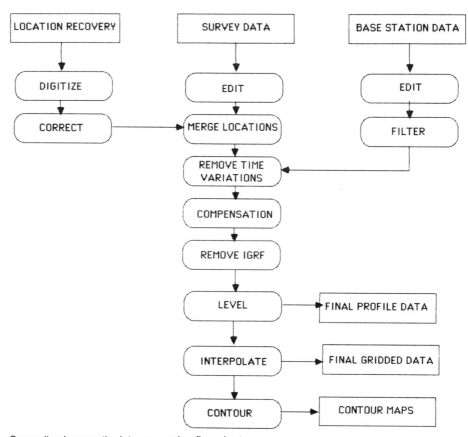

FIGURE 16-4   Generalized magnetic data processing flow chart.

ing errors, electrical interference, and the like, are present to a greater or lesser degree in essentially all raw digital data sets. Uncorrected, spikes can create wildly erroneous final data, particularly if filtering is applied.

A noise spike in the data is normally only one to two samples wide. Careful visual examination of the data will generally show these defects without difficulty. Figure 16-5 shows an expanded portion of a magnetic profile with single-sample spikes. Usually if such anomalies are wider than two samples, they may represent actual near-surface geologic features. However, in determining whether an outlying value is a spike, consideration must be given to the sample interval, distance to the source, and expected source geometry.

Many different algorithms have been developed for deleting and replacing spikes. All such techniques fail on some data sets, particularly data containing large numbers of spikes interspersed with large, high-frequency anomalies. In such cases, a program which allows erroneous values to be flagged manually (preferably using an interactive graphics terminal) is indispensable. However, isolated spikes can generally be detected by comparing each data value with a

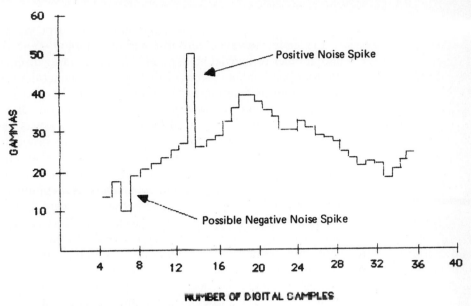

FIGURE 16-5   Expanded magnetic trace showing noise spikes.

group of adjacent ones, and flagging those values which differ from the neighboring values by an amount exceeding some threshold. This general principle underlies most spike detection algorithms (Nyman,[5] Hood et al.,[3] Halpenny[6]).

Algorithms for replacing spikes are as plentiful as those for spike detection and have the same pitfalls. Often, the predicted value used to detect the spike also serves as a replacement. Another method which generally produces good results on magnetic data is replacement by cubic splines (Deboor[7]). This latter technique has the advantage that all spikes in a line can be replaced simultaneously. However, it may be necessary to select replacement values manually in extreme cases. Here again, interactive editing is essential. Any lines for which doubt remains about erroneous values should be plotted as a final quality control and corrected as necessary.

Locations

The methods for determining and plotting locations depend to a great extent on the positioning system used. For example, electronic positioning systems such as Loran C, VLF, and GPS often yield absolute location data recorded on digital tape and synchronized with the magnetic data. Beyond spike removal and possibly some filtering, these data require few adjustments except for calibration and conversion. Electronic systems such as these are almost always used in marine surveys, and sometimes in airborne work.

Typically, however, airborne surveys employ some combination of visual and doppler or inertial navigation. The procedures discussed here are applicable to a positioning system of this type. The general strategy is to exploit the redundancy in location information between the two positioning systems to reduce the errors that invariably occur in either one alone.

Until recently, only visual flight-path recovery was used for data location. This consisted of using the aircraft position recorded on film to locate the aircraft relative to ground features found on topographic maps or on aerial photos. Since most data were collected on a time base (e.g., one sample per second), a large number of points [as many as one point every 2300 ft (700 m)] were required if well-located, airborne data were expected. Because of the influence of wind velocity, the ground speed is rarely if ever constant. A considerable and variable error thus results in the desired uniform spacing.

As the doppler system came into common use, data were collected on a spatial base, e.g., one sample every 50 m. This reduced the effect of variable aircraft ground speed and allowed definition of bad visual locations. Since the doppler acted as a "ruler" when flying a straight line, and the deviation (cross-track error) from a predetermined line could be measured and digitally recorded, this provided the necessary data to improve location accuracy by as much as a factor of 5 to 10. At the same time, the number of recovered points could be significantly reduced.

In the newer digital doppler systems, X, Y coordinates in a specified grid system can be directly recorded on digital tape. The doppler uses a magnetically slaved gyro compass as reference. Since this reference is subject to directional heading errors, the recorded location data will drift slowly from the actual position during the course of a flight.

On the other hand, if several points along a line are located "absolutely" by use of visual recovery methods, the doppler location errors can be greatly reduced. This approach is the one commonly used by many of today's aerial survey contractors.

The track recovery is performed in the usual way by film or video methods. As few as two to four visual points along the profile are required, though more complete recovery is desirable. These station numbers, along with their coordinates, are then digitized. The doppler data are then fitted to the visually located data, in the least-squares sense, by use of a low-order polynomial adjustment in X and Y. A ground-speed check is performed for each profile line to validate the results. Since the doppler ground-speed measurement has a repeatability of better than 1 percent, and the errors are not cumulative, overall location precision can be expected to be within 50 m if a reasonable map base is available.

The flight path is then plotted to evaluate the overall performance of both the positioning and the adherence to the survey specifications.

Once location is complete, these position data are merged with the geophysical data.

It should be noted that the above applies only to surveys over land, since water surface movement adds a velocity component to the doppler measurement. As a result, airborne doppler-controlled surveys over water are limited in their location precision. This is the reason for using other positioning methods in offshore surveys.

Data Correction

The magnetic data must be corrected for the time variations of the earth's magnetic field and aircraft platform motion. In addition, a model such as the international geomagnetic reference field (IGRF) is used to remove the non-crustal effects from the data.

Time Variations

The magnetic variations experienced during the survey are the result of both geologic (spatial) and external (time) influences on the earth's magnetic field. Significant time variations with periods of seconds, minutes, and hours are the effect of solar-induced activity. This activity distorts the magnetosphere (or external magnetic field) of the earth. Daily or diurnal variations are generally most pronounced during local daylight hours (see Fig. 16-6). The range of these variations is not predictable and may be as large as 100 gammas. Superimposed on these diurnal variations are micropulsations which occur more or less

FIGURE 16-6   Typical diurnal variations in total-field intensity. (*Breiner.*[20])

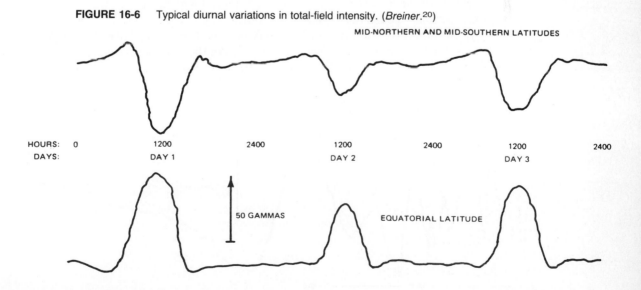

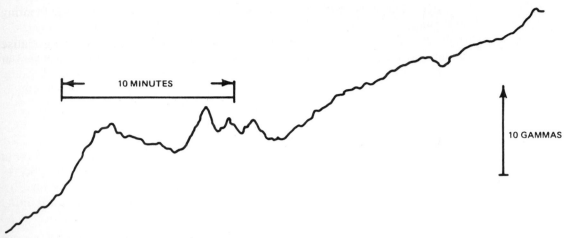

FIGURE 16-7 Typical micropulsations. (*Breiner.*[20])

randomly in time. These can have almost any amplitude, but are generally smaller than the diurnal variations except during periods of sunspot activity. Figure 16-7 shows a typical micropulsation. Micropulsations will have periods ranging from 0.01 s to several minutes. Of much greater concern are magnetic storms, which can occur several times per month. These are directly related to solar active regions and may reoccur with the solar period of 28 days. Since these can have amplitudes of up to several hundred gammas and periods from seconds to minutes, they may be interpreted as geologic features on an airborne record. The magnetic storms cause the most concern to those responsible for magnetic surveys. Figure 16-8 shows a typical magnetic storm trace. Operations normally cease during magnetic storms.

Information on the time variations is obtained from the base-station data. These data are processed as previously noted in the editing section. Depending on the type of survey and the activity of the time variations, these data may be

FIGURE 16-8 Typical magnetic storm. (*Breiner.*[20])

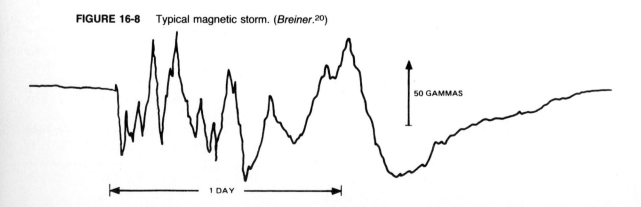

subtracted directly from the airborne data, or a low-order curve, representing the activity, may be removed from the airborne data. For direct removal, the base-station data are normally low-pass filtered, as propagation effects cause phase shifts between the variations observed at the base station and those at the survey position.

Compensation

A major source of error in airborne and marine magnetic measurements is the field of the survey vehicle. In marine surveys, these effects are minimized (but not eliminated) by towing the sensor up to 1500 feet (500 m) from the ship. In airborne work, the standard procedure is to obtain passive compensation by three-axis coil systems and permalloy (Mumetal) strips to correct for the induced and permanent fields of the aircraft. This method can remove only certain components and has a limited accuracy. For example, it does not remove errors introduced by aircraft motion in the earth's field. Hardware and software have been developed for military applications which allow compensation for these effects (Leliak[8]). These techniques are now being adopted for geophysical survey work. The aircraft attitude, rate of change of attitude, and, in some cases, electric current and control surface position are recorded digitally. Prior to a survey, a set of maneuvers is performed to "calibrate" these sensors. The coefficients for the 16 terms of the aircraft magnetic field are calculated and used in conjunction with the physical attitude of the platform during survey to correct the data. Figure 16-9 shows a sample of aeromagnetic data before and after such correction. Note the apparent anomalies in the uncompensated data. These would appear as a real, near-surface geologic feature during interpretation. The end result would be an erroneous view of the area of concern, providing misleading information.

IGRF Removal

The IGRF is a mathematical representation of the earth's main magnetic field due to sources in the core. Once this field is removed from the data, the results are actually residual magnetic anomalies due solely to the geology. This assumes, of course, that the core field is accurately described by the IGRF model. Since the dynamics of the core field are not completely understood, this is not truly the case. In actuality there are a number of earth field models to choose from (Peddie,[9] Langel et al.[10]). All of these models are based on empirical fits to observatory and, in some cases, satellite data; each one is slightly different and produces different results. The major application of the IGRF removal is in the survey of large areas which will be surveyed over long periods of time (several months to years). In small area surveys, particularly those which will not be matched to adjoining areas, a local regional trend removal may suffice. Both tables and analytical forms of the IGRF exist from which these corrections may be made.

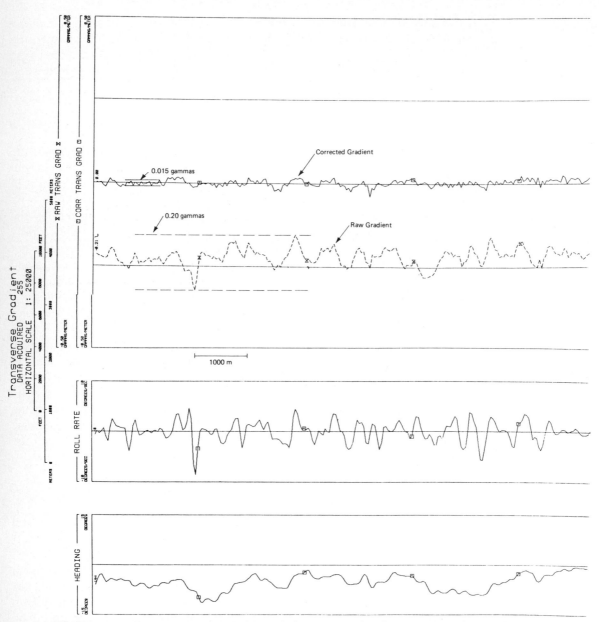

FIGURE 16-9 Transverse gradient before and after computer heading corrections. Average background noise level = 0.015 gammas/m peak to peak.

Leveling

The location procedure, and the data corrections just described, always leave residual errors in the data. In addition, altitude variations from line to line are always present to a greater or lesser degree in airborne surveys. To distribute these errors in such a way as to minimize their effect on localized anomalies, some leveling or tieing procedure is always used. For this purpose, a series of tracks, called tie lines, perpendicular to the survey lines and generally at a wider spacing are used.

The general strategy of all leveling algorithms is to reduce or eliminate the differences between the corrected magnetic field values at intersections between the survey and tie lines. This is accomplished by applying an empirically determined correction to one or both of the lines. The form of the correction varies widely. At one extreme, a single value may be allowed for each line and adjusted to minimize, by least-squares methods, the residual differences. At the other extreme, a linear or higher-order polynomial (up to third order) correction may be allowed along each line between intersections, with the residual differences eliminated completely (Bhattacharya[11]). Other methods, generally lying between these extremes, are also in common use (Foster et al.,[12] Green,[13] Ray[14]). There are other variations used by some contractors, such as the adjustment of the location of the intersections. Whatever algorithm is employed, the adjustments almost always reduce to a linear least-squares system to be solved for the corrections.

Since the leveling procedure is essentially empirical, no single algorithm will perform best in all situations. Consideration of the major contributions to the residual errors for a particular survey may suggest a preferred procedure. In any case, final manual adjustments must often be made by visual examination of a preliminary map.

Interpolation to a Regular Grid

The data now consist of a series of profile lines with a high data density along the line and a low data density between lines. In order to prepare contour maps, it is necessary to reduce these data to a regular grid. This process is known as *interpolation*. A number of algorithms exist to interpolate irregular data to a regular grid (see, for example, James,[15] Crain and Bhattacharya,[16] Bhattacharya,[17] Briggs,[18] Royle et al.[19]). In some cases, interpolation is done in two stages. The first stage produces a coarse grid, which is further refined by techniques such as the bicubic spline (DeBoor[7]). Whatever the method, the computer requirements are generally quite large.

This interpolation process is critical to good, usable contour maps. One measure of quality is that a profile exhibited from the resultant grid should agree with the original profile data to within one-half of a contour interval. For example, if a survey is to be contoured to a 5-gamma level, then, when a profile is laid over the contour map, all data should match to within 2.5 gammas.

FIGURE 16-10 Residual total field contour map. (*Data courtesy of Minnesota Geological Survey, Dr. M. Walton, Director, and compiled by EG & G Geometrics.*)

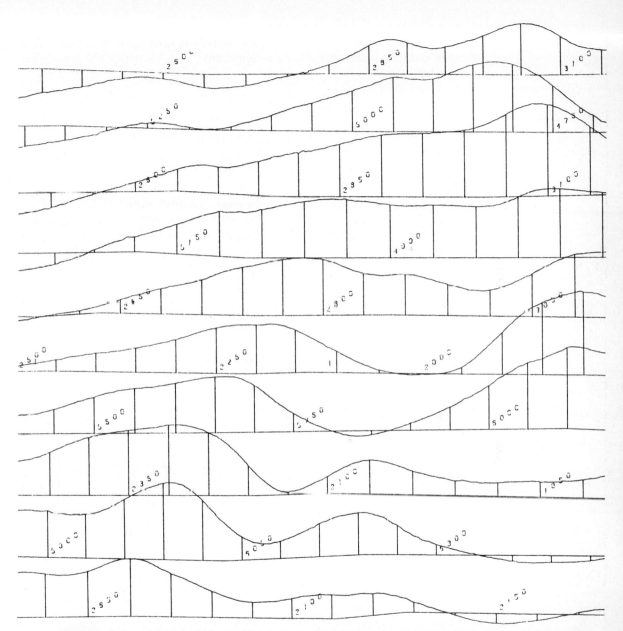

FIGURE 16-11 Offset magnetic profiles shown as "fence" diagram. (*Processing and display by Comap Geo-surveys, Inc.*)

The gridded data from the interpolation process provide the database from which most methods of presentation are derived (exclusive of profiles). These include contour maps and other presentations, such as perspective plots and pseudoimage maps.

Data Display

The types of data displays are limited only by the user's imagination. There are, however, a number of common types. These include residual contour maps, offset profiles, and multiparameter profiles.

A typical contour map is shown in Fig. 16-10. The following survey specifications were used: sensitivity 0.25 gammas, sampling interval 250 ft (75 m), altitude 500 ft (150 m) mean terrain clearance-radar controlled. The flight lines are north-south spaced 1300 ft (400 m) apart with tie lines east-west spaced at 6500 and 13,000 ft (2.0 and 4.0 km). A geomagnetic reference field was removed, based upon the American World Charts Model, 1975, updated to 1980.

FIGURE 16-12   Typical digital plot of magnetic profile. Full-scale deflection is 500 gammas. Trace is "stepped" to retain sensitivity, yet accommodate over ranging.

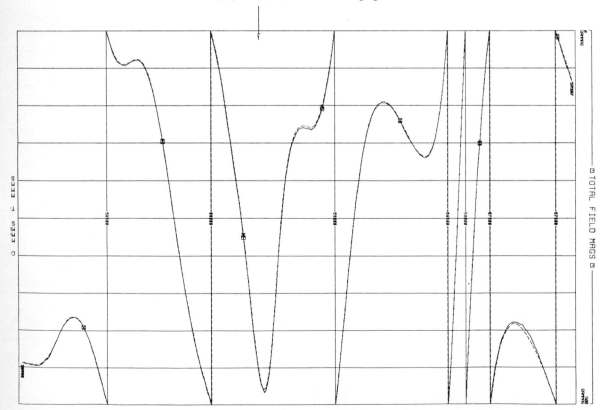

At 47° 30′N and 92°W the American World Charts Model gives a magnetic inclination of 75° 17′N, a magnetic declination of 3° 13′E, and a field intensity of 60,195 gammas. The contour-mapping process used approximately one-fourth of all data samples to create a 213 m by 213 m primary grid with minimum curvature interpolation. The final grid was refined with a bicubic spline technique. The primary contour interval is 20 gammas with down-gradient shading at 10 gammas.

Offset profiles are another common method of displaying magnetic data. Figure 16-11 shows a typical set of offset profiles. The data are from the U.S. Department of Energy and were collected under the National Uranium Resource Program.

Digitally plotted magnetic profiles are usually obtained as a part of an aeromagnetic survey. Figure 16-12 shows a a typical profile. These profiles are invaluable even in qualitative interpretation of magnetics. From these, estimates of source depth and source dimension can be made.

REFERENCES

1 Jensen, H.: Important Details and Applications of a New Airborne Magnetometer, *Geophysics*, vol. 45, pp. 973–976, 1965.

2 Reid, A. B.: Aeromagnetic Survey Design, *Geophysics*, vol. 45, pp. 973–976, 1980.

3 Hood, P. J., M. T. Holroyd, and P. H. McGrath: Magnetic Methods Applied to Base Metal Exploration, pp. 77–104, in P. J. Hood (ed.), "Geophysics and Geochemistry in the Search for Metalic Ores," *Geol. Surv. Can. Econ. Geol. Rep. 31*, Ottawa, 1979.

4 Hansen, R. O.: Two Approaches to Total Field Reconstruction from Gradiometer Data, *54th Annu. Int. SEG Meeting*, Atlanta, Georgia, 1984.

5 Nyman, D.: The Interpolation Error Operator: Time Series Error Detection and Correction, *Geophysics*, vol. 42, pp. 773–777, 1977.

6 Halpenny, J.: A Method of Editing Time Series Observations, *Geophysics*, vol. 49, pp. 521–524, 1984.

7 DeBoor, C.: Bicubic Spline Interpolation, *J. Math. und Phys.*, vol. 41, pp. 212–218, 1962.

8 Leliak, P.: Identification and Evaluation of Magnetic-Field Sources of Magnetic Airborne Detector Equipped Aircraft, *IRE Trans. Aerospace Navigational Elect.*, vol. 8, pp. 95–105, 1961.

9 Peddie, N. W.: International Geomagnetic Reference Field 1980, *PAGEOPH*, vol. 120, 1982.

10 Langel, R. A., R. H. Estes, G. D. Mead, E. B. Fabiano, and E. R. Lancaster: Initial Geomagnetic Field Model from MAGSAT Vector Data, *Geophys. Res. Lett.*, vol. 7, pp. 793–796, 1980.

11 Bhattacharya, B. K.: An Automatic Method of Compilation and Mapping of High-Resolution Aeromagnetic Data, *Geophysics*, vol. 36, pp. 695–716, 1971.

12 Foster, M. R., W. R. Jines, and K. van der Weg: Statistical Estimation of Systematic Errors at Intersections of Lines of Aeromagnetic Data, *J. Geophys. Res.*, vol. 75, pp. 1507–1511, 1970.

13 Green, A. A.: A Comparison of Adjustment Procedures for Leveling Aeromagnetic Survey Data, *Geophysics*, vol. 48, pp. 745–753, 1983.

14 Ray, R. D.: "Correction of Systematic Error in Magnetic Surveys: An Application of Ridge Regression and Sparse Matrix Theory," preprint, Western Geophysical Company of America, Houston, Tex., 1984.

15 James, W. R.: FORTRAN IV Program Using Double Fourier Series for Surface Fitting of Irregularly Spaced Data, Computer Contribution 5, State Geological Survey, The University of Kansas, Lawrence, 1966.

16 Crain, I. K., and B. K. Bhattacharya: Treatment of Non-equispaced Two-Dimensional Data with a Digital Computer, *Geoexploration,* vol. 5, pp. 173–194, 1967.

17 Bhattacharya, B. K.: Bicubic Spline Interpolation as a Method for Treatment of Potential Field Data, *Geophysics,* vol. 34, pp. 402–423, 1969.

18 Briggs, I. C.: Machine Contouring Using Minimum Curvature, *Geophysics,* vol. 39, pp. 39–48, 1974.

19 Royle, A. G., F. L. Clausen, and P. Fredericksen: Practical Universal Kriging and Automatic Contouring, *Geo-Processing,* vol. 1, pp. 377–394, 1981.

20 Breiner, S.: Application Manual for Portable Magnetometers, EG&G Geometrics, 1973.

CHAPTER 17

INTERPRETATION OF MAGNETIC DATA

The techniques employed for interpreting magnetic data have many similarities to those on which gravity interpretation is based. This is to be expected in view of the fact that the laws of potential theory are fundamental to both methods. The similarities are the greatest when one compares gravity data (for which the acceleration is always vertical) with total-field magnetic data that have been reduced to the pole, a processing technique presented in Sec. 17-2. This step transforms the total-field data measured at an arbitrary magnetic latitude to the data that would have been recorded over vertically magnetized bodies in a vertical magnetic field pointing down (as it is at the north magnetic pole). With this technique and symmetric bodies, symmetric anomalies will be displayed centered over the causative body, an aid to the interpretation and comparison of anomalies.

Airborne and ship-towed magnetometers, as well as land instruments other than the flux-gate type, record total fields, the most common magnetic field measurement today. The challenge of developing fast, accurate, and automated total-field interpretation methods and the large amount of airborne and ship-borne data available for such analysis have stimulated the development of many ingenious computer techniques for this purpose. The literature on the subject has been particularly voluminous since the middle 1960s.

Earlier editions considered single-component (vertical or horizontal) and total-field interpretation separately and presented some equations with which to calculate the vertical field. This edition concentrates on total-field interpretation techniques, since they constitute the most practical and common approaches available. Nearly all these techniques are computer driven, due to the complexity of the equations involved and the widespread availability of suitable computers. Software for total-field magnetic interpretation is available for computers ranging in size from desk top machines to large mainframes.

17-1 QUALITATIVE INTERPRETATION OF MAGNETIC DATA

A large amount of the effort put into interpreting data obtained in magnetic exploration might go no farther than a qualitative evaluation of magnetic maps or profiles. The presence or absence of a fault or an intrusive body may be of much more importance than its shape or its depth of burial, neither of which can be uniquely determined from magnetic data anyway. In many magnetic surveys, the objective is to describe the boundary between sedimentary basins and surrounding areas where the basement is shallow. Such information can often be obtained by visual inspection of a magnetic map. A basin is characterized by smooth contours and low magnetic relief, while the surrounding platform area shows steep gradients and high relief in the magnetic contours.

FIGURE 17-1   Magnetic map of southwestern Oklahoma showing sudden changes in magnetic relief. One is at the southern edge of Anadarko Basin to the north of the Wichita Mountain belt, in which the magnetic gradients are high. The other transition is between the mountain belt and the basin to the south of it. (*From V. L. Jones, Vertical-Intensity Magnetic Map of Oklahoma, Proc. Geophys. Soc. Tulsa, vol. 8, p. 43, 1961–1964.*)

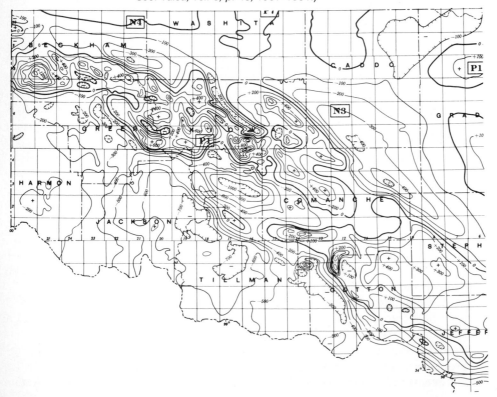

Often a well-defined boundary between zones with appreciably different degrees of magnetic relief can indicate the presence of a major basement fault. Figure 17-1 illustrates two boundaries of this kind observed in southwestern Oklahoma at the edge of the Anadarko Basin.

A diapiric feature observed in a seismic reflection section may be interpreted as either a salt dome or an igneous intrusive. The best way to identify its composition may be to run a magnetic survey across the feature. This could indicate the lithologic nature of the diapir (whether it is salt or igneous material), information that probably could not be obtained from the seismic data alone.

Significance of Magnetic Contours

Magnetic contours can look so deceptively similar to contours of subsurface structure that it is easy for those not familiar with magnetic maps to interpret the magnetic features indicated by the contours as if they were structural. In areas where the hard rocks are shallow and uniformly magnetized such an assumption might give useful qualitative information on the structure of the rocks, particularly when linear trends are observed. Magnetic maps over sedimentary basins, where the magnetized rocks are deep, can almost never be relied on for reliable information about the structure of the basement surface.

The magnetic relief observed over sedimentary basin areas is almost always controlled more by the *lithology* of the basement than by its topography. Changes in lithology that give rise to lateral contrasts in susceptibility and remanence show up in the magnetic contours more conspicuously than do topographic features on the basement surface. Changes in the magnetization of basement rocks a mile or more deep may result in magnetic anomalies up to several thousand gammas in magnetic readings at the surface. At the same depth, structural relief on the basement surface as great as 500 ft would seldom produce anomalies larger than 50 gammas. Figure 17-2 illustrates why anomalies due to magnetic contrasts can be so much larger than those resulting from topography. The vertical effect of a field of intruded magnetic material having a susceptibility contrast of 0.005 cgs units with respect to the rocks alongside it is $2\pi \times 0.005$ cgs units, or about 3000 gammas. An erosional remnant 1000 ft high and 5000 ft in diameter on an otherwise flat andesite surface covered by 5000 ft of nonmagnetic sediments produces an anomaly of only about 120 gammas. This example indicates how relatively small variations in susceptibility of basement rocks can cause anomalies with greater amplitude than anomalies produced by large topographic relief on the basement.

Use of Magnetic Data in Mapping Surface Geology

One of the most useful geological applications of magnetic surveys is to map structural trends by following lineations in magnetic contours. In some cases the lineations reflect the strike lines of elongated intrusive features or the

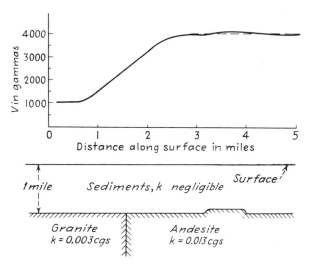

FIGURE 17-2 Comparison of magnetic effect of lateral susceptibility change in basement with effect of structural feature on basement surface.

surfaces of large faults reflected in the basement topography or lithology. Such features are often concealed under sedimentary cover and show up only on magnetic maps. Magnetic data-processing techniques for trend analysis are presented at the end of Sec. 17-2. The U.S. Geological Survey has been carrying out detailed aeromagnetic surveys over many parts of the United States. These have been of particular value for mapping geology in areas where igneous and metamorphic rocks occur near the surface but are hidden from view because of vegetation or other cover. Even where the surface geology is well exposed, geological maps can be made with a minimum of expense for field work if only scattered data points from surface outcrops are connected by use of aeromagnetically observed trends. The magnetic data facilitate interpolation of the field measurements, making a high density of ground observations unnecessary. This approach can be particularly fruitful in remote areas or those areas where surface access is difficult, provided that at least some of the geologic lineations have magnetic expression.

Figure 17-3 shows an aeromagnetic map of the Southern Cross area of Western Australia, which has well-defined magnetic anomalies indicating the trend, width, and dip of banded iron formations which act as marker beds to trace the folding axes of concealed metavolcanics and metasediments. The map is from a paper by Rayner.[1]

In mining exploration it is common to plot contacts, dips, strikes, faults, and similar features observed at the surface on aerial photographs along with identification of all outcropping rocks, usually by dabs of color at the positions where they are mapped. Magnetic contours superimposed on the same photographs make it easier to fill in the gaps between outcrops.

Often the general shape of a magnetic anomaly will help in determining the basic geologic nature of its buried source. If the contours show circular symme-

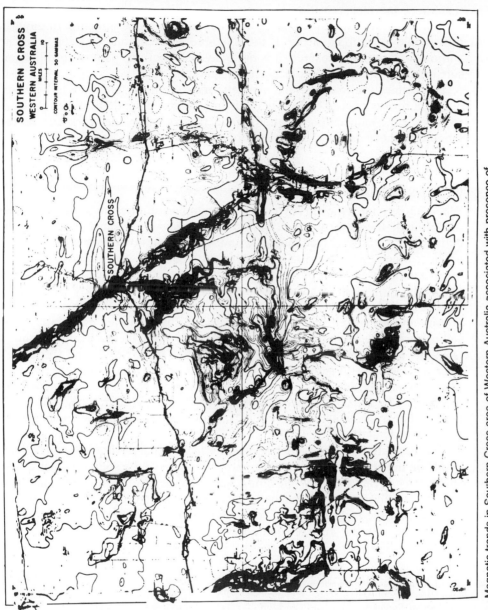

FIGURE 17-3 Magnetic trends in Southern Cross area of Western Australia associated with presence of banded iron formations, which show structure of concealed metavolcanics and metasediments. *(From J. M. Rayner,[1] "Mining and Groundwater Geophysics," The Queen's Printer, Ottawa, 1967.)*

try where the magnetization is vertical, the body may be a plug. If closed contours are elongated, the source may be a dike and the direction of elongation should indicate its strike. If there is an elongated zone of steep gradient without well-defined closures, it is quite possible that this pattern results from subsurface faulting that has displaced magnetized rocks.

The delineation from surface magnetic measurements of contacts between different rock types can be helpful in planning other, more detailed geophysical surveys, e.g., induced-polarization or electromagnetic. The work can be restricted to those areas where the rock type is indicated as favorable.

Effect of Flight Elevation on Observed Fields

When an aeromagnetic survey is run at a number of different altitudes above the ground, the data obtained at the lower elevations show more sharply defined and better-resolved magnetic anomalies than those made at the greater heights. Since there is virtually no difference between the magnetic effect of most sediments and that of the air, an aeromagnetic profile made at a height h above the ground showing an anomaly from a magnetized body buried at a depth z should be identical to a profile that would be obtained with a total-field ground magnetometer over the same feature if it were buried under a layer of sediments having a depth $z + h$. As the flight elevation increases, the anomaly from any buried, magnetized feature is attenuated in amplitude and spread out over a wider area. Figure 17-4 shows three profiles flown over the Benson Mines magnetite deposit in St. Lawrence County, N.Y., at heights ranging from 1000 to 10,000 ft above the ground. The very sharp magnetic peak recorded near the center of the profile from the 1000-ft altitude becomes almost unobservable at 10,000 ft.

The resolution of individual anomalies from separate buried sources depends on the height of the flight line above the level of the sources. Figure 17-5 shows how flying at a low elevation will indicate two anomalies while at a greater elevation the two magnetic features merge into one because of the spreading of the magnetic effect from each source with increasing distance in accordance with the inverse-square law.

FIGURE 17-4 Effect of flying at different elevations over Benson Mines. (*U.S. Geological Survey.*)

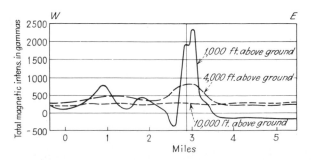

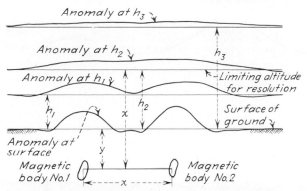

FIGURE 17-5   Resolution of anomalies from two buried magnetic bodies a distance x apart. Magnetic profiles shown at surface and at three flight elevations (h_1, h_2, and h_3). Anomalies will not generally be resolved if flight-line altitude is greater than distance $x - y$.

Dependence of Total-Field Anomalies upon Magnetic Latitude and Orientation of the Source

The magnetic anomaly observed from a buried magnetized body will depend upon the magnetic latitude as well as upon the orientation (with respect to the magnetic meridian) of any axis of elongation associated with the body. In the previous chapter it was pointed out that the flight lines are generally oriented in a direction normal to the geologic strike where that is known. If the flight paths make an oblique angle with the strike or axis of elongation, the interpretation of anomalies thus recorded can be very complicated.

North-South Flight Line Perpendicular to Axis of Elongated Body with Square Cross Section   Where the flight line is normal to the axis of elongation of a magnetized body, the anomaly obtained from it near the magnetic equator will appear quite different from that at middle latitudes or at the magnetic poles. Consider the two-dimensional magnetized body with its height equal to its width illustrated in Fig. 17-6. Its magnetization is entirely of the induced type. Its east-west axis, normal to the north-south flight line, is perpendicular to the plane of the cross section and is infinitely long. The total-field anomalies that would be observed over the body are shown for the magnetic north pole, the magnetic equator, and for a magnetic latitude of 26.6°N.

If the magnetization is vertical, as at the north pole (Fig. 17-6a), the flux lines associated with the induced magnetization are symmetrical about a vertical axis through the center of the body. Where they are directed downward at the level of the flight line, they reinforce the earth's field and give a positive anomaly. Where the field is horizontal (as it is on both sides of the body), the anomaly is zero. Where the field has an upward component (as is the case still farther in each direction from the center of the body), it opposes the earth's field and the anomaly becomes negative.

When the earth's field is horizontal, as it is at the magnetic equator, the lines of force from the magnetized body will oppose the earth's field over the center

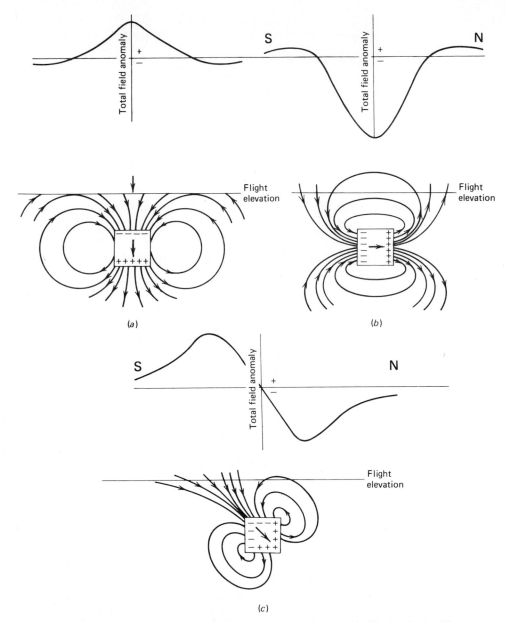

FIGURE 17-6 Total-field anomalies observed when flight line is perpendicular to axis of buried body with square cross section elongated perpendicular to page: (*a*) at north magnetic pole; (*b*) at magnetic equator; (*c*) at magnetic latitude of 26.6°N. All magnetization is induced. Anomaly is positive when the field of the buried body reinforces the earth's field and is negative when the field opposes the earth's field.

of the body, giving rise to a negative anomaly. If the axis of the body trends in the magnetic east-west direction and the flight line is in the north-south direction, the total-field anomaly will have the character indicated in Fig. 17-6*b*. At the two positions along the flight line where the lines of force are vertical, the anomaly becomes zero, and at greater distances on either side the field from the magnetic source will reinforce that of the earth. Thus, as the figure shows, the anomaly at the magnetic equator has about the same form as it does at the north pole, but it will be inverted in sign.

If the same two-dimensional body, oriented in the east-west direction, is at a magnetic latitude of 26.6°N (Fig. 17-6*c*) the poles will be distributed symmetrically with respect to the direction of the field, the two faces that are closest to the north pole containing positive poles and the two farthest from it containing negative poles. The lines of force are symmetrical about a diagonal through the cross section and are perpendicular to the earth's field at a point on the surface above the center of the body. As a field having this direction neither increases nor decreases the earth's field, the anomaly is zero at this point.

Effect of Orientation of Axis of Body on Anomaly Obtained when Flying Perpendicular to Axis   The direction of the axis of a buried, magnetized body will also affect the total-field anomaly it produces along a flight line across this axis. Let us consider a buried slab having the form of a rectangular parallelepiped, with its long direction horizontal and with its horizontal dimension perpendicular to the axis substantially greater than its height. The flight line is always normal to the long axis (perpendicular to the paper) regardless of its orientation. Figure 17-7 shows the geometry for the three cases where the axis is respectively north-south (Fig. 17-7*a*), east-west (Fig. 17-7*b*), and N45°E (Fig. 17-7*c*), the flight lines being perpendicular to the respective directions.

For the slab with its axis oriented north-south, the anomaly is positive over the body itself and negative on either side. The amplitude of the anomaly becomes greater as the magnetic latitude becomes higher. When the axis of the slab is in the east-west direction, the anomaly depends on the magnetic inclination. If the magnetic inclination is 45°, the anomaly is unsymmetrical, being positive over the updip end of the inducing field and negative over the downdip end. If there is no inclination, the field is symmetrical and negative directly over the body. When the axis of the slab has an orientation of 45° with the north-south direction, the anomaly is rather similar to that observed across the body when oriented east-west at a magnetic inclination of 45°, although the amplitude is lower and the point where the field changes direction is not quite the same.

17-2 INTERPRETATION OF TOTAL-FIELD DATA

The interpreter is usually given a set of magnetic profiles or a contoured magnetic map, preferably in digital form, and must relate the anomalies to subsurface magnetic bodies. Since an infinite number of solutions exist, i. e.,

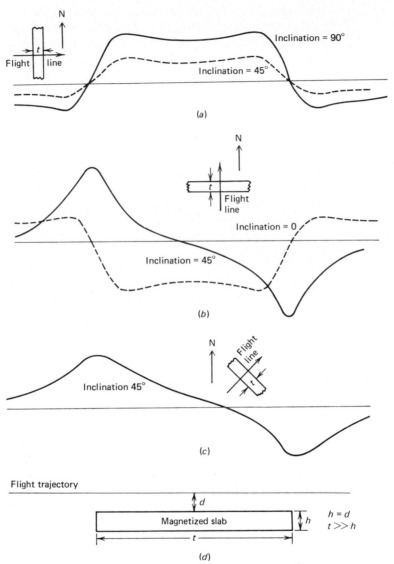

FIGURE 17-7 Total-field anomalies observed over a two-dimensional magnetized slab with long axis horizontal and horizontal dimension perpendicular to axis much greater than thickness (vertical dimension). Flight lines always perpendicular to long axis. (a) Orientation of axis north-south; (b) orientation of axis east-west; (c) orientation of axis N45°E. (d) Cross section showing position of slab in vertical plane-of-flight line.

the problem is inherently nonunique, it is essential that all additional geophysical and geological constraints be incorporated into the analysis. There are three basic approaches to this interpretation challenge: forward modeling, inverse methods, and data enhancement. Each is discussed in the following sections.

Forward Modeling

Forward modeling is the "art" of estimating the geometry of the source or the distribution of magnetization within the source by trial-and-error modeling. As discussed in Sec. 15-4, many different forward-modeling algorithms are available with which to calculate the precise field of a hypothetical source. The result is compared with the observed data, and the model is adjusted in order to improve the fit for a subsequent comparison. Many of the classic algorithms have been adapted to modern interactive-graphics hardware, so this is probably the most widely used interpretive technique. Magnetic modeling and interpretation code, suitable even for microcomputers, exists. As microcomputers drop in price and rise in power, more sophisticated and powerful software packages will become available for potential-field interpretation. The model may be two- or three-dimensional, and the calculations may be done in the space domain or in the Fourier domain.

The decision on how to adjust the model at each iteration in the trial-and-error approach is subjective and can be time-consuming. Consequently, various workers have written algorithms to perform the forward-modeling iterations by computer. The theoretical profile is calculated from the initial model, "goodness of fit" (e.g., mean-squared error) is determined between the observed and the calculated profiles, one or more body parameters are adjusted so that the fit can be improved, and the field is recalculated. Although iterative forward modeling is the core of the technique, when an algorithm automatically determines a parameter of the source, the technique may thereupon be classified among the inverse methods.

Inverse Methods

Inverse methods involve the direct determination (as opposed to the trial-and-error or indirect determination) of some parameter(s) of the source from the measured data. It is important to realize that every anomaly has an infinite number of permissible sources. One way to narrow infinity down to some smaller number is to constrain the parameters in some way. Constraints may be imposed mathematically: for example, magnetization values may be required to have a minimum amount of variation from point to point. Independently measured geophysical data could constrain the solutions: for example, permissible magnetizations might be restricted according to sample measurements, or gravity or seismic data can constrain body shape. Geologic constraints are determined from field studies or analogous field situations: for example, boundaries between magnetic bodies may be required to be vertical.

In general, two parameter sets govern the shape of the anomaly: the shape of the body and the distribution of magnetic material within it. During any given computer run, usually one of the two is held fixed. In some cases, the calculation of depth to source or depth to bottom of source is a desired quantity. The following section discusses these three approaches to the inversion of magnetic data.

Calculation of Magnetic Distribution Given the Geometry of the Source
Sometimes geologic evidence or other geophysical field measurements are available to describe the geometry of the source. With the source geometry fixed, calculations of the distribution of magnetization directly from the measured field is a linear inverse problem, since potential fields are linear functions of the magnitude of the source. For example, doubling the magnetization throughout all source bodies doubles the amplitude but not the shape of the magnetic anomaly. The following four sections present four ways to handle the linear inverse problem.

Matrix Method The matrix method, a space-domain technique, seeks a numerical solution for a linear integral equation. Bott[2], Bott and Hutton[3], and others[4,5] divided the source geometry into cells, each with uniform magnetization, and solved for the best set of magnetizations. Figure 17-8 shows Emilia and Bodvarsson's[6] use of this technique to determine the set of magnetizations associated with a magnetic anomaly profile across a (marine) spreading center. If the number of observations exceeds the number of cells, a least-squares method is used to achieve the best set of magnetizations. Bott[2] stated that this matrix method can be applied to irregularly shaped bodies which are not amenable to Fourier methods of inversion.

Bott and Hutton[4] point out an important instability in this method. If the widths of the magnetic cells are too small with respect to the depth to the cells, the calculated magnetizations vary unrealistically from cell to cell. Similar

FIGURE 17-8 From top to bottom: Magnetic anomaly profile across a spreading ridge. Cell-by-cell distribution of magnetization determined for the source body. Outline of the source body with sections of normal magnetization in black. *J, O,* and *M* represent previously identified time events (Jaramillo, Olduvai, and Mammoth events, respectively). The thickness of the source layer was assumed to be 2 km. (*From Emilia and Bodvarsson.*[5])

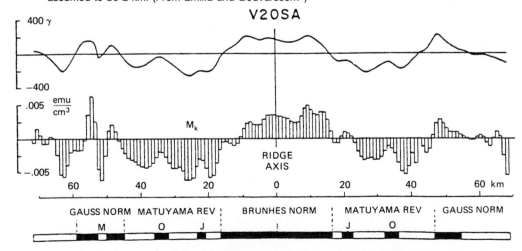

instabilities are inherent in all inverse calculations and are most apparent when resolution of too much detail is attempted.

Divide by the Earth Filter The benefits of working in the Fourier domain have attracted several workers. For example, in the special situation where sources are confined to a horizontal layer and magnetization varies only in one horizontal direction, the magnetic anomaly can be written as the one-dimensional convolution integral. Following Schouten's[7,8] development, the anomaly may be written as

$$m(x) = \int_{-\infty}^{+\infty} j(\xi) \, K(x - \xi) \, d\xi \qquad (17\text{-}1)$$

when defining the quantities according to Fig. 17-9. The quantity K is a kernel that depends upon a and b (the depths to the top and bottom of the body) and upon the orientation of the magnetization vector. The strike of the body is along the y axis. The Fourier transform of $f(x)$ is $F(s)$, with the convention that

$$F(s) = \int_{-\infty}^{+\infty} f(x) \, e^{-isx} \, dx \qquad (17\text{-}2)$$

and

$$f(x) = \frac{1}{2\pi} \int_{-\infty}^{+\infty} F(s) \, e^{isx} \, ds$$

and where s is wave number which is inversely proportional to wavelength. The Fourier transform of the anomaly $m(x)$ can be written

$$M(s) = J(s) \, K(s) \qquad (17\text{-}3)$$

Hence the Fourier transform of the magnetic survey is equal to the Fourier transform of the magnetization (assumed to be a function only of x) times the "earth filter." When one starts with a given earth model and a set of magnetiza-

FIGURE 17-9   Earth model giving rise to the observed anomaly, $m(x)$, at $(x, 0)$. ξ is the x coordinate of the body. The intensity of magnetization $j(\xi)$ is a function of ξ alone within the body and zero without. (*From* Schouten.[7])

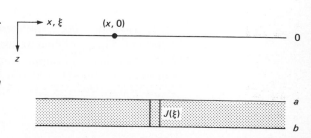

tions, the multiplication of the Fourier transforms of these two is simply the forward problem discussed in Sec. 15-4. The inverse problem is solved by dividing the Fourier transform of the survey data by the earth filter, which thus yields the magnetization[7-9]. In the case where magnetization varies in both horizontal directions, the above equations should be written as two-dimensional integrals, and the earth filter has a similar but two-dimensional form. It is important to note that certain instabilities are inherent in this procedure: The longest and shortest wavelengths are greatly amplified and often need to be filtered[9]. The earth filter is determined by the source geometry. The source geometry must be rather simple, i.e., confined by horizontal planes and varying in only one (or two) horizontal directions.

Parker's Method Parker generalized his Fourier-domain forward-modeling algorithm (as discussed in Sec. 15-4) to do the inverse calculation. With some assumptions concerning the source geometry, he derived an iterative scheme involving Fourier transforms at each step to find the distribution of magnetization between two undulating surfaces given the measured magnetic field.[10]

Determination of the Single Best Direction of Magnetization Modeling and inverse methods must account for significant components of remanent magnetization. If the geometry of a source is known, a forward method, such as the method of Talwani,[11,12] can be used to calculate three fields due to three orthogonal components of magnetization, respectively. These fields can be compared with observed data by the use of least-squares techniques to ascertain the relative importance of each of the three magnetic components, thereby providing the best average direction of magnetization.

Marine magnetic data over seamounts are often analyzed by this technique. Each seamount is treated as a single paleomagnetic sample so that the average magnetization vector associated with the seamount is treated as an estimate of a VGP (virtual geomagnetic pole). VGPs calculated in this way for Pacific seamounts provide a Cretaceous polar wander curve for the Pacific plate relative to the earth's rotation axis and independent of other plate motions (Francheteau et al.,[13] Parker[14]).

Calculation of Source Geometry Given the Distribution of Magnetization Potential fields are rather complicated functions (involving logarithms and arctangents) of the coordinates of the boundary of their sources. Hence, the determination of shape or size of the source is a nonlinear inverse problem and is more difficult than the linear one. The two styles of approach to this problem are discussed below.

Approximate the Nonlinear Equation by Linear Ones and Use Least Squares The nonlinear relationship between the measured anomaly and the body coordinates is approximated by a Taylor's series. The problem is rendered approximately linear by dropping the higher-order terms. This approach is often used[15-17] for 2-D problems starting with the equations of Talwani and Heirtzler.[11]

A method of rapid convergence described by Marquardt[18] was used by Johnson[15] to interpret efficiently a 2-D magnetic structure. Here, two parameters, the positions in x and z of one corner point of the body cross section, were altered until the sum of the squared differences between observed and calculated anomalies reached a minimum value. Figure 17-10, from Johnson,[15] illustrates the initial and final model deduced from the best fit of a calculated anomaly. This approach was implemented for microcomputers by Reeves and MacLeod.[19] They showed how a rough initial model (Fig. 17-11) could be refined through iterative (inverse) modeling, resulting in the final model depicted.

Webring[17] has published a gravity and magnetic inversion program to derive an ensemble of 2-D prisms (a structural cross section) whose calculated anomaly best approximates the observed data in a least-squares sense. The 2-D prisms are formed by linking vertices into a network which may be deformed by a modified Marquardt algorithm. The location of the prism vertices and the density or magnetic property of each prism can all be investigated.

Linear Programming   The source region is divided into a large number of small cells, with the number of cells exceeding the number of field observations. Linear programming is used with constraints to find magnetizations for each cell. Magnetizations determined are not treated as "real" but are used to estimate certain key parameters about the geometry of the body (e.g., maximum thickness). Heustis and Parker[20] discussed how to calculate the source distribution that has the minimum intensity yet fits data and is confined to a given thickness layer. "Because the minimum intensity must be a monotonically decreasing function of layer thickness, it follows that an upper bound on the intensity allows a lower limit of the thickness."[20] They applied their theory to the oceanic magnetized layer.

Calculation of Depth to Source or Depth to Bottom of Source   The depth to the top of the source is a useful tool for finding depths of sedimentary basins, and sometimes for locating major structures in basement rocks. (Some anomalies arising from basement rocks, however, may be due to lithologic changes rather than to structural features.)

In certain geologic situations, the depth to the bottom of magnetic sources is sought: It can correspond to the depth to the Curie-temperature isotherm. The Curie point is the temperature above which crustal rocks lose their magnetization and no longer generate detectable magnetic anomalies. Magnetic data can be used to learn about the thermal structure of the upper crust. Aeromagnetic data have significant potential as a rapid, regional geothermal reconnaissance tool. Curie-point determination is an exceedingly difficult task because the bottoms of magnetic sources contribute very low-amplitude and long-wavelength components to the observed anomaly as compared to shallower sources. Furthermore, the bottom of a magnetic source may be a lithologic change, not the Curie-point isotherm.

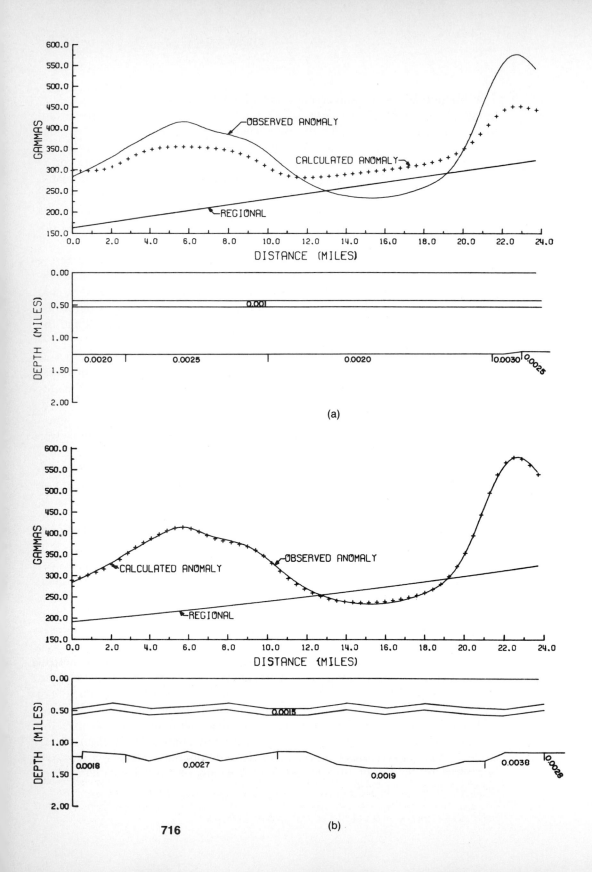

(a)

(b)

716

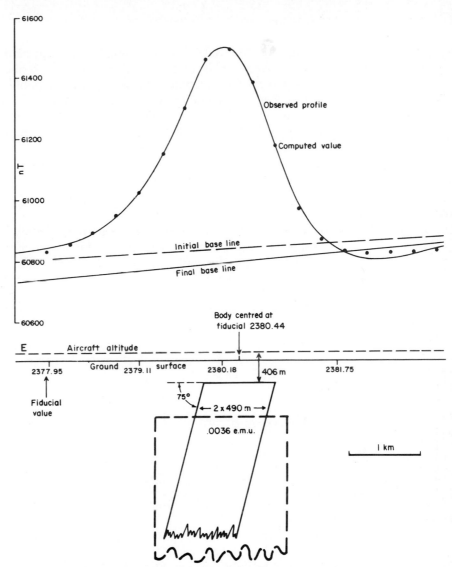

FIGURE 17-11   The fit obtained through iterative inverse modeling between an observed magnetic profile at a high magnetic latitude and a computed profile from a source body. The starting model, a dipping dike, is shown in dashed outline. The final model, with numerical values for the parameters, is shown in true scale section below the profile. This modeling was accomplished on a microcomputer. (*Reeves and MacLeod.*[19])

FIGURE 17-10   (a) The initially assumed geological configuration and susceptibilities are shown in the section in the bottom part of the figure. The anomalies due to this configuration with the initial regional curve are shown in the top part of the figure by the crosses. The solid curve represents the observed data. (b) The changed geological configuration and susceptibilities are shown in the section. The altered regional curve is shown above. The anomalies due to this configuration and with this regional curve are shown by the crosses. (*Johnson.*[15])

Calculations of depth to source or depth to bottom of source can be made from the shape of anomalies, or the shape of the power spectrum computed from magnetic data. Several examples are described below.

Werner Method This method makes use of a semiempirical calculation which is quite easy to apply. Werner's original publication is not readily accessible, but the technique has been summarized by Hartman et al.[21]

Consider a thin dike with infinite strike length and depth extent. The total anomalous field $\Delta T(x)$ at a distance x along a measuring line perpendicular to the dike can be expressed in the empirical form

$$\Delta T(x) = \frac{A(x - x_0) + Bz}{(x - x_0)^2 + z^2} \tag{17-4}$$

where x_0 is the horizontal distance to a point immediately over the center of the dike's top and z is the depth to the top. A and B are functions (to be determined) of the field strength, dip, and strike as well as the inclination and declination of the dike's magnetization.

Equation (17-4) has four unknowns, A, B, x_0, and z. If observations are made on a level surface and if the thin dikes satisfy certain other requirements, the above equation can be put into the form

$$a_0 + a_1 + b_1 F + b_1 xF = x^2 F \tag{17-5}$$

where

$$a_0 = -Ax_0 + Bz, \ b_0 = -x_0^2 - z^2, \ a_1 = A, \ b_1 = 2x_0, \text{ and } F = \Delta T(x)$$

It is easy to show that

$$x_0 = \frac{b_1}{2} \quad \text{and} \quad z = \pm \tfrac{1}{2} \sqrt{-4b_0 - b_1^2}$$

It is only necessary to substitute the $\Delta T(x)$'s at four different values of x to obtain a_0, a_1, b_0, and b_1. From them one solves for x_0 and z.

The above technique uses a dike (thin sheet) as the "unit building block" for the source geometry. Hartman et al.[21] also discussed the extension to Werner's theory that utilizes interfaces as the building block. They noted that a thin sheet is actually two parallel interfaces located arbitrarily close together. Moreover the anomaly due to a thin sheet is equivalent to the anomaly of an interface. By applying Werner deconvolution to both the total-field anomaly and its calculated derivative, the depth to the source can be automatically calculated for semi-infinite, homogeneous, thin-sheet bodies, contacts, or faults, with the assumption that the bodies of the above type strike perpendicular to the flight line.

For automated magnetic interpretation, Ku and Sharp[22] built upon the Werner deconvolution approach by additionally employing some of Marquardt's inverse modeling techniques. Naudy[23] presented an automated determination of source depth from aeromagnetic profiles.

Moments of Anomalies   The moment of the individual anomaly has also been used to calculate depth to source or depth to bottom of source.[24] The nth moment of a function $f(x)$ is defined, in this context, as $M_n = x^n f(x)$. The nth x and y moments of $f(x,y)$ are defined as $M_n^x(x,y) = x^n f(x,y)$ and $M_n^y(x,y) = y^n f(x,y)$. Bhattacharyya and Leu[24] described a method for spectral analysis of gravity and magnetic anomalies due to 2-D structure. This approach evaluated the spectra of moments of data along a profile. (An earlier paper by Bhattacharyya[25] had discussed some general properties of potential fields in the space and frequency domains.) Bhattacharyya and Leu[26] extended their spectral approach to the analysis of anomalies due to 3-D structures representable by vertical rectangular prismatic bodies. They showed that the ratios of the spectra of the x moments (and y moments) to the Fourier transform of the potential-field data are related to the depth and dimensions of the causative body. The source is assumed to be a vertically dipping rectangular prism. The original data were reduced to the pole on the assumption of induced magnetization of all bodies. The upper edge of the prism, relative to the deeper edges, dominates the spectrum of the anomaly. The moments of the anomaly contain the larger effects of the bottom edges, and so their spectra are useful for estimating the depth to the bottom of the causative bodies.[27] Figure 17-12 is their interpretation of a magnetic anomaly in Yellowstone National Park.

Power Spectra   The simple relationship between the shape of the spectra to the depths to the top and bottom of the source has been utilized by various

FIGURE 17-12   Interpretation of filtered total-field magnetic anomaly shown in solid lines. Dashed contour lines show the anomaly due to a rectangular prismatic body. The horizontal cross section of the body is shown by a thin line. Contour interval is 50 gammas. Location: Yellowstone National Park, U.S.A. (*Bhattacharyya and Leu.*[27])

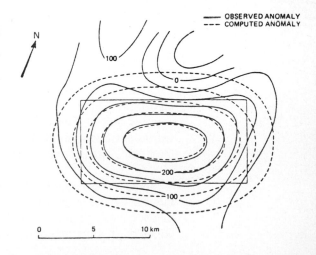

workers. Spectra are generated for profiles[28,29] or for gridded data[30,31] and compared with model spectra to determine the key body parameters.

Data-Enhancement Techniques

In many cases, much can be learned directly from gridded magnetic data without explicitly modeling the anomalies. The product of this (computer) approach is usually a map, often contoured, which accentuates certain attributes of the source. Most of these filtering-type techniques can be applied in either the space or Fourier domain, but the latter approach is often the more efficient and instructive.

Reduction to the Pole The shape of a magnetic anomaly not only depends on the shape and the susceptibility of the perturbing body, but also on the direction of its magnetization and the direction of the regional field. Reduction to the pole transforms an anomaly into the anomaly that would be observed if the magnetization and regional field were vertical (as if the anomaly was measured at the north magnetic pole). A symmetric body produces a symmetric anomaly at the magnetic poles. Hence, reduction to the pole is a way to remove the asymmetries caused by a nonvertical magnetization or regional field and to produce a simpler set of anomalies to interpret. (Symmetric anomalies are visually easier to interpret and to compare.) In particular, anomalies are more nearly centered over their respective causative bodies, a positioning that facilitates comparison with gravity or seismic maps. Space-domain convolution algorithms[32] or Fourier-domain algorithms[33,34] may be employed to accomplish reduction to the pole. Figure 17-13 shows Blakely and Cox's[35] model test of the reduction to the pole.

Upward and Downward Continuation Upward continuation is the process of transforming potential-field data measured on one surface to some other higher surface. No assumptions are required about specific sources. Because the data are being "moved" away from sources, this procedure is generally stable mathematically. Downward continuation, the transforming of data to some lower surface, is extremely unstable, however, because moving nearer the source amplifies shorter-wavelength information (including the noise). These operations can be carried out in the space domain, using the convolution algorithm[32,36] or the Schwarz-Christoffel transformation, which deals with 2-D sources only.[37] The Fourier domain may be employed for upward- or downward-continuation calculations from a horizontal surface to a horizontal surface[33] or from an uneven surface to an uneven surface.[38,39]

Vertical Derivatives Vertical derivatives amplify short-wavelength information at the expense of long-wavelength information. Vertical-derivative maps, usually the first or second vertical derivative, accentuate gradients along edges of shallow magnetic sources. Hence they are sometimes used to locate

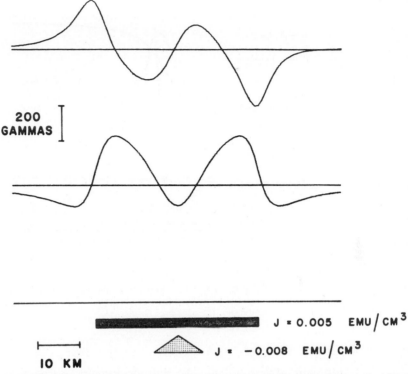

FIGURE 17-13   Model data showing reduction to the pole. The source bodies have been generalized to change with depth—the cross-sectional boundary of the source and the intensity of the magnetization both are functions of z. The source magnetization that produced the top profile has a declination D_M of 0° and an Inclination I_M of 40°. The regional field has declination D_H and inclination I_H of 0° and 30°, respectively. The strike S of the source is 105°. The second profile is the result of transforming the first profile to the north magnetic pole. (*Blakely and Cox.*[35])

edges of magnetic bodies and to emphasize sources at shallow depths. The calculations may be carried out in the space domain[32] or in the Fourier domain.[33]

Pseudogravity Transformation   Poisson's relation states that the magnetic potential and the gravitational attraction over a bounded mass with uniform density and uniform magnetization are proportional. It is a straightfoward procedure, therefore, to calculate from magnetic data, given a density contrast and a magnetic contrast, the gravitational attraction that would be observed if the magnetization distribution were replaced by an identical density distribution. (Pseudomagnetic maps may also be produced from gravity data.) We might do this not because we believe that such a mass distribution actually exists but because certain properties of gravity anomalies are easier to analyze than certain properties of magnetic anomalies, principally the location of the edge of the anomalous source body (Fig. 17-14). Algorithms exist for the space-

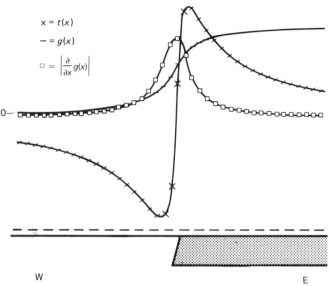

FIGURE 17-14 Model data showing the magnetic anomaly $t(x)$, its pseudogravity counterpart $g(x)$, and the magnitude of the horizontal gradient of the pseudogravity $|\partial/\partial x \cdot g(x)|$. Inclination $= 60°$, declination $= 0°$. Units are arbitrary. (*Cordell and Grauch*.[41])

domain approach[40] and the Fourier-domain approach.[33] Most algorithms that perform pseudogravity transformations require that the declination and inclination of the magnetic vector associated with the magnetic source are known. This may be difficult if the remanent magnetization component is significant.

Horizontal Gradients   Horizontal gradients of gravity anomalies are steepest approximately over edges of tabular masses. Horizontal gradients of pseudogravity anomalies can be calculated and mapped, and the maxima on such maps can be inspected to aid in the location of magnetization contrasts.[41,42] In Fig. 17-14, Cordell and Grauch[41] illustrate the relationship between the total-field magnetic anomaly $\Delta T(x)$, its pseudogravity counterpart $g(x)$, and the magnitude of the horizontal gradient of the pseudogravity.

Attenuation of Terrain Effects   Topography that includes magnetic rock types (e.g., young volcanic terranes) can cause significant anomalies in magnetic surveys, obscuring other anomalies of more interest for which the survey was conducted. Removal of the effects of a magnetic terrane is a more difficult problem than gravity terrain corrections. Magnetizations vary by orders of magnitude and by sign from point to point and from rock type to rock type, whereas densities vary typically by only a few percent.

Blakely and Grauch[43] statistically correlated observed magnetic anomalies with the magnetic field calculated from a uniformly magnetized topographic model in order to objectively identify areas in which topographic effects are pronounced. The areas of low or no correlation are interpreted as areas exhibiting anomalies unrelated to topography, and hence are areas of geologic interest.

Grauch[44] presented an approach to automatically separate anomalies caused by magnetic terrane from anomalies caused by subsurface sources. It is based upon the premise that anomalies due to subsurface sources are uncorrelated with topographic effects, and it requires no information about distribution of magnetization.

Another quantitative approach to this problem, using Fourer-domain analysis techniques, was carried out by Blakely,[45] who compared the spectral differences between observed anomalies and anomalies calculated from topographic relief. The magnetic field due to topographic sources was calculated by Parker's method,[46] in which the top of the source is the digitized terrain, the bottom is flat and horizontal, and the magnetization is uniform.

Wavelength Filtering Wavelength filtering is sometimes used to calculate the regional or residual fields. Low-pass filters pass the long-wavelength anomalies (broad slow changes in the potential-field data) typically attributed to deep-crustal or subcrustal sources and termed the regional field. High-pass filters pass the short-wavelength anomalies (residuals) usually associated with shallow features. Hence, wavelength filters are sometimes used to separate anomalies due to shallow sources from anomalies due to deep sources. These techniques were discussed and illustrated in Chap. 14. The validity of this separation rests upon the assumption that the cutoff wavelength of the filter is related to the maximum depth of the source. When a long-wavelength anomaly is caused by a broad, shallow feature, the premise that wavelength filtering separates deep and shallow sources is invalidated (Hildenbrand,[33] Simpson et al.[47])

Trend analysis is a filtering technique that passes anomalies whose strike is between two specified directions. It is important to note that anomalies can become falsely elongated by directional filters; only trends that are visible on the unfiltered map should be believed. Trend analysis maps can be useful for enhancing subtle geologic features in the potential-field data and for attenuating noise with specific trends (e.g., navigational errors along parallel flight lines).

Caveats

Interpolation Fourier-domain techniques for potential-field data require uniform gridded coverage. To establish a regular grid of data, the initial data may have to be interpolated. For successful interpolation, a sufficiently fine grid should be used so that the values of the original data set are not degraded

(Gibert and Galdeano[48]). When coverage is irregular, interpolated values may be inserted by use of an interpolation algorithm (e.g., Hildenbrand[33]), usually without ill effects. Input grids containing appreciably large regions of missing data are inappropriate for Fourier-domain techniques. Such grids usually display unwanted characteristics in the Fourier domain, which give erroneous results.

Most Fourier-domain magnetic interpretation or filtering techniques that use the fast Fourier-transform (FFT) algorithm (Cooley and Tukey[49]) assume that both the normal field vector and the magnetization vector have constant directions over the entire gridded data. In reality, this is not true if the area of investigation is too large or if a substantially heterogeneous area is under study. Gibert and Galdeano[48] present a Fourier-domain approach that is slower than one using the FFT but which addresses these and other problems.

Edge Effects   Magnetic surveys are of necessity finite in lateral extent. The abrupt termination of data at the edge of the survey can cause distortion (Gibbs phenomenon) upon filtering in the Fourier domain. The best (but often not the most practical) way to remove edge effects is to have available sufficient amounts of real data outside the zone of interest, so the zone of interest may be accurately treated by various filtering techniques (Hildenbrand[33]).

It is not just the Fourier methods which have problems with irregular or missing data coverage. Convolution methods (i.e., space-domain operators) must also deal with the abrupt termination of data and the irregular spacing of data. As in seismic surveys, anomalies of interest on the edge of a survey generally will require a new survey centered over the anomaly in order to be defined and believed.

17-3   GENERAL CONSIDERATIONS IN MAGNETIC INTERPRETATION

Regionals and Residuals   The removal of regional effects to obtain residual anomalies is of course as important in magnetic interpretation as it is for gravity data. The method of wavelength filtering to obtain residual anomalies was presented at the end of Sec. 17-2. The mathematical methods for obtaining residual gravity fields discussed in Chap. 14 are all applicable (directly or with modifications) to magnetic interpretation. The techniques actually employed, however, may be somewhat different. In mining exploration with the ground magnetometer, the fields from magnetic minerals in relatively shallow ore bodies are probably so large that the background field will not affect the desired results significantly. In the analysis of anomalies from such sources it is seldom worthwhile to remove the regional field except when regional variations are large, in which case they can often be removed visually.

Where large areas are covered, the simplest approach is to fit the magnetic data over as large an area as possible around the zone of interest to a polynomial of appropriate order and to subtract the polynomial surface from the observed surface. The principal problem in removing a magnetic regional, as in the corresponding gravity case, is one of interpretation. It may not be possible to determine whether an apparent residual feature has structural significance or is the result of a lithologic change deep within the basement.

Ambiguity of Magnetic Data   The statements made in Chap. 14 on the ambiguity of gravity data hold for magnetic data as well. The laws of potential theory that tell us why gravity data by themselves can never be accounted for by a single, unique interpretation apply also to the magnetic case. Here again independent geological information is necessary if the interpreter is to choose the most reasonable of an indefinite number of subsurface pictures that might fit the magnetic observations equally well. Just as it is often impossible to differentiate between structure and density contrast in determining the source of a gravity anomaly, it may be infeasible for the same reason to say whether an observed magnetic anomaly results from structural relief or from a lateral change in susceptibility.

Even when concentrations of magnetic material are accurately located by magnetic methods, it is not generally possible to evaluate their economic possibilities from magnetic data alone. There is often such wide divergence in the susceptibilities of various minerals that very small quantities of one may have more effect than very large quantities of another. Because this fact was not recognized, the early magnetic prospecting for iron deposits in Wisconsin, Michigan, and Minnesota was spectacularly unsuccessful. A large-scale program of magnetic exploration begun about 1875 showed up innumerable magnetic anomalies which were suggestive of commercial iron deposits. When these were investigated further, it was found that in most cases no economic concentrations of iron were present. Other areas exhibiting no magnetic anomalies at all often turned out to be highly productive. This puzzle remained unsolved for 50 years until Mason, Slichter, and Hay began to investigate the fundamental magnetic properties of various minerals associated with iron deposits. Discovering that magnetite has a much greater susceptibility than any other iron-bearing mineral, they were the first to realize that magnetic data reflect percentages of magnetite, but not of most other ferrous constituents. A minute amount of magnetite disseminated in nonferrous minerals could give a greater magnetic anomaly than a large, commercially productive deposit of hematite, which is a much less magnetic ferrous mineral. This discovery immediately led to new and more successful interpretation techniques in magnetic prospecting for iron. Weaver[50] has cited this example to show how empiricism not supported by proper analytical reasoning can lead to trouble in exploration.

17-4   INTERPRETATION OF DATA FROM MAGNETIC SURVEYS

In this section we shall consider the results of some magnetic surveys, ground, airborne, and ship-towed, with particular reference, where the information is available, to the relationship between the magnetic data and the geology of the area involved. Examples will be presented from mineral, petroleum, geothermal, and archaeological exploration.

Magnetic exploration for minerals is generally undertaken with one of three objectives in mind: (1) to look for magnetic minerals, such as iron ores rich in magnetite, directly; (2) to use associated magnetic minerals as tracers in the search for nonmagnetic minerals; or (3) to determine the depth, size, or structure of mineralized zones for which there is no surface evidence because of alluvial or vegetative cover. Faults and similar structural features that have a bearing on the depths of ore deposits can often be found by magnetic surveys.

There are reported cases where the occurrence of oil in an individual pool can be related to a magnetic anomaly, such as one from a buried basement ridge causing entrapment in overlying sediments that have draped over the magnetic source, or a magnetic anomaly attributable to the epigenetic near-surface magnetite which formed through the chemical reactions of seeping hydrocarbons with the local ground conditions. Except for such cases, most magnetic surveys are primarily useful in oil exploration for determining basement depths so as to cast light on the existence and geometry of sedimentary basins, particularly in relatively unexplored areas.

Geothermal exploration uses the various interpretation techniques available to determine the base of the magnetic source. This is postulated to be the Curie-point isotherm, i.e., the temperature at which rocks lose their magnetization due to heating. Areas of anomalously shallow Curie-point isotherms are identified as potentially prospective for the harnessing of geothermal energy.

Magnetic Exploration for Iron Ore   Approximately 90 percent of the world's iron production comes from sedimentary sources which are primarily oolitic or siliceous in composition. The remainder is from igneous rocks, the ores generally being in close proximity to intrusive masses from which the iron was derived or from weathering of nonferrous constituents of the igneous material. Ores associated with igneous rocks are likely to have a high magnetite-hematite ratio, and they can be detected by magnetic measurements directly. Hematitic ore bodies are nonmagnetic, but they often can be related genetically or structurally to surrounding formations containing magnetite. Magnetic surveys in such cases would then be used for indirect location of the ore.

The applicability as well as the limitations of magnetic surveys for locating economic deposits of hematitic ores are illustrated in Fig. 17-15, which shows the total-field magnetic contours over the Northern Middleback Range of South Australia, the major source of iron in the continent. The shaded area bounded by heavy lines is the area within which iron-bearing formations crop out. The black patches represent ore bodies where the iron occurs in economic quantities. The magnetic contours indicate the general area where iron is found, but the magnitudes give no clue to the locations of the ore bodies themselves. Two important deposits, the Iron Prince and Iron Baron, are somewhat outside the zone of magnetic anomalies. The ore bodies do yield diagnostic gravity anoma-

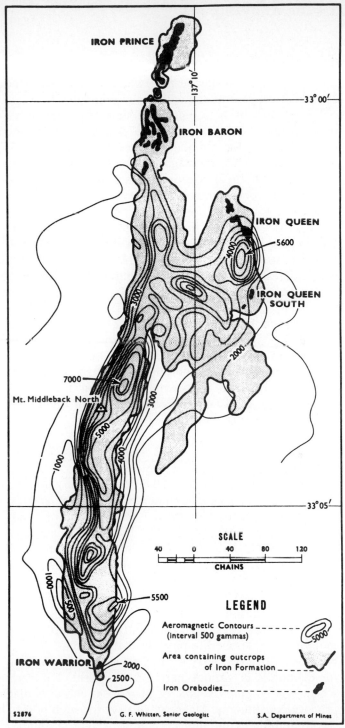

FIGURE 17-15   Total-field magnetic contours over Northern Middleback Range of South Australia. Note correlation of anomalies with shaded areas, where iron formations outcrop. (*From Webb.*[51])

727

lies, however, and the standard exploration procedure here has been to block out areas on the magnetic map where iron is indicated and then to look for economic concentrations with the gravimeter.

Where the iron is taconitic, the state of oxidation has a considerable effect on its magnetic character. Figure 17-16 shows the magnetic field over a portion of the western Mesabi Range. Here the oxidized portions of Biwabik iron formation are much less magnetic than the taconitic rocks that are not oxidized. This is because the oxidation breaks down magnetite. As the less-oxidized ore is easier to process, areas with magnetic highs should be more prospective as sources of commercial ore.

Figure 17-17 shows the aeromagnetic contours observed over Pea Ridge, Mo., where an ore body which was expected to produce 2 million tons a year was discovered at a depth of about 1250 ft. The drilling that led to the discovery was undertaken to investigate the source of the 3200-gamma anomaly indicated on the map. The ore body is about 3000 ft across with its center slightly north of the magnetic peak. The iron bodies are hydrothermal fracture fillings and replacements in Precambrian volcanics.

Figure 17-18 shows the surface vertical magnetic profile and the aeromagnetic total-field profile over the Dayton ore body in Nevada, which was formed by replacement of metamorphosed limy sediments. A granodiorite intrusion adjacent to the body apparently folded and fractured the sediments, allowing the replacement to take place. The effect of flight elevation on the aeromagnetic anomaly is pronounced.

Magnetic Exploration for Other Minerals   Although not magnetic themselves, base metals (e.g., nickel and copper) and gold are often found in association with magnetic minerals such as magnetite and pyrrhotite. Some metallic ores are found in the margins of batholiths and other intrusives which can be detailed under glacial drift by magnetic surveys.

Figure 17-19 shows the vertical magnetic anomaly observed by Galbraith[54] over a nickel and copper sulfide ore body beneath a norite contact in the Sudbury district of Canada. The ore was discovered by a borehole, located on the basis of magnetic measurements, which penetrated 100 ft of drift before reaching the desired target.

Magnetic surveys have frequently been employed in prospecting for diamond-bearing kimberlite pipes in various areas. This type of exploration has been described by Gerryts[55] in a review of geophysical methods of exploring for diamonds in various parts of the world. Kimberlite, an ultrabasic rock which is a common source of diamonds, contains magnetite and ilmenite as primary constituents. Magnetic surveys for such bodies have been reported in the United States and the U.S.S.R. as well as in South, East, and West Africa. Figure 17-20 illustrates the aeromagnetic anomaly observed over some pipes in the Koffiefontein area of South Africa.

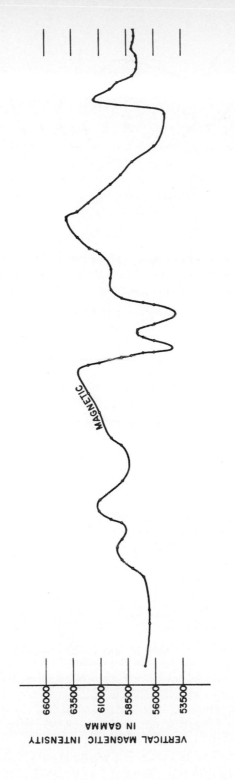

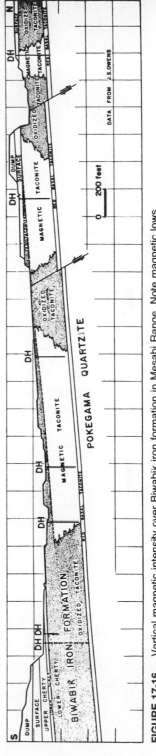

FIGURE 17-16 Vertical magnetic intensity over Biwabik iron formation in Mesabi Range. Note magnetic lows over oxidized zones. DH indicates drill hole. (*From Leney.*[52])

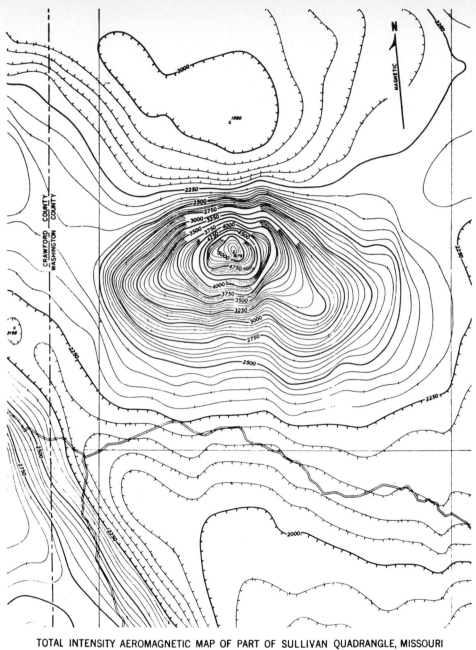

TOTAL INTENSITY AEROMAGNETIC MAP OF PART OF SULLIVAN QUADRANGLE, MISSOURI

RELATIVE TO ARBITRARY DATUM

Contour interval 50 and 250 gammas
Flown 1800 feet above sea level
1951

FIGURE 17-17 Aeromagnetic contours over Pea Ridge, Mo., ore body. The ore, 1250 ft deep and 3000 ft in horizontal dimensions, is located in the area where the magnetic intensity is highest. (*From Leney.*[52])

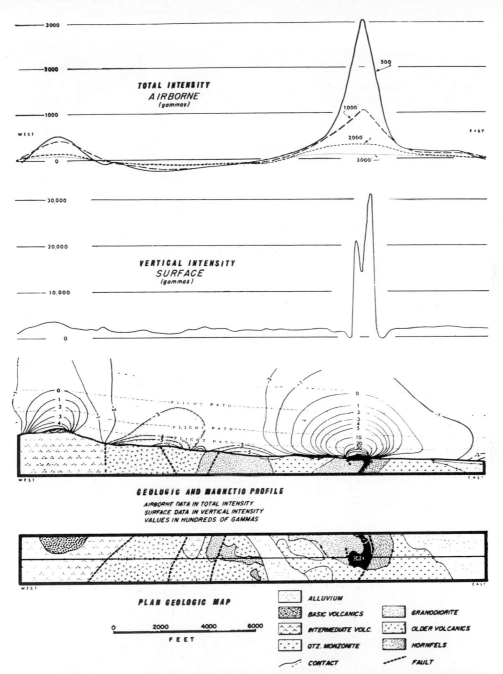

TOTAL INTENSITY
AIRBORNE
(gammas)

VERTICAL INTENSITY
SURFACE
(gammas)

GEOLOGIC AND MAGNETIC PROFILE
AIRBORNE DATA IN TOTAL INTENSITY
SURFACE DATA IN VERTICAL INTENSITY
VALUES IN HUNDREDS OF GAMMAS

PLAN GEOLOGIC MAP

ALLUVIUM	
BASIC VOLCANICS	GRANODIORITE
INTERMEDIATE VOLC.	OLDER VOLCANICS
QTZ. MONZONITE	HORNFELS
CONTACT	FAULT

0   2000   4000   6000
FEET

FIGURE 17-18   Airborne profiles of total intensity at various flying heights compared with vertical intensity measured on surface over Dayton ore body in Nevada for which geological map and section are shown. (*From Riddell.*[53])

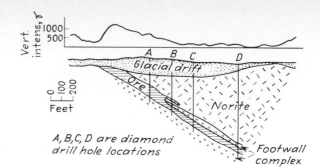

FIGURE 17-19 Magnetic field over drift-covered sulfide-ore body at Sudbury, Ontario. (*After Galbraith.*[54])

FIGURE 17-20 Aeromagnetic anomaly over kimberlite pipes in Koffiefontein area, South Africa. (*From Gerryts.*[55])

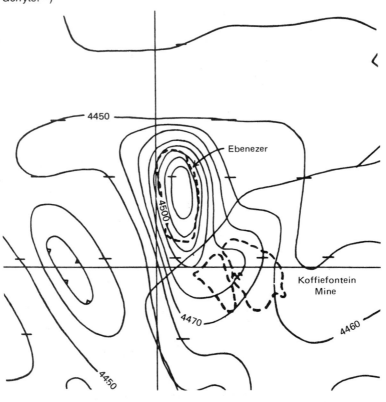

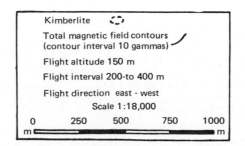

In the Ellendale area of Western Australia (Fig. 17-21), detailed airborne surveys were used to search for kimberlites and related lamproitic* rocks for economic diamond deposits (Smith,[56] Jenke[57]). A known lamproite pipe near Big Spring (Fig. 17-21) was surveyed with a variety of geophysical methods. The ground magnetic survey there revealed an 80-nT (gamma) anomaly (Fig. 17-22). The subsequent airborne magnetic survey in the Ellendale area, covering 3500 km², used a terrain clearance of 80 m and a line spacing of 250 m. The survey revealed 26 anomalies of from 4 to 20 nT, appropriate for detailed follow-up (numbered in Figs. 17-23 and 17-24). The flat-lying Devonian and Permian limestones, sandstones, and shales provided a very quiet background for the kimberlitic or associated kimberlitic rocks. Through auger drilling and trenching, 24 of the 26 anomalies proved to be indeed kimberlites or related lamproitic rocks. Further airborne electromagnetic test surveys were used to detect possibly nonmagnetic kimberlites or to upgrade very weak magnetic responses. Although the Ellendale field is not economic at present, the presence of large subeconomic pipes provided encouragement for further exploration, with the result being the commercial discovery of diamonds at Argyle. In 1984, the Argyle Diamond Mines produced 5,689,546 carats from alluvials. Production of diamonds from the Argyle pipe (the main orebody) was scheduled to start by 1986.

Magnetic Exploration for Hydrocarbons The most widespread application of magnetic prospecting to oil exploration since World War II has been to determine the present extent and thickness of sedimentary basins in previously unexplored areas. This is done by mapping the depths to the tops of intrusives in the basement from aeromagnetic or ship-towed magnetic data by methods discussed earlier in this chapter. Steenland[59] reports that the discrepancy between basement depths estimated by this means and those indicated by drilling in northern Alberta and northeastern British Columbia has been on the average no greater than 5 percent.

Figure 17-26 shows contours of basement depth over the Bass Strait area between the Australian mainland and Tasmania based on analysis of magnetic

---

* Definitions

1 *Kimberlite*   Mica peridotite (olivine plus pyroxene, biotite, melilite); host rock for diamonds.

2 *Peridotite*   An ultramafic rock that is 30–90 percent olivine.

3 *Mafic*   Magnesium, iron(Fe)-bearing igneous rock (used as a term in opposition to "silicic," silica-aluminum-rich rock).

4 *Phyre* or *phyry* (as a suffix)   Coarse grains (large crystals) set in a finer groundmass which may be crystalline or glassy or both.

5 *Lamprophyre family*   Ultramafic and mafic dike rocks rich in alkali and in (FeO + MgO). Are dark-colored (mafic) dike rocks containing euhedral mafic phenocrysts (large crystals) of biotite, amphibole, pyroxene, or olivine. Typically porphyritic with mafic minerals in two generations: biotite and/or barkevikite, with augite, olivine, and, rarely, melilite as possible additional minerals.

6 *Lamproitic*   Ultramafic dark rocks. By removing the "phyre" suffix, the implication is that the coarse grains (set in a finer groundmass) are not present.

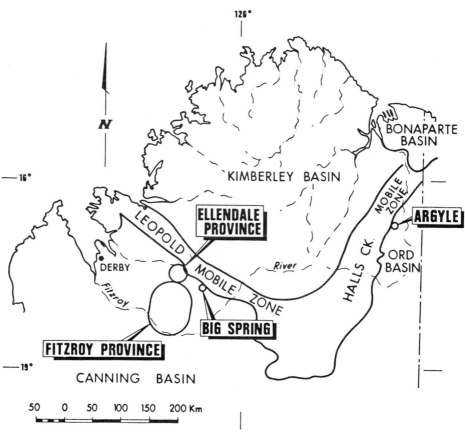

FIGURE 17-21 Locality plan, Kimberley Basin, Western Australia, showing Ellendale kimberlite province and Argyle diamond mine. (*Smith*. [56])

anomalies. The map, made before any offshore seismic work or drilling had been carried out, indicates two underwater basins which were considered to be prospective for oil. One was an offshore extension of the then nonproductive Ottway Basin, previously located on land by drilling in southeastern Victoria. The existence of the other basin, in the center of Bass Strait, had not been known before the magnetic survey. The information on basin geometry thus obtained made it possible to program subsequent seismic lines over areas where the sedimentary basins appeared to be best developed. On the basis of this shooting, large quantities of gas have been discovered in fields that are well placed for supplying the energy needs in population centers such as Sydney and Melbourne.

Even in known basin areas, magnetic surveys can show topographic trends in the basement that might have an important bearing on overlying sedimentary

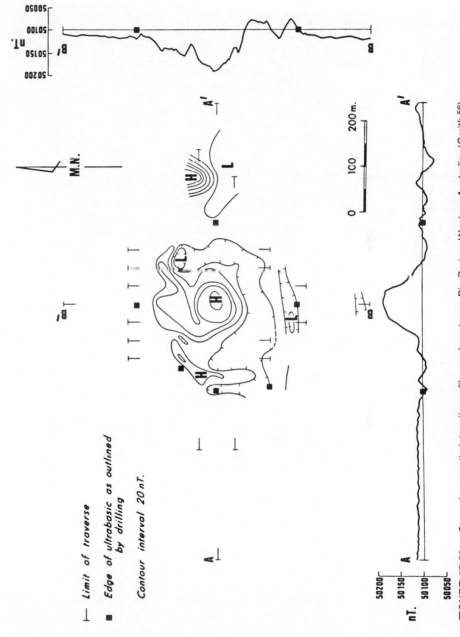

┴ Limit of traverse

■ Edge of ultrabasic as outlined by drilling

Contour interval 20 nT.

FIGURE 17-22 Ground magnetic intensity profiles and contours, Big Spring, Western Australia. (*Smith.*[56])

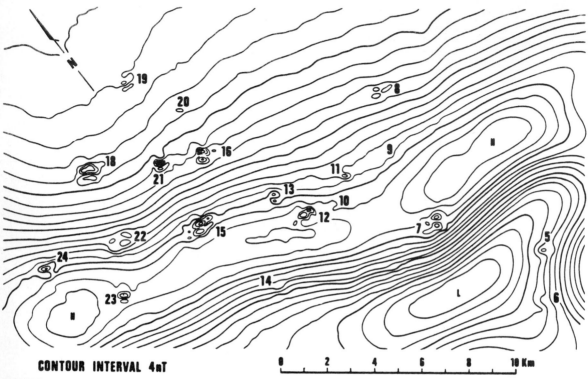

CONTOUR INTERVAL 4ɴT

FIGURE 17-23
Contours of airborne total magnetic intensity, Ellendale, Western Australia. (*Smith*.[56])

structures. Figure 17-27 shows a map of total fields from an aeromagnetic survey over the Wichita Mountain area of southwestern Oklahoma. The northwest-southeast lineation of magnetic contours follows the trend of the Wichita Mountains, but no igneous rock is exposed along this axis. An analysis by Vacquier et al.[61] led to the conclusion that the zone of high intensity is not the axis of the buried Wichita Mountains but a linear band of gabbro about 3 mi wide buried along the southwest slope of the mountains. A depth of burial of 2300 ft is estimated from the magnetic gradients. A purely qualitative analysis would put the highest ridge of the buried Wichitas along the axis of the magnetic high several miles from that determined by Vacquier's computations. Such a displacement could have a significant bearing on conclusions that might be reached by a petroleum geologist looking for sedimentary structures in the area that might be controlled by buried basement topography.

A number of oil fields have been discovered entirely or primarily through magnetometer surveys. In most of them the production is from porous serpentine plugs which have a high magnetic susceptibility compared with surrounding sediments. These fields are all quite small. Sometimes a sedimentary oil trap is formed by draping over a structural high on the basement surface. The

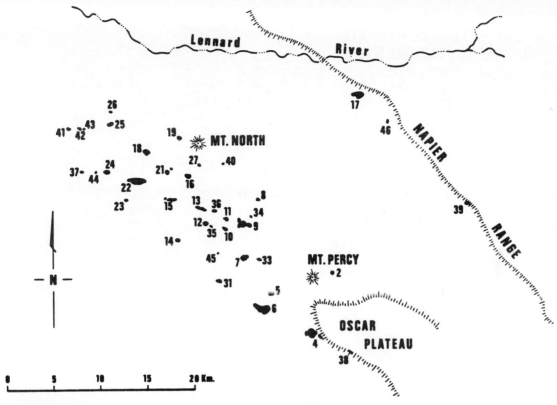

FIGURE 17-24
Summary map show-
ing known kimberlitic
bodies in the Ellendale
province, Western Aus-
tralia. (*Smith*,[56])

FIGURE 17-25   Magnetic field, gold values, and
geologic structure along profile at
Portage Creek, Alaska. (*After
Joesting*.[58])

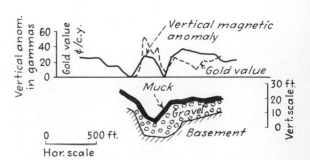

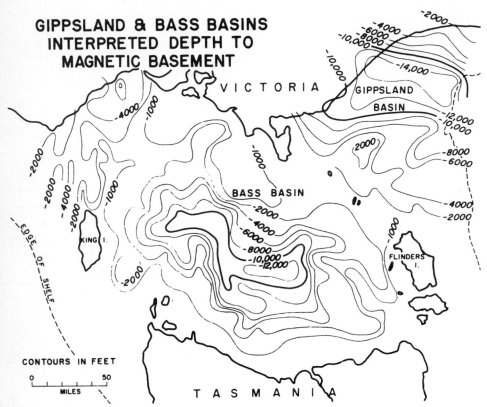

FIGURE 17-26 Depths to magnetic basement in Gippsland and Bass basins south of Victoria, Australia as interpreted from aeromagnetic data. (*From Wallis.*[60])

Cumberland Field, in Oklahoma (Fig. 17-28) is located along the axis of a magnetic high with a 100-gamma reversal. The cross section in the figure was inferred by Cram[62] on the basis of subsurface and magnetic information. The Jackson Field in Mississippi is located over a magnetic high with the closing magnetic contour of lowest intensity 20 mi in diameter. The greatest magnitude of the anomaly is more than 1200 gammas. The origin of the anomaly is believed to be an igneous plug, very possibly cryptovolcanic, but it has never been penetrated by the drill. The largest field ever discovered directly by the magnetometer is the Hobbs Field of Lea County, N.M. The discovery well was drilled in 1927 on the basis of magnetic and torsion-balance surveys.

Weak negative anomalies are to be expected over salt domes because of the contrast between the slightly negative susceptibility (about -6×10^{-6} SI units) of the salt or cap rock and the small positive susceptibility (125 to 630 $\times$ 10^{-6} SI units) of the surrounding sediments. So far as is known, no oil has been associated with salt domes exhibiting such a magnetic effect, although several experimental surveys have revealed anomalies of the predicted size.

TOTAL INTENSITY AEROMAGNETIC MAP RELATIVE TO ARBITRARY DATUM
MANGUM, OKLAHOMA

Flown 1935' above sea level

FIGURE 17-27
Aeromagnetic contours over area of Wichita Mountains near Mangum, Okla. (*From Vacquier et al.*[61])

The use of high-sensitivity magnetometers has enabled the delineation in some sedimentary basins of small ($\frac{1}{2}$ to 2 gamma) high-frequency anomalies attributable to diagenetic magnetite over oil fields (Donovan et al.[63]). In the Arctic National Wildlife Refuge, Alaska, Donovan et al.[64] reported that the chemical reduction of iron oxides in the presence of seeping hydrocarbons gave

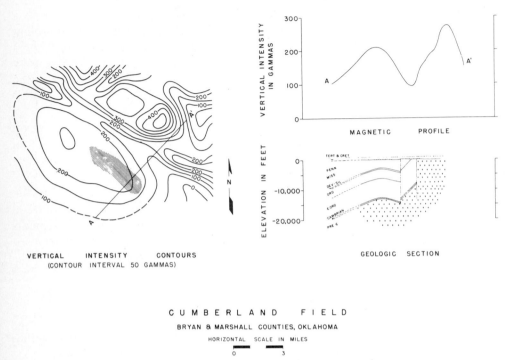

VERTICAL INTENSITY CONTOURS
(CONTOUR INTERVAL 50 GAMMAS)

GEOLOGIC SECTION

C U M B E R L A N D   F I E L D

BRYAN & MARSHALL COUNTIES, OKLAHOMA

HORIZONTAL SCALE IN MILES

0   3

FIGURE 17-28   Magnetic intensities observed over Cumberland Field, Okla., along with geologic section. (*After J. W. Peters, Mines Mag., 1949.*)

rise to magnetic anomalies detected in a low-altitude aeromagnetic reconnaissance survey for petroleum. "The magnetic contrast between sedimentary rocks of normally low magnetic susceptibility and those locally enriched with this epigenetic magnetite resulted in distinctive high-wavenumber and low-amplitude total field anomalies."[64] The role that permafrost may play in inhibiting epigenetic processes was not addressed, but magnetic anomalies were recorded onshore over seeps and known accumulations. Magnetometers were mounted in each wingtip and in a tail stinger, permitting the calculation of the resultant horizontal gradient relative to the flight path. The gradient data were not significantly affected by the diurnal variations and solar storms common at high magnetic latitudes. The application of this technique to other basins would require careful study of the local conditions.

Basalt-Covered Areas   Prieto et al.[65] interpreted aeromagnetic, gravity, and magnetotelluric (MT) data to discern the thickness of the Columbia River Basalts in southern Washington. Since seismic reflection techniques do poorly in near-surface thick basalts, other geophysical surveys often provide a cost-effective exploration approach.

A deep well in the area provided some resistivity and density data with a generalized lithologic column. Numerous gas shows, though not of sufficient volume for commercial production, no doubt offered encouragement for hydrocarbon exploration. The magnetic data were first interpreted; the initial gravity model used the model deduced from the magnetic data. Refinements of the earth model were provided by the gravity data; the MT data were next interpreted using the best model to date.

They stated that "in general MT data are more sensitive to vertical resistivity changes and less to lateral changes, in contrast with gravity and aeromagnetic data, which are more sensitive to lateral rock property changes than to vertical changes." Thus the approximate depth to base of basalt can be approximately determined by use of the MT data, and lateral variation in the depth to base of basalt is best determined by use of the gravity data. The aeromagnetic data allowed a good estimate to the top of magnetic basement, which here appears to correspond to top of electrical basement, thus giving an estimate of the thickness of sediments under the basalt flows.

Geothermal Exploration Using Aeromagnetic Data

Yellowstone National Park Bhattacharyya and Leu[27] studied the spatial variation of the Curie-point isotherm level in Yellowstone by analyzing aeromagnetic data. The spectral analysis of residual magnetic anomalies allowed an estimate to the bottom of the magnetized crust, the level often interpreted as the Curie-point isotherm. Their study documented a strong correlation between a shallow Curie-point isotherm and the caldera (where most of the park's boiling springs, fumaroles, and hydrothermal alterations are). See Fig. 17-29.

Central Oregon Cascades Young silicic volcanism, hot springs, and high heat flow indicate the Cascade Range of central Oregon to be potentially significant for geothermal resources. Connard et al.[31] further studied the geothermal potential of the central Oregon Cascades through an aeromagnetic survey (Fig. 17-30). The survey over 17,700 km^2 consisted of 16,000 km of flight lines flown at 2.74 km (9000 ft) above sea level. This flight elevation allowed almost the entire area to be covered at one observational level with a minimum terrain clearance. In one area, the summits of high mountain peaks did extend above the flight elevation, which caused "holes" in the flight lines. The holes were filled in with 1000 km of flight lines flown at 3.35 km (11,000 ft) extending well beyond the gap in the data caused by the peaks. The east-west traverses were spaced 1.6 km (1 statute mile) apart, the north-south traverses 8.05 km (5 statute miles) apart. Spectral analysis of the magnetic anomalies suggested that the High Cascades are underlain by Curie-point isotherm depths as shallow as 9 km (Fig. 17-31). These shallow Curie-point isotherm depths imply thermal gradients greater than 50°C/km and surface heat flow greater than 100 mW/m^2.

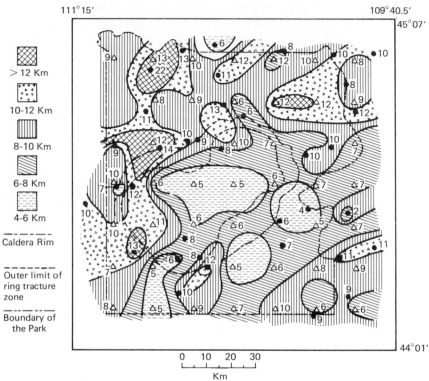

FIGURE 17-29 Contoured map of the depths to the Curie point isotherm. Circles and triangles represent the locations of the centers of individual anomalies and grid blocks, respectively. (*Connard et al.*[31])

A spectral technique was used to calculate the average depth to an ensemble of magnetic sources because it was difficult to isolate magnetic anomalies caused by individual sources in the geologically complex Cascade Range.

A low-pass-filtered magnetic anomaly map attenuated wavelengths shorter than 25 km, "eliminating or substantially reducing most of the correlation between anomalies and topography." Analysis of this map in conjunction with geologic mapping in this and surrounding areas allowed major fault trends and structural elements to be identified. Magnetic source depth calculations showed that the High Cascades occupy a structural depression or graben on the eastern side of the Western Cascades.

Magnetic Exploration and Applications for Archaeological Purposes One of the most strikingly straightforward and successful magnetic surveys was that conducted to discover huge basalt monuments buried up to 18 ft (6 m) in East

FIGURE 17-30 Aeromagnetic survey area (black square) shown in Fig. 17-31 (*Connard et al.*[31])

QUATERNARY VOLCANIC ROCKS

WESTERN CASCADES

COLUMBIA RIVER BASALTS

PRE-TERTIARY ROCKS

Boundary of Basin and Range

Quaternary volcanic centers

Fault zones:

B = Brothers Fault Zone

E-D = Eugene-Denio Zone

M = McLoughlin Zone

V = Vale Zone

S = Sisters Fault Zone

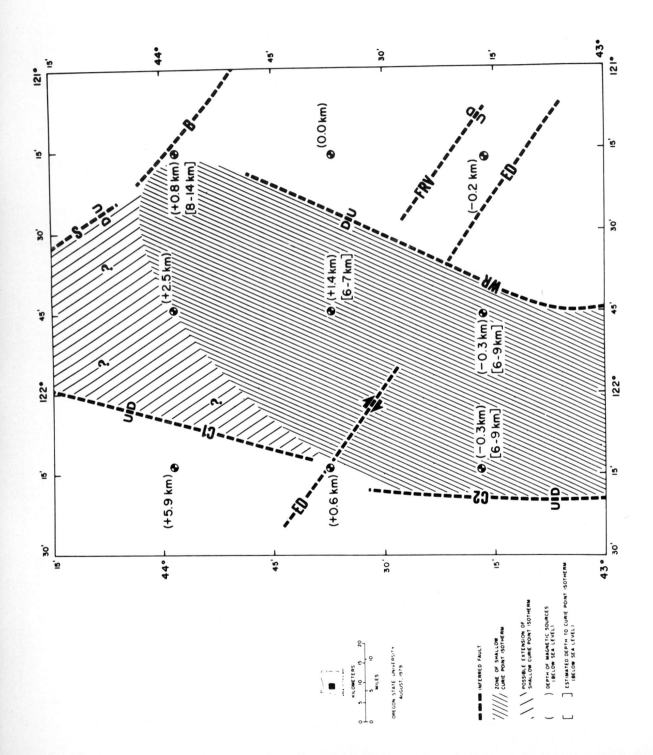

Central Mexico (Breiner[66]). Many of the objects had very simple shapes (round or rectangular slab), which led to relatively straightforward, easily modeled anomalies. Of the over 100 large anomalies located, 20 were excavated, yielding various large objects. One such object was a rectangular basalt altar weighing 20 tons; another was an Olmec head weighing 10 tons. These and the other large objects gave high-amplitude, sharp anomalies.

The remanent magnetism of archaeological baked clays has been studied to construct secular variation curves of the magnetic pole.[67] The remanent magnetism of the baked clays of known age determines the secular variation curve; baked clays of unknown age can then be assigned a likely age based upon the orientation of their remanent magnetism.

Overview of Gravity and Magnetic Surveys Paterson and Reeves[68] have discussed the current applications, survey methods, processing, and interpretation techniques for gravity and magnetic surveys. Their paper includes excellent examples of modern data, including vertical magnetic gradient data, various types of filtering and transformations of potential-field data, and many references to recent work. They reiterate the continuing worldwide demand for magnetic and gravity surveys, and they present the recent types of solutions to long-term problems (positioning requirements, noise, etc.).

REFERENCES

1 Rayner, J. M.: The Role of Geophysics in the Development of Mineral Resources, pp. 259–266, in "Mining and Groundwater Geophysics/1967," *Geol. Surv. Can. Econ. Geol. Rep. 26*, Ottawa, 1970.

2 Bott, M. H. P.: Solution of the Linear Inverse Problem in Magnetic Interpretation with Application to Oceanic Magnetic Anomalies, *Geophys. J. Roy. Astr. Soc.*, vol. 13, pp. 313–323, 1967.

3 Bott, M. H. P., and M. A. Hutton: A Matrix Method for Interpreting Oceanic Magnetic Anomalies, *Geophys. J. Roy. Astr. Soc.*, vol. 20, pp. 149–157, 1970.

4 Bott, M. H. P., and M. A. Hutton: Limitations on the Resolution Possible in the Direct Interpretation of Marine Magnetic Anomalies, *Earth Planet. Sci. Lett.*, vol. 8, p. 317, 1970.

5 Emilia, D. A., and G. Bodvarsson: Numerical Methods in the Direct Interpretation of Marine Magnetic Anomalies, *Earth Planet. Sci. Lett.*, vol. 7, p. 194, 1969.

6 Emilia, D. A., and G. Bodvarsson: More on the Direct Interpretation of Magnetic Anomalies, *Earth Planet. Sic. Lett.*, vol. 8, pp. 320–321, 1970.

7 Schouten, J. A.: A Fundamental Analysis of Magnetic Anomalies over Oceanic Ridges, *Marine Geophys. Res*, vol. 1, pp. 111–114, 1971.

8 Schouten, H., and K. McCamy: Filtering Marine Magnetic Anomalies, *J. Geophys. Res.*, vol. 77, pp. 7089–7099, 1972.

FIGURE 17-31 Map of the Central Oregon Cascades area showing areas of shallow Curie-point isotherm and regional structural interpretation of aeromagnetic data. (*Connard et al.*[31])

9 Blakely, R. J., and H. Schouten: Comments on Paper by Hans Schouten and Keith McCamy, "Filtering Marine Magnetic Anomalies," *J. Geophys. Res.*, vol. 79, pp. 773–774, 1974.

10 Parker, R. L., and S. P. Huestis: The Inversion of Magnetic Anomalies in the Presence of Topography, *J. Geophys. Res.*, vol. 79, pp. 1587–1593, 1974.

11 Talwani, M., and J. R. Heirtzler: Computation of Magnetic Anomalies Caused by Two-Dimensional Structures of Arbitrary Shape, pp. 464–480, in "Computers in the Mineral Industries," *Stanford Univ. Pub. Geol. Sci.*, vol. 9, pt. 1, 1964.

12 Saltus, R. W., and R. J. Blakely: Hypermag: An Interactive, Two-Dimensional Gravity and Magnetic Modeling Program, U.S. Geol. Surv. Open-File Rep. 83–241, 91 pp., 1983.

13 Francheteau, J., C. G. A. Harrison, J. G. Sclater, and M. L. Richards: Magnetization of Pacific Seamounts: A Preliminary Polar Curve for the Northeastern Pacific, *J. Geophys. Res.*, vol. 75, p. 2035, 1970.

14 Parker, R. L.: The Determination of Seamount Magnetism, *Geophys. J. Roy. Astr. Soc.*, vol. 24, pp. 321–324, 1971.

15 Johnson, W. W.: A Least-Squares Method of Interpreting Magnetic Anomalies Caused by Two-Dimensional Structures, *Geophys.*, vol. 34, pp. 65–74, 1969.

16 McGrath, P. H., and P. J. Hood: An Automated Least-Squares Multimodel Method for Magnetic Interpretation, *Geophysics*, vol. 38, pp. 349–358, 1973.

17 Webring, M.: SAKI: A Fortran Program for Generalized Linear Inversion of Gravity and Magnetic Profiles, U.S. Geol. Surv. Open-File Rep. 85–122, 28 pp., 1985.

18 Marquardt, D. W.: An Algorithm for Least-Squares Estimation of Non-linear Parameters, *J. Soc. Indust. Appl. Math.*, vol. 11, pp. 431–441, 1963.

19 Reeves, C. V., and I. N. MacLeod: Modelling of Potential Field Anomalies—Some Applications for the Micro-computer, *First Break*, vol. 1, pp. 18–24, 1983.

20 Huestis, S. P., and R. L. Parker: Bounding the Thickness of the Oceanic Magnetized Layer, *J. Geophys. Res.*, vol. 82, pp. 5293–5303, 1977.

21 Hartman, R. R., D. J. Tesky, and L. L. Friedberg: A System for Rapid Digital Aeromagnetic Interpretation, *Geophysics*, vol. 36, pp. 891–918, 1971.

22 Ku, C. C., and J. A. Sharp: Werner Deconvolution for Automated Magnetic Interpretation and Its Refinement Using Marquardt's Inverse Modeling, *Geophysics*, vol. 48, pp. 754–774, 1983.

23 Naudy, Henri: Automatic Determination of Depth on Aeromagnetic Profiles, *Geophysics*, vol. 36, pp. 717–722, 1971.

24 Bhattacharyya, B. K., and Lei-Kuang Leu: Spectral Analysis of Gravity and Magnetic Anomalies due to Two-Dimensional Structures, *Geophysics*, vol. 40, pp. 993–1013, 1975.

25 Bhattacharrya, B. K.: Some General Properties of Potential Fields in Space and Frequency Domain, *Geoexploration*, vol. 5, pp. 127–143, 1967.

26 Bhattacharyya, B. K., and Lei-Kuang Leu: Spectral Analysis of Gravity and Magnetic Anomalies due to Rectangular Prismatic Bodies, *Geophysics*, vol. 42, pp. 41–50, 1977.

27 Bhattacharyya, B. K., and Lei-Kuang Leu: Analysis of Magnetic Anomalies over Yellowstone National Park: Mapping of Curie Point Isothermal Surface for Geothermal Reconnaissance, *J. Geophys. Res.*, vol. 80, pp. 4461–4465, 1975.

28 Treitel, S., W. G. Clement, and R. K. Kaul: The Spectral Determination of Depths to Buried Magnetic Basement Rocks, *Geophys. J. Roy. Astro. Soc.*, vol. 24, pp. 415–429, 1971.

29 Blakely, R. J., and Siamak Hassanzadeh: Estimation of Depth to Magnetic Source

Using Maximum Entropy Power Spectra, with Application to the Peru-Chile Trench, pp. 667–682, in "Nazca Plate: Crustal Formation and Andean Convergence," *Geol. Soc. Am. Mem.* 154, 1981.

30 Spector, A., and F. S. Grant: Statistical Models for Interpreting Aeromagnetic Data, *Geophysics*, vol. 35, pp. 293–302, 1970.

31 Connard, G., R. W. Couch, and M. Gemperle: Analysis of Aeromagnetic Measurements from the Cascade Range in Central Oregon, *Geophysics*, vol. 48, pp. 376–390, 1983.

32 Grant, F. S., and G. S. West: "Interpretation Theory in Applied Geophysics," McGraw-Hill, New York, 1965.

33 Hildenbrand, T. G.: FFTFIL: A Filtering Program Based on Two-Dimensional Fourier Analysis, U.S. Geological Survey Open-File Rep. 83-237, 61 pp., 1983.

34 Blakely, R. J.: Documentation for REDUC3, an Algorithm for the Linear Filtering of Gridded Magnetic Data, U.S. Geological Survey Open-File Rep. 77-784, 27 pp., 1977.

35 Blakely, R. J., and Allan Cox: Identification of Short Polarity Events by Transforming Marine Magnetic Profiles to the Pole, *J. Geophys. Res.*, vol. 77, pp. 4339–4349, 1972.

36 Bhattacharyya, B. K., and K. C. Chan: Reduction of Magnetic and Gravity Data on an Arbitrary Surface Acquired in a Region of High Topographic Relief, *Geophysics*, vol. 42, pp. 1411–1430, 1977.

37 Parker, R. L., and K. D. Klitgord: Magnetic Upward Continuation from an Uneven Track *Geophysics*, vol. 37, pp. 662–668, 1959.

38 Grauch, V. J. S.: TAYLOR: A Fortran Program Using Taylor Series Expansion for Level-Surface or Surface-Level Continuation of Potential Field Data, U.S. Geological Survey Open-File Rep. 84-501, 31 pp., 1984.

39 Cordell, L.: Techniques, Application and Problems of Analytical Continuation of New Mexico Aeromagnetic Data Between Arbitrary Surfaces of Very High Relief, *Proc. Int. Meet. Potential Fields in Rugged Topography*, Bull. No. 7, Institut de Géophysique de Université de Lausanne, Lausanne, Switzerland, pp. 96–101, 1985.

40 Baranov, V.: A New Method for Interpretation of Aeromagnetic Maps: Pseudo-Gravimetric Anomalies, *Geophysics*, vol. 22, pp. 359–383, 1957.

41 Cordell, Linn, and V. J. S. Grauch: Mapping Basement Magnetization Zones from Aeromagnetic Data in the San Juan Basin, New Mexico, pp. 181–197, in W. J. Hinze (ed.), "The Utility of Regional Gravity and Magnetic Anomaly Maps," Society of Exploration Geophysicists, Tulsa, Okla., 1982.

42 Blakely, R. J., and R. W. Simpson: Approximating Edges of Source Bodies from Magnetic or Gravity Anomalies, *Geophysics*, vol. 51, pp. 1494–1498, 1986.

43 Blakely, R. J., and V. J. S. Grauch: Magnetic Models of Crystalline Terrane: Accounting for the Effect of Topography, *Geophysics*, vol. 48, pp. 1551–1557, 1983.

44 Grauch, V. J. S.: A New Magnetic-Terrain Correction Method for Aeromagnetic Mapping, *Proc. Int. Meet. Potential Fields in Rugged Topography*, Bull. No. 7, Institut de Géophysique de Université de Lausanne, Lausanne, Switzerland, pp. 110–113, 1985.

45 Blakely, R. J.: The Effect of Topography on Aeromagnetic Data in the Wavenumber Domain, *Proc. Int. Meet. Potential Fields in Rugged Topography*, Bull. No. 7, Institut de Géophysique de Université de Lausanne, Lausanne, Switzerland, pp. 102–109, 1985.

46 Parker, R. L.: The Rapid Calculation of Potential Anomalies, *Geophys. J. Roy. Astr. Soc.*, vol. 31, pp. 447–455, 1973.

47 Simpson, R. W., T. G. Hildenbrand, R. H. Godson, and M. F. Kane: A Description

of Colored Gravity and Terrain Maps for the U.S. and Adjacent Canada East of 104°, U.S.G.S. Open File Rep. 82-877, 18 pp., 1982.

48 Gibert, D., and A. Galdeano: A Computer Program to Perform Transformations of Gravimetric and Aeromagnetic Surveys, *Computers and Geosciences*, vol. 11, pp. 553–588, 1985.

49 Cooley, J. W., and J. W. Tukey: An Algorithm for the Machine Calculation of Complex Fourier Series, *Math. Comput.*, vol. 19, pp. 297–301, 1965.

50 Weaver, P.: The Relative Place of Empirical and Analytic Methods of Geophysical Interpretation, *Geophysics*, vol. 7, pp. 281–292, 1942.

51 Webb, J. E.: The Search for Iron Ore, Eyre-Peninsula, South Australia, "Mining Geophysics," vol. 1, pp. 379–390, Society of Exploration Geophysicists, Tulsa, Okla., 1966.

52 Leney, George W.: Field Studies in Iron Ore Geophysics, "Mining Geophysics," vol. 1, pp. 391–417, Society of Exploration Geophysicists, Tulsa, Okla., 1966.

53 Riddell, Paul A.: Magnetic Observations at the Dayton Iron Deposit, Lyon County, Nevada, "Mining Geophysics," vol. 1, pp. 418–428, Society of Exploration Geophysicists, Tulsa, Okla., 1966.

54 Galbraith, F. M.: The Magnetometer as a Geological Instrument at Sudbury, *Trans. Am. Inst. Min. Met. Eng.*, vol. 164, Geophysics, 1945, pp. 98–106, 1945.

55 Gerryts, E.: Diamond Prospecting by Geophysical Methods: A Review of Current Practice, pp. 439–446, in "Mining and Groundwater Geophysics/1967," *Geol. Surv. Can., Econ. Geol. Rep. 26*, Ottawa, 1970.

56 Smith, R. J.: Geophysics in Australian Mineral Exploration, *Geophysics*, vol. 50, pp. 2637–2665, 1985.

57 Jenke, G. P.: The Role of Geophysics in the Discovery of the Ellendale and Fitzroy Kimberlites, *Abstracts, Austral. Soc. Explor. Geophys., Biennial Conf.*, Brisbane, 1983.

58 Joesting, H. R.: Magnetometer and Direct-Current Resistivity Studies in Alaska, *Trans. Am. Inst. Min. Met. Eng.*, vol. 164, Geophysics, 1945, pp. 66–87, 1945.

59 Steenland, N. C.: An Evaluation of the Peace River Aeromagnetic Interpretation, *Geophysics*, vol. 28, pp. 745–755, 1963.

60 Wallis, W. E.: Offshore Petroleum Exploration, Gippsland and Bass Basins—Southeast Asia,* *Proc., 7th World Petrol. Congr.*, vol. 2, pp. 783–791, Elsevier, London, 1967.

61 Vacquier, V., Nelson C. Steenland, Roland G. Henderson, and Isidore Zietz: Interpretation of Aeromagnetic Maps, *Geol. Soc. Am. Mem. 47*, 1951.

62 Cram, Ira H.: Cumberland Oil Field, Bryan and Marshall Counties, Okla., pp. 341–358, in "Structure of Typical American Oil Fields," American Association of Petroleum Geologists, 1948.

63 Donovan, T. J., R. L. Forgey, and A. A. Roberts: Aeromagnetic Detection of Diagenetic Magnetite over Oil Fields, *Bull. Am. Assoc. Petrol. Geol.*, vol. 63, pp. 245–248, 1979.

64 Donovan, T. J., J. D. Hendricks, A. A. Roberts, and P. T. Eliason: Low-Altitude Aeromagnetic Reconnaissance for Petroleum in the Arctic National Wildlife Refuge, Alaska, *Geophysics*, vol. 49, pp. 1338–1353, 1984.

* This title undoubtedly contains an error. "Asia" should be "Australia."

65 Prieto, C., C. Perkins, and E. Berkman: Columbia River Basalt Plateau—An Integrated Approach to Interpretation of Basalt-Covered Areas, *Geophysics*, vol. 50, pp. 2709–2719, 1985.

66 Breiner, S.: A Magnetic Survey for Buried 3000 Year Old Basalt Monuments in Mexico, *Abstracts 54th Annu. SEG Meet.*, pp. 179–182, 1984.

67 Sternberg, R. S.: Archaeomagnetism in the American Southwest, *Abstracts 54th Annu. SEG Meet.*, pp. 197–199. 1984.

68 Paterson, N. R., and C. V. Reeves: Applications of Gravity and Magnetic Surveys: The State of the Art in 1985, *Geophysics*, vol. 50, pp. 2558–2594, 1985.

CHAPTER 18

ELECTRICAL AND ELECTROMAGNETIC PROSPECTING METHODS

Electrical prospecting is far more diversified than the other geophysical methods we have studied. Some electrical techniques (e.g., the self-potential, telluric-current, and magnetotellurics) depend for a source on naturally occurring electromagnetic (EM) fields. Other methods require electric currents or fields which are introduced into the earth artificially and in this respect are similar to the seismic techniques. In the latter category belong the potential-drop methods (e.g., resistivity) as well as EM and induced-polarization prospecting. The number of different surface and airborne EM methods and their variants is quite large.

Electrical prospecting has been an integral part of the exploration process since its early times. The various EM techniques have been used in a wide range of exploration and other geophysical applications, from oil and gas prospecting through mining and geothermal to groundwater, engineering geophysics, and waste disposal problems.

Because of the wide diversity of electrical and EM exploration methods and the range of their past and future applications, they will not be treated here with the same detail as the seismic methods in previous chapters. The material presented here is not intended to be comprehensive enough to cover all the various techniques and applications. The objective is to give a descriptive treatment of the more important aspects, concentrating on developing fundamental understanding of these methods and the physical principles on which they are based. For further information the reader will be referred to pertinent books and publications in the open scientific literature. Fortunately, the subject is well covered by numerous books and articles. Consequently the references for this chapter are not intended to be all inclusive.

TABLE 18-1 PROMINENT ELECTRICAL AND ELECTROMAGNETIC GEOPHYSICAL METHODS

Natural field source	Artificial controlled source
A. Magnetotellurics (MT)	A. Electrical resistivity (dc)
Tellurics-MT (TMT)	B. Transient soundings (TEM)
Audio-frequency MT (AMT)	C. Induced polarization (IP)
Audio-frequency magnetic (AFMAG)	D. EM induction
Telluric current	E. Ground penetrating radar
B. EM array profiling (EMAP)	
C. Self-potential (SP)	

The general theory of electromagnetics has been the subject of numerous, excellent books, from the fundamental work of Maxwell[1] to more recent texts such as Stratton[2] or Jackson,[3] which provide the necessary preliminary background and can also serve as references for advanced studies. Several books address more specifically EM geophysics and related subjects (Keller and Frischknecht,[4] Wait,[5,6] Rokityanski,[7] Porstendorfer,[8] Kaufman and Keller,[9–11] and Sumner[12]). Of special importance are the reviews presented in the SEG publication Mining Geophysics.[13] Review chapters also exist in general geophysical textbooks, such as Grant and West,[14] Parasnis,[15] and Telford et al.[16]

One way to classify the main categories of electrical and geophysical tools is according to the mechanism of the source involved in each one. Table 18-1 lists separately those methods that use naturally occurring fields and those that employ artificial surface (or airborne) source signals. When a natural field is used for the source in telluric-magnetotelluric methods and their generalization into array profiling techniques, deep penetration is achieved. Such methods are more important in petroleum exploration. On the other hand, the active source methods are limited in their practical range of penetration but have advantages in their ability to control the source and to choose the acquisition parameters that are suited for resolution of the exploration objective.

Historically, EM exploration methods have seen wider use in the U.S.S.R., especially for oil and gas exploration. That work has been described in publications, a number of which have been translated into English. Kaufman and Keller[9–11] and Rokityanski[7] provide fairly extensive coverage of this literature.

18-1 ELECTRICAL PROPERTIES ASSOCIATED WITH ROCKS

Electrical prospecting uses three phenomena and properties associated with rocks: (1) Resistivity, or the reciprocal of conductivity, governs the amount of current that passes through the rock when a specified potential difference is applied. (2) Electrochemical activity caused by electrolytes in the ground is the basis for magnetic, self-potential, and induced-polarization methods. (3) The dielectric constant gives information on the capacity of a rock material to store electric charge and governs, in part, the response of rock formations to high-frequency alternating currents introduced into the earth by conductive or inductive means.

Resistivity The electrical resistivity of any material is defined as the electrical resistance of a cylinder with a cross section of unit area and with unit length. If the resistivity of a conducting cylinder having a length l and cross-sectional area S is ρ, the resistance R is expressed by

$$R = \frac{\rho S}{l} \qquad (18\text{-}1)$$

The generally accepted unit of resistivity is the ohm-meter ($\Omega \cdot m$), although the ohm-centimeter is sometimes used. The current density J is related to the electric field E and the resistivity through Ohm's law:

$$J = \frac{1}{\rho}E \qquad \text{or} \qquad J = \sigma E \qquad (18\text{-}2)$$

(for a continuous medium, not a circuit board). The conductivity σ of a material is defined as $1/\rho$, the reciprocal of its resistivity. The unit of conductivity in SI is mho/m or siemens/m.

In most rock materials the porosity and the chemical content of the water filling the pore spaces are more important in governing resistivity than is the conductivity of the mineral grains of which the rock itself is composed. The salinity of the water in the pores is probably the most critical factor determining the resistivity. When porous rocks lie above the water table at shallow depths, or when they occur at such great depths, that all pore spaces are closed by ambient pressure, the current flow through them is maintained through electronic conduction and takes place within the mineral grains themselves. Under these conditions the resistivity of the rock will depend on the intrinsic microscopic rock properties. When the pores are saturated with fluids, it will be governed by the fluid resistivity, and the main conduction mechanism is electrolytic. An empirical relationship for the dependence of the resistivity on the porosity ϕ and fluid resistivity ρ_w is given by Archie's law:

$$\rho = a\phi^{-m}s^{-n}\,\rho_w$$

where s is the fraction of the pores that are fluid filled, $n \cong 2$, and a and m are constants: $0.6 < a < 2.5$; $1.3 < m < 2.5$.

All resistivity-sensing, surface-electrical methods detect the bulk resistivity of a volume of rock at depth (in situ) with resistivity values reflecting the combined effects of all conduction modes.

The range of resistivities among rocks is quite large, extending from under 10^{-2} to $10^8 \ \Omega \cdot m$ and above. Rocks and minerals with resistivities below 1.0 $\Omega \cdot m$ are considered good conductors; those from 1 to 100 $\Omega \cdot m$, intermedi-

TABLE 18-2 RESISTIVITIES (IN OHM-METERS) FOR WATER-BEARING ROCKS OF VARIOUS TYPES

Geologic age	Marine sand, shale, graywacke	Terrestrial sands, claystone, arkose	Volcanic rocks (basalt, rhyolite, tuffs)	Granite, gabbro, etc.	Limestone, dolomite, anhydrite, salt
Quaternary, Tertiary	1–10	15–50	10–200	500–2000	50–5000
Mesozoic	5–20	25–100	20–500	500–2000	100–10,000
Carboniferous	10–40	50–300	50–1000	1000–5000	200–100,000
Pre-Carboniferous Paleozoic	40–200	100–500	100–2000	1000–5000	10,000–100,000
Precambrian	100–2000	300–5000	200–5000	5000–20,000	10,000–100,000

Source: G. R. Keller, in "Handbook of Physical Constants," rev. ed., *Geol. Soc. Am. Mem.* 97, 1966.

ate conductors; and those from 100 and up, poor conductors. Table 18-2 lists the ranges within which resistivities have been observed for several types of water-bearing rocks.

Figure 18-1 shows the effect of geologic age upon the resistivity of sedimentary rocks. The horizontal lines show the range of resistivities measured around radio stations for sedimentary rocks with apparently similar lithologic characteristics having ages which cover the entire range of geologic time. Normally one would expect a fairly uniform increase of resistivity with geological age because of the greater compaction associated with increasing thickness of overburden. But the anomalously high resistivities of the Tertiary rocks may reflect the fact that the deposition at this time was mainly in fresh water rather than in saltwater, as was the case during the Mesozoic.

There is no consistent difference between resistivity ranges of many rock types, although metamorphics and igneous rocks appear to have a higher resistivity, statistically, than do sedimentary rocks. Certain rock materials, including some that are sought in mineral exploration, tend to have anomalously low resistivities (high conductivities) with respect to surrounding rocks. This makes it possible to locate them by measuring resistivity anomalies at the surface. Similarly, many geothermal systems are characterized by very conductive rock at depth. Contrasts in resistivity, which can be large among the different rock types, allow EM surface sensing of information related to the geoelectrical structure at depth. This type of information in general has lower resolving power compared to reflection seismics.

Electrochemical Activity   Electrochemical activity in rocks depends on their chemical composition and on the composition and concentration of the electrolytes dissolved in the groundwater with which they are in contact. Such activity governs the magnitude and sign of the voltage developed when the rock material is in equilibrium with an electrolyte. The electrochemical activity at depth is responsible for the self-potentials measured at the surface.

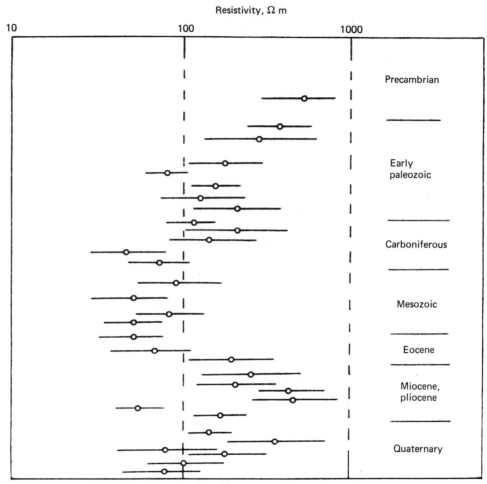

FIGURE 18-1 Average resistivity for sedimentary rocks of various geologic ages. Each bar indicates the range within which 95 percent of the values fall for the group indicated. (*From Keller and Frischknecht.*[4])

Dielectric Constant The dielectric constant is a measure of the polarizability of a material in an electric field. The polarization, or electrical moment per unit volume, **P** is proportional to the impressed electric field **E**, and the proportionality constant is χ, the electrical susceptibility. The total electrical flux per unit area (corresponding to magnetic flux density) is $\mathbf{E} + 4\pi\mathbf{P}$ or $(1 + 4\pi\chi)\mathbf{E}$. The quantity $1 + 4\pi\chi$ is designated as ϵ, the dielectric constant, which is analogous to magnetic permeability. The quantity $\epsilon\mathbf{E}$ is called the displacement current, **D**. It represents another conduction mechanism, which is of significant magnitude only in very resistive material and for high frequencies. In electrostatic units **E**, **D**, and **P** are in V/cm while χ and ϵ are dimensionless.

The dielectric constant determines the effective inductive capacity of a rock material and, consequently, its static response to any applied electric field, either direct or alternating. The dielectric constant of a vacuum is unity. For most hard rocks it ranges from about 6 to 16 electrostatic units (esu). For wet soils and clays it is somewhat greater than this, extending up to 40 or 50 esu. The dielectric constant is generally independent of frequency below 100 Hz, but at higher frequencies a dependence is observed. It is also quite sensitive to temperature—the value of ϵ increases as the rocks become hotter.

18-2 DIRECT-CURRENT RESISTIVITY METHODS

As resistivity is a fundamental electrical property of rock materials closely related to their lithology, the determination of the subsurface distribution of resistivity from measurements on the surface can yield useful information on the structure or composition of buried formations. A common method for carrying out such measurements involves the transmission into the earth of direct current. Four-electrode arrays are generally used at the surface: one pair for introducing current into the earth, the other pair for measurement of the potential associated with the current. The potential drop ratio method, also used for determining resistivity, is a variation of this procedure.

The direct-current (dc) resistivity-soundings method is one of the oldest geophysical techniques. Comprehensive studies of the method have been presented in a wide range of books and scientific articles. More detailed and deeper general discussion of the physical principles and mathematical treatment of the method can be found in Koefoed,[17] Parasnis,[18] Keller and Frischknecht,[4] Patra and Mallick,[19] and Van Nostrand and Cook.[20] A compact review of a tutorial nature with case histories was presented by Ginzburg.[21]

The method has been applied to a wide variety of exploration problems. The most successful and beneficial surveys have been in mining, groundwater, and engineering applications. Some successful applications in petroleum exploration have been reported, although the limited depth of penetration and the conductive nature of many structures of petroleum interest have restricted the applications to relatively shallow problems (under 5000 ft) and as a supplement to other EM methods with deeper penetration.

Current Flow and Potentials between Electrodes at Surface

If two electrodes are inserted into the ground and an external voltage is applied across them, there will be a flow of current through the earth from one electrode to the other. The lines of flow are always perpendicular to surfaces along which the potential is constant, the latter being referred to as *equipotentials*. This relationship is illustrated by the cross section in Fig. 18-2a. The potential difference (or voltage) impressed across electrodes A and B is distributed along the space between them. In a homogeneous conductor, the potential with respect to A along a vertical plane cutting the surface at C, which

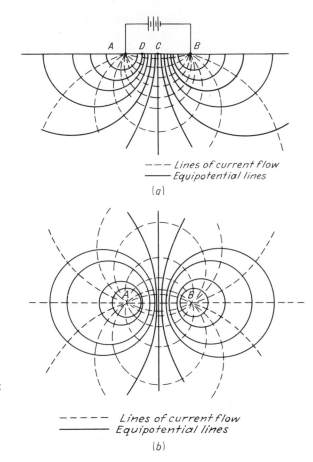

FIGURE 18-2 Equipotential lines and flow lines: (a) below the earth's surface in the vertical plane through the electrodes; (b) on plane of earth's surface; electrodes at *A* and *B*.

is midway between *A* and *B*, will be half as great as its value at *B*. If one could measure the potential underground, one would observe that the potential is the same as at any surface point, such as *D*, wherever the ratio of distances from the point to *A* and to *B*, respectively, is the same as the ratio at the surface point. In the case of *D*, this ratio is one-third. The full line extending downward from *D* and bending back under *A* is the trace of this equipotential surface on the vertical plane containing *A* and *B*. Figure 18-2*b* shows where a family of such surfaces intersects the horizontal surface plane containing *A* and *B*. The equipotential lines must always be perpendicular to the lines of current flow, since no component of the current at any point can flow along the equipotential line.

The electric field **E** of Eq. (18-2) is defined everywhere by the gradient of a potential function *V*:

$$\mathbf{E} = -\nabla V \qquad (18\text{-}3)$$

This potential decreases as l/r, the distance from the current electrode. If the current I is injected into a homogeneous half-space of resistivity ρ through an electrode at the surface, the potential at another surface point P at a distance r from the source electrode will be

$$V_P = \frac{I\rho}{2\pi} \cdot \frac{1}{r} \tag{18-4}$$

The configuration of the equipotential lines everywhere on the surface can, in principle, be detected through measurements of potential differences or voltages between pairs of grounded electrodes. This voltage, ΔV, is the surface expression resulting from the interaction between the source that drives direct current I through the resistive medium and the subsurface geoelectrical structure. The objective of dc soundings is to deduce from surface measurements of the source strength, I, and the induced voltages, ΔV, the nature and distribution of electrical resistivities under the surface.

The simplest case of exploration interest is the one where the variation of the subsurface resistivities is entirely vertical along the depth (z) axis. In this 1-D case the geoelectrical model can consist of several horizontal and laterally homogeneous, discrete or continuously varying layers whose resistivity is expressed by $\rho(z)$. This is a relatively simple case even though some practical limitations exist on the uniqueness and resolution with which the subsurface resistivities can be sensed. As a general rule, one can say that as the spacing and areal extent of the surface current and voltage electrodes increase, the resistivity variations are sensed at greater depth. This last property is true even if some lateral variations or heterogeneities of the subsurface resistivities exist.

As illustrated schematically in Fig. 18-3, the very regular pattern of current flow is distorted by buried bodies. Conductive anomalies tend to concentrate electric currents while relatively resistive bodies cause the currents to flow around them. The location of such bodies can be found relatively easily, for some cases, through the detection of surface anomalies. However, if multidi-

FIGURE 18-3   Distortion of current flow lines by bodies having (*A*) anomalously high or (*B*) anomalously low conductivity.

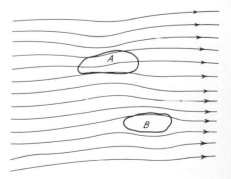

mensional structural resistivity information is needed, the problem becomes more involved and requires the application of forward- and inverse-modeling techniques.

Apparent Resistivity

It is convenient and customary for most resistivity techniques to define a response function called apparent resistivity, ρ_a, which can be evaluated or estimated from surface measurements. These apparent resistivities are usually functions of a variable that is related to the depth of penetration. Consequently, the apparent resistivities are of important intuitive value and help in practical quality control and interpretation procedures.

To illustrate this concept, let us consider a semi-infinite solid with uniform resistivity ρ. Assume that a current I is introduced into this material through electrodes at positions A and B on its surface (Fig. 18-4). Assume also that the potential gradient associated with this current is measured across two other electrodes at positions C and D on the same surface. The potential at electrode C will be [from Eq. (18-4)]

$$V_C = \frac{I\rho}{2\pi}\left(\frac{1}{r_1} - \frac{1}{r_2}\right) \tag{18-5}$$

where r_1 is the distance from potential electrode C to current electrode A and r_2 is the distance from this electrode to current electrode B. Similarly, the potential at electrode D is

$$V_D = \frac{I\rho}{2\pi}\left(\frac{1}{R_1} - \frac{1}{R_2}\right) \tag{18-6}$$

where R_1 is the distance from D to A and R_2 the distance from D to B.

The potential difference ΔV that would be measured by a potentiometer across electrodes C and D is then $V_C - V_D$. Subtracting Eq. (18-6) from Eq. (18-5) and solving for ρ, we obtain a value which we designate as

FIGURE 18-4   Arrangement of current electrodes (A and B) and potential electrodes (C and D).

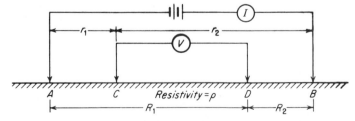

$$\rho_a = \frac{2\pi\Delta V}{I} \frac{1}{1/r_1 - 1/r_2 - 1/R_1 + 1/R_2} \qquad (18\text{-}7)$$

In SI units, if the voltage ΔV is in volts, I in amperes and distances in meters, then ρ_a has the resistivity units of ohm-meters ($\Omega \cdot$ m). The result is independent of the positions of the electrodes and is not affected when the current and potential electrodes are interchanged.

The value ρ_a obtained from Eq. (18-7), the *apparent resistivity*, is equal to the true resistivity only when the latter is uniform throughout the subsurface. Otherwise it must be looked upon as a convenient way to represent a response of the actual distribution of laterally homogeneous resistivities in the subsurface on the basis of surface measurements. If the electrodes are laid out along a line and their separations are increased in a systematic manner, the change in the apparent resistivity [as defined in Eq. (18-7)] as a function of electrode spacing makes it possible to determine the variation of resistivity with increasing depth within limits of resolution that depend on the subsurface resistivity layering and data quality.

To illustrate how this concept is applied, let us assume that the subsurface consists of two layers separated by a horizontal boundary. The upper layer has resistivity ρ_1, the lower $\rho_2 < \rho_1$. The current between electrodes A and B will no longer flow along the same arcs as it did in a homogeneous earth as shown in Fig. 18-2. The lines of flow are moved downward as shown in Fig. 18-5 because the lower resistivity below the interface results in an easier path for the current within the deeper zone. For the same reason, the total current is greater than it would be if the upper material extended downward to infinity. The deeper the interface, the smaller the increase in current flow. The greater the current-electrode separation in proportion to the depth of the interface, the greater the effect of the low-resistivity substratum on the current that flows between these electrodes.

The distortion of the lines of current flow from the simple pattern shown in Fig. 18-2 for a homogeneous earth to the more complicated one of Fig. 18-5 for a two-layer subsurface results in a corresponding distortion of the equipotential

FIGURE 18-5   Lines of current flow between electrodes A and B in two-layered earth with higher conductivity in deeper layer. Compare with flow lines for homogeneous earth (Fig. 18-2).

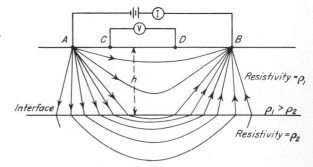

lines which are mapped where they intersect the surface. As the apparent resistivity depends only on the potential difference between the voltage electrodes divided by the current that flows into the earth, any irregularities in the positions where the equipotentials intercept the surface indicate departures from homogeneity in the subsurface resistivity.

It is easy to see that the apparent resistivity would be virtually the same as the resistivity ρ_1 of the upper medium when the separation of current electrodes is very small compared with the thickness h of the upper layer. This is because very little current would penetrate to the substratum below the interface. At spacings that are large compared with h, the apparent resistivity approaches ρ_2 because the portion of the current confined to the surface layer becomes negligible. Figure 18-6 shows a schematic curve of apparent resistivity versus the current-electrode spacing for the two-layer case. The asymptotic behavior of the apparent resistivity can provide important intuitive guidance concerning very shallow and very deep resistivities.

Electrode Arrangements and Field Procedures

In actual practice a number of different conventional surface configurations are used for the current and potential electrodes. In many arrangements, both sets of electrodes are laid out along a line. The current electrodes are generally placed on the outside of the potential electrodes. The most widely used configurations will be described in the paragraphs that follow. For convenience V will denote the measured voltage while the potential difference is ΔV.

FIGURE 18-6 Apparent resistivity as function of electrode separation for two-layer case illustrated in Fig. 18-5 (schematic).

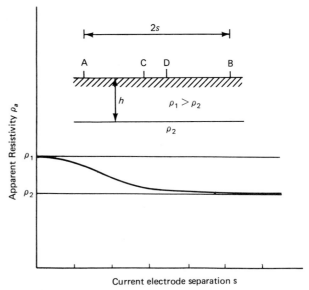

Wenner Arrangement One common electrode arrangement for resistivity measurement is the Wenner configuration illustrated in Fig. 18-7*a*. Here each potential electrode is separated from the adjacent current electrode by a distance *a* which is one-third the separation of the current electrodes. For this geometry, Eq. (18-7) becomes

$$\rho_a = 2\pi a \frac{\Delta V}{I} \tag{18-8}$$

The Wenner arrangement is a special case of the Schlumberger array, discussed next.

Schlumberger Arrangement In the Schlumberger configuration, the operator expands the electrode spacing by increasing the distance between current electrodes, typically on a logarithmic scale, during the course of a measurement. The potential-electrode spacing is assumed to be infinitesimal, and the observed values of potential can be adjusted accordingly. The Schlumberger electrode arrangement is illustrated in Fig. 18-7*b*.

The apparent resistivity at the center of a Schlumberger array is

$$\rho_a = \frac{\pi(s^2 - a^2/4)}{a} \frac{\Delta V}{I} \tag{18-9}$$

where *s* is half of the current-electrode separation (i.e., *AB*/2). The separation *a* between the potential electrodes *MN* is typically very small. For a "point dipole," Eq. (18-9) becomes

$$\rho_a = \frac{\pi s^2}{a} \frac{\Delta V}{I} \tag{18-10}$$

As a practical matter, when we consider attainable instrument accuracies, $a < 0.05s$ is sufficient and (18-10) can be used to compute the apparent resistivity from the field measurements of *V* and *I* versus current-electrode spacing, *S*.

Dipole Methods Dipole methods, more recently introduced than the Wenner or Schlumberger methods, are widely used, especially in the U.S.S.R., for deep penetration. Such a dipole-dipole array is illustrated in Fig. 18-7*c*. The current electrodes are usually well separated from the potential electrodes. If the separations *a* and *b* are equal and the distance between the centers of the respective pairs is $(n + 1)a$, the apparent resistivity determined by this arrangement is

$$\rho_a = n(n + 1)(n + 2) \cdot \pi a \frac{\Delta V}{I} \tag{18-11}$$

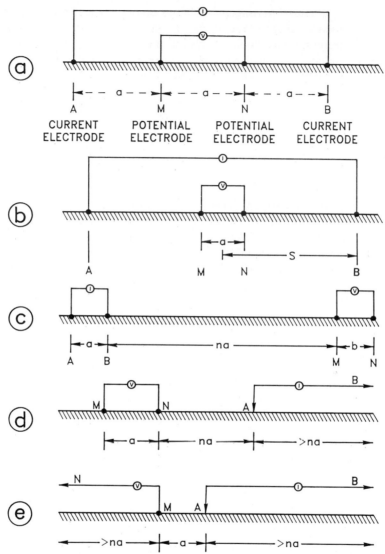

CURRENT
ELECTRODE   POTENTIAL
ELECTRODE   POTENTIAL
ELECTRODE   CURRENT
ELECTRODE

FIGURE 18-7   Collinear electrode configurations in common use: (*a*) Wenner arrangement; *a* is spacing as used in (18-8); (*b*) Schlumberger arrangement; *a* is very small and constant, and *S* is increased during the measurement; (*c*) dipole-dipole or axial dipole arrangement; separation $r = na$ between respective electrode pairs is changed during the measurement; (*d*) pole-dipole array, second current electrode is far from measurement location. This becomes three-electrode array for $u = 1$. (*e*) Pole-pole array.

Another collinear dipole arrangement is the pole-dipole (Fig. 18-7d). The second current electrode, *B*, is assumed to be a great distance from the measurement location (infinite electrode). For this configuration

$$\rho_a = 2\pi a n(n + 1) \frac{\Delta V}{I} \qquad (18\text{-}12)$$

If one of the potential electrodes, *N*, is also at a great distance, the configuration is called pole-pole (Fig. 18-7e). The apparent resistivity is then

$$\rho_a = 2\pi a \frac{\Delta V}{I} \qquad (18\text{-}13)$$

The apparent resistivities from dipole arrays are commonly plotted on a pseudo cross section along the traverse of measurements. Such a section cannot be construed as a vertical section showing resistivity variations. ρ_a values are plotted at the midpoint between the current transmitter and the potential (voltage) receiver. The vertical axis corresponds to *n*, the separation parameter.

Other, nonaxial, dipole arrays are used. Figure 18-8 describes some of these arrays in plan view. As before, *A* and *B* are the current electrodes while *M* and *N* denote the potential electrodes.

The variety of electrode configurations in dc resistivity soundings allows sufficient flexibility in adjusting the acquisition geometries and parameters to suit the field conditions and the exploration objective. They all share similar types of sources and receivers, all have a common characteristic of responding

FIGURE 18-8   Dipole arrays for several nonaxial dipole-dipole configurations. *A* and *B* are current electrodes and *M* and *N* are potential electrodes.

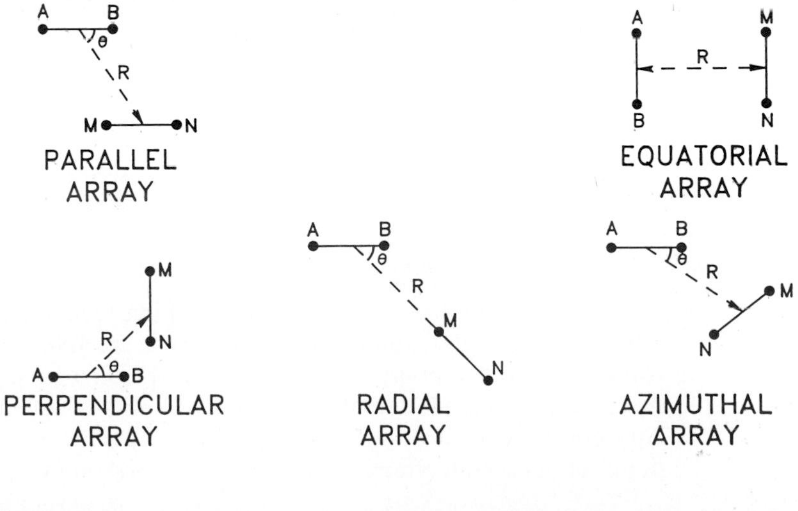

to deeper structures as the size of the array separation increases, and all tend to respond more strongly to resistive, as opposed to conductive, anomalies.

Equipment for Resistivity Soundings

The equipment required for dc resistivity sounding is simple in principle. A wide range of such equipment to suit different possible exploration needs and operating conditions is available. The basic requirement on a dc transmitter is to provide a constant-current source while this current is introduced into the ground. Various polarity reversals and switching periods are used to help reduce spurious electrode potentials as discussed below. The power is generated normally by a portable generator, although rechargeable batteries can be used for shallow exploration where the power requirements are not large. The range of source strength is quite wide, from as little as 100 mA produced by a portable, backpackable system to several hundreds of amperes. Recent transmitters allow the operator wider choices of signal types and application for other electrical methods.

A receiver for dc sounding data is basically a sensitive milliammeter or voltmeter. Historically, the meter readings were recorded by hand with some repetition or averaging. Current systems, which are controlled by a microprocessor, can perform automatic recording of both voltage and current, stack the results, and compute the pertinent apparent resistivity in real time.

Cancellation of Spurious Potentials at Electrodes

In addition to the potential difference associated with the current introduced into the earth by the current electrodes, the voltage reading may include spurious electrochemical potentials between the electrodes and electrolytes in the earth. Nonpolarizing electrodes (such as copper/copper–sulfate porous pots) are often used to avoid such effects. A long-established technique for eliminating contact potentials of this kind is that of Gish and Rooney.[22] It uses a commutator that reverses the directions of the current flow as well as the potential polarities. Any polarizing potentials at the electrodes, being reversed in sign with each half revolution of the commutator, will cancel. Spurious electrode potentials can also be canceled by use of low-frequency alternating current.

Fixed- versus Variable-Electrode Separations

Two general approaches are used for making resistivity measurements in the field. With the first, the electrode spacings are fixed, and the array of electrodes is moved laterally along a profile with constant separation, the apparent resistivities being plotted at the midpoints. This is called *continuous profiling*. Any ore body having anomalous conductivity and which is shallower than the depth of maximum effective penetration should show up as an anomaly on the resulting map. In the second type of measurement the center of the electrode spread remains fixed, but the separation of electrodes is progressively increased. Continuous profiling with a fixed configuration is more cost effective for detection of anomalies along a traverse but is inadequate for exploration objectives requiring depth control, which can only be achieved through expanding the geometry of the electrode configuration.

Interpretation

The quantitative interpretation of dc resistivity soundings has been the subject of numerous mathematical modeling studies for several decades. The simplest form of interpretation is the case of anomaly detection along a continuous profile. This only requires identification of the anomaly above the noise level. The next level of complexity in interpretation is the construction of a 1-D model, whose calculated response matches the field observations. Many geological features of economic interest can be represented quite adequately by a simple layering picture. Where there is an unconsolidated overburden over bedrock, it may be possible to estimate the depth to solid rock from resistivity measurements by use of the formulas for a two-layer configuration. A frequent use is the determination of depth to the water table. Many resistivity surveys carried out for engineering purposes are designed to yield this type of information. The interpretation of apparent resistivity curves in terms of a 1-D model is relatively well understood, and a number of forward- and inverse-modeling solutions exist. Some will be discussed below.

As the geoelectrical situation becomes more complex and includes 2-D and 3-D lateral heterogeneities, the interpretation becomes more involved and requires multidimensional modeling algorithms. This occurs when the objective itself is inhomogeneous or in the interpretation of deep structure complicated by variations in shallow resistivity and topographic relief.

Some ore bodies with anomalous conductivity can be represented as spheroids, and their dimensions and depth of burial can be calculated from resistivity data by the closed mathematical expressions worked out for these geometrical forms. The same approach can be applied to the study of filled sinks, as will be shown later.

Layered Media with Horizontal Interfaces   The simplest configuration for which theoretical solutions are available is that involving a few discrete layers, each having a uniform but different resistivity and separated from adjacent layers by plane horizontal interfaces.

Hummel[23] has worked out the theory for the two- and three-layer cases, using the method of images. This technique is based on the premise that there are current sources at all positions of the mirror images of the electrodes with respect to the various interfaces across which there is a discontinuity in resistivity. Multiple reflections result in an infinite number of such images for each interface. Since each reflection involves a loss of intensity (as with partly silvered mirrors) and successive reflections correspond to increasingly distant sources, it is only necessary to consider the effect of the first few multiples to obtain a usable value for the potential. For a surface layer of thickness h and resistivity ρ_1 overlying an infinitely thick substratum of resistivity ρ_2, the apparent resistivity ρ_a is

$$\rho_a = \rho_1\left\{1 + 4\left[\frac{k}{\sqrt{1 + (2h/a)^2}} - \frac{k}{\sqrt{4 + (2h/a)^2}}\right.\right.$$
$$\left.\left. + \cdots + \frac{k^n}{\sqrt{1 + (2nh/a)^2}} - \frac{k^n}{\sqrt{4 + (2nh/a)^2}} + \cdots\right]\right. \quad (18\text{-}14)$$

where a is the separation parameter for the Wenner arrangement and k is the resistivity reflectivity for dc currents:

$$k = \frac{\rho_2 - \rho_1}{\rho_2 + \rho_1} \quad (18\text{-}15)$$

Since $|k| < 1$, the series converges—i.e., the terms rapidly approach zero—and only a limited number of terms (each corresponding to a successive multiple reflection) is needed in carrying out the summation.

Hummel's work was based on that of Stefanescu et al.,[24] who had previously developed a more general integral expression suitable for the computation of the apparent resistivities for 1-D models.

With the Wenner arrangement of electrodes, the apparent resistivity ρ_a as calculated in the field is simply $2\pi aV/I$. When ρ_a is determined over a range of a values, the unknown quantities h and k can be found by matching the curves of ρ_a versus a, as observed, with theoretical responses based on various assumed layering conditions.

One-Dimensional Interpretation Aided by Master Curves

Historically, the most common device for interpreting resistivity data for a *small* number of horizontal layers was an assemblage of master curves. Each such curve is a plot of apparent resistivity versus electrode separation for the arrangement of electrodes employed in the field and for a specified layering configuration, various thicknesses and resistivity ratios being assumed for the individual layers. The use of master curves will be demonstrated for a two-layer, simple case. Similar master curves are available for models with more layers.

Two-Layer Case In the two-layer case involving a single layer of specified thickness h overlying an infinitely thick homogeneous substratum, a family of curves is plotted for different values of h and k. The apparent resistivity (actually $2\pi a\Delta V/I$ for the Wenner configuration of electrodes) is plotted versus *a* at the same scale as the master curves, and the curve of observed data is matched with the theoretical master curves. The correct values of *h* and *k* are established from the characteristics of the master curve giving the best match.

It is customary to plot such curves on a logarithmic scale like that shown in Fig. 18-9 for the Schlumberger configuration. The abscissa is the logarithm of *s/h*, the ratio of half the current-electrode separation to layer thickness. The ordinate is the logarithm of the ratio of the apparent resistivity to its limiting value ρ_1. If the assumption of two horizontally bounded layers is correct, the only unknowns are ρ_2 and *h*, the deeper-layer resistivity and thickness. The advantage of using log-log plots for the observed data and the master curves is that the experimental curve giving the best fit to the field measurements will be parallel to the applicable master curve. When *h* is not known, as is generally the case, it is only necessary to assume an arbitrary value for the depth in plotting the experimental points. The *s/h* value of the master curve which most closely parallels the plot of observed data enables one to determine *h*.

FIGURE 18-9   Typical master curves for Schlumberger electrode arrangement when layer of resistivity ρ_1 and thickness *h* overlies substratum of resistivity ρ_2. (*From Parasnis.*[15])

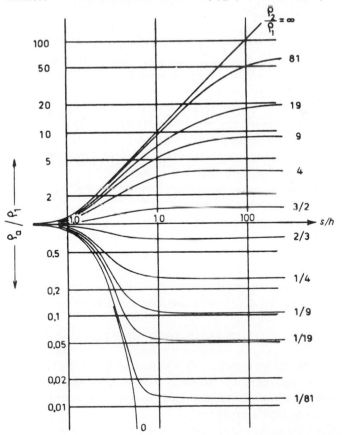

One-dimensional interpretation of dc sounding by use of master curves is of historic and, perhaps, educational value only and has become obsolete with the availability of computers. Fast and efficient algorithms (for an early one, see Argelo[25]) have become available even for small computers. Such 1-D interpretation can be done in the field with portable computers that execute both forward and inverse programs. Multidimensional interpretation usually requires a larger computer.

Resistivity Interpretation through 1-D Modeling

The objective of 1-D modeling of an apparent-resistivity curve for certain dc sounding arrays is to arrive, given ρ_a, at the best estimate of the 1-D true-resistivity profile versus depth, $\rho(z)$, under the measurement location. This can be done either through direct transformation or through iterative, curve-fitting procedures that are of a least-squares nature. A few of those fitting approaches can also provide some resolution analysis of the parameters of the best-fit model.

Some early works on 1-D dc modeling make significant contributions toward the understanding of the problem. Slichter[26] published a solution to the basic potential equation for which resistivity varies continuously with depth. This case, which can theoretically be used for direct interpretation, unfortunately has little practical application in prospecting. Van Nostrand and Cook,[20] following Pekeris,[27] have developed a method for solving the problem where the variation of resistivity with depth is stepwise. This, of course, corresponds to a multilayered earth. Koefoed[28] has published papers on a method also based on Pekeris' theory for rapid computation of the layering configuration from an apparent-resistivity curve. Marsden[29] has demonstrated computer techniques to interpret electric soundings directly from apparent-resistivity-versus-electrode-spacing data obtained in the field.

Recently, more powerful inversion processes have been applied to the 1-D dc interpretation problem. Inman et al.[30] have used a singular-value-decomposition approach iteratively to arrive at a model which fits, in the least-squares sense, apparent-resistivity data estimated from field measurements (ρ_D). This inverse approach linearizes the relationship between apparent resistivities for various electrode spacings $\rho(s_i)$, $i = 1, \ldots, m$, and the set of parameters, p_j, $j = 1, \ldots, n$ (layer resistivities and thicknesses), defining a 1-D model. The apparent-resistivity data are a function G of p_j:

$$\rho_D(s_i) = G(p_1, \ldots, p_m) \qquad i = 1, \ldots, n$$

The nonlinear function G will be expanded into a Taylor series, and terms of order higher than 1, assumed to be small, are dropped. This achieves effective linearization of the problem, which allows execution of an iterative least-squares-fitting process:

$$\rho_k(s_i) = \rho_D(s_i) + \sum_{j=1}^{n} \frac{\partial G_i}{\partial p_j}\bigg|_{p_j^{(k)}} \left(p_j^{(k)} - p_j^{(k+1)}\right) \qquad i = 1, \ldots, m \qquad (18\text{-}16)$$

where k is the iteration number.

In order to obtain the correction term for the model parameters $p_j^{(k)} - p_j^{(k+1)}$, which will give the new model $p_j^{(k+1)}$, from the one of the previous iteration $p_j^{(k)}$, one has to invert the Jacobian matrix A:

$$A_{ij} = \frac{\partial G_i}{\partial p_j}\bigg|_{p_j^{(k)}} \qquad \begin{matrix} i = 1, \ldots, n \\ j = 1, \ldots, m \end{matrix} \qquad (18\text{-}17)$$

which is of arbitrary dimensionality ($m \times n$) and rank. As described by Jackson[31] this can be accomplished by use of the natural inverse (Lanczos[32]). A is inverted, Eq. (18-16) is solved for a correction step, and a new model represented by $p_j^{(k+1)}$, $j = 1, \ldots, n$, is obtained. The process continues iteratively until the data are fitted closely enough (below the noise level for example) or until the corrective steps are insignificant.

The iterative solution process described above allows evaluation of a resolution matrix that can be interpreted quantitatively to yield relative resolution estimates for the model parameters and measures of their interdependences. The latter can be considered as a more complete assessment of coupling between the effect of certain model parameters on the measured response. A special case of this coupling, the joint product effect of resistivity and thickness of a resistive layer which lies between two conductors, was called "the equivalence problem" in the early literature. Resolution analysis will also typically reveal that resistive layers have a greater effect on dc resistivity results than do conductive ones.

The iterative inversion process based on the singular value decomposition can be viewed as a discrete case of the more general continuous approach described by Oldenburg.[33]

A time-consuming part of the automatic inverse procedure above is the computation of the Jacobian matrix elements of Eq. (18-7), namely the partial derivatives of every data point with respect to each of the model parameters. A linear filtering method first presented by Ghosh[34,35] can be of considerable help. The apparent resistivity can be represented (Koefoed[28]) as an integral transform of a kernel function $T(\lambda)$ (e.g., for a Schlumberger array):

$$\rho_a(s) = s^2 \int_0^\infty T(\lambda) J_1(\lambda) \lambda \, d\lambda \qquad (18\text{-}18)$$

where $s = AB/2$ and $\lambda = 1/s$.

Following Ghosh,[34,35] Eq. (18-18) may be inverted by use of Hankel's inversion of the Fourier-Bessel integral

$$T(\lambda) = \int_0^\infty \frac{1}{s} \rho_a(s) J_i(\lambda s) \, ds \qquad (18\text{-}19)$$

Substituting $s = e^x$ and $\lambda = e^{-y}$, one gets

$$T(y) = \int_{-\infty}^\infty \rho_a(x) J_1(e^{-(y-x)}) \, dx \qquad (18\text{-}20)$$

which is an expression of a linear, convolutional relationship that exists between $\rho_a(s)$ and $T(\lambda)$. Figure 18-10 (after Ginzburg et al.[36]) depicts two convolution filters for transforming the kernel function $T(\lambda)$ into the apparent resistivity $\rho_a(s)$ and back.

The kernel function is convenient to use since it can be computed analytically and recursively very efficiently for a stack of $N - 1$ layers, each with resistivity ρ_j and thickness h_j, over a half-space of resistivity ρ_N. Propagating through the 1-D model upwards to the surface,

$$T_j(\lambda) = \rho_j \frac{\rho_j(1 - e^{-2\lambda h_j}) + T_{j+1}(\lambda)(1 + e^{-2\lambda h_j})}{\rho_j(1 + e^{-2\lambda h_j}) + T_{j+1}(\lambda)(1 - e^{-2\lambda h_j})}$$

$$j = N - 1, \ldots, 1 \quad (18\text{-}21)$$

$T_1(\lambda)$ is the kernel function at the surface. The apparent resistivity can be easily obtained from $T_1(\lambda)$ by use of the convolution filters of Fig. 18-10. Moreover, all the partial derivatives of $T_1(\lambda)$ can be computed recursively just as easily, as shown by Ginzburg et al.[36] Consequently, an iterative 1-D inversion scheme on $T(\lambda)$ can be more efficient. Figure 18-11 presents an example of the application of least-squares iterative inversion to the kernel function obtained from actual data. The resistivity profile obtained is compared to borehole lithological information.

The linear filtering approach can be effectively used to transform resistivity soundings obtained with one electrode configuration into another (Kumar and Das[37]), and it can be applied to other EM geophysical methods.

Two- and Three-Dimensional Modeling

Two- and three-dimensional buried inhomogeneities can produce significant anomalies at the surface. Buried conductors tend to concentrate the current flow lines while resistive bodies cause the current to diverge and flow around them. Figure 18-12a and b demonstrates both effects.

The 2-D and 3-D modeling problem is by far more complicated than the 1-D one. While analytical solutions exist for some limited geometries (Van Nostrand[38]), finite-difference and finite-element methods (Das and Verma,[39] Dey and Morrison[40]) as well as integral equations (Hohman[41]) are generally used.

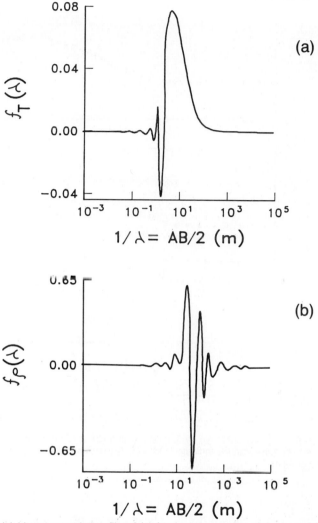

FIGURE 18-10 (a) Linear convolution filter $f_T(\lambda)$ for the computation of the kernel function from the apparent resistivity. (b) Similar filter for the computation of the apparent resistivity from the kernel function.

The mathematical treatment of these modeling problems is beyond the scope of this text. However, computers, especially those with vectorized computational capabilities, make 2-D modeling practically feasible, and even 3-D forward modeling can be undertaken, albeit with some limitations. Two-dimensional iterative inversion can follow a similar strategy to the least-squares fitting one described above. Due, however, to the large number of possible couplings between model parameters, a completely automatic iterative process, though feasible, is hazardous. A more practical approach calls for user-guided iterative, inverse processes.

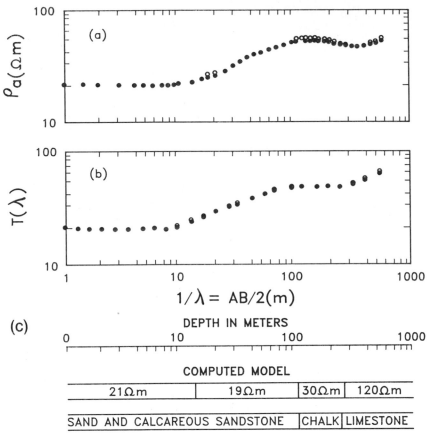

FIGURE 18-11   Apparent resistivity curve (*a*), its kernel function (*b*), and the computed model compared to the well log (*c*). Open circles indicate field data, full circles indicate values computed from the interpreted model.

Of special importance (though too often neglected) are 2-D and 3-D topographic and shallow effects. These can be problematic and cause severe interpretational pitfalls, especially for dc resistivity techniques, since depth control is achieved through expanding surface electrode geometry, and the distortion effects of lateral currents can be large. Surface effects are of special importance to the relatively high-resolution cavity-detection problem as described and treated by Spiegel et al.[42]

At times the shallow 3-D body can itself be the survey objective. Its location can be revealed simply through an anomalous response on continuous profiling that can be compared to the analytical response. Such an example is given by Cook and Van Nostrand.[43] They have compared the horizontal resistivity profiles observed over a shale sink in Cherokee County, Kansas, with theoretical curves for a sunken hemispherical boss having a plane boundary flush

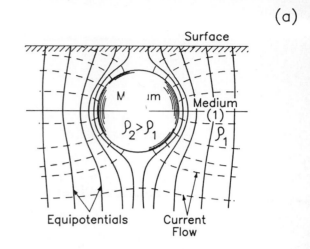

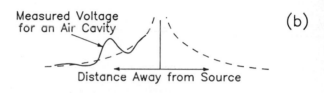

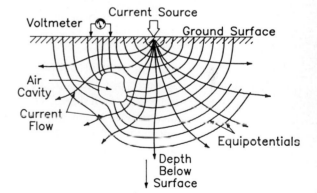

FIGURE 18-12   Equipotentials and current flow lines for (a) buried conductive sphere (*Telford et al.*[16]) and (b) buried resistive air cavity (*South West Research Institute, San Antonio, Texas*).

with the free surface. Figure 18-13 indicates the close resemblance that was shown between their theoretical and observed curves.

18-3   NATURAL-SOURCE ELECTROMAGNETIC TECHNIQUES

Electromagnetic geophysical techniques that utilize naturally occurring EM phenomena have been used in exploration for petroleum, mineral resources, and geothermal energy since the early 1950s. As with many other electrical and

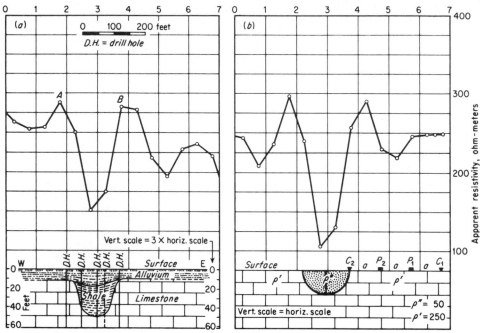

FIGURE 18-13   Comparison of observed and theoretical horizontal resistivity profiles over filled sink for Wenner configuration: (*a*) observed field curve with geologic cross section; (*b*) theoretical field with assumed data points only at electrode positions. Diameter of sink is 3*a*/2. Assumed value of $\rho''/\rho' = \frac{1}{5}$. (*After Cook and Van Nostrand.*[43])

electromagnetic geophysical methods, natural-source techniques remotely sense, from the surface of the earth, the spatial distribution of electrical resistivity with depth. The last decade has seen increased use of natural-source techniques for petroleum exploration. In addition to the obvious advantage of not having to carry a source with the exploration group, such EM energy can usually penetrate well below exploration depths. This deep-penetration property alone makes natural-field EM techniques the most suitable among the various EM methods for resistivity surveying in petroleum exploration. Natural-source EM techniques retain their deep-penetration power even where penetration by conventional reflection seismic techniques is difficult, as in the presence of overlying basalts or other volcanics. However, the resolving power of EM methods is well below that of most reflection seismic techniques. Consequently, most applications of the natural-source EM methods have been in reconnaissance of large, relatively unexplored basins. Natural-source methods are generally used as a prelude or supplement to seismic exploration or as a substitute for seismic surveying where such surveys yield poor or no results.

Aside from petroleum exploration, the sensitivity of natural-field EM techniques to conductive anomalies make them especially suitable for exploration for geothermal energy sources. Use of these techniques for mining exploration has been limited because other geophysical tools, such as active-source electromagnetics, are more suitable.

The development of natural-source EM array techniques presents a significant improvement over older EM methods. These methods, which use high redundancy, adequate spatial sampling, and proper array design, are capable of yielding increased resolution and of reducing the effects of the near surface on the resolution of deeper formations.

Early work on the development of natural-source EM techniques was carried out in the Soviet Union by Tikhonov[44] and in France by Cagniard.[45] Both have recognized in their pioneering work the applicability of natural EM sources for exploration purposes. They recognized the plane-wave nature of that source and its ability to penetrate to great depths. Once this idea was conceived, the theoretical background was already there. Maxwell,[1] in his fundamental work on electromagnetism, solved the problem of plane EM waves propagating through a layered medium. This solution was adapted by Tikhonov[44] and Cagniard[45] to formulate an exploration method in a 1-D layered earth. Their work lays a foundation for what became known as the magnetotelluric (MT) method of exploration. Since the early work of Cagniard and Tikhonov, the MT method has evolved to cover wider frequency ranges and to handle more field components in order to interpret multidimensional geoelectrical situations. Robust signal-enhancement techniques have been added, and the method has been generalized to EM array techniques. We shall cover all of these subjects in this section.

The Source Signal

The source signal for natural-field EM methods consists of naturally occurring fluctuations in the earth's magnetic field. This source is present at any place on earth and at practically any time. It exists over a wide range of frequencies. The commonly used frequency range for exploration is from 0.0001 to about 10,000 Hz. In the frequency range below 1 Hz most of the source energy comes from micropulsations of the natural EM field caused by disturbances in the ionosphere. Such micropulsations are caused primarily by the interaction of the solar wind with the ionosphere. The strengths of micropulsations vary with the diurnal rise and fall of the ionosphere and are strongly dependent on the presence and magnitude of solar flares. Figure 18-14 shows the general range of this source signal-power spectrum. As the figure shows, the energy of the ionospheric source increases significantly as frequency decreases. As we shall see later, this will be the main reason for the high penetrating power of natural-field source signals.

In the frequency range above 1 Hz, most of the energy comes from electrical phenomena in the atmosphere, such as thunderstorms. This locally generated energy propagates over great distances in the space between the conductive surface of the earth and the ionosphere or the ionospheric cavity. Short-wave radio broadcasting depends for its range on transmission in the same manner.

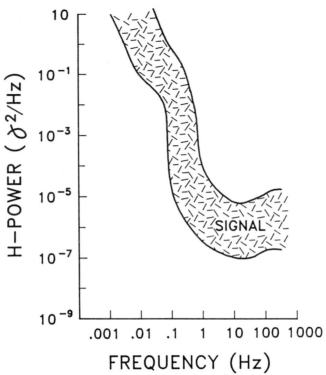

FIGURE 18-14   Natural-source electromagnetic signal. Note the relatively high signal levels at low frequencies.

When micropulsations are received at short-wave frequencies, they interfere with communications and are called *sferics*. The power in this higher-frequency part of the source is relatively lower than that in the lower frequencies, and the source strength dependence on time can be more irregular. The source-signal strengths for both ionospheric and thunderstorm-generated sources can vary by an order of magnitude within a few minutes.

Studies have been carried out to characterize this natural EM source. It is generally accepted, at least as a working assumption, that at the surface of the earth natural sources generate plane EM waves. Their stochastic nature is generally stationary. Due to the large resistivity contrast between the more conductive earth and the air, these plane EM waves penetrate vertically into the earth.

The validity of the plane-wave assumption has been studied by a number of workers; Madden and Nelson[46] have shown that it is generally acceptable as a working assumption for frequencies greater than 10^{-3} Hz in midlatitudes. Hermance and Peltier[47] studied the effects of equatorial and auroral electrojet wind currents and concluded that in generally conductive environments the basic source assumptions still hold for frequencies between 10^{-4} and 1 Hz.

For the high-frequency part of the source spectrum, above 1 Hz, the validity of the plane-wave assumption has been studied by Bannister,[48] who calculated the field of an electrical dipole in the atmosphere over a homogeneous earth model and concluded that the plane-wave assumption will still be valid as close as 7 skin depths from the source. This means that in the high-frequency range, the plane-wave assumption will be valid closer to the source for conductive geologies, while in a resistive earth one has to maintain a greater separation.

The frequency range for classical MT exploration is from 10^{-4} Hz to several hundred hertz. Some applications utilize the higher part of the frequency range occupied by the natural EM spectrum, namely from 1 to 10,000 Hz. The latter is referred to in the literature as "audio" magnetotellurics (AMT). The difference between MT and AMT is only in the depth ranges for which they are used. The same mathematical descriptions and physical principles apply to both.

The magnetic induction field vector **H** generated by ionospheric and thunderstorm activities at a given spot on the surface of the earth produces a plane wave that penetrates vertically into the geology. The field interacts with the geoelectrical structure. The plane waves undergo reflections, transmissions, and other phenomena common to plane waves interacting with a conductive structure of one or more dimensions. In addition, one can look at the various parts of the geoelectrical structure as a system that consists of conductors in a time-dependent, magnetic field. According to the fundamental laws of electromagnetism, an electric field is induced in the geoelectrical structure by the time-varying magnetic field. An observer at the surface of the earth can measure both fields—the magnetic field **H** and the induced electric field **E**. The magnetic field acts primarily as a source field, whereas the electric field is a secondary phenomenon induced by the interaction between the magnetic field and the geoelectrical structure. The penetrating magnetic-source field vector has only horizontal components, H_x and H_y. Once the source field interacts with a 2-D or 3-D structure, a vertical field component is also generated due to the interaction of the source field with the multidimensional medium. This vertical field component can be measured as well.

The fundamental equations describing the behavior of EM waves were formulated by Maxwell:

$$\nabla \cdot \mathbf{E} = \frac{1}{\epsilon} \bar{\rho} \qquad \text{Coulomb's law}$$

$$\nabla \cdot \mathbf{H} = 0$$

$$\nabla \times \mathbf{E} = -\mu \frac{\partial \mathbf{H}}{\partial t} \qquad \text{Faraday's law}$$

$$\nabla \times \mathbf{H} = \epsilon \frac{\partial \mathbf{E}}{\partial t} + \mathbf{J} \qquad \text{Ampere's law}$$

$$(18\text{-}22)$$

Equations (18-22) cast these fundamental equations in a form suitable for description of EM wave propagation in rock material. μ indicates the permeability of the rock, which for all practical purposes is the same as that for free space, μ_0, and ϵ is the dielectric constant. Two additional important relationships associated with Maxwell's equations are Ohm's law, mentioned in Eq. (18-2), and the continuity equation

$$\nabla \cdot \mathbf{J} + \frac{\partial \bar{\rho}}{\partial t} = 0 \tag{18-23}$$

Note that $\bar{\rho}$ conventionally denotes charge density rather than resistivity. The continuity equation relates the current density $\mathbf{J}$ to the time dependence of the charge density, and it plays an important role in the understanding of the behavior of the natural-source EM response to both vertical and lateral resistivity variations.

Conventionally, we shall assume a harmonic time dependence of the form of $e^{-i\omega t}$, where ω is the frequency in radians per second, and we shall neglect the first term on the right in Ampere's law, which represents displacement currents. These currents are small for the frequency range and resistivities encountered in rock material with natural-source EM techniques. Simple algebra will lead us from Maxwell's equations under the assumptions stated above into a wave equation, which in one dimension for the electric field is written as

$$\frac{d^2E}{dz^2} = -i\omega\mu\sigma E \tag{18-24}$$

where σ is the conductivity.

Figure 18-15 describes schematically the interaction of the source magnetic induction field with the geoelectrical medium.

Equation (18-2) has two independent solutions:

$$E \propto \exp\{\pm i \sqrt{i\omega\mu\sigma}\, z\} \tag{18-25}$$

These solutions describe the behavior of the electric field as a function of depth z. The magnetic field obeys a similar wave equation and thus is described by similar exponential solutions. These two solutions differ only by the sign of the exponent. In our notation, the plus sign represents the down-going wave while the minus sign represents the up-going wave. In either case the amplitude of such solutions will decay exponentially, and the skin depth is defined as the depth in a homogeneous medium at which the amplitude decays by a factor of $1/e$ from some initial value. The skin depth δ is derived directly from Eq. (18-25):

$$\delta = \sqrt{\frac{2}{\mu\omega\sigma}} = \sqrt{\frac{2\rho}{\omega\mu}} \tag{18-26}$$

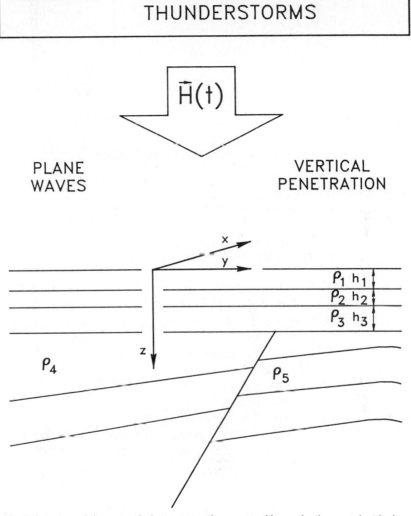

FIGURE 18-15   The interaction of the natural electromagnetic source with conductive geoelectrical model.

The physical meaning of the functional expression for the skin depth of EM waves in a homogeneous conductive medium is important. First, the skin depth increases with decreasing frequency. This means that, as is the case for acoustic waves, EM waves penetrate deeper as frequencies are lower. That behavior is described in Fig. 18-16. Two EM plane waves, with frequencies of ω_1 and ω_2, respectively, where $\omega_1 > \omega_2$, will both decay. However, the rate of decay for the wave of the lower frequency is lower. Second, the skin depth depends on

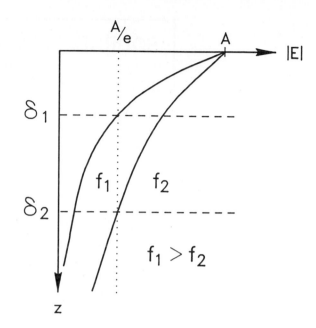

FIGURE 18-16 The decay of the amplitude of electromagnetic waves for two different frequencies in a homogeneous medium. Lower frequencies decay more slowly with depth and penetrate deeper.

the conductivity σ or, inversely, the resistivity ρ. The higher the resistivity, or the lower the conductivity, the greater is the skin depth for a given frequency.

Note that this behavior is different for EM waves than for direct currents. Direct currents penetrate easily through conductors and are blocked by resistors, whereas EM waves exhibit the opposite behavior. Electromagnetic waves penetrate easily through resistive material and suffer no attenuation as they propagate through an infinite resistor; on the other hand, conductors will block them. The exploration implications of these properties are significant. Exploration in localities such as basalt-covered areas can be done relatively easily with EM waves which propagate through the resistive basalt and are not significantly attenuated. Another implication is that a sensing technique using EM waves will be more sensitive and will resolve conducting bodies to a greater degree.

Both frequency and conductivity dependence of the skin depths are described in Fig. 18-17. The skin depths for a homogeneous earth of given resistivity and given frequency can be read from the diagonal lines. For example, an EM wave with frequency of 1 Hz will decay by a factor of $1/e$ after it has traveled in homogeneous material with resistivity of $100 \ \Omega \cdot m$ a distance of 5 km. If, however, the material is conductive with a resistivity of only $1 \ \Omega \cdot m$, the same EM wave will decay by a factor of $1/e$ after traveling 500 m. If a penetration of 5 km is desired, one has to look for that conductive material at a frequency of 0.01 Hz.

As we have seen, the natural source normally has increased energy in low frequencies and is generally sufficient to ensure penetration, even in conductive materials. In order to achieve that penetration, however, one must resort to low frequencies or long wavelengths and therefore must sacrifice resolution. This means that in areas with a thick cover of conductive material, $2 \, \Omega \cdot m$ or less, one must be careful in using natural-field EM techniques. Examples of such areas are basin-and-range provinces or offshore in deep water. Low frequencies will have to be used to achieve penetration, and then the resolution obtained will be relatively lower, and the recording time for information at these extremely low frequencies will be long, which may make the application of this technique prohibitively expensive.

Data Acquisition

Two types of EM fields can be acquired in geophysical exploration methods by use of the natural source. One is the magnetic induction **H**, which is the source field, and the other is the electric field **E**. Early in the development of natural-field EM techniques, as reported in the works of Cagniard[45] and Tikhonov,[44] only two field components were acquired: the magnetic field component and the electric field component perpendicular to it. The basic concept was that in a laterally homogeneous, 1-D medium the result is independent of the direction as long as one measures two such components. This is indeed the case for laterally homogeneous media.

FIGURE 18-17
Skin-depth chart for a homogeneous earth.

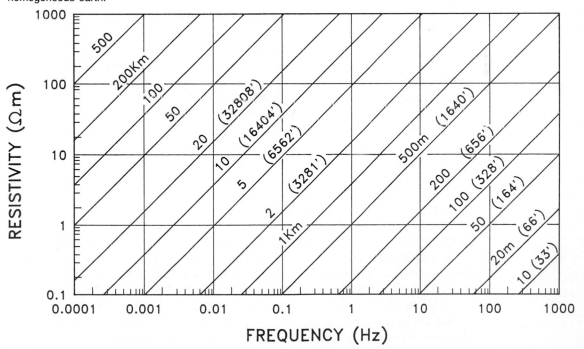

In geophysical exploration with the natural ionospheric source, however, one has to consider the source polarization as well. The polarization of that source varies continuously. As a result, if one measures only those two components, a method called scalar MT, different results might be obtained for different source polarizations. Consequently, the geophysical information and its interpretation may reflect the source polarization at the time of measurement as well as the geoelectrical structure and thus will not be repeatable. Once this was realized, it was clear that in utilizing the natural EM source for geophysical exploration, vector quantities have to be measured at each and every location (Swift[49]).

Typical MT measurements are done on a station-by-station basis. Each station consists of both magnetic and electric field sensors. A 3-D coordinate system is established at the MT site with the z axis pointing downward. The magnetic field is measured vectorially by measuring all three components along the three axes of the coordinate system. The magnetic field components are measured by either induction coils or a Superconducting Quantum Interference Device (SQUID). Several different designs of induction coil magnetometers exist. They are all similar in principle; they all include a core of Mumetal around which several tens of thousands of turns of copper wire are wound. Some coils are passive, and some include a built-in preamplifier system.

During the last decade, a superconducting magnetometer, SQUID, has become common in some applications of MT data acquisition. SQUID magnetometers are generally quieter and more sensitive than are coils, especially in the low-frequency range. Each type of sensor offers advantages and disadvantages. Coils tend to be bulky and heavy. Some weigh over 35 kg and are about 2 m long, although some recent coil designs are smaller. Coils are relatively trouble-free and service-free. On the other hand, the SQUID magnetometer is easier to install and carry around because all three components are packaged into a single device. However, it requires a good supply of liquid helium to provide the near absolute-zero temperature at which superconductivity is present, a severe limitation in some remote areas. The discovery in late 1986 of higher temperature superconducting ceramics may remove this limitation.

The electric field is measured through sensing the potential difference between a pair of ground electrodes. Typical chemical-electrode materials are copper, copper sulfate, cadmium, and cadmium chloride. In some cases, a lead plate may be used. The distance between the electrodes is typically 50 to 300 m. Longer electric field dipoles will yield higher signals and also average over more near-surface effects, but they may acquire more ambient noise. Figure 18-18 shows schematically the sensor layout for a typical MT station.

In a practical application, the site does not have to be laid out exactly symmetrically. Electrode configurations in the form of an L or a T or even nonperpendicular arrays can be used. Figure 18-19 shows a typical electrode installed in mud, sometimes with added chemicals to decrease the electrode contact resistance with the ground. Figure 18-20 shows a typical induction coil that can sense one component of the magnetic induction field.

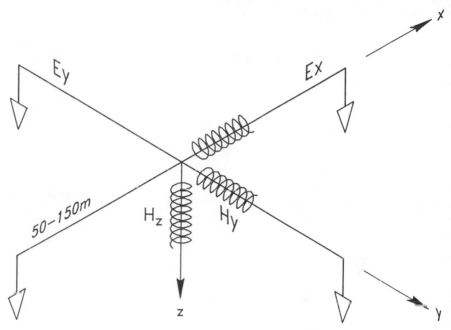

FIGURE 18-18   Sensor layout for an individual, five-component, classical magnetotelluric station.

FIGURE 18-19   Electric field sensor; an electrode installed in a conductive mudcake to reduce contact resistance.

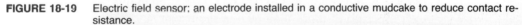

FIGURE 18-20   Induction coil installed vertically to measure the H_z component of the magnetic field.

A typical set of five traces representing the five components measured at an MT site is shown in Fig. 18-21. The information in this figure has been recorded over a period of more than 60 s in the frequency range of 0.1 to 5.0 Hz. One characteristic natural-source event is observed after the 40-s mark on all five channels. Note that the vertical component of the electric field is not measured, since for most geological situations, just underneath the surface of the earth, this component is small because the large conductivity difference between the rocks and the air will make the reflection coefficient at the surface − 1.

Several different data acquisition systems capable of recording five-component MT information exist. They all divide the several-decade-wide frequency range into subbands. The information from the electric and magnetic field sensors is fed into electric and magnetic field preamplifiers where it receives its appropriate first stage of amplification and filtering. A second stage of both amplification and filtering is common and is followed by an analog-to-digital (A/D) conversion. State-of-the-art systems perform data enhancement and analysis at the site in real time or near real time. The time-domain information and/or the processed results are recorded on magnetic tape.

Common MT systems operate from below 10^{-3} Hz to several hundred hertz, while AMT systems operate from several hertz up to 10,000 Hz. Some systems are designed to record more than one MT station simultaneously. The information can be brought into the A/D or processing unit via cable or radio telemetry. This allows enhanced and more robust data processing through cross-referencing information from different stations, as will be explained in the next section. Some systems have high-precision clocks built into them to allow data from other stations that are recorded synchronously and simultaneously with a base station to be postprocessed together. Such a procedure requires transportation of data tapes from one location to another and allows cross-referencing techniques in data processing between stations separated by virtually unlimited distances. Figure 18-22 shows a schematic block diagram of a natural-field, EM data acquisition system.

Utilization of the natural field presents, in addition to several obvious advantages such as plane-wave geometry and source availability, some disadvantages. When using the natural source, one has to deal with whatever is provided naturally. The natural source, as is evident from Fig. 18-14, can be very weak, especially in the middle-frequency range around 0.5 to 5 Hz. Hence

FIGURE 18-21
Natural-source magnetic induction, **H**, signals and induced field components.

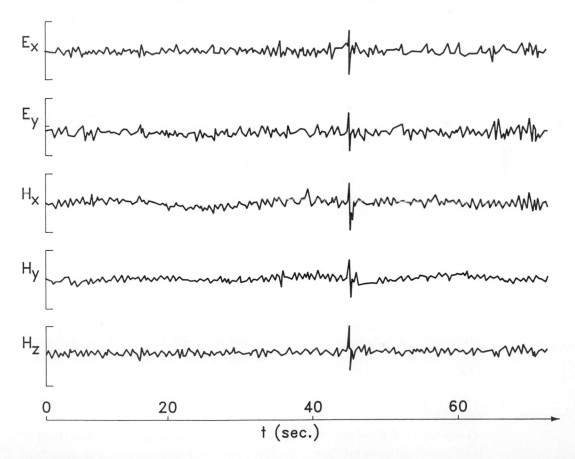

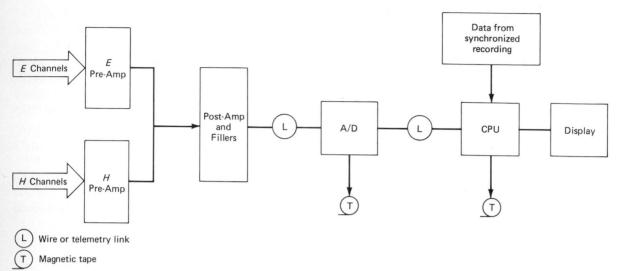

FIGURE 18-22   Schematic block diagram of a typical natural-source electromagnetic data-acquisition and real-time-processing system.

there is a requirement for high-quality, sensitive, and quiet instrumentation. As with all electrical methods, electrodes should not be set up in the immediate vicinity of near-surface conducting bodies.

Many noise sources can interfere with the natural-source information. Obvious noise sources are associated with the electric power grid in power lines, electrical generators, and switching stations. Some less-obvious noise sources are underground pipelines with electrical corrosion protection, the seismic-electric effect from microseisms, or even electrified fences. Radio transmitters and microwave repeater stations have also been known to cause noise problems.

Typically, in remote areas that are far from cultural activity, industrial areas, and power lines, all of these noise sources are of secondary importance. As we get closer to populated areas, however, these noise sources have to be overcome, usually through acquisition of greater quantities of data, followed by stacking and robust data enhancement. Cultural noises tend to be weaker at night, and, in general, all kinds of electromagnetic noise which interfere with natural-source EM geophysical exploration vary as a function of time. As a result, one can often get significantly better data by waiting a few hours or by reoccupying a station a few days or a few weeks later. In extreme noise situations, the acquisition of useful, natural-source EM data becomes impractical.

Data Processing

As we have seen before, the plane-wave, magnetic induction source field **H** penetrates vertically into the geological formations and induces an electric field vector $\mathbf{E}$ through its interaction with the subsurface conductive material. The source field is related to the induced field through a transfer function relationship involving an impedance function Z:

$$\mathbf{E} = Z\mathbf{H} \tag{18-27}$$

where the source field, induced field, and Z are functions of frequency. This multiplicative relationship in the frequency domain between $\mathbf{E}$ and $\mathbf{H}$ implies linearity of the relationship between the source and the induced fields. The transfer function or the impedance Z transforms as a tensor because it relates two vector quantities.

Working in the frequency domain is natural because of the linear impedance relationship. In addition, it gives an added advantage of a domain that is directly related to skin depth or penetration. Similarly, the relationship between the magnetic induction field and the electric field can be expressed by an admittance function Y:

$$\mathbf{H} = Y\mathbf{E} \tag{18-28}$$

In order to be able to use this impedance or admittance relationship, one has to transform the measured signal for the source field $\mathbf{H}$ and the induced field $\mathbf{E}$ into the frequency domain using some standard technique. The method can be a fast Fourier transform (FFT). In some field systems that use a small CPU, another technique, known as *cascade decimation* (Wight et al.[50]), is commonly used. Using cascade decimation, one can perform a Fourier transform without the requirement common to FFT techniques of keeping the entire time series in memory at one time.

Let us review how the elements of this impedance tensor are estimated. The equations

$$E_x = Z_{xx} H_x + Z_{xy}H_y \tag{18-29}$$
$$E_y = Z_{yx}H_x + Z_{yy}H_y \tag{18-30}$$

express the relationship between the source field and the induced electric field, Eq. (18-27), explicitly. All the quantities are complex functions of frequency. In a similar way, one can express the relationship between the source field, which has only horizontal components (H_x and H_y) for the magnetic induction field, to the vertical component of the magnetic field. That component is generated by the interaction of the source field with those parts of the geoelectrical subsurface structure which are not layered and laterally homogeneous. The relationship is

$$H_z = AH_x + BH_y \tag{18-31}$$

where A and B are complex transfer functions.

The six transfer functions in Eqs. (18-29), (18-30), and (18-31)—the four elements of the impedance tensor $\mathbf{Z}$ and the functions A and B—include all the information estimated from the measured field components at a given MT station. For another presentation of measured quantities and their relationship to estimated quantities, see Eggers.[51] In order to estimate each of these six complex transfer functions, one has to measure redundant information, such as measuring the fields for the same frequency at two or more different times. This will allow evaluation of these independent equations, for example, Eq. (18-29), at least twice, and we thus obtain at least two equations with two unknowns that can be solved simultaneously. Similar treatment can be given to Eqs. (18-30) and (18-31). This type of solution requires independent polarizations between the two instances of measurement of the source and induced field at a given frequency.

Any practical measurements of the MT signals involve a certain amount of noise. Consequently, one would like to acquire large quantities of redundant information in order to obtain better estimates of the transfer functions. If one has acquired independent measurements of the field for a given frequency, an estimate for the impedance element, for example those in Eq. (18-29), can be obtained by requiring minimization of the least-squares function

$$\Psi = \sum_{i=1}^{n} (E_{x_i} - Z_{xx}H_{x_i} - Z_{xy}H_{y_i})(E_{x_i} - Z_{xx}H_{x_i} - Z_{xy}H_{y_i})^* \quad (18\text{-}32)$$

which expresses the absolute value of the difference between the measured electric field and the one predicted from the measured source field using the estimated impedances. By taking derivatives of Eq. (18-32) with respect to the real and imaginary parts of each impedance element, we obtain two equations with the two unknowns Z_{xx} and Z_{xy}, which are the same unknowns as in Eq. (18-29) (Sims et al.[52]):

$$\langle E_x R_1^* \rangle = \langle H_x R_1^* \rangle Z_{xx} + \langle H_y R_1^* \rangle Z_{xy}$$
$$\langle E_x R_2^* \rangle = \langle H_x R_2^* \rangle Z_{xx} + \langle H_y R_2^* \rangle Z_{xy} \quad (18\text{-}33)$$

The quantities in angle brackets are the auto- or cross-power spectra between two signals representing any of the five components measured in the classical MT station over a narrow frequency band around a given frequency ω; the bandwidth is $\Delta\omega$. The definition of the spectral quantities is given by

$$\langle S_1 S_2^* \rangle = \frac{1}{\Delta\omega} \int_{\omega-\Delta\omega/2}^{\omega+\Delta\omega/2} S_1(\omega') \cdot S_2(\omega')^* \, d\omega' \quad (18\text{-}34)$$

The bandwidth $\Delta\omega$ has to be sufficiently small so that a given function does not vary much within this frequency band. The fields R_1 and R_2 can be any of the horizontal field components E_x, E_y, H_x, or H_y.

Since there are six independent ways to choose a combination of two out of four signals, the system of two equations with two unknowns, Eq. (18-33), can be reviewed in six different ways by a choice of different reference signals R_1 and R_2. The most commonly used possibility is that for which R_1 is chosen to be H_x and R_2 is chosen to be H_y. Another possibility is R_1 and R_2 being chosen as E_x and E_y, respectively. Two other possibilities involving perpendicular components of the electric and magnetic field, such as E_x and H_y, tend to be relatively unstable, especially in laterally homogeneous media, since these components are highly coherent and the denominator for one of the solutions of Eq. (18-33) becomes very small. Consequently, there are four independent ways to solve Eq. (18-33). Equations (18-30) and (18-31) can be solved in similar ways for the other unknowns—the other two elements of the impedance tensor and the quantities A and B. Completely analogous treatment can be given to Eq. (18-28) if one desires to estimate the admittance tensor elements.

In practice, measurements are going to be contaminated by certain amounts and types of noise. In general, the amount and nature of this noise is not known. Its effect can, however, be characterized and estimated in several different ways. One way of estimating noise effects is through the phasor coherency function defined by

$$C_p = 1 - \frac{1}{m|R|}\sum_{i=1}^{m}|Z_i - Z|$$

where   (18-35)

$$Z = \frac{1}{m}\sum_{i=1}^{m}Z_i$$

The phasor coherency expresses the scatter between different estimates of the impedance elements by use of Eq. (18-33) for different selections of R_1 and R_2.

As we have seen before, up to four different references can normally be used, although not all of them may yield stable estimates. In Eq. (18-35), m represents the number of stable estimates while Z_i represents each one of the independent estimates and Z is defined as the average of those estimates. The phasor coherency is the measure of the scatter of each independent estimate in the complex plane around the mean value. For ideal, noise-free data all of these independent estimates should fall on the same point on the complex plane, and the phasor coherency will attain the value of 1 (Word et al.[53]). Another quality control measure can be the ordinary coherency expressing the coherency between two signals S_1 and S_2:

$$\text{Coh} = \frac{|\langle S_1 S_2^* \rangle|^2}{\langle S_1 S_1^* \rangle \langle S_2 S_2^* \rangle}$$ (18-36)

Yet another quality measure which can be more effective is the multiple or predicted coherence function for two different input signals. All of the above quality measures as well as the estimated quantities can be computed and readied for review in real time by present-day field systems while the data are being acquired.

The effect of noise on the estimated impedance elements can be described if we consider each of the information channels as pure signal, $\mathbf{E}_s$, plus additive noise, $\mathbf{E}_n$.

$$\mathbf{E} = \mathbf{E}_s + \mathbf{E}_n \qquad \mathbf{H} = \mathbf{H}_s + \mathbf{H}_n \qquad (18\text{-}37)$$

If we assume that the signals are independent of the noise and, for the sake of algebraic simplicity, treat the 1-D case, namely a layered and laterally homogeneous medium, Z_{xx} is zero, as we shall see later in the section. The solution for the estimated Z_{xy} is related to the noise-free Z_{xy} through a multiplication by the factor expressed in the equation

$$\hat{Z}_{xy} = Z_{xy} \left(1 + \frac{\langle E_{x_n} E_{x_n}{}^* \rangle}{\langle E_{x_s} E_{x_s}{}^* \rangle} \right) \qquad (18\text{-}38)$$

The important implication is that for a noise source that is independent of the signal, and even if the noise is white, a choice of an electric field signal as a reference signal for estimating the impedance in Eq. (18-33) will bias the estimated impedance upward by a multiplicative factor given in Eq. (18-38). Similarly, choosing magnetic field signals as references R_1 and R_2 in Eq. (18-34) will bias the estimate downward by the factor in equation

$$\hat{Z}_{xy} = \frac{Z_{xy}}{1 + \langle H_{y_n} H_{y_n}{}^* \rangle / \langle H_{y_s} H_{y_s}{}^* \rangle} \qquad (18\text{-}39)$$

Implicit in Eqs. (18-38) and (18-39) is that it is difficult to avoid the effect of local noise if one measures only a single, five-component MT station. If only five channels are available, it is preferable to use all of the available stable estimates for each of the impedance tensor elements and average them for a somewhat less-biased estimate.

Goubau et al.[54] have suggested that in order to reduce the bias effect due to autospectral components of the noise recorded locally, one should record simultaneously with a given five-component MT station at least two other channels to serve as estimating reference signals in Eq. (18-33). Magnetic fields are most commonly used since they are less affected by local geology.

A typical way of applying this method of remote referencing is to measure two complete MT stations in two different locations. In such a case, the autospectral elements between noise terms in Eqs. (18-38) and (18-39) will become cross-spectral elements between noises recorded in two different locations. If those two locations are sufficiently far apart so that the noise processes in those locations are uncorrelated, the cross-correlation term will tend to be small and the bias effect will be reduced.

To obtain independent noise contaminations in some areas may require station separations of several tens of kilometers, particularly in the lower-frequency ranges. For such applications, telemetry systems and synchronized recordings have been developed and implemented in some data acquistion systems. Recording more than one station at a time and using channels from one station as reference signals for estimating the impedance signal in another may be helpful, even if those stations are close together and not sufficiently far apart to enjoy independent external noise processes. Cross-referencing between the two locations can thus reduce the effects of random channel noise in the acquisition system itself.

Modeling and Interpretation of Magnetotelluric Data

Modeling of MT data has received wide coverage in the scientific literature with reports of a large number of case histories. We shall describe MT modeling and interpretation in increasing order of generality. First the 1-D problem will be treated. The nature of the 1-D MT impedance will be discussed together with the relevant mathematical formulations. We shall describe both the forward- and inverse-modeling processes for this 1-D case and analyze the resolving power of naturally occurring plane EM waves with respect to a 1-D structure.

Following the 1-D discussion, we shall generalize the situation into a 2-D model and show that the forward-modeling problem for a 2-D case separates into two independent modes of EM wave propagation in the conductive medium. Naturally, the final generalization will be into 3-D situations. Both the resolving power of the method in the vertical and horizontal dimensions will be discussed, and the resultant understanding of the effects of shallow structure of resistivity variations on MT data will be highlighted. To make full use of the natural resolving power of plane EM waves and combat distortive effects that can be caused by shallow resistivity variations or topography, the most recent development of EM array profiling techniques will be presented and analyzed.

One-Dimensional Magnetotelluric Modeling

Let us begin with a 1-D problem. A 1-D geoelectrical structure is one that can be adequately described by a subsurface model for which electrical resistivities do not vary laterally. For such models, the resistivity structure consists of horizontal layers, each with a discrete resistivity and thickness. We include the case of continuously varying resistivity as a function of depth as long as it does not change laterally. Any cross section of such an earth in any location and in any direction will appear identical.

Calculating the MT impedance for a 1-D earth is relatively simple. Actually the mathematical formulation for a plane wave interacting with a layered medium was described by Maxwell[1] in his nineteenth-century fundamental work. His solution treats plane EM waves (light) interacting with the layered medium of a crystal lattice. Maxwell did provide the formulation, but it wasn't until many decades later that Tikhonov[44] and Cagniard[45] recognized the usefulness of applying the same solution to naturally occurring, EM plane waves of ionospheric and upper atmospheric origin interacting with a layered earth medium.

A 1-D model which consists of $N-1$ layers of resistivities ρ_j and thicknesses h_j, respectively, overlaying a half-space of resistivity ρ_N is described in Fig. 18-23. The impedance for such a model is

$$Z(\omega) = \frac{E_x(\omega)}{H_y(\omega)} = -\frac{E_y(\omega)}{H_x(\omega)} \tag{18-40}$$

The electric and magnetic fields at the surface above a 1-D model are perpendicular and independent of the direction of measurement. The 1-D impedance is simply the ratio, in the frequency domain, of perpendicular electric and magnetic field components. Due to this property of the MT impedance for a 1-D model, it was thought by Cagniard and other early workers that it is sufficient to measure only the electrical component and a perpendicular magnetic field component. Unfortunately, this rather simplistic approach is not workable, since the source-field polarization varies with time. Consequently, if one measures only one component of each of the interacting fields, the impedance results are not repeatable. In order to obtain repeatable results, vector measurements have to be acquired at every MT station, and the tensor relationship, such as that in Eqs. (18-29) and (18-30) between the horizontal components of the magnetic and electric fields, has to be evaluated. For a 1-D model the diagonal elements of the impedance, Z_{xx} and Z_{yy}, are zero regardless of the orientation of the measurement directions, while Z_{xy} and Z_{yx} are equal in magnitude and opposite in sign, as reflected in Eq. (18-40).

In order to evaluate the MT impedance at the surface on top of the 1-D structure as described in Fig. 18-23, it is convenient to start at the top of the half-space. The impedance for the homogeneous half-space of the resistivity ρ_N is

$$Z_N = \sqrt{i\omega\mu\rho_N} \tag{18-41}$$

Note that this impedance has a phase of 45°. Beginning at the top of the homogeneous half-space in Fig. 18-23, which is overlain by a stack of $N-1$ laterally homogeneous layers, one can evaluate progressively the impedance at the top of layer j, Z_j, using the recursive relationship

$$Z_j = \gamma_j\rho_j \frac{\gamma_j\rho_j(1-u) + Z_{j+1}(1+u)}{\gamma_j\rho_j(1+u) + Z_{j+1}(1-u)} \qquad j = N-1, \ldots, 1 \tag{18-42}$$

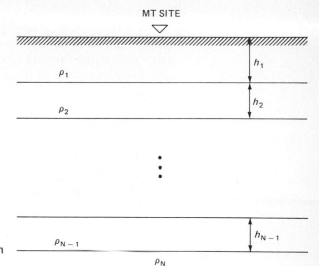

MT SITE

FIGURE 18-23 One-dimensional resistivity-depth model.

Equation (18-42) is a formulation which allows one to propagate the MT impedance recursively from the top of one layer to the top of the layer just above it until the surface is reached. γ_j in Eq. (18-42) is given by

$$\gamma_j = \sqrt{\frac{i\omega\mu}{\rho_j}} \tag{18-43}$$

whereas the propagation operator u is given by

$$u = e^{-2\gamma_j h_j} \quad \text{(MT)} \tag{18-44}$$

Notice the clear functional resemblance between Eq. (18-42) and Eq. (18-21) for the kernel function in the dc resistivity case. Indeed if one uses the propagation operator u given by

$$u = e^{-2\lambda h_j} \quad \text{(dc)} \tag{18-45}$$

Eq. (18-42) becomes analogous to (18-21). This implies that the kernel function in Eq. (18-21) describes the transfer function for a layered model after the source geometry has been properly removed from the data by an integration or filtering operation as described in a previous section.

It is customary to describe the impedance at the surface as apparent resistivity and phase functions of frequency. The apparent resistivity is defined by

$$\rho_a = \frac{1}{\omega\mu} |Z|^2 \tag{18-46}$$

The apparent resistivity as a function of frequency has intuitive significance. Its high-frequency value converges asymptotically to the actual resistivity of the upper layer while its low frequency will approach the resistivity for the half-space underlying the 1-D model. Similarly, the phase of the complex impedance function on top of the 1-D model is defined by

$$\phi = \tan^{-1} \frac{\text{Im}[Z]}{\text{Re}[Z]} \tag{18-47}$$

as the phase of the complex impedance function. In practice, when the electric field is measured in millivolts per kilometer, the magnetic field in gammas, and the period T in seconds or the frequency in hertz, the apparent resistivity is

$$\rho_a = 0.2T \left| \frac{E_x}{H_y} \right|^2 \tag{18-48}$$

The apparent resistivity and the phase of an impedance function for a 1-D earth are not independent functions. A Hilbert-transform type relationship (Bohel et al.[55]) exists between them. The first-order approximation for this Hilbert-transform relation is given by

$$\frac{d \log \rho_a}{d \log \omega} \cong \frac{\phi°}{45} - 1 \tag{18-49}$$

The relationship in Eq. (18-49) is of great value for quality control and robust impedance enhancement for 1-D and 2-D structures.

The apparent resistivity for 1-D structures responds to the variations of resistivity in a smooth fashion. Long-period values correspond to greater depths. Figure 18-24 illustrates a typical example in which a resistive shallow layer, such as volcanics, basalts, or carbonates, overlays the conductive target layered sediments, which are underlain by a resistive basement and a deep conductive material. The apparent resistivity for a typical MT station measured on the surface of such a model will display the resistive nature of the shallow material for short periods. It becomes more conductive in response to the sediments in the middle-period range. An increase in resistivity occurs at longer periods as the resistive basement is detected. Finally, a decline in apparent resistivity takes place in response to the conductive half-space underneath the model. Note that the phase for the same impedance described in Fig. 18-24 does obey the Hilbert-transform relationship described in Eq. (18-49).

The Inverse Problem for One-Dimensional Magnetotelluric Response

The inverse problem for 1-D MT structures is defined as finding a 1-D subsurface resistivity structure whose response closely fits impedance information estimated from the field data. A number of approaches have been reported,

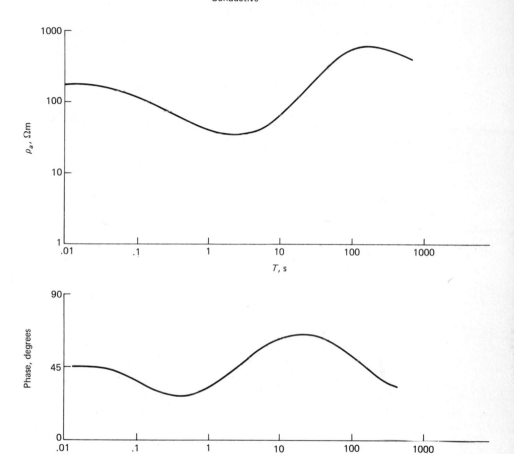

Resistive	(Volcanics)
Conductive	(Sediments)
Resistive	(Basement)
Conductive	

FIGURE 18-24   Typical apparent resistivity and phase curves for a one-dimensional model with a resistive cover such as a layer of volcanic rocks.

including least-squares fitting procedures or one based on singular value decomposition (Shoham et al.[56]). An adaptation of the Backus-Gilbert approach (Oldenburg[57]) has also been reported. All of these inverse methods arrive at a 1-D model by finding one with a response that fits the impedance estimated from the field observations.

A simple approximate transformation devised by Bostick[58] is of special importance to achieve an approximate, quick 1-D inversion of MT impedance. We start with asymptotic expressions of the apparent resistivity as a function of frequency for one layer of thickness D and resistivity ρ_1 overlaying a half-space

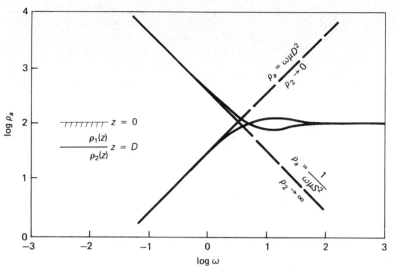

FIGURE 18-25 Low-frequency asymptotes for one layer of thickness D and resistivity ρ_1 overlaying a half-space of resistivity ρ_2.

with resistivity ρ_2, as described in Fig. 18-25. The low-frequency, low-apparent-resistivity asymptote for the case in which the underlying half-space becomes infinitely conductive is expressed by

$$\lim_{\substack{\omega \to 0 \\ \rho_2 \to 0}} \rho_a(\omega) = \omega\mu D^2 \qquad (18\text{-}50)$$

The complementary case of the low-frequency asymptote for an infinitely resistive half-space is

$$\lim_{\substack{\omega \to 0 \\ \rho_2 \to \infty}} \rho_a(\omega) = \frac{1}{\omega\mu S^2} \qquad (18\text{-}51)$$

The conductance term S is defined as the ratio between thickness and resistivity or the conductivity thickness product:

$$S = \frac{D}{\rho_1} = \int_0^D \frac{1}{\rho_1(z)}\, dz \qquad (18\text{-}52)$$

This equation is given as an integral expression for a continuously varying resistivity as a function of depth.

One can look at these asymptotes as defining a new coordinate system in D and S in which apparent resistivity is expressed. At any given frequency the depth with which that frequency is associated can be read directly from the apparent-resistivity value for that frequency or from the intercept of the apparent-resistivity curve with the infinite-conductor, low-frequency asymptote in Eq. (18-50). Manipulating this equation, one gets

$$z = \sqrt{\frac{\rho_a}{\omega\mu}} \tag{18-53}$$

for an approximate frequency-depth relationship for 1-D MT data.

In order to get an estimate of the true resistivity as a function of depth, a further approximation is made by considering the range between the two extreme asymptotes at every point of an apparent-resistivity curve in the coordinate system defined by the various D and S lines of Fig. 18-25. If we look at two infinitesimally close points on the apparent-resistivity curve, we can show (Bostick[58]) that an approximate expression for the true resistivity versus depth is

$$\rho(z) = \rho_a(\omega) \frac{1 - C}{1 + C} \tag{18-54}$$

where

$$C = \frac{d\,(\log \rho_a)}{d\,(\log \omega)} \tag{18-55}$$

is the slope of the apparent-resistivity curve in the logarithmic apparent-resistivity-versus-frequency display. This inverse transformation has the effect of sharpening the relatively sluggish response of the apparent resistivity to the resistivity profile as described in Fig. 18-24.

An example of the application of this approximate inverse transformation is given in Fig. 18-26. A 1-D model consisting of three layers over a conductive half-space was chosen, and the exact apparent resistivity for that model was calculated as a function of frequency by use of the recursive expression (18-42). This apparent resistivity was then transformed into the depth domain by Eqs. (18-53), (18-54), and (18-55) to obtain the continuous resistivity-versus-depth profile. The continuous profile displays the nature of this approximate inversion or inverse transformation and the sharpening effect it has over the apparent-resistivity function. Note that the inverted curve tends to respond more strongly to conductive layers than to resistive layers, as one might expect from the physics of EM wave propagation. Also note that if the slope of the apparent resistivity as expressed in Eq. (18-55) is difficult to estimate for noisy actual field data, the phase values can be used to estimate that slope according to the Hilbert-transform relationship between the phase and the slope in apparent resistivity as described in Eq. (18-49).

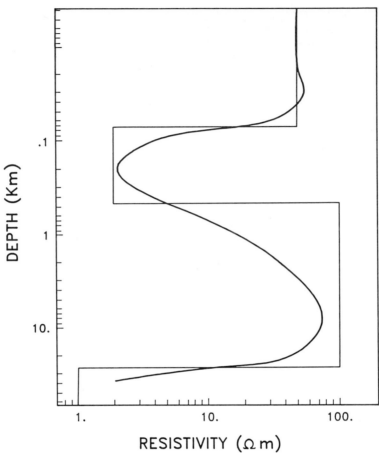

FIGURE 18-26 A resistivity–depth profile and a continuous profile obtained from the application of the approximate Bostick's 1-D inversion to the synthetic apparent resistivity for this model.

The Resolving Power of Magnetotellurics with Respect to One-Dimensional Structures

The understanding of the resolving power of MTs with respect to 1-D structures is of great importance to proper application of this low-resolution method. When assessing the resolving power of a geophysical method, it is important first to investigate whether the mathematical solution is unique. Weidelt[59] made such an investigation and concluded that the 1-D MT inverse problem is unique in principle. That means that for an ideal data set, which has an infinite amount of data of infinite accuracy, there is one and only one 1-D model that will yield an impedance calculated according to the recursive relationship (18-42) and the associated equations will perfectly match that 1-D response.

Theoretical uniqueness distinguishes EM methods from potential-field methods, such as gravity and magnetics, which are inherently nonunique, even for ideal data sets. In practice, however, we always have to interpret data sets that are nonideal. The data quantity is finite, and each data point has a limited accuracy. For such situations, even a method that is unique in principle has only a finite resolution. The resolving power can be studied by taking a 1-D model and perturbing its various parameters. Doing so, it has been observed by workers that specific model parameters are coupled to produce an effect known as equivalence of the EM response. More specifically, for a conductive, sedimentary layer which lies on top of the basement and is covered with resistive basalt or carbonate formations, resolution is best for the conductivity-thickness product of that layer or its conductance S as defined in Eq. (18-52). The product of these two parameters is better resolved than is each of them separately, and one can increase the resistivity while increasing the thickness of the intermediate conductive layer by the same relatively small factor without changing the observable response by an appreciable amount. Similar equivalences exist for other EM and electrical methods.

A revealing description of the resolving power of 1-D structure when plane EM waves are used was given by Bostick et al.[60] The forward MT problem was linearized, and it was found that for a small perturbation of the resistivity structure around the base model, such as a uniform resistivity with depth, the linearized problem can be represented as a convolutional relationship. This means that in the description of Fig. 18-27 a layered resistivity structure, shown on the left, will yield the apparent resistivity on the right by means of a convolver g defined by

$$g(x) = [\cos (e^x) + \sin (e^x)] \, e^{x - e^x} \tag{18-56}$$

where

$$x = \ln z \tag{18-57}$$

This convolver g, described in Fig. 18-28, was termed the MT wavelet for its resemblance to a seismic wavelet. The width of this convolver on a logarithmic depth scale is, however, large and extends beyond one decade of depth. Consequently, the shape of this convolver describes the relatively sluggish resolution of the 1-D MT inversion process for such models.

Figure 18-27 describes the result of applying the convolver g to a resistivity structure according to

$$\Delta \ln \rho * g = \Delta \ln \rho_a \tag{18-58}$$

The apparent resistivity obtained from this convolution is outlined by the dotted function of apparent resistivity with respect to frequency, whereas the exact apparent resistivity obtained from the recursive relationship (18-42) is described by the solid line. Observing Fig. 18-27, one concludes that the

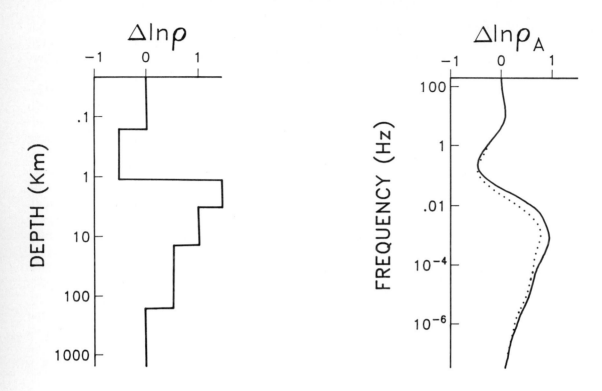

FIGURE 18-27   The linearized response, $\Delta \ln \rho_A$, is related to a one-dimensional resistivity-depth model $\Delta \ln \rho$ through a convolution with the "wavelet" g.

forward 1-D MT process—calculating the apparent resistivity as a function of frequency given a 1-D resistivity distribution with depth—is only weakly a nonlinear process. The resolving power of the 1-D MT problem is described by the convolver g. The width and length of the tail actually indicate that the 1-D MT problem which is purely inductive—a magnetic induction field interacting with a conductive medium and producing an electric field—is a process of relatively low resolution. One may use the same convolver for deriving an optimal inverse filter by some criterion such as a Wiener inverse with added noise.

Figure 18-29 describes the application of an optimal Wiener inverse filter for the forward process described by the convolver in Eq. (18-56) to a three-layer model over a half-space. The resistivity as a function of depth is described by the solid straight line, whereas the optimal inverse using the convolver g for an approximately 30 percent noise-to-signal ratio is described by the curve designated by crosses. Note that this curve has about equal response to resistive or

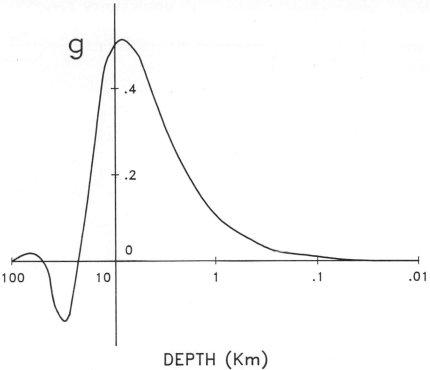

FIGURE 18-28   The 1-D natural-field electromagnetic inductive wavelet *g*.

conductive layers, since it is obtained from the inverse to a linearized process, whereas the different response of EM waves to resistive or conductive anomalies is expressed in higher-order terms. For comparison purposes, the curve designated by circles describes a response of the approximate Bostick 1-D transformation of Eqs. (18-53), (18-54), and (18-55) to the same model. This inverse transformation is similar in resolving power to the optimal Wiener inverse for average noise levels, but responds more strongly to conductive layers than to resistive layers, as one may expect from a nonlinearized transformation which uses the approximate asymptotic expressions for true physical waves interacting with the layered medium.

To summarize the nature of the 1-D MT problem, one may say that the interaction of plane EM waves with a layered medium enjoys large depths of penetration due to the high energy in the low-frequency part of the spectrum of the natural EM field. However, the same mechanism that provides the deep penetration also reduces the resolving power, since we obtain depth control through the exponential decay of the amplitude as function of frequency.

Presently, this is the only way to obtain depth control for EM waves of a natural source interacting with a 1-D earth structure. An individual reflection of

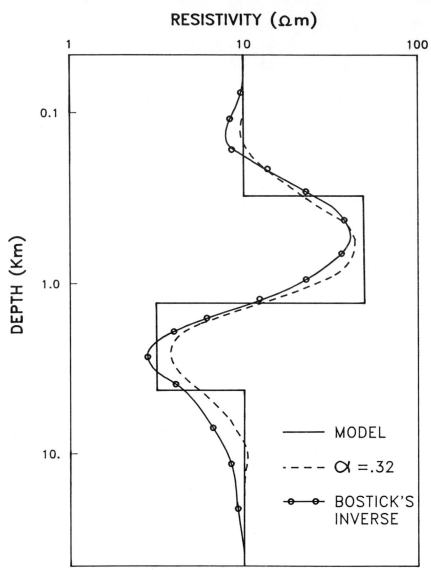

FIGURE 18-29   Two approximate inversions for the synthetic response of a one-dimensional model. A Wiener inverse using the forward wavelet *g* and a Bostick inverse.

such EM waves from the various interfaces and reflectors is not separately measurable by available technology despite repeated claims to the contrary.

The nature of this low-resolution, 1-D process is described by the MT wavelet. As we shall see, naturally occurring EM waves can achieve a higher resolution by interacting with 2-D or 3-D structures with laterally discontinuous resistivities.

The Two-Dimensional Magnetotelluric Modeling Problem

We now wish to generalize our discussion of the interaction of plane EM waves generated by ionospheric and atmospheric sources with the crust of the earth. A 2-D geoelectrical structure is one for which the electrical resistivity or the electrical conductivity varies as a function of only one horizontal coordinate, for example x, while the resistivity is not a function of the other coordinate, y. The direction along which the electrical properties do not vary, y, is called the *strike direction*, and the perpendicular direction, x, is called the *dip direction*.

For a 2-D model the equations describing the interaction of plane EM waves with such a medium separate completely into two sets of equations. One describes the case for which the electric field component is parallel to the strike while the magnetic field component is perpendicular to it. The first mode of interaction is called *E-parallel* $(E_\parallel)$ or the *transverse electric* (TE) mode. The other set of equations describes the normal or perpendicular mode in which the electric field component is perpendicular to the strike or in the dip direction, while the magnetic field component is in the strike direction. This is called *E-perpendicular* $(E_\perp)$ or the *transverse magnetic* (TM) mode.

The two modes of EM wave propagation in 2-D media behave differently. An early, and the clearest, description of this different behavior was given by d'Ecreville and Kunetz.[61] Their simple model, described in Fig. 18-30, consists of two quarter-space blocks extending to the surface with a vertical contact between them. The block on the left is more resistive than the one on the right, and the strike is in the direction of the y axis. This 2-D problem separates into the two fundamental modes of EM wave propagation, the $E_\parallel$ mode and the $E_\perp$ mode.

Let us examine the behavior of these two modes for this simple, single-vertical-contact model since this behavior can shed light on other models that are significantly more complicated. If we measure a number of MT stations along the x axis, i.e., along the line traversing the model from the left to the right, and plot the apparent-resistivity information for the two fundamental modes for a single frequency as a function of x, we obtain the apparent resistivities as described in the middle part of Fig. 18-30.

First, let us start with the $E_\parallel$ or TE mode. As we measure the response of the stations to the far left, away from the contact, the asymptotic value of this apparent resistivity is equal to the resistive value of the block on the left or ρ_1. As we move along the x axis to the right toward the vertical contact of the resistivity discontinuity, this $E_\parallel$ mode senses the existence of the discontinuity and smoothly plunges down due to the effect of the more conductive block to the right. The curve goes *smoothly* through the location of the discontinuity and eventually, as we approach the far right side of the model, asymptotically converges to the true value of the resistivity for the block on the right side.

An entirely different behavior is exhibited by the $E_\perp$ or TM mode. Just as $E_\parallel$ mode, it starts, as we move from the left to the right, from the true value of the resistivity for the resistive block on the left. However, as we approach the

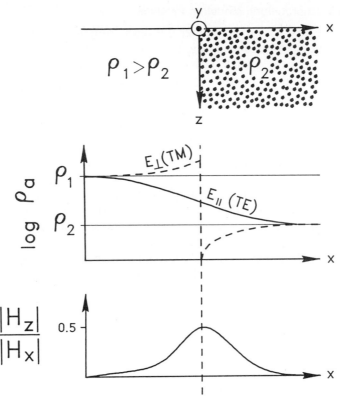

FIGURE 18-30 Natural-field electromagnetic response to a two-dimensional, single lateral contact, model. (*After d'Ecreville and Kunetz*[61], *1968.*)

point of discontinuity from the resistive side the $E_\perp$ mode exhibits an even more resistive response than does the resistivity of the block on the left or ρ_1. As we cross the resistivity discontinuity, the $E_\perp$ drops and has a discontinuous behavior. Immediately across the resistivity discontinuity, the resistivities are even lower (more conductive) than those of the block on the right with a relatively low resistivity ρ_2. Again, as we move to the far right, it converges to the true value for that block. The third portion of Fig. 18-30 shows that, as we move across the discontinuity, higher values of the vertical component of the magnetic field, H_z, which is purely a secondary field, occur at the lateral discontinuity. The vertical magnetic field is induced by the structure and is not present in the source. It reaches a maximum at the point of discontinuity.

The physical reason behind this characteristic behavior is that, for the $E_\parallel$ mode, the electric field is in the direction of the geoelectric strike. Electric currents, which tend to follow the direction of the electric field component, are flowing in the structure parallel to the strike, never trying to cross the lateral resistivity discontinuity. Consequently, although this current flow senses the presence of the discontinuity as we get closer to it, it passes through the discontinuity in a smooth fashion. This means that the information carried by the $E_{\parallel}$ response is less distorted by lateral discontinuities but also less sensitive to them. On the other hand, the $E_{\perp}$ mode has an electric field component in the x direction. That electric field component drives electric currents across, perpendicular to the vertical contact. There is a discontinuity in the magnitude of this electric current due to the contrast in resistivities. This discontinuity is compensated by surface charges formed along the vertical plane of contact. We denote the surface charge density by ρ_s.

If we take the equation of continuity in the frequency domain and substitute Ohm's law, we get

$$\nabla \cdot (\sigma \mathbf{E}) = -i\omega\rho_s \tag{18-59}$$

which relates the discontinuity in the electric current density to the charge density. If we substitute from Maxwell's equations and make the usual assumption of neglecting the displacement currents (for the frequency range used in natural-field EM geophysics the currents are small), we get an expression for the magnitude of the surface charge density ρ_s:

$$\rho_s = \epsilon_0 \frac{\sigma_1 - \sigma_2}{\sigma_1} E_x \tag{18-60}$$

For the low-frequency range used in natural-field electromagnetics, the effect of these surface charges on the $E_{\perp}$ response is essentially frequency independent (Kaufman[62]). Consequently, the discontinuity effect described in Fig. 18-30 will cause a change of equal magnitude for all frequencies on the $E_{\perp}$ apparent resistivities. This frequency-independent change appears as a vertical shift on typical logarithmic apparent-resistivity-versus-logarithmic-frequency plots and thus has been termed the *static effect*.

Figure 18-31 sheds light on the response of the simple 2-D model through examination of the frequency-domain effects. Two sites are considered: site A on top of the resistive block to the left, and site B on top of the more conductive block to the right. As one observes the apparent resistivity as a function of frequency for those $E_{\parallel}$ and $E_{\perp}$ modes for either site, it is evident that for the higher frequencies these curves approach the true value of the resistivity for the corresponding block on top of which the site is located. As the frequency gets lower, the response of the $E_{\perp}$ mode on site A, which is on the resistive block, appears more resistive than even the relatively high resistivity value of ρ_1. The opposite happens for site B, which is on top of the conductive block. This phenomenon is another description of the discontinuity in the $E_{\perp}$ response described earlier in Fig. 18-30. The $E_{\perp}$ mode will see a conductive block as being more resistive because a lateral contrast is being approached from its resistive side. We also see in Fig. 18-31 that the $E_{\parallel}$ mode behaves in a more

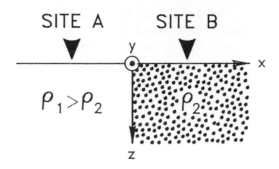

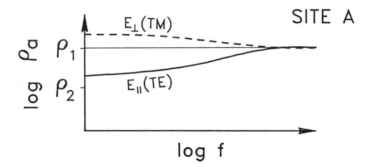

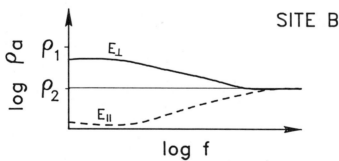

FIGURE 18-31 The effect of a vertical resistivity contrast on frequency-domain, natural-field, electromagnetic impedance.

continuous fashion. Low-frequency response for the $E_\parallel$ mode at site A is more conductive than the resistivity value of the block on the left due to the influence of the conductive block on the right.

Further insight into the interpretation of MT data obtained over 2-D structures can be gained by analyzing the response described in Fig. 18-32 (Patrick and Bostick[63]). This response describes both $E_\parallel$ and $E_\perp$ modes measured over a

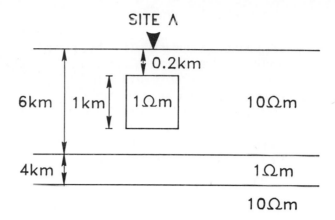

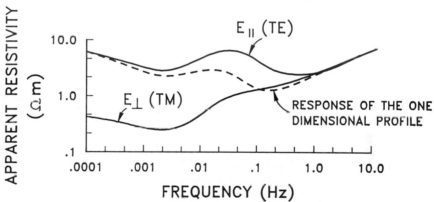

FIGURE 18-32   *E*-parallel and *E*-perpendicular responses for a two-dimensional model.

model consisting of a 2-D conducting (1-Ω · m) block imbedded in the 6-km-thick surface layer. The model is 1-D otherwise. The lower part of Fig. 18-32 shows that, as we expect, both curves start from the same values for very high frequencies. As the frequency decreases, both curves sense the presence of the relatively more conductive 1-Ω block. Both curves dip downward in resistivity, and, as the frequency decreases further, the relatively resistive material under the block expresses itself around 0.03 Hz. With a further decrease of frequency, the conductive effect of the 1-Ω · m, 4-km layer is seen around 0.002 Hz. Both curves show resistive trends for very low frequencies responding to the relatively resistive, underlying formation.

A fundamental difference between the behavior of the $E_\parallel$ and $E_\perp$ modes is, however, also evident. The $E_\parallel$ mode responds more faithfully to the resistivity profile directly under the location, as we might expect from the 1-D resistivity profile for that station. It eventually does converge at low frequencies to the true value of the resistivity for the half-space. Comparing the $E_\parallel$ mode obtained from the 2-D computation of the MT response with the one obtained for the 1-D profile underneath the A station (indicated in Fig. 18-32 as a dashed line), we see that the $E_\parallel$ line eventually converges for low frequencies to the same response obtained from the 1-D calculation. This means that with decreasing frequency the $E_\parallel$ mode achieves greater depths of penetration while losing or "forgetting" the effects of shallow heterogeneities. On the other hand, the $E_\perp$ mode did sense the shallow heterogeneity, and this effect never disappears from the $E_\perp$ response even for the lowest frequencies.

If one applies a 1-D inverse to either curve described in Fig. 18-32, the inverted resistivity-versus-depth models are seen in Fig. 18-33. These inverted profiles are obtained with the approximate Bostick transformation of equating (18-53), (18-54), and (18-55) and are compared to the true-resistivity model under site A, which is indicated by the dashed line. Inverting the $E_\parallel$ mode produces a resistivity profile that more closely approximates the true one under the site, whereas the $E_\perp$ mode will yield a distorted resistivity profile.

This important characteristic difference in behavior between the two modes is fundamental to the interpretation of classical MT soundings. The MT responses estimated from the field data are analyzed to identify the $E_\parallel$ and $E_\perp$ modes. Then if we wish to use a 1-D inverse as a first interpretive approximate step, we can invert the $E_\parallel$ mode and display the resulting model on a cross section. The rationale behind this interpretive approach is that the $E_\parallel$ mode will be less affected or distorted by 2-D and 3-D lateral heterogeneities. This 1-D approximate interpretation to data obtained over a multidimensional structure can be misleading and has to be followed, verified, and checked through the use of 2-D and 3-D techniques.

It is important to note that depth conversion obtained by placing a higher emphasis on the $E_\parallel$ mode, which has been, and still is, prevalent in MT interpretation, can result in significant loss of resolution. Indeed, the $E_\parallel$ mode is less sensitive to lateral changes than the $E_\perp$ mode. If the target resembles a layered or slowly varying earth, the $E_\parallel$ mode interpretation may be preferred. If, however, the target has strong lateral resistivity variations, such as in faulting or overthrusting environments, prime importance should be given to the interpretation of the $E_\perp$ mode since it usually carries the highest resolving power with respect to lateral resistivity changes.

A further physical insight into the behavior of the two separate modes of EM excitation displayed in the model of Fig. 18-32 can be found by analyzing a model displayed in Fig. 18-34. A 2-D conductive body interacts with two separate modes of excitation. The parallel mode drives currents along the axis of the body, which never try to get across lateral boundaries. Consequently, the response for the $E_\parallel$ mode shown in the lower part of the figure has only a

SITE A

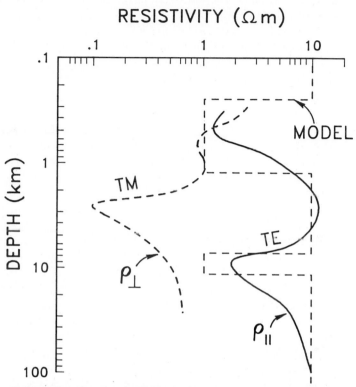

FIGURE 18-33 Comparison between inverted resistivity-versus-depth profiles obtained using the E-parallel and the E-perpendicular response to the model of Fig. 18-32 for site A.

weak indication of the presence of the conductive body underneath. In the $E_\perp$ mode, however, the electric field in the x direction drives electric current across this conductive, 2-D body. Different current densities occur outside and inside the body, just as in the vertical-contact model described before, and are counteracted by surface charges on the vertical sides of the buried body. These surface charges produce much stronger effects, which are observable at the surface; consequently the $E_\perp$ mode shown in the lower part of Fig. 18-34 responds to this body in a much more positive way. As before, the effect of these surface charges is frequency independent for frequencies low enough to have penetrated below the depth of the buried body. The surface expression is not, however, discontinuous as in the model of Fig. 18-30 because the buried conductive body is covered with a homogeneous overburden which acts to smooth the discontinuity effect of the lateral contact.

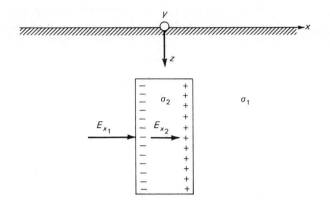

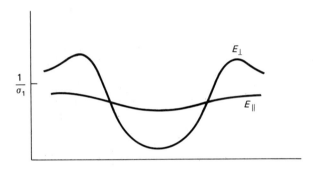

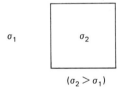

FIGURE 18-34 *E*-parallel and *E*-perpendicular schematic profiles for a natural-field response across a 2-D conductive buried body.

The Impedance Relationship

We have seen that the general impedance transfer relationship between the source magnetic field signal, which has H_x and H_y components, and the induced electric field components is given by Eqs. (18-29) and (18-30). Impedances Z_{xx}, Z_{xy}, Z_{yx}, and Z_{yy} are elements of a complex tensor which is a function of frequency. Additionally, a transfer relationship exists between the source signal and the vertical component of the magnetic field, as shown in Eq. (18-31). This impedance relationship reduces to

$$E_x = Z_{xy}H_y \qquad E_y = Z_{yx}H_x \qquad (18\text{-}61)$$

when the x and the y axes are aligned along the principal axes of the structure, i.e., the strike and dip directions. In this case, as mentioned above, the problem becomes two scalar problems—the $E_{\parallel}$ and the $E_{\perp}$ modes. This separation is described by Eq. (18-61), which implies that in the principal coordinates the diagonal Z_{xx} and Z_{yy} components vanish and each of the electric field components relates to just a single magnetic source component.

In practice, when an MT station is acquired, we do not know the directions for the strike and the dip of the subsurface structure. In such a case, all the impedance elements described in Eqs. (18-29) through (18-31) are present. However, the expected behavior of the impedance relationship for a 2-D structure in the principal coordinate system, Eq. (18-61), can be used to find the closest approximation to this direction and to the impedances for the two principal modes of excitation. The coordinate system is rotated about the z axis in order to find a direction for which the diagonal elements Z_{xx} and Z_{yy} vanish. The resulting relationships set the impedances for the $E_{\parallel}$ and $E_{\perp}$ modes:

$$Z_{xy} = Z_{\perp} = Z_{TM} \qquad Z_{yx} = Z_{\parallel} = Z_{TE} \qquad (18\text{-}62)$$

The subscripts TM and TE stand for transverse magnetic and transverse electric, respectively.

The angle θ_0 for the directions at which these conditions occur and where the two modes of excitation separate is given by Vozoff[64] as

$$\tan(4\theta_0) = \frac{(Z_{xx} - Z_{yy})(Z_{xy} + Z_{yx})^* + (Z_{xx} + Z_{yy})^*(Z_{xy} + Z_{yx})}{|Z_{xx} - Z_{yy}|^2 - |Z_{xy} + Z_{yx}|^2} \qquad (18\text{-}63)$$

These conditions are met every 90°. Consequently, unique determination of the strike and dip directions from the elements of the impedance tensor relating horizontal components of the fields is not possible. The ambiguity can be removed by use of the relationship between the source signal and the vertical component of the magnetic field or the Tipper defined by Eq. (18-31).

As shown by Word et al.,[53] if the x axis is along the dip direction and the y axis is along the strike direction, rotation into the principal coordinate system will make H_z dependent on H_x only. This condition, which sets B of Eq. (18-31) to zero, is satisfied once every 180° and thus can resolve the 90° ambiguity in the rotation angle.

In the general 3-D case, no strike direction can be defined, so the electric field drives electric currents across the lateral discontinuities, to some extent, in any direction. Consequently, Z_{xx} and Z_{yy} will, in general, never vanish for any direction or any axis of symmetry. Nevertheless, it has become customary in classical magnetotellurics to estimate the direction that minimizes the diagonal elements Z_{xx} and Z_{yy} and maximizes the off-diagonal elements Z_{yx} and Z_{xy}. This direction provides an approximation for an idealized strike direction. Different maximization and minimization criteria have been used. However, one frequently used criterion is

$$|Z_{xy}(\theta) + Z_{yx}(\theta)| \mapsto \text{maximum} \qquad (18\text{-}64)$$

for the maximization of the absolute value of the sum of off-diagonal elements. This problem has been solved (Swift[49]). After an approximate strike direction has been found, the impedance is rotated to the principal directions and the two principal modes of excitation—$E_{\parallel}$ and $E_{\perp}$—are identified even for the 3-D case as an aproximate approach guided by the 2-D case.

The direction of the principal coordinates, or the geoelectrical strike direction as a function of frequency, is by itself a valuable quantity which can be estimated from the MT data, since the MT information is recorded vectorially. In certain types of applications and for certain geological models, this quantity may be the most important one derived from the MT data.

A word of caution is needed here. Traditionally, in MT data processing and interpretation, it is customary to rotate the impedance to its principal coordinates as computed separately for each frequency. Though sometimes useful, this may yield $E_{\parallel}$ and $E_{\perp}$ apparent resistivities which, for different parts of the frequency spectrum, correspond to geometrically different coordinate systems. Such quantities are not physically meaningful and may give an erroneous interpretation. Use of a single rotation angle for each MT station or even a single rotation angle for an entire area may be more reliable.

The application to 3-D geoelectrical structures of rotation and diagonalization principles that apply to 2-D models is approximate by nature. Consequently, it is customary to define quantities that allow an assessment of the success in finding principal strike directions. Such quantities are, for example, the skewness, defined as

$$\alpha = \frac{|Z_{xx} + Z_{yy}|}{|Z_{xy} - Z_{yx}|} \qquad (18\text{-}65)$$

and the ellipticity

$$\beta(\theta_0) = \frac{|Z_{xx} - Z_{yy}|}{|Z_{xy} + Z_{yx}|} \qquad (18\text{-}66)$$

Both quantities vanish in the principal coordinate system for a 2-D subsurface model.

The quantities discussed above are illustrated in Figs. 18-35 through 18-37 and show results from a typical MT station recorded in a basalt-covered area in the Columbia Plateau of Washington state. The period rather than the frequency in all of these figures increases to the right. Figure 18-35*a* demonstrates both the *xy* and *yx* components of the MT impedance. Each curve has been

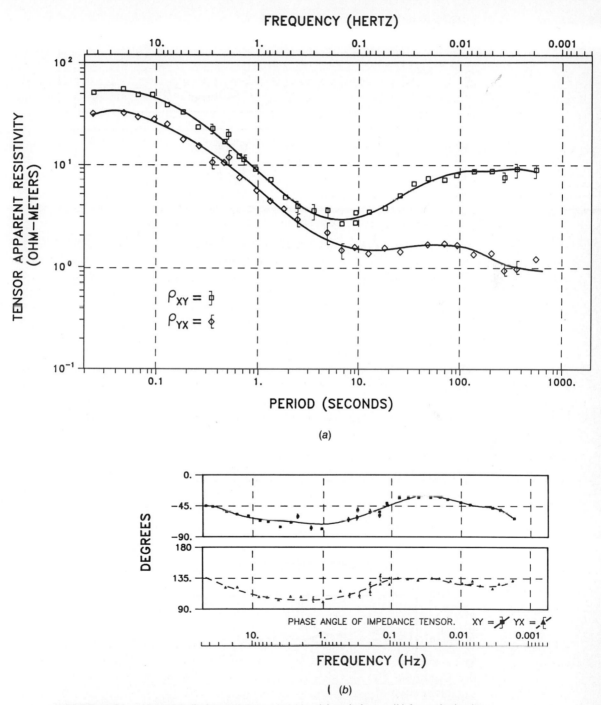

FIGURE 18-35 Magnetotelluric apparent resistivities (a) and phases (b) for a single site.

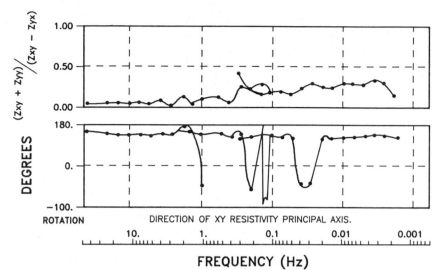

FIGURE 18-36 Magnetotelluric tensor impedance skewness and rotation angle to a principal strike-dip system.

smoothed with a polynomial function. Note that both curves start with a highly resistive value for the short-period or high-frequency part of the figure to the left and that the apparent resistivity decreases toward the middle-frequency range responding to conductive sediments present beneath the thick basalt cover in the Columbia Plateau. Finally, the curves respond to a more resistive basement, although not equally. One curve becomes more resistive, whereas the other shows a fair amount of anisotropy with respect to the previous one.

FIGURE 18-37 Tipper amplitude and phase for an MT site. (*Courtesy AET.*)

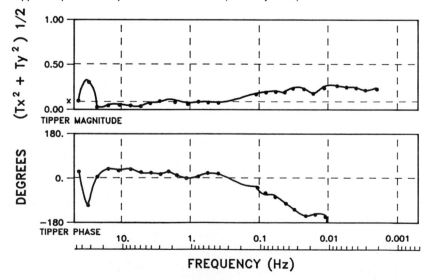

This anisotropy, while it can be explained by local structure, is more likely a result of a basinwide phenomenon.

Figure 18-35*b* shows the phase functions corresponding to each apparent resistivity. Notice that the Hilbert-transform relationship between the phase and the apparent resistivity holds within the noise level for these curves.

Two other quantities shown in Fig. 18-36 relate to the 2-D and 3-D nature of these responses. The rotation angle (in degrees) is shown in the lower part and generally indicates that the strike direction is about 170° relative to north for short periods and about 160° for a very long period, corresponding most likely to a deeper structure. The upper part indicates the magnitude of the skewness function, Eq. (18-65), as a function of frequency. The skewness is not high for this particular site, and it increases for the lower-frequency range where the anisotropy between the two curves in Fig. 18-35*a* is increasing as well.

Figure 18-37 describes the Tipper for this site both in magnitude and phase. Note again that the Tipper response at low frequencies is somewhat analogous to the anisotropy between the ρ_{xy} and ρ_{yx} curves with decreasing frequency.

Shallow Effects on Natural-Field Electromagnetic Data

Shallow effects on natural-field EM data can be significant. These effects are caused by topographical features or shallow resistivity distributions or both. These shallow features are commonly 3-D. It would, however, help our understanding if we look at the shallow effects for 2-D structures first, keeping in mind that the $E_\perp$ mode is more relevant for the description of similar effects for 3-D topographical or shallow resistivity distributions.

It will be easier to illustrate the shallow effects using the example of a 2-D surface structure in Fig. 18-38. In this case, a ridge 450 m in height and 2 km wide represents the 2-D topography. The ridge is infinitely long in the y direction, and the x direction is across the figure. The two curves in Fig. 18-38 show the response of such a homogeneous, 100-$\Omega \cdot$ m half-space, with this small ridge on top of it, to plane EM waves.

As we might expect, the response involving the electric field parallel to the axis of the ridge ($E_\parallel$), described in the dashed line, shows only a mild effect of the presence of the ridge. Electric currents flowing along the axis of the ridge are affected to a minor extent by this relatively small structure. On the other hand, the $E_\perp$ mode, in which the electric field is in the x direction, shows dramatic effects due to the presence of these topographical features. This $E_\perp$ electric field drives current across the structure. This structure, although 100 $\Omega \cdot$ m in resistivity, is significantly more conductive than the air about it; thus it is a conductive intrusion into a resistive medium. Consequently, the electric current flowing across the feature in the dip direction will try to flow and fill the complete volume of the conductive ridge.

Following the description, we might expect that these currents show the strongest variation and anomalies around places in which the topography changes most abruptly, and this is indeed the case. Note that the most dramatic

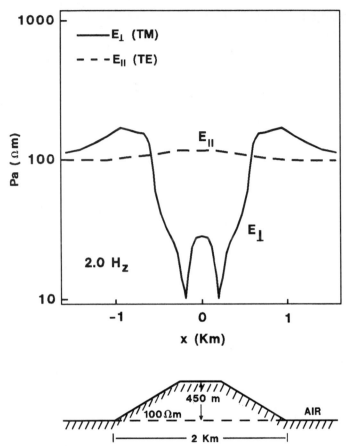

FIGURE 18-38   Effect of a two-dimensional surface elevated structure on the $E_{\parallel}$ and $E_{\perp}$ responses (*Ngoc,*[65] *Wannamaker et al.*[66])

changes in the $E_{\perp}$ response have been at the foot of the ridge where the horizontal surface breaks into the uphill slope and at the top of the ridge where the slope flattens. As explained before for the other 2-D model, another interesting feature is that the $E_{\perp}$ response of such a ridge shows weak dependence on the frequency for the frequency range used in natural-field EM prospecting. Consequently, the effect of this ridge on the natural-field EM data will be especially strong in places where the slope of the ridge changes abruptly and will show a frequency-independent, or static, nature. This model has been presented before by Ngoc[65] and Wannamaker et al.[66] The same observation about the strong static effect due to change of the resistivity was also made by Holcombe and Jiracek.[67]

In a complementary fashion, Fig. 18-39 describes the effect of a valley. In this case we have a 1-km-deep and $4\frac{1}{2}$-km-wide valley on the top of the 100-$\Omega \cdot$ m half-space. Not surprisingly, the $E_{\perp}$ response, again for a 2-Hz

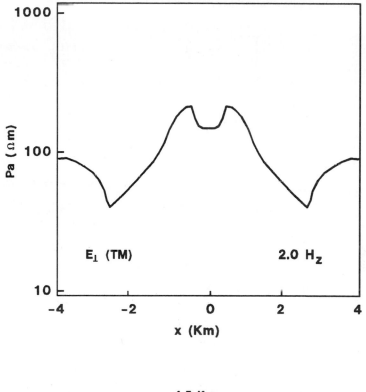

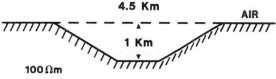

FIGURE 18-39   Effect of a surface depression on the $E_{\parallel}$ and $E_{\perp}$ responses.

frequency, shows the most significant change exactly at the locations where the slope of this 2-D valley changes.

A similar effect is described by Fig. 18-40. We start with the basic model of a resistive shallow layer on top of the conductive layer underlain by a resistive and a conductive sequence. This is the typical model for basalt- or carbonate-covered areas. The resistive rocks cover the conductive, sedimentary column which lies on top of the basement features. This simple, 1-D model will produce an apparent-resistivity curve, described on the right side of Fig. 18-40 by the dashed-dotted line. If, however, shallow, 3-D heterogeneities are added to this model, as described by the dark features in the upper part of the resistive top layer of Fig. 18-40, a major change will occur. These small heterogeneities represent either shallow resistivity variations or topographical features. Since these features are fairly small, even the highest frequency described in the

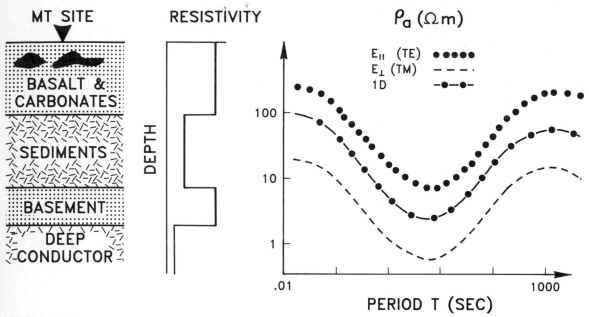

FIGURE 18-40
Effect of shallow 3-D heterogeneities.

response of Fig. 18-40, namely 0.01 s or 100 Hz, penetrates below the depths of burial of these shallow, 3-D features.

For those EM waves that penetrate well below the depth of burial of the 3-D heterogeneities, the effect of the heterogeneities is similar to surface features observed before in the $E_\perp$ mode. Note that for 3-D features, the pure $E_\parallel$ mode does not exist and the response is of an $E_\perp$ nature. An effect produced by this 3-D shallow feature is independent of frequency (i.e., a statics effect). On the display on the right side of Fig. 18-40, this effect will appear as a shift of the entire resistivity curve. One of these curves, which, only by analogy to the 2-D terminology, is identified as $E_\parallel$, will be shifted by a certain amount; the other one ($E_\perp$) will be shifted by a different amount.

In the general case of shallow heterogeneities of 3-D nature, either curve can be shifted up or down by arbitrary amounts. This shift, in the logarithmic scale, corresponds to a multiplicative factor, K, on the apparent resistivity. Figure 18-41 shows the effect on the inverted resistivity profile of this multiplicative statics effect, K. It is not difficult to demonstrate from the approximate Bostick transformation described above in Eqs. (18-53) through (18-55) that this will cause the logarithmic-resistivity-versus-logarithmic-depth profile to slide along a 2:1 slope in that description, as demonstrated by Fig. 18-40.

Since, as we mentioned before, the magnitude of the statics effect may not be related to the geometric size of the surface feature or shallow resistivity distribution, but it is related to how fast the topography or the shallow resistivity varies laterally; even small features can cause significant statics effects. Consequently, unless one has control of the statics effects, any depth-related interpretation can be strongly affected and distorted. These effects cannot in general be corrected for a single, MT station, although some interpretive assumptions may help. A typical assumption may be a tie to known or independently measured surface resistivity or known well-log information.

Motivated by the need to help MT interpretation with some additional information to resolve the statics-effects problem, several investigators (Sternberg et al.,[68] Andrieux and Wightman[69]) have attempted to solve this statics ambiguity using independently measured EM data such as dc resistivity data or transient EM soundings. The approaches are reasonable and can prove very helpful in many cases, although as always where two different kinds of data which respond to the same physical properties are jointly interpreted, extreme caution should be taken since different measurements may have different types of responses to the same resistivity feature.

FIGURE 18-41   The effect of "static" shift on an inverted, resistivity-versus-depth, profile is a shift along a 2:1 slope in the log ρ vs. log z domain.

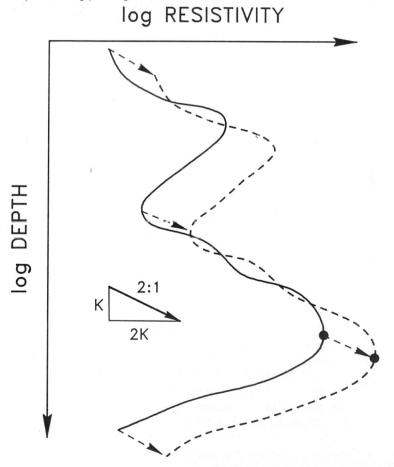

Electromagnetic Arrays

A significant step toward the removal of certain statics effects from earth responses to natural-field EM data was achieved with the development of the electromagnetic array profiling (EMAP) method (Bostick[70]). The basic idea behind the method is that certain statics effects affecting MT data for 3-D and 2-D, $E_\perp$ mode responses can be significantly reduced through low-pass filtering of properly acquired data in the spatial wave-number domain.

In order to demonstrate the principle of the EMAP method, let us consider a half-space with average conductivity σ_0 which is perturbed by relatively small conductivity features represented in the wave-number domain by $\sigma\,(k_x,k_y,k_z)$, where z is the depth. The electric field measured on top of such a perturbed half-space as a function of temporal frequency ω and wave numbers k_x and k_y is obtained by multiplying the conductivity variation with a Green's function, G, which is a function of the temporal frequency, wave numbers, and depth:

$$E(\omega,k_x,k_y) \;=\; G(\omega,k_x,k_y,z) \cdot \sigma(k_x,k_y,z) \tag{18-67}$$

which is an expression of the type of linearization we have imposed on this transfer relation problem. In a generalized way, Eq. (18-67) is analogous in three dimensions to Eq. (18-58), presented before as a comparable relationship in one dimension. The Green's function G of Eq. (18-67) acts as a spatial filter whose characteristics depend on the nature of the model. Equations

$$G(\omega,0,0,z) \;=\; \frac{\omega\mu\sigma_0}{k}\, e^{-2ikz} \tag{18-68}$$

$$G(\omega,0,k_y,z) \;=\; \frac{\omega\mu\sigma_0}{k_z}\, r_1 e^{-i(k_z+k)z} \tag{18-69}$$

give this filter in the wave-number domain for the 1-D case and the 2-D, $E_\parallel$ mode case. Expression (18-68) is functionally identical to the wavelet described in Eq. (18-56). Note the functional similarity between the Green's function for the 1-D case and for the 2-D parallel case. This mode of excitation is purely inductive, does not involve any current crossing of lateral boundaries, and consequently exhibits similar physical behavior and resolving power. Additionally, it is evident from the functional shape of the Green's function in Eqs. (18-68) and (18-69) that for this inductive case the Green's functions act as low-pass filters reducing and smoothing the effects of resistivity perturbations at depths as observed by the electric field measured on the surface. This effect is similar in nature to that of the MT wavelet discussed before [Eq. (18-56)]. This low-pass filtering effect will tend to reduce the aliasing if the fields are sampled at the surface at relatively sparse locations.

On the other hand, the responses for the 2-D, $E_\perp$ mode and the 3-D case are

$$G(\omega,k_x,0,z) \;=\; \left(\frac{\omega\mu\sigma_0}{k_z} + \frac{k_x{}^2}{ik_z}\right) \cdot e^{-i(k_z+k)z} \tag{18-70}$$

$$G(\omega,k_x,k_y,z) = \left(\frac{\omega\mu\sigma_0}{k_z} r_2 + \frac{k_r^2}{ik_z}\right) \cdot e^{i(k_z + k)z} \qquad (18\text{-}71)$$

where $k_z^2 = k^2 - k_x^2 - k_y^2$

$\qquad k^2 = -i\omega\mu\sigma_0$

$\qquad \frac{1}{2} \le |r_1, r_2| \le 1$

$\qquad k_x^2 < \omega\mu\sigma_0 \cong \omega\mu_0/\rho_a$

In this case, the response consists of two separate additive terms. The first acts similarly to the inductive mode of propagation and excitation discussed before. However, the second term approaches values which are independent of frequency for the low-frequency limit. The bandpass represented by this Green's function in the wave-number domain increases with decreasing temporal frequency ω. This enhancement of high-wave-number (short-wavelength) response increases the possibility of aliasing if the electric field is undersampled.

In the EMAP method, the statics effects are attenuated through low-pass filtering in the wave-number domain in order to compensate for the high-pass characteristics of the Green's functions for the 3-D and 2-D, $E_\perp$ cases discussed above. A way to determine the desired low-pass filter may be developed by requiring that the contribution of the two terms in Eq. (18-70) or (18-71), representing both conductive and inductive responses, be approximately equal. Note that the ratio of the temporal frequency times the permeability to the apparent resistivity is the reciprocal of the square root of the apparent depth of penetration, as we have seen from the Bostick inverse transformation. Consequently, a reasonable filter width can be related to the apparent depth of penetration.

As described before, we sense the electric field using dipoles or pairs of electrodes over typical distances ranging from 50 m to many hundreds of meters, connected with wires. These dipoles themselves cause a low-pass spatial filtering effect on the data, since the response of such dipoles amounts to boxcar averaging between its terminals. However, if the depth of penetration or the depth of the target is greater than the length of the single dipole, several dipoles may be combined in a weighted-average fashion to form a low-pass filter with a cutoff adequate for the desired depth of penetration.

When the desired depth of penetration is larger than the number of dipoles that can be acquired simultaneously with existing hardware, it is necessary to combine or synthesize the output of several dipoles resulting from data acquisition during different time periods. To allow such synthesis and for proper normalization, each of the dipoles covering a given line is recorded simultaneously with a reference station that remains fixed in a single location. Estimating impedances vectorially, in a very similar fashion to the MT impedance estimation, yields a set of line impedances obtained with respect to a single reference station. This allows in-line, low-pass filtering operations regardless of the specific time a given dipole has been acquired. Note that the

Green's functions in Eqs. (18-68) and (18-69) representing the 1-D or the 2-D inductive modes of excitation do not suffer from statics effects. The other two Green's functions in (18-70) and (18-71) for the 2-D perpendicular case and the 3-D case have the term representing statics effects that can be significantly attenuated by such wave-number-domain, low-pass filters. Consequently, recording a set of in-line dipoles covering a line allows the acquisition of a data set for which the short-wavelength statics caused by topography and near-surface resistivity distributions can be controlled. Figure 18-42 shows the layout of such a line. This control is achieved by use of the data acquired for natural-source EM fields only and does not require involvement of other types of data.

Several surveys using these new array techniques have been presented and have demonstrated extremely good results (Bostick,[70] Shoemaker et al.[71]). At this time, development of EM array techniques is just beginning and shows great promise for enhanced resolution and good statics control. Figure 18-43 shows one cross section obtained from that mode of acquisition and processing of the natural-field EM array data (Word et al.[72]).

FIGURE 18-42   Electromagnetic array profiling (EMAP) layout for data acquisition array.

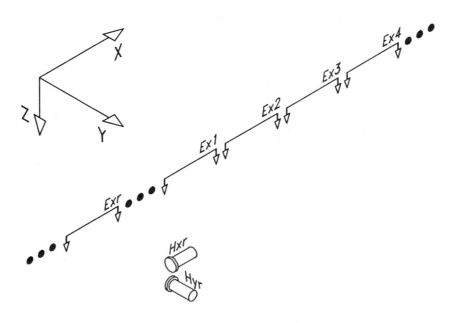

EMAP ACQUISITION GEOMETRY

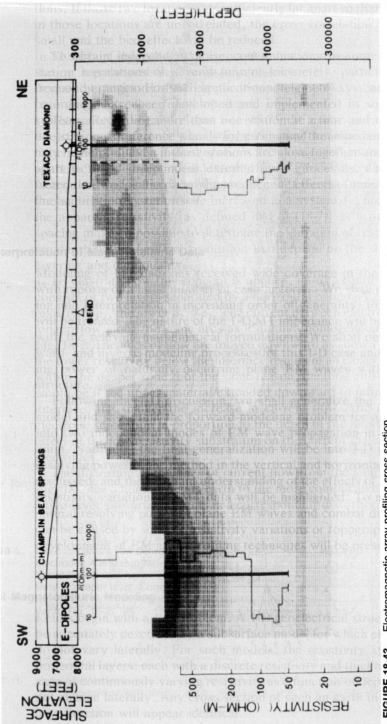

FIGURE 18-43   Electromagnetic array profiling cross section.

18-4 THE SELF-POTENTIAL METHOD

The self-potential method involves measurement at the surface of electric potentials developed in the earth by electrochemical action between minerals and the solutions with which they are in contact. No external electric fields are applied with this technique. When different portions of an ore body are in contact with solutions of different composition, chemical reactions take place which result in different solution pressures along the respective areas of contact. The difference in solution pressure gives rise to a potential difference which causes current flow in the ground.

Source of Potential The potential anomaly observed over a sulfide or graphite body is invariably negative. Earlier theories attributed the anomaly in sulfides to oxidation of the portion of the body penetrating the aerated zone above the water table. The process was presumed to generate sulfuric acid. Neutralization of this acid would form salts with an equilibrium potential that would cause current to flow through the sulfide to solutions below it with a different potential. The theory of Sato and Mooney[73] is now more widely accepted. The mechanism they have proposed is not based on oxidation of the sulfide. The ore body, being a good conductor, carries current from oxidizing electrolytes above the water table to reducing ones below it without being oxidized itself. The flow pattern is shown in Fig. 18-44 and it is detected by the negative potential the current introduces as it passes along the surface.

While the strongest potentials of this kind are excited in ores such as pyrites, a number of other minerals, e.g., pyrrhotite and magnetite, generate diagnostic self-potential patterns. Kruger and Lacy[74] describe an alunite body which was responsible for a 1700-mV potential anomaly at Cerro de Pasco in Peru. The polarization was attributed by them to free acid released during alunitization of the country rock, a mechanism that does not conform to more recent thinking.

FIGURE 18-44 Natural potential profile and pattern of current flow where sulfide body penetrates oxidizing zone above water table.

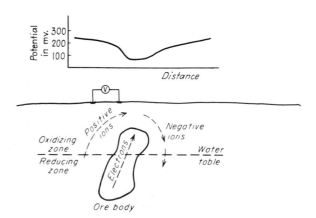

Not all near-surface sulfide bodies exhibit anomalous potentials, since there are many surface conditions that inhibit oxidation. Beneath the water table or permafrost, oxidation is virtually absent.

Spurious sources of potential often obscure effects of subsurface electrochemical action. Elevation changes (on account of normal atmospheric potential gradient) cause voltages in the earth which may not be easy to predict. Telluric currents (natural earth currents of global extent flowing through the earth's crust) may result in potential differences which are sometimes difficult to separate from electrochemical potentials. Streaming potentials can also cause anomalies, the largest of which are greater than those associated with oxidation of an ore body.

Field Procedure and Interpretation Self-potential anomalies, often hundreds of millivolts in magnitude, can be detected by nonpolarizing porous electrodes connected to the respective terminals of a millivoltmeter. The potentials can be measured along profiles with pairs of such electrodes maintained at uniform separation. With this arrangement, gradients are usually mapped rather than actual potential differences. Equipotential lines are sometimes determined by maintaining one electrode in a fixed position and finding the line along the surface for which no potential difference is observed between it and a movable probe.

The theory of interpretation is quite similar to that for magnetic prospecting since dipole potential fields are involved in both cases. Theoretical studies by Petrovski,[75] Stern,[76] de Witte,[77] and Yüngül[78] have led to quantitative techniques for interpreting potential anomalies. These are useful only when the polarized body can be represented by a sphere or some other simple geometrical form.

Self-potential surveys have often led to the discovery of sulfide-ore bodies at shallow depths of burial. Among these are several at Noranda and one near Sherbrooke, Quebec. The possibilities of the technique have been investigated in other areas, such as the tristate zinc and lead district (see Jakosky et al.[79]), where no correlation was found between natural potentials and lead and zinc mineralization.

Yüngül[78] has described a self-potential survey in the Sariyer area of Turkey which led to the discovery of a sulfide mass containing zones with copper concentrations as high as 14 percent. A cross section of this ore body, as determined from boreholes, shafts, and tunnels, is shown in Fig. 18-45 along with the potential profile observed on the overlying surface. The steep topography required the use of terrain corrections which resulted in a displacement of the predicted center of the ore body northwestward from the polarization minimum that was measured on the ground. A drill hole at the position of minimum potential would have encountered only pyrite, as was learned subsequently when the adit shown in figure was excavated.

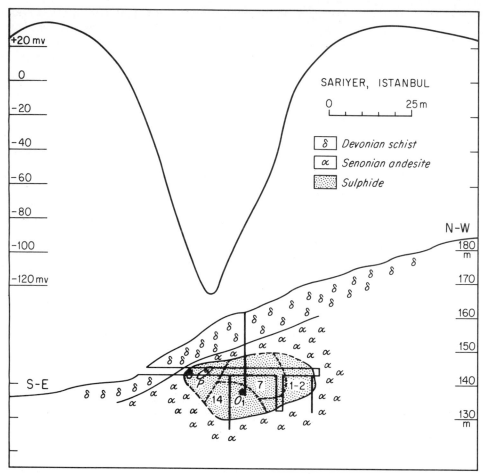

FIGURE 18-45 Self-potential profile and geologic section, Sariyer, Turkey. (*After Yüngül.*[78])

18-5 ELECTROMAGNETIC PROSPECTING OF THE INDUCTIVE TYPE

Principles

One of the most widely used electrical techniques in mineral exploration is the EM method. It is based on the induction of electric currents in buried conductors, such as certain ore bodies, by the magnetic components of electromagnetic waves generated at the earth's surface or in aircraft above its surface. The waves originate from alternating currents at frequencies ranging from a few hertz to a few megahertz which are passed through loops of wire on the ground or in the air. With some methods, current is introduced into the earth by grounded lengths of wire. The oscillating magnetic fields thus generated are propagated as waves into the earth, attenuating at a rate that depends on the frequency and the electrical properties of the rock material through which they travel. The higher the frequency, the greater the rate of attenuation. When the waves pass through a conducting body, they induce alternating electric currents in the conductive materials. These currents become the source of new EM waves which can be detected by suitable pickup coils.

There is such a large selection of specific techniques which are available for ground and airborne EM surveys that it will not be possible to discuss them in any detail here. For further information on such techniques the reader is referred to Keller and Frischknecht,[4] Parasnis,[15] Grant and West,[14] Bosschart,[80] and Ward.[81]

An early application of inductive methods is the location of buried metal, e.g., military mines, by sappers with search coils which respond to waves induced in metallic materials by high-frequency currents. Current sources are generally circular loops in either the horizontal or the vertical plane or elongated horizontal wires. The most commonly used frequencies are in the neighborhood of 500 Hz.

During the 1930s, Peters and Bardeen[82] worked out the theory for determining the depth of penetration of EM waves as a function of frequency. They showed that there is an optimum frequency f that will give the greatest strength of returned signal from a conductor at a depth h where the resistivity in the overlying material is ρ. It can be determined from the relation

$$h \sqrt{\frac{f}{\rho}} = 10 \qquad (18\text{-}13)$$

where h is in meters, f in hertz, and ρ in ohm-centimeters.

For a depth of 100 m and a resistivity of $10^2 \ \Omega \cdot m$, this equation shows that the best frequency is 100 Hz, while penetration to 300 m is best accomplished at 10 Hz. If the resistivity is abnormally high, say $10^4 \ \Omega \cdot m$, a conducting layer 1000 m deep would give the best energy return with a 100-Hz signal, while a layer of 100 $\Omega \cdot m$ resistivity would have to be 100 m deep to have its maximum response at this frequency. Presently available techniques of measuring EM waves at very low frequencies allow penetrations as deep as many kilometers, even through sedimentary sections.

Depth Sounding and Horizontal Profiling

Most inductive methods were originally designed to locate the horizontal positions of buried conductors, but techniques have been developed for estimating their depth as well. The two kinds of methods are analogous in many ways to the horizontal and vertical sounding used in dc (or low-frequency) resistivity prospecting.

Depth Sounding In applying the EM method to depth sounding, one can either vary the spacing between the transmitting loop and receiving coil or vary the frequency while maintaining fixed positions of the transmitter and receiver. Varying the frequency is generally preferred, as any change in the positions of the surface units may introduce undesired effects. If the boundaries to be located occur over a range of depths, it may be necessary to work with a number of spacings on the surface, as the best resolution will be obtained at a separation of coils which depends on the depth of the target. Either loops or long wires may be used as sources. A long grounded wire can usually be considered as an infinite linear source; very large rectangular loops can be treated in the same way if the measuring coil is much nearer to one side of the loop than it is to any of the others.

The theory by which vertical sounding data are interpreted is not difficult to apply where simple models can be fitted to the subsurface structure. The depth to the top of a thick, perfectly conducting layer underlying an infinitely resistant overburden can be ascertained by measuring the ratio of the amplitudes of the horizontal to the vertical magnetic fields observed on the surface. The depth h of a thin horizontal conducting sheet can be determined by comparing this ratio at various values of x, the horizontal source-receiver distance, using a logarithmic curve computed for different ratios of h to x.

Sundberg Method   The Sundberg method, described by Zuschlag[83] gives data which are interpreted by use of the equations and curves computed for one or more thin conducting sheets. The current flows through an insulated copper cable, connected to a source of alternating current, which runs along the surface either as a long grounded wire or as a large insulated loop which forms a rectangle. A number of transverse receiving profiles are laid out perpendicular to the grounded wire or to one side of the loop. The magnetic component of the induced EM field is measured at discrete points along the profile by special search coils consisting of several hundred turns of wire. At least two frequencies are employed, and depth soundings can be made by comparing results at the different frequencies. The quantity actually mapped is the ratio of field intensity at each measuring point to the current in the source loop.

Figure 18-46 illustrates an application of the Sundberg method. Here the loop constituting the source is a rectangle 4000 by 1500 ft in dimensions. The position of the body is indicated, as shown, by the zone over which an observable magnetic response is recorded. If the ore body could be approximated as a sheet, its depth could be determined by measuring the respective components of the field in phase and out of phase with the source signal.

The Sundberg method was used to explore for oil at shallow depths before seismic methods were developed for effective mapping of shallow structures. The Bruner fault in Texas was mapped by this technique. Here a discontinuity was traced in a thin conducting formation about 500 ft deep; this was later shown to coincide with the boundary of the oil-producing zone associated with the fault. The method is now employed only for mining exploration.

Turam Method   The Turam method is similar to the Sundberg method but differs from it in that the ratio of field intensities at two points is observed rather than the intensity at a single point. As with the Sundberg method, two

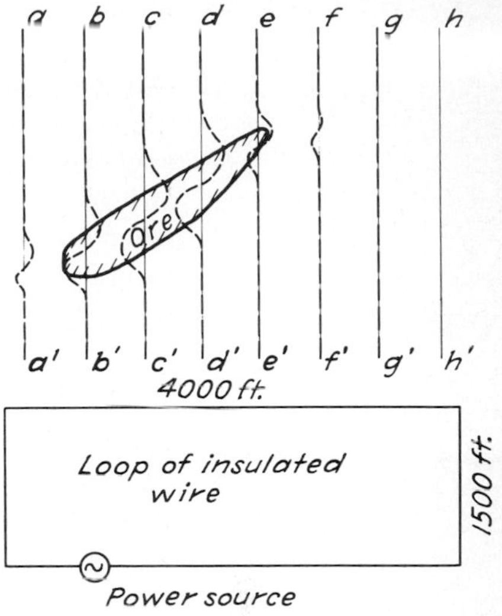

FIGURE 18-46 Detection of conducting ore body under shallow overburden by electromagnetic induction. Current flows through ground loop, and search coils are moved along traverse lines such as *aa'*, *bb'*, etc. Dashed lines show relative response of vertical search coil as function of position along traverses.

frequencies within the 100- to 800-Hz range are employed. A cable several kilometers long is laid out as a source parallel to the expected strike and is grounded at both ends. Measuring coils are read in pairs along lines perpendicular to the cable, the spacing between them generally being about 25 m. In-phase and out-of-phase ratios are observed as well as amplitude ratios and phase-angle differences.

Horizontal Profiling   Most EM surveys are carried out with the object of locating the horizontal positions of buried conducting bodies rather than of determining their depths. Both fixed and moving sources are used in surveys conducted for this purpose. The fixed-source methods are generally designed in such a way that the transmitter is kept at a single location and the receiving loop is moved over the area being explored. The moving-source method involves shifting both source and receiver, usually in a way that maintains a fixed separation between the two. The principal complication that arises in the moving-source method is variable coupling between the source and the conductor. This could cause variations in the response which, not being associated with the subsurface conductor, might be hard to interpret.

The moving-source method requires smaller and more portable generators and source loops than the fixed-source technique, which often employs large insulated loops or long grounded wires.

Some methods are designed to measure only the direction of the induced magnetic field; they can be highly sensitive and do not require complicated instruments. They avoid the necessity for measuring a reference signal associated with the source itself, a difficult requirement in determining relative amplitudes of induced fields. The ratio of the fields observed at two locations or the ratio of two components observed at the same place will give information on subsurface resistivity although the results are more difficult to interpret. The direction of the field is most generally measured by the dip-angle method (also called the vertical-loop method). The source loop is in the vertical plane, and the receiving loop is linked to an inclinometer which is used to measure the angle with the horizontal of the plane in which it lies when the voltage induced in it is a maximum. The azimuth for minimum response of the receiving loop when it is vertical is first measured in the manner illustrated in Fig. 18-47. This technique can be used either with a fixed-source or a moving-source configuration. Dip-angle measurements when properly interpreted can yield information on horizontal location, strike, dip, depth, length, and conductivity of a buried conducting sheet.

FIGURE 18-47 Configuration of transmitting and receiving coils for the vertical-loop or dip-angle method of electromagnetic surveying. Measurement is made in two stages as shown.

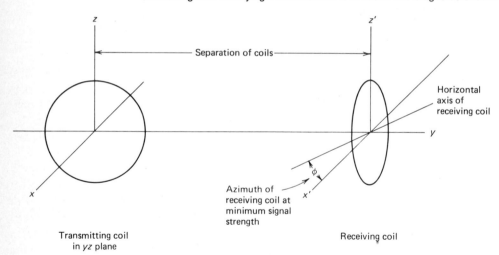

Stage 1: Determining azimuth for dip-angle measurement.

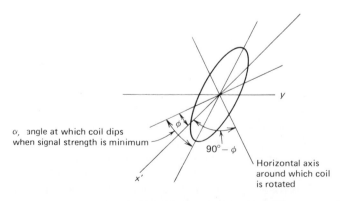

Stage 2: Measuring dip-angle for minimum response.

The *Slingram* method uses portable loops similar to those employed for measuring dip angles with a moving source but the ratio of in-phase and out-of-phase components of the induced voltage is observed with a ratiometer. Both loops are generally horizontal. One or two fixed frequencies are employed, and the loop spacing is kept constant. Traverses are usually laid out normal to regional trends. The information obtainable from Slingram measurements is quite similar to that indicated in the previous paragraph for the dip-angle method when the conductor is a single dipping sheet or a series of parallel, closely spaced sheets equivalent in electrical properties to a wide dike.

The greatest source of difficulty in the interpretation of horizontal profiling data is the effect of conductive material in the rock laterally adjacent to prospective ore bodies and in the overburden above them. Variations in the conductivity of the overburden can give rise to anomalies which resemble those from ore bodies and which might conceal effects from deep conductors of economic interest.

Airborne Electromagnetic Prospecting

Since the early 1950s an increasing proportion of EM surveys has been carried out with airborne instruments. The primary objective of most airborne inductive surveys is to locate sulfide ores. The advantage of airborne surveys in speed of coverage and consequent economy is obvious, but technical problems not encountered in ground surveys make it more difficult to obtain useful electromagnetic data from the air than from the earth's surface. Among these problems are (1) the limited separation between source and receiver compared with that possible on the ground; (2) the exceptional sensitivity required in the measuring system to pick up the weak signals returned to the surface when the source of the primary EM energy must, for reasons of safety, be from 200 to 500 ft above the ground surface; and (3) the higher noise level introduced by motion of the receiving loop in the earth's magnetic field.

A review article by Pemberton[84] describes methods for obtaining the necessary sensitivity in airborne surveys. The simplest arrangement is to attach both the transmitting and receiving loops to opposite wing tips. Another is to receive with a loop towed in a bird connected with the transmitting aircraft by a long cable. The receiving loop may also be in a second plane flying close behind the one containing the transmitter. Still another system is designed to send out transient pulses intermittently, reception being measured during the intervals when the primary field is cut off.

A variety of systems is employed for airborne EM operations. The Törnqvist[85] method makes use of two transmitting loops attached to the aircraft, one in the horizontal plane and the other in the vertical. Two receiving loops, towed in a bird from the same or a second plane, are oriented in the same respective directions. Figure 18-48 illustrates this arrangement as adopted by International Nickel Company. The two transmitters send out alternating magnetic fields of the same frequency and amplitude but 90° different in phase. A rotating mag-

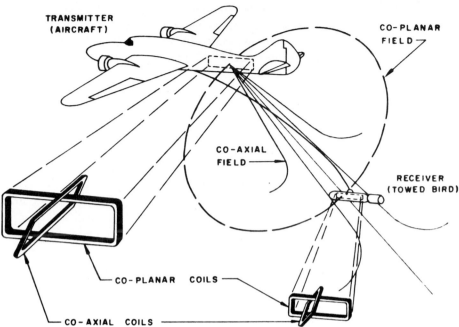

FIGURE 18-48 Arrangement of coils in airborne electromagnetic recording as carried out by International Nickel Co. (*After Dowsett.*[86])

netic field is generated in this way. The signal from one receiving element is shifted in phase 90° with respect to that from the other, and any difference between them is registered by a pen recorder. If there were no conductor below the plane, the two signals would be identical, so that the difference after shifting would be zero and the recorder trace would show only noise. A conductor such as an ore body would cause the signals to be different from each other and the difference would be observed as a signal on the record. The difference amplitude and the phase shift are recorded by separate pens, and any conducting ore body below the aircraft should show up on both traces.

Using a single plane, it is generally necessary to tow the receiver 500 ft or so behind the aircraft. To keep the bird containing the receiver from hitting the ground, the plane must fly at a height of at least 400 ft. The two-plane arrangement makes it possible to trail the bird by a much shorter cable, say 50 to 60 ft, so that a flying height as low as 300 ft is possible. At this height, with an 800-ft separation between planes, conducting bodies as deep as 1500 ft below the ground surface can be detected on the signal traces.

A number of other airborne EM techniques are in common use. The Slingram system, for example, has been adapted for aircraft, providing a highly sensitive measurement technique. Fixed loops are attached either to opposite wingtips (for vertical orientation in the same plane) or to the nose and a boom projecting from the tail (for a vertical coaxial arrangement). The method makes use of a single frequency in the range from 300 to 4000 Hz. The input system records on six channels simultaneously, each representing a different range of frequencies. Because of noise, the data are generally not as good as with ground measurements, and interpretation is likely to be more qualitative. This limitation is generally acceptable, as the principal objective of such a survey is to separate anomalies which have possible economic potential from those which do not, thus localizing interesting areas for further investigation.

Typical Results of Electromagnetic Surveys

After the data obtained in EM prospecting are reduced, they are generally presented in the form of cross sections showing the amplitudes of the signals recorded by the receiving element versus the horizontal position. The latter is expressed in terms of distance in ground surveys and in terms of time in airborne surveys. Generally the components of the signal that are in phase and out of phase with the primary signal are plotted separately. Comparison of the two signatures facilitates interpretation.

Figure 18-49 illustrates the data obtained over the Brunswick sulfide body, consisting of massive pyrite and sphalerite. A highly magnetic iron formation is adjacent to the sulfide ore body. Respective in-phase and out-of-phase profiles are shown both for 400- and 1000-Hz signals. Curves are presented both for coplanar and coaxial coils. These responses were obtained by mixing received and primary signals in such proportion as to null the outputs. A number of important lead-copper-zinc bodies such as this were discovered in northern New Brunswick by surface EM surveys in 1952 and 1953. Both sulfide and graphite bodies give rise to EM anomalies in this mineral province.

The coplanar coil configuration shows a positive response over the iron and a negative one over the sulfide body. The coaxial coils show in-phase effects with signs the reverse of these, but the out-of-phase field gives a positive response over the sulfides and none over the iron. This combination of effects makes it possible to identify the sulfide deposits from the signatures made with the different recording configurations.

Figure 18-50a shows a series of EM profiles crossing a sulfide body in the Muskeg prospect of northwestern Quebec. The survey was carried out from the air using horizontal coplanar coils. Ore bodies in this area are covered by clay and glacial material averaging 50 ft in thickness. Although the outline of the conductor is easily traceable across the profiles, it is not possible to tell from the EM data alone that the conducting material changes from sulfides to graphite as one goes north from line 4W to line 8W. This information can be obtained from magnetic readings. Figure 18-50b relates the EM data to the geological results obtained from diagonal drill holes at the center of profile O and on profile 8W. The sulfides here are in the form of andesites, which are embedded in tuffs and rhyolite.

A third example comes from the Pipe nickel mine in north central Manitoba, which has been discussed by Dowsett.[86] Here the ore body is long, thin, and

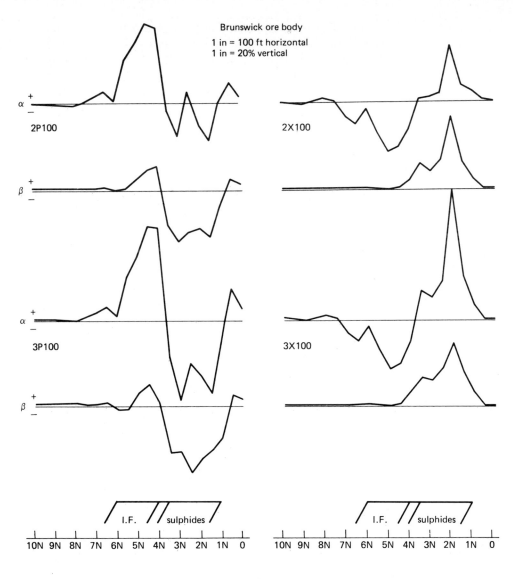

FIGURE 18-49 Electromagnetic profiles over New Brunswick sulfide body and adjacent iron formation (I.F.). Top set and third set of curves from top show in-phase responses to primary field. The other two show out-of-phase responses. The 2 × 100 label indicates, from legend below, that the frequency was 400 Hz, that the coils were coaxial, and that the spacing was 100 ft. Other symbols can be related to legend in a similar way. (*After Brant et al.*[87])

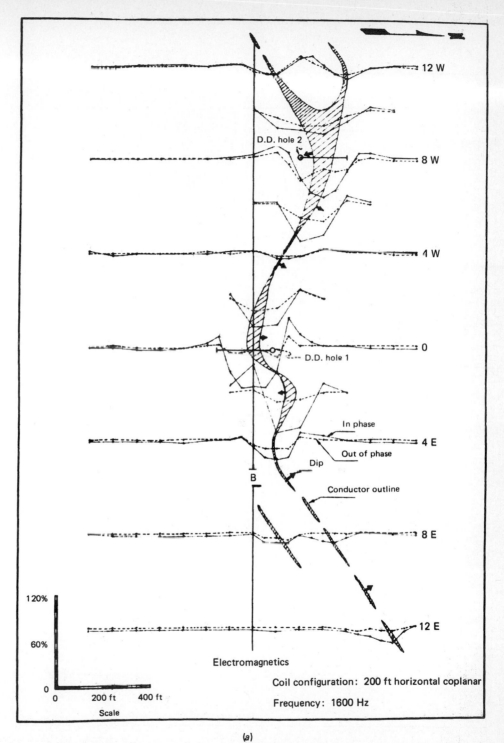

12 W

D.D. hole 2

8 W

4 W

0

D.D. hole 1

In phase

4 E

Out of phase

Dip

B

Conductor outline

8 E

12 E

120%

60%

0

0   200 ft   400 ft

Scale

Electromagnetics

Coil configuration: 200 ft horizontal coplanar

Frequency: 1600 Hz

(a)

FIGURE 18-50   Results of electromagnetic survey over sulfide body in Muskeg area, northwestern Quebec: (a) electromagnetic profiles along lines crossing ore body. Crosshatched areas show interpreted configurations of conducting bodies; (b) geology indicated by two slanting drill holes at locations shown in (a). (*After White*.[88])

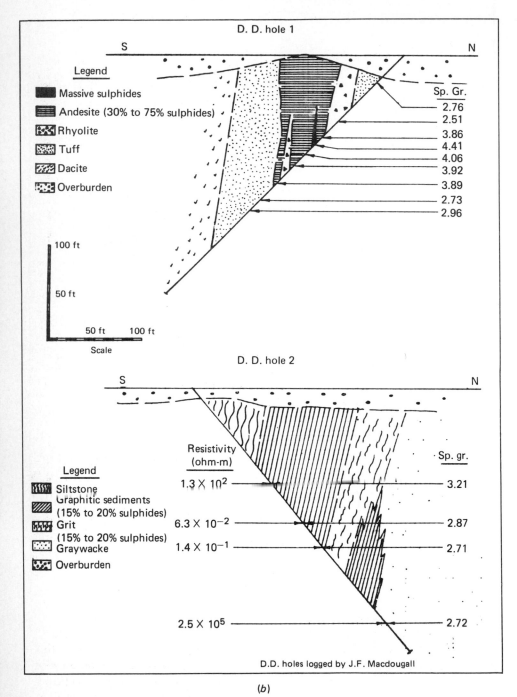

(b)

FIGURE 18-50   continued

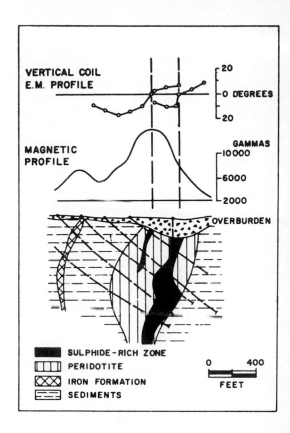

FIGURE 18-51 Electromagnetic and magnetic profiles obtained over the Pipe nickel mine, Manitoba.(*From Dowsett.*[86])

inclined at a large angle with the horizontal. It consists primarily of pyrrhotite, which is both conductive and magnetic. Alongside the pyrrhotite is an iron formation which is only weakly magnetic compared with the sulfide body. Figure 18-51 illustrates the relationship between the EM profiles recorded on the ground using a vertical loop and the magnetic profile obtained over the same traverse. Both are plotted over a geologic section obtained from five drill holes in close proximity. The magnetic anomaly appears better defined than the EM response.

18-6 INDUCED POLARIZATION

The induced-polarization method, first used in the late 1940s has been put to extensive use in the search for disseminated sulfide ores. During the 1960s this method became the most widely employed of all ground-based techniques in mining geophysics. For more detailed information on induced polarization a review paper by Madden and Cantwell[89] and the book by Sumner[90] as well as the discussions in Parasnis[15] and Keller and Frischknecht[4] are suggested.

Principles   When a current is passed through earth materials not containing metallic minerals, the amount of current is related to the driving potential only by the ohmic resistance of the formations involved. When the formations contain metallic minerals, the currents give rise to an exchange of ions at the surface of contact between the minerals and the electrolytes dissolved in the fluid filling the intergranular pore spaces. This electrochemical exchange creates a voltage which opposes the current flow through the material, and an added voltage is necessary to overcome the barrier thus created. The extra voltage necessary to drive current through the barrier is sometimes referred to as the *overvoltage*. When the externally applied current is turned off, the electrochemical voltages at the metallic grain surfaces are dissipated, but not instantaneously. The decaying voltages can be measured for a time after the current is switched off. The voltage is observed to vary with time, as shown in Fig. 18-52. The ratio between the amplitude of the overvoltage just after the current stops to that just before gives a measure of the concentration of metallic minerals in the material through which the current flows.

If an alternating current is put into the earth, the overvoltage observed at the metallic surface will decrease with increasing frequency because the buildup of the opposing voltage to its full value requires a longer time than the period between changes in direction of the applied current. As the frequency of the alternating current increases, the peak overvoltage it induces attains a maximum value that represents a decreasing proportion of the ac amplitude. The ratio of the alternating induced polarization potential at two different frequencies, as well as that of the ac to that of dc, is related to the concentration of metallic minerals along the path of the current.

Field Procedures   The techniques used in the field to measure induced polarization are similar in many ways to those employed for resistivity measurements. Current is introduced into the earth with two electrodes, and a potential is measured across the other two electrodes after the current is shut off. Generally the geometry of the electrode configuration is kept uniform while the position is changed laterally along a profile. This procedure is better adapted for reconnaissance of new areas than the vertical-sounding field arrangement, which, as with resistivity and EM measurements, involves changing the electrode spacing while maintaining a fixed center position.

FIGURE 18-52   Decay of electric field strength in rock sample when external voltage is shut off. (*Keller and Frischknecht.*[4])

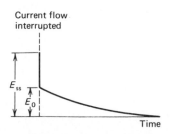

The current introduced into the earth may be in the form of pulses, generally shaped as square waves, or of low-frequency (1 Hz or less) alternating currents. With the second arrangement data are usually compared at a variety of frequencies.

Two pulsing techniques are employed; one involves a single abrupt interruption of a direct current flowing through the earth, with subsequent measurement of its decay characteristics. The current flows for 1 to 5 min before it is cut off, the duration of the pulse being measured precisely. The transient voltage is read at closely spaced intervals after termination of the current when it is not recorded continuously. Either way it is customary to measure the area beneath the voltage-time curve (up to the time that the voltage is no longer detectable) to determine the overvoltage created while the current was flowing. Sometimes special integrating elements (such as RC circuits or fluxmeters) are employed to give a direct reading of the area.

A somewhat different approach makes use of a series of identical pulses repeated at short, uniform intervals. The form of the signal may not be quite the same as that for the single-pulse arrangement unless the interval between the repeated pulses is large. This is because the decay signal from the cutoff of one pulse may be superimposed on the correponding signal from the subsequent pulse or pulses, the amount of superposition depending on the time constant. In any case the voltage observed during the period between pulses is averaged, and this average is used in the interpretation.

The *variable-frequency method* is designed to measure changes in apparent resistivity when the frequency is changed. Polarization opposing externally impressed potential drops would have the same effect as a resistance in series with the actual resistance of the formations except that the effect would vary with frequency. In rocks without minerals that give rise to induced polarization, there will be a very small decrease in resistivity with increasing frequency, usually less than 1 percent. But where there is induced polarization, the decrease of resistivity will be much larger, sometimes becoming as great as 10 to 20 percent for a tenfold frequency increase. The percentage P of decrease may be expressed in the form

$$P = \frac{\rho_2 - \rho_1}{\sqrt{\rho_2 \rho_1}} \times 100\% \qquad (18\text{--}73)$$

where ρ_2 is the resistivity measured at a particular frequency and ρ_1 the resistivity at another frequency 10 times as high. According to Marshall and Madden,[91] rocks with concentrated sulfides would give rise to a P greater than 10 and porphyry copper ores (2 to 10 percent sulfides) to a P between 5 or 10. Rocks with a trace of sulfide mineralization would have a P value from 2 to 5, sandstones and siltstones from 1 to 3, basalt from 1 to 2, and granite from 0.1 to 0.5.

Applicability of the Method In addition to its primary use in exploration for disseminated sulfides, induced polarization has been proposed as a tool for groundwater exploration. Vacquier et al.[92] have carried out polarization experiments with sand-clay mixtures saturated with different electrolytes. Clay particles can cause polarization by blocking the flow of electrolyte-bearing fluid through pore spaces. Ionic exchanges in the clay molecules can cause the clay-sand mixture to act as a distributed electronegative membrane. Proper interpretation of induced-polarization data can show the depth at which these effects take place, thus establishing the position of the water table. Frische and von Buttlar[93] give formulas for computing the depth of the water table from such data.

Rogers[94] has endeavored to evaluate the induced-polarization method as a means of locating disseminated sulfide ores. He concludes that within certain limits of size, depth, and sulfide concentration, the method can establish the presence or absence of sulfides showing a metallic luster in 80 percent of the cases where it is used alone and in a higher percentage of cases when other criteria are available. The lateral extent of the sulfide ore body can be determined to an order of magnitude while the percent of sulfides by volume, said to be the least reliable and generally least important estimate of all, can "sometimes be squeezed out of the data."

Examples Figure 18-53 illustrates the type of data obtained by induced polarization over a sulfide body in Arizona. The method of presenting the

FIGURE 18-53 Presentation of induced-polarization data as illustrated by plot along traverse over sulfide body in Arizona. Above the horizontal line, conventionally determined apparent resistivities are plotted. Below the line a polarization factor based on the difference between apparent resistivities at two frequencies is shown. The exponents for the resistivity values show polarization effects expressed in a different way from those indicated below the line. It is evident that the induced-polarization data are more diagnostic of the presence of sulfides than are the resistivity data. (*After Rogers.*[94])

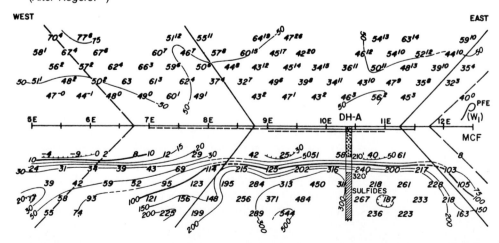

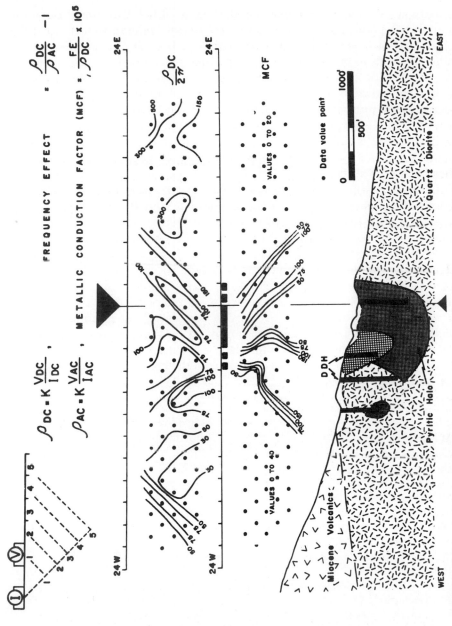

FIGURE 18-54 Induced-polarization profile over Krain sulfide deposit, British Columbia. Contours have the same significance as in Fig. 18–53. The metallic conduction factor (MCF), contoured below the line, is defined at the top of the figure. Ore body is indicated by coarse crosshatching. (*After Hansen and Barr.*[95])

electrodes and the pair of potential electrodes is systematically increased. The polarization ("the metallic conduction factor") based on the difference in resistivity at two frequencies is plotted at a depth of half the separation of the pairs below a point midway between them. As the separation increases, the "depth" at which the value is plotted increases. It is not intended for such a plotting of depth to be looked upon as anything but a rough approximation.

Above the line of stations at the center are contours of the apparent resistivity, determined by conventional techniques, plotted in the same way (with the polarization presented in terms of percentage difference of resistivity at the two frequencies shown as an exponent of the resistivity value). Increasing penetration here is indicated as an increasing distance *above* the horizontal midline. The resistivity contours appear much less diagnostic of anomalous bodies below the surface.

Drilling has confirmed the indication in the polarization data that there is a zone of sulfide mineralization between stations 12E and 9E. The log of the drill hole shown near 10½E shows 210 ft of gravel below the surface, a zone of oxidation in the bedrock from 210 to 320 ft, and a zone with 3 to 5 percent of sulfides by volume from 320 to 600 ft.

Results in a similar form are presented in Fig. 18-54 from the Krain copper deposit in British Columbia. The induced-polarization data gave better definition of the copper ore than magnetometer or self-potential data did, according to a report on the investigation by Hansen and Barr.[95] The definition of the metallic conduction factor, which is contoured on the same basis as in Fig. 18-53, is indicated in the figure. In this case also the resistivity contours above the baseline do not appear to be as diagnostic of the copper concentration as do those of induced polarization.

REFERENCES

1 Maxwell, J. C.: "A Treatise on Electricity and Magnetism," Clarendon Press, United Kingdom, 1891, republished by Dover, 1954.
2 Stratton, J. A.: "Electromagnetic Theory," McGraw-Hill, New York, 1941.
3 Jackson, J. D.: "Classical Electromagnetics," Wiley, New York, 1975.
4 Keller, George V., and Frank C. Frischknecht: "Electrical Methods in Geophysical Prospecting," Pergamon, London, 1966.
5 Wait, J. R.: "Electromagnetic Waves in Stratified Media," Pergamon Press, Macmillan, New York, 1962.
6 Wait, J. R. (ed.): "Electromagnetic Probing in Geophysics," Golem Press, 1971.
7 Rokityanski, I. I.: "Geoelectromagnetic Investigation of the Earth's Crust and Mantle," Springer-Verlag, New York, 1982.
8 Porstendorfer, G.: "Principles of Magnetotelluric Prospecting," Gebruder Borntrager, Stuttgart, 1975.
9 Kaufman, A. A., and G. V. Keller: "The Magnetotelluric Sounding Method," Elsevier, New York, 1981.
10 Kaufman, A. A., and G. V. Keller: "Frequency and Transient Soundings," Elsevier, New York, 1983.
11 Kaufman, A. A., and G. V. Keller: "Inductive Mining Prospecting," Elsevier, New York, 1985.

12 Sumner, J. S.: "Principles of Induced Polarization for Geophysical Exploration," Elsevier, New York, 1976.

13 "Mining Geophysics," Society of Exploration Geophysicists, Tulsa, Okla., 1966.

14 Grant, F. S., and G. F. West: "Interpretation Theory in Applied Geophysics," McGraw-Hill, New York, 1965.

15 Parasnis, D. S.: "Principles of Applied Geophysics," Chapman & Hall, London, 1986.

16 Telford, W. M., L. P. Geldart, R. E. Sheriff, and D. A. Keys: "Applied Geophysics," Cambridge Univ. Press, 1976.

17 Koefoed, O.: "Geosounding Principles," vol. 1, "Resistivity Soundings Measurements," Elsevier, New York, 1979.

18 Parasnis, D. S.: "Mining Geophysics," Elsevier, Amsterdam, 1966.

19 Patra, H. P., and K. Mallick: "Geosounding Principles," vol. 2, "Time Varying Geoelectric Soundings," Elsevier, New York, 1980.

20 Van Nostrand, G., and K. L. Cook: Interpretation of Resistivity Data, U.S. Geol. Surv. Prof. Paper 499.

21 Ginzburg, A.: Resistivity Surveying, *Geophys. Surv.*, vol. 1, pp. 325–355, 1974.

22 Gish, O. H., and W. J. Rooney: Measurement of Resistivity of Large Masses of Undisturbed Earth, *Terr. Mag. Atm. Electr.*, vol. 30, pp. 161–188, 1925.

23 Hummel, J. N.: A Theoretical Study of Apparent Resistivity in Surface Potential Methods, *Trans. Am. Inst. Min. Met. Eng.*, vol. 97, *Geophys. Prospect.*, pp. 302-422, 1932.

24 Stefanescu, S., C. Schlumberger, and M. Schlumberger: Sur la Distribution Electrique Potentielle autour d'une Prise de Terre Ponctuelle dans un Terrain a Couches Horizontales Homogenes et Isotopes (The Distribution of Electrical Potential about a Point Electrode in an Earth of Horizontal, Homogeneous, and Isotropic Beds), *J. Phys. Radium*, vol. 1, pp. 130–141, 1930.

25 Argelo, S. M.: Two Computer Programs for the Calculation of Standard Graphs for Resistivity Prospecting, *Geophys. Prospect.*, vol. 15, pp. 71–91, 1967.

26 Slichter, L. B.: The Interpretation of the Resistivity Prospecting Methods for Horizontal Structures, *Physics*, vol. 4, pp. 307–322, 407, 1933.

27 Pekeris, C. L.: Direct Method of Interpretation in Resistivity Prospecting, *Geophysics*, vol. 5, pp. 31–42, 1940.

28 Koefoed, O.: "The Application of the Kernel Function in Interpreting Geoelectrical Resistivity Measurements," Borntraeger, Berlin, 1968.

29 Marsden, D.: *Eur. Assoc. Explor. Geophys., 34th Meet.*, Paris.

30 Inman, J. R., J. Ryn, and S. H. Ward: Resistivity Inversion, *Geophysics*, vol. 38, pp. 1088–1108, 1973.

31 Jackson, D. D.: Interpretation of Inaccurate, Insufficient, and Inconsistent Data, *Geophys. J. Roy. Astr. Soc.*, vol. 28, pp. 97–109, 1972.

32 Lanczos, C.: "Linear Differential Operators," Van Nostrand, London, 1961.

33 Oldenburg, D. W.: The Interpretation of Direct Current Resistivity Measurement, *Geophysics*, vol. 43, pp. 610–625, 1978.

34 Ghosh, D. P.: The Application of Linear Filter Theory to the Direct Interpretation of Geolectric Resistivity Soundings Measurements. *Geophys. Prospect.*, vol. 19, pp. 192–217, 1971.

35 Ghosh, D. P.: Inverse Filter Coefficients for the Computation of Apparent Resistivity Standard Curves for Horizontally Stratified Earth, *Geophys. Prospect.*, vol. 19, pp. 769–775, 1971.

36 Ginzburg, A., D. Loewenthal, and Y. Shoham: On the Automatic Interpretation of

Direct Current Resistivity Soundings, *Pure Appl. Geophys.*, vol. 114, pp. 983–995, 1976.

37 Kumar, R., and U. C. Das: Transformation of Dipole to Schlumberger Soundings Curves by Means of Linear Digital Filters, *Geophys. Prospect.*, vol. 25, pp. 780–789, 1977.

38 Van Nostrand, Robert G.: Limitations on Resistivity Methods as Inferred from the Buried Sphere Problem, *Geophysics*, vol. 18, pp. 423–433, 1953.

39 Das, U. C., and S. K. Verma: Electromagnetic Response of an Arbitrary Shaped Three-Dimensional Conductor in Layered Earth—Numerical Results, *Geophys. J. Roy. Astr. Soc.*, vol. 69, pp. 55–66, 1982.

40 Dey, P., and H. F. Morrison: Resistivity Modeling for Arbitrary Shaped Three Dimensional Structures, *Geophysics*, vol. 49, pp. 753–780, 1979.

41 Hohman, G. W.: Three Dimensional Induced Polarization and Electromagnetic Modelling, *Geophysics*, vol. 40, pp. 309–324, 1975.

42 Spiegel, R. J., V. R. Sturdivant, and T. E. Owen: Modeling Resistivity Anomalies from Localized Voids under Irregular Terrain, *Geophysics*, vol. 45, pp. 1164–1183, 1980.

43 Cook, K. L., and R. G. Van Nostrand: Interpretation of Resistivity Data over Filled Sinks, *Geophysics*, vol. 19, pp. 761–790, 1954.

44 Tikhonov, A. V.: Determination of Electrical Characteristics of the Deep Strata of the Earth's Crust, *Dokl. Akad. Nauk*, vol. 73, p. 295, 1950.

45 Cagniard, L.: Basic Theory of the Magnetotelluric Method of Geophysical Prospecting, *Geophysics*, vol. 18, pp. 605–635, 1953.

46 Madden, T. R., and P. H. Nelson: A Defense of Cagniard's Magnetotelluric Method, ONR Report Project NR-371-401, Geophysics Lab, M.I.T.

47 Hermance, J. F., and W. R. Peltier: Magnetotelluric Field of Line Current, *J. Geophys. Res.*, vol. 75, pp. 3351–3356, 1970.

48 Bannister, P. R.: Source Distance Dependance on the Surface-Impedance Conductivity Measurement Technique, *Geophysics*, vol. 34, pp. 785–788, 1969.

49 Swift, C. M., Jr.: A Magnetotelluric Investigation of an Electrical Conductivity Anomaly in the Southwestern United States, Ph.D. Thesis, M.I.T., 1967.

50 Wight, D. E., F. X. Bostick, Jr., and W. H. Smith: Real-Time Fourier Transformation of Magnetotelluric Data, Elect. Geophys. Res. Lab., Univ. of Texas, Austin, p. 93.

51 Eggers, D. E.: An Eigenstate Formulation of the Magnetotelluric Impedance Tensor, *Geophysics*, vol. 47, pp. 1204–1214, 1982.

52 Sims, W. E., F. X. Bostick, Jr., and W. H. Smith: The Estimation of Magnetotelluric Impedance Tensor Elements from Measured Data, *Geophysics*, vol. 36, pp. 938–942, 1971.

53 Word, D. R., H. W. Smith, and F. X. Bostick, Jr.: An Investigation of the Magnetotelluric Impedance Tensor Method, EGRL report No. 82, Univ. of Texas, Austin, 1970.

54 Goubau, W. M., T. D. Gamble, and J. Clarke: Magnetotelluric Data Analysis: Removal of Bias, *Geophysics*, vol. 43, pp. 1157–1166, 1978.

55 Bohel, J. E., F. X. Bostick, Jr., and W. H. Smith: An Application of the Hilbert Transform to the Magnetotelluric Method, Elect. Geophys. Res. Lab., Univ. of Texas, Austin, p. 98.

56 Shoham, Y., A. Ginzburg, and F. Abramovici: Crustal Structure in Central Israel from the Inversion of Magnetotelluric Data, *J. Geophys. Res.*, vol. 83, pp. 4431–4440, 1978.

57 Oldenburg, D. W.: One Dimensional Inversion of Natural Source Magnetotelluric Observations, *Geophysics*, vol. 44, pp. 1218–1244, 1979.

58 Bostick, F. X., Jr.: A Simple, Almost Exact Method of Magnetotelluric Analysis, Workshop on EM Methods, Univ. of Utah, January, 1977.

59 Weidelt, P.: The Inverse Problem of Geomagnetic Induction, *Z. Geophysik*, vol. 38, pp. 257–289, 1972.

60 Bostick, F. X., Jr., Y. Shoham, and W. H. Smith: An Optimal Inverse for the Linearized One Dimensional Magnetotelluric, *Abstract, SEG Annu. Int. Meet,* 1979.

61 d'Ecreville, I., and G. Kunetz: The Effect of a Fault on the Earth's Natural Electromagnetic Field, *Geophysics*, vol. 27, pp. 651–665, 1962.

62 Kaufman, A. A.: Tutorial, Distribution of Alternating Electrical Charges in a Conducting Medium, *Geophys. Prospect.*, vol. 33, pp. 171–184, 1985.

63 Patrick, F. W., and F. X. Bostick, Jr.: Magnetotelluric Modeling Techniques, Elect. Geophys. Res. Lab, Report No. 59, Univ. of Texas, Austin, 1969.

64 Vozoff, K.: The Magnetotelluric Method in the Exploration of Sedimentary Basins, *Geophysics*, vol. 37, pp. 98–141, 1972.

65 Ngoc, P. V.: Magnetotelluric Survey of the Mount Meager Region of the Squamish Valley (British Columbia), Rep. Geomagnetic Service of Canada, Dept. of Energy, Mines, and Resources, Ottawa, p. 26, 1980.

66 Wannamaker, P. E., J. A. Stodt, and L. Rijo: Two Dimensional Topographic Responses in Magnetotellurics Modeled Using Finite Elements, *Geophysics*, vol. 51, pp. 2131–2144, 1986.

67 Holcombe, H. T., and G. R. Jiracek: Three-Dimensional Terrain Corrections in Resistivity Surveys, *Geophysics*, vol. 49, pp. 439–452, 1984.

68 Sternberg, B. K., J. C. Washburne, and R. G. Anderson: Investigation of MT Static Shift Correction Methods, *Expanded Abstract, SEG Annu. Int. Meet.* October, 1985.

69 Andrieux, P., and E. W. Wightman: The So-Called Static Corrections in Magnetotelluric Measurements, *Expanded Abstract, SEG Annu. Int. Meet.*, December 1984.

70 Bostick, F. X., Jr.: Electromagnetic Array Profiling (EMAP), *Expanded Abstract, SEG Annu. Int. Meet.*, November 1986.

71 Shoemaker, C. L., Y. Shoham, and R. L. Hockey: Interpretation of Natural Source Electromagnetic Array Data, *Expanded Abstract, SEG Annu. Int. Meet.*, November 1986.

72 Word, D. R., R. Cross, and D. M. Chambers: An EMAP Case Study, *Expanded Abstract, SEG Annu. Int. Meet.*, November 1986.

73 Sato, M., and H. M. Mooney: The Electrochemical Mechanism of Sulfide Self-Potentials, *Geophysics*, vol. 25, pp. 226–249, 1960.

74 Kruger, F. C., and W. C. Lacy: Geological Explanation of Geophysical Anomalies near Cerro de Pasco, Peru, *Econ. Geol.*, vol. 44, pp. 485–491, 1949.

75 Petrovski, A.: The Problem of a Hidden Polarized Sphere, *Phil. Mag.*, vol. 5, pp. 334–353, 914–933, 1928.

76 Stern, Walter: Relation between Spontaneous Polarization Curves and Depth Size and Dip of Ore Bodies, *Trans. Am. Inst. Min. Met. Eng.*, vol. 164, Geophysics, 1945, pp. 180–196, 1945.

77 deWitte, L.: A New Method of Interpretation of Self-Potential Field Data, *Geophysics*, vol. 13, pp. 600–608, 1948.

78 Yüngül, Sulhi: Interpretation of Spontaneous Polarization Anomalies Caused by Spherical Ore Bodies, *Geophysics*, vol. 15, pp. 237–246, 1950.

79 Jakosky, J. J., R. M. Dreyer, and C. H. Wilson: Geophysical Investigation in the Tri-State Zinc and Lead Mining District, *Univ. Kans. Eng. Exp. Stn., Bull.* 24, 1942.

80 Bosschart, Robert A.: Ground Electromagnetic Methods, pp. 67–80, in "Mining and Groundwater Geophysics/1967," *Geol. Surv. Can. Econ. Geol. Rep.* 26, Ottawa, 1970.

81 Ward, Stanley H.: Airborne Electromagnetic Methods, pp. 81–108, in "Mining and Groundwater Geophysics/1967," *Geol. Surv. Can. Econ. Geol. Rep. 26*, Ottawa, 1970.

82 Peters, L. J., and John Bardeen: Some Aspects of Electrical Prospecting Applied in Locating Oil Structures, *Physics*, vol. 2, pp. 103–122, 1932; reprinted in "Early Geophysical papers," pp. 145–164, Society of Exploration Geophysicists, Tulsa, Okla., 1947.

83 Zuschlag, Theodor: Mapping Oil Structures by the Sundberg Method, *Trans. Am. Inst. Min. Met. Eng.*, vol. 97, *Geophysical Prospecting*, pp. 144–159, 1932.

84 Pemberton, Roger H.: Airborne Electromagnetics in Review, *Geophysics*, vol. 27, pp. 691–713, 1962.

85 Törnqvist, G.: Some Practical Results of Airborne Electromagnetic Prospecting in Sweden, *Geophys. Prospect.*, vol. 6, pp. 112–126, 1958.

86 Dowsett, John S.: Geophysical Exploration Methods for Nickel, pp. 310–321, in "Mining and Groundwater Geophysics/1967," *Geol. Surv. Can., Econ. Geol. Rep. 26*, Ottawa, 1970.

87 Brant, A. A., W. M. Dolan, and C. L. Elliot: Coplanar and Coaxial EM Tests in Bathurst Area, New Brunswick, Canada, 1956, "Mining Geophysics," vol. 1, pp. 130–141, Society of Exploration Geophysicists, Tulsa, Okla., 1966.

88 White, P. S.: Airborne Electromagnetic Survey and Ground Follow-up in North-western Quebec, "Mining Geophysics," vol. 1, pp. 252–264, Society of Exploration Geophysicists, Tulsa, Okla., 1966.

89 Madden. T. R., and T. Cantwell: Induced Polarizations: A Review, "Mining Geophysics," vol. 2, pp. 373–400, Society of Exploration Geophysicists, Tulsa, Okla., 1967.

90 Sumner, J. S.: "Principles of Induced Polarization for Geophysical Exploration," 2d ed., Elsevier, New York, 1985.

91 Marshall, D. J., and T. R. Madden: Induced-Polarization: A Study of Its Causes, *Geophysics*, vol. 24, pp. 790–816, 1959.

92 Vacquier, V., C. R. Holmes, P. P. Kintzinger, and Michel Lavergne: Prospecting for Ground-Water by Induced Electrical Polarization, *Geophysics*, vol. 22, pp. 660–687, 1957.

93 Frische, R. H., and H. von Buttlar: A Theoretical Study of Induced Electrical Polarization, *Geophysics*, vol. 22, pp. 688–706, 1957.

94 Rogers, George R.: An Evaluation of the Induced-Polarization Method in the Search for Disseminated Sulfides, "Mining Geophysics," vol. 1, pp. 350–358, Society of Exploration Geophysicists, Tulsa, Okla., 1966.

95 Hansen, Don A., and David A. Barr: Exploration Case-History of a Disseminated Copper Deposit, "Mining Geophysics," vol. 1, pp. 306–312, Society of Exploration Geophysicists, Tulsa, Okla., 1966.

INDEX